ENGINEERING-TECHNICAL

DRAFTING AND GRAPHICS

J. W. GIACHINO
Head, Department
of Engineering and Technology,
Western Michigan University
Kalamazoo, Michigan

HENRY J. BEUKEMA
Supervisor of Drafting,
Department of Engineering and Technology,
Western Michigan University
Kalamazoo, Michigan

AMERICAN TECHNICAL SOCIETY
CHICAGO, ILLINOIS

2nd Printing 1962
3rd Printing 1963
4th Printing 1964
5th Printing 1965
6th Printing 1966
7th Printing 1966
8th Printing 1967
9th Printing 1968
10th Printing 1969

Library of Congress Card Catalog No.: 61-11297.

Printed in the United States of America.

PREFACE

Drafting is the accepted medium of communication in all phases of industrial and engineering work; consequently, engineering and technical personnel must possess a good understanding of drafting techniques. In addition they must have outstanding abilities in spatial visualization so they can readily solve engineering problems, create design requirements, and convey engineering ideas.

In taking up an engineering or technical course of study, students are required in most cases to obtain a fairly comprehensive knowledge of drafting. Unfortunately there is often a lag between the drafting procedures taught in educational institutions and the drafting practices used in the field. It is a generally accepted fact that drafting programs—no matter how comprehensive they are—cannot prepare students to be highly competent in drafting; in reality, they can only give them an opportunity to acquire the principles. Nevertheless, industries do expect that the principles taught be consistent with the best practices used by draftsmen and engineers.

The purpose of this book is to present an overview of the significant fields of drafting, using practices currently recognized by industry, and basic graphical forms of representation which are needed by students of engineering and technology. This objective was achieved as a result of an extensive study of the drafting techniques employed in a variety of industrial and engineering drafting departments. Numerous companies cooperated in this study by making available their drafting standards manuals as well as prints of their products. These manuals and prints were carefully analyzed and notations made of practices that were considered to be important in teaching drafting courses. Every effort was then made to incorporate the essential elements in the manuscript. Furthermore, all of the latest drafting standards have been included that have been published by such standardizing agencies as the American Standards Association, Society of Automotive Engineers, American Society of Mechanical Engineers, Joint Army and Navy Standards, and Military Standards.

Considerable attention has also been given to the drafting problems included at the end of each section. Many of these problems represent actual products manufactured in industry. To avoid mere copy work as much as possible, the problems frequently require a certain amount of design effort; in some instances dimensions have been purposely omitted to stimulate design imagination.

Acknowledgments

The writers are extremely grateful to the following industries who generously supplied material which made the preparation of this text possible:

ACF Industries, Incorporated
Aluminum Company of America
American Machine and Foundry Corporation
American Motors Corporation
American Radiator and Standard Sanitary Corporation
Baldwin-Lima-Hamilton Corporation
Bausch & Lomb Optical Company
Bendix Products Division, Bendix Aviation Corporation
Benton Harbor Engineering Company

Browne & Sharpe Mfg. Company
Burndy Engineering Corporation
Burroughs Corporation
Caterpillar Tractor Company
Checker Motors Company
Chicago Pneumatic Tool Company
Chicago Screw Company
Chrysler Corporation
Clark Equipment Company
Convair Div., General Dynamics Corporation
Crane Company
Cutler-Hammer, Inc.
Dictaphone Corporation
Douglas Aircraft Company
Eastman Kodak Company
Engineered Precision Casting Company
Fairbanks-Morse & Company
Fairchild Engine & Airplane Corporation
Ford Motor Company
General Motors Corporation
Goodyear Tire & Rubber Company
Hapman Corporation
Ingersoll Kalamazoo Div., Borg-Warner Corporation
Jack & Heintz, Inc.
Johns-Manville Products Corporation
Kawneer Company
Kelsey-Hayes Wheel Company
Link-Belt Company
Lionel Corporation
Lockheed Aircraft Corporation
Mack Manufacturing Corporation
Maytag Company
Millers Falls Company
Minneapolis-Honeywell Regulator Company
Motor Wheel Corporation
Mueller Brass Company
Pacific Car & Foundry Company
Philco Corporation
Pratt & Whitney Aircraft Company
Radio Corporation of America
Raytheon Manufacturing Company
Republic Aviation Corporation
Rohm & Haas Company
Royal Typewriter Company
Ryan Aeronautical Company
St. Louis Car Company
Smith Corona, Inc.
Sterling Electric Motors, Inc.
Sylvania Electric Products, Inc.
Thor Corporation
Timken Roller Bearing Company
Veeder-Root, Incorporated
Waukesha Motor Company
Whirlpool Corporation
S. S. White Dental Mfg. Company
Willys Motors, Inc.
Wyman-Gordon Company
Yale & Towne Manufacturing Company

Special appreciation is expressed to the following for their cooperation and assistance in preparing the various designated chapters:

Miller-Davis, Structural Engineers: Section 18, Structural Drawing.

Louis C. Kingscott & Associates, Architects: Section 17, Architectural Drafting.

Wilkins & Wheaton Engineering Co.: Section 20, Map Drawing.

Frederick Post Co.: Section 27, Reproduction of Drawings.

Dale King, Assistant Professor of Drafting, Department of Engineering and Technology, Western Michigan University: Section 14, Gears and Cams.

Don Nantz, Professor of Machine-Tool, Department of Engineering and Technology, Western Michigan University: Section 24, Tool and Die Drawing.

Robert Angerman, Project Engineer, Ingersoll Kalamazoo Division, Borg-Warner Corp.: Section 23, Graphs and Charts.

Eugene Kirchherr, Assistant Professor of Geography and Geology, Western Michigan University: Section 20, Map Drawing.

J. H. Bergen, formerly Director Engineering Services Laboratory, American Machine and Foundry Co.: Section 25, Simplified Drafting.

Earl Willmarth, Drafting Instructor, Central High School, Battle Creek: Cam and Gear problems in Section 14.

James Conners, Elwyn Englcter, William Snyder, David Bowen, and Carl Holkeboer, for drawings and checking the problems.

J. W. GIACHINO

HENRY J. BEUKEMA

CONTENTS

INTRODUCTION

IMPORTANCE OF DRAFTING IN ENGINEERING DEVELOPMENT

CHARLES A. CHAYNE,
Vice President in Charge of Engineering Staff
General Motors Corporation

Drafting is probably the engineer's most important form of communication. Just as picture writing, the first form of written communication, was used to express thoughts and records, so do engineers working with graphics mold intangible ideas and theories into tangible goods and products. Yet, there is a tendency in present engineering education to minimize the importance of drafting.

In applying for their first job after graduation, the majority of young engineers express a definite preference for experimental and testing work rather than for design. To them, design is associated with the drawing board, and they have been led to believe that work on a drawing board is of a menial nature, perhaps all right for a tradesman, but certainly beneath the dignity of a graduate engineer.

We have found, however, that these same young engineers, after two or three years in experimental or test activities, usually request a transfer to design work. They have learned by actual experience that the real creative engineering is done in the drafting room and that there must be a design before there can be a test or experimental program. They have discovered that drafting has a vital, dual function in the engineering organization:

(a) As a means of communication whereby ideas can be presented to others quickly and vividly.

(b) As a tool whereby these ideas may be developed and expanded by graphical methods.

As with any language, skill can be obtained only by practice and certainly a few months of minimum drafting training received in college cannot be considered adequate practice for mastering such a vital skill. Consequently, young engineers should not only expect, but should seek several years of full-time design work.

It has been our experience that the most valuable men in an engineering development group are those whose broad background in designing permits them to follow a project from the initial freehand sketch to the finished prototype. Men of initiative and vision who have the ability to draw a good working layout, draw or supervise the drawing of the details, check the finished drawings, and then follow the parts in the shop through the assembly and testing phases are the type of "all-around" engineers constantly being sought to fill positions of higher responsibility.

As demonstrated by engineers of this type, drafting is by no means losing its place as an engineering tool.

Drawing equipment, materials and instruments 1

Engineering drawing is a graphic language that expresses and conveys ideas of shape, size and construction of parts or mechanisms. To have optimum value, engineering drawings must be clear, concise and subject to but one interpretation. In order to produce drawings that conform to accepted standards and practices, professional draftsmen and engineers utilize certain types of equipment, drafting materials and instruments. Since time is an important element in any industrial work, a clear understanding of all the drafting tools and drawing techniques is important to speed up the process of drawing preparation. The equipment, material and instruments used by professional draftsmen and engineers are described in this section.

1.1 Drafting table and board

Professional draftsmen and engineers do most of their drawing on tables similar to those shown in Fig. 1-1. Although the construction details may vary somewhat on different tables, in general they are made either to a standard height or so they can be adjusted to any desired working height. A turn of a hand knob or lever also permits the top to be regulated to various angles; on some tables the top can be moved to full easel position. Many tables have a steel cleat on each end of the top which is designed to hold and keep a straight edge as well as to prevent warpage.

The draftsman usually covers the table top with a special buff or green colored waterproof board cover paper, which not only minimizes glare but provides a smooth, firm working foundation under the drawing sheet, thereby helping to produce sharp clear-cut pencil lines. It also makes erasing easier.

To facilitate the work of the draftsman, many drafting rooms are equipped with posture chairs in place of the customary drafting stool, as illustrated in Fig. 1-2. The posture chair has a free floating back rest with a seat that can be raised or lowered to desired positions, and an independently adjustable foot ring.

Figure 1-1
The professional draftsman and engineer do their work on drafting tables like these. Mayline Company, Inc., and Frederick Post Co.

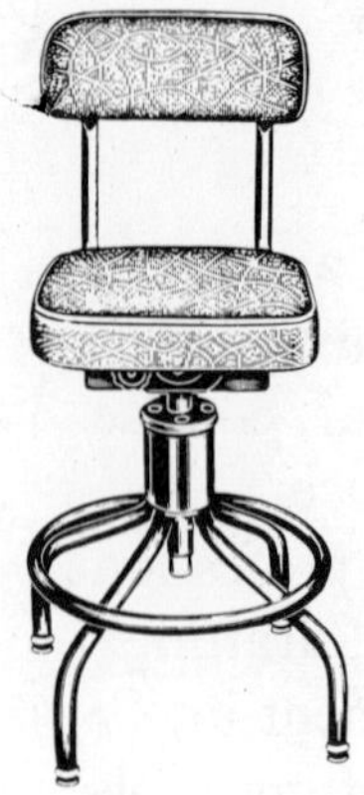

Figure 1-2
To facilitate the work of the draftsman, this posture stool is often provided. Keuffel and Esser Co.

Figure 1-3
The drafting board is used when drafting tables are not available. Mayline Company, Inc.

The drawing board shown in Fig. 1-3 is used by draftsmen primarily for field work. It is commonly found in schools when professional drafting tables are not available. These boards are made of either white pine or basswood and come in a variety of sizes. The 20 inch × 26 inch is the most practical for ordinary drawing.

1.2 T-square

The T-square is used for drawing horizontal lines and as a supporting straightedge for triangles when vertical and slanted lines are to be made. The two types of T-squares are the *fixed head* and the *adjustable head*. See Fig. 1-4. The fixed head is intended for most ordinary work while the adjustable head is designed especially for drawing parallel inclined lines.

The length of T-squares ranges from 18 inches to 60 inches. For maximum effectiveness, the T-square should extend along the entire length of the drafting board. The most popular T-squares have plastic or celluloid edges which permit lines to be visible underneath the edge of the blade.

Since a T-square must be perfectly square to be accurate, care should be taken never to drop it or use it as a hammer. The device shown in Fig. 1-5 is often fastened to the T-square to insure lifelong rigidity and squareness. This metal clamp is easily installed and is extremely valuable in situations where inexperienced students are learning to draw.

1.3 Testing a T-square for straightness

Since accurate work can only be achieved if the drafting tools are in proper working condition, a draftsman should periodically check his T-square for straightness. To test the edge of the T-square for straightness, a sharp line is drawn through two widely separated points. Then the square is turned over and another line drawn through these points using the same edge. If the square is true, the two lines will coincide. Any deviation from the straight line will indicate an error in the blade equal to one-half the space between the two lines. See Fig. 1-6.

1.4 Parallel straightedge

The parallel straightedge is preferable to the T-square for large drawings. While the T-square is satisfactory for small work, it becomes unwieldy and inaccurate in lengths over four feet. Since the parallel straightedge is supported at both ends, it has the advantage over the T-square in that it maintains parallel motion automatically and may be moved up or down with slight pressure at any point along its length.

The straightedge can be mounted on either the drafting table top or on the drafting board. It is operated by a cord which runs through both ends of the straightedge. The arrangement of the cord and guiding pulleys varies, depending on the manufacturer of the equipment. Fig. 1-7 illustrates two common types.

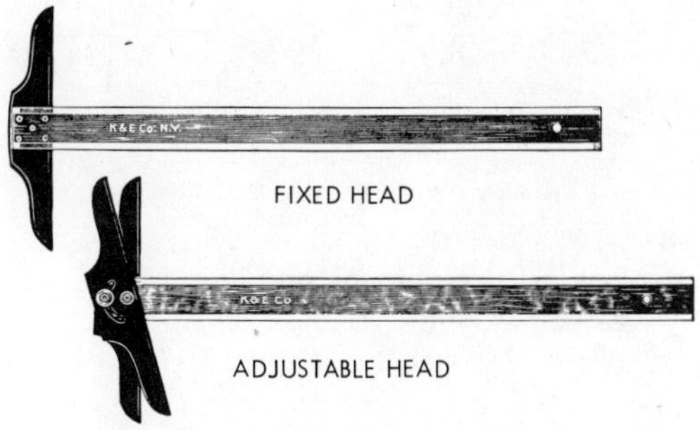

Figure 1-4
T-squares are used by draftsmen to draw horizontal lines and as a straightedge for triangles. Keuffel and Esser Co.

Figure 1-5
This Allen clamp keeps the head of the T-square securely fastened to the blade. Floyd L. Allen

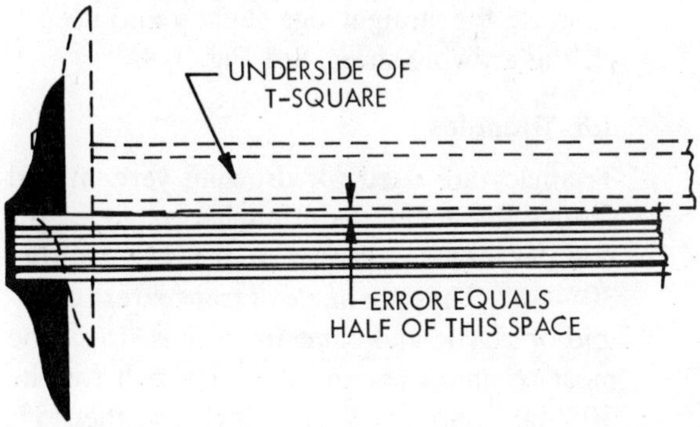

Figure 1-6
This is how a T-square should be tested for straightness.

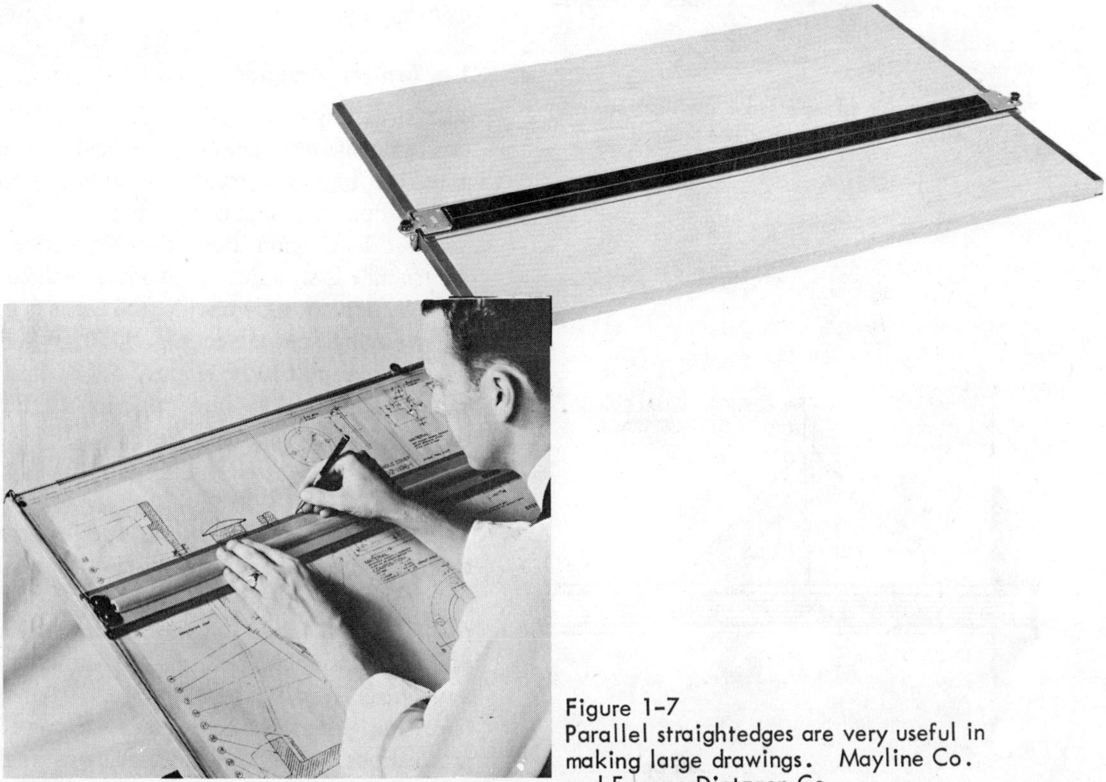

Figure 1-7
Parallel straightedges are very useful in making large drawings. Mayline Co. and Eugene Dietzgen Co.

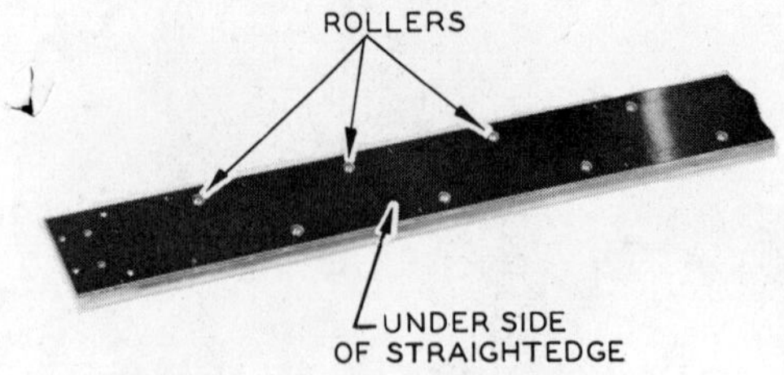

Figure 1-8
The roller raises the straightedge and prevents smudging the lines.
Mayline Co.

Figure 1-9
Triangles are used to draw vertical and slanted lines. Mayline Co.

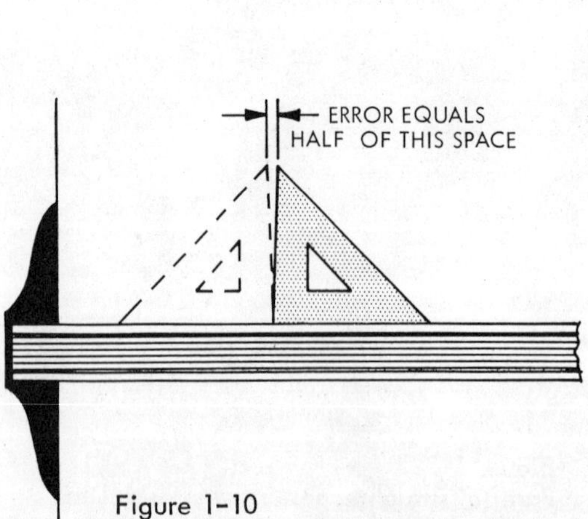

Figure 1-10
This is how a triangle can be checked for straightness.

On some makes of parallel straightedges, smudging of lines by the straightedge is avoided by using spring-mounted rollers on the under side of the straightedge. These rollers raise the straightedge slightly and keep it off the drawing sheet. See Fig. 1-8.

1.5 Triangles

Triangles are used for drawing vertical and slanted lines. The two triangles employed for this purpose are known as the 45° and the 30°–60°. They are made of transparent celluloid or plastic and come in various sizes. The most common are the 8 or 10 inch for the 30°–60° and the 6 or 8 inch for the 45°. See Fig. 1-9.

1.6 Testing triangles

The straightness of a triangle is tested by placing it against the T-square and drawing a vertical line. The triangle is then reversed and without the T-square being moved, the line is drawn again along the same edge. If the triangle is straight, the two lines will coincide; if they do not coincide, the error is half the resulting space. See Fig. 1-10. When a triangle is found to be slightly out of line, it can be corrected by sandpapering or filing the edges where necessary.

1.7 Adjustable triangles

The professional draftsman and engineer frequently use what is known as the *adjustable triangle* (see Fig. 1-11) instead of the regular types. Since it has a protractor, the adjustable triangle permits the drawing of any angle from 0° to 90° direct from the base line. The protractor has two rows of graduations—the outer row indicates angles from 0° to 45° from the longer base, and the

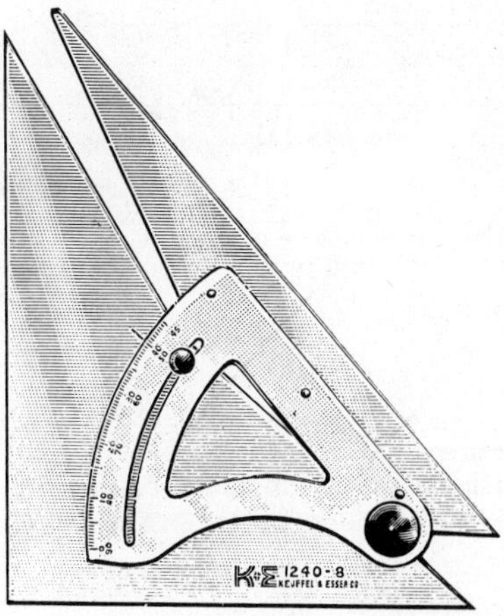

Figure 1-11
This adjustable triangle is often preferred by draftsmen.
Keuffel and Esser Co.

inner row indicates angles from 45° to 90° from the shorter base. The graduations are marked to half degrees and the adjustable arm is held firmly at any angle by a clamp screw, which also serves as a handle for lifting or moving the instrument.

1.8 Scales

The scale has a twofold function: (1) to measure distances accurately, and (2) to produce a drawing to certain sizes, that is, *making a drawing to scale*. Drawing to scale simply means that objects are represented on paper either in full size, reduced size, or enlarged size. For some parts, the dimensional units must be reduced to properly make the drawing on the required size sheet. The size of other objects may have to be increased to show all the necessary details with any degree of clarity. Scales are therefore constructed to permit production of drawings to any desired size.

The most common scales used in drawing are the *Mechanical Engineer's*, sometimes known as the *Mechanical Draftsman's scales*, the *Architect's scales*, and the *Civil Engineer's* or *decimal scales*. These scales are available in either a flat or triangular shape. See Fig. 1-12. An advantage of the triangle scale is that more measuring faces are incorporated on one stick; however, with such a scale, a scale guard, as shown in Fig. 1-13, is necessary to keep the required measuring edge in a constant position.

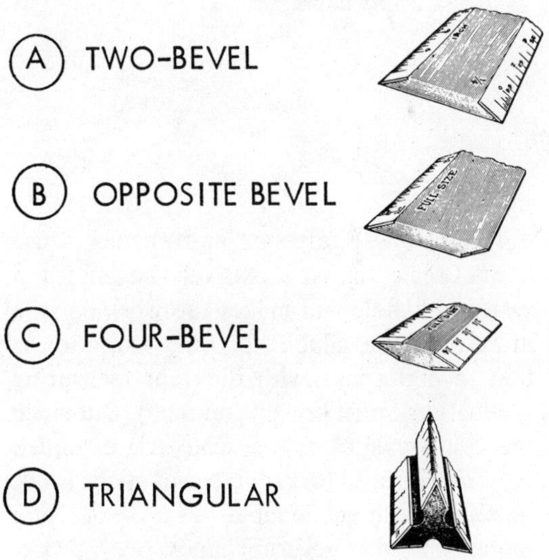

Figure 1-12
Scales of these shapes are used for drawing. Keuffel and Esser Co.

Figure 1-13
This scale guard keeps a triangular scale in position for instant use.

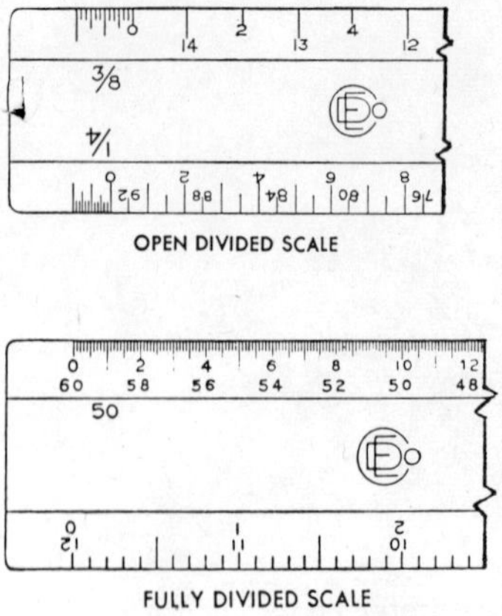

Figure 1-14
A scale may be either "open divided" or "fully divided."
Eugene Dietzgen Co.

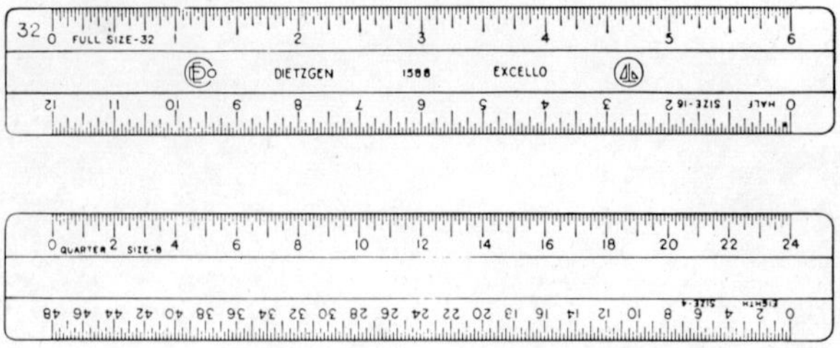

Figure 1-15
Units on the Mechanical Engineer's scale. Eugene Dietzgen Co.

Professional draftsmen and engineers use the flat scale almost exclusively because it is easier to handle and makes the working face more readily available. Its only limitation is that several sticks with different measuring graduations must be kept on hand. But since the draftsman uses one scale for extended periods, the need for a number of sticks is not particularly objectionable. Flat scales are manufactured in several shapes.

The *two-bevel* scale has the advantage of a wide base and the scale faces are always visible. See *A,* Fig. 1-12. The *opposite-bevel* scale is easy to handle and easily lifted from the board by tilting. See *B,* Fig. 1-12. The *four-bevel* scale has four faces and is especially convenient as a pocket rule in the 6″ size. See *C,* Fig. 1-12.

All scales are either *open divided* or *fully divided.* See Fig. 1-14. *Open divided scales* are those on which the main units are numbered along the whole length of the edge with an extra unit fully subdivided in the opposite direction from the zero point. When the subdivided unit represents one foot, as in the Architect's scale, the subdivided graduations designate fractional parts of the foot. When the subdivided unit represents one inch as in the Mechanical Engineer's scale, the graduations indicate 1/4, 1/8, 1/16, etc., of an inch. Open divided scales often have two complete measuring systems on one face, one double the other and reading in opposite directions.

Fully divided scales have all the subdivisions along the entire length of the stick so that several values from the same origin can be read without having to reset the stick. They are sometimes double numbered, either to permit both right-to-left and left-to-right reading, or to provide two different scales on one face.

1.9 Mechanical Engineer's scale

This scale is used for drawing machine and structural parts. The measuring units are designed to produce drawings that are to be 1/8, 1/4, 1/2 or full size. The graduations represent inches and fractional parts of inches. Thus, to draw an object to a 1/4 scale, the 1/4 measuring face would be used. Each main division on this scale then is equal to one inch. The fractional parts of the inch are indicated by small division lines located along

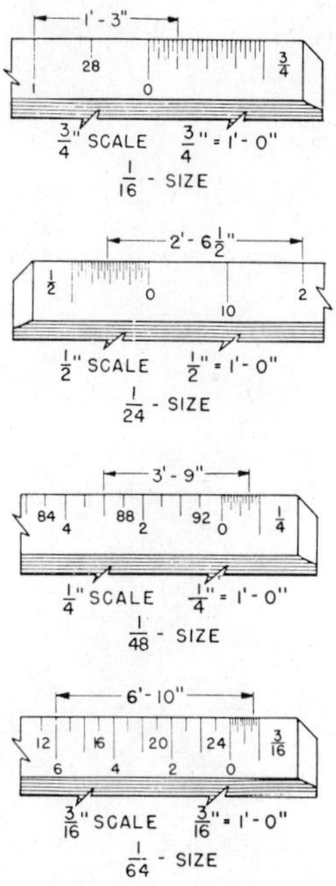

Figure 1-16
Measuring units on the Architect's scale.

TABLE I. SCALES FOR FULL SIZE AND REDUCED DRAWINGS

Full size	12 in. equals 1 ft or 1" = 1"
3/4 size	9 in. equals 1 ft or 3/4" = 1"
1/2 size	6 in. equals 1 ft or 1/2" = 1"
1/4 size	3 in. equals 1 ft or 1/4" = 1"
1/8 size	1-1/2 in. equals 1 ft or 1/8" = 1"
1/12 size	1 in. equals 1 ft or 1" = 12"
1/16 size	3/4 in. equals 1 ft
1/24 size	1/2 in. equals 1 ft
1/48 size	1/4 in. equals 1 ft

the entire edge (fully divided), or only one unit opposite the zero mark (open divided) is subdivided. See Fig. 1-15. As mentioned earlier, the Mechanical Engineer's scale is made in either the flat or triangular shape. The flat shape comes with one, two or four measuring faces.

1.10 Architect's scale

The Architect's scale is used for making drawings of buildings, as well as for structural and machine parts. This stick provides a wider range of scale reductions. The basic measuring faces are designated as 3, 1–1/2, 1, 3/4, 1/2, 3/8, 1/4, 3/16, 3/32, 1/8, and full size. In each case these scales represent the proportions to which drawings can be reduced in terms of feet and inches. Thus, the measuring edge marked with a 3 means 3 inches equals one foot. The edge labeled 1–1/2 indicates that 1–1/2 inches equals one foot, and so on. See Fig. 1-16.

With the Architect's scale the sizes with which drawings can be produced are shown in Table I. Notice that in the scale reductions, whenever an object has to be enlarged, the units on the 3 or 1–1/2 scale can be used to represent inches instead of feet. For example, if a part has to be drawn several times larger than its actual size, and the number 3 scale is used, the 3 instead of representing units where 3 inches equals one foot, the same divisions can represent one inch. This produces a drawing three times its actual size. Similarly, the 1–1/2 scale may be employed for the same purpose.

1.11 Civil Engineer's or Decimal scale

The graduations on this scale represent decimal units. Originally the Engineer's scale was employed primarily where large reductions were necessary, such as for making maps and charts. Today, however, it is more widely utilized in engineering drawing because the decimal system of dimensioning is now being followed more extensively in industry. See Section 7.

Decimal scales are made with decimal units divided into 10, 20, 30, 40, 50 and 60 parts to the inch. Thus the edge marked 10 simply means that one inch has been subdivided into 10 equal parts. A scale where the inch is divided into 50 parts, which is the one most often used in industry, means each part

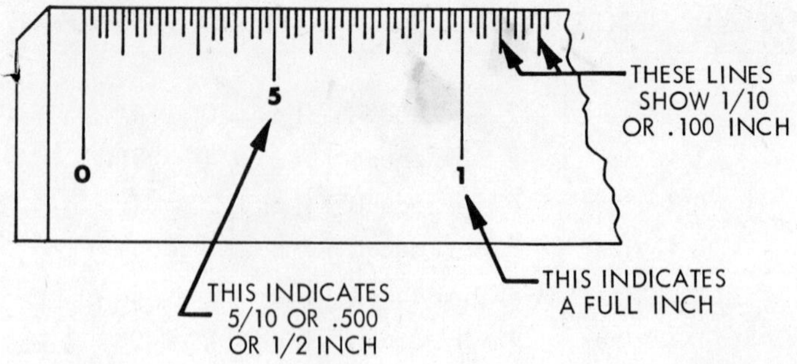

Figure 1-17
How to use the decimal scale for a full-size drawing.

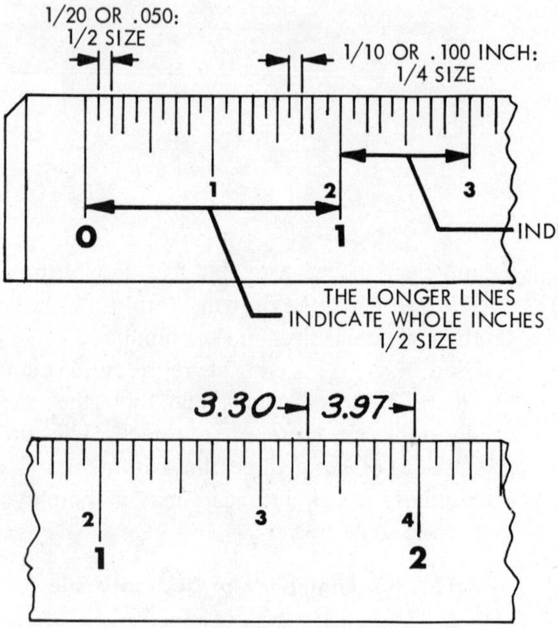

Figure 1-18
How to use a decimal scale for half-size and one-quarter size drawings.

is 1/50 of an inch, or a decimal equivalent of .02 inch. Notice in Figs. 1-17 and 1-18 how this scale can be used to produce full, one-half and one-quarter size drawings.

1.12 Protractors

A protractor is a semicircular form divided into units called *degrees*. Two scales are shown on the protractor with each scale having units running from 0 to 180 degrees. The outer scale is designed for laying out angles that extend to the left and the inner scale for angles that must be laid off to the right. See Fig. 1-19.

There are three other types of protractors frequently used by the draftsman: The *Transparent Arm Protractors,* the *Pro-Tract-Angle* and the *Draft-Scale-Angle*. See Fig. 1-20. These protractors are time saving devices since they permit laying out angles and drawing angular lines in one operation. Notice particularly the versatility of the Pro-Tract-Angle and the Draft-Scale-Angle. The Pro-Tract-Angle has two triangular arms,

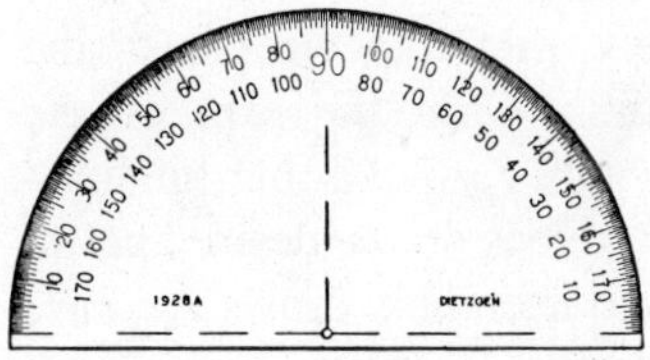

Figure 1-19
A protractor is used to lay out angles.
Eugene Dietzgen Co.

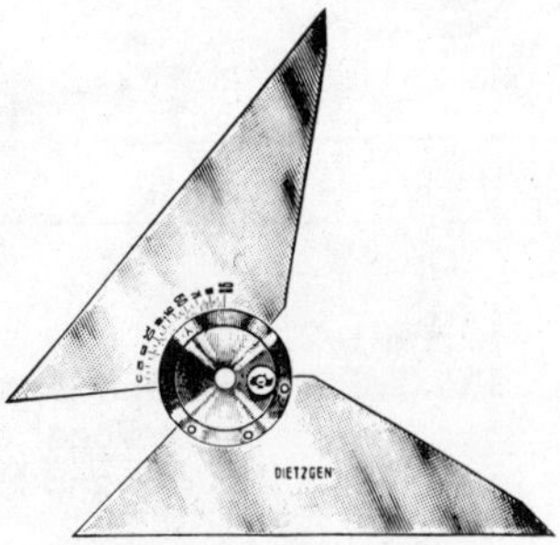

PRO-TRACT-ANGLE

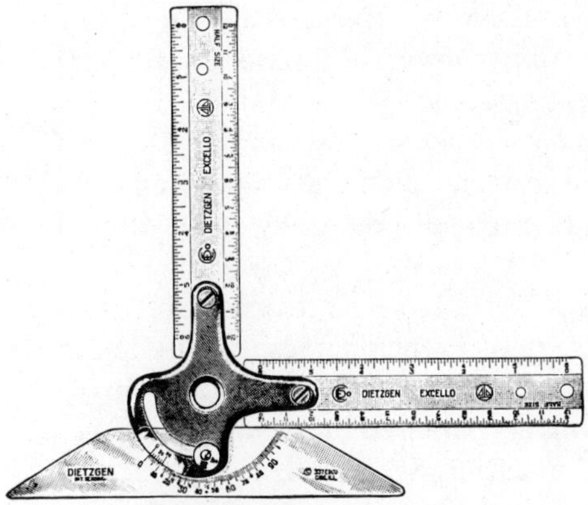

DRAFT-SCALE-ANGLE

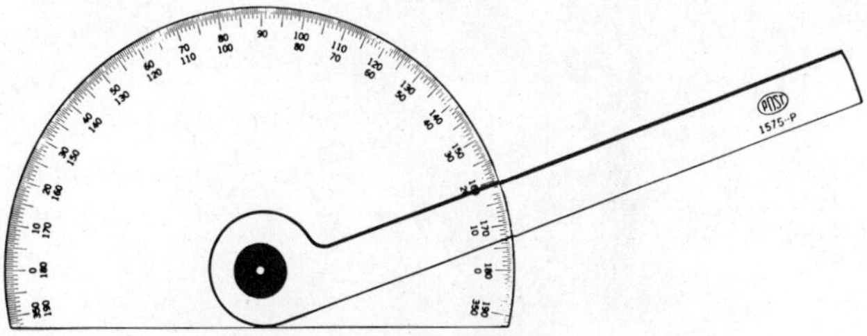

TRANSPARENT ARM PROTRACTOR

Figure 1-20
These special types of protractors are time saving devices.
Frederick Post Co., Eugene Dietzgen Co.

one is attached to a fixed center having a protractor index; the other arm, containing the protractor graduations is attached to a movable concentric disk. This permits the drawing of any angle from a line parallel to the base line to any angle 90° to the base line. The movable arms can be locked in any position by means of the clamp screw, which also serves as a handle for lifting or moving the instrument. Each of the two triangles is made with a 45° angle and a 30°–60° angle, so they can be used as standard triangles.

The Draft-Scale-Angle consists of a triangular base to which is attached a movable arm for holding the two detachable scales. The arm has a protractor with a vernier reading to ten minutes.

1.13 Drafting machine

The drafting machine is now a standard piece of equipment in most industrial drafting rooms. See Fig. 1-21. It is an extremely useful device since it eliminates the need for separate scales, triangles, protractor and T-square. All of the essential drawing units are attached in such a manner as to permit their instant use. Its time saving value lies in the fact that many drawing operations can be combined, such as laying out horizontal and vertical lines, measuring, and laying out angles. The centralized control units allow the draftsman to accomplish these operations with his left hand, leaving his right hand free for drawing. Thus, to draw a line of a predetermined length at a given angle, the draftsman, using

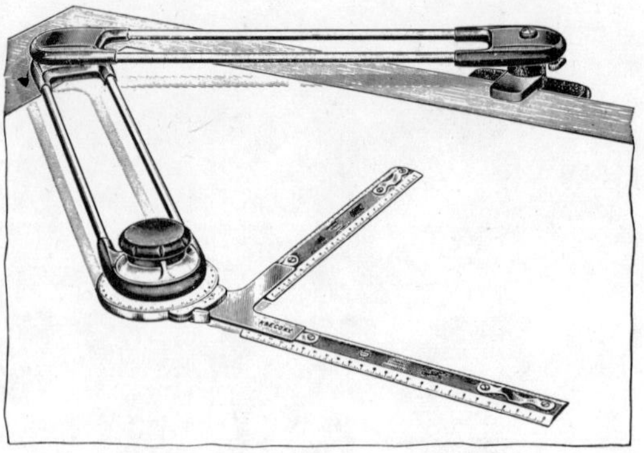

Figure 1-21
The drafting machine is standard equipment for the professional draftsman and engineer. Keuffel and Esser Co.

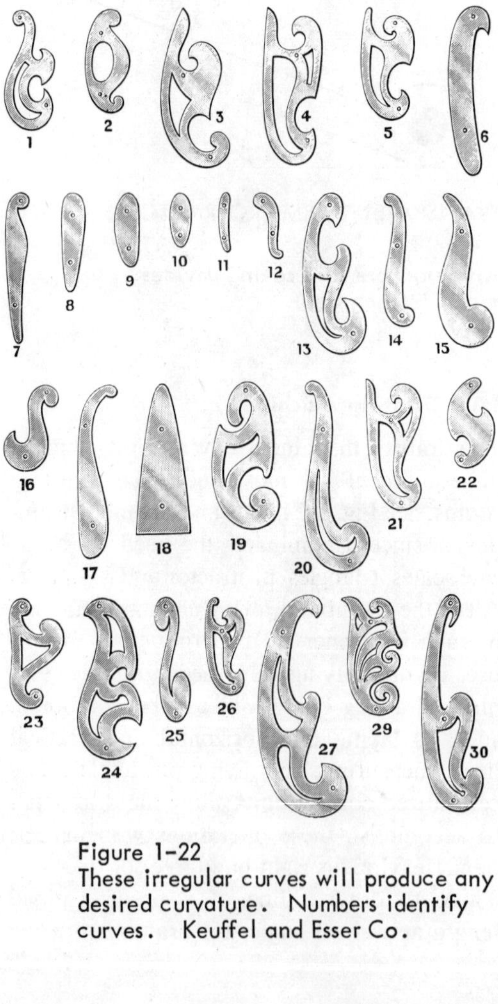

Figure 1-22
These irregular curves will produce any desired curvature. Numbers identify curves. Keuffel and Esser Co.

his left hand only, simultaneously sets the correct angle, and swings the arm of the drafting machine until zero of either the horizontal or vertical scale is on the desired point. With his right hand he simply draws the lines of the required length. Without resetting the controls, parallel or perpendicular lines can be drawn anywhere on the board.

1.14 Curves

When it is necessary to draw curves other than standard circles or arcs, special devices are used. These devices are called *Irregular (French) Curves, Mechanical Engineer's Curves, Ship Curves, Railroad Curves* and *Flexible Curves.*

Irregular Curves as shown in Fig. 1-22 are available in many different shapes and sizes and can produce practically any desired curvature.

Mechanical Engineer's Curves are actually a group of French curves, usually ten in a set, selected to provide patterns of curves commonly encountered in the work of a mechanical engineer. See Fig. 1-23.

Copenhagen Ship Curves are another set of curved patterns which are often used for work requiring more extended curvatures. These curves are not known to be based on any mathematical formula or principle. Undoubtedly they were originally laid out to combine two arcs which had been proven over the years to be of practical curvature for hull design. See Fig. 1-24.

Railroad Curves are especially designed to meet highway and road engineering requirements. They are cut to definite radii in which one inch equals 100 feet. Both edges of the curves have the same radius. Each curve is usually stamped with its designated degree of radius and tangency value. See Fig. 1-25.

Flexible Curves consist of long, narrow strips of flexible metal with either metal or rubber ruling edges which can be bent to fit any desired curvature. See Fig. 1-26. The spline shown in Fig. 1-27 is another type of flexible curve used considerably in lofting work where full size contours of objects must be laid out. Spline weights or "ducks" hold the spline in any desired position.

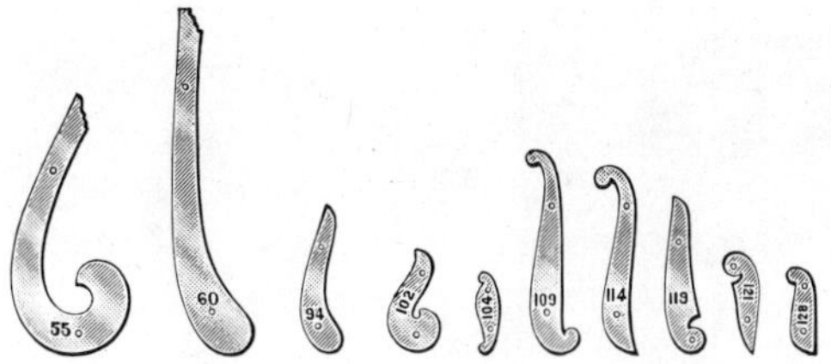

Figure 1-23
These curves are especially useful to the industrial draftsman. Numbers identify curves. Keuffel and Esser Co.

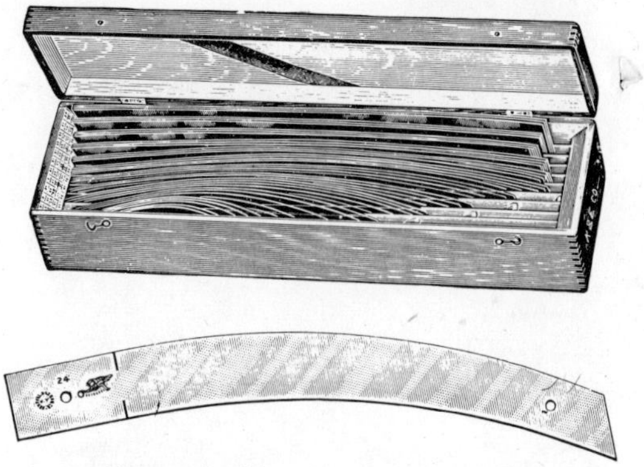

Figure 1-25
Railroad Curves are designed for highway and railroad engineering work. Keuffel and Esser Co.

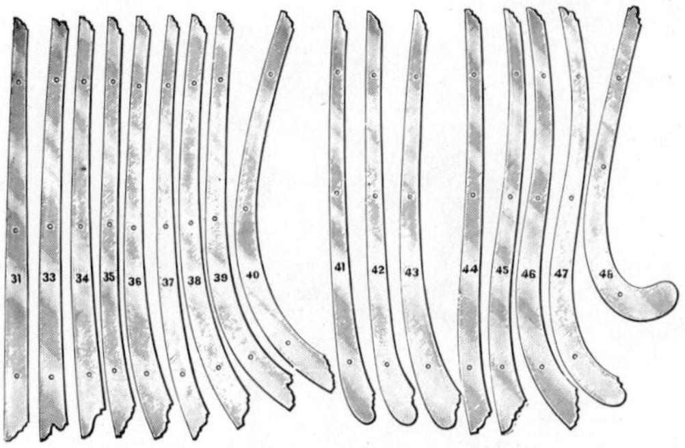

Figure 1-24
Ship Curves are used to produce more extended lines of curvature. Numbers identify curves. Keuffel and Esser Co.

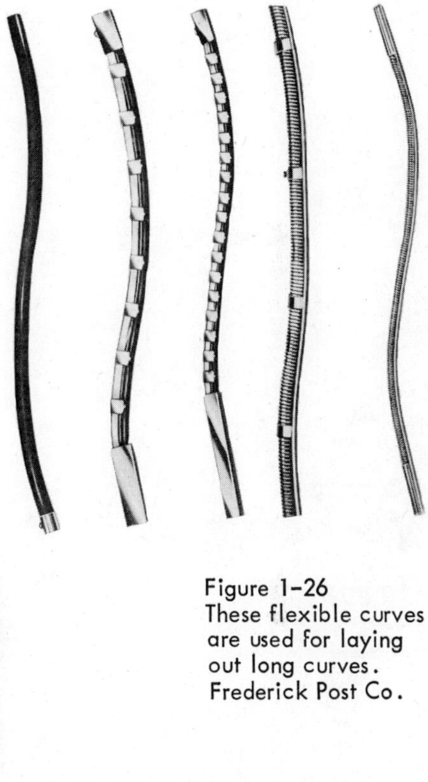

Figure 1-26
These flexible curves are used for laying out long curves. Frederick Post Co.

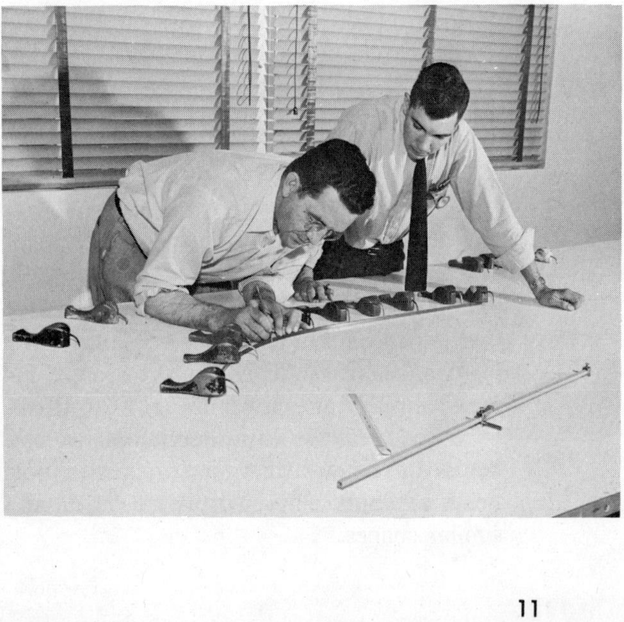

Figure 1-27
Spline and spline weights are used a great deal for lofting work. Boeing Airplane Co.

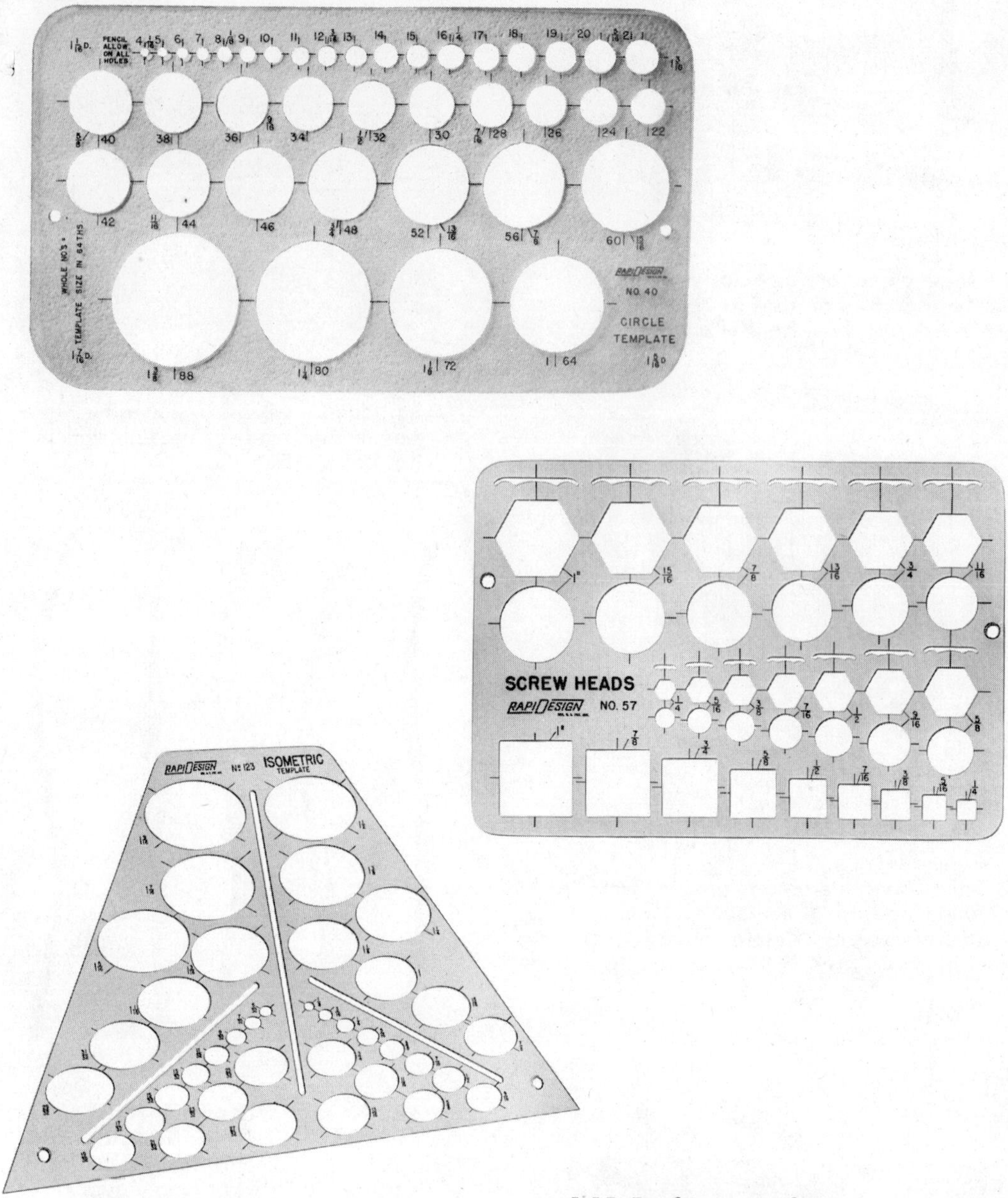

Figure 1-28
These templates are a must for the professional draftsman and engineer.
Rapidesign, Inc.

1.15 Drafting templates

A variety of templates have been designed to simplify the job of the draftsman and to minimize many time consuming operations. These templates save hours of tedious work in laying out holes, standard symbols and other figures that are constantly necessary in plans, drawings and sketches. Several of the more common templates are shown in Fig. 1-28. It will be noticed that the illustrated templates may be used to draw such figures as circles, bolt heads and nuts, ellipses of various sizes, and similar shapes.

Figure 1-29
Some draftsmen prefer a mechanical pencil. Frederick Post Co.

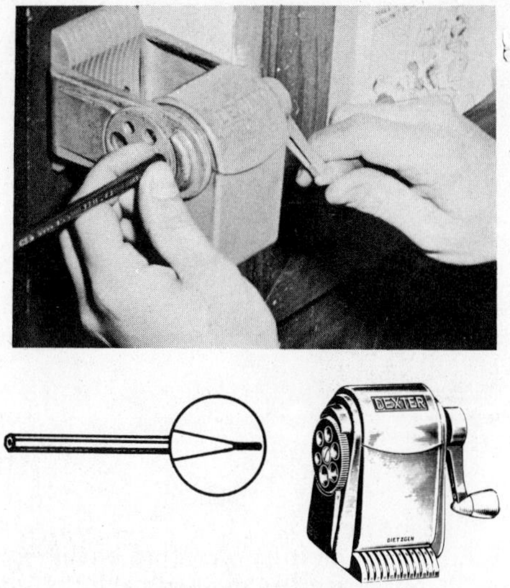

Figure 1-30
This sharpener is equipped with special cutters which remove the wood only on a pencil and not the lead.

1.16 Drawing pencils

Drawing pencils are made with leads of different grades of hardness. The hardness is designated on the pencil by numbers and letters. These symbols range from 7B, which is very soft, through 6B, 5B, 3B, 2B, B, HB, F, H, 2H, 3H, 4H, 5H, 6H, 7H, 8H and 9H, which is the hardest.

Many draftsmen prefer the mechanical pencil because its length remains constant and it can easily be refilled with new leads. See Fig. 1-29.

1.17 Pencil sharpeners

To simplify the process of sharpening a pencil, most drafting rooms have mechanical sharpeners equipped with special draftsman's cutters. This sharpener removes the wood only, leaving the lead exposed so it may be pointed to any desired shape. See Fig. 1-30.

The pencil pointer illustrated in Fig. 1-31 is another piece of standard equipment found in drafting rooms. This pointer is used to shape the lead to a conical point after the wood is removed. Electrically operated pencil pointers as shown in Fig. 1-32 are now found in larger drafting rooms.

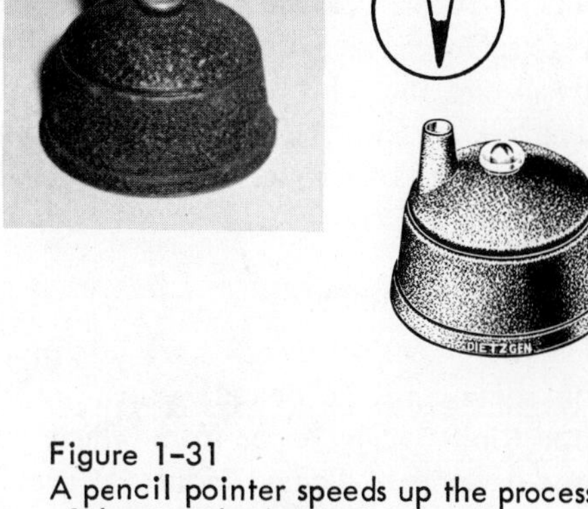

Figure 1-31
A pencil pointer speeds up the process of shaping the lead of a pencil.

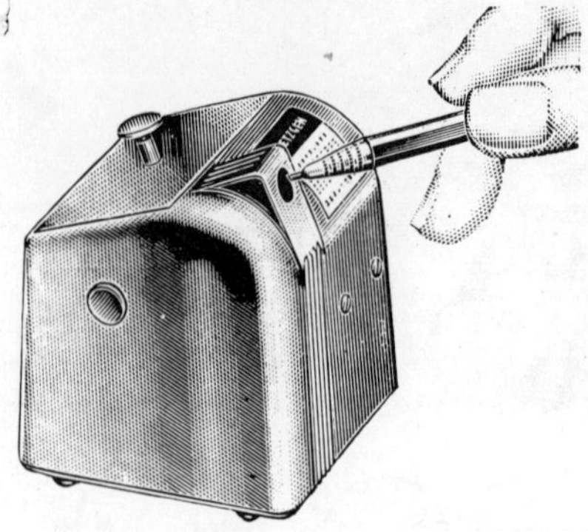

Figure 1-32
Some drafting rooms are equipped with electrically-operated pencil pointers.
Eugene Dietzgen Co.

1.18 Drawing paper

Most industrial drawings are made on tracing paper or cloth rather than on paper. However, beginning students of drawing usually start their work on drawing paper and then transfer to tracing paper after some skill in drawing is mastered.

Drawing paper is produced in roll and sheet form and comes in white, cream and light green color. The light green paper has the advantage of not showing dirt as readily as the others and reduces glare to a minimum.

Several grades of drawing paper are available; however, it is advisable to use a good quality paper because it withstands erasing better. One surface of the paper has a smooth finish and the other surface a rough finish. The smooth finish is more adaptable for ink work whereas the rough finish is better suited for pencil drawings.

1.19 Tracing paper

Formerly, most drawings were first prepared on some kind of opaque paper and then traced on tracing paper from which a print was developed. Today, industrial draftsmen make their drawings directly on tracing paper in order to accelerate the drawing process.

Tracing paper is a thin transparent paper which is either left in its natural state or treated with some transparentizing agent. The treated papers are called *vellums* while the untreated types are referred to as *natural* tracing papers. Natural tracing papers are manufactured in many different grades in either pure white or blue tinted colors. These papers do not, as a rule, possess the high degree of transparency as the vellums. The vellums are made of 100 percent pure white rag stock and are particularly noted for their high transparency. They withstand repeated erasing without leaving ghost marks, have good pencil and ink taking qualities, do not discolor with age, and stand a considerable amount of handling without damage.

1.20 Tracing cloth

Tracing cloth is a transparentized fabric and is used when the original tracing has to be preserved for a long period of time. It is available in either white or blue tinted colors. One side is usually dull and the other glazed. Tracing cloth will take both pencil and ink. In making drawings on cloth, the dull side should always be used. For inking purposes, a tracing cloth powder or pumice is sprinkled over the cloth and then dusted off with a felt pad or brush. The pumice prepares the cloth to take ink more readily.

1.21 Glass cloth

Glass cloth is a transparent material which has been impregnated and processed to provide an excellent drawing surface for ink or pencil. Because of its high dimensional stability, it is used extensively in industry for tool drawings such as of jigs, fixtures, and dies; for maps, comparator work, and shop layouts. Glass cloth eliminates the need for laying out a design on tool stock by hand. The design of the tool is drawn full scale on the glass tracing cloth and the design is then transferred to the tool stock by contact printing. See Section 24. Duplicates of the original can readily be made by various reproduction processes. See Section 27.

Figure 1-33
A dusting brush is a necessary part of the draftsman's "kit of tools." Keuffel and Esser Co.

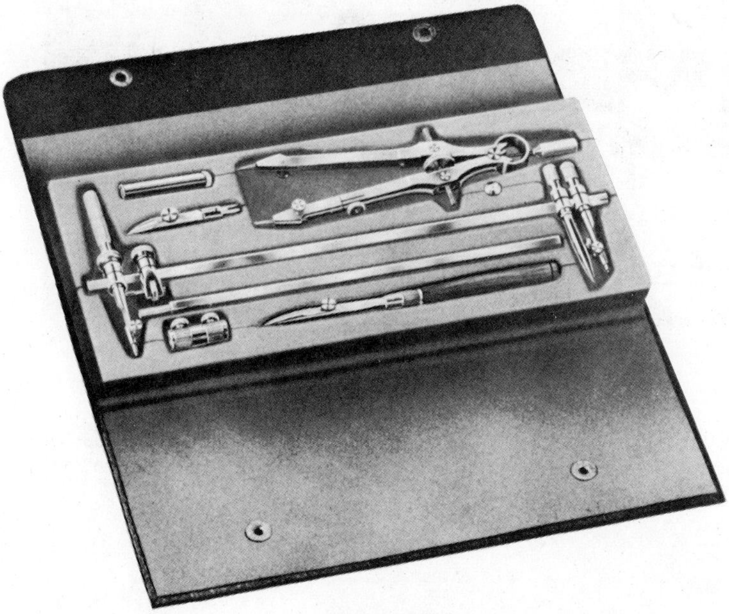

Figure 1-34
This standard set contains the instruments for preparing most drawings. Frederick Post Co.

1.22 Dusting brush

The brush shown in Fig. 1-33 is a necessary item for the professional draftsman. It is extremely valuable for removing eraser particles and dust from a drawing.

1.23 Drawing instrument set

A serviceable set of instruments is very essential for producing good drawings with a minimum amount of effort and in the shortest possible time. There are many different kinds of sets. Some contain numerous special accessories while others include only the basic instruments. Most industrial draftsmen and engineers usually possess a set having the following instruments: (1) 6 inch adjustable bow compass with pen and pencil point attachment, (2) 8 and 10 inch beam compass, and (3) ruling pen. See Fig. 1-34.

The adjustable bow compass draws circles from 3/16 to 8 inches in diameter. By replacing the lead with a steel point, this instrument also serves as a divider. The beam compass with the two bars permits drawing large circles. Most beam compasses include a center point assembly with a micrometer adjustment for accurate settings. The ruling pen is used for inking straight lines. See Section 15. Pen points can be inserted in both the bow and beam compasses for inking purposes.

Figure 1-35
A modern industrial drafting room.

Basic drawing techniques 2

The value of any mechanical drawing depends entirely on how skilfully the draftsman can present the essential data of the object involved. This degree of skill is governed to a considerable extent by how effectively various drafting tools and materials are used. The basic drawing practices and drafting tools which must be mastered by the draftsman are described in this section.

2.1 Drawing sheet sizes

The size of sheet used for a drawing is determined by the object to be drawn. Thus a small size sheet is usually preferable for a small object while larger size sheets are needed for large parts and assemblies. Actually all industries use a variety of sheet sizes although they often standardize on some sizes for certain types of work.

Drawing sheet sizes are based on standards recommended by the *Society of Automotive Engineers* and the *American Society of Mechanical Engineers.* These associations have, over the years, undertaken the standardization of drafting practices which have generally been accepted by industry as a whole. The basic drawing sheets as recommended by both associations are shown in Table I.

For drawings which require sheets larger than the standard size sheets, the practice is to use *roll stock.* Most roll stock is available in 36 inch and 42 inch widths. When roll stock is used, the sheet is commonly designated as *R-size.* There is no industry-wide standard for R-size sheets. Manufacturers have established their own specifications governing the limits of these sheets to suit their particular needs.

2.2 Covering the drafting board

Sub-section 1.1 stated that draftsmen make it a practice to cover their drafting boards with a special board cover paper. To apply such a cover, dampen the underside of the cover paper with a sponge or wet cloth. Lay the cover paper on the drafting board and staple it onto the board at about three inch intervals. Trim the ends of the cover paper with a knife or razor blade and allow it to dry and shrink to a smooth tight surface. See Fig. 2-1.

TABLE I. DRAWING SHEET SIZES

A-size	8 1/2 x 11	or 9 x 12
B-size	11 x 17	or 12 x 18
C-size	17 x 22	or 18 x 24
D-size	22 x 34	or 24 x 36
E-size	34 x 44	or 36 x 48

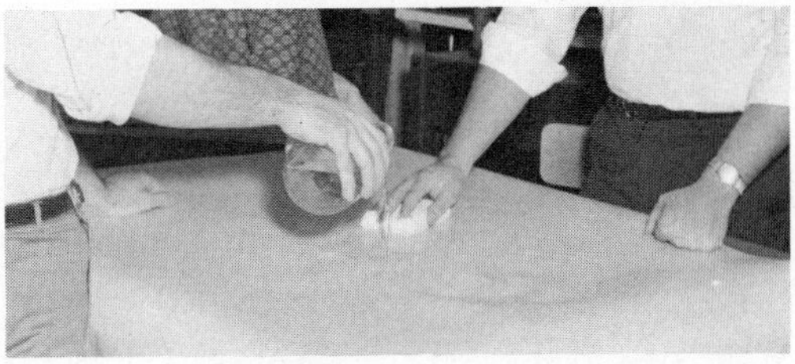

Figure 2-1
Draftsmen usually cover their boards with a special board-cover paper.

2.3 Fastening the sheet to the board

The drawing sheet should be conveniently located on the board so there is sufficient room to use the T-square or straightedge at the bottom of the sheet. When a drafting machine is employed, many draftsmen prefer to place the sheet at an angle as shown in Fig. 2-2. This position reduces the effects of light shadows from the scales and makes lettering much easier.

Although thumbtacks are sometimes used to secure the sheet to the board, most draftsmen prefer drafting tape or staples. The cor-

Figure 2-2
With a drafting machine, the drawing process is simplified if the sheet is placed in this position.

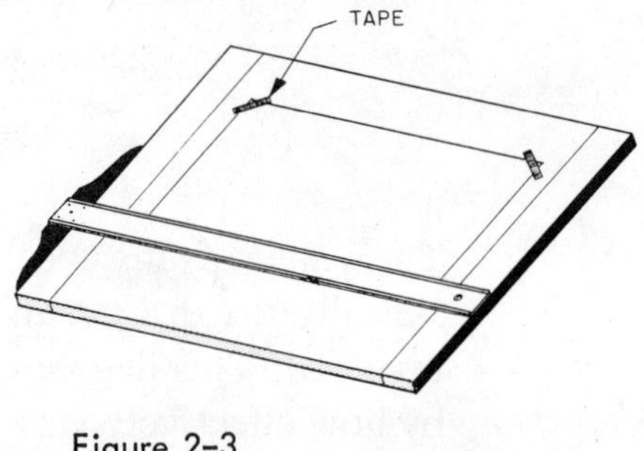

Figure 2-3
This is an example of how the sheet should be secured to the board.

rect procedure in fastening the sheet is to staple or place a piece of tape across the upper left hand corner. The T-square is then moved up to the bottom edge or printed border line of the sheet and another staple or strip of tape is fastened on the upper right hand corner. See Fig. 2-3. This is followed by securing the two bottom corners as well. Frequently, a draftsman will use a continuous strip of tape along the four edges rather than small pieces across the corners. The continuous strip serves to protect the edges of the sheet and keep them from becoming torn during the drawing operations.

2.4 Selecting the correct pencil

The hardness of lead to be used depends on such factors as grade of paper, kinds of lines required and the prevailing humidity in the room. See Sub-section 1.16 for hardness designations. Generally, a 4H, 5H, or 6H pencil produces satisfactory lines when preparing layout drawings or drawings which require extreme accuracy. For drawings which necessitate heavier lines, a 3H or 4H is recommended. A softer pencil such as H or 2H is advisable when drawings are to be produced on tracing paper or cloth. Sketching is best accomplished with an HB, F or H pencil.

2.5 Sharpening the pencil

To produce clear sharp lines, a pencil must be sharpened correctly. Two types of points are used for drawing: the conical point and the wedge or chisel point. See Fig. 2-4. The conical point is best for all-purpose work. Some draftsmen prefer the wedge-shaped point for drawing straight lines and the conical point for lettering and curved-line work.

In sharpening a pencil, the end opposite the hardness symbols should be cut in order that the grade of the pencil used is always known. The pencil should first be sharpened in a regular pencil sharpener and then about 3/8 inch of the lead uncovered with a knife. See Fig. 2-5. Notice the slight shoulder where the lead is exposed. The advantage of shaping the wood section in this manner is that the pencil can be held closer to the T-square and triangle and the lead may be repointed several times without having to use the sharpener. The use of a knife to uncover the lead is not necessary if a sharpener with draftsmen's cutters is employed.

After the wood is removed, the pencil is pointed on a sandpaper pad or smooth file by a rotating, reciprocating motion until the point assumes the shape of a cone. If a wedge-shaped point is desired, the point is rotated slightly, as in shaping a cone, and the operation completed by rubbing both sides of the point flat on the sandpaper or file. See Fig. 2-6. Whenever possible the pencil pointer should be used.

2.6 Sheet margins

The actual margin allowance for drawing sheets varies slightly with different manufacturers. Many engineering departments require a uniform margin of 1/2 inch to 1 inch on all sides of the sheet. Frequently sheets with printed margins are provided.

ASME Standards recommend the following margins:[1]

A and B-size sheet—1/4 inch on all sides

C-size sheet—3/8 inch on all sides

D and E-size sheet—1/2 inch on all sides

SAE recommends a uniform 1–1/4 inch margin at the left edges of all sheet sizes with the remaining margins varying from 1/4 inch to 1/2 inch.[2] See Fig. 2-7.

If the sheets are to be bound, a 1 inch margin should be provided on the left side of all sheet sizes. See Fig. 2-8.

To protect roll-size drawings at points of greatest wear, a 4 inch to 8 inch blank space should be provided on one or both ends of the sheet.

2.7 Title block and title strip

A title block or title strip provides space for recording the part number, part name, drawing date, scale, date first used, reference, material specifications, heat treatment, and initials or signature of the draftsman, tracer, checker and two or more approving officials. The use of all these spaces is not mandatory. Spaces not required are omitted, re-labeled for specific requirements, or consolidated with other spaces to provide more room for required information.

Location of the title block on the drawing is optional; however, the predominant practice in industry is to place the title block in the lower right corner of the sheet. The dimensions of the various spaces vary with different industries. Figs. 2-9 and 2-10 illustrate the sizes and forms of title blocks as

1. *American Drafting Standards Manual, Section I* (New York: The American Society of Mechanical Engineers, 1956), P—1–4.

2. *SAE Automotive Drafting Standards* (New York: Society of Automotive Engineers, Inc., 1952), A1.03.

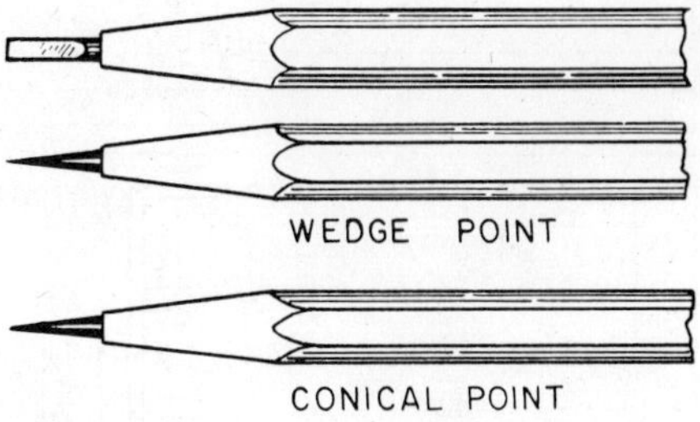

Figure 2-4
A pencil is sharpened so the point is conical or wedge shaped.

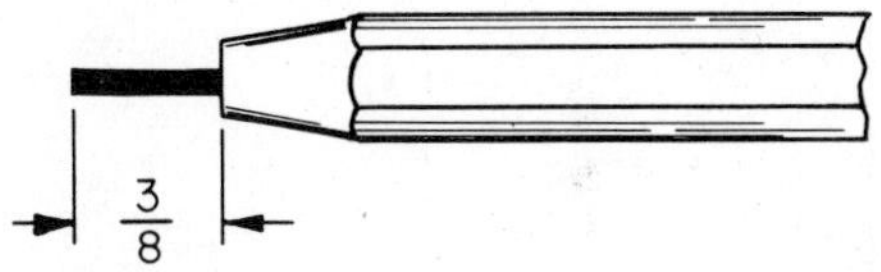

Figure 2-5
If a slight shoulder is provided like this, the pencil can be held closer to the straightedge.

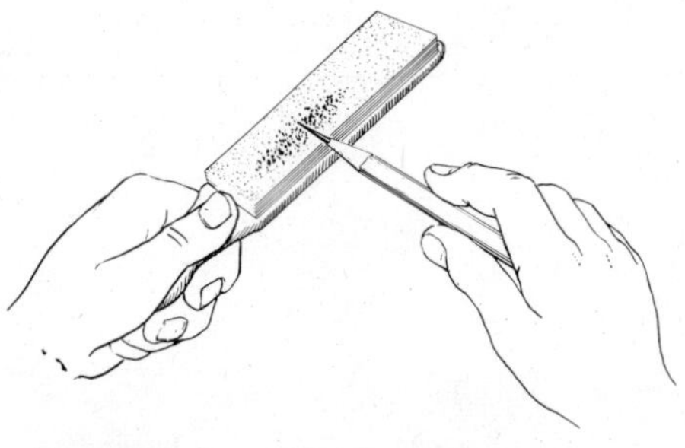

Figure 2-6
The pencil point is formed by shaping it on a sandpaper pad or file.

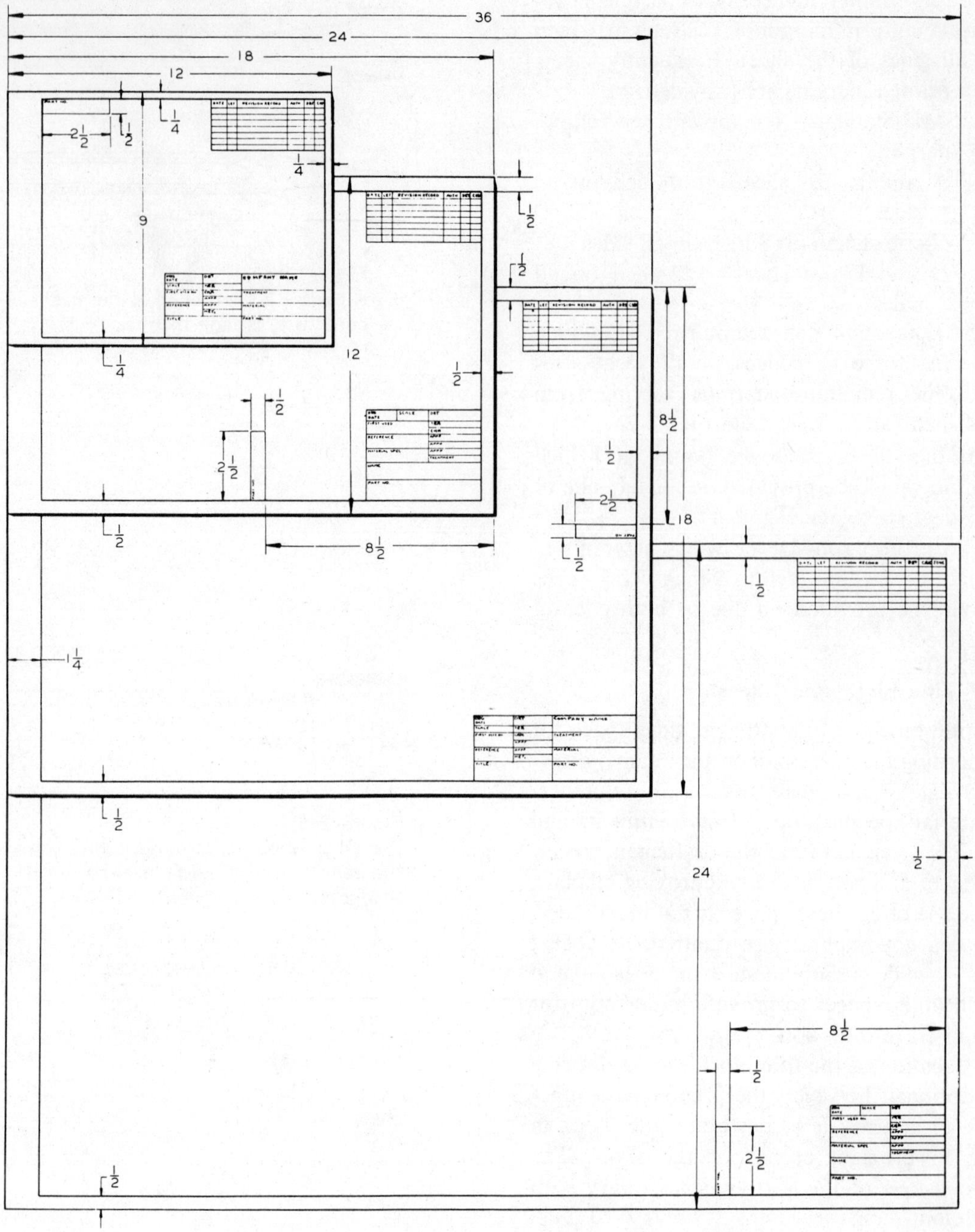

Figure 2–7
Examples of margin allowances recommended by SAE. SAE

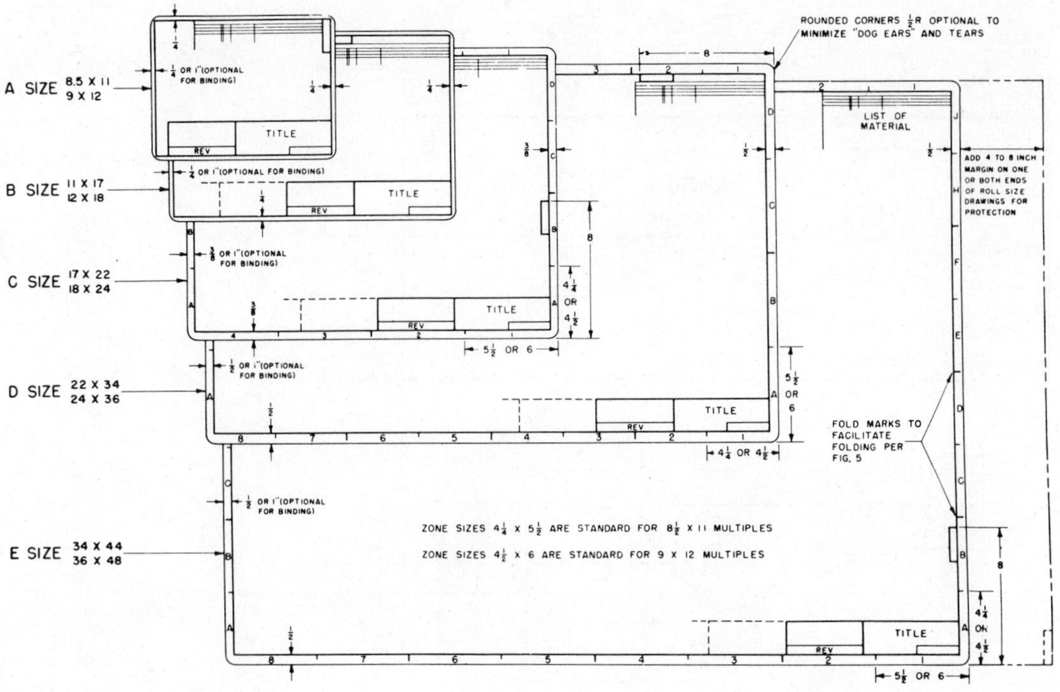

Figure 2-8
Examples of margin allowances recommended by ASA Standards. ASME

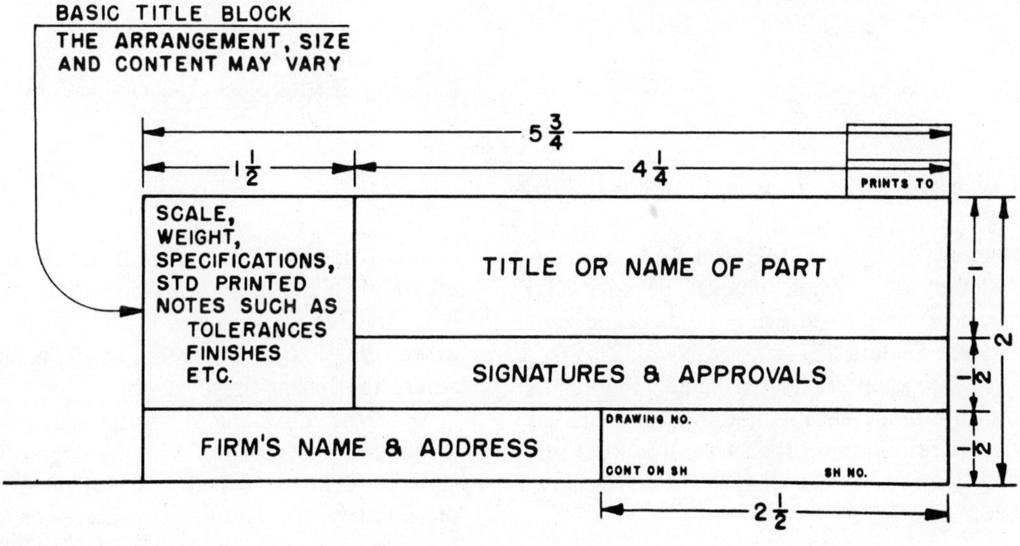

Figure 2-9
Example of title block suggested by ASA. ASME

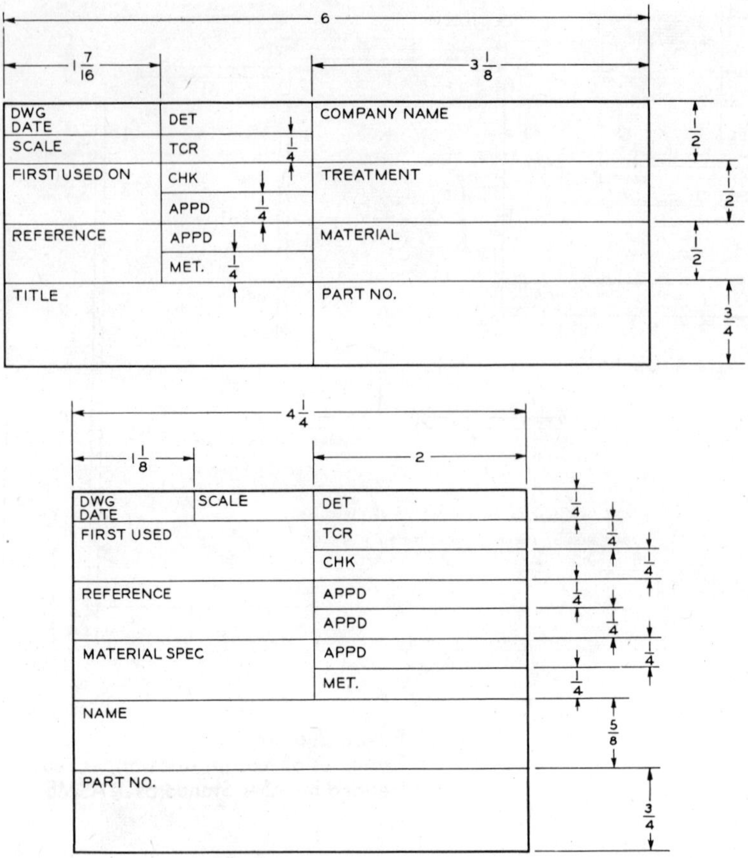

Figure 2-10
Examples of title blocks recommended by SAE.
SAE

suggested by the ASME and SAE. For description of revision blocks, primary and secondary part or drawing number, and zoning, see Section 13.

A title strip serves the same function as the title block except that it extends across the entire bottom of the sheet. It is used primarily on A-size drawings to conserve space. See Fig. 2-11.

2.8 Drawing horizontal lines

To draw horizontal lines, place the head of the T-square firmly against the left edge of the board. Hold the head of the T-square with the left hand as shown in Fig. 2-12 and slide it near the point where the line is to be drawn. Then position the hand so the fingers are on the blade of the square and the thumb is on the board as shown in Fig. 2-13, and move the T-square to the exact position where the line is to be made.

With the T-square in position, place the pencil point against the working edge of the square. Hold the pencil at an angle of approximately 60° and tilt it to the right; that is, in the direction of the line being drawn. Also incline the pencil slightly away from the working edge since this will keep the pencil point closer to the T-square. As the line is drawn, the little finger of the hand holding the pencil should glide lightly on the blade of the T-square. It is good practice to rotate

INGERSOLL STEEL & DISC DIVISION
BORG-WARNER CORPORATION
KALAMAZOO, MICHIGAN
APPROVED
DATE
UNLESS NOTED DIMENSIONS ARE IN INCHES WITH LIMITS + −
WAS
DATE
BY
PART
MAT'L.
CUSTOMERS PART NO.
NO. REQ'D. PER UNIT
DWG. BY
DATE
CHECKED BY
SCALE
PART NO. A

Figure 2-11
A title strip is sometimes used on A-size sheets. Ingersoll Steel and Disc Div. of Borg-Warner Corp.

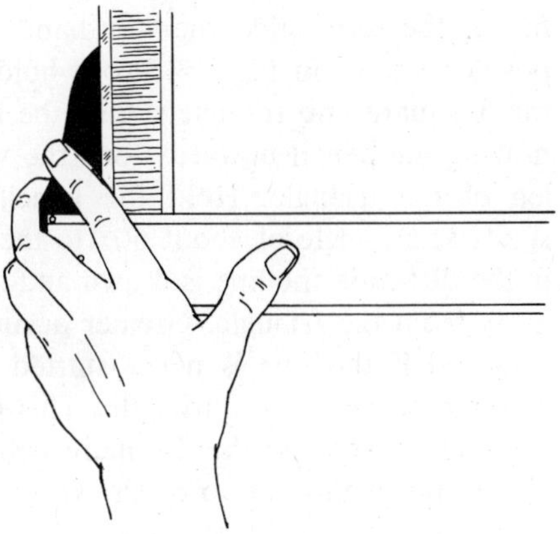

Figure 2-12
This is the first position in manipulating the T-square.

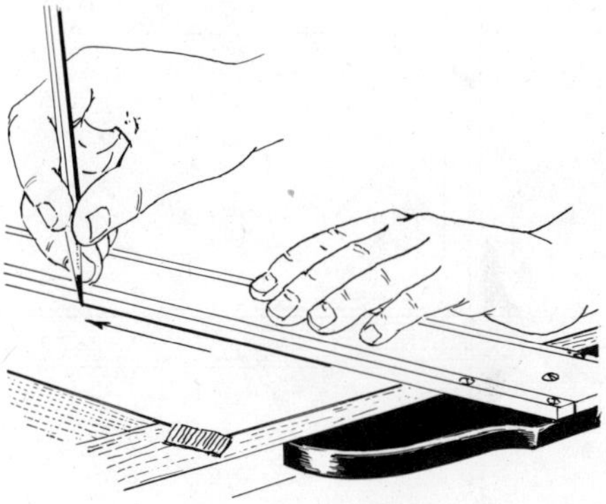

Figure 2-14
This is the position of the T-square and pencil for drawing horizontal lines.

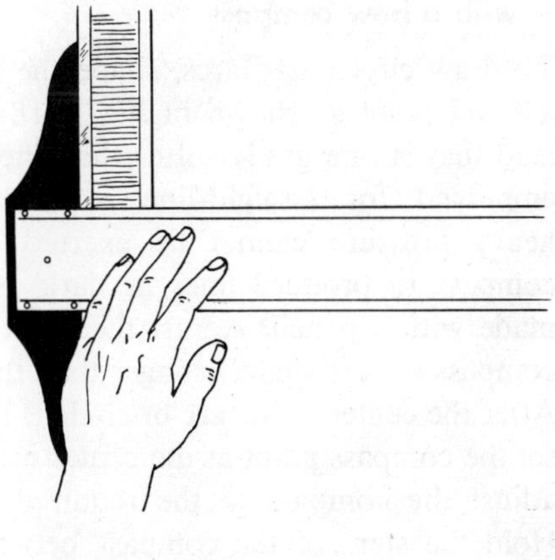

Figure 2-13
Hold the T-square like this when the line is drawn.

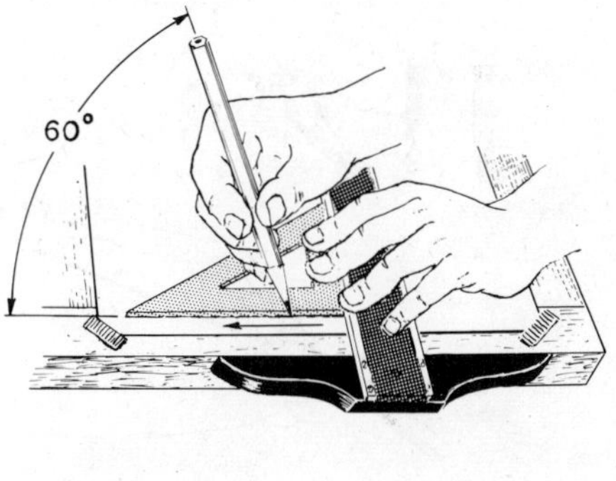

Figure 2-15
This is how vertical lines are drawn.

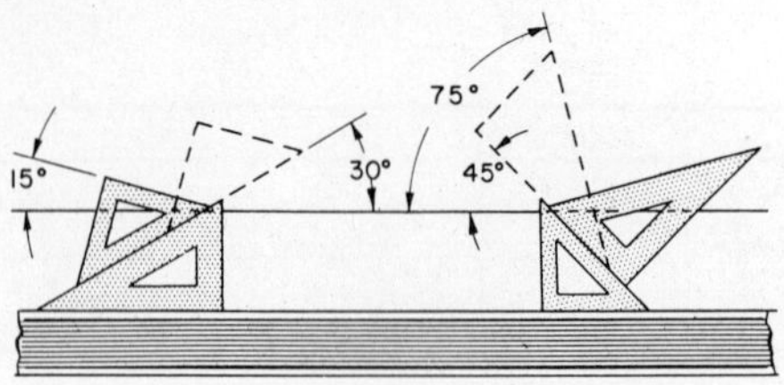

Figure 2-16
Various inclined lines can be drawn by combining the two triangles as shown here.

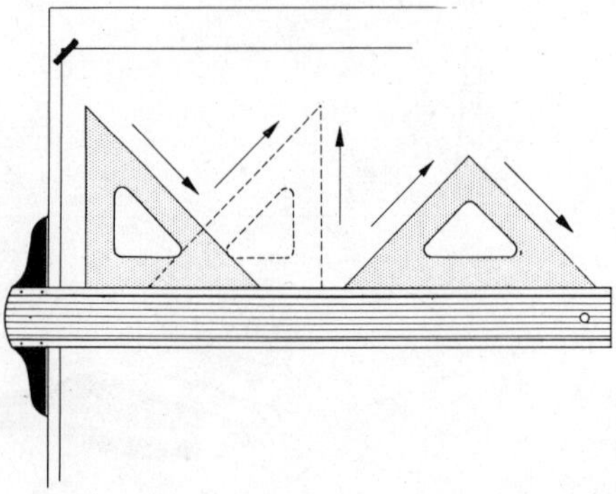

Figure 2-17
Notice the direction in which the pencil should move in drawing inclined lines with the aid of triangles.

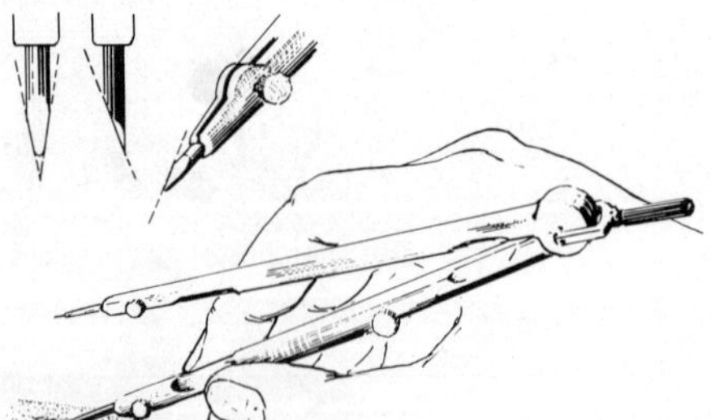

Figure 2-18
Shape the lead of the compass to a bevel point.

the pencil between the thumb and fingers when drawing the line because such a motion keeps the conical pencil point symmetrical for longer periods and produces more uniform lines. Remember that horizontal lines are always drawn from left to right. See Fig. 2-14. For a left handed person the entire procedure described above may be reversed.

2.9 Drawing vertical lines

Place one leg of either the 45° or 30°–60° triangle on the T-square with the other leg facing the left. Slide the left hand to the position shown in Fig. 2-15 so it holds both the T-square and triangle. Draw the line by moving the pencil upward along the vertical leg of the triangle. Hold the pencil so it slants at an angle of about 60° to the paper in the direction the line is drawn and slightly away from the triangle. Greater accuracy is achieved if the line is never started at the extreme corner of the triangle. This can be avoided by keeping the T-square below the lower end of the line to be drawn.

2.10 Drawing inclined lines

Many inclined lines can be made at standard angles using the two triangles. Fig. 2-16 illustrates how the triangles are combined to obtain these various angles. To insure a high degree of accuracy, inclined lines should be drawn in the directions illustrated in Fig. 2-17.

2.11 Drawing circles and arcs with a bow compass

To draw circles and arcs, shape the lead to a bevel point as shown in Fig. 2-18. Use a lead that is one grade softer than the pencil employed for straight-line work because heavy pressure cannot be exerted on the compass to produce lines as dark as those made with a pencil. Adjust the point of the compass so it is slightly longer than the lead. After the center of the arc or circle is located, set the compass point at the center mark and adjust the compass to the required radius. Hold the stem of the compass between the thumb and forefinger. Draw the circle in a clockwise direction, tilting the compass slightly in the direction the circle is being

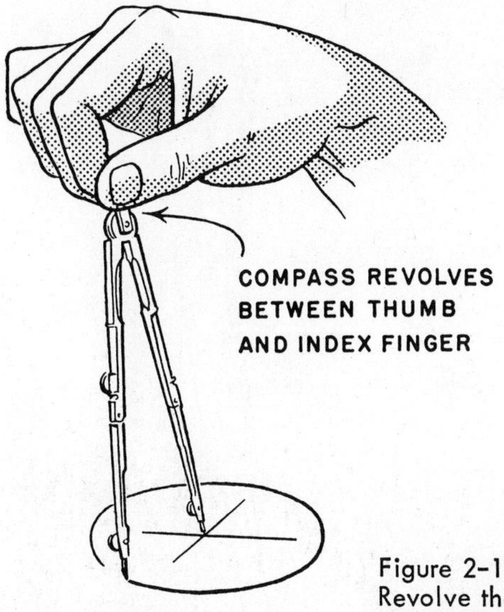

Figure 2-19
Revolve the compass between the thumb and forefinger to draw the circle.

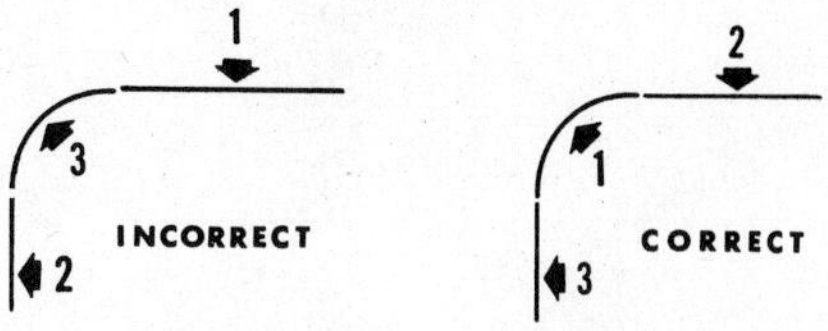

Figure 2-20
Always draw the arc first and then connect the lines to the arc.

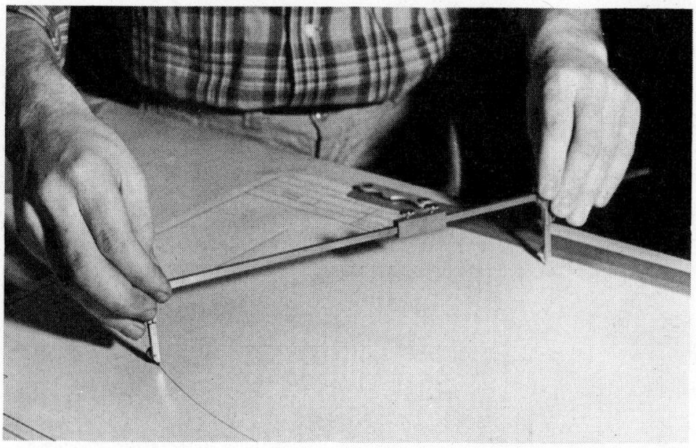

Figure 2-21
Hold the beam compass in this position to draw large circles and arcs.

made. Complete the circle in one sweeping motion. See Fig. 2-19.

When arcs and straight lines tangent to them are required, it is best to draw the arcs first, since it is easier to connect straight lines to an arc than to adjust the arc to the straight lines. See Fig. 2-20.

2.12 Drawing circles and arcs with a beam compass

When the required circles or arcs are too large to be drawn with a regular bow compass, the beam compass is used with either the short or long bar. For exceptionally large circles or arcs the two bars may be joined together with the bar coupler. See Sub-section 1.23.

To use a beam compass, set the points to the required radius, employing the micrometer adjustment for accurate settings. Hold the beam compass with two hands as shown in Fig. 2-21 and draw the circle or arc.

2.13 Using dividers

Dividers are used to space off equal distances, to divide lines into equal parts, and to transfer dimensions.

To space off equal distances, set the points

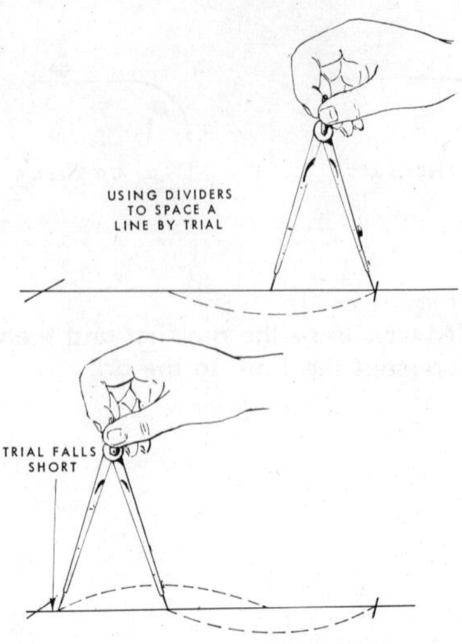

Figure 2-22
Here is how dividers should be used to space off equal distances or to divide a line into equal parts.

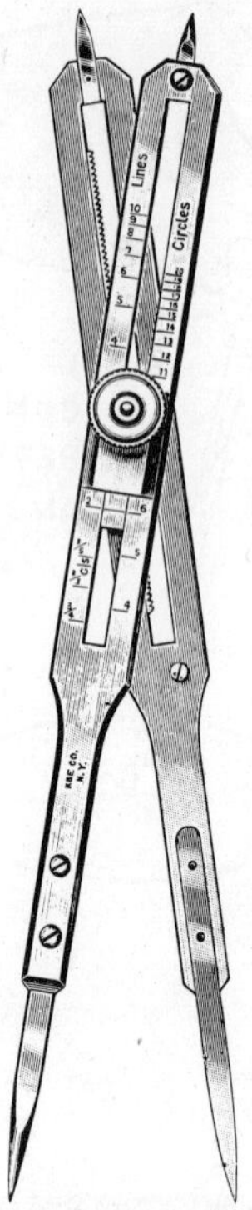

Figure 2-23
Proportional dividers are a time saving device when making copies of drawings to a specified scale.
Keuffel and Esser Co.

of the dividers to the required length. Hold the dividers as shown in Fig. 2-22 and set off the spaces by rotating the dividers between the thumb and forefinger. Rotate the dividers first on one side of the line and then on the other to equalize any accumulating error.

To divide a line into equal parts, adjust the dividers to the approximate space required. Step off the distances, rotating the dividers first to the right and then to the left until the number of units required have been stepped off. See Fig. 2-22. If the line falls short or beyond the given line, lengthen or shorten the dividers proportionately and repeat the operation. For example, to divide a line into four equal parts, set the dividers by eye to approximately one-quarter of the length. After this distance is stepped off and it is found that the space is too small, increase the distance between the divider points by one-quarter of the remaining distance. Similarly, if the last prick of the dividers is beyond the end of the given line, shorten the dividers one-quarter of the extended distance.

To transfer a distance from one part of the drawing to another, simply adjust the dividers to the required length and press the points lightly on the paper in the new position. Avoid too much pressure on the dividers; it will leave unsightly holes in the paper and also may cause the dividers to spread.

Proportional dividers. When a draftsman is required to make copies of drawings to an enlarged or reduced scale, he frequently employs the proportional dividers. See Fig. 2-23.

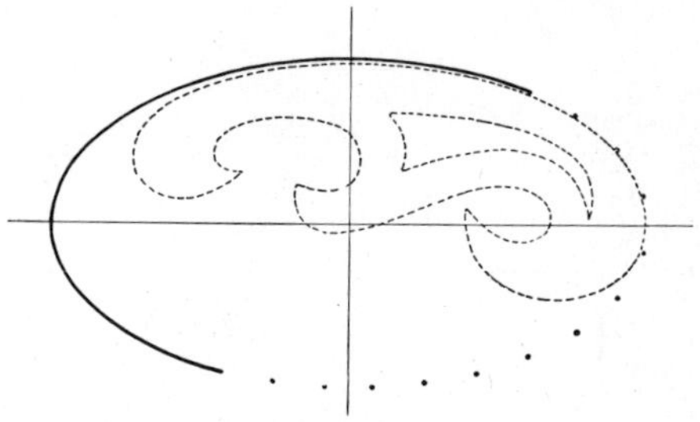

Figure 2-24
An irregular curve should be used in this manner to secure a smooth line.

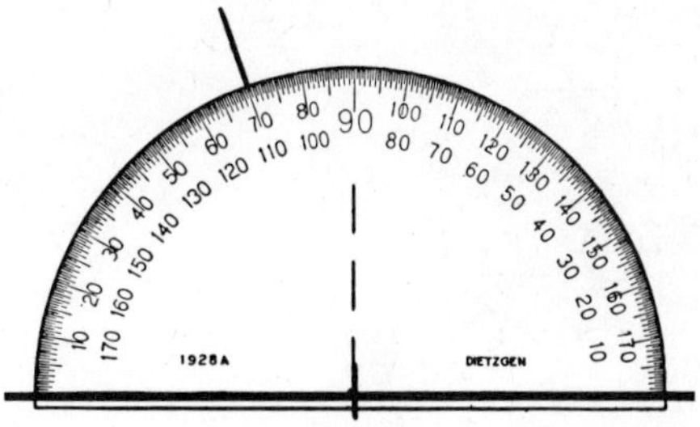

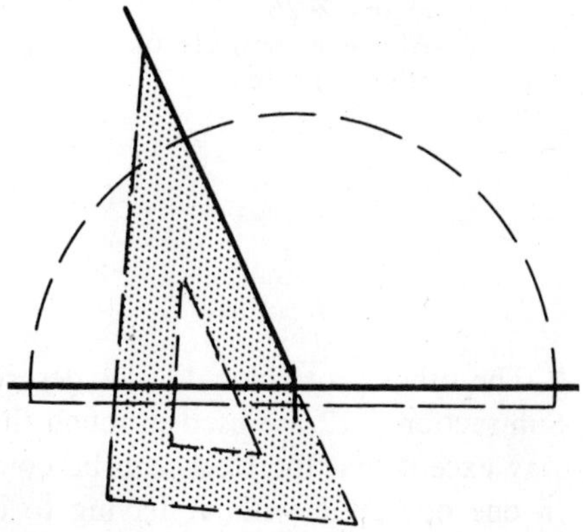

Figure 2-25
How to lay out angles with a protractor.

This instrument permits (1) reproducing the lines of a drawing so the lines in the copy are of a known ratio to the original, and (2) producing a drawing so the content of a solid or area of a plane surface will be in proportion to the original.

Proportional dividers consist of two legs on a sliding, adjustable pivot, making it possible, when the legs are open, to have the distance between the points at one end bear a definite proportion to the distance between the points at the opposite end. The legs are marked with correctly divided scales and when the sliding pivot is set to the proportion desired on any particular scale, that proportion is established. By means of the sliding pivot set to the various scales on the legs, (1) lines may be divided into a given number of parts or elongated to given proportions, (2) the circumference of a circle may be divided into any number of equal parts, and (3) the area of plane circles and squares and the volumes of cubes and spheres may be reduced or enlarged.

2.14 Drawing irregular curves

To draw an irregular curve, first lay off a series of points to indicate the shape of the curve and sketch in a very light line connecting these points. Then select a part of the irregular curve or Mechanical Engineer's curve that fits a portion of the line, as shown in Fig. 2-24. Arrange the curve so its curvature increases in the direction the curvature of the line increases. Be sure the curve used matches the curved line to be drawn for some distance beyond the point where the curved line and irregular curve appear to coincide. If this is done, each successive position of the curved line will be tangent to the other without any abrupt breaks in the line. Continue to move the irregular curve to new positions until the entire line is completed.

2.15 Using a protractor

Occasionally, it is necessary to measure or set off angles other than those which can be obtained with triangles. For such operations, a protractor is necessary. To use a protractor, place it on the T-square with its center point on the mark where the angle is to be located, as shown in Fig. 2-25. Find the desired angle on the protractor, using either the inner or outer scale, and mark it with a point. Remove the protractor and, with the edge of a triangle or straightedge, draw a line connecting the two points.

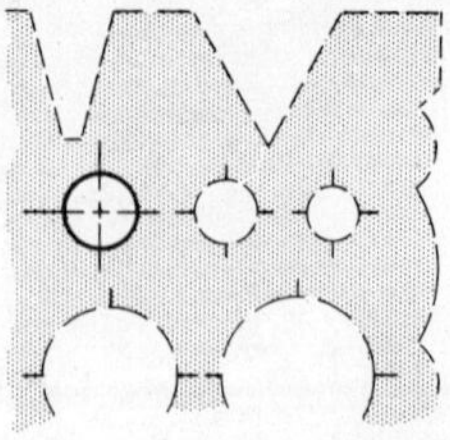

Figure 2-26
Whenever possible use a template to draw a circle.

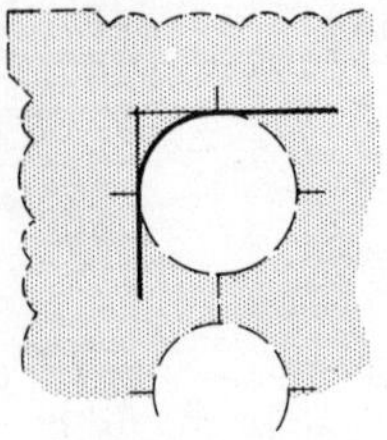

Figure 2-27
A template will expedite the process of drawing arcs.

The other protractor devices described in Sub-section 1.12 are used in much the same way except that the work can be completed in one operation without having to employ separate triangles or straightedges in drawing the angular line.

2.16 How to use a draftsquare or hole template

To draw small circles, lay out the center lines of the circle. Place the template so the quadrant lines of the required circle coincide with the center lines drawn on paper, and trace the circle. See Fig. 2-26.

To draw an arc, lay out the tangent lines. Set the template so the quadrant lines of the correct size radius coincide with the tangent lines, and trace the arc. See Fig. 2-27.

2.17 Alphabet of lines

For pencil work two widths of lines are used —*medium-thick* for visible, hidden, cutting-plane and short break lines; and *thin* for center, dimension, extension, section, long-break and phantom lines. In general, pencil lines will be the same width as ink lines, except that thicker pencil lines will usually be somewhat thinner than corresponding ink lines.

Pencil lines should be clean, dense-black and uniform with a distinct contrast in thickness between the medium-thick and thin lines. Pencil leads should be hard enough to prevent smudging but sufficiently soft to produce black lines. Fig. 2-28 illustrates the various types of lines used in making a drawing. Fig. 2-29 shows how these lines are actually employed in a drawing.

Visible lines. Visible lines are used to show the visible edges of objects. They are the most prominent lines on a drawing.

Hidden lines. These lines are used to show hidden edges of an object. The dashes should be approximately 1/8 inch long with about 1/32 inch spaces. However, the lengths may vary slightly to suit the size of the drawing.

Section lines. Section lines are used to show the cut surfaces of an object in a sectional view. They should be drawn thin to contrast well with visible lines, be equally spaced and proportionate to the size or mass of the section.

Center lines. Center lines are used to indicate axes of symmetrical parts, circles, and paths of motion. The long dashes may vary from 3/4 inch long to 1–1/2 inches or more, depending on the size of the drawing. The short dashes should be approximately 1/16 inch long. Center lines should start and end with the long dashes and should not intersect at spaces between the dashes.

Dimension lines, extension lines, and leaders. Dimension lines are used to indicate the extent and direction of dimensions and are terminated with arrowheads. Extension lines

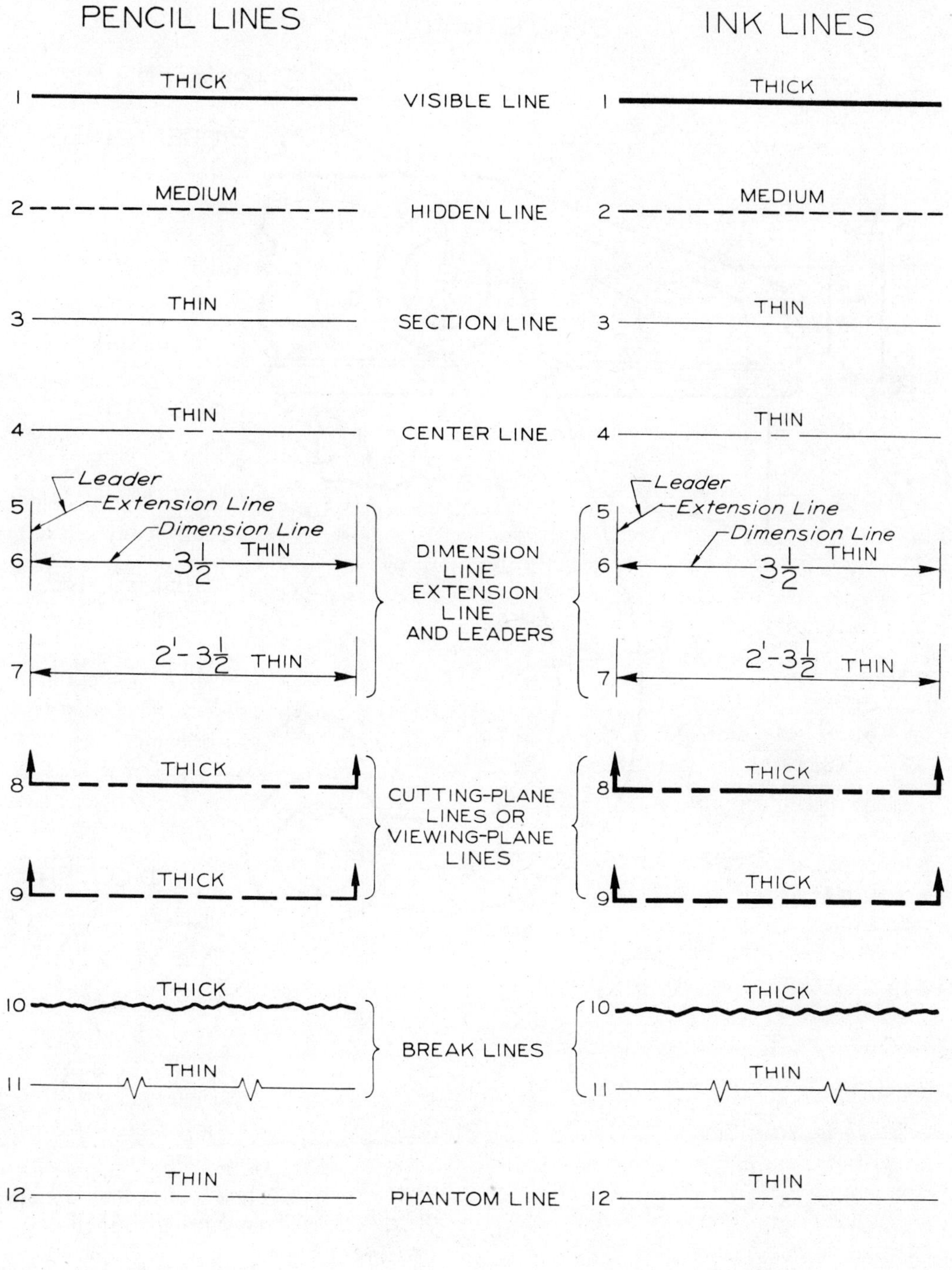

Figure 2–28
Alphabet of lines. ASME

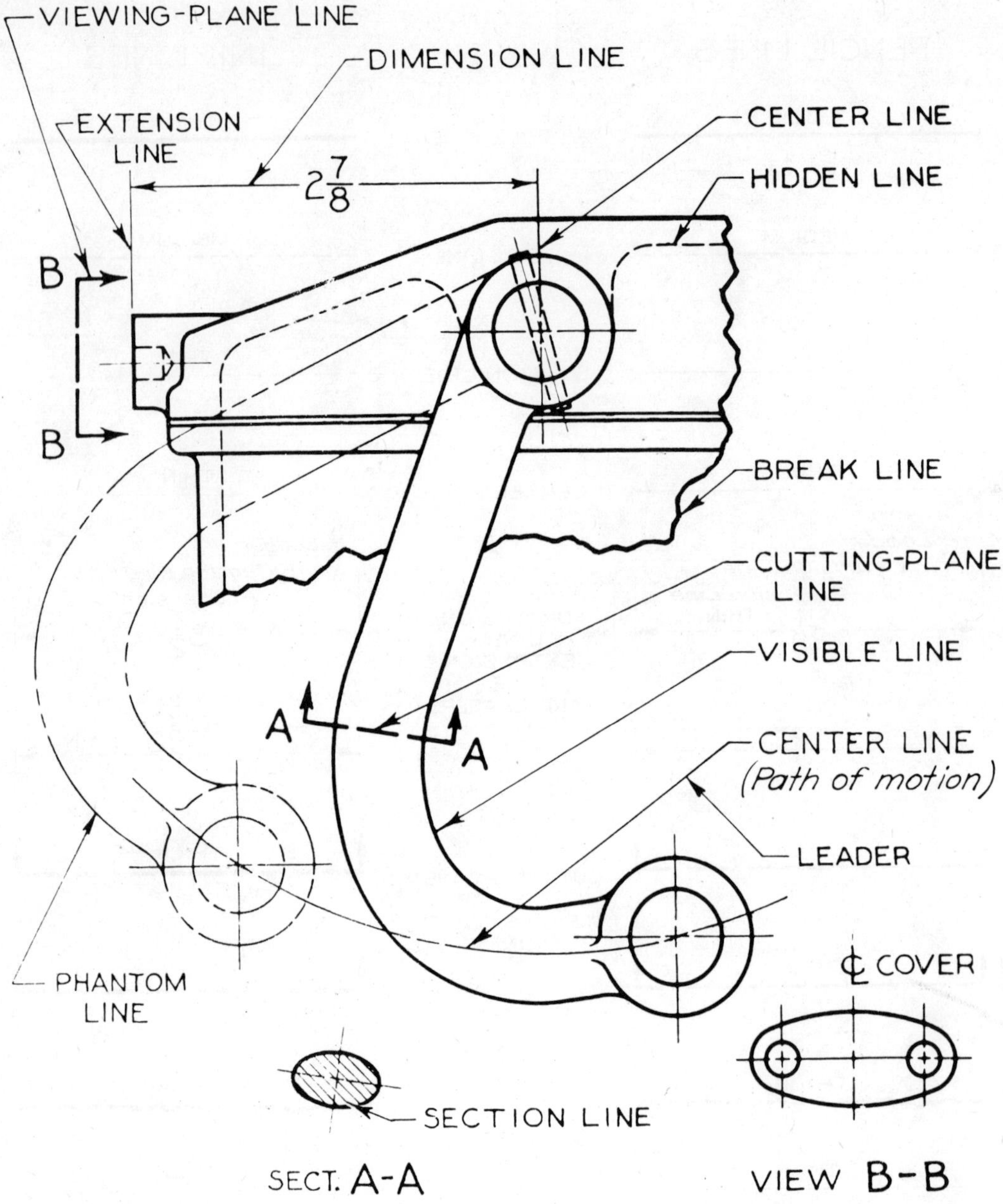

Figure 2-29
Here is how various lines are used in making a drawing. ASME

DRAWING SCALES			
FULL SIZE	12" = 12"	1/1	
HALF SIZE	6" = 12"	1/2	6" = 1 FT
QUARTER SIZE	3" = 12"	1/4" = 1"	3" = 1 FT
EIGHTH SIZE	1-1/2" = 12"	1-1/2" = 1 FT	
TWICE SIZE	24" = 12"	2/1	2 x SIZE
FOUR TIMES SIZE	48" = 12"	4/1	4 x SIZE

Figure 2-30
The scale of a drawing may be shown in any one of these ways.

are used to indicate the termination of a dimension. They should begin 1/16 inch from the object and extend 1/8 inch beyond the outermost arrowhead. Leaders are used to direct notes or identification symbols to features on the drawing.

Cutting plane lines. These lines are used to indicate the location of cutting planes in sectioning and the viewing position of removed pieces. Two forms of lines may be used. The first consists of alternating long dashes and pairs of short dashes. The long dashes should be approximately 3/4 to 1–1/2 inches or more in length, depending on the size of the drawing, and the short dashes 1/8 inch long with 1/16 inch spaces.

The second fórm of line is composed of equal dashes approximately 1/4 inch long. The ends of cutting-plane lines are bent at 90 degrees and terminated by arrowheads to indicate the direction of sight for viewing the section.

Break lines. Break lines are used to limit a broken section. For short breaks an uneven freehand line is recommended. For long breaks, the practice is to use long, thin-ruled dashes joined by freehand "zig-zags".

Phantom lines. Phantom lines are used to show adjacent parts, alternate positions, and lines of motion. They are thin lines composed of long dashes varying from 3/4 to 1–1/2 inches or more alternated with pairs of short dashes 1/8 inch in length with 1/16 inch spaces.

2.18 Indicating the scale on a drawing

As stated in Section 1, a drawing is made so the object is shown in its full or natural size, its reduced size, or its enlarged size. Whenever possible, the practice is to make the drawing full size. If the size has to be reduced, most industries usually limit the scale to 1/2, 1/4, or 1/8. For parts which are too small to be drawn full size, the common procedure is to draw them two or four times larger.

The scale of a drawing is always included in the title block. If more than one detail occurs on a drawing and different scales are used, the scale of the principal detail is shown in the title block along with the notation "and noted." The other scales are specified under each detail. Fig. 2-30 illustrates several methods of designating the scale on a drawing.

2.19 Laying out accurate measurements

Measurements should not be taken off the scale with dividers and laid off on the drawing. This practice ruins the scale and tends to pro-

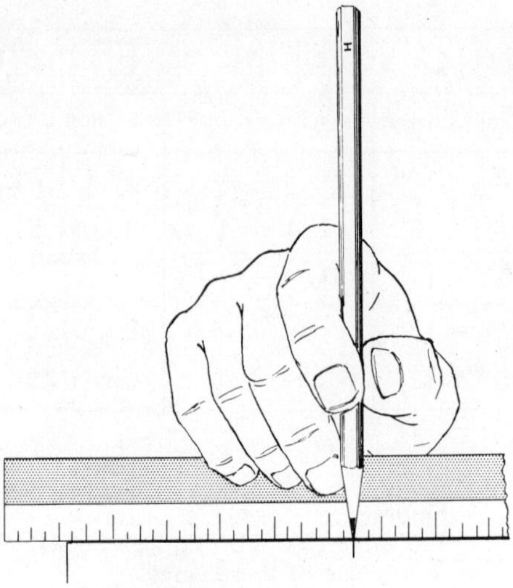

Figure 2-31
For accurate results lay out dimensions in this manner.

Figure 2-34
The electric erasing machines speed up the erasing operation.

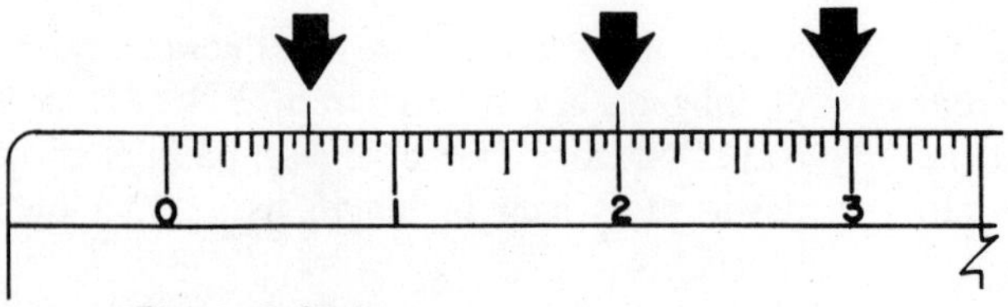

Figure 2-32
Avoid cumulative error by laying out all distances without moving the scale.

Figure 2-33
An eraser of this type simplifies the task of removing heavy lines.
Keuffel and Esser Co.

duce errors. For accurate results, place the scale on the drawing and make a small mark with the point of the pencil next to the graduation desired. See Fig. 2-31. When a number of distances are to be laid off end-to-end on the same line, mark off all of the distances without moving the scale. If each distance is laid off individually by moving the scale to a new position each time, there is always a possibility that accumulative errors will be introduced. See Fig. 2-32.

2.20 Erasing a drawing

In the process of making a drawing, a draftsman will need to make certain corrections and changes which will involve some amount of erasing. Most pencil marks or lines can be eradicated with an ordinary pencil eraser. Heavy lines are removed more easily and quickly with the special drawing eraser shown in Fig. 2-33. Extremely hard or gritty erasers should be avoided since they damage the surface of the paper.

The electric erasing machine is a common tool in many drafting rooms. See Fig. 2-34. It is built so the motor can be started and stopped and the erasing operation performed with one hand. A special built-in blower blows away the erased particles while the machine is erasing.

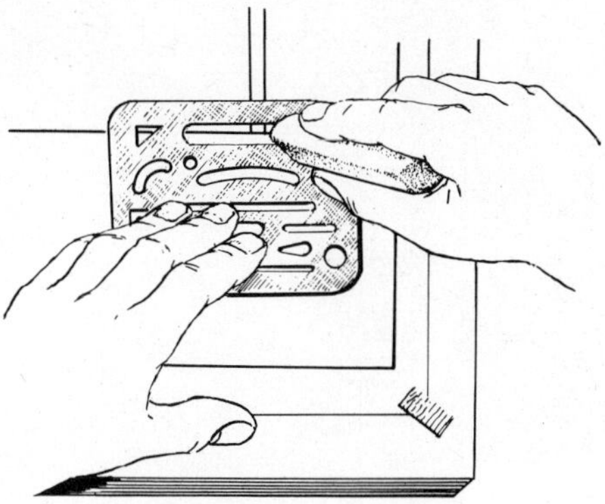

Figure 2-35
An erasing shield simplifies the task of removing pencil marks.

Before proceeding with any erasing operation, be sure that the eraser is clean. A simple way to clean an eraser is to rub it on a piece of clean paper. Very often if a considerable amount of erasing is necessary, it is a good idea to place a triangle under the paper. The triangle provides a hard surface which permits erasing to be accomplished more effectively. To prevent tearing the paper, however, care should be exercised to erase only on the wider sections of the triangle.

To erase, place the fingers of the left hand near the mark that is to be removed and rub the eraser back and forth. Hold the paper firmly, otherwise it may wrinkle or tear. Rub slowly, without too much pressure, to avoid overheating the eraser and leaving a stain on the drawing.

If erasing is to be done near lines which are to be left intact, the use of an erasing shield will facilitate the process. See Fig. 2-35. To use this shield, select an opening that best fits the mark to be removed. Hold the shield firmly over the pencil mark and erase through the opening. If a shield is not available, the same results can be obtained by covering the area not to be touched with a piece of stiff paper.

When the erasing is completed, wipe off the paper with a clean cloth or dusting brush, and touch up any of the lines that might have been damaged during the erasing process. To help keep a drawing clean, draftsmen often sprinkle granulated rubber over the paper. These small particles act as bearing surfaces which keep the T-square and triangles from actually touching the paper. As a result, dirt and pencil graphite are prevented from spreading over the drawing.

Occasionally after erasing some lines a groove may remain in the paper. The groove, if not too deep, can be removed by rubbing over with a burnisher or even with the thumb nail.

2.21 Keeping a drawing clean

One of the true marks of a good draftsman is his ability to produce clean drawings. Very often what might be an excellent drawing is ruined because of its dirty appearance. The professional draftsman and engineer are very meticulous in keeping their drafting equipment clean and refraining from practices that may contribute to producing a dirty drawing. To produce clean drawings, therefore, the student of drafting should faithfully observe and carry out the following:

1 Always wipe off the board, T-square, triangle, and other tools before proceeding to draw. Any ordinary soft cloth or cleansing tissue will serve this purpose. Soap and lukewarm water may be used. Hot water should be avoided since it may cause wooden, celluloid or plastic articles to warp.

2 Be sure the hands are clean at all times. If the hands tend to perspire they should be washed frequently during the drawing period. Sprinkling talcum powder on the hands will often counteract excessive perspiration.

3 Keep the hands or sleeves off the penciled area. It is a good idea to roll up the sleeves. If additional work must be done in the penciled area, such as lettering or erasing, cover the remaining section with a clean sheet of tracing paper.

4 Do not slide triangles, T-square, or other drafting devices over penciled lines. When these instruments must be moved over pen-

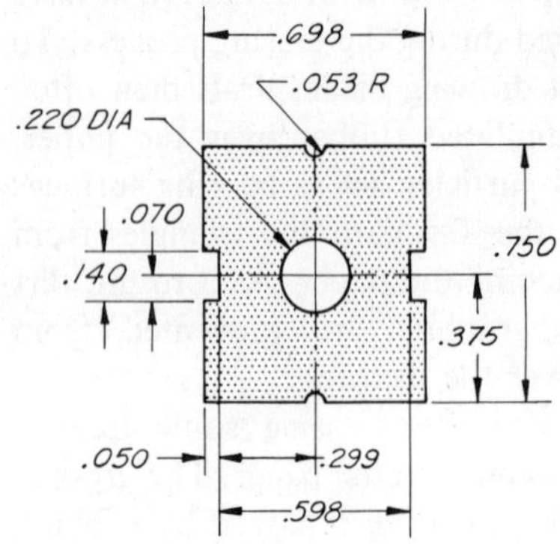

Figure 2-36
Bracket Insulation. The Lionel Corp.

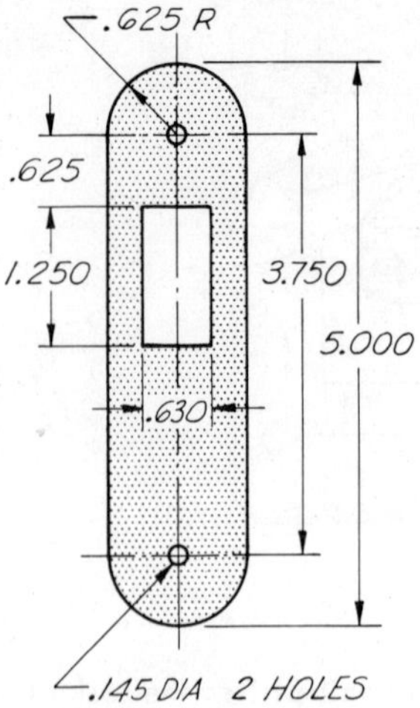

Figure 2-37
Latch Front.
Yale and Towne
Manufacturing Co.

ciled areas, it is better to pick them up. Sliding them will tend to spread tiny dirt or graphite particles, thereby smearing the surface. Sprinkling granulated rubber over the paper will reduce smearing to a minimum.

5 Do not remove erasing particles with the fingers or palm of the hand. Use a draftsman's dusting brush or flick the particles off with a clean cloth.

6 Never sharpen a pencil over the drawing. After sharpening or pointing, wipe the pencil point with a clean cloth to remove small particles of loose graphite.

7 Never place the sandpaper pad in contact with any other drafting equipment while it is stored in the drawer unless it is completely enclosed.

8 Always cover a drawing at the end of the drawing period.

9 Do not allow drawings to overhang drafting or reference table edges, or be mishandled in other ways that will result in folds or creases.

Problems, section 2

1 Make a drawing of the Bracket Insulation on A-size sheet. See Fig. 2-36. Scale = 4/1. Material: .062 Black Phenolic Plate.

2 Construct a full-size drawing of the Latch Front shown in Fig. 2-37. Material: Aluminum, 63S-T5.

3 Prepare a drawing of the Bail Adjusting Link shown in Fig. 2-38. Scale = 4/1. Material: .050 Full Hard Brass.

4 Construct a drawing of the Octal Contact Blank. See Fig. 2-39. Scale = 10/1.

5 Make a 3/4 size drawing of the Nose Piece shown in Fig. 2-40.

6 Produce a drawing of the Gasket shown in Fig. 2-41. Use any convenient scale. Material: 1/16 Black Rubber, Garlock #353.

7 Using any suitable scale, make a layout of the Baffle shown in Fig. 2-42. Material: .125—61S-T6 Aluminum.

8 Make a drawing of the Shim shown in Fig. 2-43. Scale = 2/1. Material: .020 Plastic Shim Stock.

9 Construct a drawing of the Gasket shown in Fig. 2-44. Use any convenient scale. Material: 1/16 Asbestos Fibre.

10 Produce a 1—1/2 size drawing of the Gasket shown in Fig. 2-45. Material: 3/32 Neoprene.

11 Enlarge the drawing of the Lens Diaphragm Leaf to a suitable scale. See Fig. 2-46.

12 Lay out a full-size pattern for the airfoil section shown in Fig. 2-47.

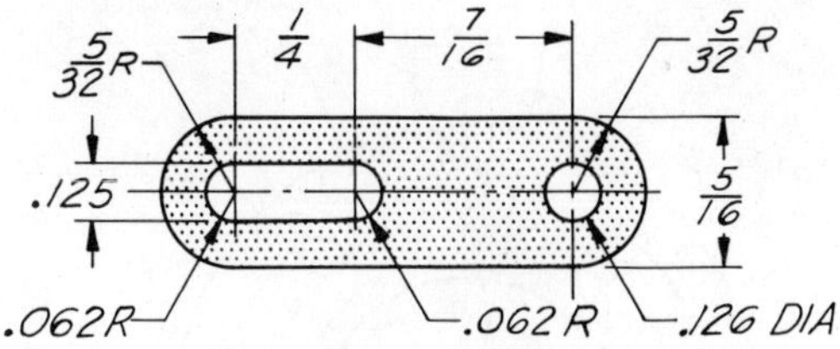

Figure 2-38
Link, Bail Adjusting
Dictaphone Corp.

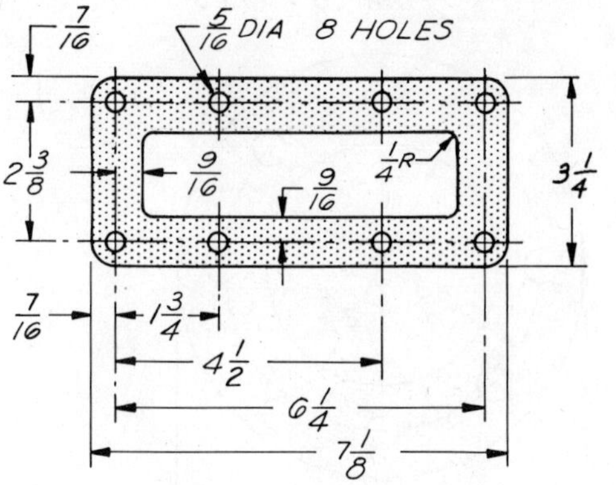

Figure 2-41
Gasket. Bendix Aviation Corp.

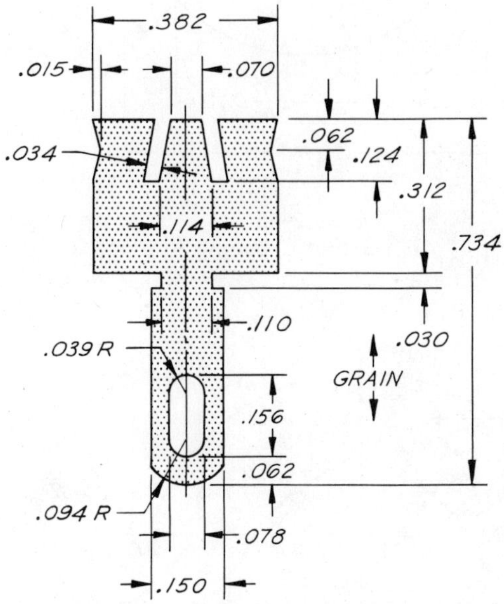

Figure 2-39
Octal Contact Blank
Sylvania Electrical Products, Inc.

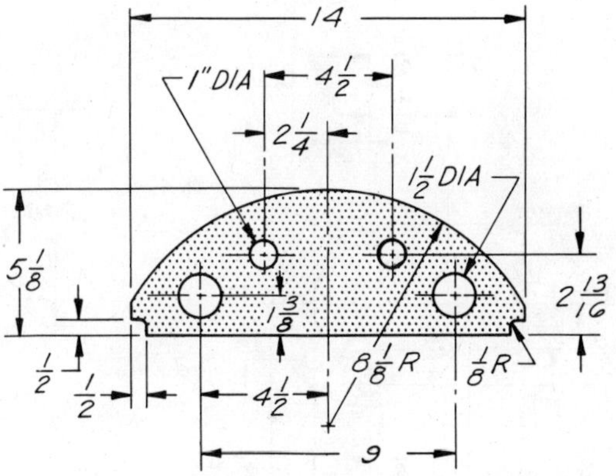

Figure 2-42
Baffle

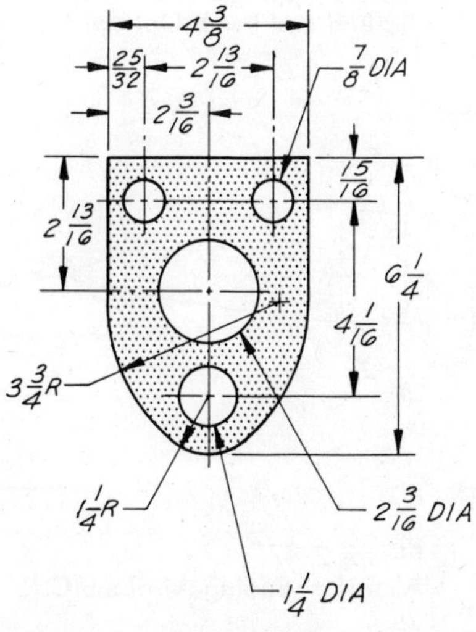

Figure 2-40
Nose Piece
Bausch and Lomb Optical Co.

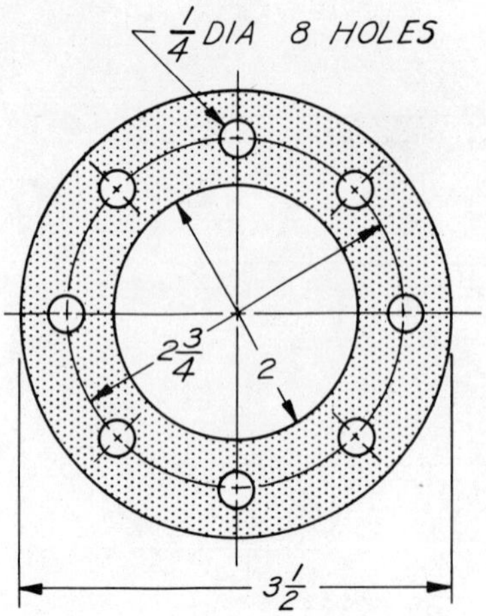

Figure 2-43
Shim. Bendix Aviation Corp.

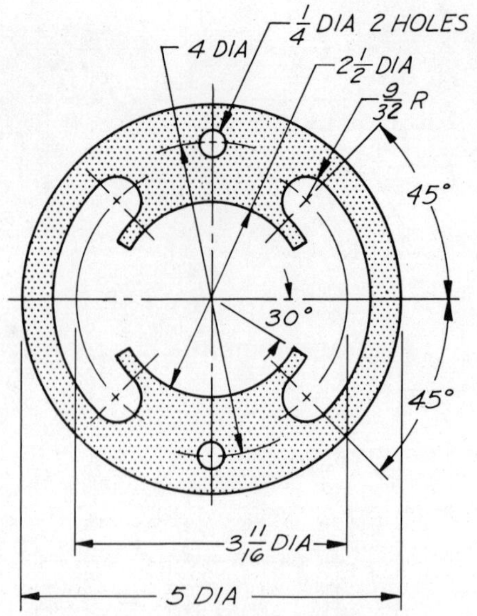

Figure 2-45
Gasket. Boeing Airplane Co.

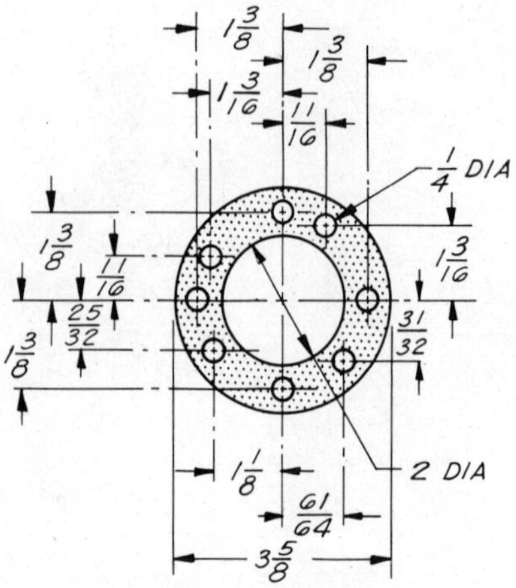

Figure 2-44
Gasket. Bendix Aviation Corp.

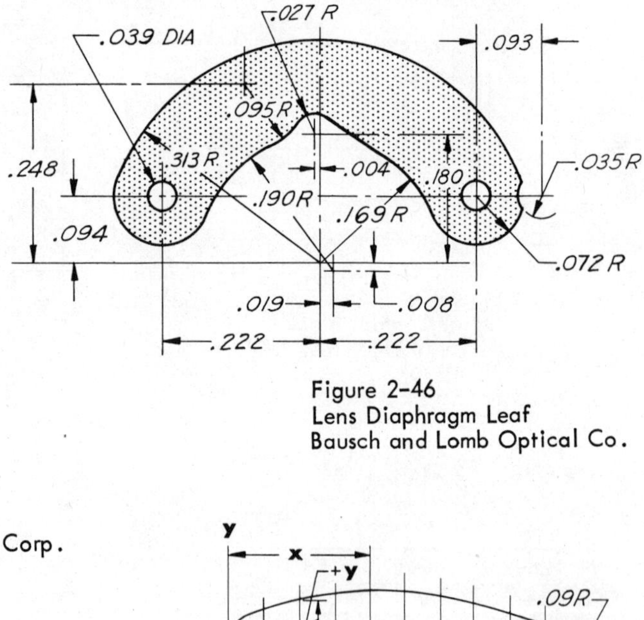

Figure 2-46
Lens Diaphragm Leaf
Bausch and Lomb Optical Co.

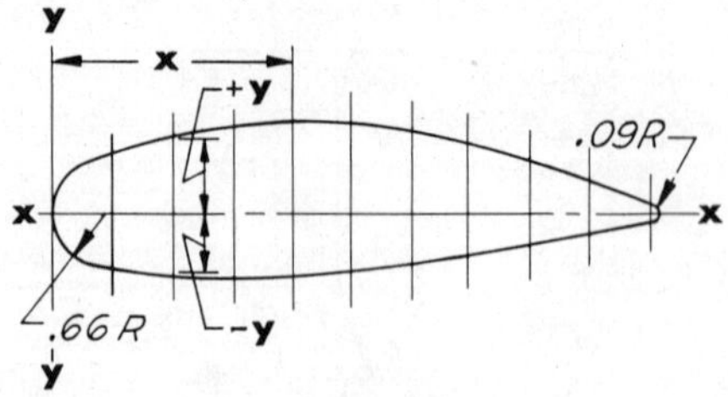

UPPER CAMBER

X AXIS	0	.75	1.5	2.25	3.00	3.75	4.50	5.25	6.00	6.75	7.50
Y AXIS	0	.74	.95	1.08	1.13	1.12	1.04	.89	.68	.43	.11

LOWER CAMBER

X AXIS	0	.75	1.5	2.25	3.00	3.75	4.50	5.25	6.00	6.75	7.50
Y AXIS	0	-.68	-.76	-.79	-.79	-.74	-.66	-.55	-.42	-.26	-.10

Figure 2-47
Airfoil. Boeing Airplane Co.

Engineering lettering 3

A drawing is prepared to convey certain kinds of information. If a drawing is to indicate clearly its intended function, two observances are necessary: (1) the object must be drawn according to accepted standards, and (2) sufficient data must be included which will supplement the readability of the graphically illustrated object.

The presentation of informational data on a drawing is known as *lettering*. Whether the data is in the form of dimensional sizes, explanatory notes, or the listing of specifications, it must be legible and pleasing in appearance. Moreover, lettering must be of such a nature that it can be executed easily and rapidly by the draftsman.

To be able to letter well is a skill which can be acquired only through practice. To acquire skill in lettering, a student of drawing must practice diligently and observe the principles described in this section.

3.1 Style of lettering

There are several different styles of letters, but in actual usage, professional draftsmen and engineers usually confine their lettering to the type known as the upper case (capital letters), single-stroke Gothic. Lower-case letters are rarely used on machine drawings. They are used more extensively for maps and other topographical drawings as well as architectural and structural drawings.

Single-stroke simply means that the width of the lines which form the letters does not vary. It does not imply that letters are begun and completed in one single stroke.

The Gothic style is universally used in industry because it is more legible and can be executed much more rapidly than other styles.

Both the vertical and inclined Gothic letters are acceptable in engineering drawing. The vertical letters are considered by some to possess greater readability. However, they are a little more difficult to produce because a slight variation from the vertical is quickly discernible. Although most industries do not prescribe any one form, some prefer that all lettering be done in one style only. Therefore, it is wise for the student of drafting to become proficient in using both the inclined and vertical letters.

3.2 Letter strokes

To acquire skill in lettering, letters and numerals should be formed with certain strokes. Although in the past there have been some divergent points of view concerning the number and direction of strokes, an examination of the practices followed by experienced draftsmen discloses that the strokes shown in Figs. 3-1 and 3-2 are more currently favored. The outstanding features of the strokes illustrated are that they permit greater speed in the lettering process and provide a more natural flow of lines with a minimum change of pencil position. The same strokes are applicable for both inclined and vertical letters.

3.3 Proportions of letters and numerals

To create the effect of balance and of stability, letters and numerals should have a certain relationship between height and width. Some letters and numbers, because of their shape, must be wider, whereas others need to be narrower. In order to understand the significance of this relationship, the letters and numbers shown in Fig. 3-3 have been enclosed in squares the sides of which have been divided equally into six parts. Notice that most letters are approximately two-thirds as wide as they are high. Letters *B, C, D, E, F, G,* etc., are four squares wide. Others such as *A, O, Q,*

Figure 3-1
These are the vertical style letters and numbers used by some draftsmen. The arrows show the direction of the strokes.

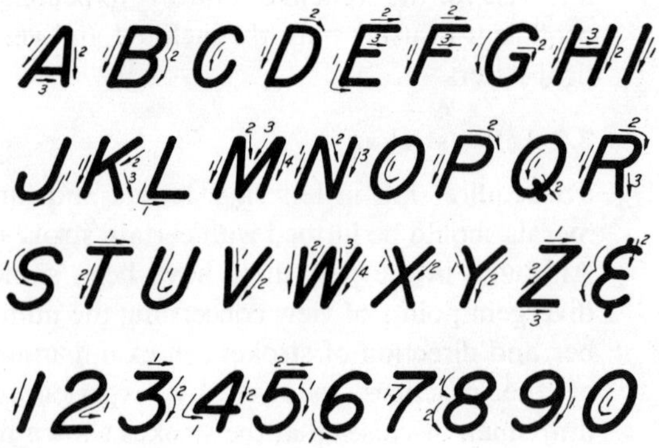

Figure 3-2
Some draftsmen prefer the inclined letters.

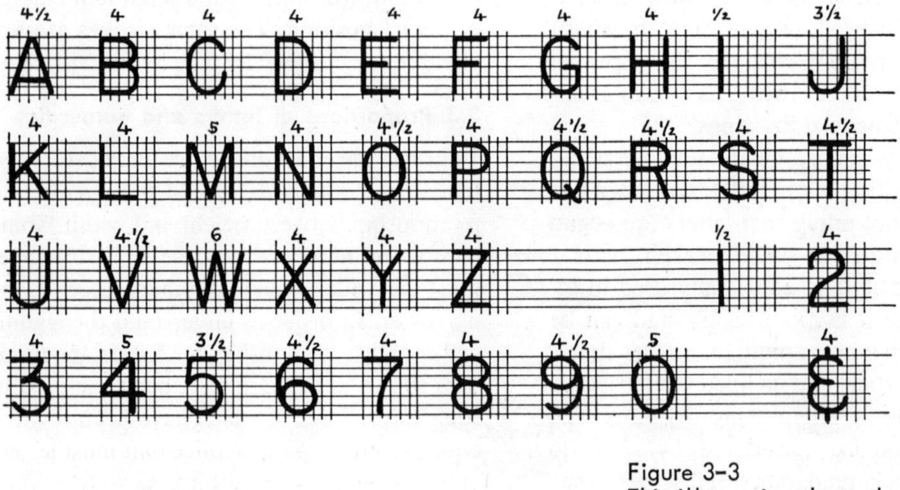

Figure 3-3
This illustration shows the correct height and width relationship for letters and numbers.

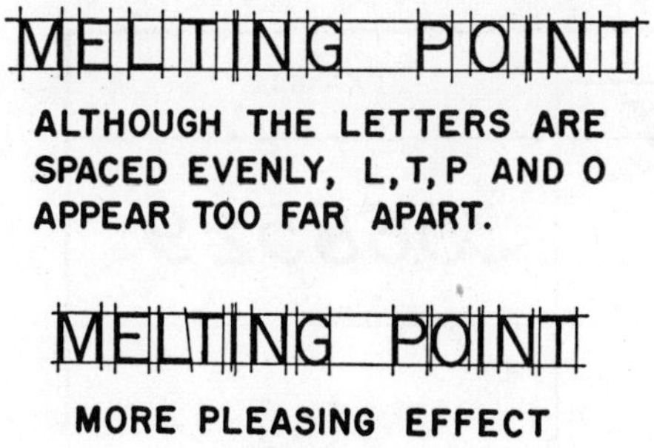

MELTING POINT
ALTHOUGH THE LETTERS ARE SPACED EVENLY, L, T, P AND O APPEAR TOO FAR APART.
MELTING POINT
MORE PLEASING EFFECT

Figure 3-4
The area between letters should appear to be equal.

Figure 3-5
Examples of condensed and extended letters.

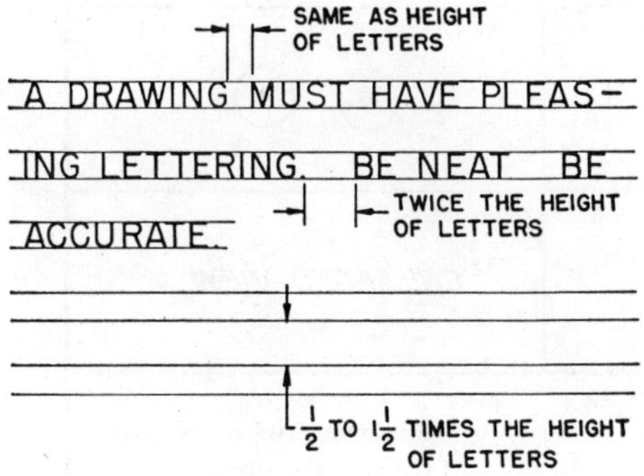

Figure 3-6
Words and sentences should be spaced like this.

R, and *V* are four and one-half squares wide, whereas *M* is five squares wide. The widest letter of the alphabet is *W,* which is almost six and one-half squares wide.

Fig. 3-3 also shows the correct proportion for numbers. Most numbers such as 2, 3, 7, 8 are about two squares narrower than they are high, whereas 4, 6, 9, and 0 are more than four squares wide. Notice also that with letters having horizontal cross bars—*B, E, F, H,* and *R,* the middle bar is placed slightly above the center, and the top portion of *B, X, Y,* 3, 5, 6, 8, etc., is made smaller than the bottom portion to avoid the effect of top-heaviness.

3.4 Spacing letters

Making properly proportioned letters is not sufficient for good lettering. Equally important is the spacing between the letters. To obtain a pleasing appearance, the areas between each letter must appear to be equal. See Fig. 3-4. This uniformity cannot always be achieved by simply placing the letters the same distance apart. For example, if the letters *L* and *T* were spaced the same distance as *M* and *E* an unbalanced effect would result. Due to the shape of *L* and *T,* less space is needed between them than for *M* and *E.* The same principle must be observed for some of the other letters in the alphabet. The

	HEIGHT		EXAMPLE
	MECHANICAL	FREE HAND	
Part Number in Title Block	.240 to .350 .350 Preferred	1/4 to 3/8 3/8 Preferred	*3568529*
Section and Tabulation Letters	.240	1/4	*A-A*
Part Name in Title Block	.140	5/32	*CRANKSHAFT*
Revision Column, Process and Dimensional Notes	.120	1/8	*FINISH ALL OVER*
Dimensions: Fractional, Decimal	.120	1/8	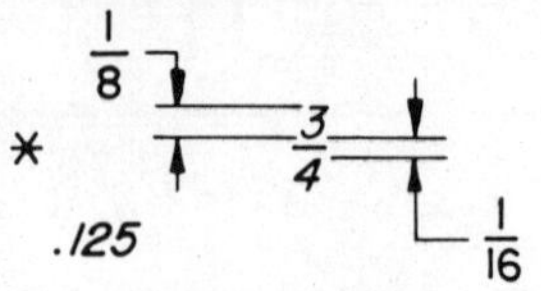
Revision Letter or Revision Number on Body of Drawing	.120	1/8	(A) (6)
Sub Titles for Special Views	.120	1/8	*ENLARGED VIEW*

*Fractions. The division sign of a binary fraction shall be parallel to the direction in which the dimension reads, except when such fractions are included in notes, tables, lists, etc., where a diagonal line may be used. Example: 15/32

Figure 3-7
SAE recommended letter heights.
SAE

accepted rule is to place adjacent letters with straight sides farther apart than those with curved sides. Sometimes it may even be necessary to overlap slightly such combinations as *LT* and *AV*, whereas in other cases the width of a letter has to be decreased. The customary practice is to judge the spacing by eye rather than try to achieve area balance by means of actual measurement.

In the process of lettering composition, the letters and numerals may have to be condensed or extended to meet certain space requirements. Thus if a space is limited in length, each letter in the composition will have to be correspondingly narrower. Similarly if a wide space is to be filled with composition, each letter may have to be extended. See Fig. 3-5.

3.5 Spacing words, sentences and lines

The distance between words should be equal to the height of the letters. See Fig. 3-6. As a

TYPE 1

ABCDEFGHIJKLMNOP

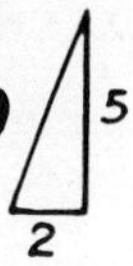

QRSTUVWXYZ&

1234567890 $\frac{1}{2}$ $\frac{3}{4}$ $\frac{5}{8}$ $\frac{7}{16}$

TO BE USED FOR MAIN TITLES & DRAWING NUMBERS

TYPE 2

ABCDEFGHIJKLMNOPQR STUVWXYZ&

1234567890 $\frac{13}{64}$ $\frac{5}{8}$ $\frac{1}{2}$

TO BE USED FOR SUB-TITLES

TYPE 3

ABCDEFGHIJKLMNOPQRSTUVWXYZ&

1234567890 $\frac{1}{2}$ $\frac{3}{4}$ $\frac{5}{8}$ $\frac{7}{16}$

FOR HEADINGS AND PROMINENT NOTES

TYPE 4

ABCDEFGHIJKLMNOPQRSTUVWXYZ&

1234567890 $\frac{1}{2}$ $\frac{1}{4}$ $\frac{3}{8}$ $\frac{5}{16}$ $\frac{7}{32}$ $\frac{1}{8}$

FOR BILLS OF MATERIAL, DIMENSIONS & GENERAL NOTES

TYPE 5

OPTIONAL TYPE SAME AS TYPE 4 BUT USING TYPE 3 FOR FIRST LETTER OF PRINCIPAL WORDS. MAY BE USED FOR SUB-TITLES & NOTES ON THE BODY OF DRAWINGS.

TYPE 6

abcdefghijklmnopqrstuvwxyz

Type 6 may be used in place of Type 4 with capitals of Type 3

Figure 3-8
ASA Standards for letter heights.
(Letters are actual size.)
ASME

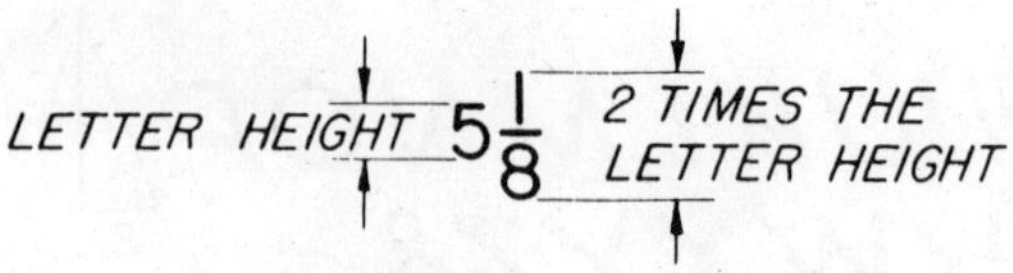

Figure 3-9
Fractions should be made like this.

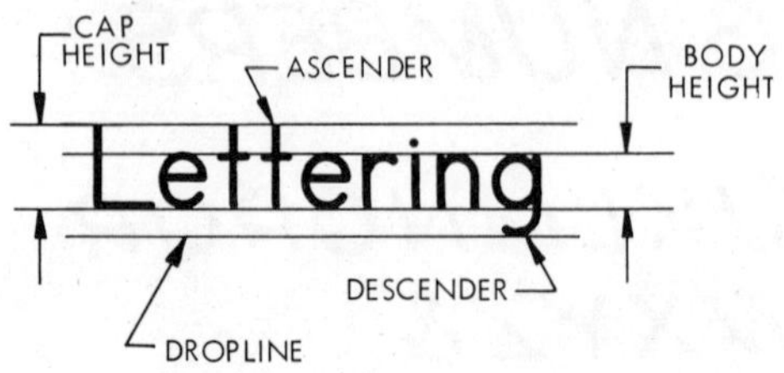

Figure 3-10
This is the correct structure of lower case letters.

(A)

(B)

Figure 3-11
Lower case letters are formed with these strokes. (A) shows vertical lettering; (B), slant lettering.

rule, sentences are spaced a distance equal to approximately twice the distance between words. When several lines of lettering are required, the spacing between them may vary from one-half to one and one-half times the height of the letters. The actual distance will depend on the amount of space available for composition.

3.6 Height of letters

The actual height of letters used on a drawing depends on the function of the composition. Titles and part numbers always have the greatest height, while letters for such items as section designation, part name, notes, dimensions, bill of materials, etc., are correspondingly smaller. Fig. 3-7 illustrates the SAE standard for height of letters. Fig. 3-8 shows the letter heights recommended by ASA.

3.7 Height of numerals

Whole numbers and decimals should be made the same height as the letters. The height of each number in a fraction should be approximately three-fourths the height of the whole number. The full height of the fraction including the fraction bar and space above and below the bar should be approximately twice that of the whole number. See Fig. 3-9.

3.8 Lower-case letters

Lower-case letters consist of three parts known as *bodies, ascenders,* and *descenders.* See Fig. 3-10. The bodies are made from three-fifths to two-thirds the height of capitals. The ascenders extend to the cap line while the descenders drop the same distance below to the dropline. The shape and strokes for lower case letters are shown in Fig. 3-11.

3.9 Guide lines

In actual practice, the draftsman draws only two guide lines to represent the height of capital letters. He then visualizes the letters to determine their correct spacing in the given area. Once he has the correct spacing, he proceeds to insert the words or numerals.

The only other guide lines used occasionally by beginning students are slanted lines for inclined letters. These slanted lines are drawn at random across the horizontal guide lines to help maintain the proper slant of the letters. Inclined letters are drawn at an angle of about 67–1/2° from the horizontal. The proper slope angle may be found by marking off two units on a horizontal line and five units on a vertical line. The point of termination of the two lines will produce a slant of approximately 67–1/2°. Then with a T-square and triangle held as shown in Fig. 3-12, the necessary lines are drawn.

To draw horizontal guide lines, mark the height of the letters desired and with the aid of a T-square, draw two light lines. If several lines of lettering are required, set the dividers to the correct height and step off the number of lines needed. With a little practice, guide lines eventually can be spaced by eye rather than measuring them with a scale or dividers. To make erasing unnecessary, all guide lines should be drawn so they are barely visible.

For lower case letters, four guide lines are drawn. Two lines serve as guides for the main bodies of the letters and the other two for the ascenders and descenders. See Fig. 3-10.

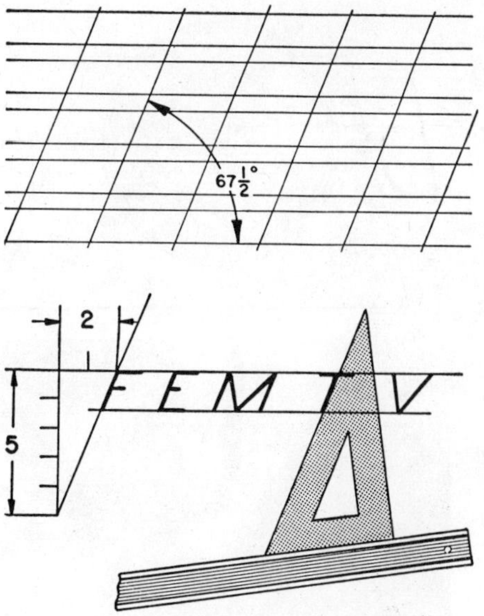

Figure 3-12
This is how the correct slant for inclined letters can be determined.

3.10 Guide line devices

To simplify the process of drawing guide lines, many draftsmen use special devices made for this purpose. The two most common are the *Braddock-Rowe Lettering Triangle* and the *Ames Lettering Instrument*.

The *Braddock-Rowe Lettering Triangle* is equipped with a series of holes arranged to provide guide lines for lettering and dimensioned figures, and for drawing section lines. See Fig. 3-13. The numbers at the base of the triangle designate the spacing of guide lines in thirty-seconds of an inch. Thus if No. 4 holes are used, the guide lines will be 4/32 or 1/8 inch apart. The slot on the left is for drawing slope guide lines for inclined letters. The column of holes on the left is used to draw guide lines for numerals 1/8 inch high and for drawing section lines 1/16 inch apart.

To use the triangle, the pencil point is inserted through the proper hole and the instrument moved back and forth along the T-square.

The *Ames Lettering Instrument* will pro-

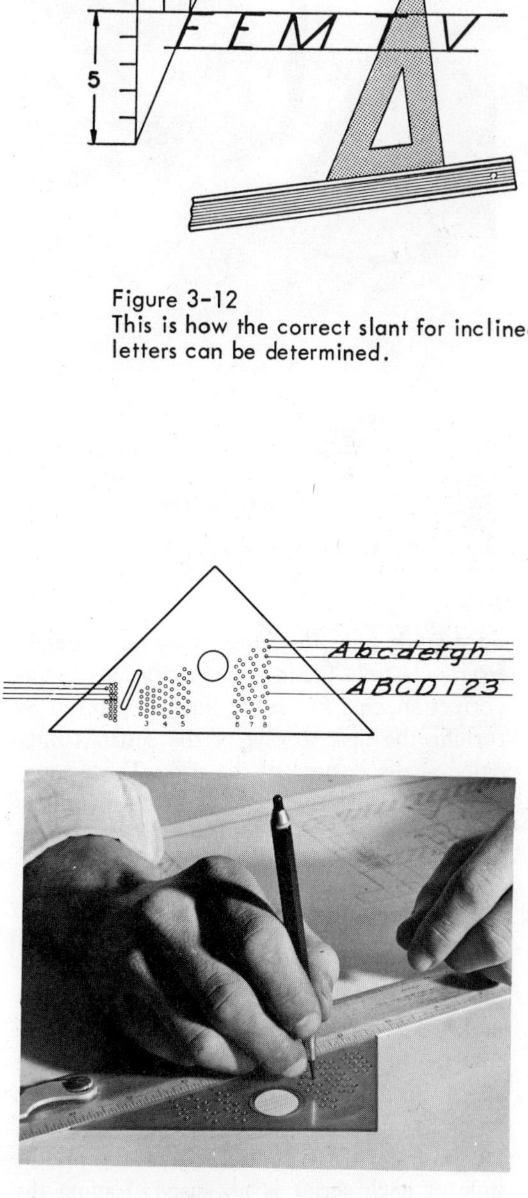

Figure 3-13
This lettering triangle simplifies the task of drawing guide lines.

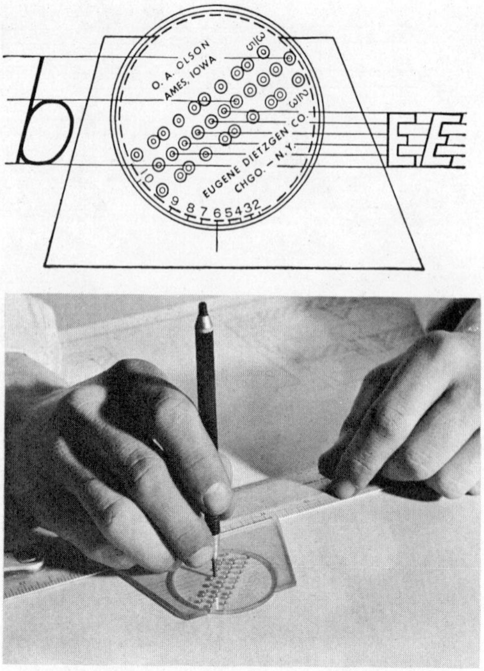

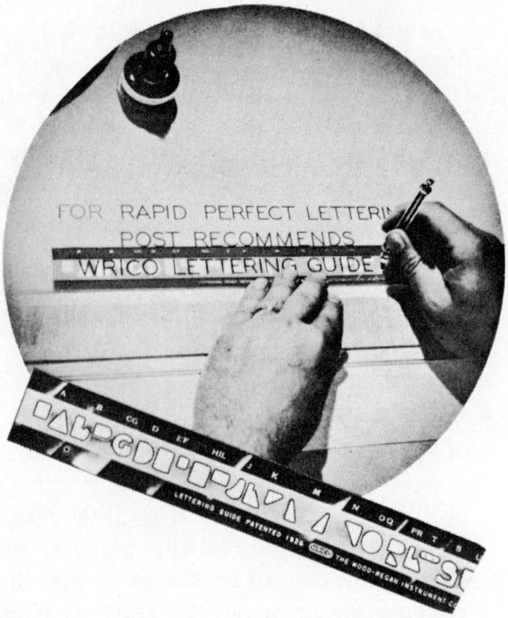

Figure 3-15
The Wrico Lettering Guide produces perfectly shaped letters when used with pencil or the special Wrico pen.

Figure 3-14
The Ames Lettering Instrument is another device for drawing guide lines and section lines.

duce guide lines for letters varying in height from 1/16 to 1–1/2 inches. See Fig. 3-14. The correct spacing for guide lines is secured by turning the disk to one of the settings indicated at the bottom of the disk. These numbers designate the height of letters in thirty-seconds of an inch. The holes in the center column are equally spaced and are used to draw guide lines for numerals and fractions, and for section lines. The two outer columns of holes are used to draw guide lines for capitals or lower case letters. The fractions 3/5 and 2/3 at the top of these columns indicate that the holes in the respective columns are spaced so the bodies of lower case letters can be made either 3/5 or 2/3 the total height of capital letters. For capital letters, the middle hole of each series is not used. Laying the instrument on either edge permits the use of the base for drawing lettering slope lines of 68° or 75°.

3.11 Pencils for lettering

An *F, H,* or *2H* pencil is used by most draftsmen for lettering. The pencil should be sharpened to a long conical point. To keep the stroke of the letters uniform, the pencil is rotated between the thumb and index finger. The pencil should be held firmly and even pressure applied. As soon as there is evidence that the strokes are broadening, the pencil should be resharpened. If the letters are made rapidly, the strokes will be more uniform in width and height.

3.12 Lettering devices

The nature of the work in some industries necessitates the use of special devices for lettering a drawing. The two most common are the *Wrico Lettering Guides* and the *LeRoy Lettering Instrument.*

The *Wrico Lettering Guides* are plastic

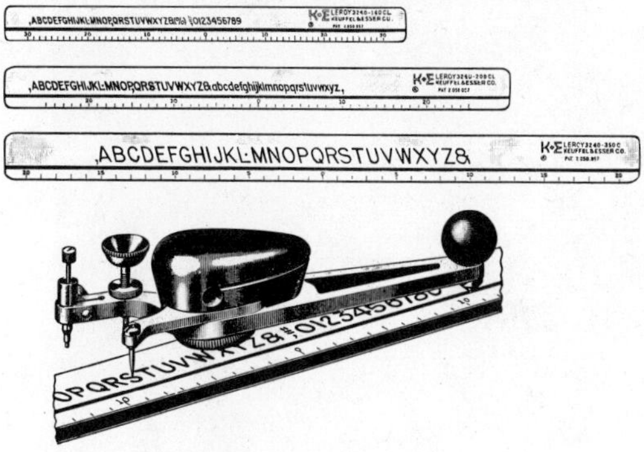

Figure 3-16
The LeRoy Lettering Instrument forms perfect letters in ink.

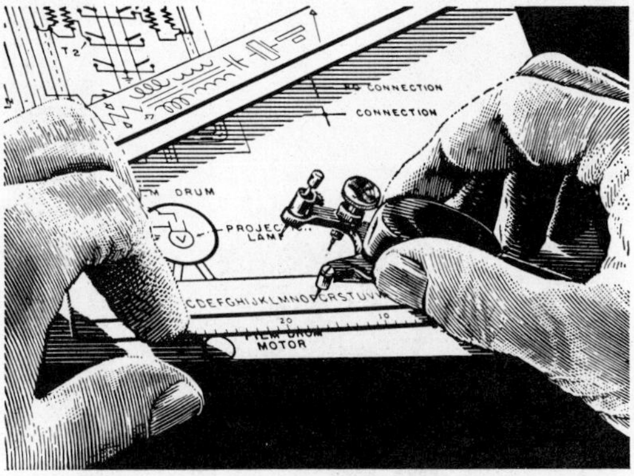

Figure 3-17
This is how the LeRoy Lettering Instrument is used.
Keuffel and Esser Co.

stencils containing outlines of letters and numerals. These guides are available with letters of various heights. See Fig. 3-15. The letters and numbers are formed by placing the guide over the portion of the paper on which the lettering is to be done and tracing the outline with a pencil. The guide is moved back and forth along the edge of the T-square or straightedge. No pencil guide lines are necessary.

For inking, a special lettering pen is provided. When the point of the pen is moved in contact with the sides of the guide, letters and numbers are quickly formed without danger of smearing. The pens are made with different sized points to produce lines of varying thicknesses.

The *LeRoy Lettering Instrument* is basically an inking lettering device. This instrument consists of a guide or template with grooved letters and numbers. The scriber is equipped with a tracer pin that follows the grooved letters on the template and a pen that forms the letters. See Fig. 3-16. The scriber is either of the fixed type, for reproducing only vertical letters, or adjustable for both vertical and inclined letters. The guides are available with letters of various heights. The thickness of the letter strokes is governed by the pen size. The instrument is used by moving the template along a T-square or straightedge as the letters are formed. See Fig. 3-17.

3.13 The Vari Typer

To reduce the time involved in lettering drawings, some industrial drafting rooms are equipped with a special lettering machine. This machine, known as a *Vari Typer,* is particularly valuable for filling in bills of materials, specifications, schematic diagrams, notes, as well as for inserting dimensional figures. The machine is operated much like a typewriter. Electrically controlled impressions permit uniform, clear and sharp composition of type directly on tracings. See Fig. 3-18.

3.14 Artype

Artype is a product occasionally used by draftsmen for special lettering work. It consists of transparent, self-adhering sheets with letters, arrows, numbers, signs and symbols. See Fig. 3-19.

These sheets are available with the letters in black or white. The white Artype is for reverse printing over dark backgrounds, and the black is opaque for light backgrounds. Application of this product is relatively simple. The general procedure for its use is as follows (see Fig. 3-20):

1 Lay out a guide line where the lettering is to be included.

2 Cut around the letter desired, using a common needle or any sharp pointed instru-

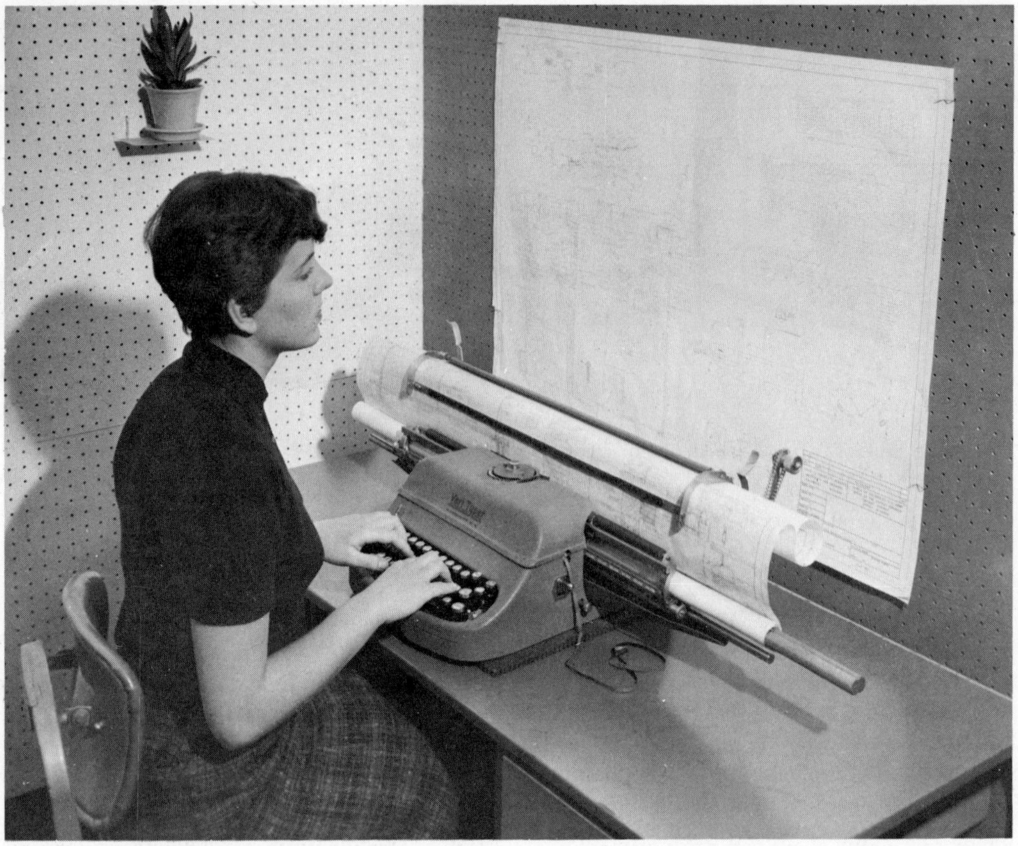

Figure 3-18
This lettering machine is often used in drafting rooms. Alfred Lant

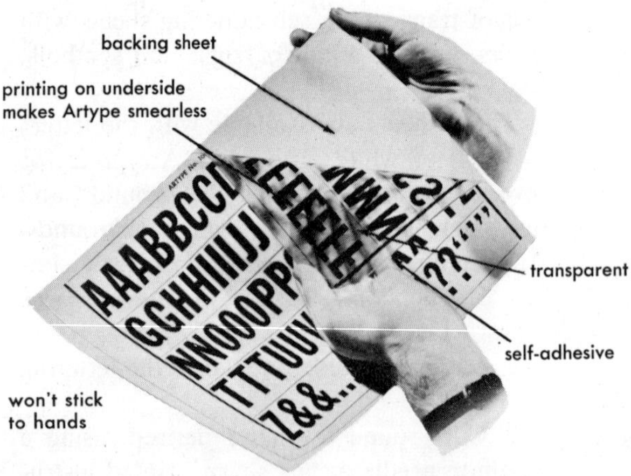

Figure 3-19
Artype is a product for special lettering work. Artype Inc.

Figure 3-20
Follow these illustrations in applying artype. Artype Inc.

ment. Press the cutter lightly, cutting through the acetate but not through the backing sheet. Be sure to include the guide line under the letter.

3 Place the point of the needle cutter under the edge of the cutout portion and lift the letter away from the backing sheet, starting at the bottom of the letter.

4 Place the letter in the desired position, lining up the guide line under the letter with the guide line drawn on the paper. A flick of the fingernail holds the letter for positioning. The letter can be easily shifted by placing the needle point under it and lifting.

5 When the letters are in the correct position, rub the Artype down firmly with the blunt end of the cutter. Do not rub down the guide line under the letters. Start at the center of each letter and work out. Cover the surface completely and be certain all edges are rubbed down tightly.

6 Remove the printed guide line under the letter by cutting through the transparent material between the letter and the guide line. Then place the needle point under the portion containing the guide line and remove.

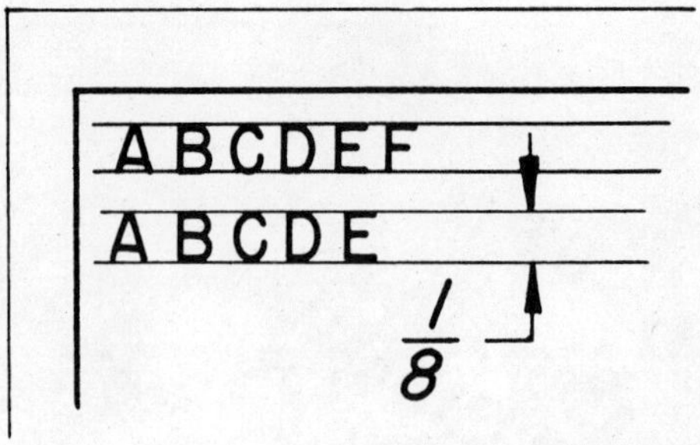

Figure 3–21
Problem 1.

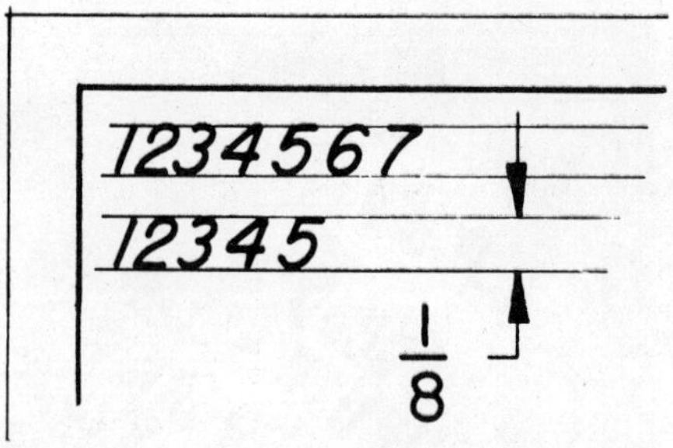

Figure 3–24
Problem 4.

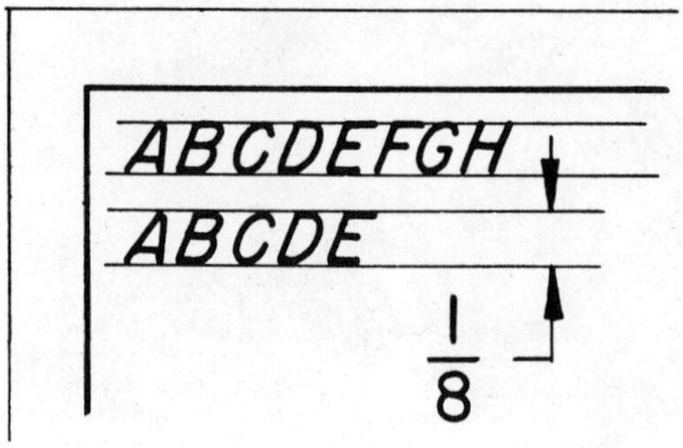

Figure 3–22
Problem 2.

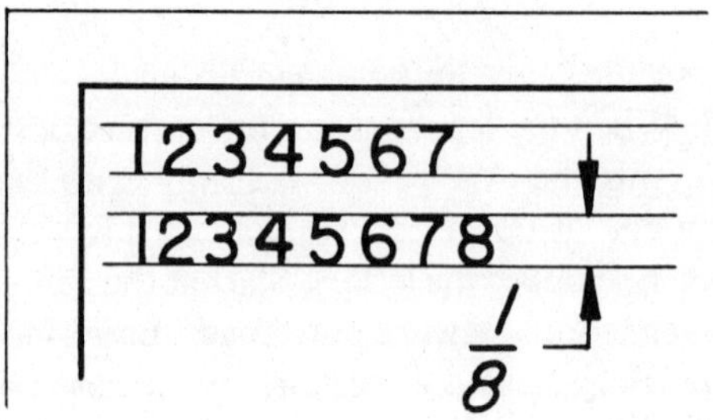

Figure 3–23
Problem 3.

Problems, section 3

1 Draw in guide lines and fill an A-size sheet using 1/8″ upper case letters. See Fig. 3-21.

2 Completely letter an A-size sheet with the alphabet using 1/8″ inclined capital letters. See Fig. 3-22.

3 Draw guide lines and complete an A-size sheet with 1/8″ vertical numerals. See Fig. 3-23.

4 Fill an A-size sheet with 1/8″ inclined numerals as in Fig. 3-24.

5 Reproduce the circumference chart shown in Fig. 3-25 by lettering the fraction and decimal equivalents with letter style as indicated.

6 Fill an A-size sheet using 1/4″ vertical upper case letters and numerals. See Fig. 3-26.

7 Fill an A-size sheet using 1/4″ inclined upper case letters and numerals. See Fig. 3-27.

8 Fill an A-size sheet with 3/8″ and 5/32″ vertical upper case letters and numerals. See Fig. 3-28.

9 Fill an A-size sheet using 3/8″ and 5/32″ inclined upper case letters and numerals. See Fig. 3-29.

10 Fill an A-size sheet with both vertical and inclined 1/8″ lower case letters. See Fig. 3-30.

11 On an A-size sheet, letter copy marked (A) and sample letters and numerals shown in Fig. 3–31. Use 1/8″ lower case letters for the composition and Wrico guide for the remaining letters and numerals in sizes as indicated.

12 On an A-size sheet, letter the composition shown in Fig. 3–32. Use 1/8″ upper case letters—either vertical or inclined.

CIRCUMFERENCES

DIAMETER	CIRC	DIAMETER	CIRC	DIA	CIRC
1/64	.0490	33/64	1.6199	2	6.2832
1/32	.0981	17/32	1.6690	3	9.4248
3/64	.1472	35/64	1.7181	4	12.5664
1/16	.1963	9/16	1.7671	5	15.7080
5/64	.2454	37/64	1.8163	6	18.850
3/32	.2945	19/32	1.8653	7	21.991
7/64	.3436	39/64	1.9145	8	25.133
1/8	.3927	5/8	1.9635	9	28.274
9/64	.4418	41/64	2.0127	10	31.416
5/32	.4908	21/32	2.0617	11	34.558
11/64	.5399	43/64	2.1108	12	37.699
3/16	.5890	11/16	2.1598	13	40.841
13/64	.6381	45/64	2.2090	14	43.982
7/32	.6872	23/32	2.2580	15	47.124
15/64	.7363	47/64	2.3072	16	50.265
1/4	.7854	3/4	2.3562	17	53.407
17/64	.8345	49/64	2.4054	18	56.549
9/32	.8835	25/32	2.4544	19	59.690
19/64	.9327	51/64	2.5036	20	62.832
5/16	.9817	13/16	2.5525	21	65.973
21/64	1.0309	53/64	2.6017	22	69.115
11/32	1.0799	27/32	2.6507	23	72.257
23/64	1.1291	55/64	2.6999	24	75.398
3/8	1.1781	7/8	2.7489	25	78.540
25/64	1.2273	57/64	2.7981	26	81.681
13/32	1.2763	29/32	2.8471	27	84.823
27/64	1.3254	59/64	2.8959	28	87.965
7/16	1.3744	15/16	2.9452	29	91.106
29/64	1.4236	61/64	2.9945	30	94.248
15/32	1.4726	31/32	3.0434	31	97.389
31/64	1.5218	63/64	3.0928	32	100.53
1/2	1.5708	1	3.1416	33	103.67

Vertical **Inclined** **Student's Choice**

Figure 3-25
Problem 5.

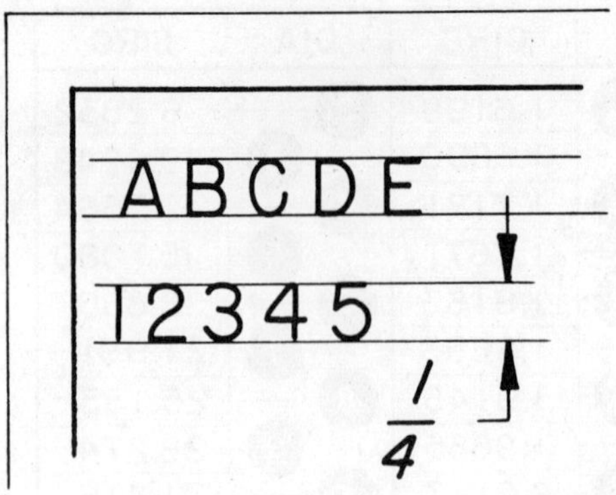

Figure 3-26
Problem 6.

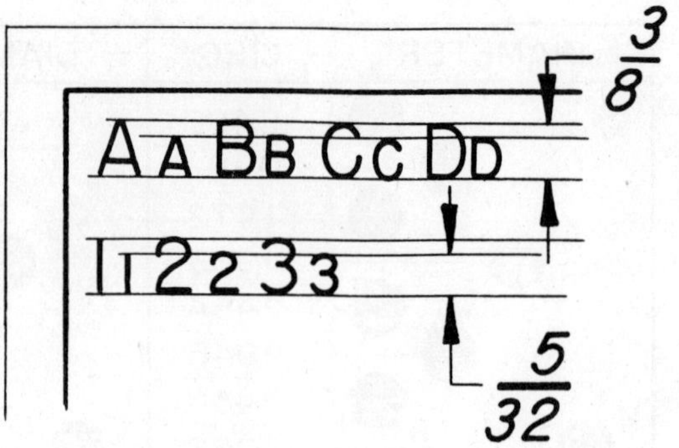

Figure 3-28
Problem 8.

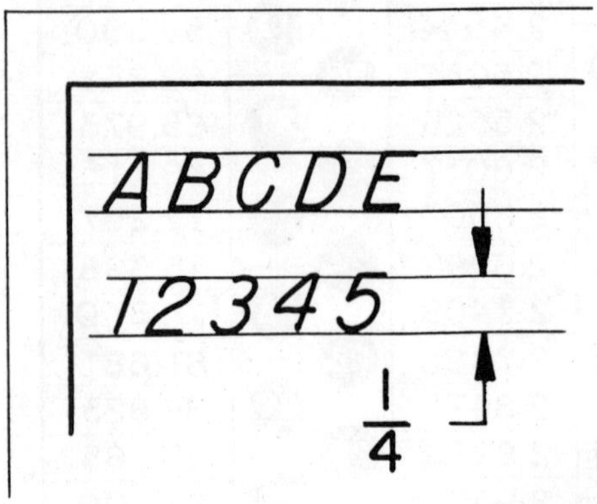

Figure 3-27
Problem 7.

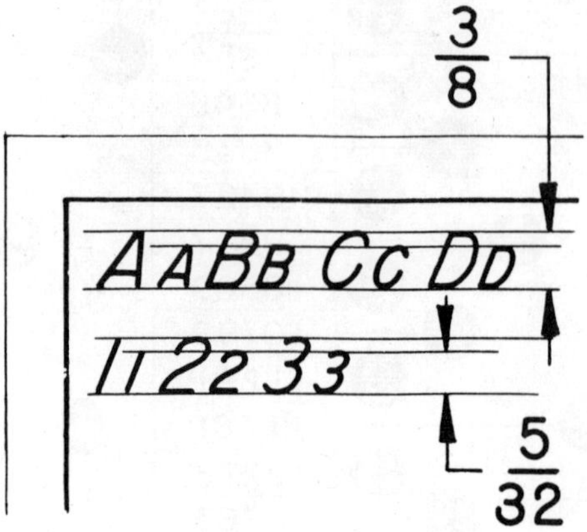

Figure 3-29
Problem 9.

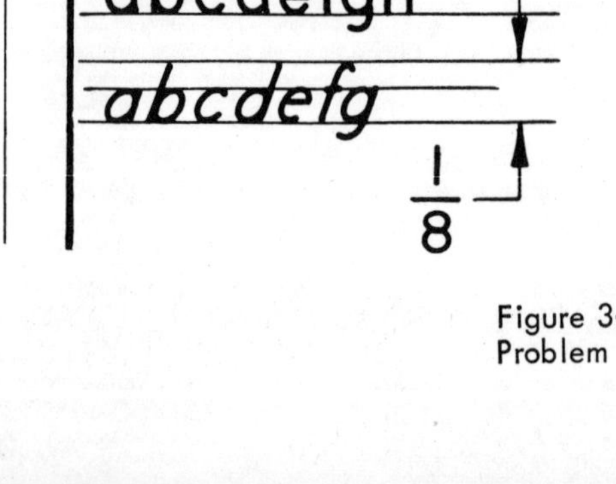

Figure 3-30
Problem 10.

LETTERING

GENERAL. The lettering must be sharp and dense to assure good reproduction. The single stroke inclined or vertical letters and numerals which are illustrated should be used for all general purposes. One style of lettering should be used throughout a drawing. Original lettering should be matched when making additions or revisions.

On mechanical drawings it is recommended that capitals be used for all lettering. On the body of structural drawings it is customary to use lower case letters with the first letters of principal words capitalized. Identifying titles, however, are in capital letters.

(A)

Figure 3-31
Problem 11.

FUNCTION OF A DRAWING

The function of a drawing is to provide a specification of the required part or assembly. A drawing should contain delineation, dimensions and tolerances, performance requirements, notes and references, as required, in sufficient clarity and detail consistent with the skills and trade practices involved, to insure correct interpretation by any manufacturing organization that may have occasion to use it.

All drawings should provide maximum latitude in the choice of manufacturing methods, processes, etc., consistent with the engineering requirements. References to specific methods of ordering material, detailed instructions for methods of manufacture and assembly, or manufacturing processes are permissible on the drawing, only if they are essential to meet engineering requirements.

Figure 3-32
Problem 12. Radio Corporation of America

Geometric constructions 4

The material in this section covers various basic geometric constructions which are used in engineering drawing. Many constructions are especially valuable when accurate, full size layouts are required such as sheet metal patterns, tool and die layouts, and layouts in lofting work. Because of the time element involved in laying out geometric constructions, the draftsman when making ordinary drawings often resorts to reasonable approximations of these constructions or uses available templates. Many of the methods the draftsman would use are included in this section along with the basic geometric methods.

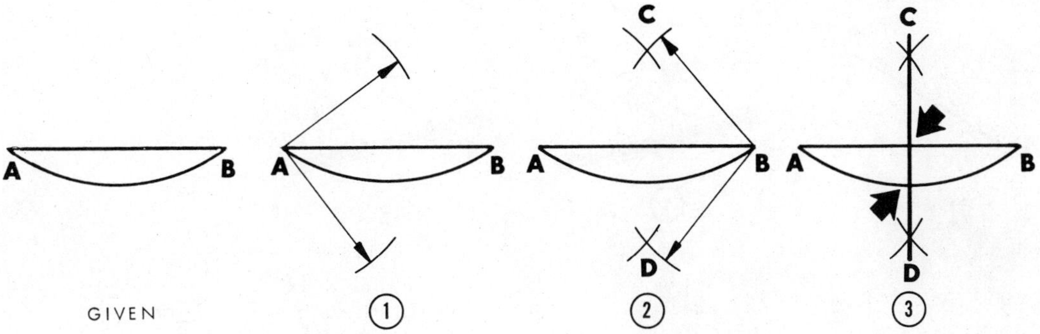

Figure 4–1
Geometric method of bisecting a line and arc.

4.1 Bisecting a line or arc

Geometric method (See Fig. 4-1)

1 Given line or arc *AB*.
2 Set the compass for any radius greater than one-half of *AB*. Using *A* and *B* as centers, draw two arcs to intersect at *C* and two arcs to intersect at *D*.
3 The point at which line *CD* crosses *AB* is the center.

Draftsman's method (See Fig. 4-2)

1 Find the center of line *AB* with dividers by the trial and error method.
2 Draw vertical line through the center with T-square and triangle.

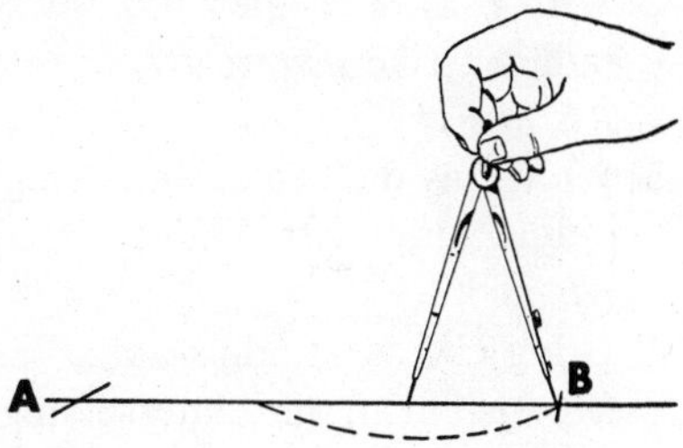

Figure 4–2
Method preferred by draftsmen in bisecting a line or arc with dividers.

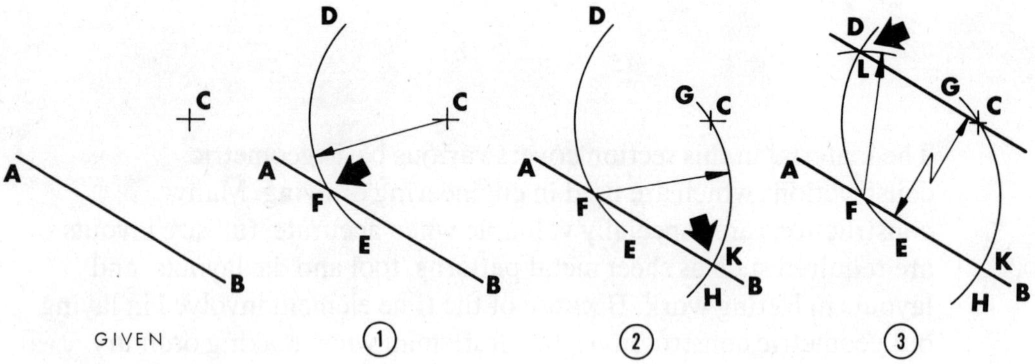

Figure 4-3
Geometric method of drawing a straight line through a point parallel to another line.

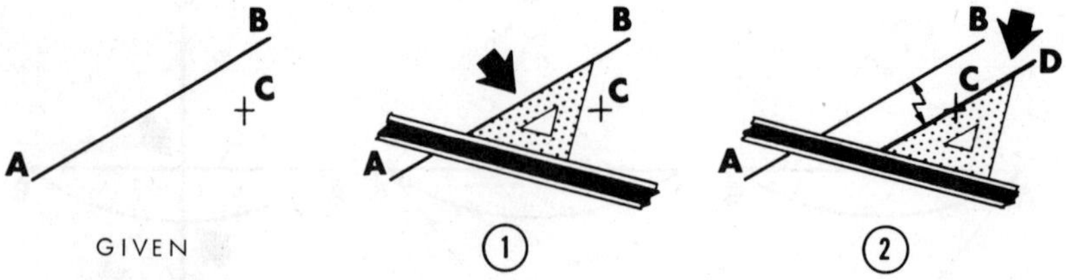

Figure 4-4
Draftsman's method of drawing a straight line through a point parallel to another line.

4.2 Drawing a straight line through a point parallel to another straight line

Geometric method (See Fig. 4-3)

1 Given line *AB* and the required point *C*.
2 With *C* as the center and any convenient radius, strike the arc *DE* to intersect line *AB* at *F*.
3 With *F* as the center and using the same radius, draw arc *GH* to intersect line *AB* at *K*.
4 Using *CK* as a radius and *F* as the center, strike an arc intersecting arc *DE* at *L*.
5 Through *L* and *C* draw the required line.

Draftsman's method (See Fig. 4-4)

1 Place a triangle on the given line *AB* with the base of the triangle resting against a T-square or another straightedge.
2 Hold the T-square in position and slide the triangle to the point for the required line *CD*.

4.3 Drawing a line parallel to another line at a given distance

Geometric method (See Fig. 4-5A)

1 *Straight lines*. Let *AB* be the line and *CD* the given distance. Using any points *E* and *F* on line *AB* as centers and *CD* as the radius, draw two arcs. The line *GH* drawn tangent to the two arcs is the required line.
2 *Curved lines*. Let *AB* be the curved line

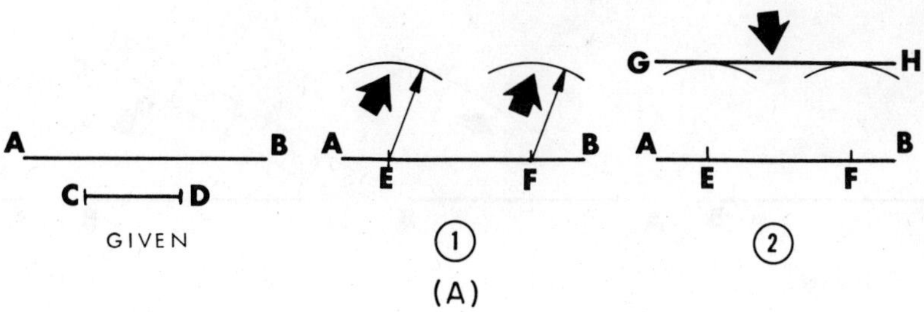

Figure 4–5A
Geometric method of drawing a line parallel to another line at a given distance.

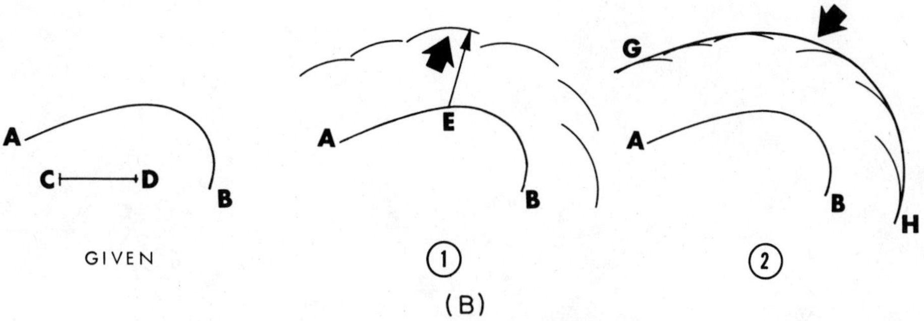

Figure 4–5B
Method of drawing curved parallel lines.

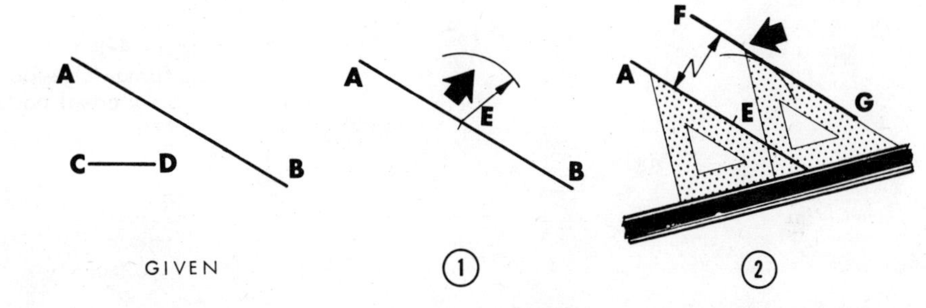

Figure 4–6
Draftsman's method of drawing a line parallel to another line at a given distance.

and *CD* the given distance. Draw a series of arcs from *AB* with a radius equal to *CD*. With an irregular curve draw a line tangent to these arcs. See Fig. 4-5B.

Draftsman's method (See Fig. 4-6)

1 With *E* as a center at any point on line *AB*, and *CD* as the given radius, draw an arc.

2 Place a triangle so one edge coincides with the given line *AB* and one other edge rests against the T-square or another straightedge. Slide the triangle against the T-square and draw the required line *FG* tangent to the arc.

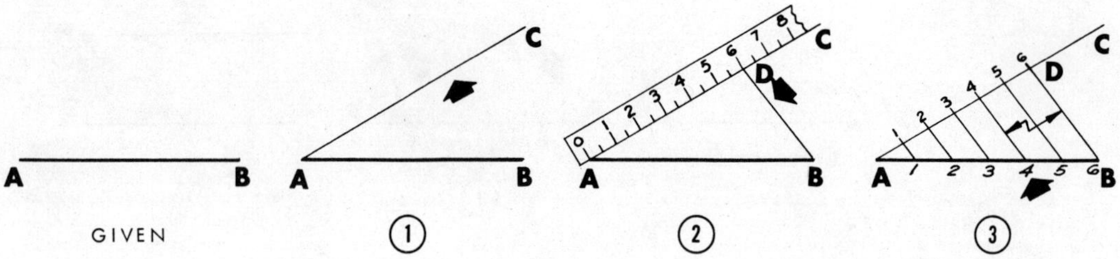

Figure 4-7
Geometric method of dividing a line into equal parts.

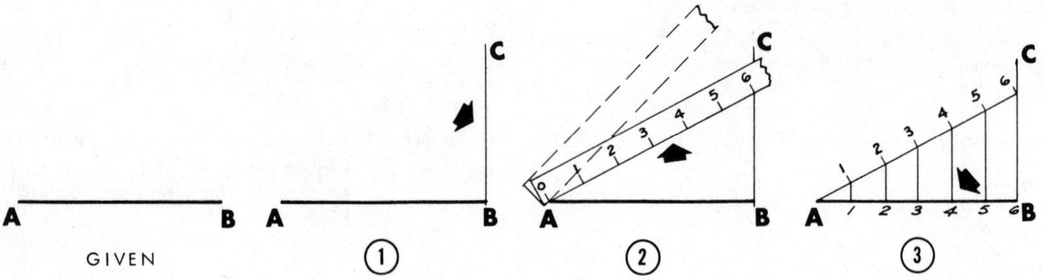

Figure 4-8
Draftsman's method of dividing a line into six equal parts.

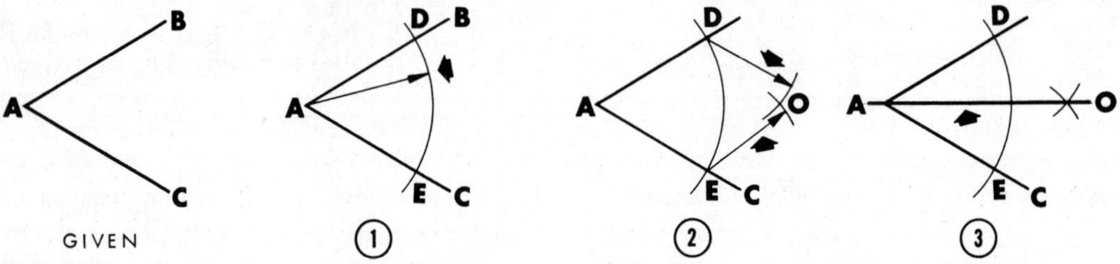

Figure 4-9
Bisecting an angle.

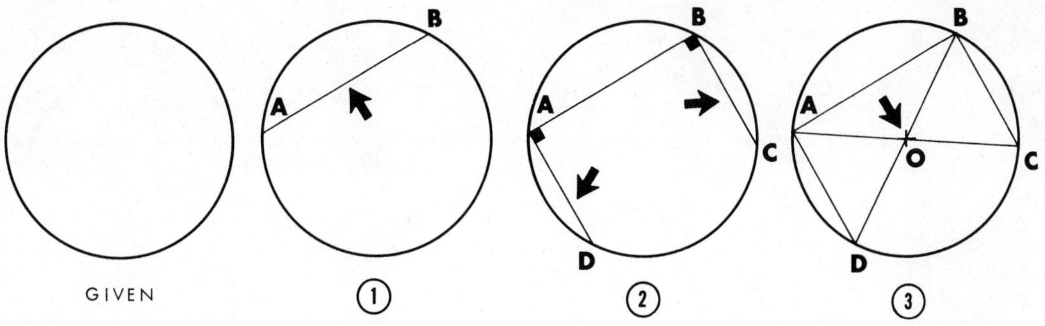

Figure 4-10
Locating the center of a circle or arc.

4.4 Dividing a line into equal parts

Geometric method (See Fig. 4-7)

1 Assume a given line is to be divided into six equal parts.
2 Draw the required line *AB* which is to be divided.
3 From one end of this line draw line *AC* at any convenient angle.
4 Starting at *A* on line *AC* lay off six equal spaces either with dividers or a scale.
5 From the termination point of the last space *D*, draw a line connecting *D* with *B*.
6 With the edge of a triangle set parallel with line *DB*, draw lines from the points on line *AC* to line *AB*. The division points will be found where the parallel lines intersect line *AB*.

Draftsman's method-A (See Fig. 4-8)

1 Assume line *AB* is to be divided into six equal parts.
2 From one point of the given line, draw a vertical line such as *BC*.
3 Place a scale so that the division point zero coincides with the end of the line *A* and the six calibration points fall on line *BC*.
4 Lay off the five intervening divisions and from these points draw lines parallel to *BC* intersecting *AB*.

Draftsman's method-B

Most draftsmen use the trial-and-error method of dividing a line. The dividers or compass is set to an approximate spacing and then adjustments made in the setting until the proper divisions are secured. See Sub-section 2.13.

4.5 Bisecting an angle (See Fig. 4-9)

1 Given angle *BAC*.
2 With *A* as a center and the compass set at any convenient radius, draw an arc cutting line *AB* at *D* and line *AC* at *E*.
3 Set the compass at a radius greater than one-half of *DE*.
4 With *D* and *E* as centers, draw two arcs to intersect at *O*.
5 Draw a line from *O* to *A*. The line *OA* bisects the angle.

4.6 Locating the center of a circle (See Fig. 4-10)

1 Draw any chord *AB* on the given circle.
2 Draw *BC* and *AD* perpendicular to chord *AB*.
3 Draw lines *DB* and *CA*, which are the diameters of the circle. The intersection of these diameters at *O* is the center of the circle.

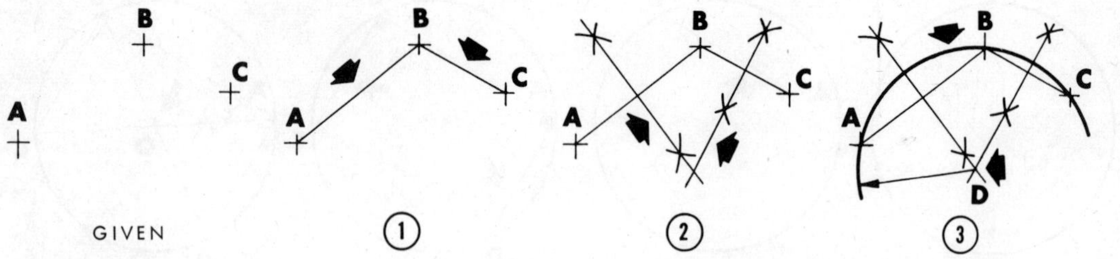

Figure 4-11
Constructing a circle or arc through three points.

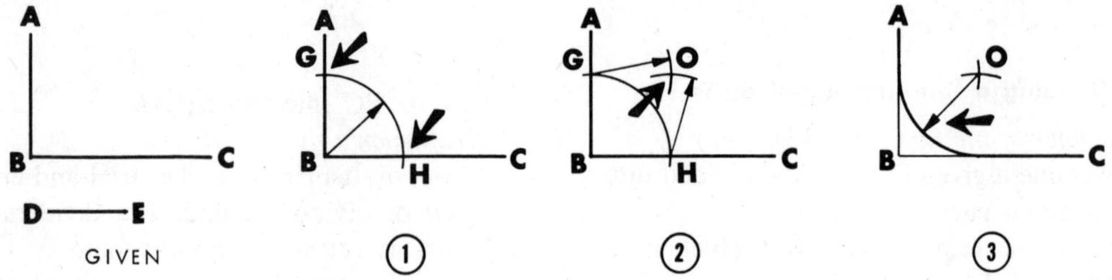

Figure 4-12
Geometric method of drawing an arc tangent to two lines at 90°.

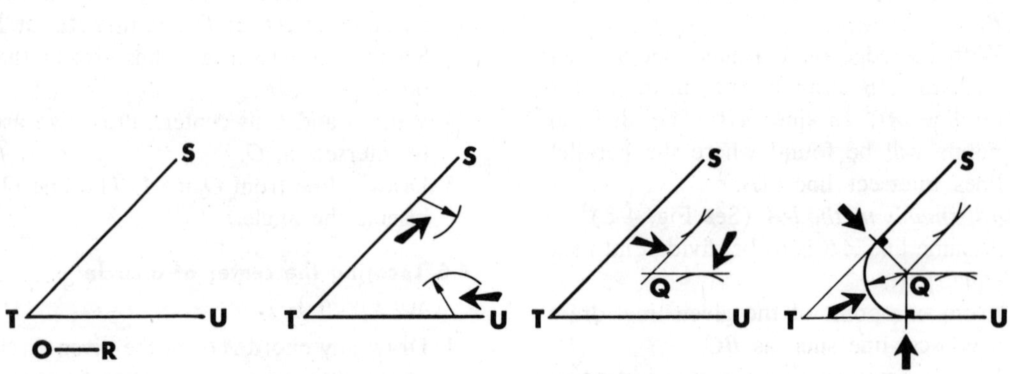

Figure 4-13
Constructing an arc tangent to two lines not at 90°.

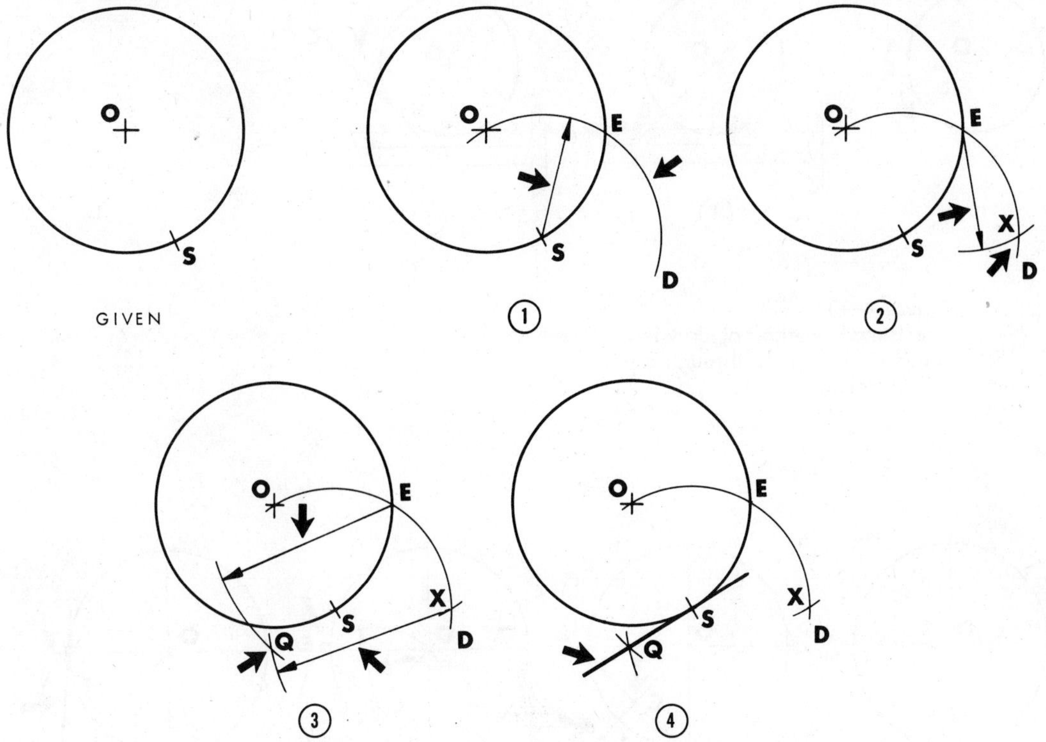

Figure 4-14
Geometric method of drawing a line tangent to a circle through a point on a circle.

4.7 Constructing a circle or arc through three given points (See Fig. 4-11)

1 Given points *ABC*.
2 Draw lines connecting *AB* and *BC* and find their bisectors.
3 The intersection of these bisectors at *D* is the center of the circle or arc.

4.8 Drawing an arc of a given radius tangent to two lines at 90°

Geometric method (See Fig. 4-12)

1 Given radius *DE* and lines *AB* and *BC* at right angles.
2 Set the compass to the given radius and, with *B* as a center, draw an arc cutting line *AB* at *G* and line *CB* at *H*.
3 Using the same radius and with *G* and *H* as centers, draw two arcs to intersect at *O*.
4 With *O* as a center and the compass set at the same radius, draw the arc tangent to lines *AB* and *BC*.

4.9 Drawing an arc tangent to two lines not at 90° (See Fig. 4-13)

1 Given radius *OR* and intersecting lines *ST* and *TU*.
2 Set the compass to the given radius *OR* and using any points on lines *ST* and *TU* draw arcs.
3 Draw straight lines parallel to *ST* and *TU* tangent to these arcs. Extend them to intersect at *Q*.
4 From *Q* draw perpendiculars to lines *ST* and *TU*.
5 With *Q* as a center and the compass set at the given radius, draw the arc tangent to lines *ST* and *TU*. The perpendiculars from *Q* determine the points of tangency.

4.10 Drawing a line tangent to a circle through a point on a circle

Geometric method (See Fig. 4-14)

1 Given point *S* on circle with center at *O*.
2 Set the compass to radius *SO* and with *S*

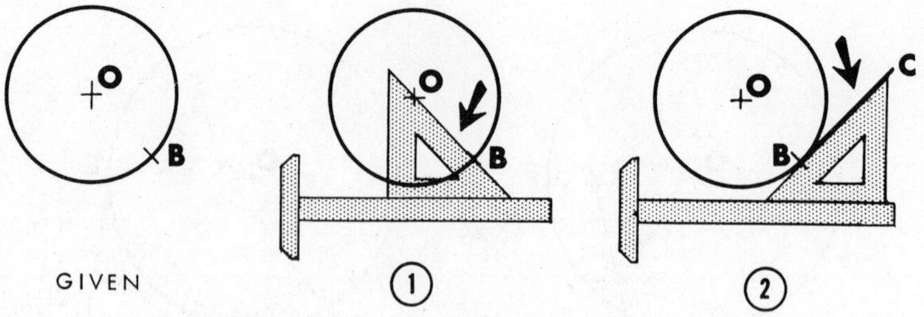

Figure 4–15
Draftsman's method of drawing a line tangent to a circle through a point on a circle.

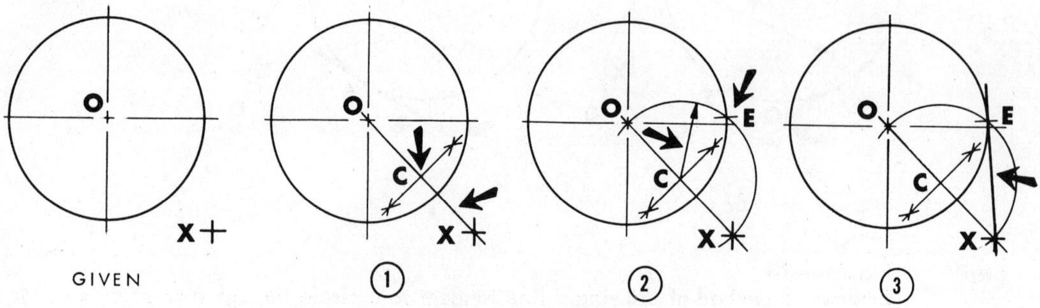

Figure 4–16
Geometric method of drawing a line tangent to a circle through a point outside the circle.

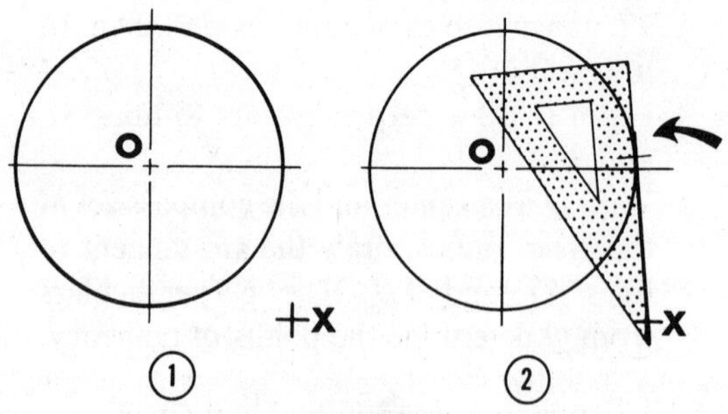

Figure 4–17
Draftsman's method of drawing a line tangent to a circle through a point outside a circle.

as a center, strike arc *OD* to cut circle *O* at *E*.

3 With *E* as a center and using the same radius, draw an arc to cut arc *OD* at *X*.

4 With *X* and *E* as centers and any convenient radius greater than *SO*, strike arcs intersecting at *Q*. This intersection provides the point for drawing the line tangent to circle with center at *O*.

Draftsman's method (See Fig. 4-15)

1 Place a triangle on the T-square so the hypotenuse of the triangle passes through the center of the circle at *O* and *B*.

2 Hold the T-square in the same position and turn the triangle so its hypotenuse passes through *B*. The line *BC* drawn along the hypotenuse of the triangle becomes the required tangent line.

4.11 Drawing a line tangent to a circle through a point outside the circle

Geometric method (See Fig. 4-16)

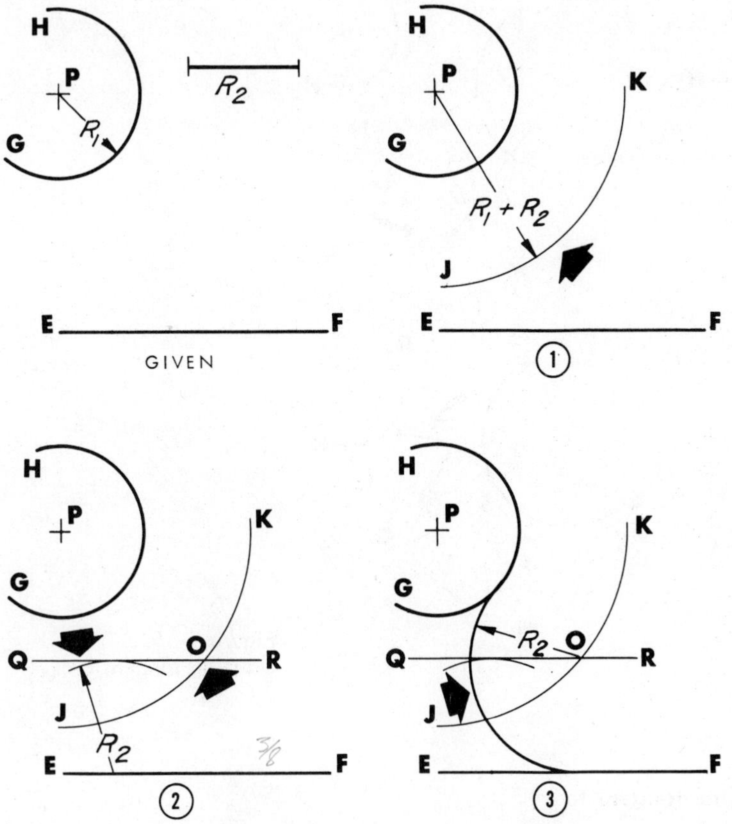

Figure 4-18
Drawing an arc tangent to a straight line and an arc.

1 Let X represent the point outside the circle.
2 Draw a line from X to the center of the circle at O.
3 Bisect line OX.
4 From the intersection at C, draw a semicircle having a radius equal to OC. The intersection of the semicircle O at E is the point of tangency for the required line.

Draftsman's method (See Fig. 4-17)

1 Place a triangle so that one side of the triangle passes through point X and is tangent to the circle.
2 Draw the line from X tangent to the circle.

4.12 Drawing an arc tangent to a straight line and an arc (See Fig. 4-18)

1 Given line EF and arc GH having radius R_1 and radius R_2.
2 Adjust the compass to a distance equal to R_1 plus the specified radius of the connecting arc R_2 and draw arc JK using P as a center.
3 Draw line QR parallel to line EF and to intersect arc JK at O. Line QR must be a distance equal to R_2 from line EF.
4 With O as a center and the compass set at the given radius R_2, draw the arc tangent to GH and line EF.

4.13 Drawing tangent arcs (See Fig. 4-19)

1 Given arc EF having radius R_1, arc GH with radius R_2 and the radius of the required tangent arc R_3.
2 Adjust compass to R_1 plus R_3 and draw arc MN.
3 Set the compass at distance to R_2 plus R_3 and draw arc ST intersecting arc MN at O.
4 Using O as a center and R_3 as a radius, draw the arc tangent to arcs EF and GH.

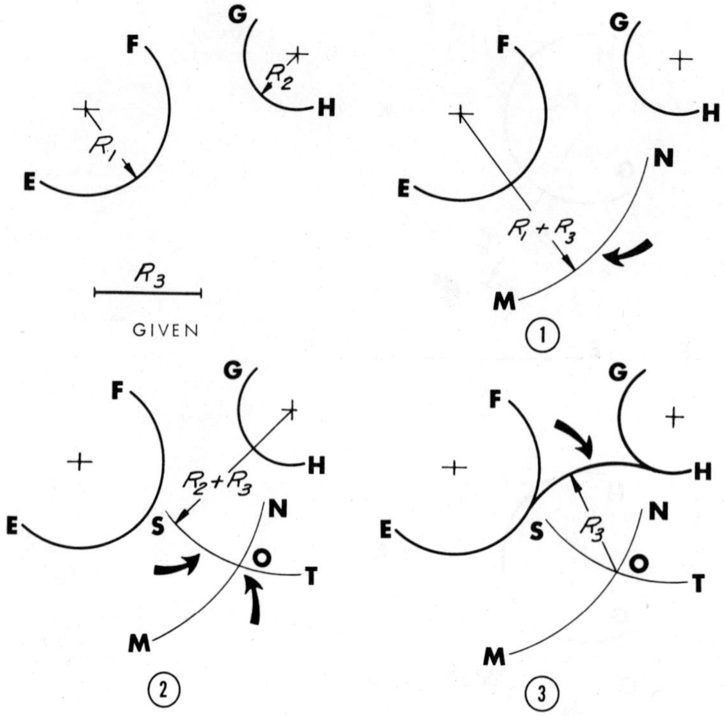

Figure 4-19
Drawing tangent arcs.

4.14 Drawing a straight line tangent to two arcs

Geometric method (See Fig. 4-20)

1 Given arcs *MN* and *RS*.
2 Find the difference between the radii of arcs *MN* and *RS*. Lay off this difference *OE* on the straight line connecting the centers of arcs *MN* and *RS*.
3 With *O* as a center and *OE* as a radius, draw the arc *KE*.
4 Find the center of line *OP*.
5 With *OG* as a radius and *G* as a center, draw arc *OP*, cutting arc *KE* at *F*.
6 Draw a line through points *O* and *F*, cutting arc *MN* at *H*. Now *H* becomes the point of tangency of arc *MN*.
7 Draw line *PJ* parallel with line *OH*. *J* is the point of tangency of arc *RS*.
8 Draw line *HJ*, which is the required tangent to the two arcs.

Draftsman's method (See Fig. 4-21)

1 Place a triangle so that one side is tangent to the two arcs. Draw the required tangent line.
2 Determine the tangent points of the arcs by sliding the triangle as shown in Fig. 4-21 along the straightedge until the side making 90° with the tangent side intersects the center of the arc. Repeat for the other tangent point.

4.15 Drawing a reverse or ogee curve
(See Fig. 4-22)

1 Let *EF* and *GH* be the two given parallel lines.
2 Connect *F* and *G* with a straight line.
3 At *F* and *G* erect lines perpendicular to *EF* and *GH*.
4 On line *FG* assume point *O* where it is desired that the ogee curve should cross. Find the perpendicular bisectors of *FO* and *GO*.
5 The intersections *X* and *Y* of these bisectors with the first two perpendiculars at *F* and *G* are the centers of the required arcs.
6 With *X* as the center and the radius *XF*, draw arc *FO*. With *Y* as a center and radius *YG*, draw arc *GO*.

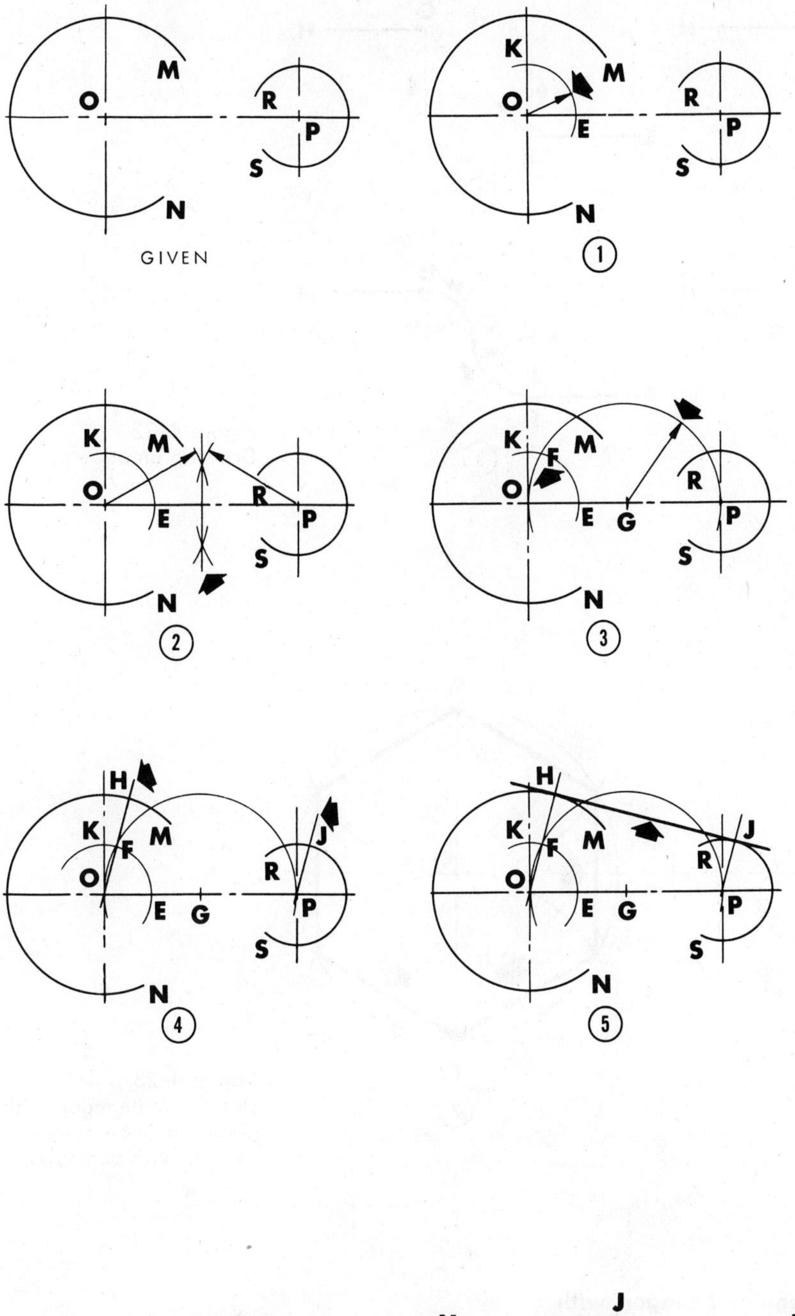

Figure 4–20
Geometric method of drawing a straight line tangent to two arcs.

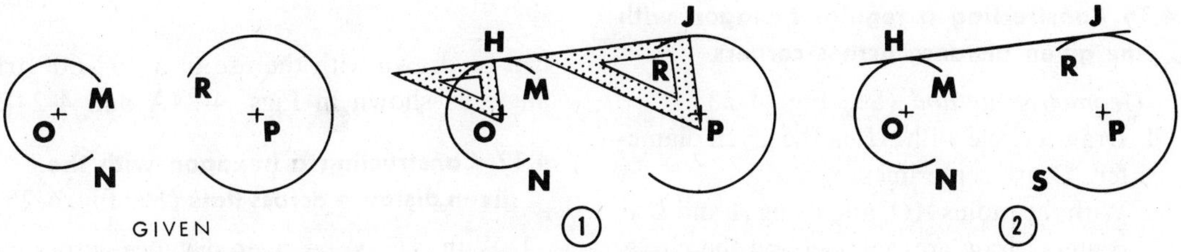

Figure 4–21
Draftsman's method of drawing a straight line tangent to two arcs.

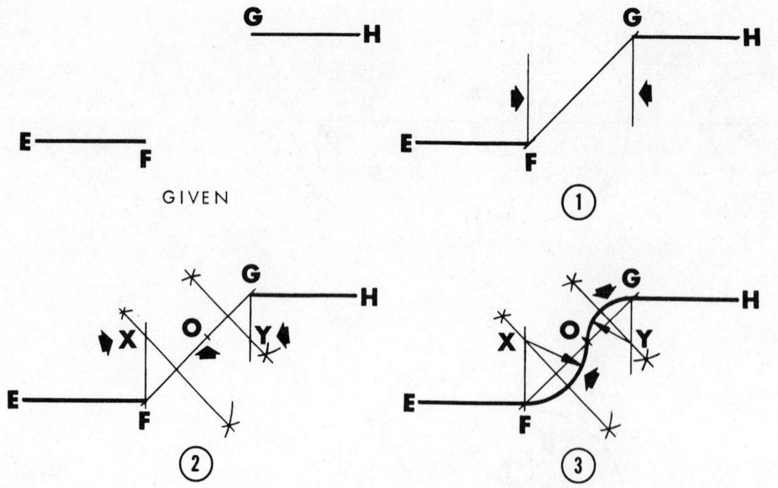

Figure 4–22
Drawing an ogee curve.

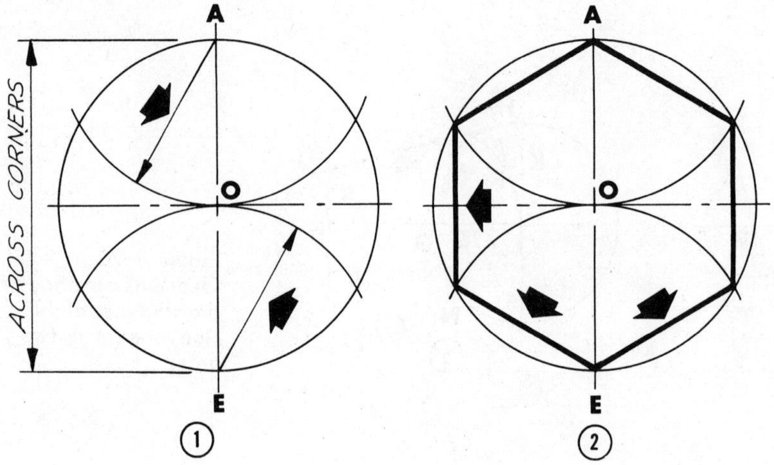

Figure 4–23
Drawing a hexagon with given distance across corners with compass.

4.16 Constructing a regular hexagon with the given distance across corners

Geometric method (See Fig. 4-23)

1 Draw a circle with *AE* as the given diameter. Draw centerlines.
2 With the radius *AO,* and using *A* and *E* as centers, draw arcs intersecting the circle.
3 Connect each point formed by the intersecting arcs with straight lines.

Draftsman's method. The same hexagon can be drawn with the use of a 30°-60° triangle as shown in Figs. 4-24A and 4-24B.

4.17 Constructing a hexagon with the given distance across flats (See Fig. 4-25)

1 With *AE* as the given distance across the flats, draw a circle.
2 Using the 30°-60° triangle, draw tangents to the circle as shown.

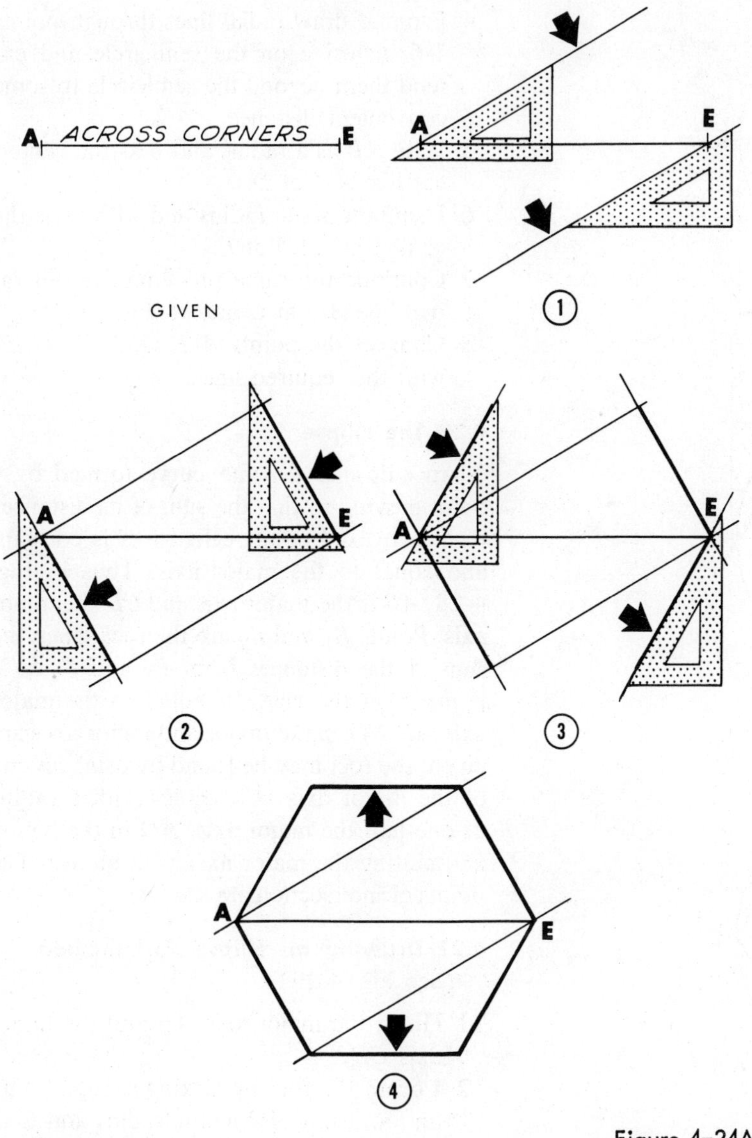

Figure 4-24A
Drawing a hexagon with given distances across corners with 30°-60° triangle.

4.18 Drawing an octagon (See Fig. 4-26)

1 Draw a square and within the square draw its diagonals.
2 Using the corners of the square as centers and a radius equal to one-half of the diagonals, draw arcs intersecting the sides of the square.
3 Connect these points with lines which form the sides of the octagon.

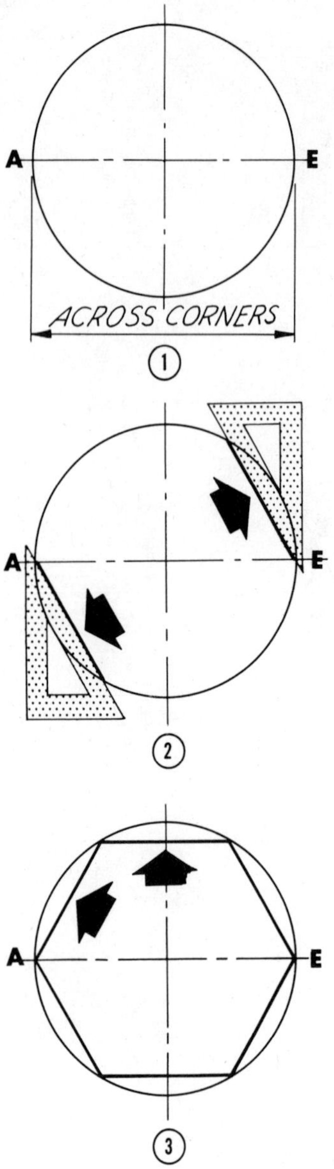

Figure 4-24 B
Drawing a hexagon within a circle using a 30°-60° triangle.

4.19 Constructing a regular polygon (See Fig. 4-27)

1 Assume the polygon is to have seven sides with *AB* as the given side.
2 With *AB* as a radius and *A* as the center, scribe a semicircle *CB*.
3 Divide the semicircle into seven equal parts and number them as shown in the figure.
4 From *A* draw radial lines through points 1-6 inclusive on the semicircle and extend them beyond the semicircle to some convenient distance.
5 With *AB* as a radius and *B* as the center, cut line *A-6* at *D*.
6 Using the same radius and with *D* as the center, cut *A-5* at *E*.
7 Continue the same procedure to cut radial line *A-3* at *G* and *A-4* at *F*.
8 Connect the points *A-2, G, F, E, D, B,* with the required lines.

4.20 The ellipse

An ellipse is a plane curve formed by a point moving so that the sum of its distances from two fixed points called *foci* is constant and equal to the major axis. Thus in Fig. 4-28, *AB* is the major axis and *CD* the minor axis. Points F_1 and F_2 are the foci. Then the sum of the distances from F_1 and F_2 to a point *P* on the curve is equal to the major axis *AB*. When the major and minor axes are given, the foci may be found by using an end of the minor axis as a center with a radius of one-half the major axis, *AO* in the figure, and cutting the major axis with an arc. The points of intersection are the foci.

4.21 Drawing an ellipse—foci method (See Fig. 4-29)

1 Given the major axis *AB* and the minor axis *CD*.
2 Locate the foci by cutting axis *AB* with an arc, using *AO* as the radius and *C* as the center.
3 Between F_1 and *O* lay off a number of equal points, such as five. For larger ellipses more points should be used to insure a smooth curve.
4 With *A-1* as the radius and F_1 and F_2 as centers scribe arcs at *1* and *1′*.
5 With *B-1* as the radius and F_2 and F_1 as centers, draw arcs intersecting arcs at *1* and *1′*.
6 Proceed in a similar manner with the remaining points to locate intersecting arcs at *2* and *2′*, *3* and *3′*, *4* and *4′*, etc.
7 Connect the points formed by the intersecting arcs with an irregular curve.

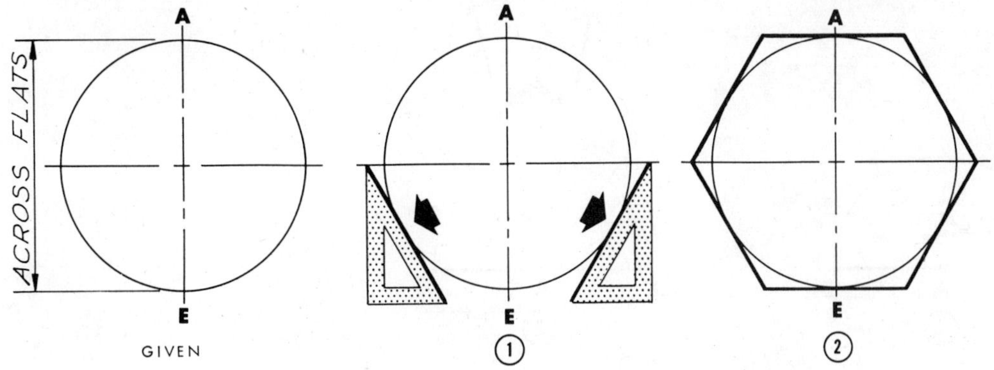

Figure 4–25
Drawing a hexagon with the given distance across flats.

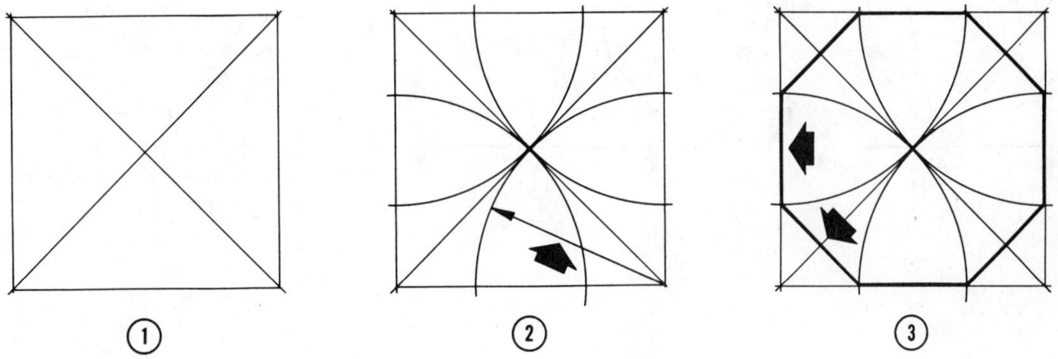

Figure 4–26
Constructing an octagon.

4.22 Drawing an ellipse—trammel method (See Fig. 4-30)

1 Secure a strip of paper or cardboard having one straightedge.
2 Lay off *EO* equal to one-half the major axis.
3 On the same strip, lay off *EF* equal to one-half the minor axis.
4 Place the strip with point *E* on the minor axis and *F* on the major axis. By moving the strip, the point *O* will provide points for the ellipse.
5 Complete the ellipse by drawing lines with an irregular curve through the points.

4.23 Constructing an ellipse—four-center method (See Fig. 4-31)

1 Given major axis *AE* and minor axis *CD*.
2 With *O* as a center and radius *OA*, draw an arc intersecting *OC* at *F*.
3 Draw line *AC*.
4 With *C* as a center and a radius *CF*, draw arc intersecting line *AC* at *X*.
5 Find the perpendicular bisector of *AX* so it intersects *AE* at *G* and the extended axis *CD* at *H*.
6 Points *G* and *H* now are centers for two of the required arcs of the ellipse.
7 Lay off *OK* equal to *OH* and *OM* equal to *OG*. With *M* and *K* as centers, draw the other two arcs of the ellipse.

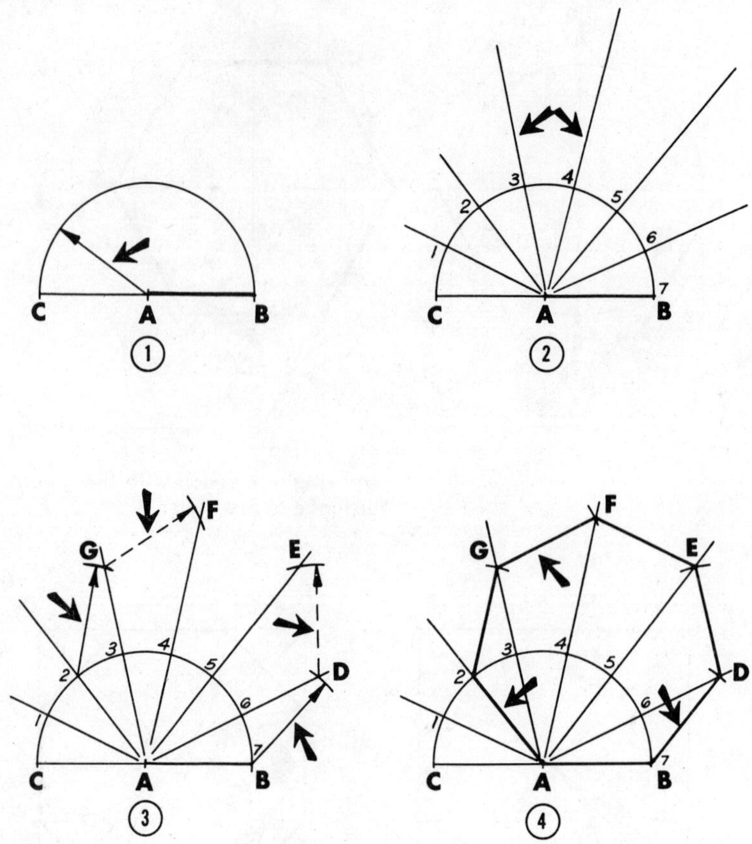

Figure 4-27
Constructing a regular polygon.

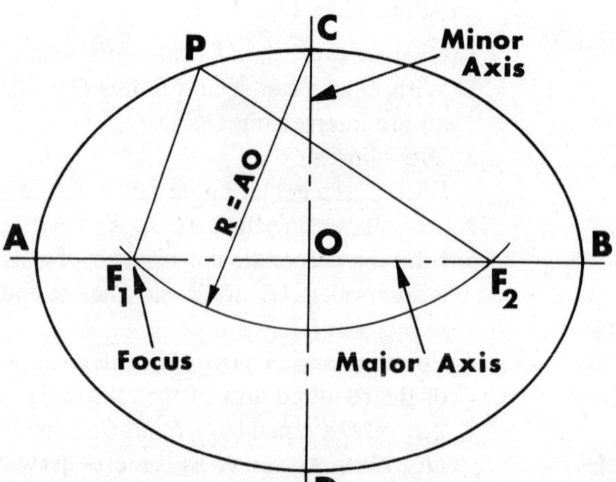

Figure 4-28
The ellipse.

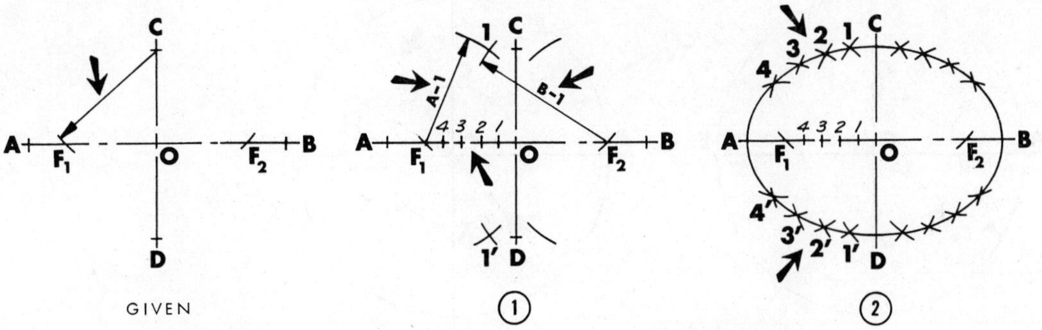

Figure 4–29
Drawing an ellipse by the foci method.

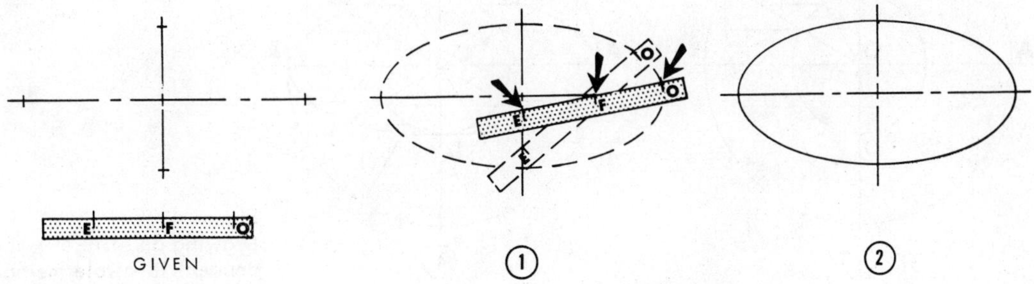

Figure 4–30
Constructing an ellipse with a trammel.

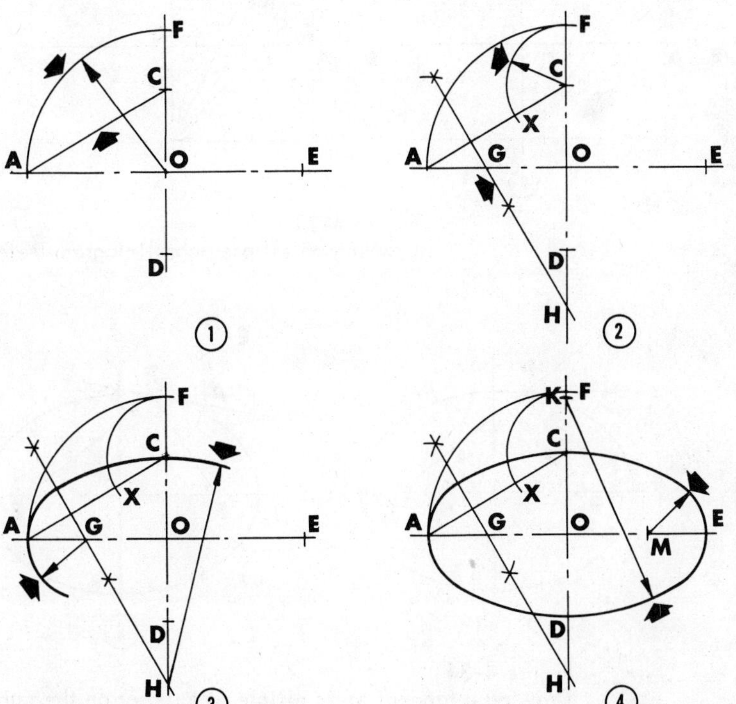

Figure 4–31
Constructing an ellipse—four-center method.

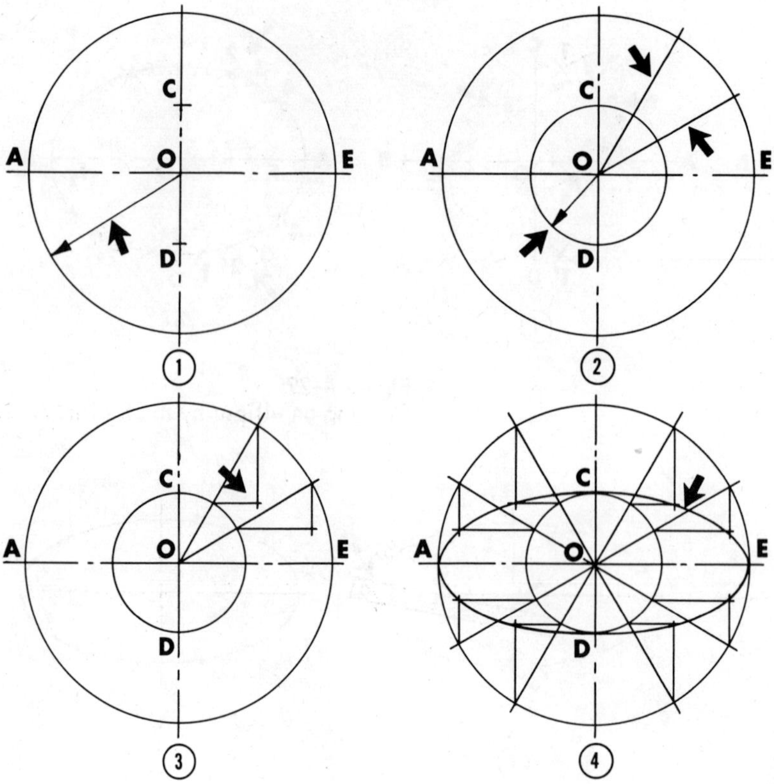

Figure 4-32
Drawing an ellipse—
concentric-circle method.

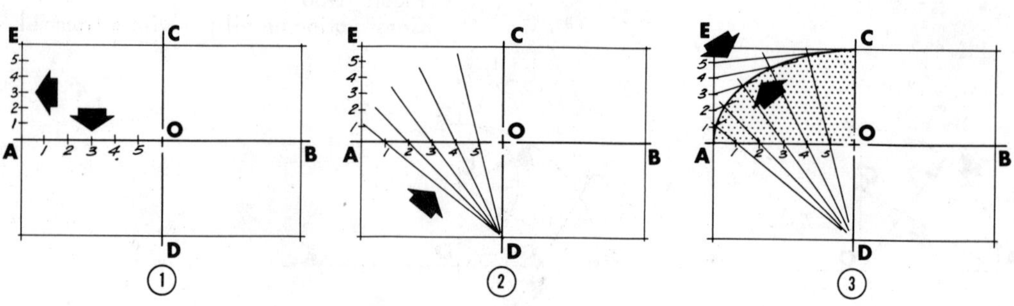

Figure 4-33
Drawing an ellipse—parallelogram method.

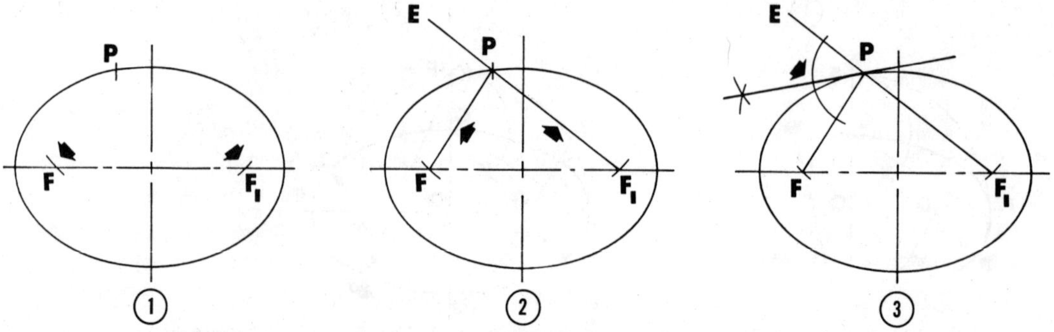

Figure 4-34
Drawing a tangent to an ellipse at a point on the curve.

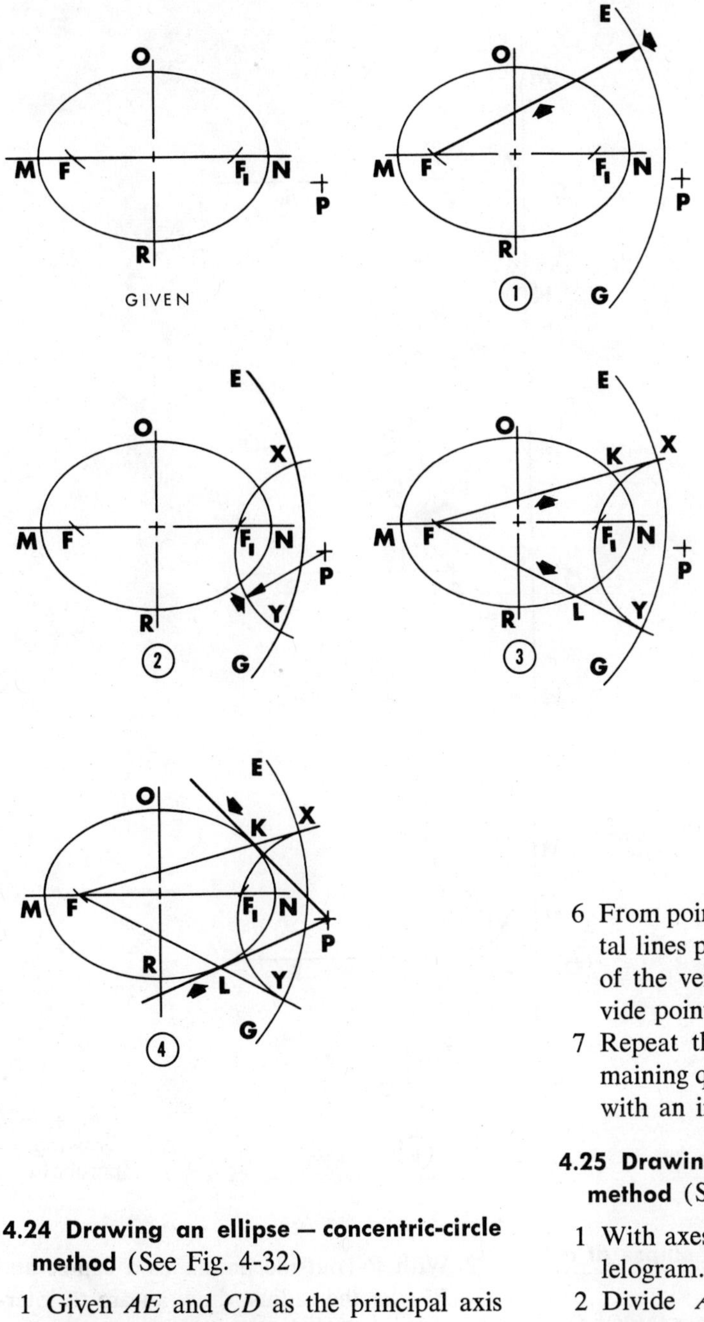

Figure 4–35
Drawing a tangent to an ellipse from a point outside the curve.

4.24 Drawing an ellipse — concentric-circle method (See Fig. 4-32)

1 Given *AE* and *CD* as the principal axis with *O* as the center.
2 With *O* as a center and radius *AO,* scribe outer circle. Draw inner circle with *CO* as a radius.
3 Divide outer circle into any number of equal parts.
4 From *O* draw radii to points on outer circle intersecting inner circle.
5 From points on outer circle draw vertical lines parallel to *CD.*
6 From points on inner circle draw horizontal lines parallel to *AE.* The intersections of the vertical and horizontal lines provide points of the ellipse.
7 Repeat the same procedure for the remaining quadrants and connect the points with an irregular curve.

4.25 Drawing an ellipse—parallelogram method (See Fig. 4-33)

1 With axes *AB* and *CD* construct a parallelogram.
2 Divide *AO* into any number of equal parts and *AE* into the same number of parts. Number these parts.
3 From *D* draw lines through points on *AO.*
4 From *C* draw lines to points on line *AE.*
5 The intersection of these lines provides points for the ellipse.
6 Proceed in a similar manner for the remaining quadrants and connect points with an irregular curve.

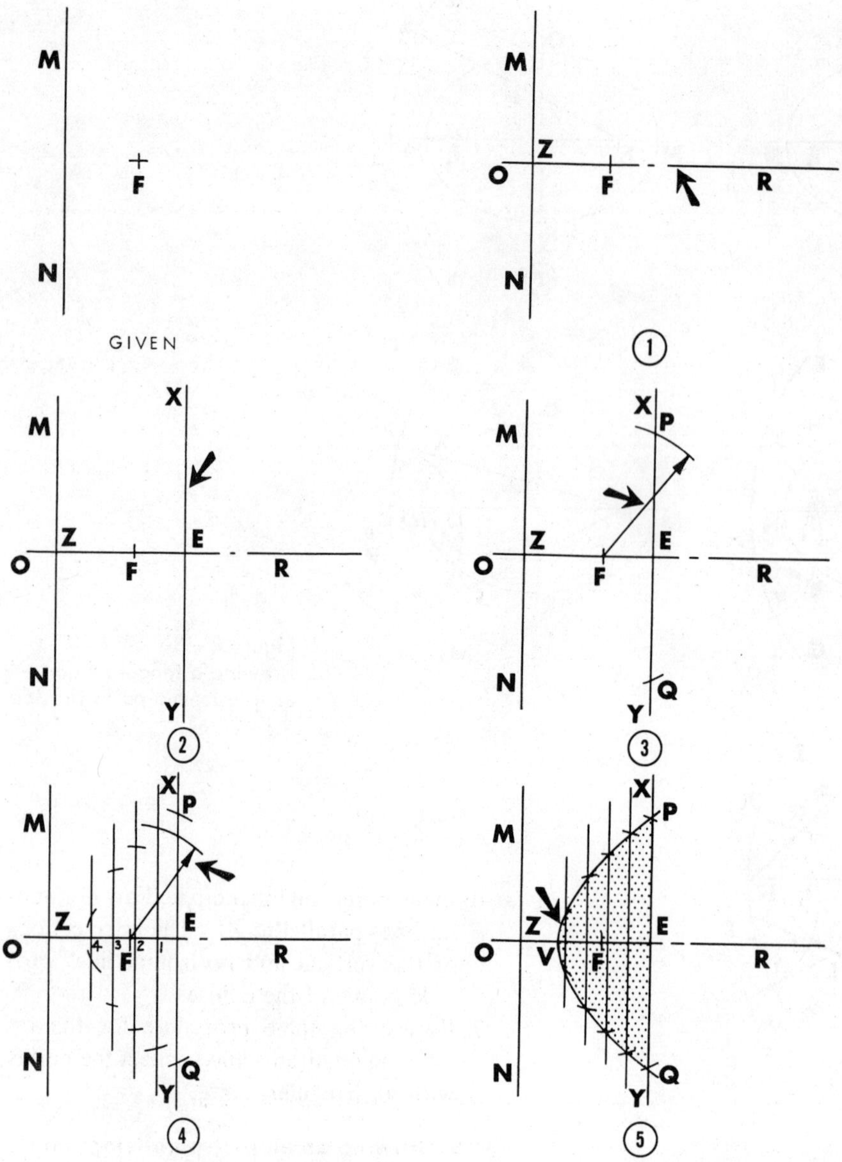

Figure 4-36 Drawing a parabola.

4.26 Drawing a tangent to an ellipse at a point on the ellipse

At point P on the curve (See Fig. 4-34)

1 Given ellipse and point P on the curve.
2 Find the foci F and F_1 on the major axis.
3 Draw lines FP and F_1P and extend to E.
4 Bisect angle EPF. The bisector of this angle is the required tangent.

From Point P outside the curve (See Fig. 4-35)

1 With focus F as the center and MN as a radius, scribe arc EG.
2 With P (outside point) as a center and PF_1 as the radius, draw an arc to intersect arc EG at X and Y.
3 Draw lines XF and YF, cutting the ellipse at K and L.
4 Points K and L are the tangent points.

4.27 Drawing a parabola (See Fig. 4-36)

A parabola is a curve that is generated by a point moving along a path equidistant from a fixed point called the *focus* and a straight line called the *directrix*.

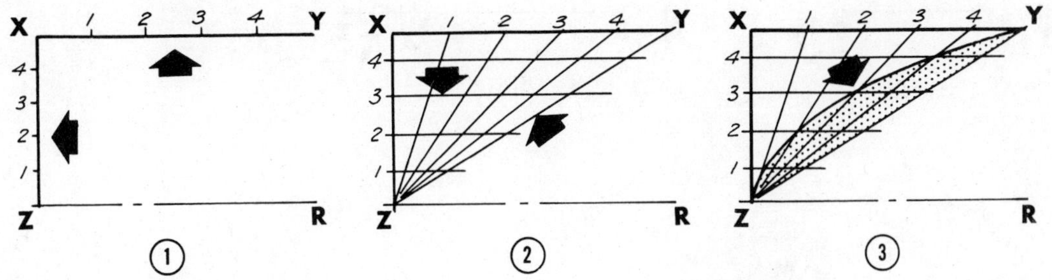

Figure 4-37
Drawing a parabola—parallelogram method.

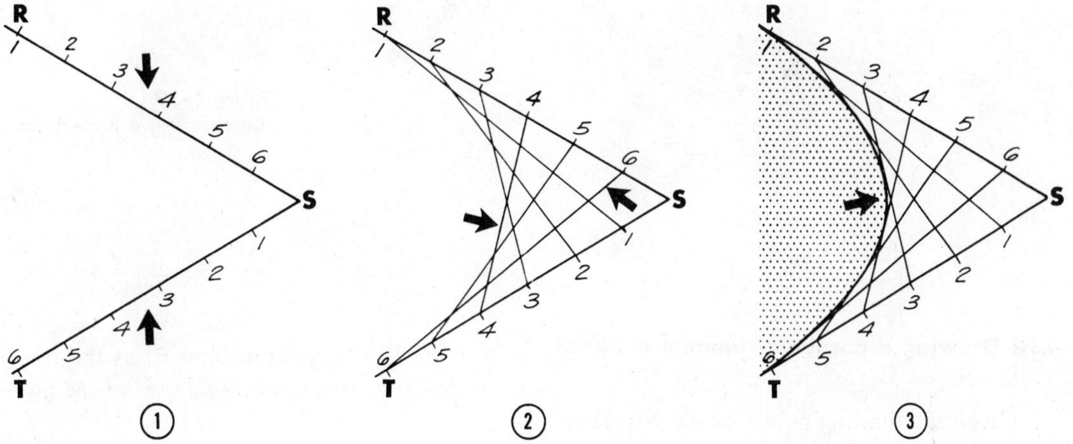

Figure 4-38
Drawing a parabola—tangent method.

1 Given focus F and directrix MN.
2 Draw line OR through F and perpendicular to MN to intersect MN at Z.
3 At any point E on line OR draw line XY parallel to MN.
4 With ZE as a radius and F as the center, draw arc intersecting line XY at P and Q. These are points on the parabola.
5 Divide distance ZE into any number of convenient spaces and draw lines through these divisions parallel to MN.
6 Repeat step 4 using distances *Z-1*, *Z-2*, *Z-3*, etc., as radii and F as center locating points on the curve.
7 The vertex V is located midway between the directrix and F on OR. Draw the curve through the points located.

4.28 Drawing a parabola—parallelogram method (See Fig. 4-37)

1 Given the rise XY and the half-span XZ of the parabola.
2 Divide XY and XZ into the same number of equal parts.
3 From division points on line XY draw lines converging at Z.
4 From the division points on line XZ draw lines parallel to the axis ZR.
5 The corresponding intersections of these lines are the points of the parabolic curve.
6 Proceed in a similar manner to find the points for the lower half of the parabola and connect points with an irregular curve.

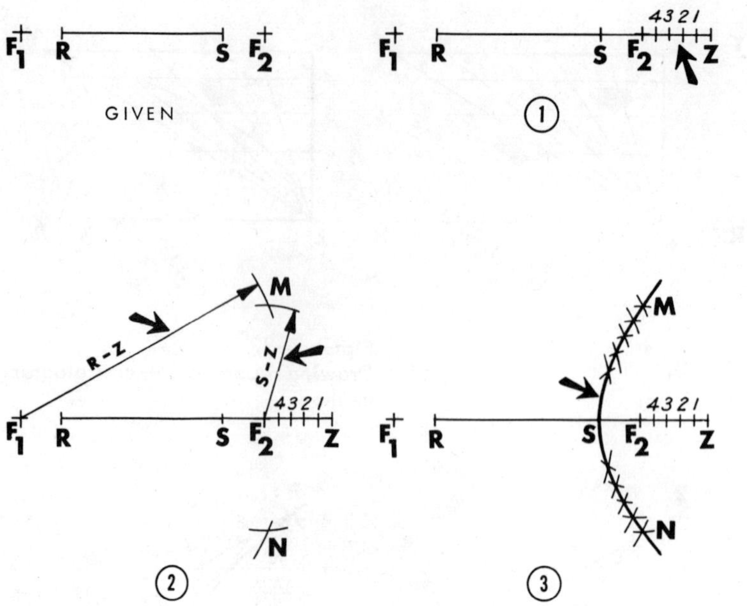

Figure 4–39
Constructing a hyperbola.

4.29 Drawing a parabola—tangent method (See Fig. 4-38)

1 Given the limiting points of the parabola *R* and *T* and the tangents *RS* and *ST*.
2 Divide lines *RS* and *ST* into any number of equal parts and number the divisions as shown.
3 Draw lines connecting like numbered points such as *1* and *1*, *2* and *2*, *3* and *3*.
4 The curve drawn tangent to these intersecting lines is the parabolic curve.

4.30 Drawing a hyperbola (See Fig. 4-39)

A hyperbola is a curve generated by a point moving so that the difference of the distances from any point of the curve to two fixed points, called the foci, is a constant equal to the transverse axis of the hyperbola.

1 Given foci F_1 and F_2 and the transverse axis *RS*.
2 Extend transverse axis to any convenient distance such as *Z*.
3 Lay off on *SZ* any number of points.
4 With *S-Z* as a radius and F_2 as the center, strike arcs at *M* and *N*.
5 With *R-Z* as a radius and F_1 as the center strike arcs to intersect arcs at *M* and *N*.
6 Proceed in a similar manner for points *1, 2, 3, 4,* etc., on the transverse axis. The points formed by the intersecting arcs represent the required curve of the hyperbola.

4.31 Constructing an involute of a polygon (See Fig. 4-40)

An involute is a spiral curve made by a point on a perfectly taut string as it unwinds from around a shape such as a circle or polygon.

1 Given polygon *LMNO*.
2 With *L* as a center and radius *LO,* scribe an arc intersecting line *LM* at *1*.
3 With *M* as a center and radius *M-1,* scribe an arc intersecting the extended line *NM* at *2*.
4 Continue this procedure and determine points *3* and *4* using radii *N-2* and *O-3*.
5 The connecting arcs determine the involute of the polygon.

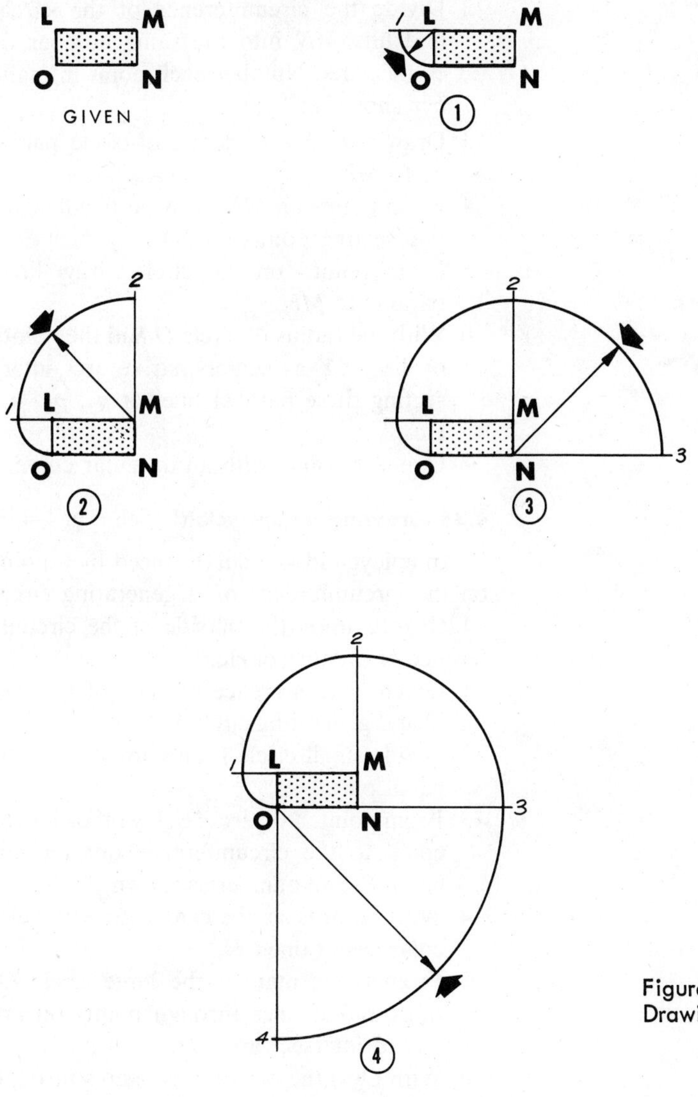

Figure 4–40
Drawing an involute of a polygon.

4.32 Drawing an involute of a circle

(See Fig. 4-41)

1 Given circle *O*.
2 Divide circle into any number of equal parts and number the parts.
3 Draw tangents to the circle at each of these points.
4 On each tangent step off the length of the corresponding arc divisions such as *1-12* on tangent line *1-A*, *2-12* on tangent line *2-B*, *3-12* on tangent line *3-C*, etc.
5 Connect the points with an irregular curve.

4.33 Constructing a spiral

(See Fig. 4-42)

A spiral of Archimedes is a curve generated when a point moves away from a fixed point so that its distance increases uniformly with the angle.

1 Given an angle of 30°.
2 From point *O* lay out a series of equal angles and draw radial lines.
3 Divide one of the radial lines *OG* into the same number of parts as there are radial lines.
4 Rotate the points on *OG* to the corre-

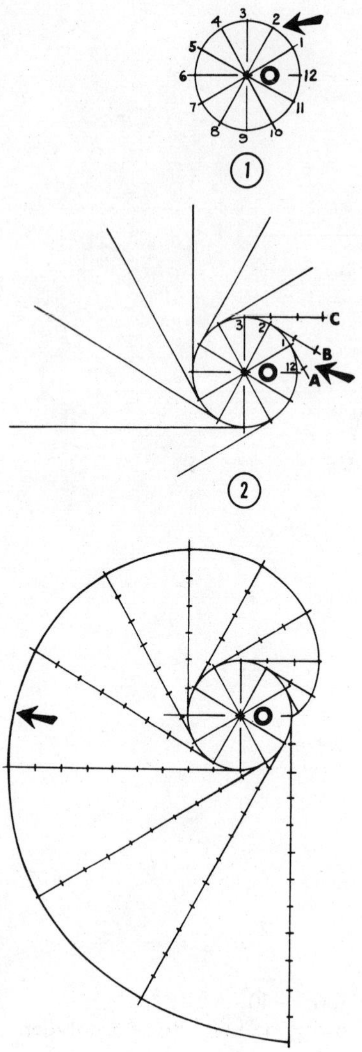

Figure 4-41
Drawing an involute of a circle.

sponding radial lines.

5 Connect points with an irregular curve.

4.34 Drawing a cycloid (See Fig. 4-43)

A cycloid is a curve generated by a point in the plane of a circle that rolls along a straight line.

1 Given circle *O* and its path-tangent line *MN* equal in length to the circumference of the circle.

2 Divide the circumference of the circle and line *MN* into the same number of equal parts. Number each point in manner shown in figure.

3 Draw path *XY* of center of circle parallel to *MN*.

4 From points on *MN* draw perpendiculars intersecting points on *XY*.

5 From points on the circle, draw lines parallel to *MN*.

6 With the radius of circle *O* and the points on line *XY* as centers, strike arcs intersecting these parallel lines at p_1, p_2, p_3, etc.

7 Connect points with an irregular curve.

4.35 Drawing an epicycloid (See Fig. 4-44)

An epicycloid is a curve traced by a point on the circumference of a generating circle which rolls upon the outside of the circumference of another circle.

1 Given circumference arc *AE* of a circle *O* and generating circle *P*.

2 Divide small circle *P* into any number of equal parts.

3 From point *Y* on arc *AE*, lay off distances equal to the circumference divisions of circle *P*, and number as shown.

4 With point *O* as the center draw the circular center line *CD*.

5 From the center of the large circle *O*, draw radial lines through points on arc *AE* to intersect arc *CD*.

6 With *O* as the center, strike arcs through points on the generating circle *P*.

7 Using points on the center line of arc *CD* as centers and radii equal to the radius of the small circle, draw arcs intersecting arcs drawn from the points on the small circle in step 6. The intersection of these arcs provides points for the epicycloid.

8 Connect points with an irregular curve.

4.36 Drawing a hypocycloid (See Fig. 4-45)

A hypocycloid is a curve generated by a point on the circumference of a circle which rolls upon the inside circumference of another circle. The same procedure is used to construct a hypocycloid as for drawing an epicycloid.

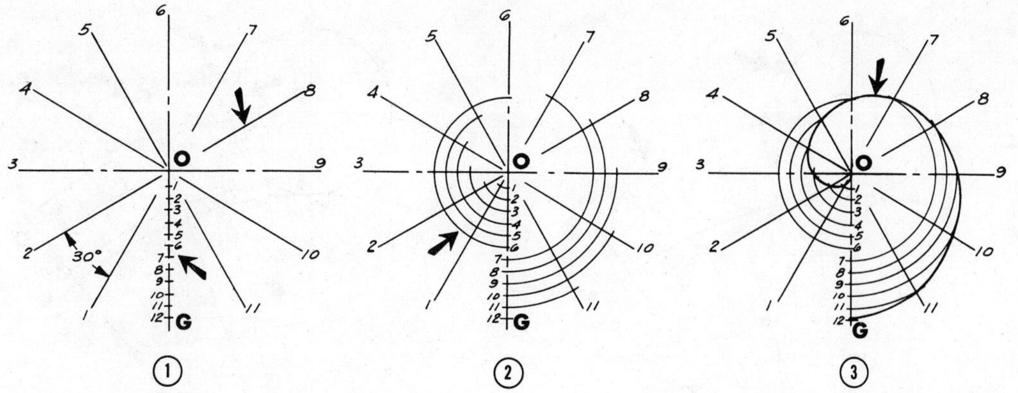

Figure 4-42
Constructing a spiral.

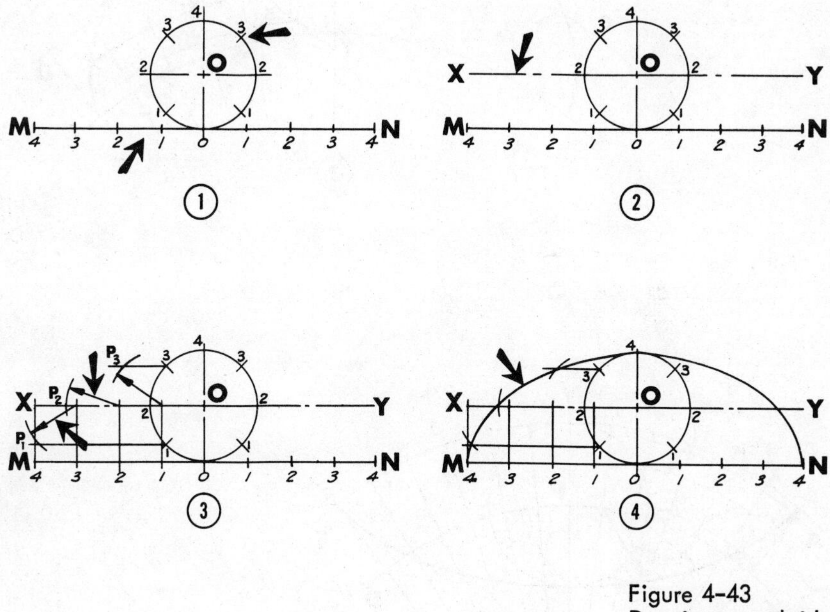

Figure 4-43
Drawing a cycloid.

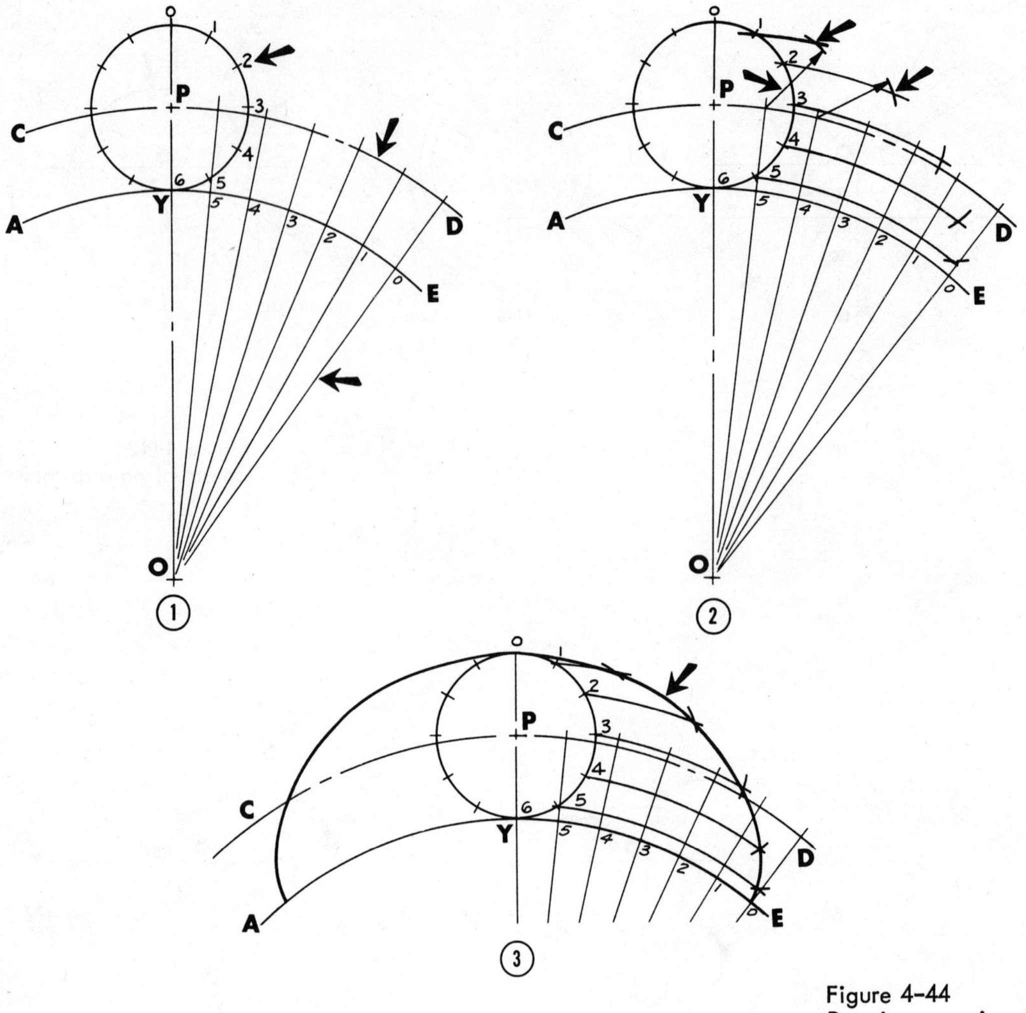

Figure 4–44
Drawing an epicycloid.

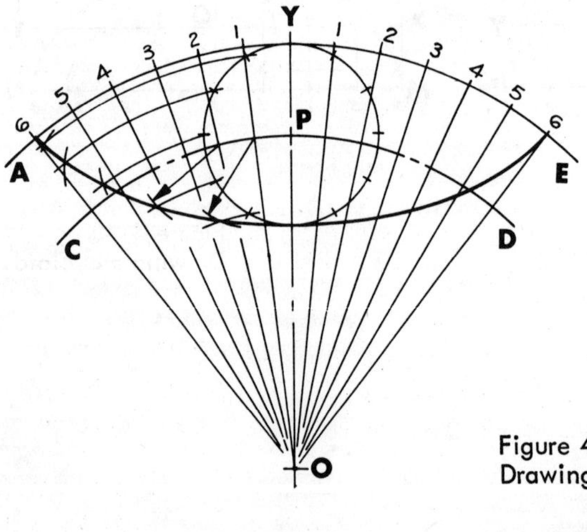

Figure 4–45
Drawing a hypocycloid.

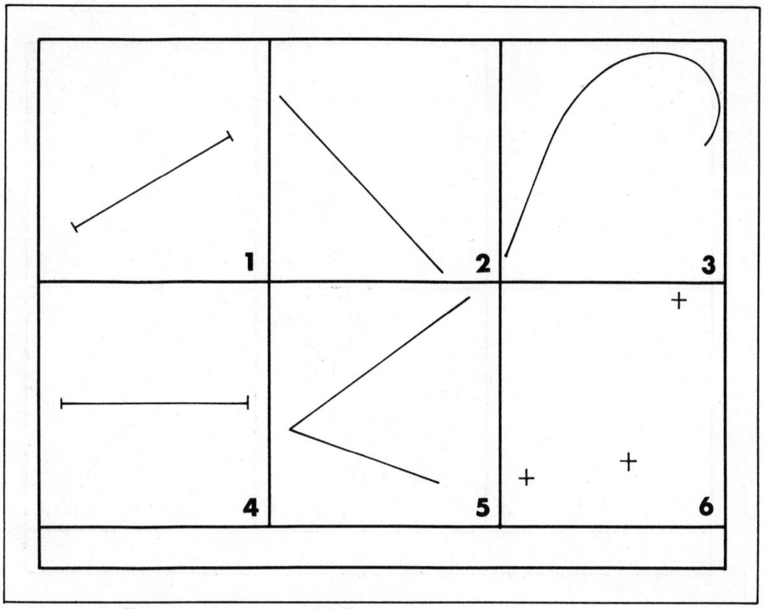

Figure 4-46
Drawing Sheet No. 1.

Problems, section 4

The following problems are designed to provide practice in basic geometric construction. To insure a high degree of accuracy, the use of a **4H** or a **6H** pencil is recommended. All construction lines should be left on the drawing. The final solution should be darkened with an **H** or **2H** pencil.

The problems should be arranged on the sheets as indicated. Dimensions and lettering may be included or omitted as determined by the instructor.

Drawing sheet No. 1 (See Fig. 4-46)

1 Bisect a line 2–17/32″ long drawn at an angle of 37°.
2 Draw a straight line parallel to another straight line at a distance of 5/8″.
3 Draw any curved line. Construct a parallel curved line at a distance of 13/16″ from the first line.
4 Divide a straight line 2–11/16″ long into five equal parts.
5 Lay out any acute angle and find its bisector.
6 Locate any three points at random. Determine the circular arc that will pass through these points.

Drawing sheet No. 2 (See Fig. 4-47)

1 Draw a 90° angle with sides of any convenient length. Construct a circular arc tangent to the two lines having a radius of 1–1/2″.
2 Construct two lines forming any convenient obtuse angle. Draw a tangent arc having a radius of 1–7/8″.

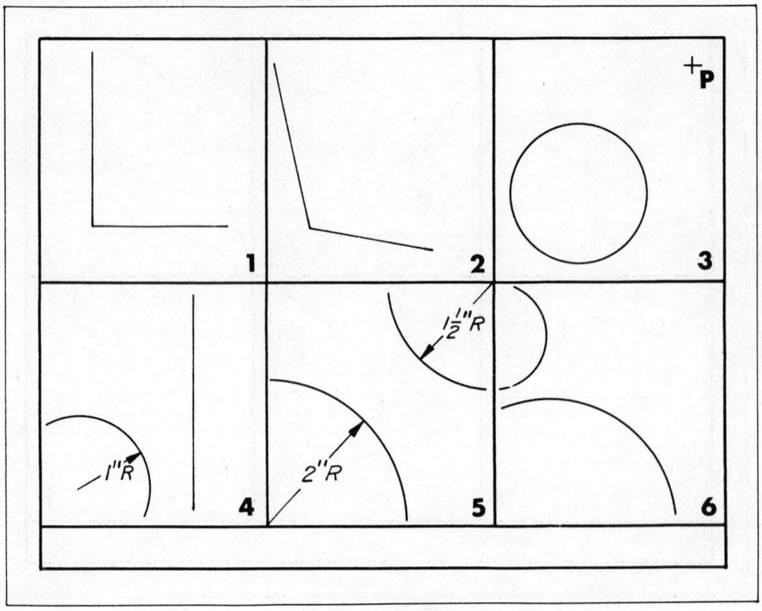

Figure 4–47
Drawing Sheet No. 2.

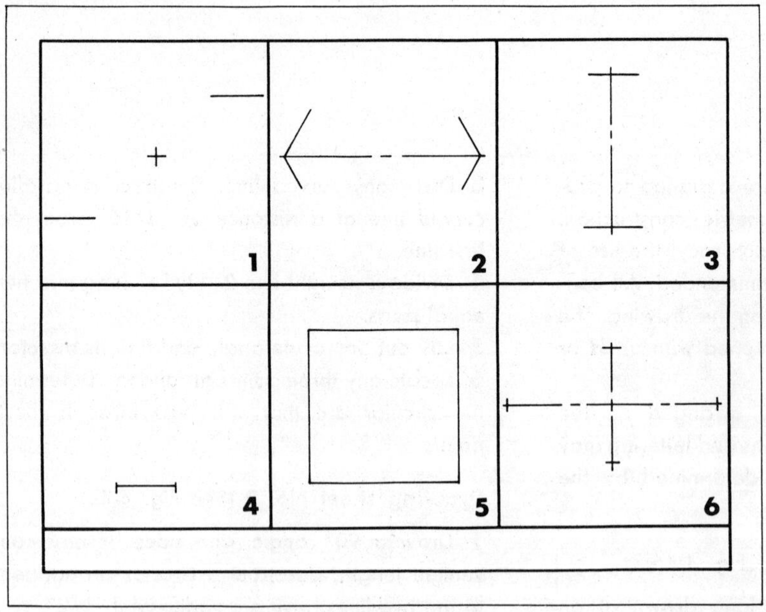

Figure 4–48
Drawing Sheet No. 3.

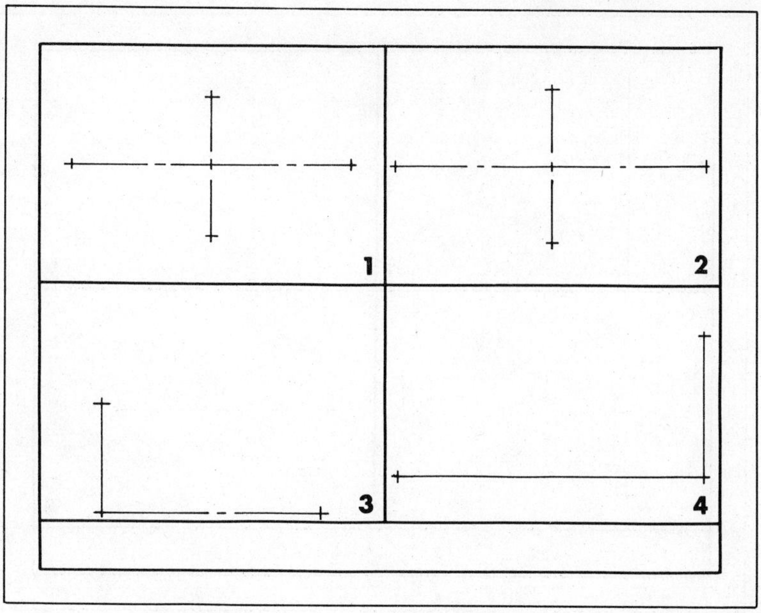

Figure 4–49
Drawing Sheet No. 4.

3 Draw a 2″ diameter circle and through any point outside the circle, such as **P,** construct a straight line tangent to the circle.

4 Draw a 5/8″ radius arc tangent to a straight line and an arc having a radius of 1″.

5 Construct an arc having a radius of 3/4″ tangent to the two given arcs.

6 Construct a straight line tangent to two arcs. Determine points of tangency.

Drawing sheet No. 3 (See Fig. 4-48)

1 Draw an ogee curve tangent to two parallel straight lines spaced 1–1/16″ apart through a point midway between the lines.

2 Construct a regular hexagon having a distance across corners of 2–7/8″.

3 Draw a regular hexagon havng a distance across flats of 2–3/32″.

4 Construct a regular hexagon having a side of 13/16″.

5 Lay out a regular octagon in a 2–1/8″square.

6 Using a major axis of 3″ and a minor axis of 1–5/8″, produce an ellipse by the foci method.

Drawing sheet No. 4 (See Fig. 4-49)

1 Lay out by the trammel method an ellipse having axes of 4″ and 2″.

2 Using the four-center method, construct an ellipse with a major axis of 4–1/2″ and a minor axis of 2–3/16″.

3 Construct a quarter of an ellipse using the concentric-circle method having a major axis of 6–1/4″ and a minor axis of 3–1/4″.

4 Using the parallelogram method, produce a quarter of an ellipse having a major axis of 9″ and a minor axis of 4″.

Drawing sheet No. 5 (See Fig. 4-50)

1 Construct a parabolic curve using a directrix and focus.

2 Construct a parabola through two points using the parallelogram method.

3 Using three points, construct a parabola using the tangent method.

4 Using a transverse axis and two foci, construct a hyperbolic curve.

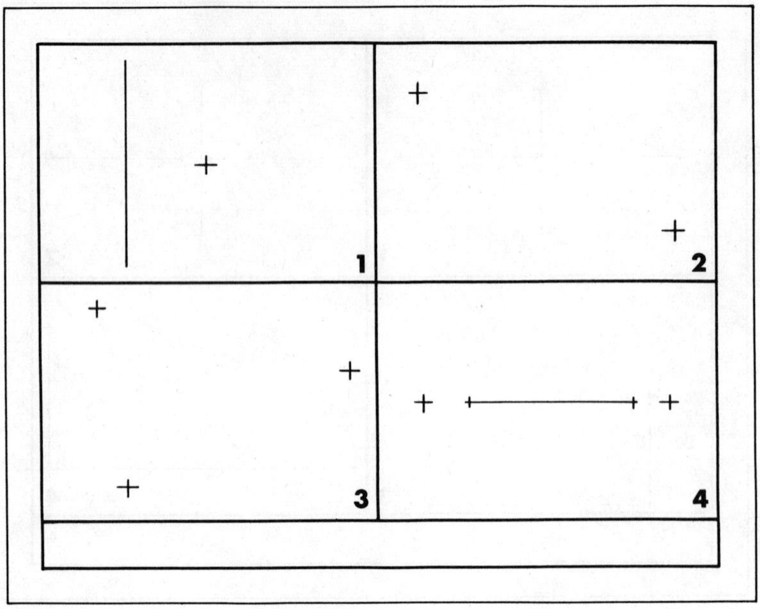

Figure 4-50
Drawing Sheet No. 5.

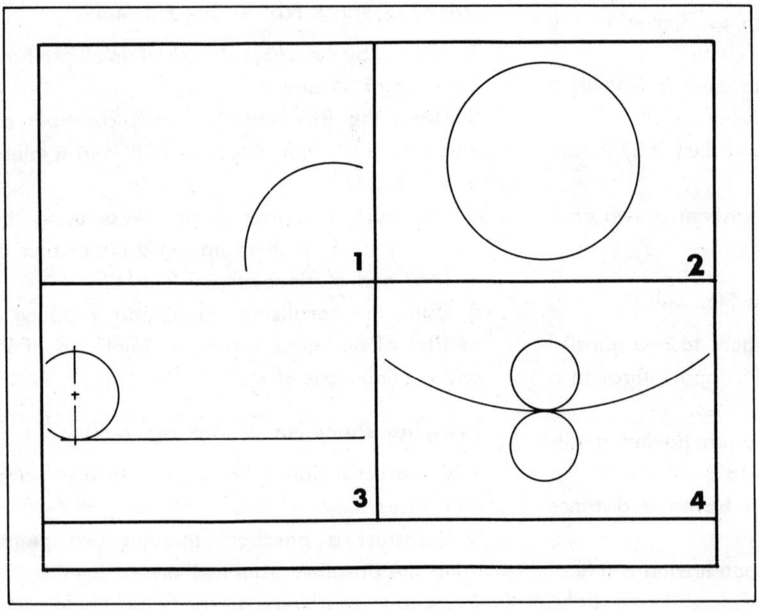

Figure 4-51
Drawing Sheet No. 6.

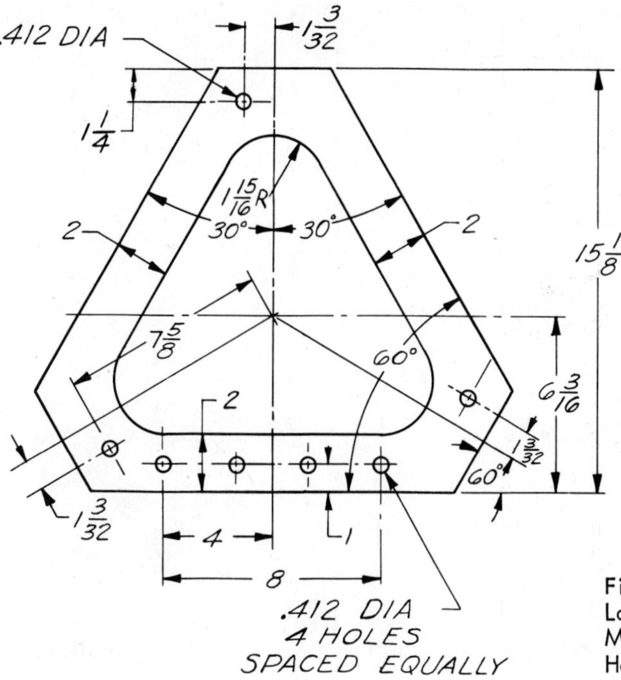

Figure 4-52
Lower Frame Plate. Hurley Machine Division of Electric Household Utilities Corp.

Drawing sheet No. 6 (See Fig. 4-51)

1 Construct the involute of the arc of a circle.

2 Construct the Spiral of Archimedes in one turn of the circle.

3 Draw a half cycloid formed by a 1–1/4″ generating circle rolling along a straight line.

4 Draw the epicycloid and hypocycloid formed by a 1″ diameter generating circle which rolls on a 4″ radius arc.

Drawing No. 7

Construct a layout of the Lower Frame Plate as shown in Fig. 4-52. Select any suitable scale. Include or omit dimensions as directed by the instructor.

Drawing No. 8

Make a drawing showing the contour of the Mixing Bowl. See Fig. 4-53. Scale—double size.

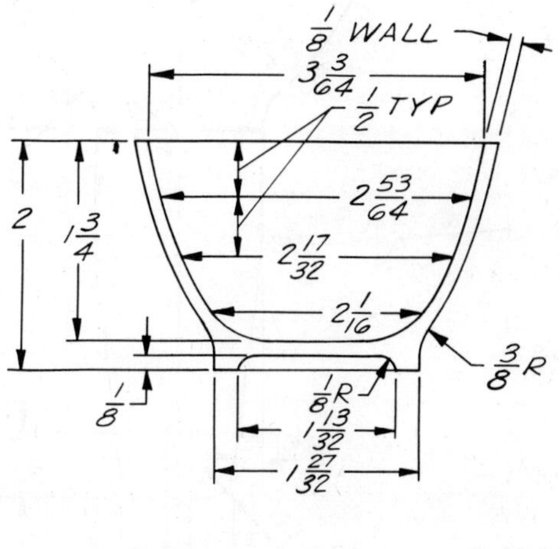

Figure 4-53
Mixing Bowl. The S. S. White Dental Mfg. Co.

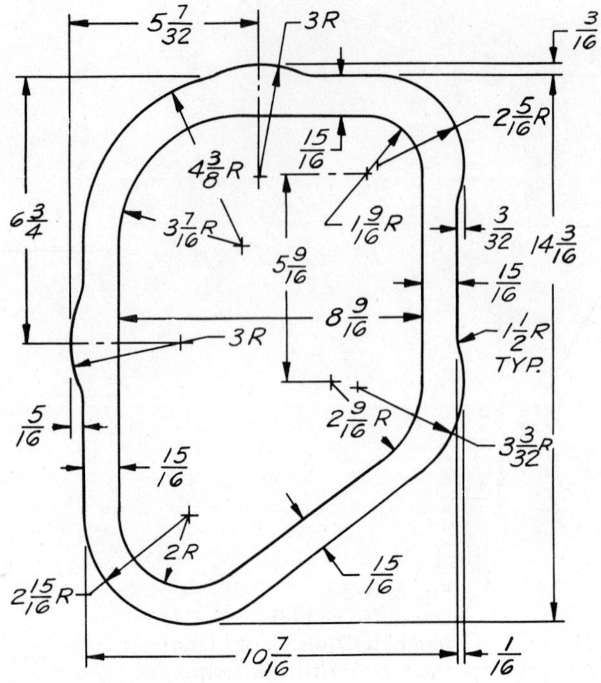

Figure 4-54
Oil Pan Gasket. Thor Corporation

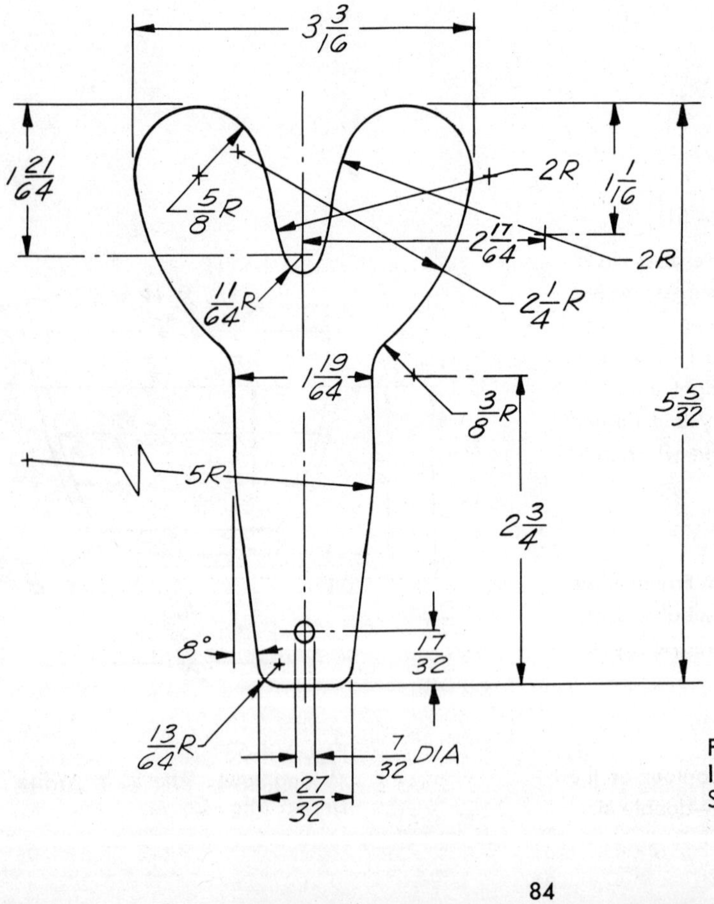

Figure 4-55
Impression Tray Blank. The S. S. White Dental Mfg. Co.

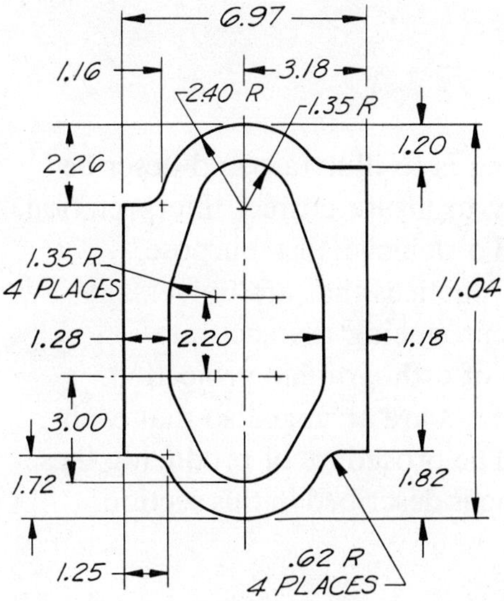

Figure 4-56
Seal Pan. Lockheed Aircraft Corp.

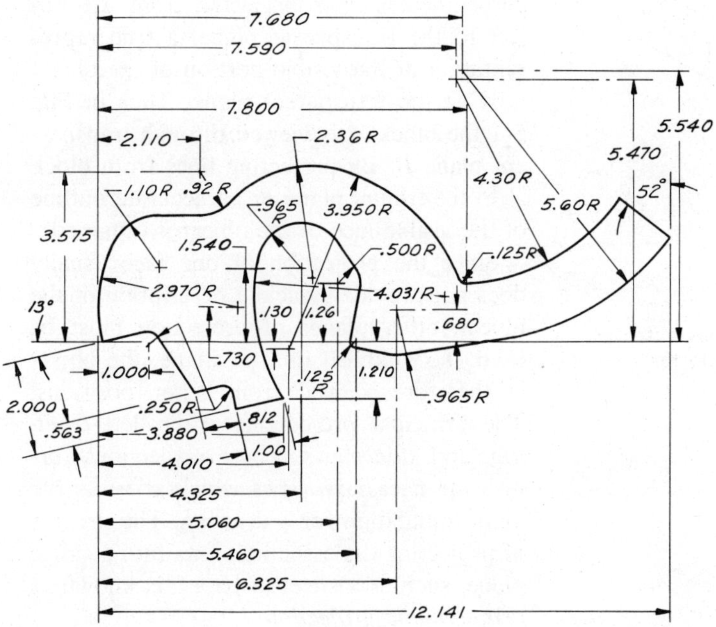

Figure 4-57
Seal
Pratt & Whitney Aircraft

Drawing No. 9

Construct a scaled layout of the Oil Pan Gasket. See Fig. 4-54.

Drawing No. 10

Lay out a full-size drawing of the Impression Tray Blank as shown in Fig. 4-55.

Drawing No. 11

Prepare a scaled drawing of the Pan Seal. See Fig. 4-56.

Drawing No. 12

Construct a full-size layout of the Seal shown in Fig. 4-57.

5 Multiview drawings

The function of any mechanical drawing is to illustrate and describe an object in sufficient detail and clarity to insure correct interpretation by any manufacturing organization. To achieve this purpose, a drawing must be made according to practices that are universally recognized. The accepted method of reproducing the accurate shape of an object is based on a system of orthographic projection. In such a system a series of separated views are arranged so that each view is definitely related to the others. The procedure of producing these views for a properly constructed drawing is described in this section.

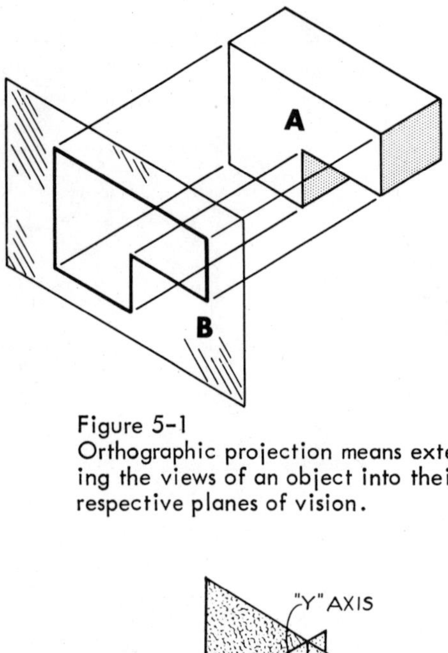

Figure 5-1
Orthographic projection means extending the views of an object into their respective planes of vision.

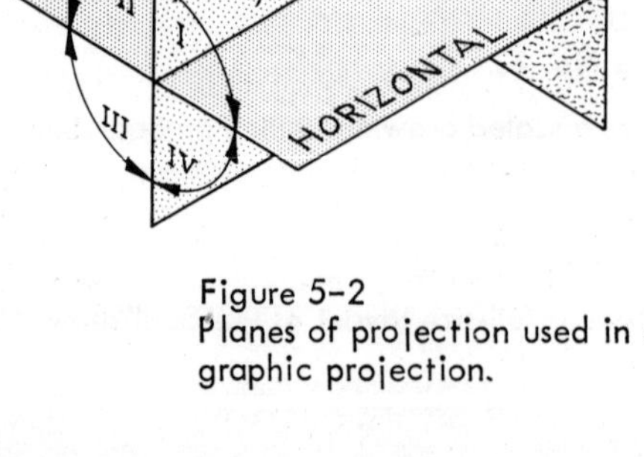

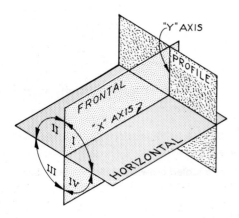

Figure 5-2
Planes of projection used in orthographic projection.

5.1 Orthographic projection

When an object is viewed through a transparent plane from a point at infinity and perpendicular lines projected from the object to the transparent plane, a true representation of the visible portion of the object falls on the transparent plane. Thus in Fig. 5-1 the block *A* is viewed through transparent plane *B*. By projecting lines from block *A* to the frontal plane *B*, an accurate outline of the visible face of the object is obtained.

Since the projection of one face usually does not provide sufficient description of the object, other planes of projection must be used. To establish its true shape, the object is therefore viewed from other positions. The principal projections are called *front, top,* and *side* views. These projections furnish the necessary views which serve as the main foundation for a drawing. The process of projecting the essential views into a single plane, such as a sheet of paper, is known as *orthographic projection.*

5.2 Planes of projection

The three planes used in orthographic projection are referred to as the *vertical* or *frontal plane*, the *horizontal plane*, and the *profile plane*. These planes are assumed to revolve about certain axes in order to bring the various views into a single plane. As shown in Fig. 5-2, the horizontal plane moves about the X-axis and the profile plane moves about the Y-axis. In orthographic projection, the horizontal and the profile planes are always revolved into the frontal plane.

The intersection of the horizontal and frontal planes generates four quadrants which are known as the first, second, third and fourth angles. An object may be placed in any one of the four quadrants and its surfaces projected onto the respective planes.

5.3 First angle projection

First angle projection is the system used exclusively in European countries in making drawings. The object is located in the first quadrant and when it is viewed from the positions shown in Fig. 5-3, and the lines of projection extended to the respective planes, the top view becomes visible on the horizontal plane, the front view on the vertical plane and the left side view on the profile plane. Upon revolving the horizontal and profile planes into the vertical plane, the various views assume the position shown in Fig. 5-4. Notice that the front view is directly above the top view and the left side view is to the right of the front view.

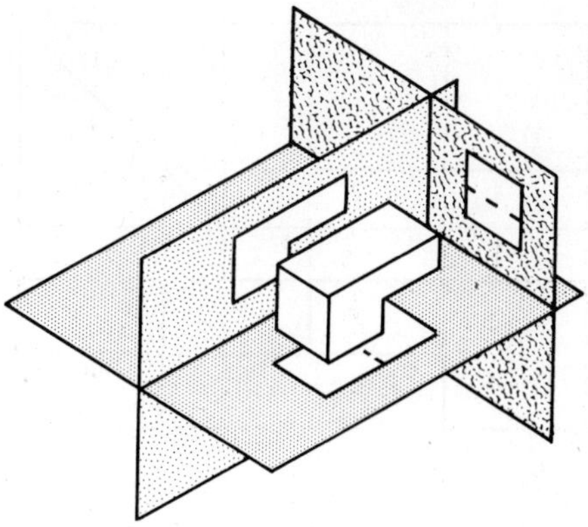

Figure 5-3
First angle projection is used exclusively in European countries.

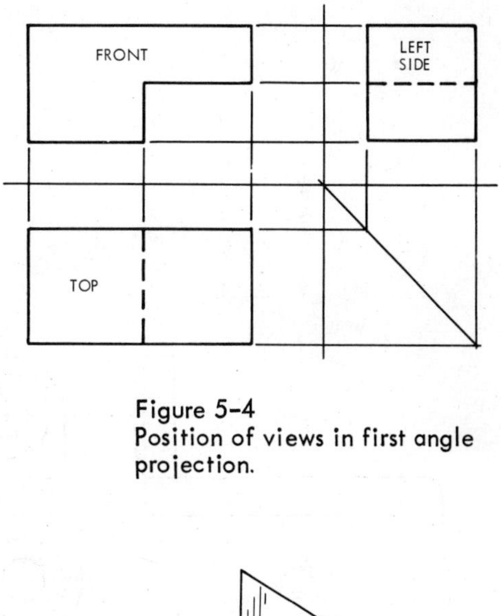

Figure 5-4
Position of views in first angle projection.

5.4 Second and fourth angle projection

If an object is placed either in the second or fourth quadrant and the horizontal and profile plane revolved into the vertical plane, both the top and front views are superimposed. This overlapping of views tends to restrict the clear visibility of either view and consequently becomes ineffective in producing an accurate drawing. Hence, the second and fourth angle projections are rarely if ever used in preparing working drawings.

5.5 Third angle projection

The third angle projection is the system of orthographic projection used for drawings in the United States and Canada. As shown in Fig. 5-5, the object is assumed to be situated in the third quadrant and when the projectors are extended to their respective planes, the top view is shown on the horizontal plane, the front view is on the vertical plane and the side view is on the profile plane. When the horizontal and profile plane are revolved into

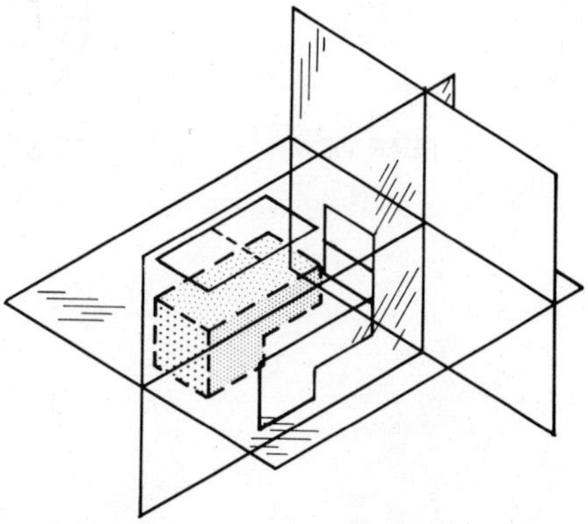

Figure 5-5
The third-angle projection is the system used for drawings in the United States and Canada.

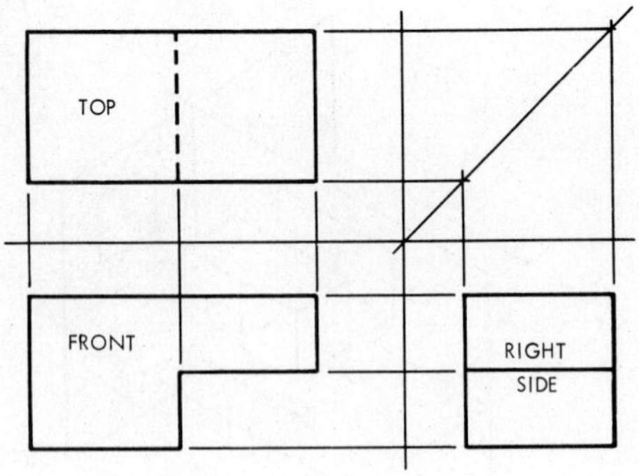

Figure 5-6
Position of views in third angle projection.

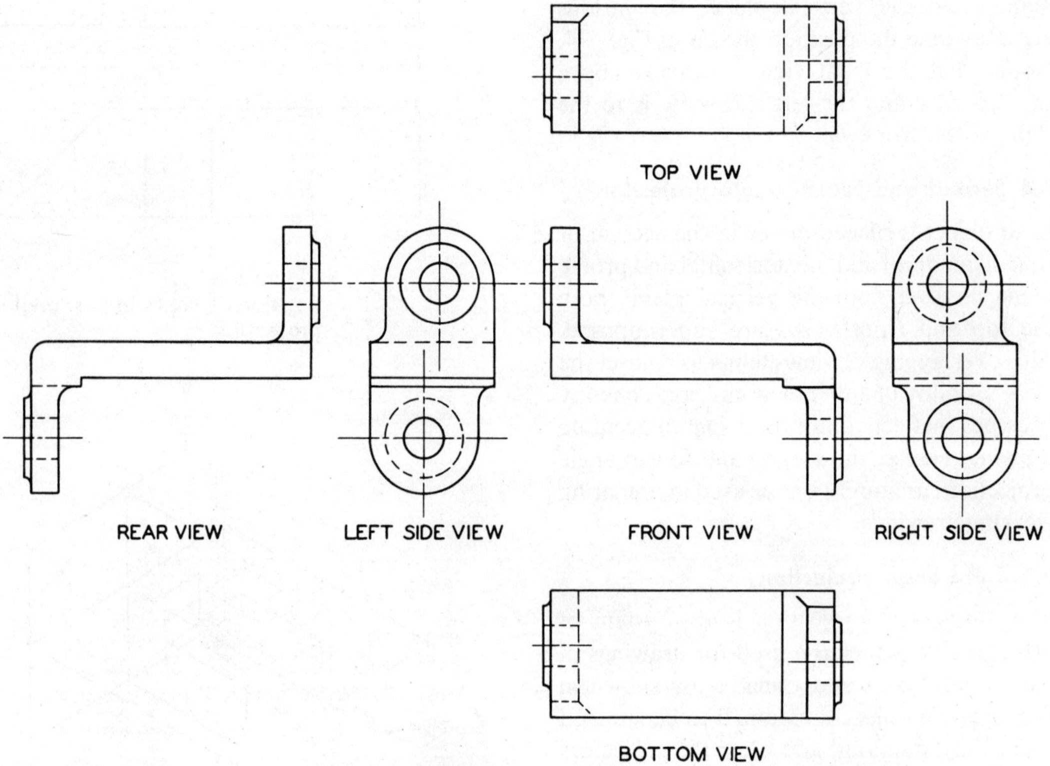

Figure 5-7
Position of views in a multiview projection system.
SAE

the vertical plane, the views fall in the position shown in Fig. 5-6. Notice that in this type of projection the top view is directly above the front view and the right side view is to the right of the front view. Compare the third angle projection method with the system used in European countries as described in Subsection 5.3.

5.6 Multiview projection

It was mentioned previously, that in order to describe an object completely, it is often necessary to show a number of projections or views. When a series of projections are used, the system is commonly referred to as *multiview projection*. With this system an object can be viewed from six different positions, namely, top, front, bottom, right side, left side, and rear. See Fig. 5-7. In all cases, the plane of projection is between the observer and the object, and except for the rear view, each plane is hinged to the vertical plane and resolved in coincidence with it in a direction away from the object. The rear view may appear at the extreme right in a reverse position to that shown in Fig. 5-7.

5.7 Visualization of views

In order to visualize better the position and relationship of the views mentioned in Subsection 5.6, assume that the rectangular box shown in Fig. 5-8 is to be unfolded into a single plane. Assume further that side A of the box represents the single plane into which the remaining sides are to be unfolded. For the purpose of swinging the respective surfaces into their correct position, each panel of the box, except the rear, is considered to be hinged to the front surface. Notice in Fig. 5-9 that when the panels of the box are swung open, panel *B* is directly above the front panel *A;* panel *C* is to the right of *A;* panel *D* is below *A*, and *E* is to the left of *A*. The rear of the box *F* unfolds so it is to the left of *E*. Thus for any third angle projection, the views of an object are always located in these positions.

Another means of visualizing the planes of projection is with the transparent box shown in Fig. 5-10. The observer views the enclosed object from various positions on

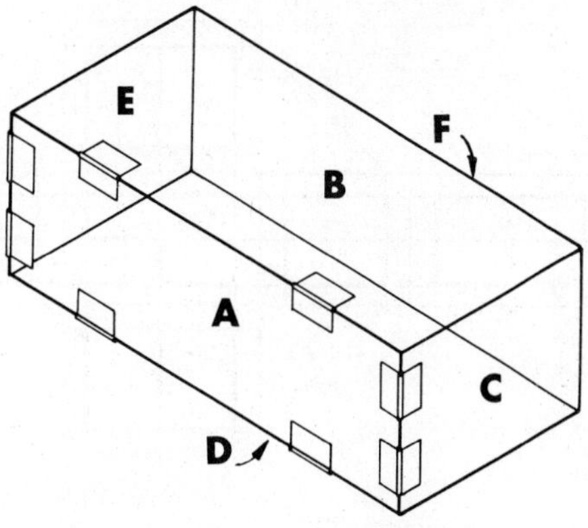

Figure 5-8
Rectangular box with its panels in a folded position.

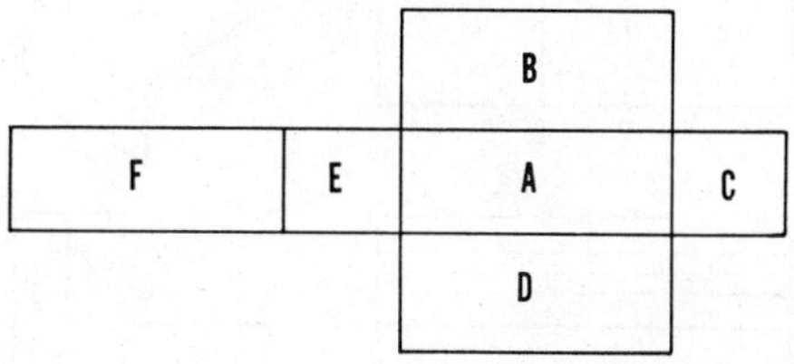

Figure 5-9
Rectangular box with its sides unfolded.

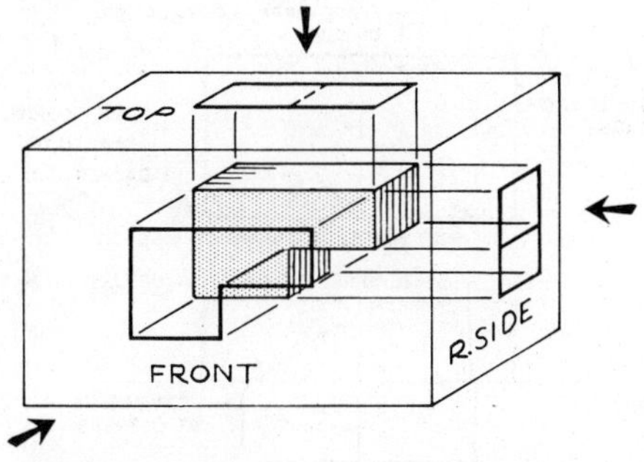

Figure 5-10
This object is enclosed in a transparent box with projectors extended to the planes.

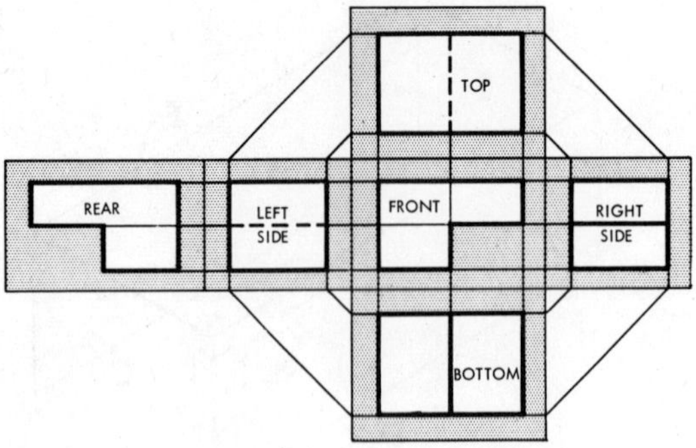

Figure 5-11
These are the six views of an object as they would appear on a drawing.

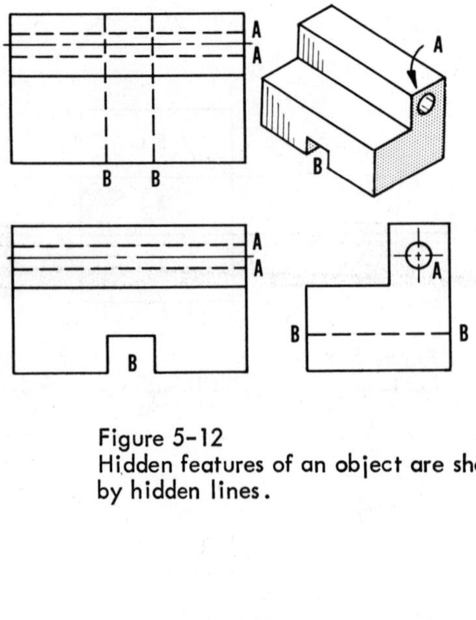

Figure 5-12
Hidden features of an object are shown by hidden lines.

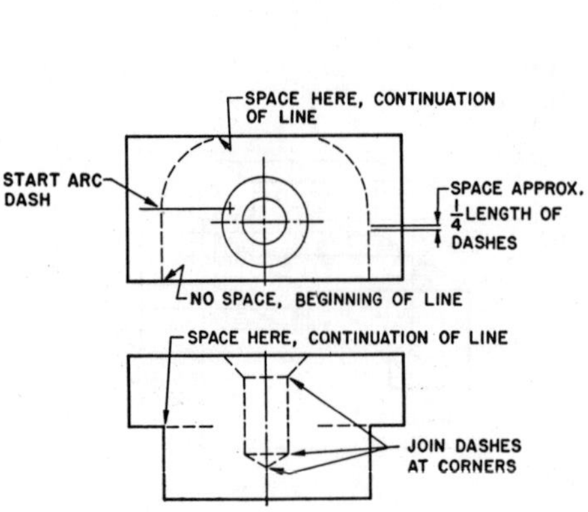

Figure 5-13
Hidden line junctures should conform to these practices.

the outside of the transparent box. If projectors are extended to the transparent planes, the six views of the object are now on their respective planes. Again all planes are assumed to be hinged as before. When the planes are revolved outwardly from their original position until they are in the front plane, they will fall in the location shown in Fig. 5-11.

Unlike the unfolded box where the sides are all joined together, the revolved planes of the transparent box show the views in positions separated from each other. Here, then are the true locations of the various views when used in a drawing. Notice that in each case the views are all the same distance from their axes. From this it becomes apparent that once the depth of one view is found, the depth of the remaining views may be determined by construction.

5.8 Showing hidden features

To describe an object completely, a drawing must show all the features of the object. In many instances certain edges, intersections, and surfaces cannot be seen from the position of the observer. The practice in drawing is to show these hidden features by means of lines made up of short dashes which are called *hidden* or *invisible* lines. Thus, in the object shown in Fig. 5-12, the hole *A* is visible in the side view but it cannot be seen when the object is viewed from the front and top. Accordingly, dashed lines *A-A* must be used in the front and top views. Similarly, the slot *B* on the bottom of the object can be seen only in the front view. This slot is therefore shown in the top and side views by dashed lines *B-B*.

Hidden lines consist of evenly spaced dashes with a space between them approximately 1/4 the length of the dash. A hidden line should always begin with a dash in contact with the line from which it starts, except when the dash would form a continuation of a full line. Dashes should touch at corners, and circular arcs should start with dashes at their points of tangency. See Fig. 5-13.

5.9 Orientation of the object

The object to be drawn conceivably can be

turned so its principal surface is parallel to any plane of projection. For example, the object in Fig. 5-14 may be orientated so the surface *A* is parallel either to the vertical, horizontal, or profile plane. In each case it will be seen that the outline of the resulting views as they would normally appear on the drawing will vary depending on the orientation of the object.

The general rule for object orientation is to place the object so the sides having the most descriptive features are perpendicular to the direction of sight lines and parallel to a plane of projection. Specifically it is important to situate the object so the least number of hidden lines will appear in the views. It is apparent in Fig. 5-15, that if the object is orientated as shown in *B*, more hidden lines would be required than if the object is placed in position *A*. It is usually not good practice to have long surfaces serve as side views as in *C*.

5.10 Number of views

Although it has been stated that an object has six possible views, it does not necessarily follow that all six views must be shown to completely describe the object in a drawing. Quite often some views will be merely duplication of others and therefore will not contribute anything to the drawing. The guiding principle in selecting views is to include only those views which are absolutely necessary to portray clearly the shape of the part. Hence, for some simple objects a single view may be sufficient, whereas, for complicated pieces two or more views may be required. For example, certain cylindrical parts may be shown by one view if the necessary dimensions are indicated as diameters. A single view is generally sufficient for thin, flat pieces of uniform thickness such as shims, gaskets, and plates, if a note is included giving the thickness. See Fig. 5-16.

Symmetrical objects can often be limited to two views. A typical example is the object shown in Fig. 5-17. A drawing of this piece needs only a front and side view since a top view would only be a duplication of the front view.

For most objects three principal views are

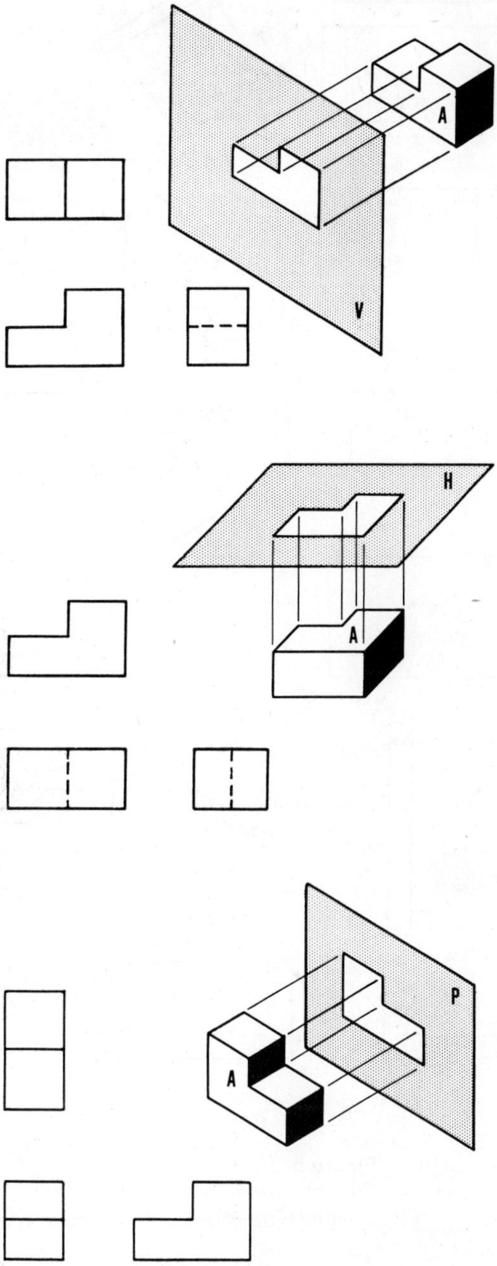

Figure 5-14
The shape of the views will depend on the orientation of the object.

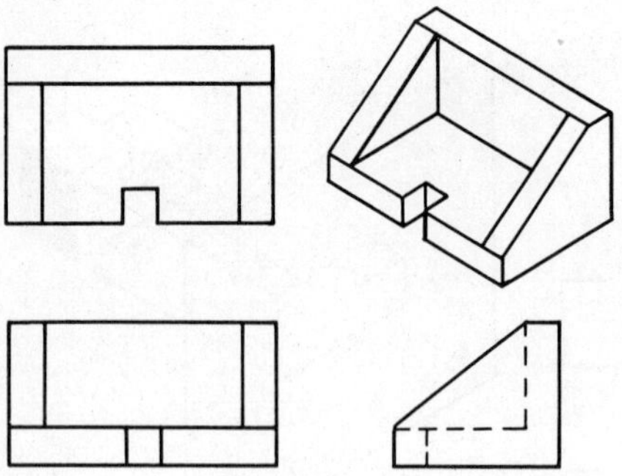

(A)

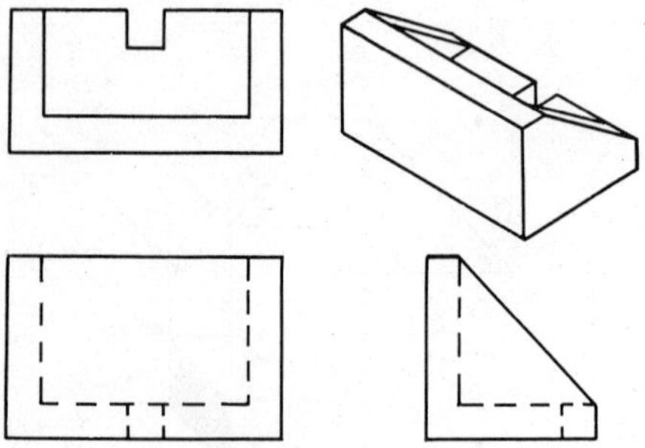

(B)

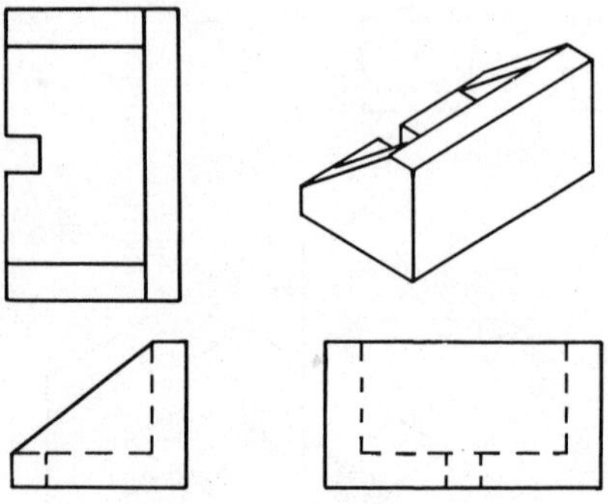

(C)

Figure 5-15
Object orientation. (A) Correct orientation; (B), (C) incorrect.

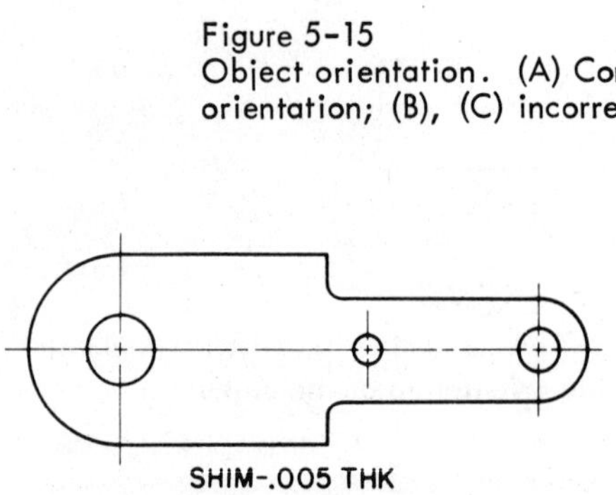

SHIM-.005 THK

Figure 5-16
A one-view drawing is sufficient for thin flat pieces having uniform thicknesses.

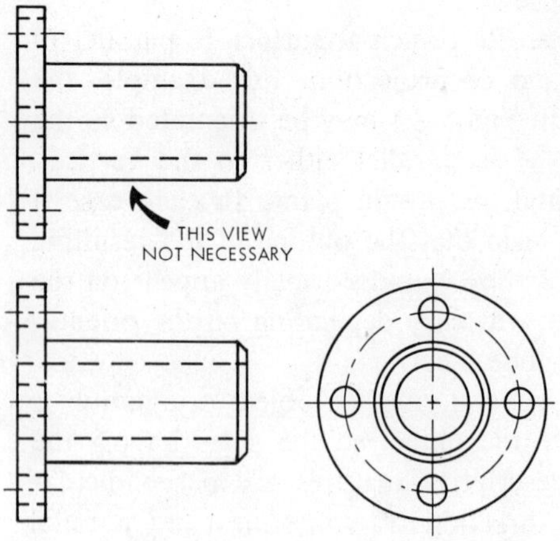

Figure 5-17
For this symmetrical object only two views are needed.

necessary—the front, the top, and a side view. The usual practice is to show the right side view only unless the shape of the two ends differs to such an extent that their true shapes cannot clearly be shown by a single side view. In the event the left side view shows more of the contour of the object, then it should be used instead of the right side view. A typical example is the object illustrated in Fig. 5-18. Notice that by using a left side view instead of the right side view all hidden lines can be eliminated.

Certain types of objects may need two side views to clearly show all of the details. See Fig. 5-19. Notice in Fig. 5-19 that without the right side view it would be virtually impossible to present a true representation of this end.

Occasionally, there will be some objects that will require a bottom view as well as a top view. See Fig. 5-20. When this problem occurs a bottom view must be included.

5.11 Partial views

When space is limited, it is permissible to represent symmetrical objects by partial views. See Fig. 5-21A. The half view drawn should always be the portion nearest the full view. The only exception is when the full view is a sectional view (see Section 8) in which case the partial view is the farthest portion. See Fig. 5-21B. Either the top, front or side views may be made as partial views.

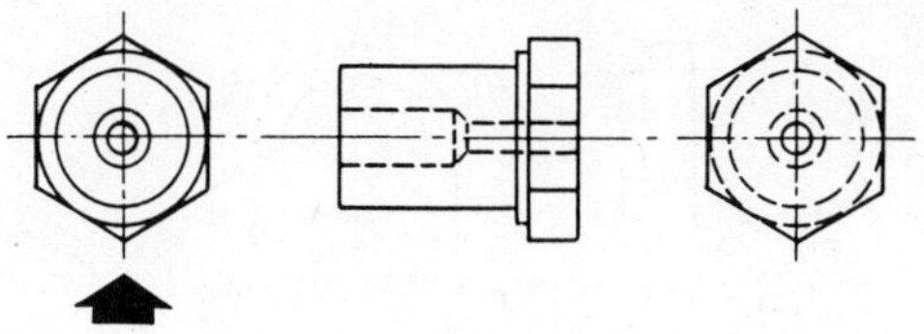

Figure 5-18
This object is clearer if the left side view rather than the right side view is shown.

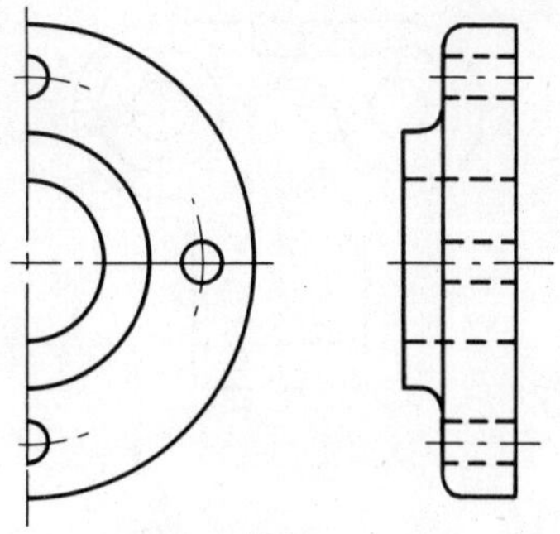

(A)

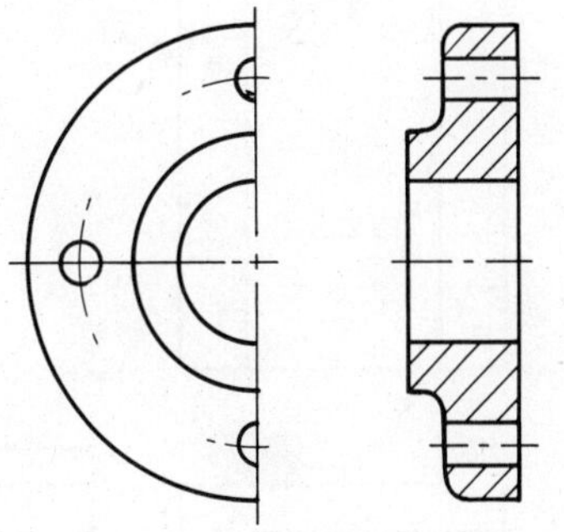

(B)

Figure 5-21
Examples of partial views.

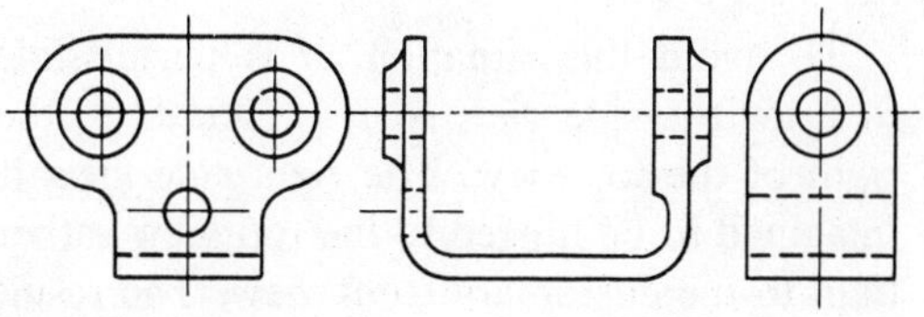

Figure 5-19
This object requires two side views for a clear presentation.

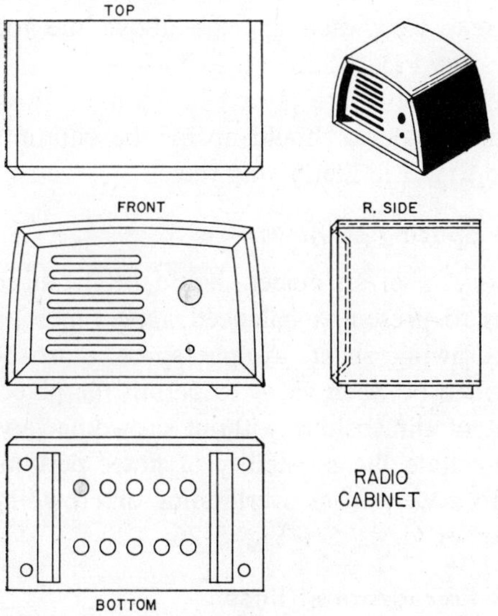

Figure 5-20
This object requires a bottom as well as a top view.

For objects where two side views can be used to a better advantage, these need not be complete views providing that, when considered together, they will fully describe the shape of the object. In such cases, only the hidden lines immediately behind the face need be shown. See Fig. 5-22.

5.12 Alternate position of side and rear views

A feature of a well made drawing is the pleasing balance of the various views. Sometimes proper spacing of views becomes a problem, especially when wide, flat objects must be drawn. If the conventional revolution of planes is used for such objects, some parts of the drawing sheet will be crowded and

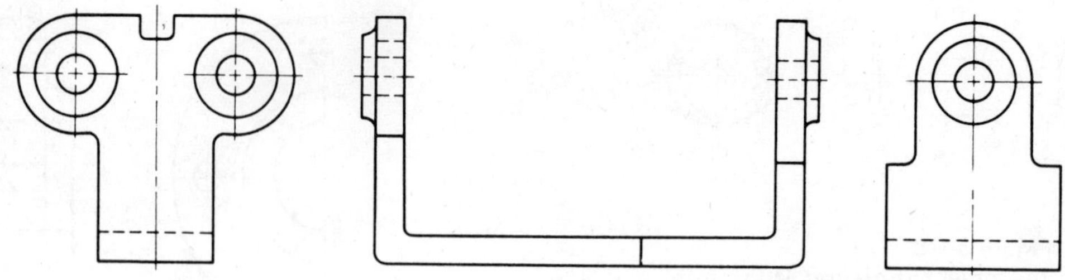

Figure 5-22
When two side views are used, they need not be complete views.

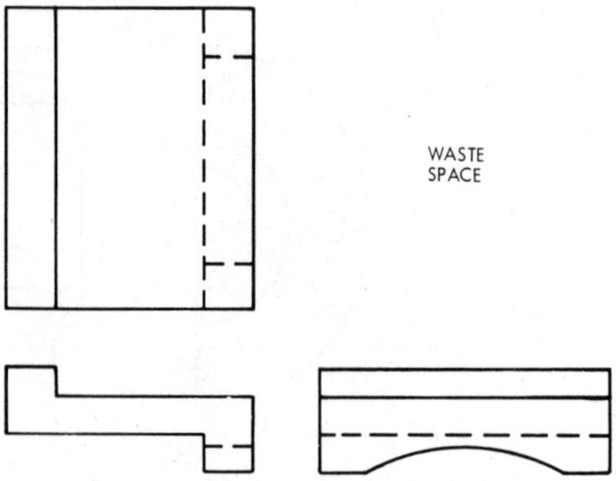

Figure 5-23
Examples of a drawing with a large open area.

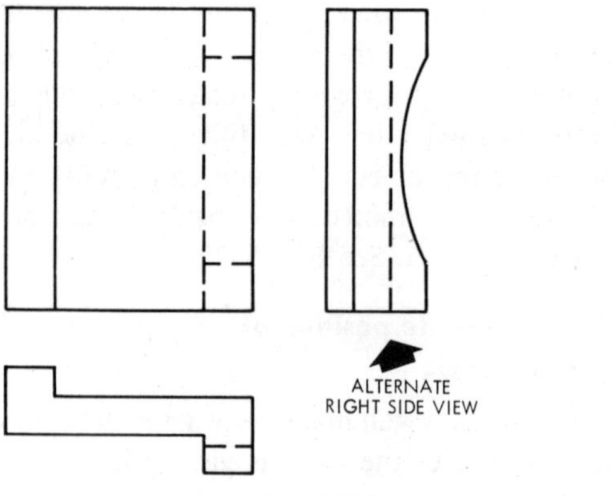

Figure 5-24
For some objects better space balance is achieved if the side view projects from the top view.

other portions will have large open areas. See Fig. 5-23.

To avoid this situation, it is permissible to draw the side view so it is located to the right of the top view. The right side view is imagined to be hinged to the top view rather than to the customary front view. The result is more satisfactory spacing arrangement. See Fig. 5-24. The same principle may be used to draw a left side view in an alternate position.

A rear view may also be drawn in an alternate position rather than in the location as shown in Fig. 5-11. In this case, the view is considered to be hinged to the top instead of to the left side view. On the drawing sheet the rear view then appears above the top view. See Fig. 5-25.

When views are placed in alternate positions, the views should always be carefully titled to aid in identifying them.

5.13 Spacing of views

The views of an object should be arranged so as to present a balanced appearance on the drawing sheet. Ample space must be provided between views to permit the placement of dimensions without crowding, and to preclude the possibility of notes pertaining to a view from overlapping or crowding the other views. See Fig. 5-26.

5.14 Precedence of lines

In laying out a view there will be instances when hidden lines, visible lines, and center lines will coincide. Since the essential features of the object are important, visible

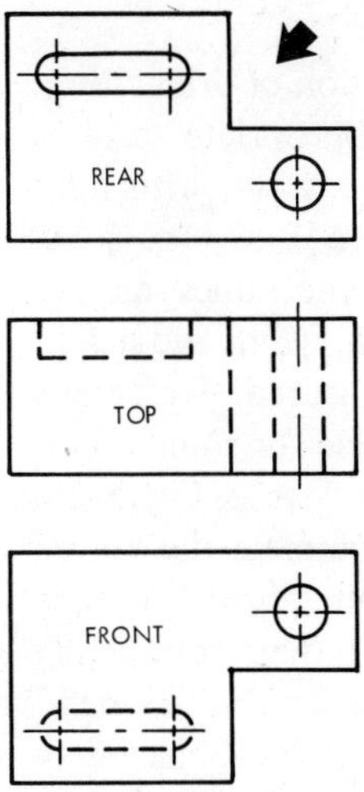

Figure 5-25
The rear view may be drawn so it is located above the top view.

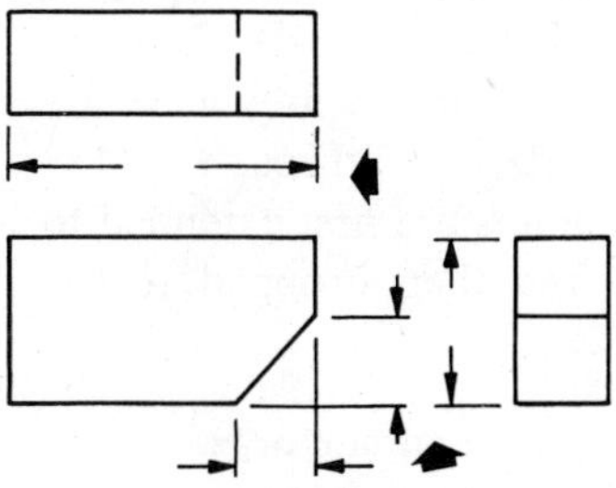

Figure 5-26
Views should be balanced on the sheet with ample space between them.

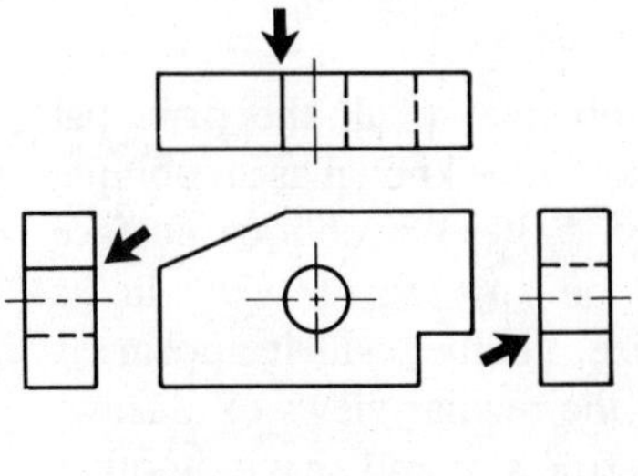

Figure 5-27
When different types of lines coincide, the accepted precedence of lines must be observed.

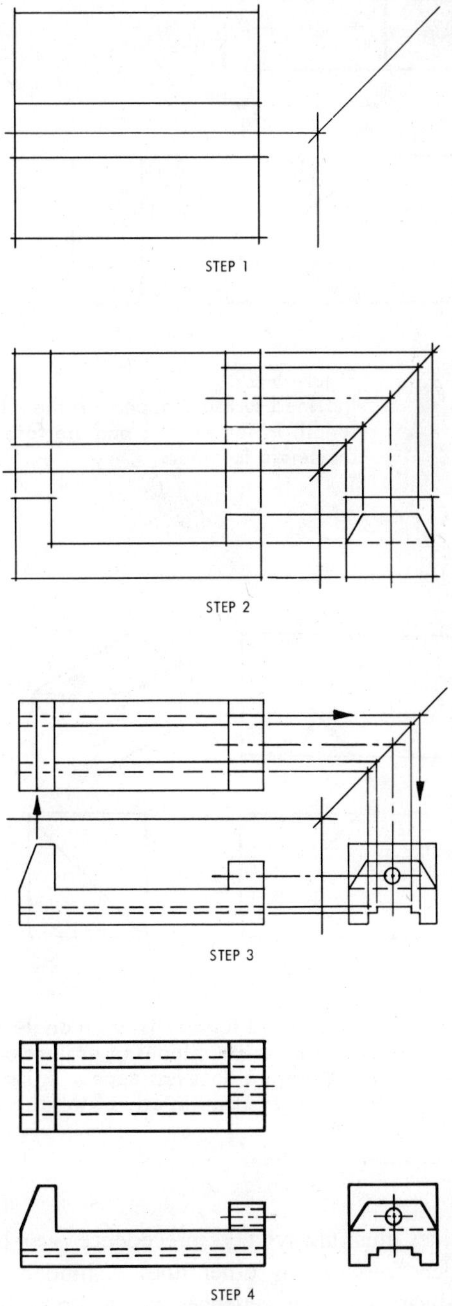

Figure 5-28
Steps in laying out a 3-view drawing.

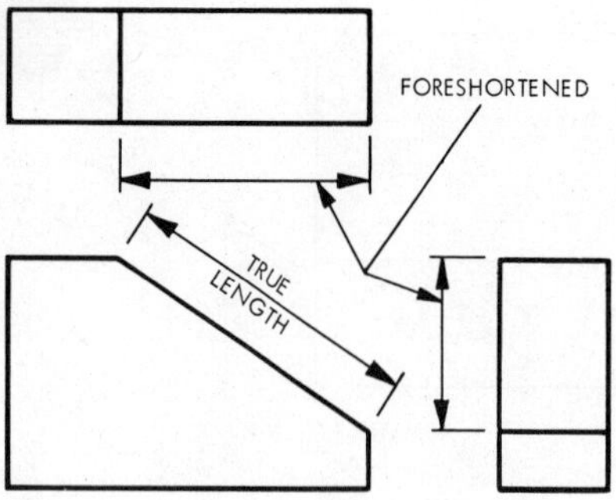

Figure 5-29
Inclined surfaces appear in their true length in some views and are foreshortened in others.

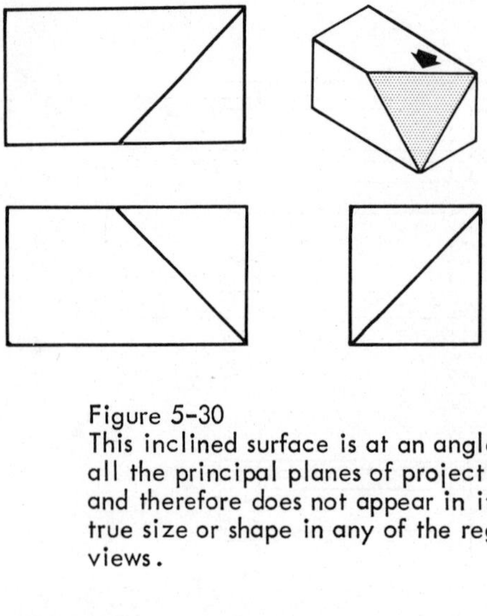

Figure 5-30
This inclined surface is at an angle to all the principal planes of projection and therefore does not appear in its true size or shape in any of the regular views.

lines must always take precedence over hidden lines or any other line. A hidden line always takes precedence over a center line. If a center line coincides with a cutting plane line, the line that contributes more to the readability of the drawing takes precedence. Dimension and extension lines should be placed so they will not coincide with other lines of the drawing. See Fig. 5-27.

5.15 Laying out a three-view drawing

The draftsman first examines the object to determine the desired position of orientation. After he decides on the appropriate scale to use, he blocks in the three views with light construction lines. See Step 1 of Fig. 5-28.

Next he lays out reference lines on the views from which the depth, width and height of the views may be measured. Reference lines can either be center lines or some dominant edge of the object. See Step 2, Fig. 5-28.

He now proceeds to complete the views. Usually construction of the three views is carried on together rather than completing one view and then going on to the next. Thus, some main feature of the object may be drawn first on the front view and then projected to the top and side views. See Step 3 of Fig. 5-28.

Points from the front view to the top and side views may be transferred by dividers or scale. The transfer procedure is sometimes simplified by means of the projection method. Points from the front view are extended to the top view and side view with the T-square and triangle. Points from the top view are projected to the side view through a 45° miter line. These points are first extended to the mitered line and then dropped to the side view.

5.16 Projection of inclined surfaces

An inclined surface is one that is perpendicular to one plane of projection and inclined to the adjacent planes. Such a surface is shown in its true length as a line only on the plane to which it is perpendicular. On other planes it will appear foreshortened. See Fig. 5-29.

5.17 Oblique surfaces

If a surface is oblique to all the principal planes of projection, it is known as an oblique surface. See Fig. 5-30. An oblique surface will not appear on any regular view in its true shape or size. Neither will it appear as a line on any of the regular views of a drawing. To show its true size and shape, another view must be drawn known as a secondary auxiliary view. This type of view is described in Section 9.

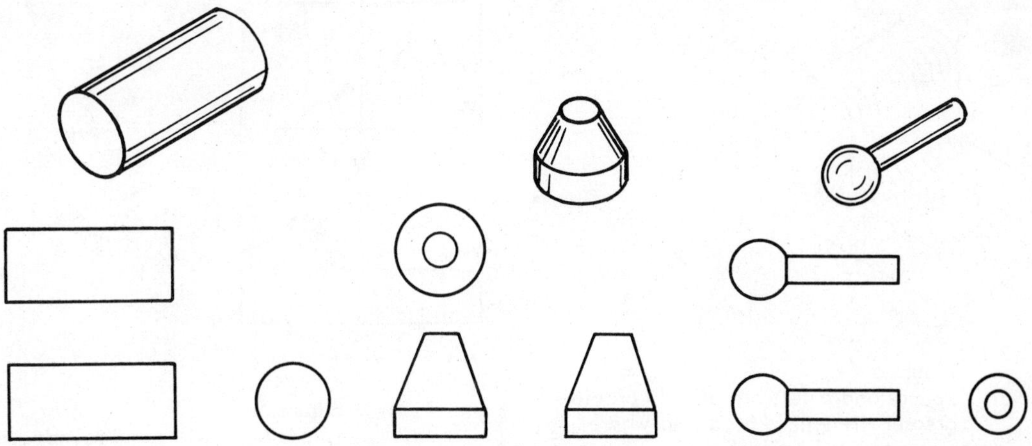

Figure 5–31
This is how a curved surface appears on the various planes of projection.

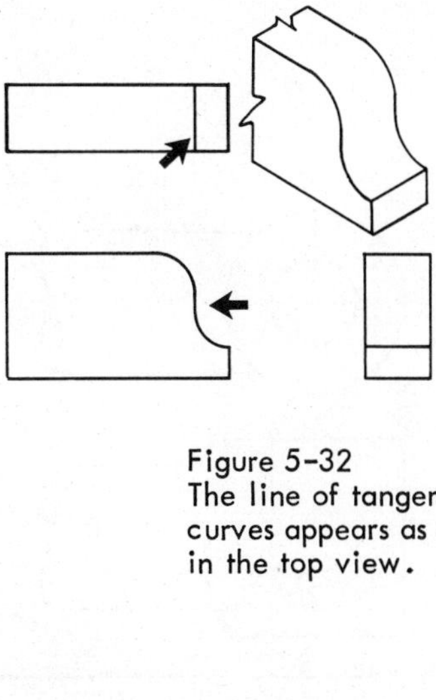

Figure 5–32
The line of tangency of these two curves appears as a straight line in the top view.

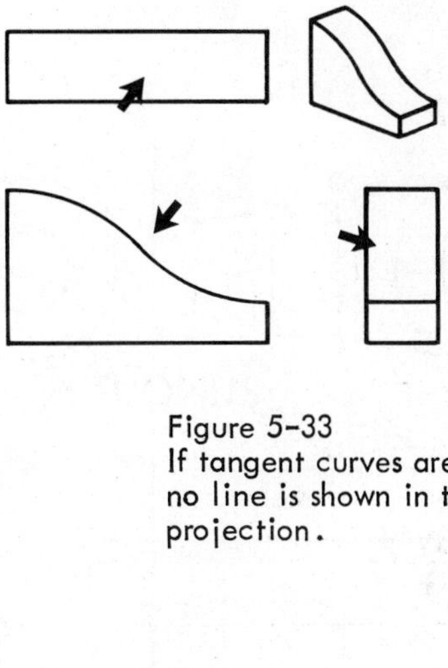

Figure 5–33
If tangent curves are at an angle, no line is shown in the plane of projection.

5.18 Projection of curved surfaces

Many objects have curved surfaces or curved edges tangent to straight planes. When a circle or curve is parallel to the plane of projection, it is shown as a circle or curve on the parallel plane, and as straight lines on the adjacent planes. See Fig. 5-31.

If an object has continuously-curved surfaces that are perpendicularly tangent to each other, their line of tangency will be perpendicular to the plane of projection as seen in Fig. 5-32.

If the tangent plane of two curves is at an angle, no line is shown in the plane of projection. See Fig. 5-33.

5.19 Runouts and filleted intersections

Many machine parts consist of castings which are made by pouring molten metal in a specially constructed mold. In making castings, precautions are always taken to eliminate sharp corners wherever two surfaces intersect. Rounded corners provide greater strength than sharp corners, and they improve the appearance and permit greater ease in handling the finished product. When

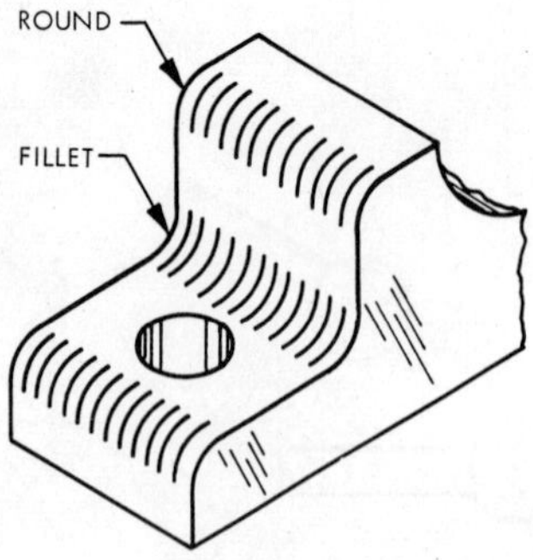

Figure 5-34
Rounds and fillets are used to provide greater strength in a casting where two surfaces intersect.

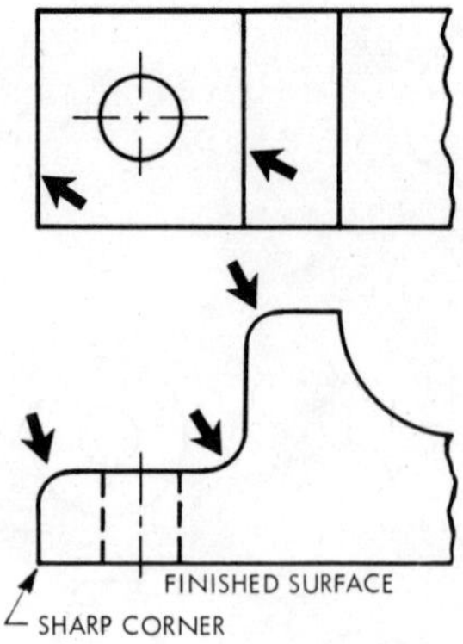

Figure 5-35
This is how fillets and rounds are shown in a drawing.

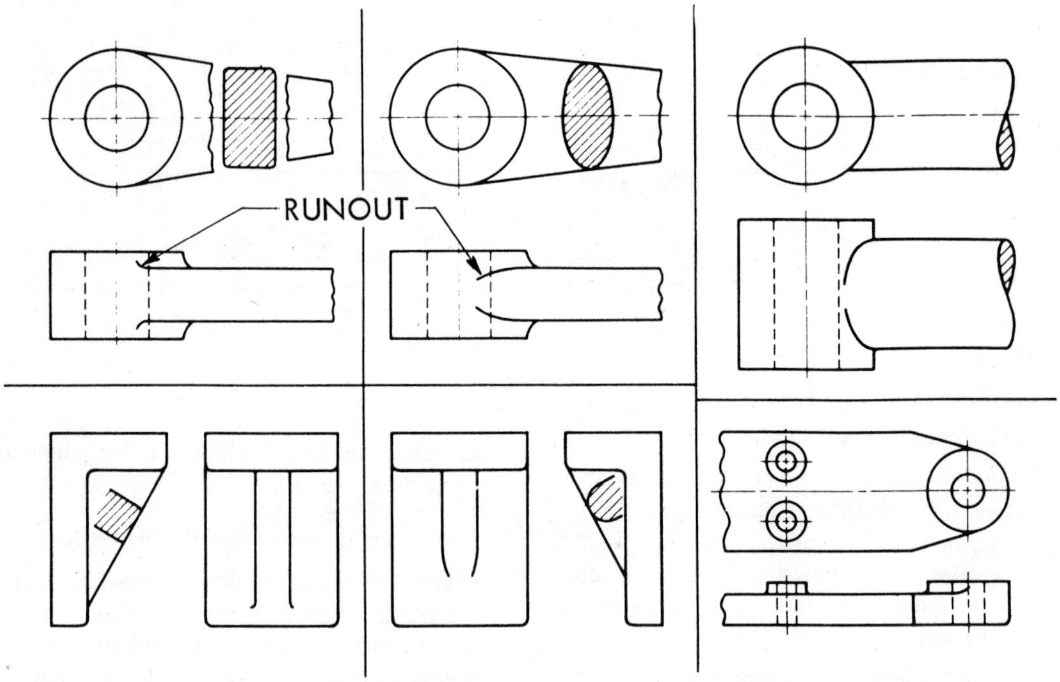

Figure 5-36
The manner in which runouts are shown is determined by the shape of the intersecting member.

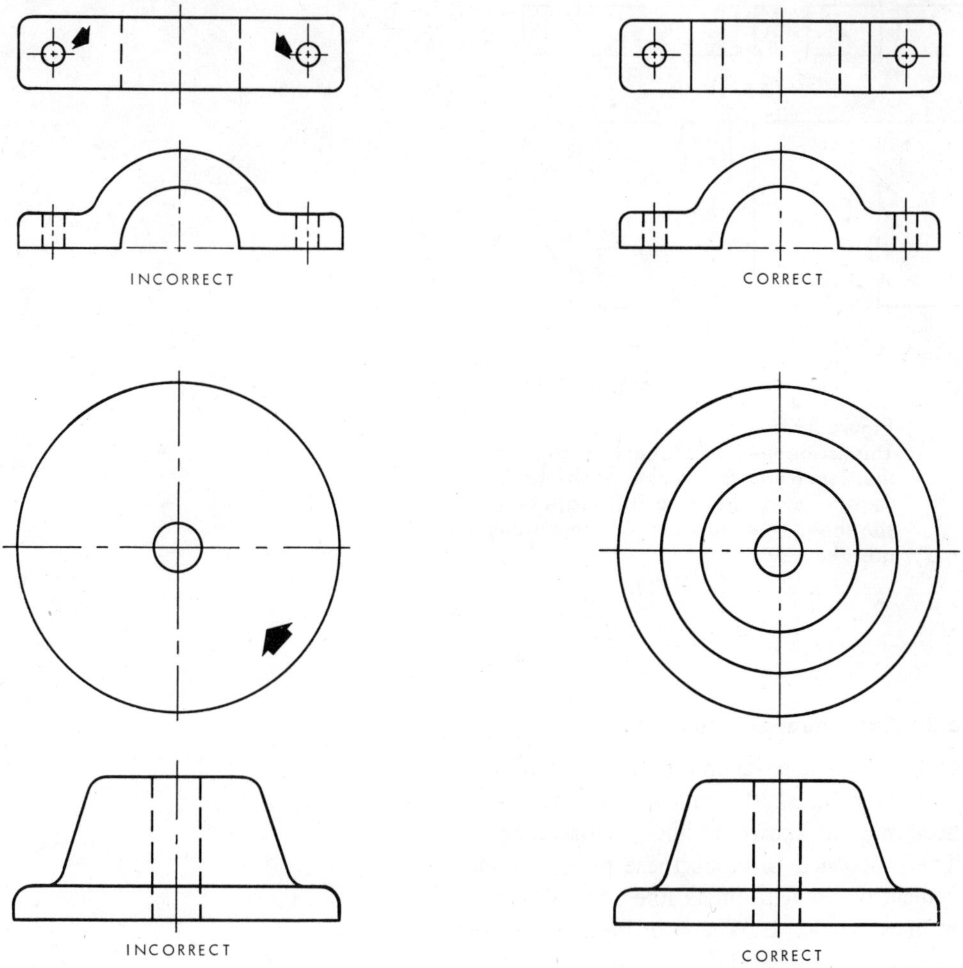

Figure 5–37
These figures illustrate the conventional method of showing filleted intersections when their true projection may be misleading.

rounded intersections of surfaces occur at outside edges they are called *rounds*. Rounded intersections of surfaces at inside corners are known as *fillets*. See Fig. 5-34.

Fillets and rounds are always shown on a drawing to indicate corners of unfinished castings. If the intersecting surfaces are to be machined, then the corners are drawn square and sharp. See Fig. 5-35. The size of fillets and rounds are designated with a note "All fillets and rounds 1/8″ radius unless otherwise specified," which is placed either near one of the principal views or included in the area designated for general notes.

When fillets and rounds intersect, the extension of the curved surfaces are commonly referred to as "runouts." See Fig. 5-36. Their tangent points should be projected to the related views where they are then shown by an arc or curve having a radius equal to the fillet or round. The required shape and thickness of the filleted area determines if the arcs are to turn inward or outward. On outside surfaces the theoretical intersections are represented on the related view by solid or dotted lines. See Fig. 5-37.

Arcs to represent fillets and rounds may be drawn freehand, with a compass or irregular curve. The curved segments should be less than a quarter of a circle.

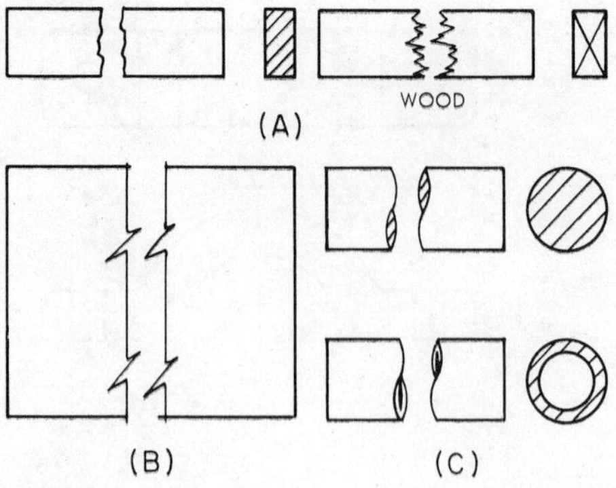

Figure 5-38
This is the method of representing conventional breaks. Although the broken feature is not drawn to full scale on the sheet, the true overall dimensions are always given.

5.20 Conventional breaks

Objects which have unusually long features such as rods, shafts, tubes, arms and bars need not be shown in their entire length. The practice is to break these parts at convenient points with break lines. See alphabet of lines, Section 2. Whenever break lines are used, the true overall dimension must always be shown. For short breaks, the break line is made freehand and the same thickness as visible lines. See A, Fig. 5-38. Where breaks are particularly long, long thin-ruled lines joined by freehand "zig-zags" are recommended. See B, Fig. 5-38. The appropriate method of representing breaks on cylindrical surfaces is shown in C, Fig. 5-38.

5.21 Right and left hand parts

As a rule, where two hands of a part are needed, only one needs to be drawn. However, the part must be marked to indicate which hand it represents. The American Standards Association recommends that the words "right hand shown" or "left hand opposite" be used. They also recommend that if the opposite hand shape is not clearly evident from the drawing, then both hands of the part should be drawn and labeled.

Problems, section 5

1-30 Make 3-view drawings approximately double size of the objects shown in Figs. 5-39 and 5-40. Supply all missing lines.

31-41 Produce multiview drawings of the objects shown in Figs. 5-41 to 5-51. Select any convenient scale and include only the essential views. On castings choose suitable size radii for fillets and rounds unless otherwise indicated.

42 Draw three views of the object in Fig. 5-52, showing the portion in front of the plane through points **A, B, C** as having been removed. Select any convenient scale.

43-45 Prepare the necessary views of the objects in Figs. 5-53 to 5-55. Use any convenient scale.

46 Make a 3-view drawing of the object in Fig. 5-56, showing portion in front of the plane through points **A, B, C** removed.

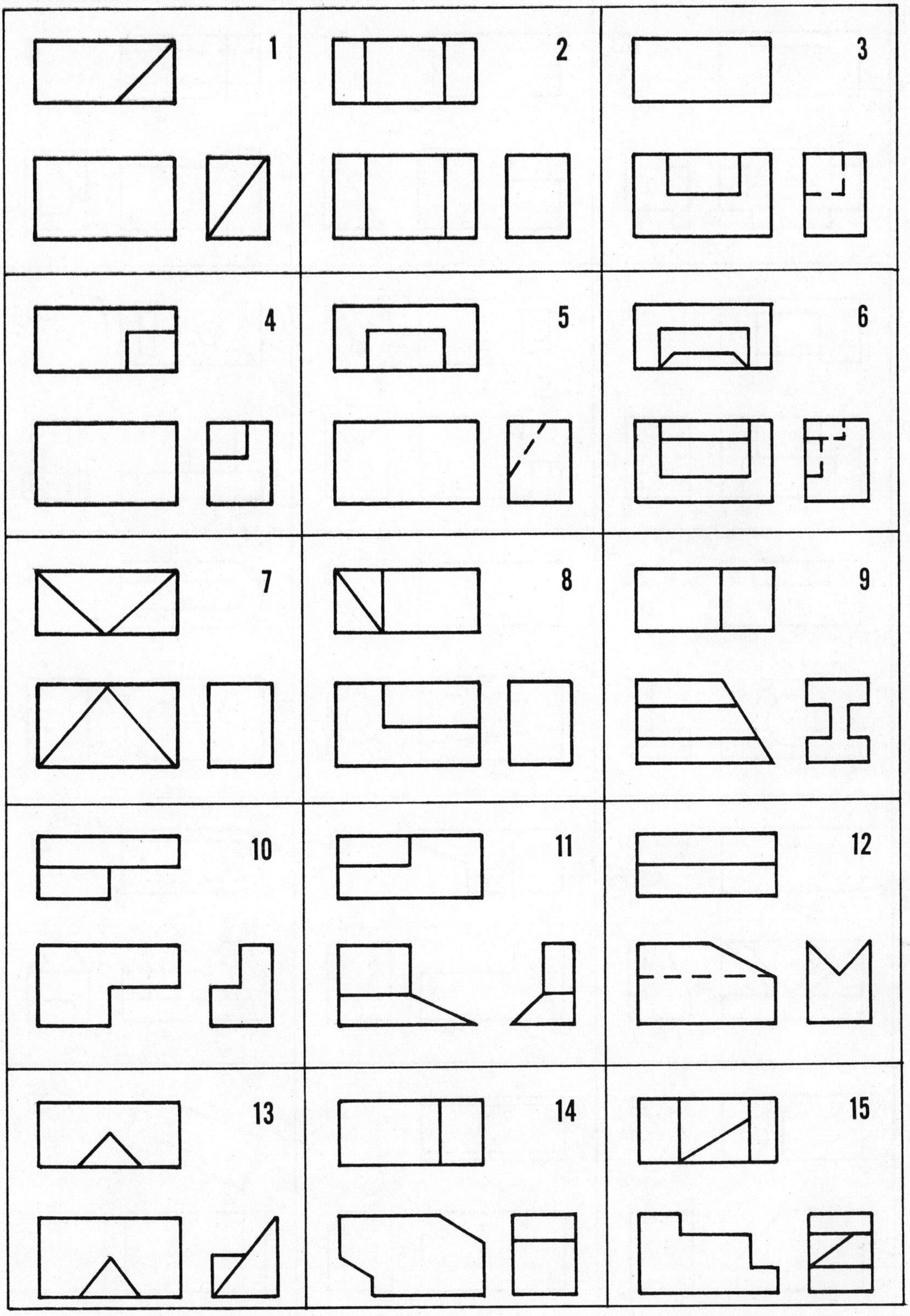

Figure 5-39
Problems 1 through 15.

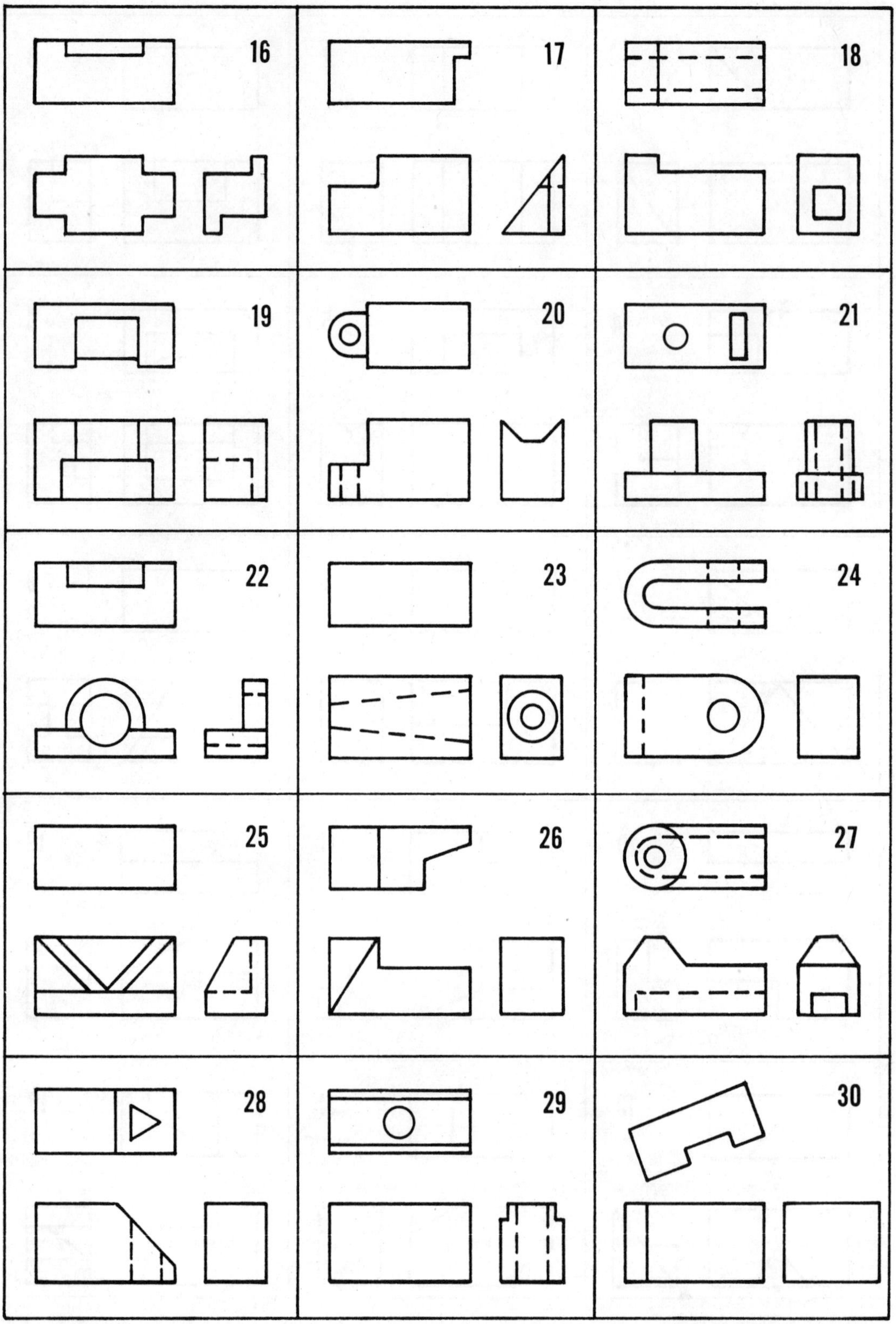

Figure 5-40
Problems 16 through 30.

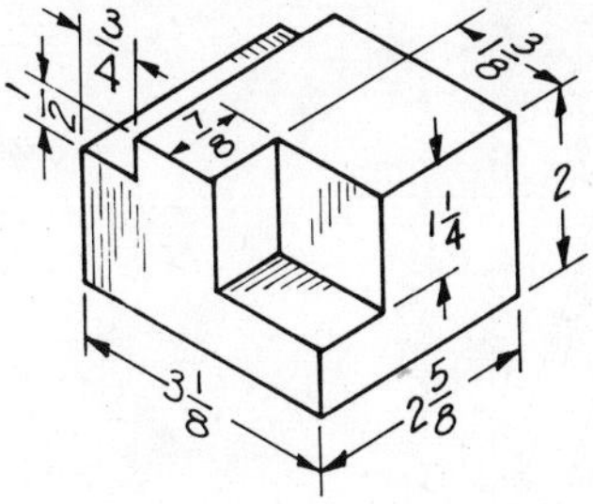

Figure 5-41
Problem 31.

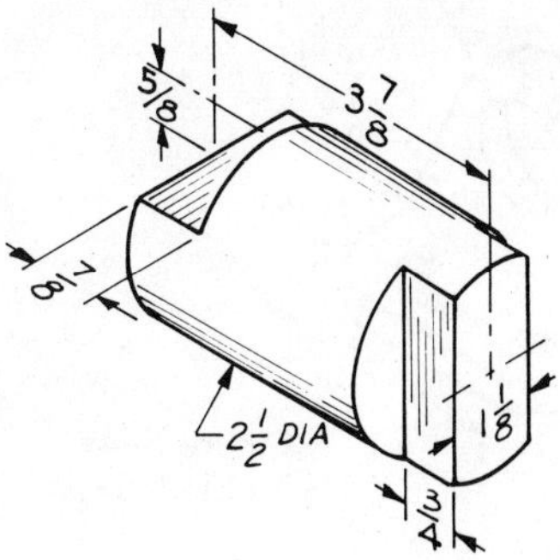

Figure 5-45
Problem 35.

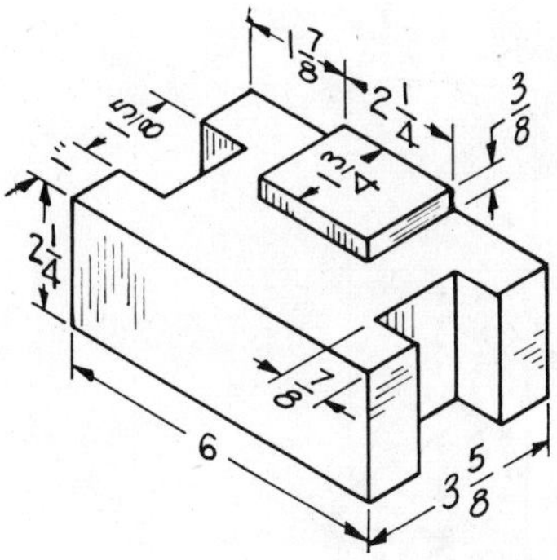

Figure 5-42
Problem 32.

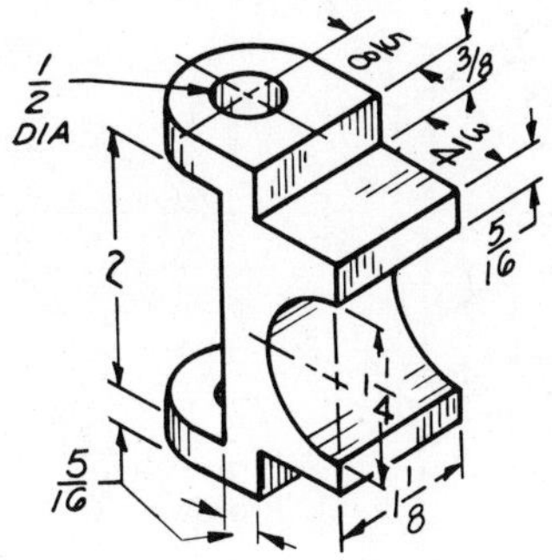

Figure 5-46
Problem 36.

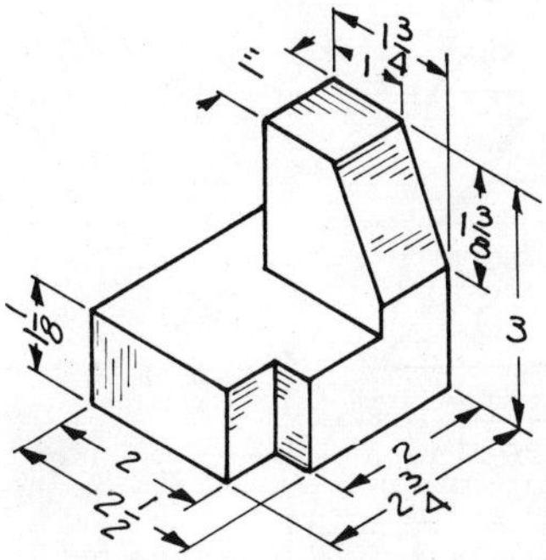

Figure 5-43
Problem 33.

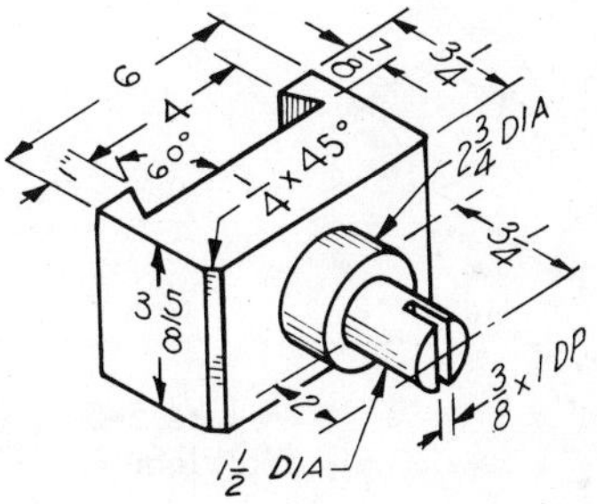

Figure 5-47
Problem 37.

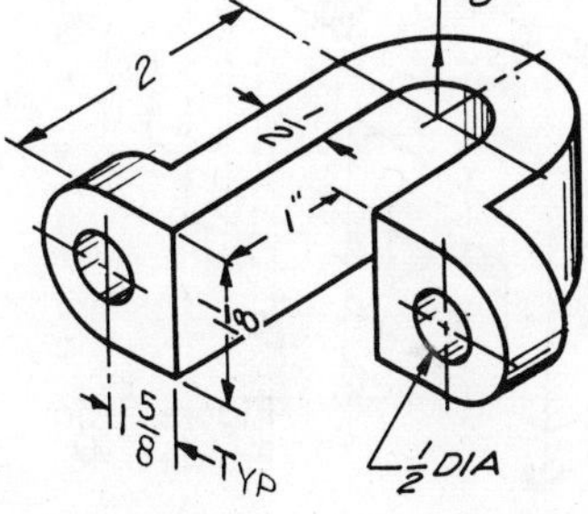

Figure 5-44
Problem 34.

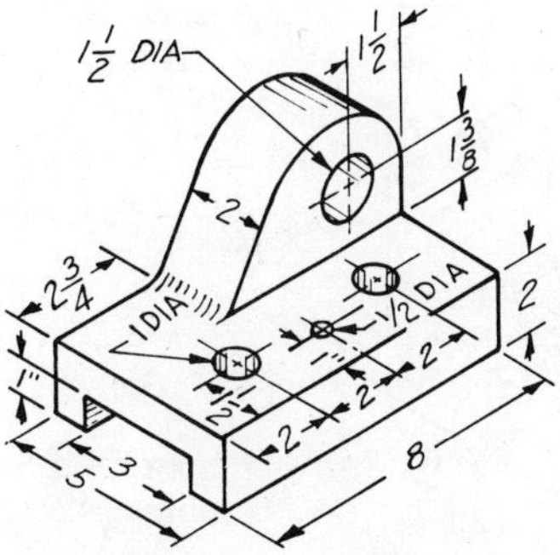

Figure 5-48
Problem 38.

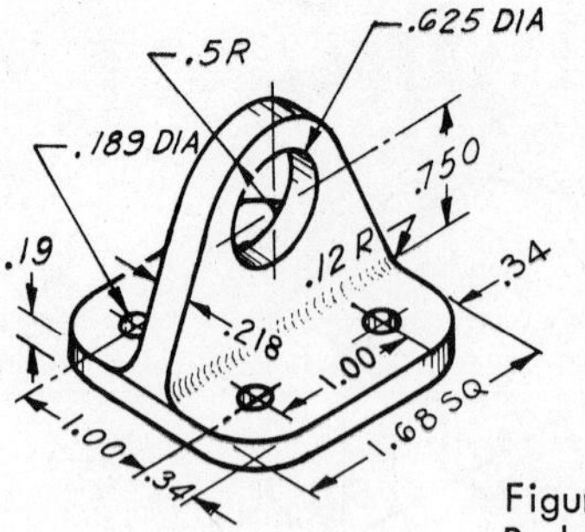

Figure 5-49
Problem 39.

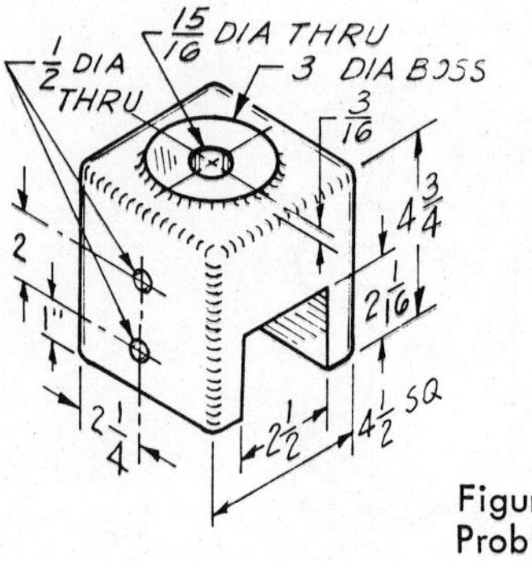

Figure 5-50
Problem 40.

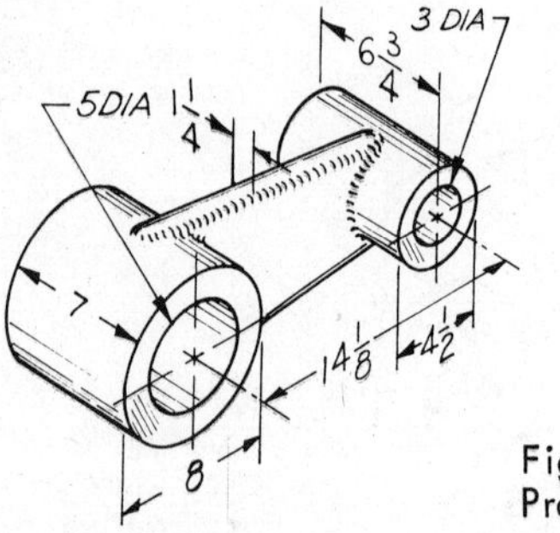

Figure 5-51
Problem 41.

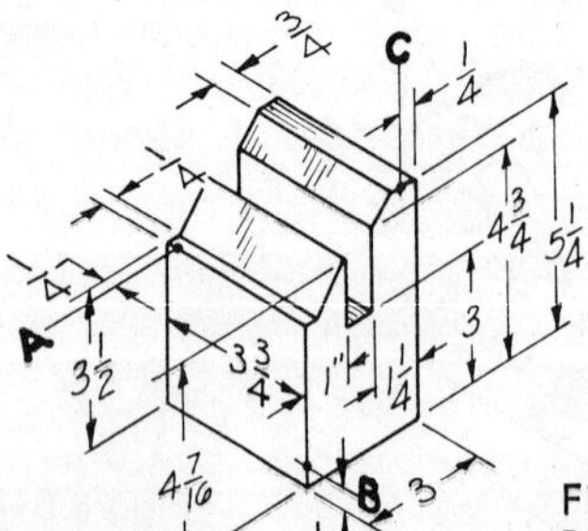

Figure 5-52
Problem 42.

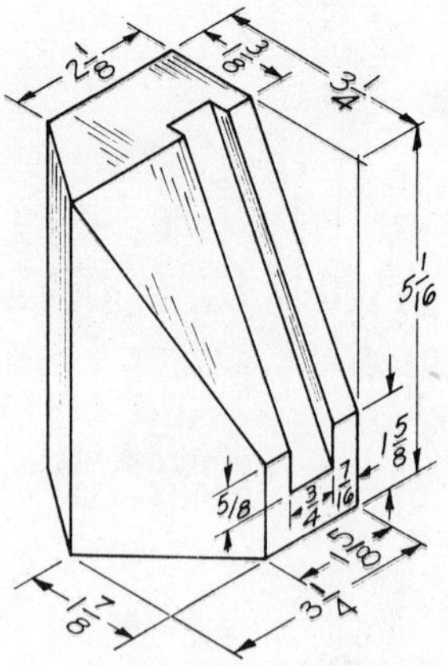

Figure 5-53
Problem 43.

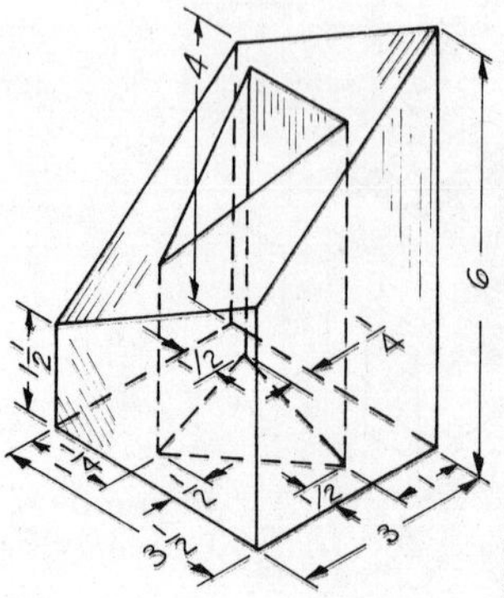

Figure 5-54
Problem 44.

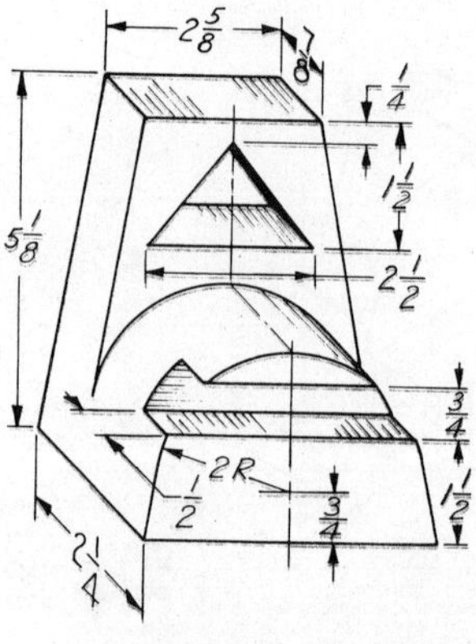

Figure 5-55
Problem 45.

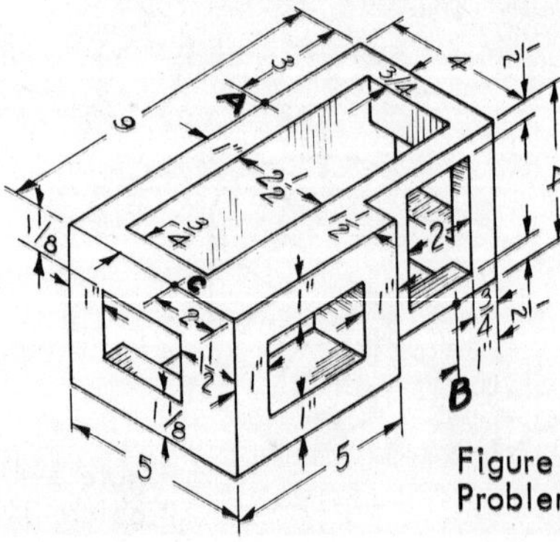

Figure 5-56
Problem 46.

Dimensioning 6

Dimensioning is the process of imparting definition to a pictorial representation. The various views if correctly placed and projected show the exact shape of the object. However, these views are meaningless unless accurate sizes are included.

A drawing is expected to convey exact and positive information regarding every detail of the represented part. Without definite specifications expressed by dimensions, it is impossible to indicate clearly any engineering intent or to achieve successful fabrication of the desired product.

An intelligently dimensioned drawing should represent the part as it is to be manufactured. It should permit mass production and interchangeability of parts regardless of the location of the manufacturing plant. A drawing should deal cautiously with the method of production, specifying the results to be obtained rather than the method of fabrication in order to allow the maximum latitude in optional methods of manufacture.[1]

Since the shopworker is expected to follow the instructions which appear on a drawing, the draftsman should be familiar with the tools, machines, materials and manufacturing facilities available. If the draftsman has an intimate knowledge of the manufacturing process, he will understand better the task of the men in the shop and greatly simplify their job. Above all, a drawing should never have to be scaled to determine a missing dimension. It should never be necessary for the shopman to have to calculate or assume any dimension in order to fabricate a product designed by the engineer or draftsman.

The dimensioning practices described in this section are those recommended by the *American Standards Association* and *The Society of Automotive Engineers* and used almost exclusively in all industries.

1. *Chrysler Drafting and Design Standards* (Detroit: Chrysler Corporation).

6.1 Fundamental dimensioning rules

According to ASA Standards, the following are the basic rules which should be observed in dimensioning any drawing:[2]

1 Show enough dimensions so that the intended sizes and shapes can be determined without calculating or assuming any distances.

2 State each dimension clearly, so that it can be interpreted in only one way.

3 Show the dimensions between points, lines or surfaces which have a necessary and specific relation to each other or which control the location of other components or mating parts.

4 Select and arrange dimensions to avoid accumulations of tolerances that may permit various interpretations and cause unsatisfactory mating of parts and failure in use.

5 Show each dimension only once.

6 Where possible, dimension each feature in the view where it appears in profile, and where its true shape appears.

7 Wherever possible, specify dimensions to make use of readily available materials, parts, tools and gages. Savings are often possible when drawings specify: (a) commonly used materials in stock sizes, (b) parts generally recognized as commercially standard, (c) sizes that can be produced with standard tools and inspected with standard gages, and (d) tolerances from accepted published standards.

2. Extracted from *American Drafting Standards Manual, ASA Y14.5—1957* (New York: American Society of Mechanical Engineers, 1957).

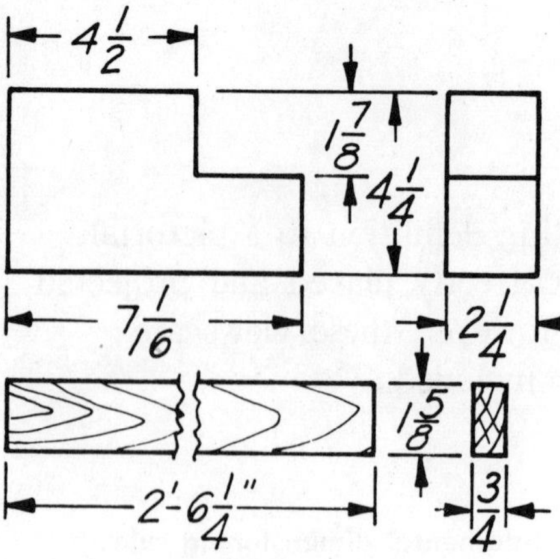

Figure 6-1
Linear dimensions are expressed in this manner.

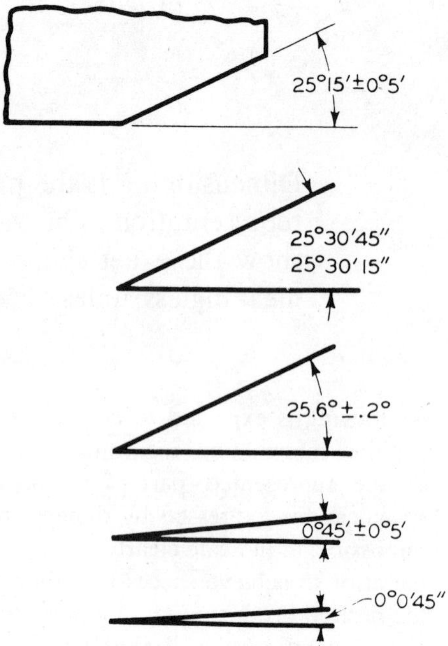

Figure 6-2
This is how angles should be dimensioned. ASA Y14.5-1957

6.2 Units of measurement

Dimensions on all drawings should be given in inches and fractional parts of an inch, or in feet and inches unless the decimal dimensioning system is used. The symbol for the inch is ″, and for the foot, ′. (See Section 7 for the decimal system of dimensioning.) The practice is to omit the inch symbol if all the dimensions are in inches. The only exception is where a dimension is likely to be misunderstood. Thus *1 Valve* should be *1″ Valve, 1 Bore* should be *1″ Bore*. Whether dimensions are all expressed in inches, or feet and inches depends on the standards adopted by individual industries. When dimensions are given in feet and inches, both the foot and inch symbols are used with a hyphen between the two figures as: 9′-7″, 5′-0¼″, 6′-4½″, 10′-0″.

In some industries dimensions are expressed in feet and inches when distances exceed 72 inches. For parts made of wood, inches are specified for lengths up to and including 12 inches, and feet and inches for lengths greater than 12 inches.[3] See Fig. 6-1.

3. *Engineering Standards* (Greenwich: American Machine and Foundry Co.).

Some industries use metric units in measuring. If dimensions are to be shown in millimeters, a general note must be included stating this fact. When both inch and millimeter dimensions are used, the inch symbol should be included on figures representing inches and the abbreviation MM on figures representing millimeters.

Angles should be dimensioned by an arc drawn with the vertex of the angle as a center and the angular dimension inserted in a break in the arc. See Fig. 6-2. As a rule, right angles need not be dimensioned unless required for clarity. Angular dimensions should be expressed in ° (degrees), ′ (minutes), and ″(seconds). When degrees are used alone, the numerical value may be followed by the symbol °, or by the abbreviation *DEG*. If minutes are indicated alone, the value of the minutes should be preceded by 0°. It is also permissible to dimension angles in degrees and decimal parts of a degree.

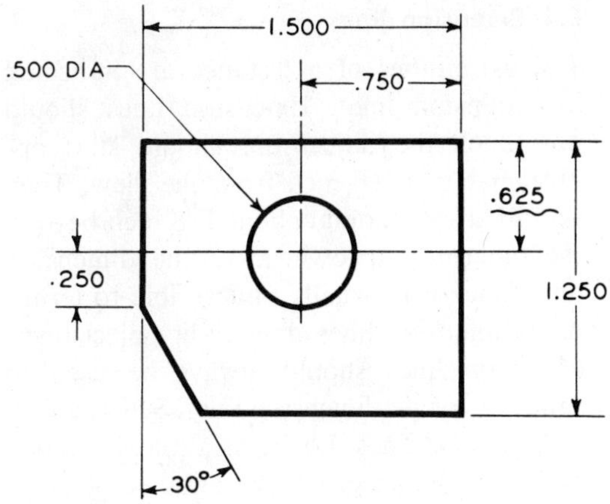

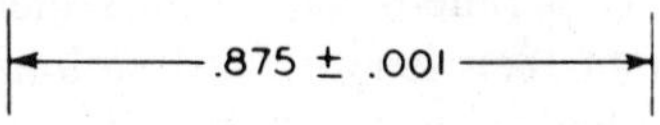

Break a dimension line for numerals in a single line

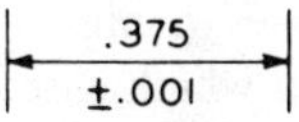

Do not break a dimension line for numerals in two lines

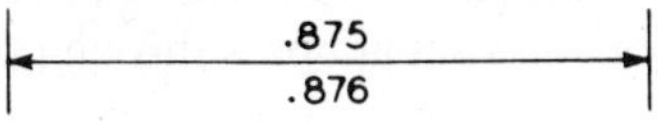

Figure 6-3
Dimensions are indicated by dimension lines which terminate with arrowheads.
ASA Y14.5-1957

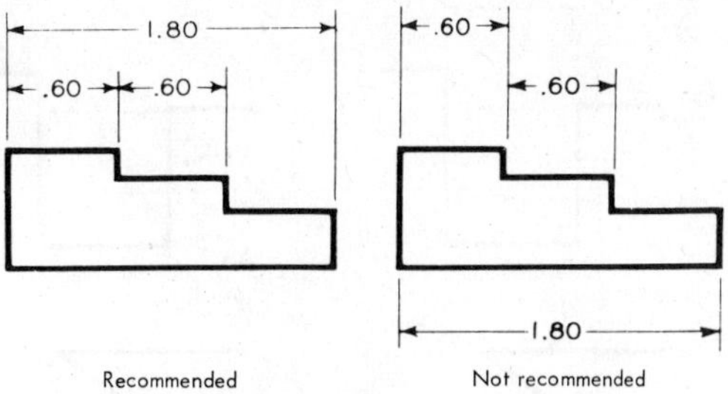

Figure 6-4
Group dimension lines so they will produce an orderly appearance.
ASA Y14.5-1957

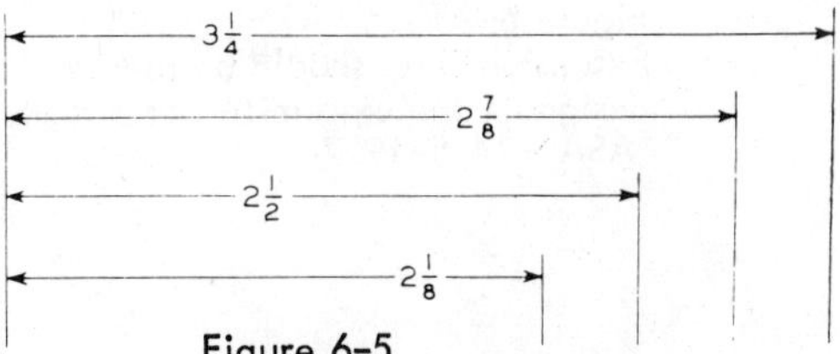

Figure 6-5
Stagger the numerals when parallel dimension lines are required.
ASA Y14.5-1957

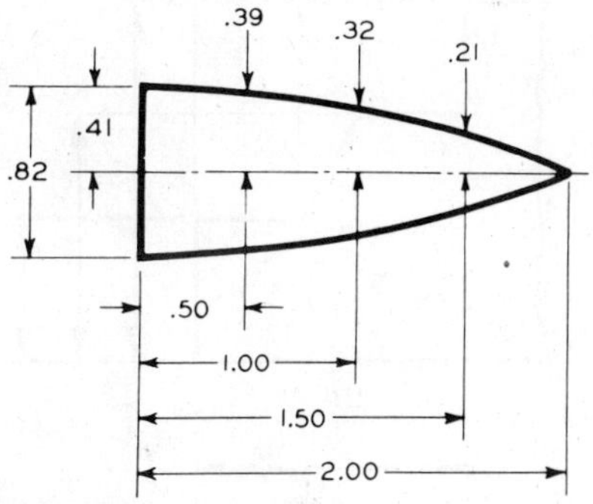

Figure 6-6
Dimension lines may be used as extension lines when situations of this nature are encountered.
ASA Y14.5-1957

6.3 How dimensions are indicated

Angular and linear distances are shown on a drawing by dimension lines. Dimension lines are thin, solid lines terminated with arrowheads. A break is left in the line for the insertion of the dimension figures if the numerals are in a single line. If the numerals are in two lines, one is placed above and the other below the line. See Fig. 6-3.

Dimension lines should be aligned whenever it is possible and grouped uniformly as shown in Fig. 6-4.

All parallel dimension lines should be about 1/4 inch apart and should not be closer than 3/8 inch to the outline of the object. If several parallel dimension lines are necessary, the numerals should be staggered for greater readability. See Fig. 6-5.

Center lines, extension lines, or object lines should never be used as dimension lines. The only exception to this rule is the situation shown in Fig. 6-6. Every effort should be taken to avoid crossing dimension lines.

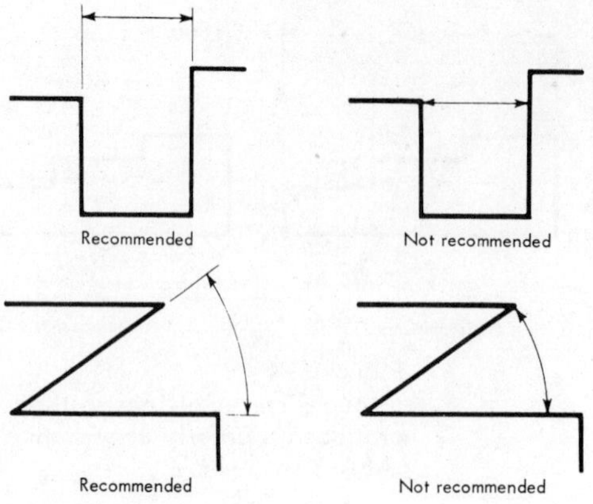

Figure 6-7
Extension lines should be used to designate the extremities of a distance. ASA Y14.5-1957

6.4 Extension lines

The extremities of a distance are indicated by extension lines. Extension lines should not touch the object but should start approximately 1/16 inch from the view. They should always extend about 1/8 inch beyond the outermost arrowhead of the dimension line. Since it is usually undesirable to terminate dimension lines directly at object lines, extension lines should always be used to properly locate dimension lines. See Fig. 6-7.

Extension lines should, as a rule, be drawn so they will not cross one another or cross dimension lines. Crossing lines can be kept to a minimum if the shortest dimension lines are drawn nearest the outline of the object. Successive parallel adjacent lines then follow in order of their length with the longest line at the outside. See Fig. 6-8.

When it is impossible to avoid crossing other extension lines, dimension lines, or object lines, the extension lines should not be broken. The exception is when an extension line crosses a dimension line close to arrowheads, in which case the extension line may be broken. See Fig. 6-9.

If a point is to be located exclusively by extension lines as shown in Fig. 6-10, the extension lines should pass through the point.

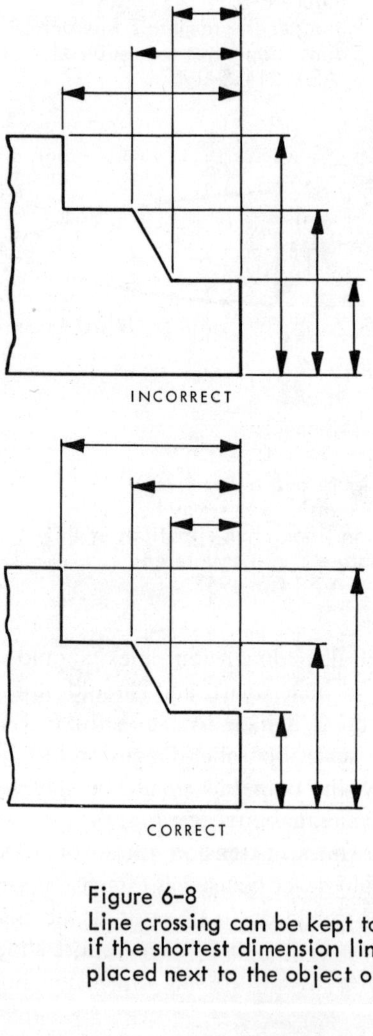

Figure 6-8
Line crossing can be kept to a minimum if the shortest dimension lines are placed next to the object outline.

6.5 Dimensioning in crowded spaces

Deviation from the customary practices of using dimension and extension lines may be necessary occasionally, particularly if dimensions must be included in crowded areas. Fig. 6-11 illustrates the common dimensioning procedure when space is limited.

6.6 Arrowheads

The arrowheads which terminate dimension lines should be made with freehand strokes as shown in Fig. 6-12. Most draftsmen prefer the solid type arrowhead instead of the single line type. The length of the arrowheads should be approximately 1/8 inch on small drawings and up to 3/16 inch on large drawings. The width of the arrowhead should be approximately one-third its length. Care should be taken to make all arrowheads the same size throughout the entire drawing.

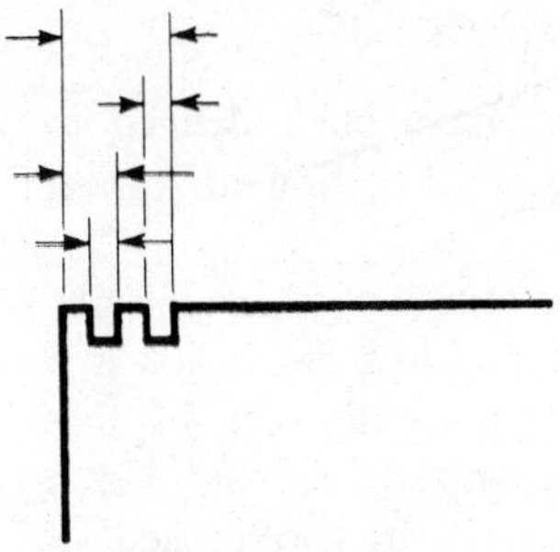

Figure 6-9
Break extension lines if they cross a dimension line near arrowheads.

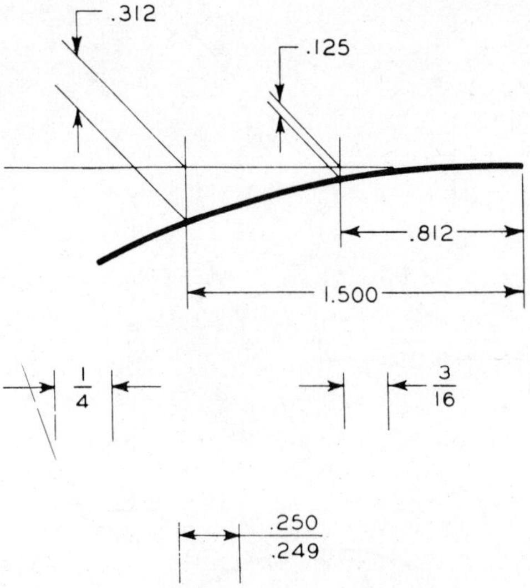

Figure 6-11
These dimensioning practices are permissible when space is limited. ASA Y14.5-1957

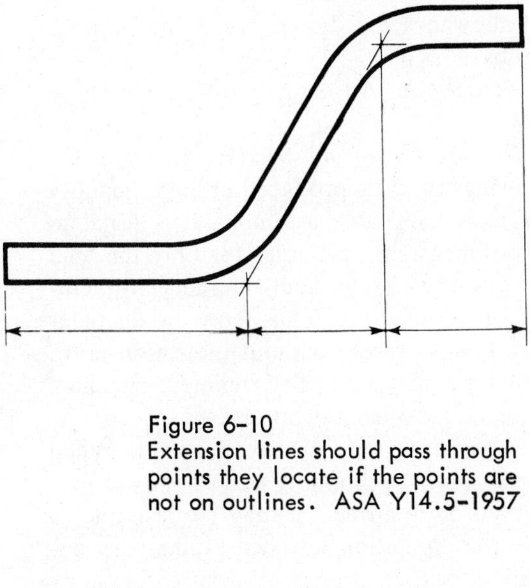

Figure 6-10
Extension lines should pass through points they locate if the points are not on outlines. ASA Y14.5-1957

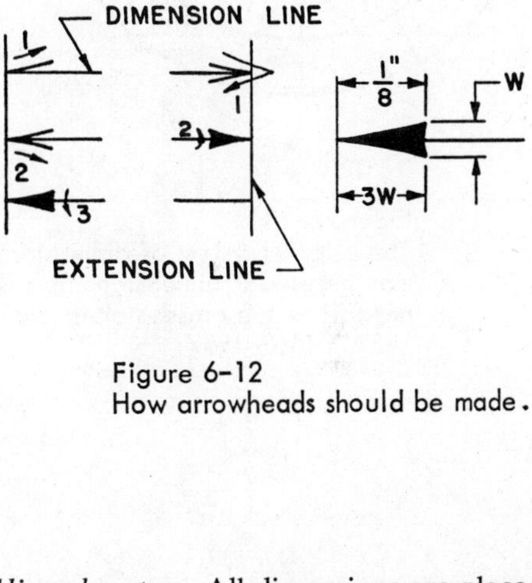

Figure 6-12
How arrowheads should be made.

6.7 Reading direction of dimensions

Two systems are used to show dimensions on a drawing—the *aligned* and the *unidirectional*. The unidirectional system is often preferred because of the greater ease in reading the figures. In fact, it is the principal system used in the automotive industry.[4]

4. *SAE Automotive Drafting Standards* (New York: Society of Automotive Engineers, Inc., 1952).

Aligned system. All dimensions are placed to read from the bottom and right-hand edge of the drawing. With this system, dimension lines that fall in a 45° zone should be avoided. See Fig. 6-13.

Unidirectional system. All dimensions are made to read from the bottom of the sheet. Fractions are written with the division bar horizontal or parallel to the bottom of the sheet. See Fig. 6-14.

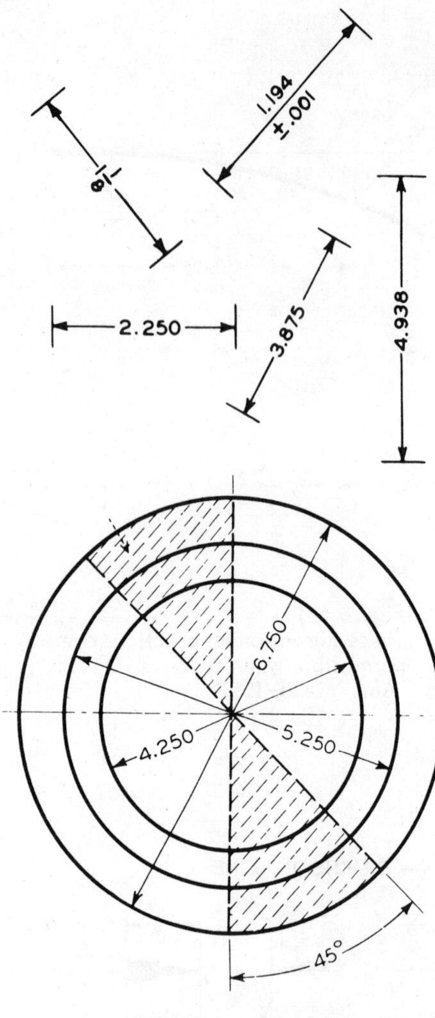

Figure 6–13
The aligned system of dimensioning may be used if dimension lines do not fall in the crosshatched area. ASA Y14.5-1957

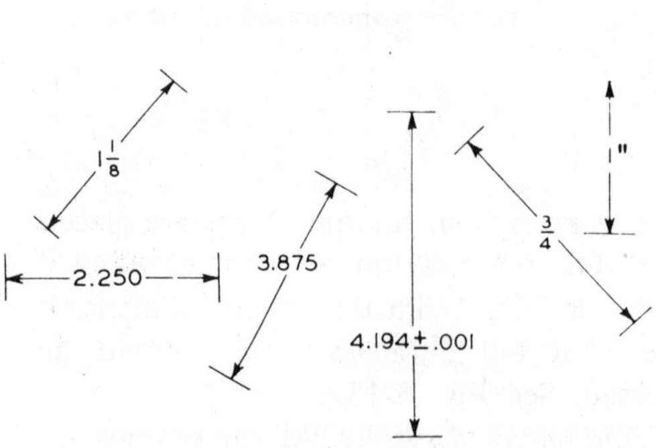

Figure 6–14
In the unidirectional system, dimensions read from the bottom of the drawing. ASA Y14.5-1957

6.8 Dimensional expressions[5]

The following terms have been defined to provide a common interpretation in respect to their use.

Size. Size is a designation of magnitude. When a value is assigned to a dimension it is referred to hereinafter as the size of that dimension. It is recognized that the words "dimension" and "size" are both used at times to convey the meaning of magnitude.

Nominal size. The nominal size is the designation which is used for the purpose of general identification. Example: 1/2″ pipe.

Basic size. The basic size is that size from which the limits of size are derived by the application of allowances and tolerances.

Design size. The design size is that size from which the limits of size are derived by the application of tolerances. When there is no allowance the design size is the same as the basic size.

Actual size. An actual size is a measured size.

Dimensions for end-product drawings. On drawings of parts produced in large quantity for interchangeable assembly, it is usual to give dimensions and notes for only the final forms and sizes, without reference to methods of manufacture. Thus, only the diameter of a hole is given, without indication as to whether it may be drilled, reamed, punched, or made by other operations.

Dimensions for process drawings. When one or more preliminary operations are performed on a surface, it may be desirable to give the dimension for each preliminary operation, with a proper allowance for stock removal and with suitable tolerances.

The choice between dimensioning as for end-product drawings or, more thoroughly, as for process drawings, will depend on the manufacturing methods and requirements, and the practice in individual industries.

6.9 Limits and tolerances

A limit indicates the largest or smallest permissible dimension. A tolerance represents

5. Extracted from *American Drafting Standards Manual, ASA Y14.5—1957* (New York: The American Society of Mechanical Engineers, 1957).

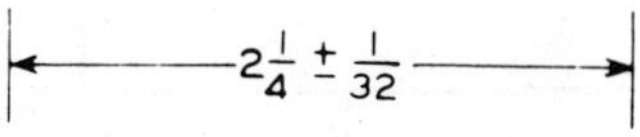

Figure 6–15
When fractional dimensioning units are used, limits and tolerances may be expressed in this manner.

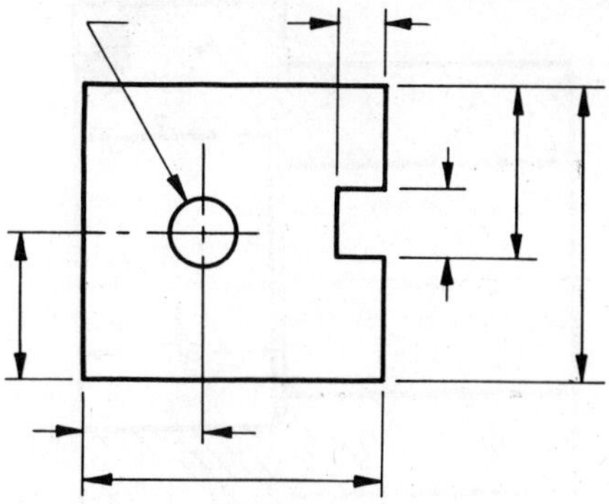

Figure 6–16
Overall dimensions should be placed outside the intermediate dimensions.

the difference between the limits. The amount of variation permitted is expressed by a plus and minus sign.

The general practice is to express limits and tolerances in decimals. Occasionally where fractional dimensioning units are used and high degrees of accuracy are not mandatory, limits and tolerances are shown in fractional numerals. See Fig. 6-15. For a more complete discussion of limits and tolerances, see Section 7.

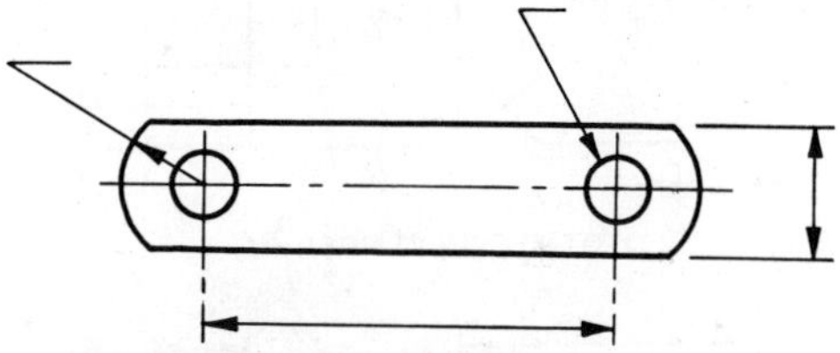

Figure 6–17
An overall dimension is not usually needed for parts with circular ends.

6.10 General dimension arrangements

Overall dimensions. When overall dimensions are used, they should be placed outside the intermediate dimensions. With an overall dimension, one intermediate distance can be omitted. The intermediate distances should be placed where the accumulated tolerance will be the least objectionable. See Fig. 6-16. On a part with circular ends, an overall dimension generally need not be given except for reference purposes. See Fig. 6-17.

Location on views. Dimensions should preferably be placed outside the outline of the parts and between the views whenever possible. See Fig. 6-18. Only in instances when the readability of a drawing is improved

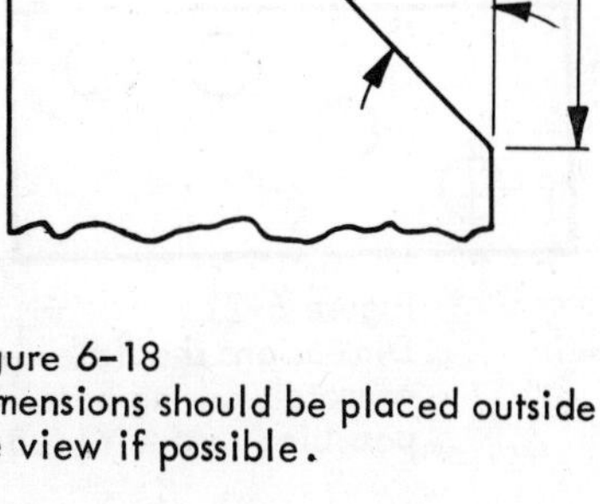

Figure 6–18
Dimensions should be placed outside the view if possible.

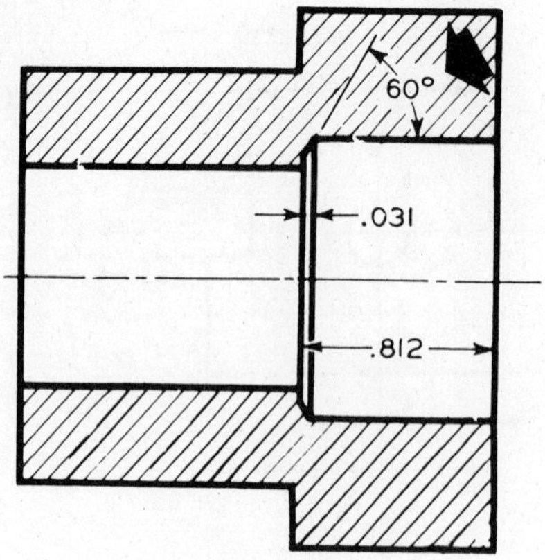

Figure 6-19
This is the practice when a dimension is placed in a sectional view.
ASA Y14.5-1957

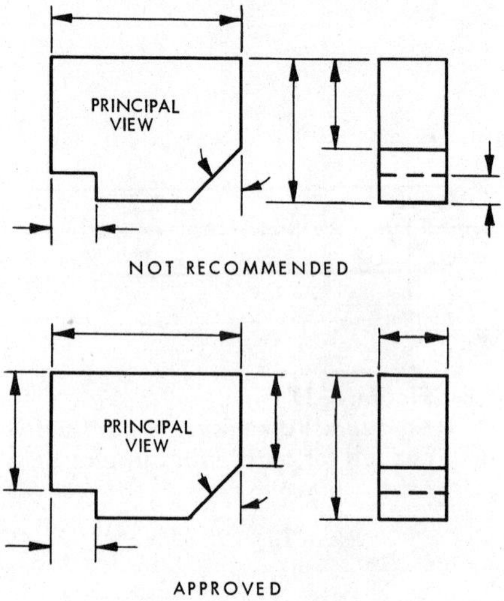

Figure 6-20
The most important dimensions should be located at the principal view.

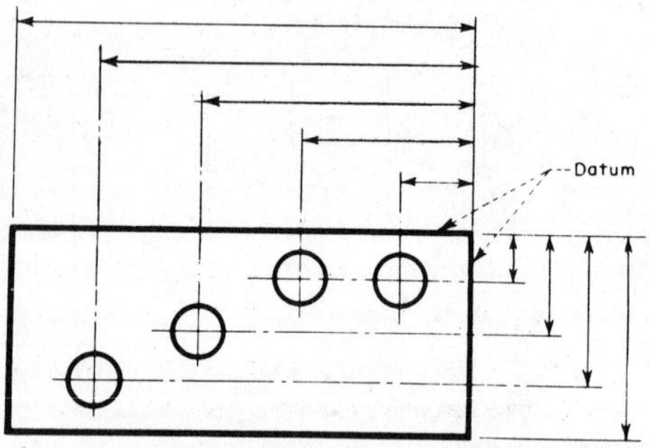

Figure 6-21
Dimensions should be given from one or more working base lines whenever possible. ASA Y14.5-1957

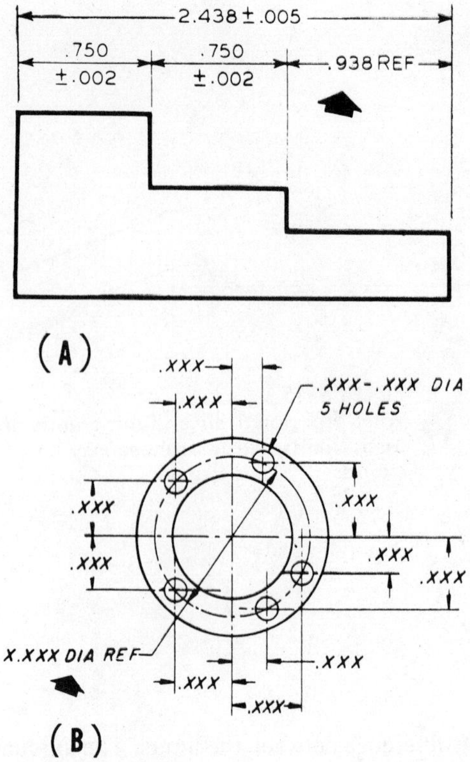

Figure 6-22
Reference dimensions often have important informational value.
ASA Y14.5-1957

should dimensions be placed within a view. If a dimension must be placed within a sectional view, a small area around each numeral should be kept free from the sectional lines. See Fig. 6-19.

Principal view. The most important dimension should be located at the principal view of a part because it is usually this view that most completely shows the essential contour characteristics of the piece. See Fig. 6-20.

Dimensions from datum. A datum is a point, a center line, or base line which establishes the location of certain elements. Whenever possible, dimensions should be given from such a line since this practice eliminates the cumulative error inherent in a chain of dimensions. See Fig. 6-21. Dimensions should never be taken from rough cast edges or other inaccurate reference points.

Reference dimensions. A reference dimension is one without a given tolerance and is

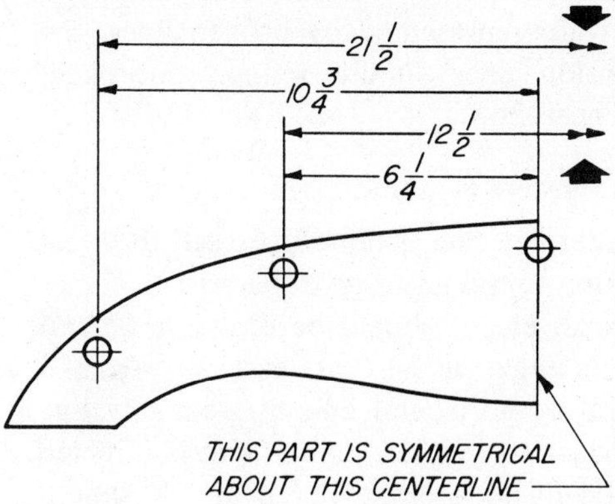

Figure 6-23
How symmetrical parts may be dimensioned.

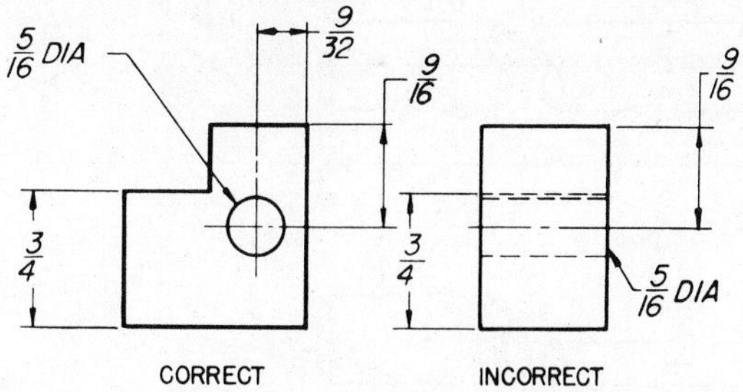

Figure 6-24
Do not dimension to hidden lines.

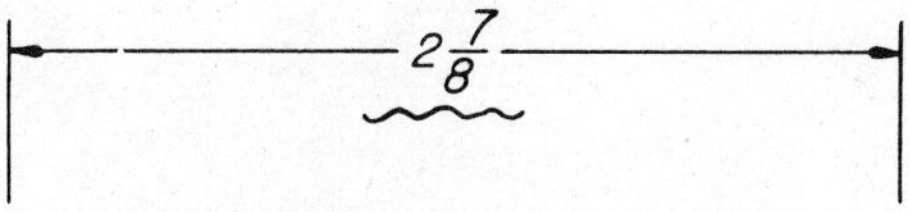

Figure 6-25
A wavy line under a dimension indicates a distance is not to scale.

used for informational purposes only. It does not govern manufacturing or inspection operations in any way. Thus there may be instances when a duplicated dimension on a drawing is not strictly essential in fabricating or inspecting the part, but has an important reference value. Such a dimension, when used, should be clearly marked with the abbreviation *REF* directly following or under the dimension. See Fig. 6-22A and 6-22B. For example, the reference dimension shown in Fig. 6-22A is simply an additional calculated distance to show the approximate overall size of the part. Also the reference dimension in Fig. 6-22B is intended primarily to indicate the approximate hole circle diameter.

Indicating symmetry. Symmetrical parts may be drawn fully dimensioned or with only one half dimensioned and with the addition of a note to specify "Part Symmetrical about this Centerline." On drawings of a symmetrical part where only a portion of the outline is pictured, due to the part's size or space limitations on the drawing, double arrows extending beyond the centerline are used to indicate symmetry.[6] See Fig. 6-23.

Hidden lines. Dimensions should not originate at or terminate to hidden lines. If dimensions cannot be placed on other views where the actual contour is visible, a sectional view may be required. See Fig. 6-24.

Dimensions out of scale. Dimensions out of scale should be avoided as much as possible. However, when the original drawing is changed or a dimension cannot be made to scale, the dimension should be underlined with a wavy line as shown in Fig. 6-25. Often the note "Not To Scale," or "Do Not Scale" is included in the general notes on the drawing.

6. *Alcoa Engineering Drafting Standards* (Pittsburgh: Aluminum Company of America).

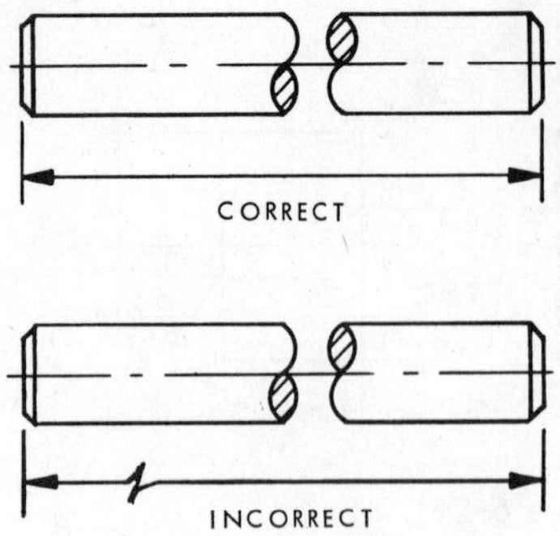

Figure 6-26
The dimension line should be unbroken when dimensioning broken outlines.

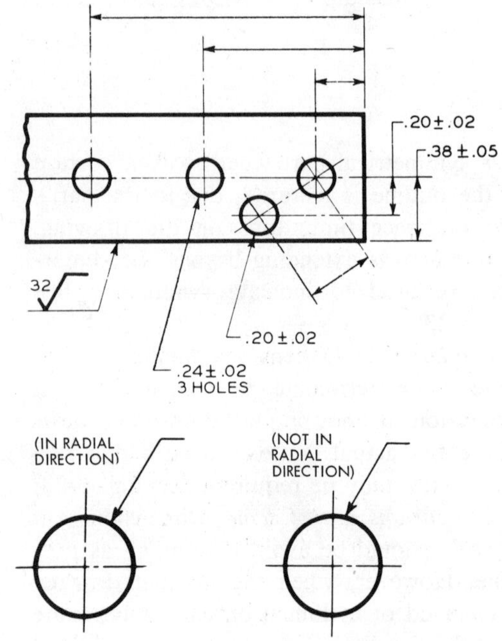

Figure 6-27
A leader is used to direct attention to a note or to indicate sizes of arcs and circles. ASA Y14.5-1957

Broken outlines. When dimensioning parts which are represented by broken lines, the dimension lines should remain unbroken. See Fig. 6-26.

6.11 Leaders

A leader is a fine oblique line used to direct attention to a note or give the size of circles and arcs, etc. It should be drawn at a convenient angle, usually at least 20° from a vertical or horizontal line or from any line or surface to which it points. If it is directed specifically to a circle or an arc, it should be drawn in a radial direction. The leader should terminate with an arrowhead drawn to the indicated outline or part. The opposite end should have a short horizontal bar about 1/8 inch long which should extend to the mid-height of the first or last letter of the note. A space of approximately 1/16 inch should be left between the end of the horizontal bar and the note or dimension.

All leaders should be short and not cross other leaders. Where several leaders are in one group, adjacent leaders are drawn parallel. Care should be taken however not to draw leaders so they are parallel to adjacent dimension or extension lines. See Fig. 6-27.

6.12 Dimensioning cylindrical or spherical surfaces[7]

Diameters of concentric elements. Where the diameters of a number of concentric elements are to be given, it is usually more convenient to show them on a longitudinal view. See Fig. 6-28. Where required, a cylindrical hole may be dimensioned in a side view. See Fig. 6-29. Where space is limited, a leader with a note may be used. The numeral may be followed by the abbreviation *DIA* to clarify the meaning.

Radii of arcs. A circular arc is dimensioned by giving its radius. Where space permits, a radius dimension line is drawn from the radius center, with the arrowhead ending at the arc and with the numeral between the arrowhead and the center. Each numeral

7. Extracted from *American Drafting Standards Manual, ASA Y14.5—1957* (New York: The American Society of Mechanical Engineers, 1957).

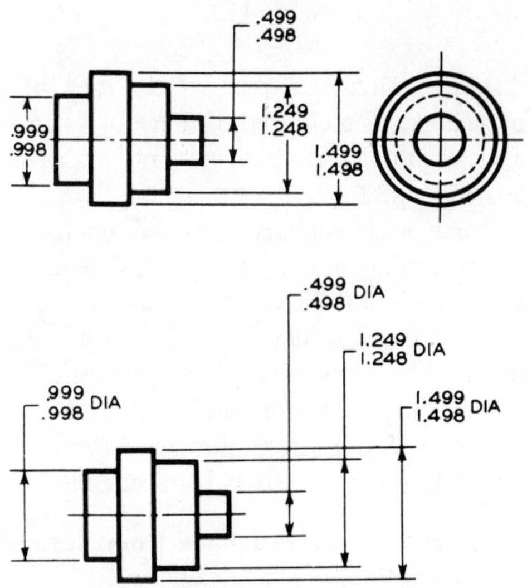

Figure 6-28
Dimensioning cylindrical surfaces on a longitudinal view, with and without a side view. ASA Y14.5-1957

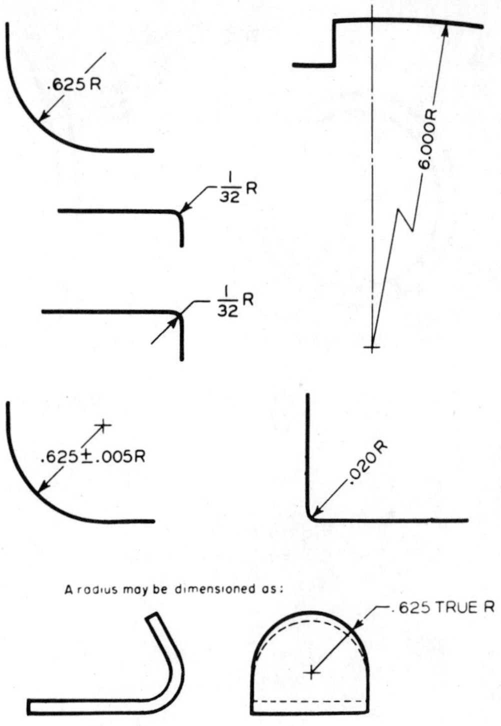

Figure 6-30
How to dimension a circular arc. ASA Y14.5-1957

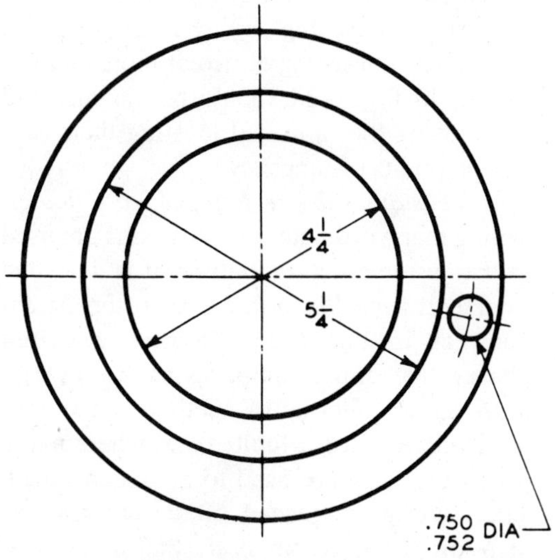

Figure 6-29
Dimensioning a side view of cylindrical surfaces. ASA Y14.5-1957

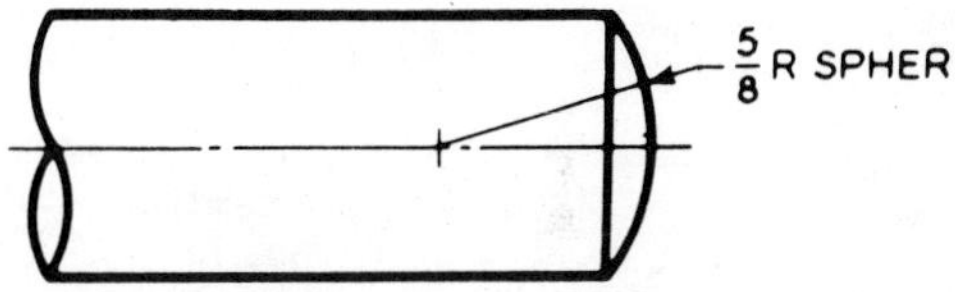

Figure 6-31
Method of indicating a spherical surface. ASA Y14.5-1957

should be followed by *R*. Where space is limited, as for a small radius, a leader may be used. Where it is inconvenient to place the arrowhead between the center of the radius and the arc, it may be placed outside the arc. The center of the radius may be indicated by a small cross to clarify the drawing. See Fig. 6-30. Where space does not permit showing the complete radius dimension line to scale, the line may be foreshortened, as in Fig. 6-30. The portion of the dimension ending in the arrowhead should be in the radial direction.

Spherical surfaces. Spherical surfaces may be dimensioned as in Fig. 6-31.

Distances along curved surfaces. Linear

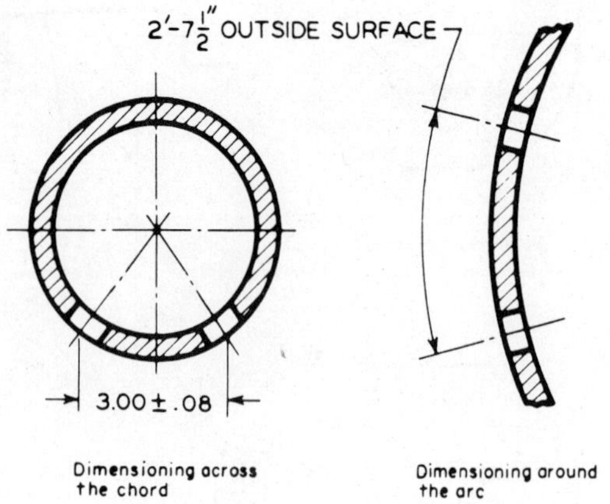

Figure 6-32
Dimensioning on curved surfaces. ASA Y14.5-1957

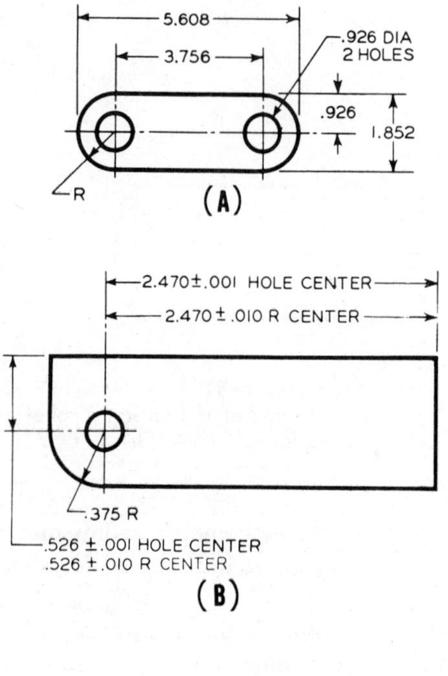

Figure 6-33
Dimensioning parts with rounded ends. ASA Y14.5-1957

distances along curved surfaces may be dimensioned as a chordal distance or as an arc, and should be so indicated on a drawing. See Fig. 6-32.

Parts with rounded ends. A method of dimensioning a part with rounded ends is shown in Fig. 6-33A. The radius is indicated, but not dimensioned; it varies with the actual width when specified in this way. Where a hole location is more critical than the location of a radius from the same center, the method of Fig. 6-33B is recommended.

6.13 Locating curved lines from datum[8]

Curved lines or surfaces should always be dimensioned from a suitable datum, which may be a center line or some other reference line which controls supplementary or matching lines or surfaces. Irregular curves may be dimensioned in the following ways:

Curves consisting of circular arcs. A curved line consisting of two or more circular arcs as in Fig. 6-34 should be dimensioned by showing the radii and locating their centers or points of tangency.

Dimensioning by rectangular coordinates. Where many ordinates and abscissas are used to dimension a curved outline, it is desirable to extend each dimension line to the datum lines, as in Fig. 6-35. Progressive datum (base) line dimensioning as shown in Fig. 6-36, is an alternative method sometimes used where space is limited and where many points on the curve need to be dimensioned. The starting arrowhead of the shortest dimension is the common starting arrowhead for the entire series.

On large panels and features, a curve may be dimensioned from numbered datum lines as in Fig. 6-37. The datum lines locate the part independently of any detail changes of the curve. The vertical and horizontal coordinates may be tabulated when many coordinates are required to describe a contour and where the points are close together as the airfoil section shown in Fig. 6-38.

8. *SAE Automotive Drafting Standards* (New York: Society of Automotive Engineers, 1952).

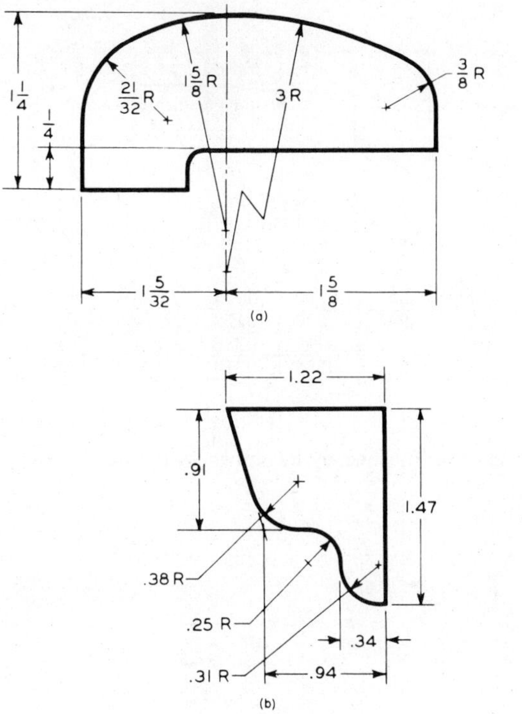

Figure 6-34
Curves consisting of circular arcs are dimensioned in this way.
ASA Y14.5-1957

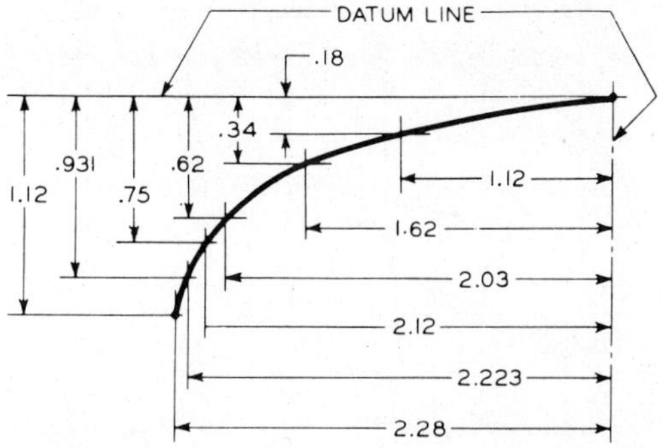

Figure 6-35
This is one method of dimensioning by rectangular coordinates.
ASA Y14.5-1957

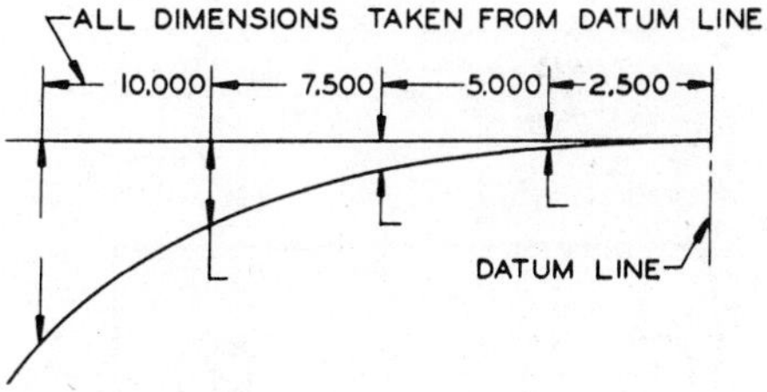

Figure 6-36
This is an alternate method of dimensioning by rectangular coordinates.

6.14 Locating holes

Methods of positioning round holes are illustrated in Figs. 6-39 to 6-43. The same techniques can also be used to locate round pins and other features of symmetrical contour.

6.15 Dimensioning round holes

Plain round holes. Diameter, depth, and number of holes should always be specified either by dimensioning or by a note. Where the hole is obviously a through hole, the depth need not be shown. If the drawing does not clearly indicate that it is a through hole, a note specifying through hole should be added. Blind holes must have the depth specified. The depth includes only the full diameter. The type of hole may be identified as a noun in note form, indicating its shape rather than the method of producing it, such

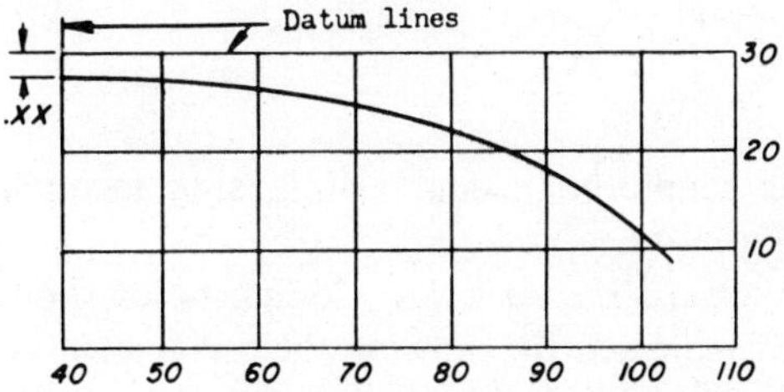

Figure 6-37
On large features a curve may be dimensioned from numbered datum lines.

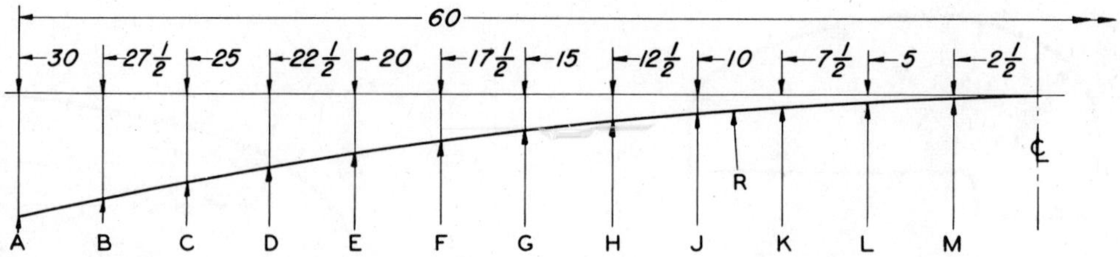

Radius	A	B	C	D	E	F	G	H	J	K	L	M
3600.0	.125	.105	.087	.070	.056	.042	.031	.022	.0140	.0079	.0035	.0009
1800.0	.250	.210	.174	.141	.111	.085	.062	.043	.0280	.0152	.0070	.0018
1200.0	.375	.315	.259	.211	.167	.128	.093	.065	.0417	.0235	.0105	.0026
900.2	.500	.420	.347	.281	.222	.170	.125	.087	.0556	.0313	.0139	.0035

Figure 6-38
When many coordinates are required the coordinates may be shown in tabular form.

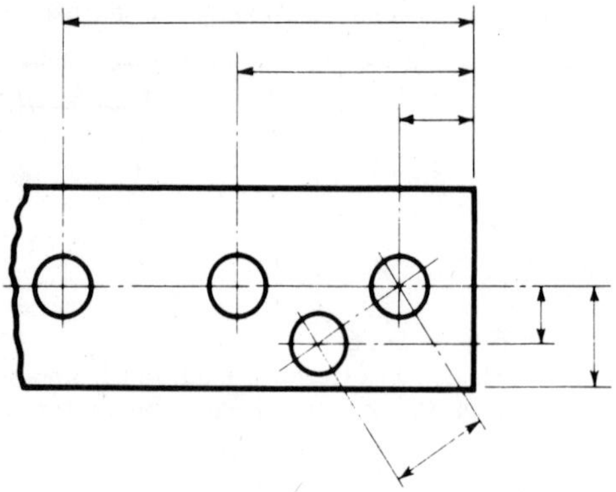

Figure 6-39
Locating holes by linear distances. ASA Y14.5-1957

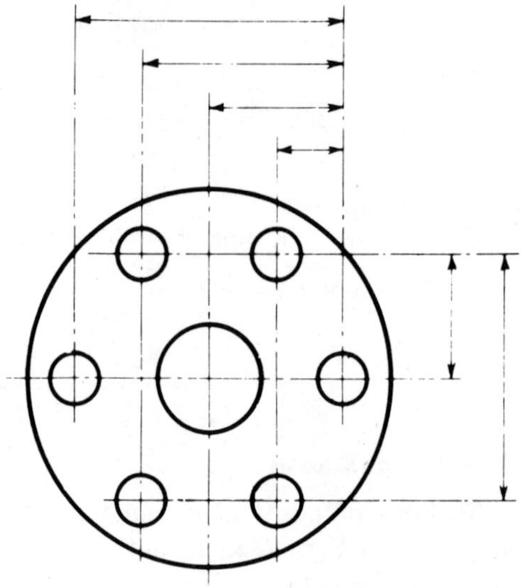

Figure 6-40
Locating holes by rectangular coordinates. ASA Y14.5-1957

as counterbore, countersink, spot face. See Fig. 6-44.

Counterbored holes. Counterbores should be indicated by showing their diameter and depth. See Fig. 6-45. In special cases the thickness of the remaining stock may be dimensioned instead of designating the depth of the counterbore.

Countersunk holes. Countersunk holes should show the diameter and angle of the countersink as in Fig. 6-46.

Spot faced holes. Spot faced holes may be dimensioned by showing the diameter of the faced area or by a note only. See Fig. 6-47.

Shaft centers. Fig. 6-48 illustrates how shaft centers or countersunk center holes should be dimensioned when located on shafts, spindles, and other cylindrical or

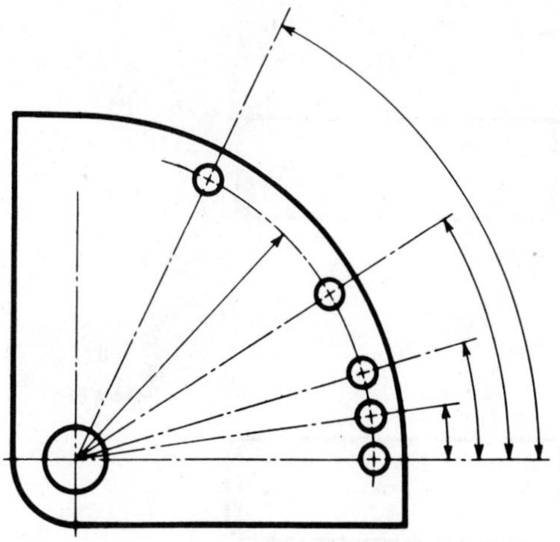

Figure 6-41
Locating holes on a circle by polar coordinates.
ASA Y14.5-1957

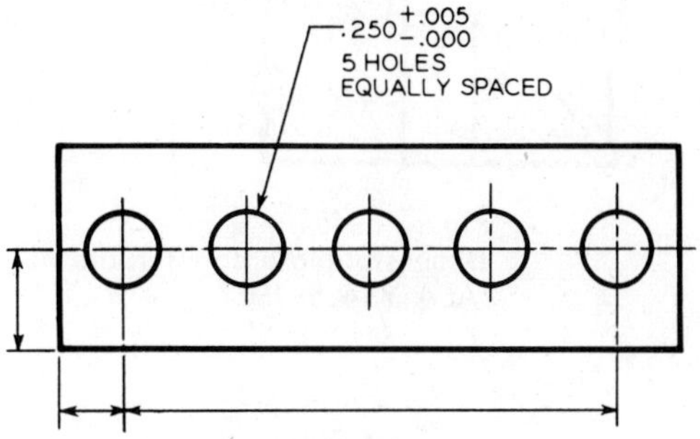

Figure 6-43
Locating holes equally spaced in a line. ASA Y14.5-1957

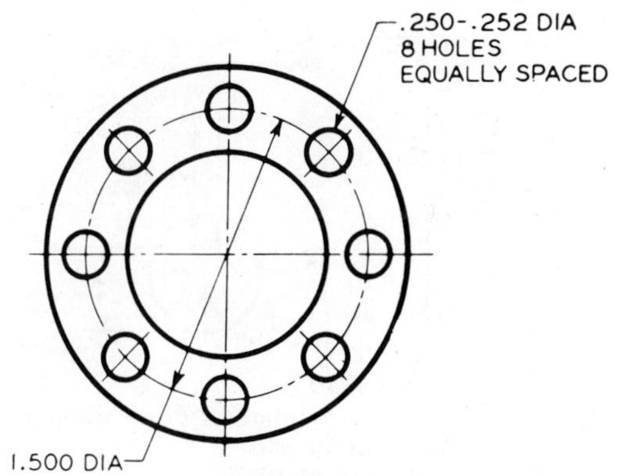

Figure 6-42
Locating holes on circles by radius or diameter and equally spaced.
ASA Y14.5-1957

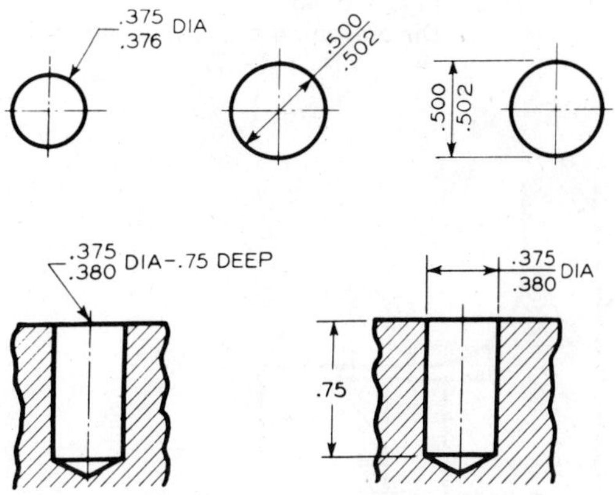

Figure 6-44
Correct method of dimensioning round holes. ASA Y14.5-1957

conical parts.

6.16 Dimensioning special features

Chamfers. Chamfers should be dimensioned by giving the angle and length as shown in Fig. 6-49A. When the angle is 45°, the chamfer may be dimensioned as illustrated in Fig. 6-49B.

Keys and keyways. Wherever possible, Woodruff keys should be specified to conform with *American Standard Woodruff Keys, Keyslots and Cutters, ASA B17F-1955*. The keys may then be specified in standard nomenclature, without making drawings. Figs. 6-50 and 6-51 illustrate satisfactory methods of expressing dimensions for keyways of the types listed in the above American standard.

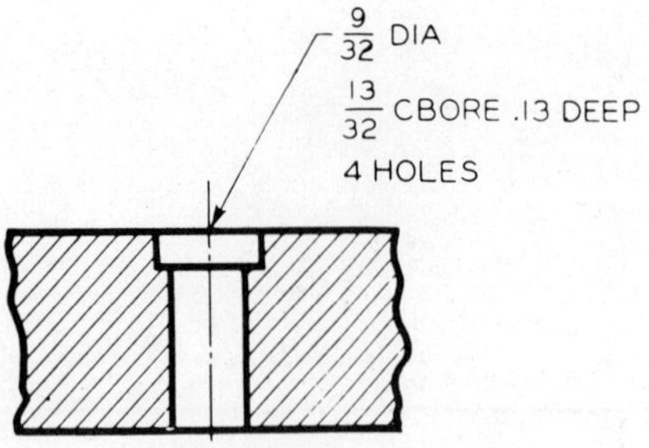

Figure 6-45
Dimensioning a counterbore hole.
ASA Y14.5-1957

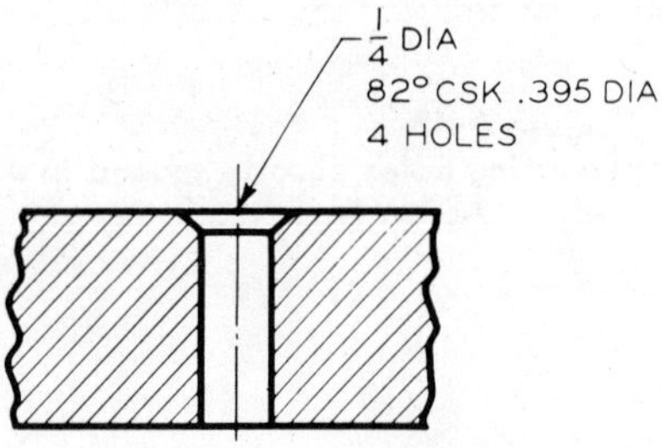

Figure 6-46
Dimensioning a countersunk hole.
ASA Y14.5-1957

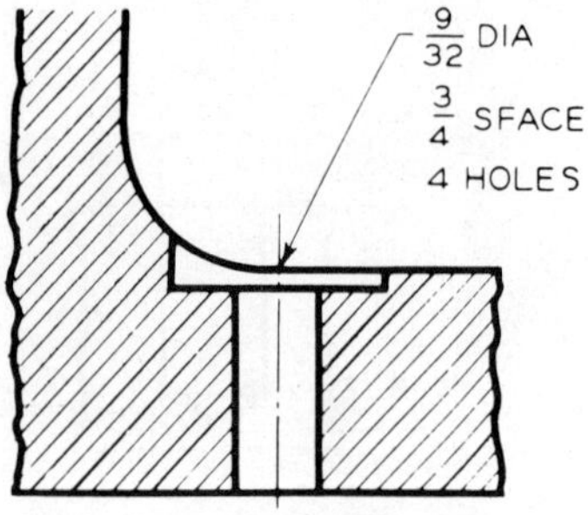

Figure 6-47
Dimensioning a spot faced hole.
ASA Y14.5-1957

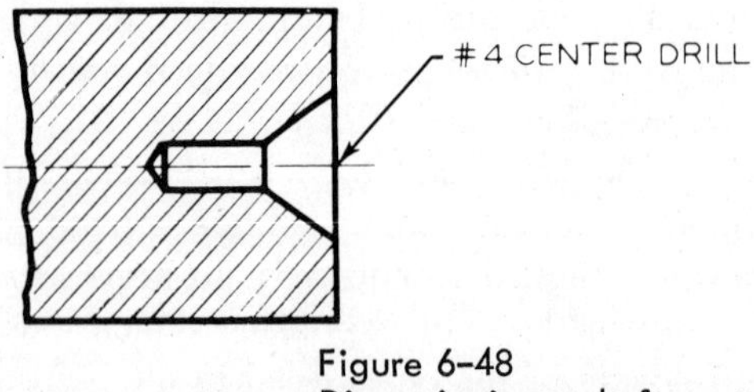

Figure 6-48
Dimensioning a shaft center.
ASA Y14.5-1957

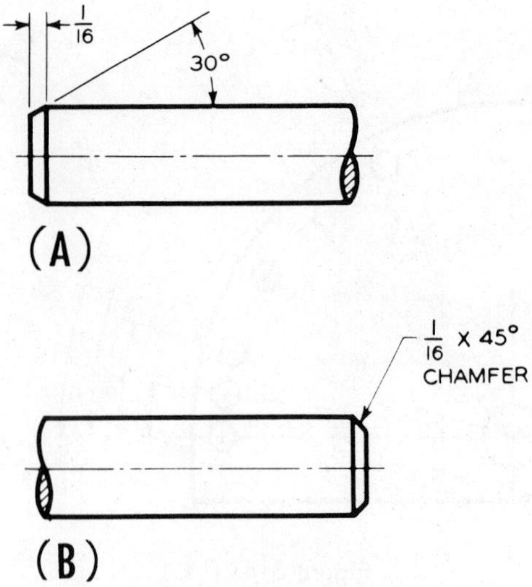

Figure 6-49
Methods of dimensioning a chamfer.
ASA Y14.5-1957

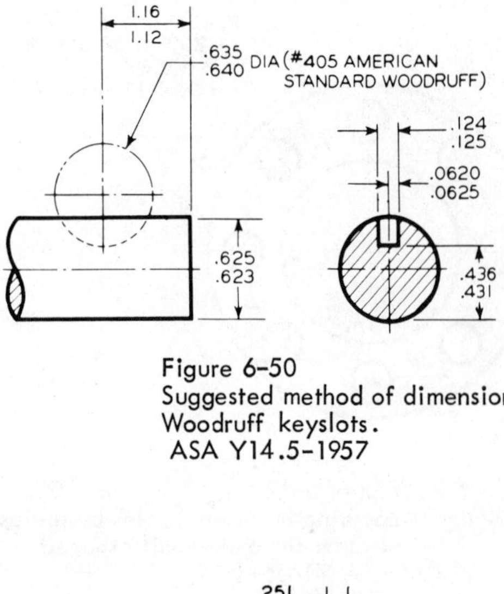

Figure 6-50
Suggested method of dimensioning Woodruff keyslots.
ASA Y14.5-1957

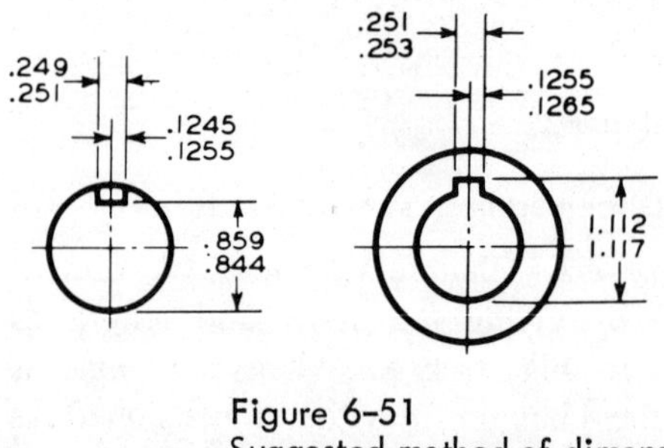

Figure 6-51
Suggested method of dimensioning Keyways for stock keys.
ASA Y14.5-1957

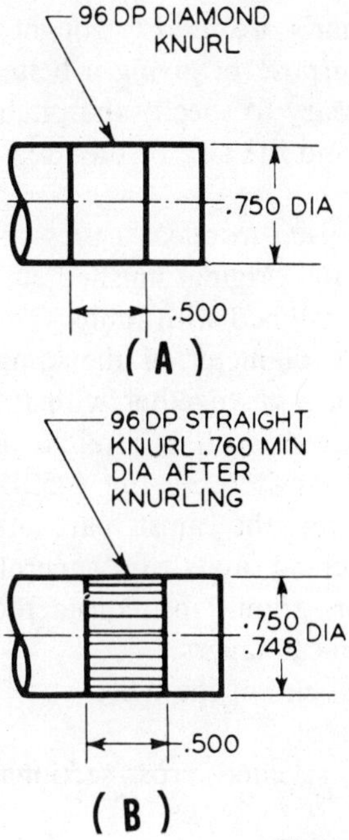

Figure 6-52
How to dimension knurls.
ASA Y14.5-1957

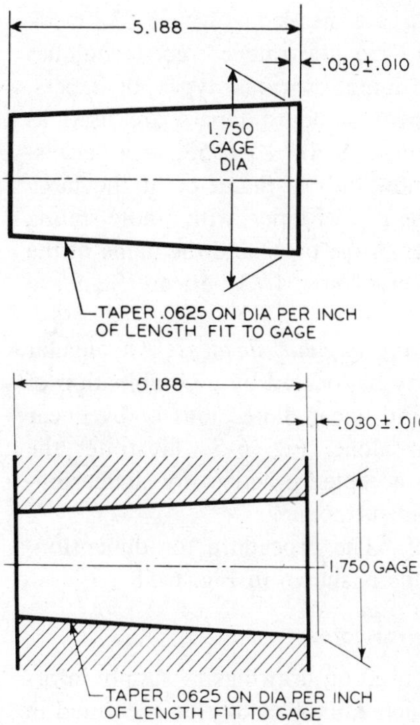

Figure 6-53
How to dimension close-fitting mating tapers. ASA Y14.5-1957

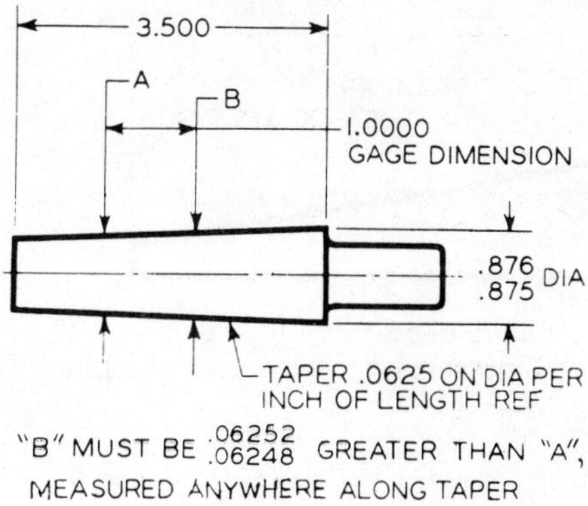

Figure 6-54
How to dimension an accurate external taper not dimensioned for a close fit with an internal taper.
ASA Y14.5-1957

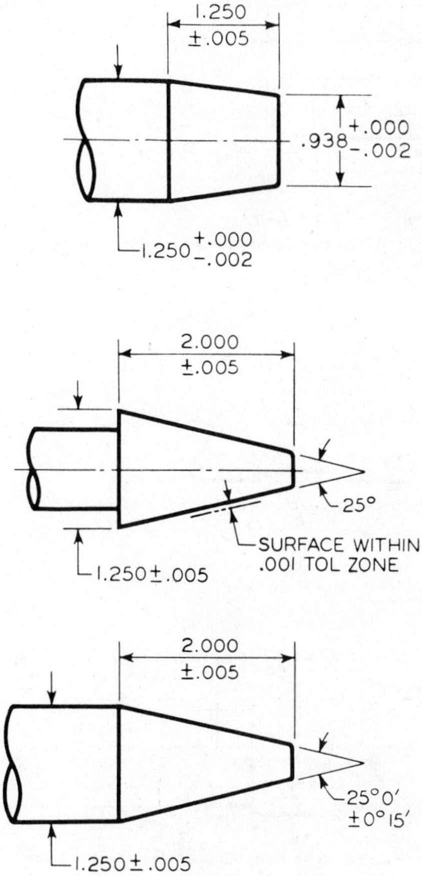

Figure 6-55
How to dimension non-critical tapers.
ASA Y14.5-1957

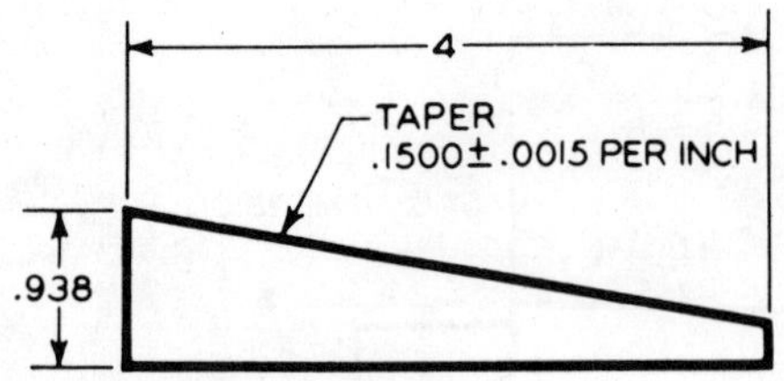

Figure 6-56
Dimensioning a taper on a flat piece.
ASA Y14.5-1957

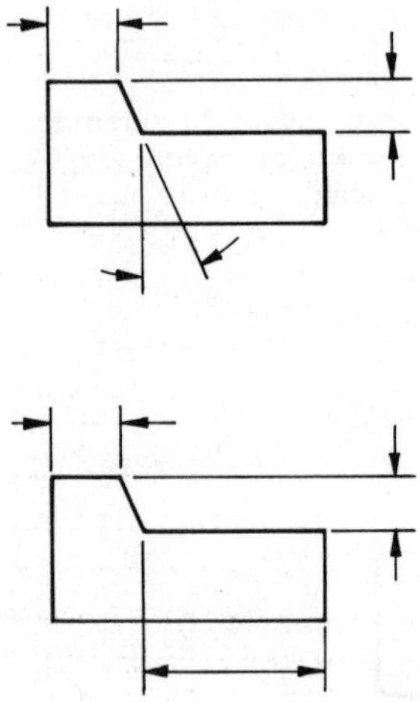

Figure 6-57
Methods of dimensioning angular surfaces.

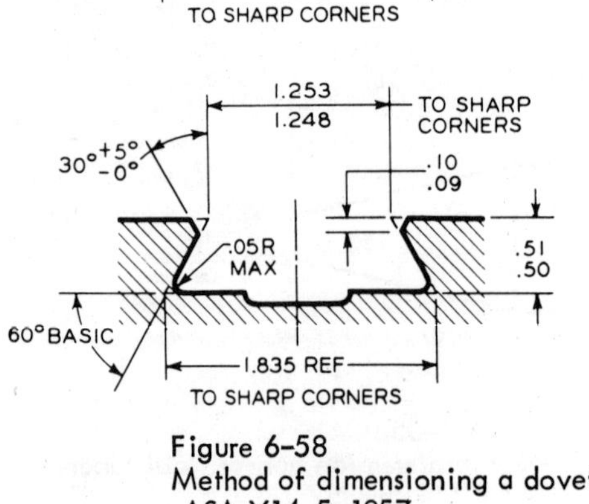

Figure 6-58
Method of dimensioning a dovetail.
ASA Y14.5-1957

Knurls. When knurls are used to roughen a surface for the purpose of giving a better grip it is only necessary to specify the pitch, and kind of knurl, and the size of the areas. See Fig. 6-52A.

When knurls are used to make a press fit between two parts, the original finished surface should be dimensioned with limits. The minimum acceptable diameter of the knurl should be given in a note together with the pitch and type of knurl, such as straight or diamond, depressed or raised. See Fig. 6-52B.

Tapers. Tapers for the most part are dimensioned in decimal units. In general, the following factors should be considered in dimensioning conical tapers:

1 Diameter at each end of the taper
2 Length of the taper
3 Diameter at a selected cross-sectional plane
4 The distance locating a cross-sectional plane at which a diameter is specified
5 Rate of taper
6 Included angle

No more of these dimensions should be given than are needed. Figs. 6-53, 6-54, 6-55, and 6-56 illustrate correct techniques for dimensioning various types of tapers. When regular standard tapers are used as specified in ASA, B5.10-1953, it is permissible to show only a diameter at the large end and the rate of taper, with a note stating the number of the taper and the name of the Standard, as "No. 4 American Standard Taper."

Positioning angular surfaces. An angular surface may be located by a combination of an angle and linear dimensions or by linear dimensions alone. Fig. 6-57 illustrates the commonly accepted practices for dimensioning angular surfaces.

Dovetails. The procedure for dimensioning dovetails is shown in Fig. 6-58.

6.17 General notes

Notes are used on drawings to supply information which cannot readily be presented in other ways or can be presented more easily in descriptive form. They are used for such a variety of purposes that it is not practical to establish a standard note for every condi-

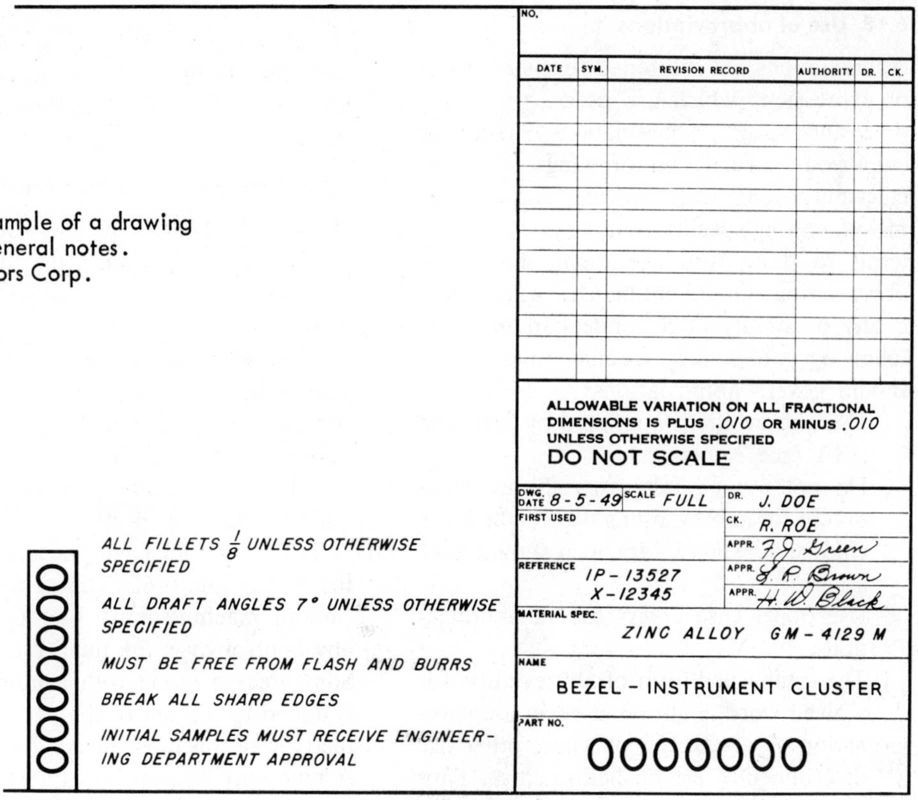

Figure 6-59
This is an example of a drawing containing general notes. General Motors Corp.

tion. The following rules generally apply for all notes:[9]

1 Information conveyed by notes shall be clear, accurate, complete, and capable of only one interpretation.
2 Only common shop trade terms and words shall be used.
3 Notes shall be as simple, brief, and concise as possible.
4 A condensed form similar to that used for telegrams shall be used.
5 Abbreviations shall be limited to the most commonly understood shop trade terms or words.
6 Notes of instruction shall preferably employ the present tense.
7 Notes which are repeatedly used on similar drawings shall preferably be identical in wording.
8 Notes shall not duplicate information recorded in the material list or repeat dimensions given elsewhere.
9 When it is necessary to make reference to information which is given elsewhere, such reference shall not lead back farther than one drawing or other source.
10 Notes shall preferably be placed horizontally on the drawing to facilitate reading.
11 Notes which apply to a specific part shall preferably be placed under or adjacent to the part circle.
12 Notes shall not be underscored. A few typical phrases in note form follow (see Fig. 6-59):

UNLESS OTHERWISE SPECIFIED FINISH ALL OVER
POLISH TO REMOVE ALL TOOL MARKS
DIMENSIONS APPLY BEFORE PLATING
HEAT TREAT PER SPECIFICATION XX
REMOVE BURRS

9. *General Electric Standards* (Schenectady: General Electric Co.).

6.18 Use of abbreviations

Abbreviations are shortened forms of words or expressions which are used to conserve time and space. Abbreviations should be employed sparingly on drawings since the chief purpose of such drawings is to convey manufacturing specifications in unmistakable terms to those who use them. Therefore, abbreviations should not be used where there is any possibility of misunderstanding. The following are a few specific rules which should govern abbreviations:

1 Use abbreviations approved by SAE and ASA (see Appendix).
2 Do not use periods after abbreviations except for abbreviations that might cause confusion. Thus *IN* for inch should have a period.
3 Use upper case letters for all abbreviations.
4 The established form of abbreviation for a given word is always used in a combination of words, except where otherwise determined by established practice. Thus the abbreviation for the combination "cubic feet per minute" is CFM, but where each word occurs separately, the abbreviations are *CU* for cubic, *FT* for feet, *MIN* for minute.

6.19 Designating finish marks

The proper functioning of a machine part depends to a large extent on the quality of its surface. Accordingly, for such parts the draftsman must not only indicate the surfaces that are to be machined but very often he must stipulate the degree of surface finish required.

Recent developments, processing and quality requirements have brought about a greater observance of surface finish. To insure correct interpretation and control of finished surfaces, certain symbols have been standardized and are recognized by all industries. These symbols are placed wherever a surface appears edgewise as a visible line. Hence, the symbols may be repeated in several views. If necessary they may even be placed on invisible lines.

The accepted symbols apply to two general classifications of surface finishes—non control surface finish and control surface finish.

6.20 Non control surface finish

Where the control of the roughness of a surface is not necessary, the following three methods may be used to indicate the surface roughness:

1 A 60 degree *V* may be drawn with its point touching the line representing the edgewise view of the surface to be machined. Occasionally the letters *R* or *G* are placed in the *V,* the *R* meaning "rough" and the *G* "grind." See Fig. 6-60.

2 The symbol *f* may be used in place of the *V*. See Fig. 6-60. This symbol specifies a smooth machine finish and does not show any control over the quality of the surface. Sometimes a circle with a number inclosed is added to the tail of the *f* to better control the type of machine surface (see Fig. 6-60). A note may be used to explain the meaning of the number.

3 A note, "Finish all over" abbreviated *"FAO"* is sometimes used if all surfaces are to be machined.

6.21 Controlled surface finish

When the height, width, and direction of surface irregularities must be controlled to exact specifications, the practice is to show the degree of control by a series of roughness symbols adopted by the American Standards Association.

The basic symbol used to designate surface irregularities is the check mark with a horizontal extension bar. The recommended proportions for construction of the surface symbol are shown in Fig. 6-61.

The point of this symbol may be placed on the line representing the surface involved, on the extension line, or on a leader line pointing to the surface. Fig. 6-62 illustrates typical applications of the symbol on a drawing.

The type, direction and magnitude of the surface irregularities are indicated by additional markings placed about the basic check

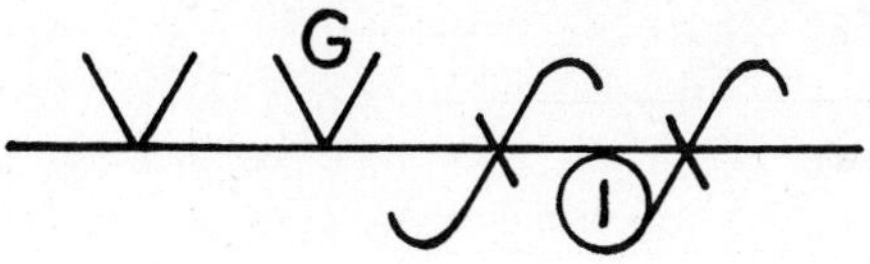

Figure 6-60
These are symbols often used to indicate non control surfaces that are to be machined.

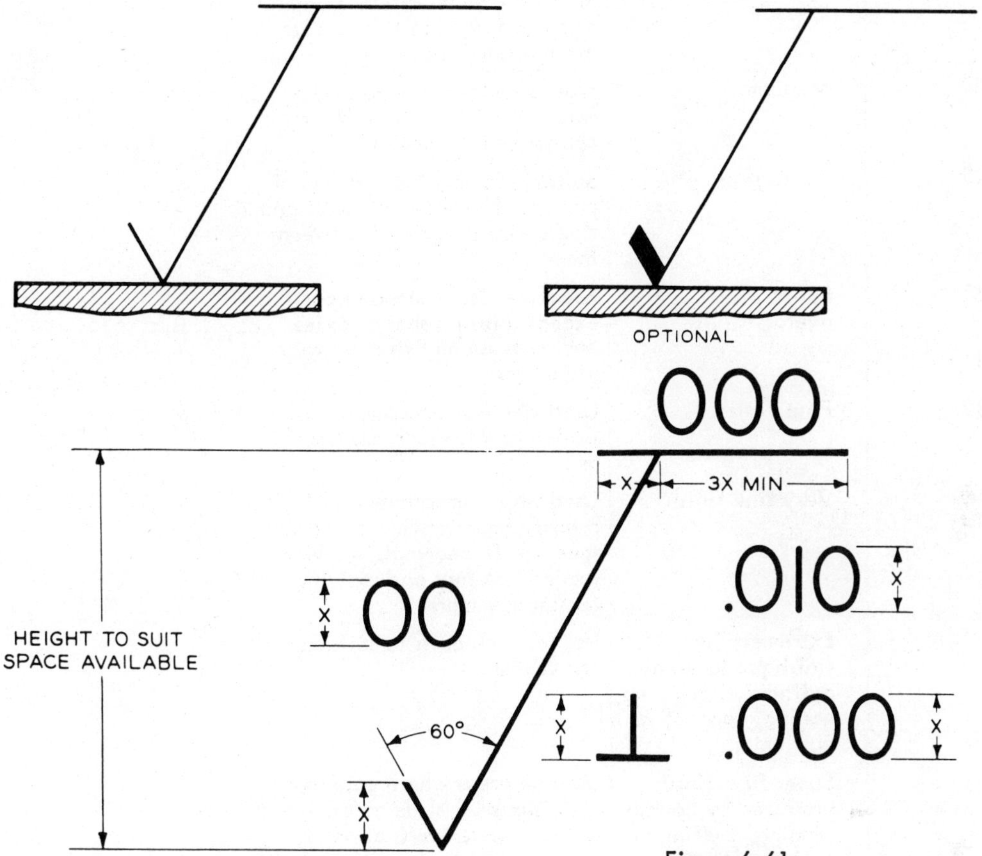

Figure 6-61
Typical proportions of a control surface symbol. ASA B46.1-1955

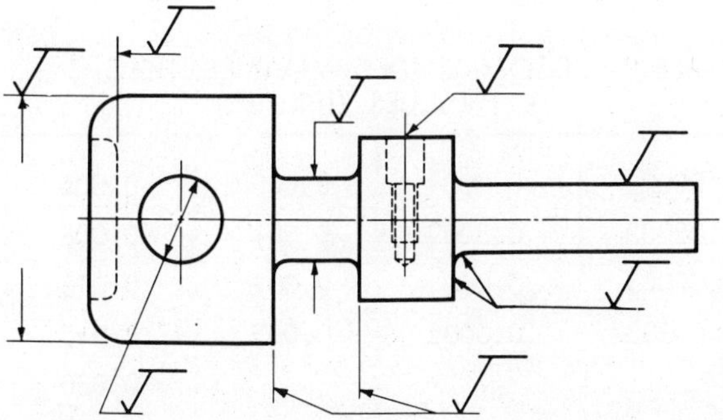

Figure 6-62
The surface roughness symbol may be located in various positions on a drawing as shown here.
ASA B46.1-1955

TABLE I. RECOMMENDED HEIGHT VALUES

Roughness value (microinches)	Type of surface	Purpose
1000	Extremely rough	Used for clearance surfaces only where good appearance is not required.
500	Rough	Used where vibration, fatigue, or stress concentration are not critical and close tolerances are not required.
250	Medium	Most popular for general use where stress requirements and appearance are essential.
125	Average smooth	Suitable for mating surfaces of parts held together by bolts and rivets with no motion between them.
63	Better than average finish	For close fits or stressed parts except rotating shafts, axles and parts subject to extreme vibrations.
32	Fine finish	Used where stress concentration is high and for such applications as bearings.
16	Very fine finish	Used where smoothness is of primary importance such as high-speed shaft bearings, heavily-loaded bearings and extreme tension members.
8	Extremely fine finish produced by cylindrical grinding, honing, lapping or buffing	Use for such parts as surfaces of cylinders.
4	Super fine finish produced by honing, lapping, buffing or polishing	Used on areas where packings and rings must slide across the surface where lubrication is not dependable.

TABLE II. RECOMMENDED WAVINESS HEIGHT VALUES (INCHES)

0.00002	0.0001	0.0008	0.005
0.00003	0.0002	0.001	0.008
0.00005	0.0003	0.002	0.010
0.00008	0.0005	0.003	0.015
			0.020

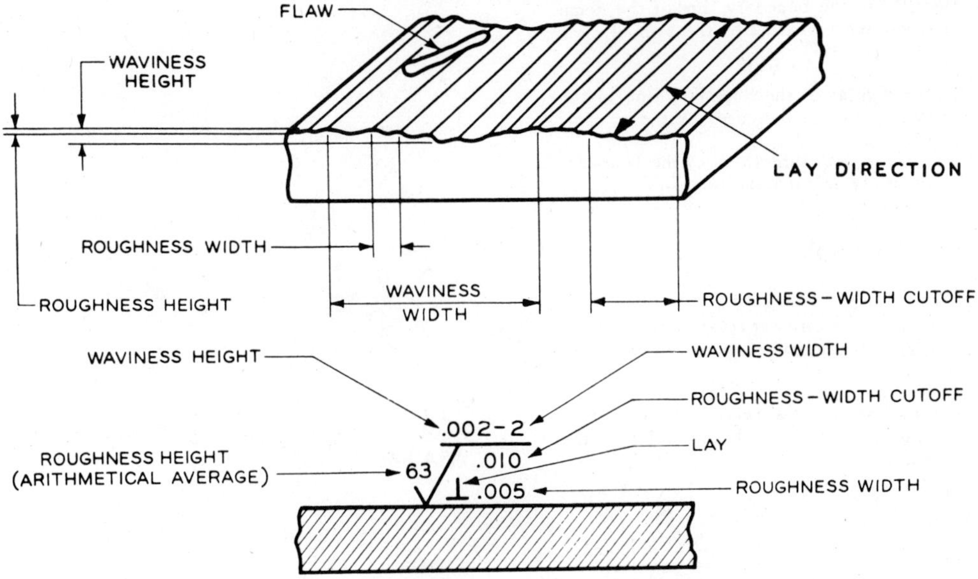

Figure 6-63
Identification and relation of symbols to surface characteristics.
ASA B46.1-1955

TABLE III. STANDARD ROUGHNESS-WIDTH CUTOFF VALUES (INCHES)

0.003	0.030	0.300
0.010	0.100	1.000

mark symbol. To understand these markings, it is necessary to know the meaning of the following terms:

Roughness. Roughness refers to the finely spaced irregularities produced by machining, abrading, extruding, molding, casting, forging, rolling, coating, plating, blasting or burnishing. The height of irregularities is rated in microinches. (A microinch is one millionth of an inch—0.000001.) The recommended height values are shown in Table I. In addition to the height, the maximum permissible spacing between repetitive units of the surface pattern is rated. This width is given in inches. See Fig. 6-63.

Waviness. Waviness refers to those surface irregularities spaced too far apart to constitute roughness. Irregularities of this category result from such factors as machine or work deflections, vibration, heat treatment, or warping strains. Both the height and width of waviness irregularities are rated in inches. See Fig. 6-63. The recommended waviness height values are given in Table II.

Roughness-width cutoff. This refers to the maximum width in inches of surface irregularities that are to be included in the measurement of roughness height. The standard values are shown in Table III.

= Parallel to the boundary line of the nominal surface indicated by the symbol.

⊥ Perpendicular to the boundary line of the nominal surface indicated by the symbol.

X Angular in both directions to the boundary line of the nominal surface indicated by the symbol.

M Multi-directional.

C Approximately circular relative to the center of the nominal surface indicated by the symbol.

R Approximately radial relative to the center of the nominal surface indicated by the symbol.

Figure 6-64
Symbols indicating direction of lay.
ASA B46.1-1955

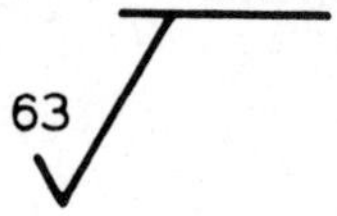

Roughness height rating is placed at the left of the long leg. The specification of only one rating shall indicate the maximum average and any lesser average shall be acceptable.

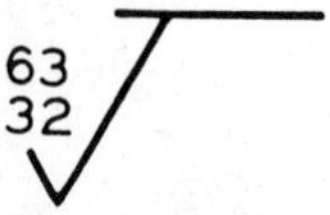

The specification of maximum average and minimum average roughness height ratings indicates permissible range of average rating.

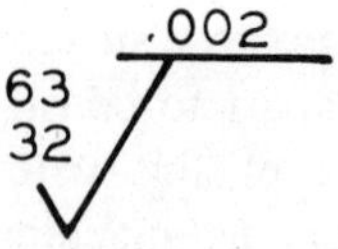

Maximum waviness height rating is placed above the horizontal extension. Any lesser rating shall be acceptable.

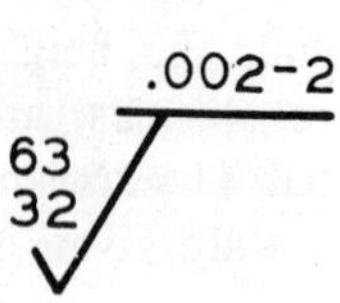

Maximum waviness width rating is placed above the horizontal extension and to the right of the waviness height rating. Any lesser rating shall be acceptable.

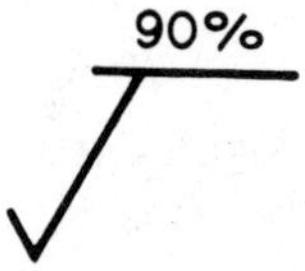

To specify contact area, when required, the percentage value shall be placed above the extension line.

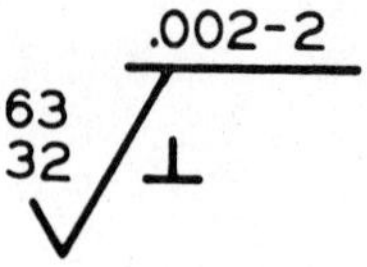

Lay designation is indicated by the lay symbol placed at the right of the long leg.

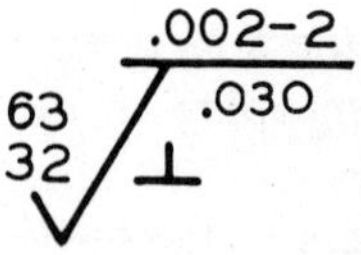

Roughness-width cutoff rating is placed below the horizontal extension.

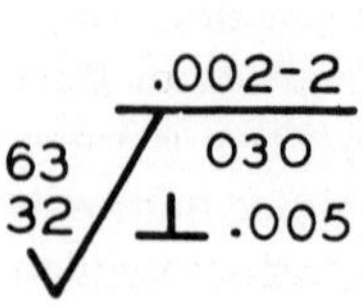

Where required, maximum roughness width rating shall be placed at the right of the lay symbol. Any lesser rating shall be acceptable.

Figure 6-65
Application of roughness, waviness, and lay symbols and ratings.

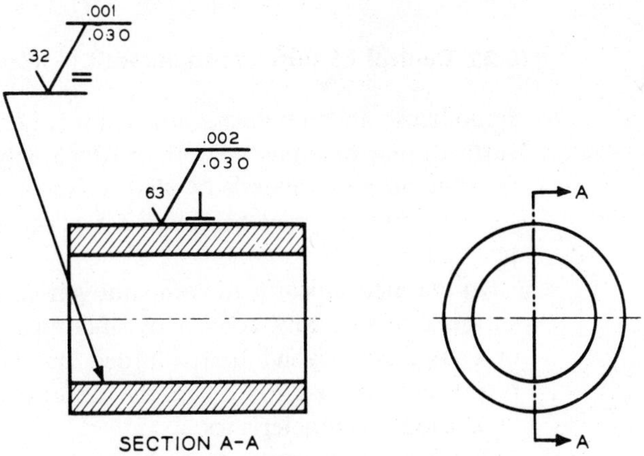

INTERPRETATION:

ROUGHNESS HEIGHT (O D) ---------------------------- 63μIN.
ROUGHNESS HEIGHT (I D) ---------------------------- 32μIN.
ROUGHNESS—WIDTH CUTOFF (O D AND I D) ---------- .030
WAVINESS HEIGHT (O D) ------------------------------ .002
WAVINESS HEIGHT (I D) ------------------------------ .001
LAY (O D) -- CIRCUMFERENTIAL
LAY (I D) -- AXIAL

Figure 6-66
Application and interpretation of roughness as it may appear on a drawing.

Lay. Lay indicates the direction of the predominant pattern of surface irregularities produced by tool marks. See Fig. 6-64.

Flaws. Flaws are irregularities such as a scratch, ridge, hole, peak, crack or check which occur at one place, or at infrequent intervals in the surface. See Fig. 6-63.

6.22 Application of symbols and ratings[10]

Fig. 6-65 illustrates the specifications of roughness, waviness and lay by insertion of the ratings in appropriate portions of the symbol. Only those ratings required to specify adequately the desired surface should be shown in the symbol.

Fig. 6-66 demonstrates the application of surface roughness symbols on drawings with explanation of the significance of the various parts of the symbol.

To insure proper interpretation of surface roughness designations, drawings may include a general note as shown in Fig. 6-67.

10. Extracted from *Surface Roughness, Waviness and Lay, ASA B46.1 — 1955* (New York: The American Society of Mechanical Engineers, 1955).

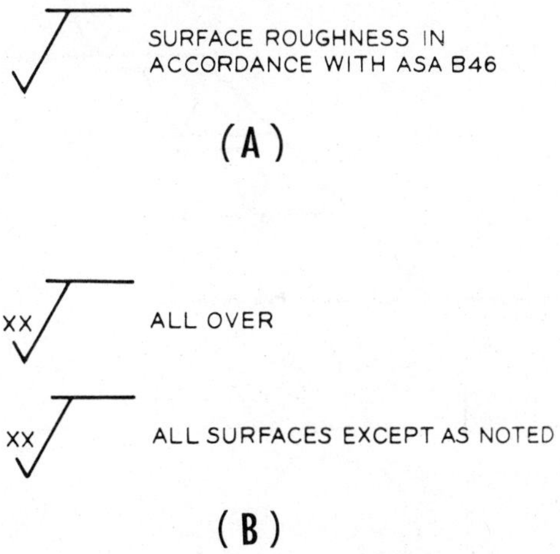

Figure 6-67
General notes for drawings to insure proper interpretation of surface roughness designations.

For parts requiring extensive and uniform surface roughness control, a general note may be added to the drawing as indicated in *B* of Fig. 6-67.

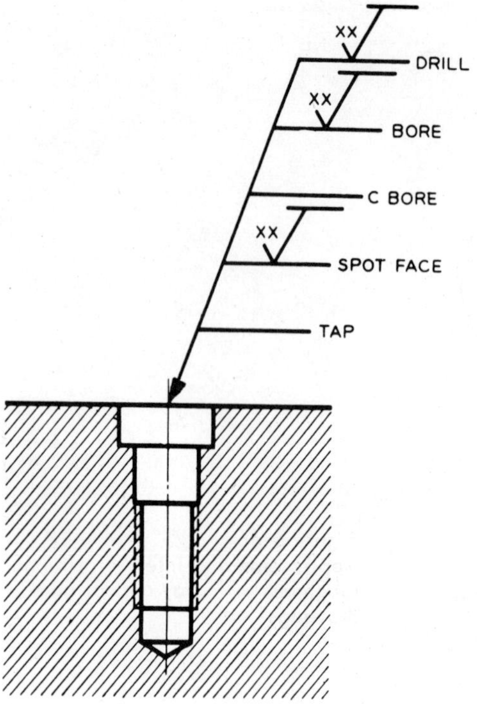

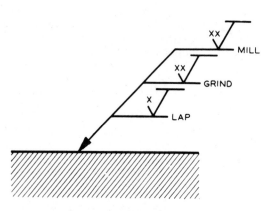

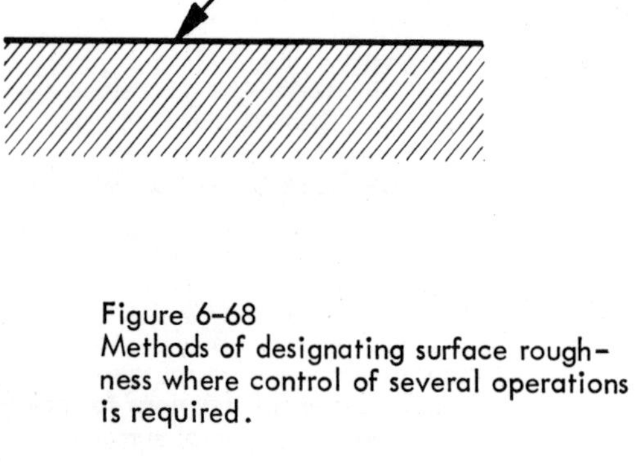

Figure 6-68
Methods of designating surface roughness where control of several operations is required.

Where surface roughness control of several operations is required within a given area, or on a given surface, surface qualities may be designated as shown in Fig. 6-68.

6.23 Control of surface roughness[11]

Smoothness and roughness are relative, i.e., surfaces may be either smooth or rough only for the purpose intended; what is smooth for one purpose may be rough for another purpose.

In the mechanical field comparatively few surfaces require any control of smoothness or roughness beyond that afforded by the processes required to obtain the necessary dimensional characteristics.

Working surfaces such as bearings, pistons, and gears are typical of surfaces for which optimum performance may require control of the surface characteristics. Non-working surfaces such as the walls of transmission cases, crank cases, or differential housings seldom require any surface control, the only exception being restrictions that may be necessary for process control and finish required for the sake of appearance.

It follows from the above that surface characteristics should not be controlled on a drawing or specification unless such control is essential to appearance or mechanical performance of the product. Imposition of such restrictions when unnecessary may increase production costs and in any event will serve to lessen the emphasis on the control specified for important surfaces.

Fig. 6-69 shows the typical range of surface roughness values which may be obtained by various production methods. The ability of a processing operation to produce a specific surface roughness depends on many factors. For example, in surface grinding, the final surface depends on the peripheral speed of the wheel, the speed of the traverse, the rate of feed, the grit size, bonding material and state of dress of the wheel, the amount and type of lubrication at the point of cutting, and the physical properties of the piece being ground. A small change in any of the above factors can have a marked effect on the surface produced. Therefore, the values shown in Fig. 6-69 should be considered flexible and not hard and fast limits.

11. *Ibid.*

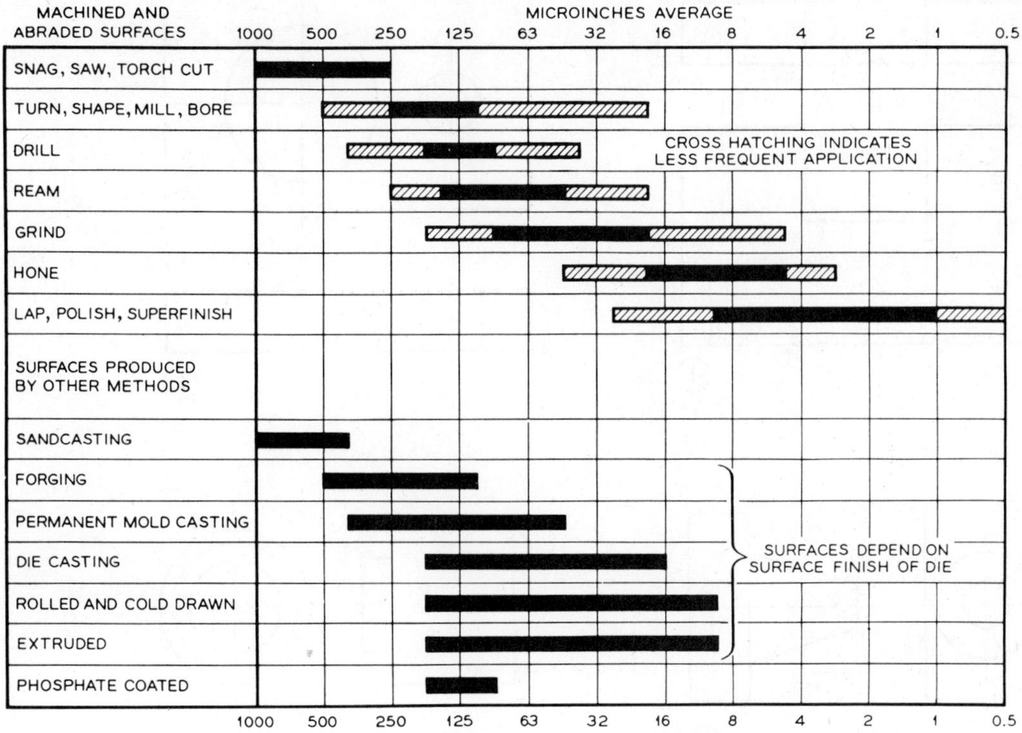

Figure 6-69
Surface roughness obtained by common production methods.

TABLE IV

Drawing problem	Scale
1	C
2	B
3	A
4	B
5	C
6	B
7	A
8	C
9	B
10	A
11	A
12	B
13	A
14	C
15	B
16	C
17	C
18	A

Problems, section 6

1-18 Reproduce the views of the problems assigned as shown in Figs. 6-70, 6-71, 6-72 and dimension completely. Determine the sizes by placing dividers on the views and obtaining their values on the scales shown below. Use scale **A, B** or **C** according to Table IV.

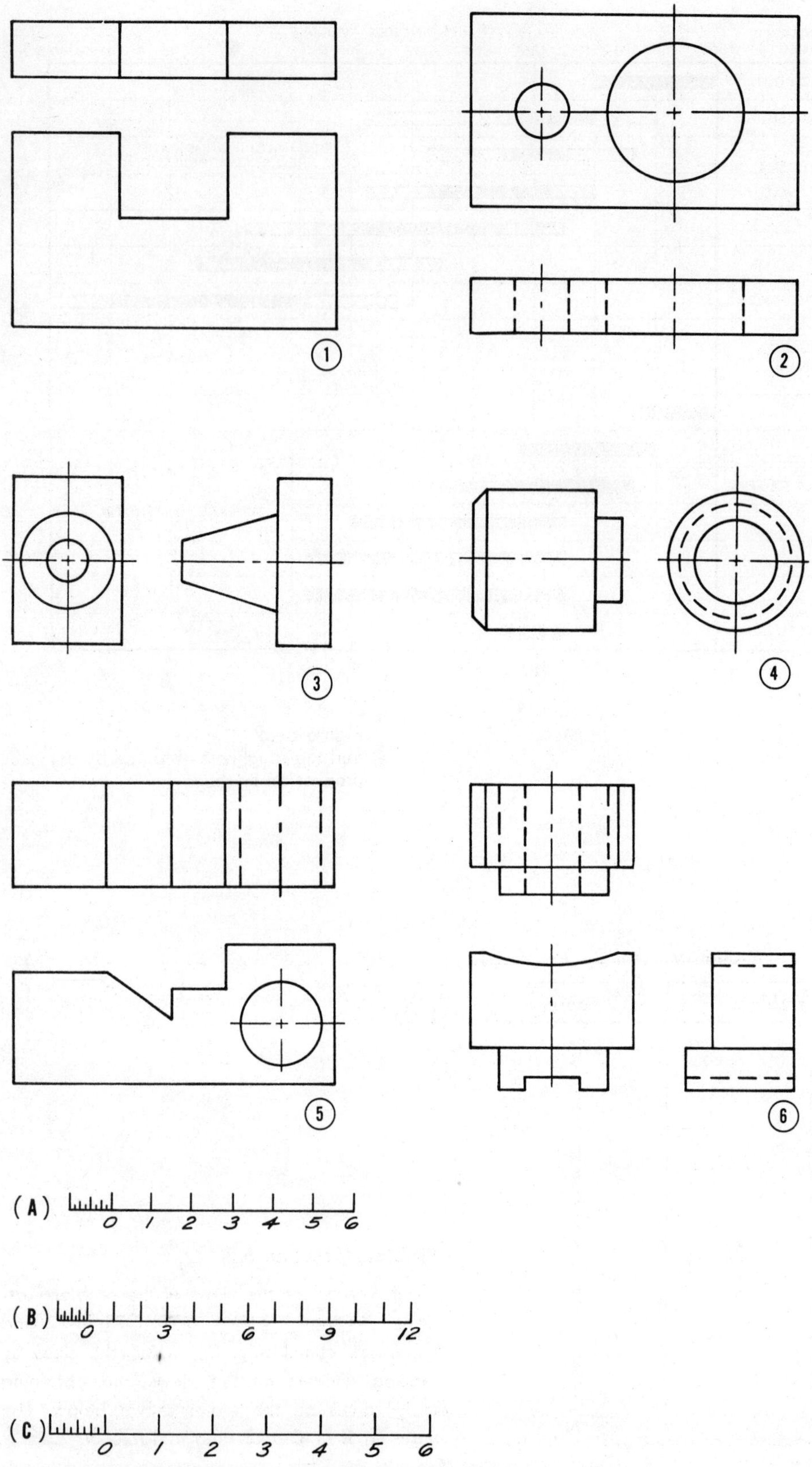

Figure 6-70
Problems 1-6.

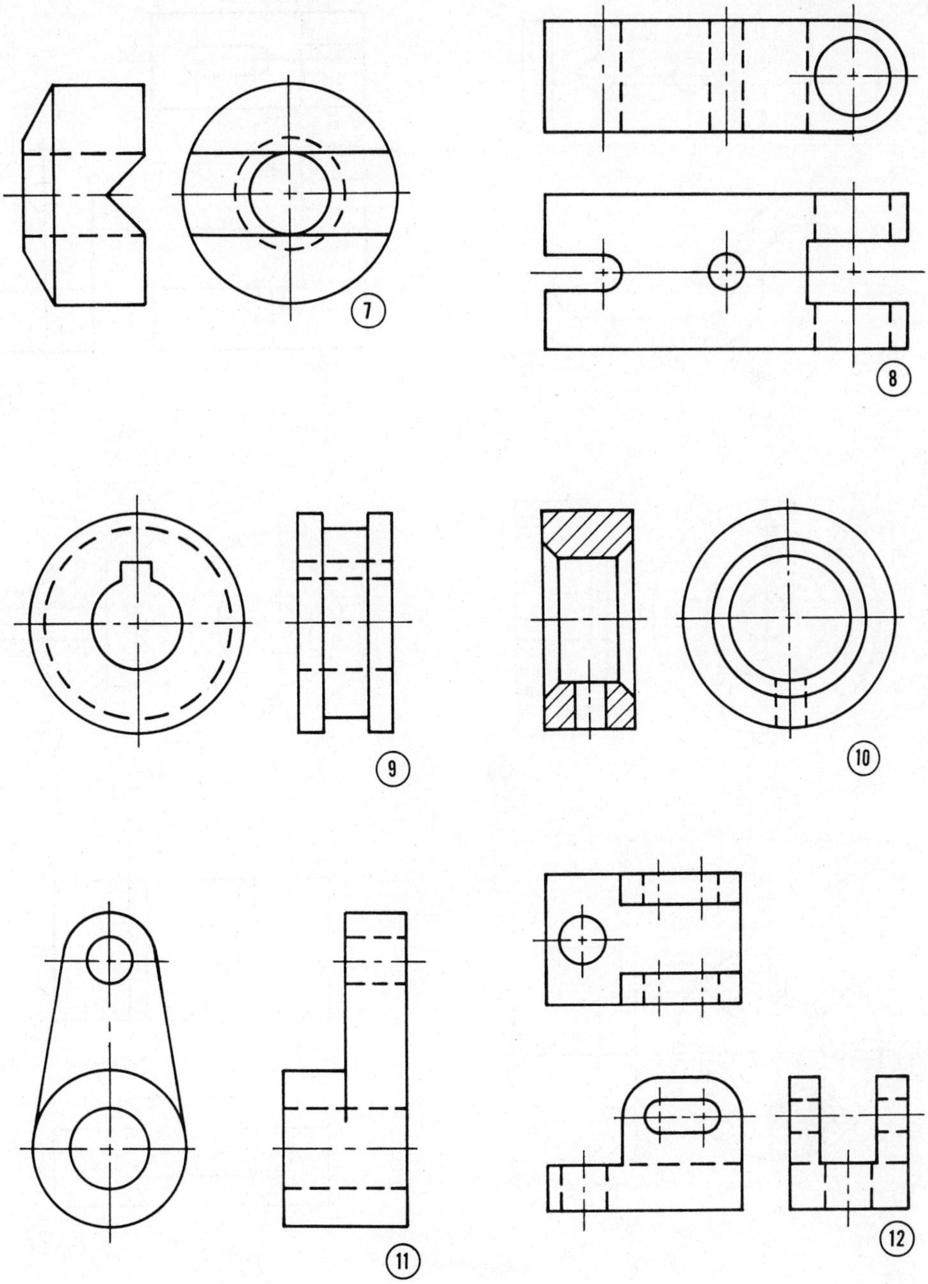

Figure 6-71
Problems 7-12.

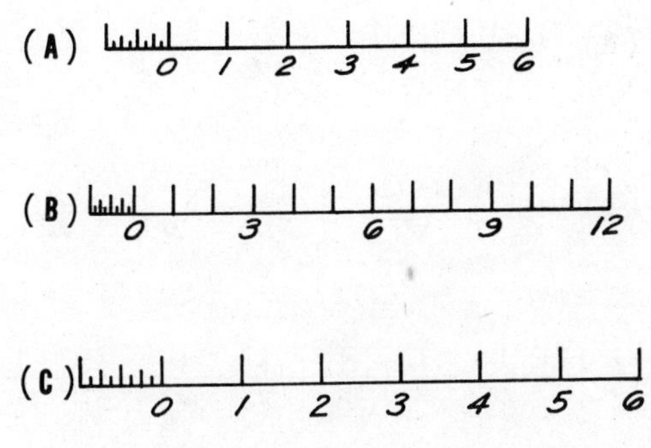

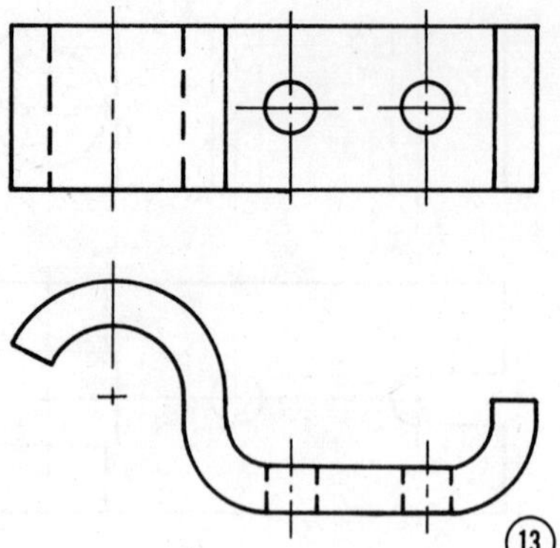

(13)

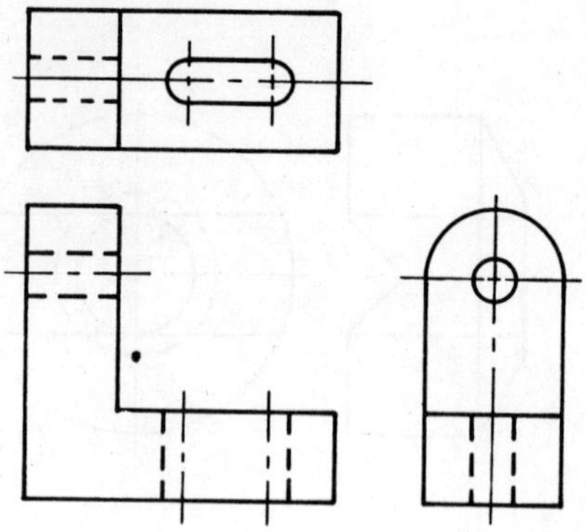

(14)

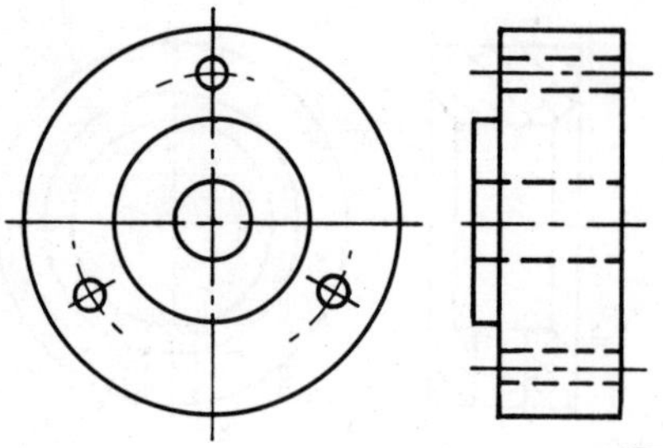

(15)

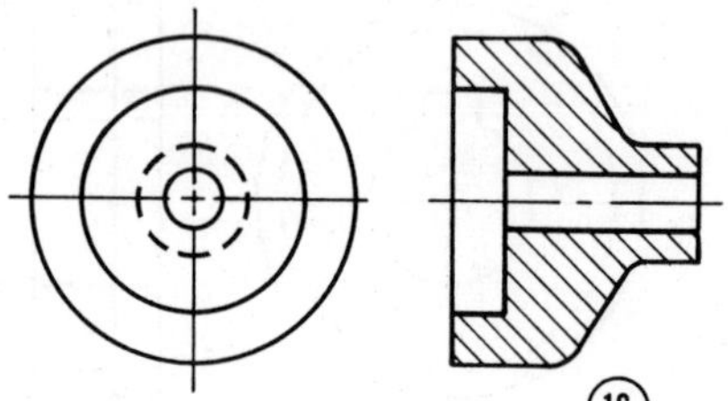

(16)

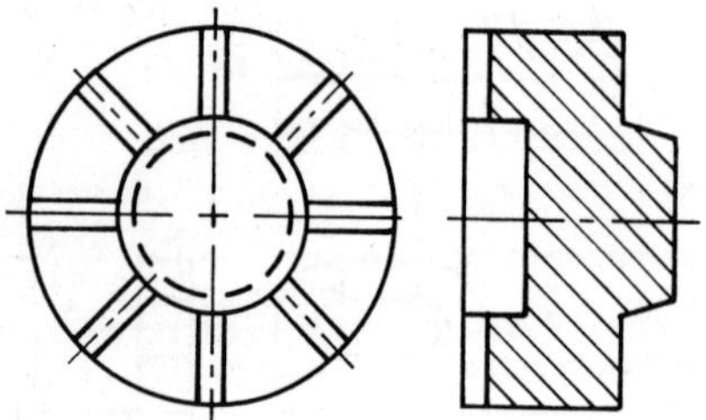

(17)

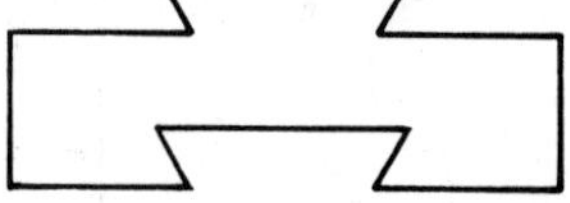

(18)

Figure 6-72
Problems 13-18.

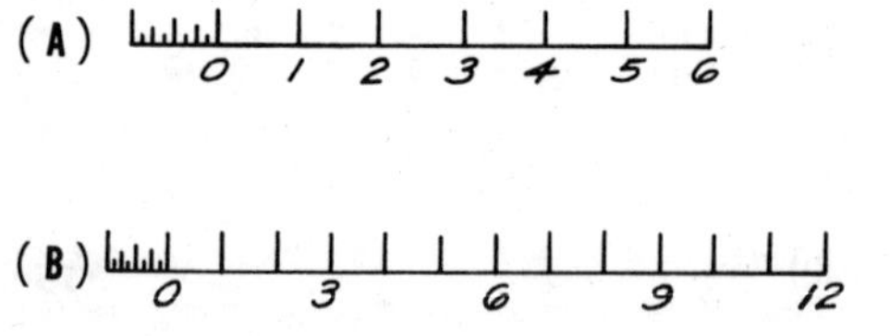

Precision dimensioning 7

With the ever increasing importance of quality control in the manufacturing process, the trend in many industries is a gradual shift to the decimal system of dimensioning. The aviation and automotive industries are now using the decimal system almost exclusively. The primary advantage that results from the use of the decimal system is the simplification of computations, since decimals can be added, subtracted, multiplied or divided more easily than fractions, all of which insures more accurate production standards.

Insofar as the actual dimensioning practices are concerned, there are no significant differences between the decimal and fractional methods. Whereas one designates sizes in fractional units, the decimal system shows all sizes in decimal values. Therefore, the material in this section will not restate the dimensioning practices described in Section 6, but present only those features which are directly related to an understanding of the decimal system of dimensioning.

In addition to the more precise method of dimensioning practices needed in the manufacturing of goods, an even more exacting control is required to regulate the interchangeability of fabricated parts. Rarely does one industry today manufacture all of the items which go into the final assembly of a product. Many parts necessary for the finished structure are sub-contracted to other industries or are purchased commercially. If pieces made in widely separated localities are to fit properly when brought together for final assembly, some control procedures are necessary, otherwise mass production of goods becomes impossible. Merely stating that a part must be made to a length of 2-1/2 inches is insufficient because exact sizes are practically impossible. The only workable solution is to design parts or components so a slight variation in the stipulated sizes is permissible. Thus if the length required for a part is 2-1/2 inches and the mating piece is engineered to fit even if the length is within a few thousandths of an inch over or under the specified size, assembly of the pieces remains possible. The control that permits interchangeability of parts regardless of the source of manufacture is a system of tolerances. The commonly accepted practices used in designating tolerances are discussed in this section.

7.1 The decimal system[1]

The decimal dimensioning system is based on the use of two-place decimals; that is, decimal dimensioning consisting of two figures after the decimal point.

The figures after the decimal point are in even hundredths as the smallest unit—.04, .34, .86, etc., rather than odd hundredths—.03, .35, .87, etc., so that when the figures are divided by two, such as converting diameter dimensions into radius dimensions, the resulting value will be two-place decimals for easier reading of the scale.

The decimal scale. For drafting room use, the scale shown in Fig. 7-1 is recommended. The inch is divided into tenths (.10, .20, etc.) and even hundredths (.02, .04, .06, etc.), the smallest increment being .02. The greater height of the center two even hundredth lines permits greater ease in reading the scale.

Converting fractions to decimals. When converting information from a drawing di-

1. *General Motors Drafting Standards* (Detroit: General Motors Corp.).

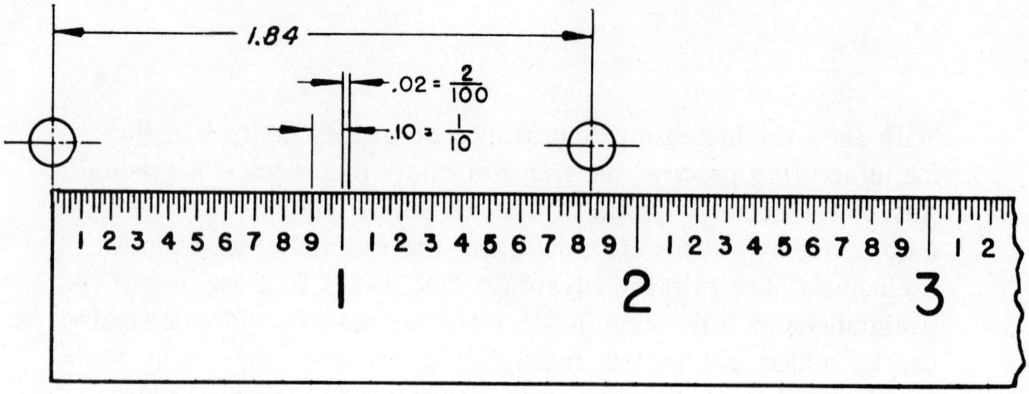

Figure 7-1
Here is a decimal scale.

mensioned in common fractions to a drawing dimensioned in decimals, the decimal equivalent of the fraction is used, if tolerances require it; but these decimals must be taken from a conversion chart like that shown in Fig. 7-2. The number of decimal places will be determined by the tolerances required. Where tolerances will permit, decimal values should be rounded off to even hundredths.

The following general practices should be observed in decimal dimensioning:

1 All dimensions are to be specified in two-place decimals except when converting from fractional dimensions or where tolerances require more than two-place decimals. See Fig. 7-3.

2 When showing limits with upper and lower dimensions in two or more decimal places, the upper and lower values are to contain the same number of decimal places. See Fig. 7-4.

3 Where tolerances are shown following the nominal dimension, the tolerance and the dimension should have the same number of decimal places. See Fig. 7-5.

4 An endeavor should be made to work to the tenth and even hundredth increment of an inch. Splitting of the even hundredth should be avoided. Odd hundredths may be used only where required for accuracy; however, this practice should be avoided as much as possible. Care should be exercised in the use of odd hundredths which will result in more than two decimal places when divided by two, as from a centerline to an

DECIMAL EQUIVALENTS OF FRACTIONS

CONVERSION CHART							
FRACTIONS		DECIMALS		FRACTIONS		DECIMALS	
64ths	32nds	Two Place	Three Place	64ths	32nds	Two Place	Three Place
1		.02	.016	33		.52	.516
	1	.03	.031		17	.53	.531
3		.05	.047	35		.55	.547
1/16		.06	.062	9/16		.56	.562
5		.08	.078	37		.58	.578
	3	.09	.094		19	.59	.594
7		.11	.109	39		.61	.609
1/8		.12	.125	5/8		.62	.625
9		.14	.141	41		.64	.641
	5	.16	.156		21	.66	.656
11		.17	.172	43		.67	.672
3/16		.19	.188	11/16		.69	.688
13		.20	.203	45		.70	.703
	7	.22	.219		23	.72	.719
15		.23	.234	47		.73	.734
1/4		.25	.250	3/4		.75	.750
17		.27	.266	49		.77	.766
	9	.28	.281		25	.78	.781
19		.30	.297	51		.80	.797
5/16		.31	.312	13/16		.81	.812
21		.33	.328	53		.83	.828
	11	.34	.344		27	.84	.844
23		.36	.359	55		.86	.859
3/8		.38	.375	7/8		.88	.875
25		.39	.391	57		.89	.891
	13	.41	.406		29	.91	.906
27		.42	.422	59		.92	.922
7/16		.44	.438	15/16		.94	.938
29		.45	.453	61		.95	.953
	15	.47	.469		31	.97	.969
31		.48	.484	63		.98	.984
1/2		.50	.500	1		1.00	1.000

Figure 7-2
Use this conversion chart to convert a drawing from fractional to decimal dimensions.

CORRECT	INCORRECT
1.00	1.
1.40	1.4
1.31	1.3125

Figure 7-3

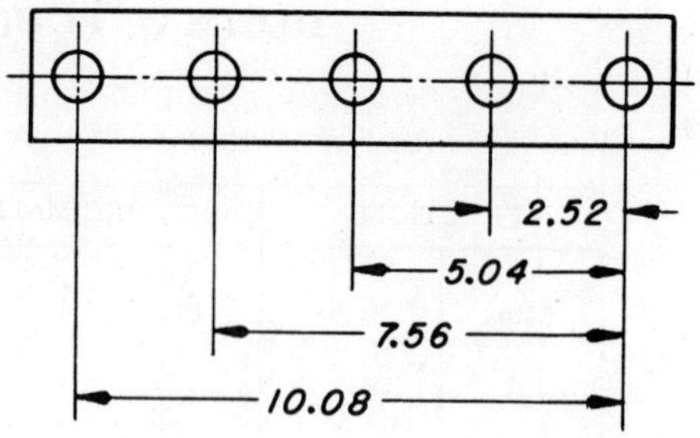

Figure 7-7

CORRECT	INCORRECT
1.212	1.212
1.210	1.21

Figure 7-4

CORRECT	INCORRECT
6.84 ± .02	6.84 ± .020
1.960 ± .005	1.96 ± .005

Figure 7-5

PREFERRED	ACCEPTABLE
1.00 or 1.02	1.01
3.12 or 3.14	3.13

Figure 7-6

edge or a hole. See Fig. 7-6.

5 Dimensions which are divided into two or more equal spaces, as between equally spaced holes, should be such that the resulting equal dimensions will be in even hundredth increments of the decimal scale, as shown in Fig. 7-7.

6 Where design requires overall dimensions which, when divided into two or more equal spaces, result in dimensions expressed in thousandths, these dimensions should be rounded off to two-place decimals wherever possible. See Fig. 7-8.

7 Where ordinates are used to dimension curves or irregular lines, all dimensions are expressed in hundredths as scaled from the layout. No effort is made to use even hundredths. See Fig. 7-9. For greater accuracy on symmetrical parts, dimensions on the overall figure should be in even hundredths to avoid any dimension from centerline to side being a three-place decimal.

Rounding off decimal values. Where it is possible to round off decimal values to a lesser number of decimal places, the following procedure should be used:

1 Where the figure following the last number to be retained is greater than five, the last number is increased by one.

2 Where the figure following the last number to be retained is less than five, the last number remains unchanged.

3 Where the figure following the last number to be retained is exactly five and the number to be retained is odd, the number is increased by one.

4 Where the figure following the last number to be retained is exactly five and the number to be retained is even, the number remains unchanged.

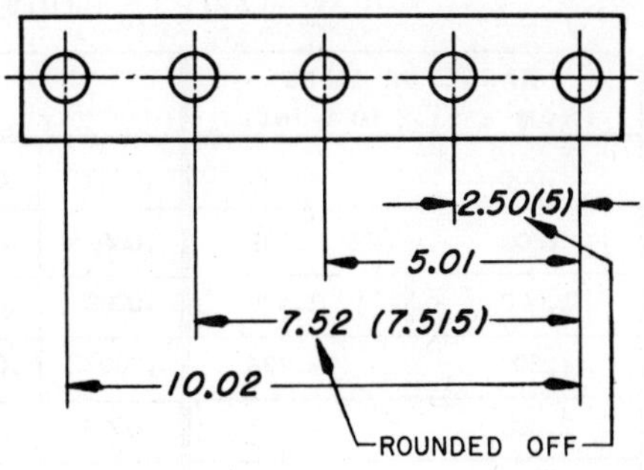

Figure 7-8

7.2 Dimensioning features

Figs. 7-10 and 7-11 are intended as a review of principal dimensioning features which were discussed in Section 6. They are included here to better orientate the student of drafting with the decimal system of dimensioning. A study of Fig. 7-12 will disclose how these various dimensioning elements are incorporated in a complete drawing.

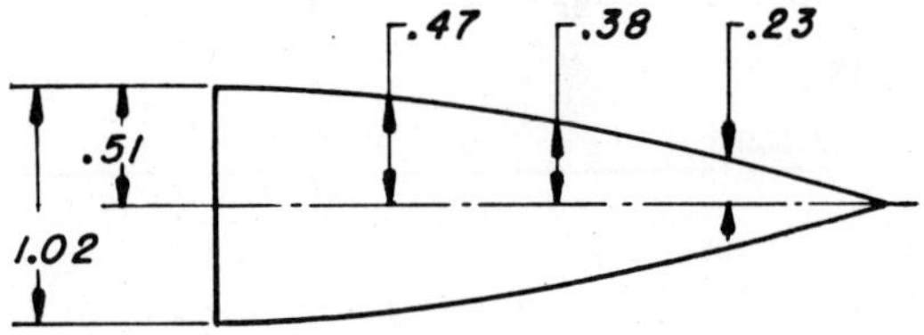

Figure 7-9

7.3 Limits and tolerances

As defined in Section 6, a tolerance is the amount of variation permitted in size and location, and a limit is the extreme permissible dimension resulting from the application of a tolerance. For example, suppose a size is shown as 3.25″. Variation from this size may be specified as being a plus .002″ and a minus .003″. Then the extreme permissible dimension could not exceed 3.25″ plus .002″ or 3.252″, or be less than 3.25″ minus .003″ or 3.247″.

There are no specific rules or formulas for establishing limits and tolerances for all phases of engineering; the draftsman must rely on good judgment, experience and knowledge of tolerances. The data in Table I is frequently used as a guide in selecting tolerances. The design and method of manufacture must determine the degree of accuracy which is expected to meet the functional requirements of each detail part.

The greater the permissible limits or tolerances, the less costly the part is to produce because of reduced amount of scrapped parts, lower labor costs and less expensive tools. Limits or tolerances should never be specified closer than necessary, either by definite specifications or by the inference of any of the general notes. In certain cases, it may be advisable to use closer tolerances to facilitate assembly. The necessity for this should be determined by ascertaining where the greatest saving lies—by close tolerances and shorter assembly time or by greater tolerances and longer assembly time.[2]

(Text continued on page 144)

2. *Chrysler Drafting and Design Standards* (Detroit: Chrysler Corp.).

TABLE I. GUIDE FOR SELECTING TOLERANCES

RANGE OF SIZES FROM	TO & INCL	TOLERANCES (TOTAL)								
.000	.599	.00015	.0002	.0003	.0005	.0008	.0012	.002	.003	.005
.600	.999	.00015	.00025	.0004	.0006	.001	.0015	.0025	.004	.007
1.000	1.499	.0002	.0003	.0005	.0008	.0012	.002	.003	.005	.008
1.500	2.799	.00025	.0004	.0006	.001	.0015	.0025	.004	.006	.010
2.800	4.499	.0003	.0005	.0008	.0012	.002	.003	.005	.008	.012
4.500	7.799	.0004	.0006	.001	.0015	.0025	.004	.006	.010	.015
7.800	13.599	.0005	.0008	.0012	.002	.003	.005	.008	.012	.019
13.600	20.999	.0006	.001	.0015	.0025	.004	.006	.010	.015	.025

TOLERANCE RANGE OF MACHINING PROCESSES

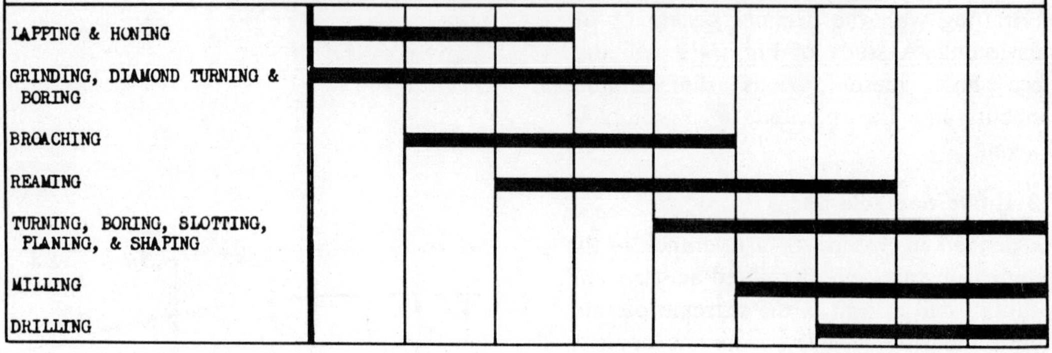

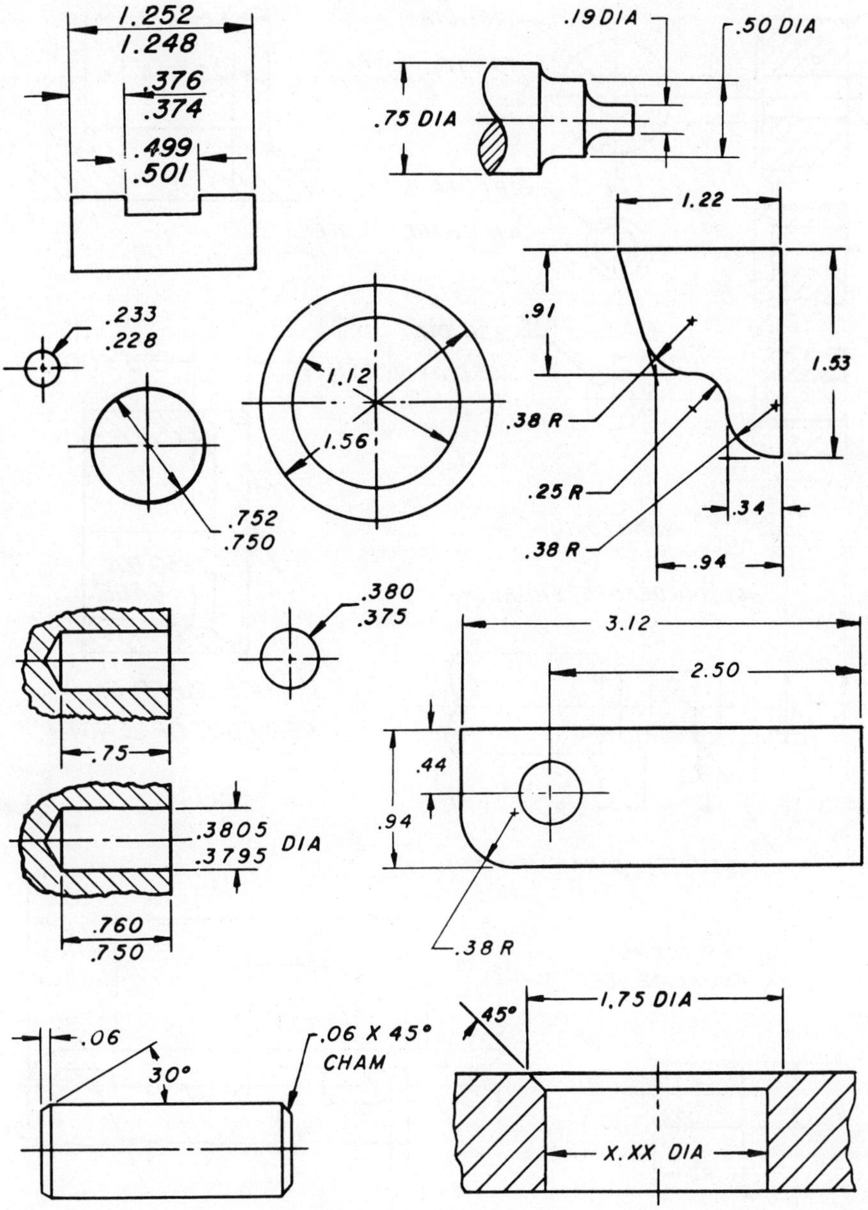

Figure 7-10
Examples of dimensioning principles with decimals.

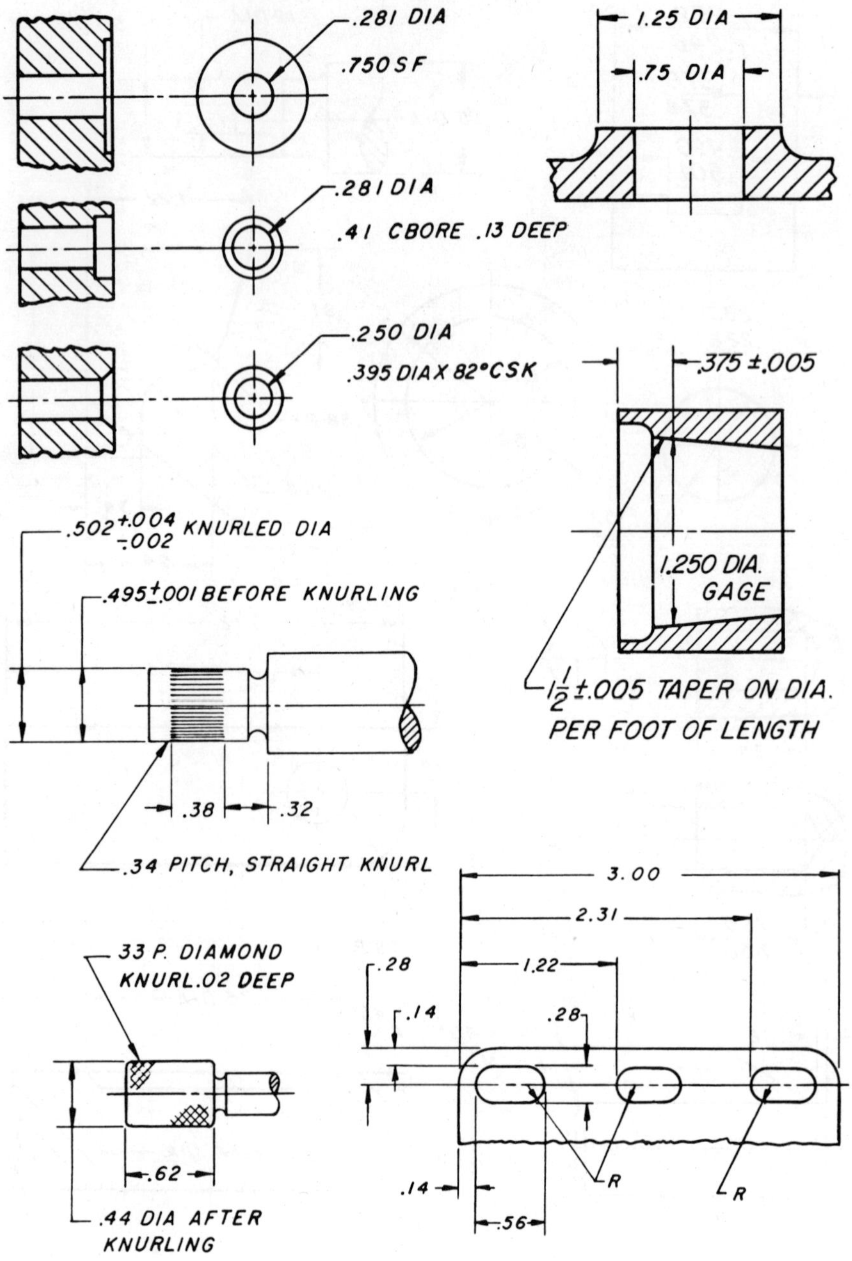

Figure 7-11
Examples of dimensioning principles with decimals.

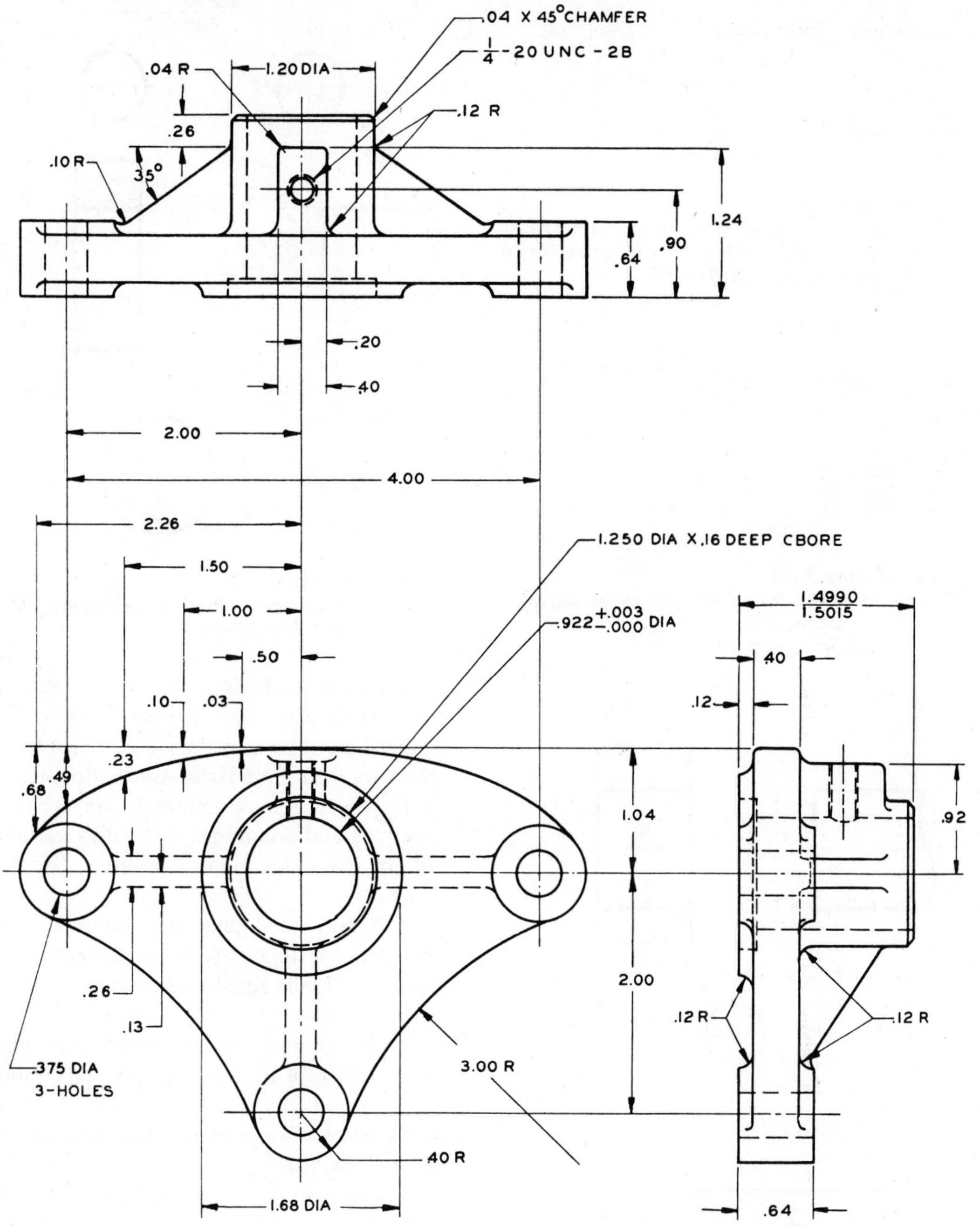

Figure 7-12
A typical drawing in which the decimal system of dimensioning is used.
Chrysler Corp.

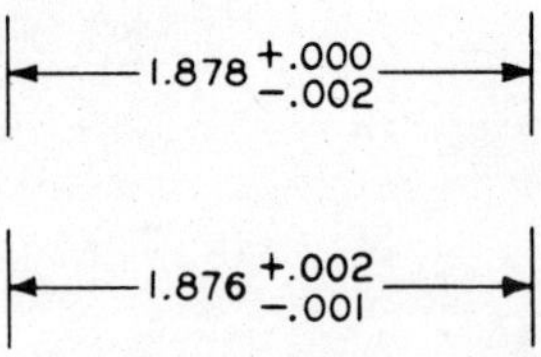

Figure 7-13
Tolerances should be as coarse as possible but still permit satisfactory functioning of the part. ASA Y14.5-1957

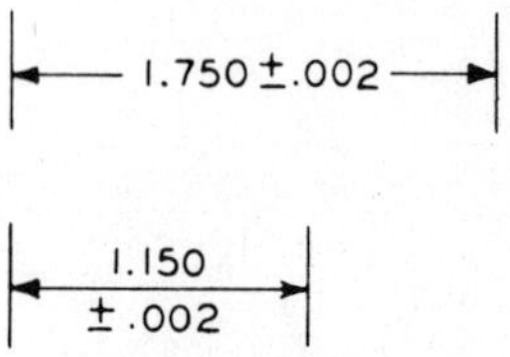

Figure 7-14
These are accepted methods of showing tolerances on a drawing.
ASA Y14.5-1957

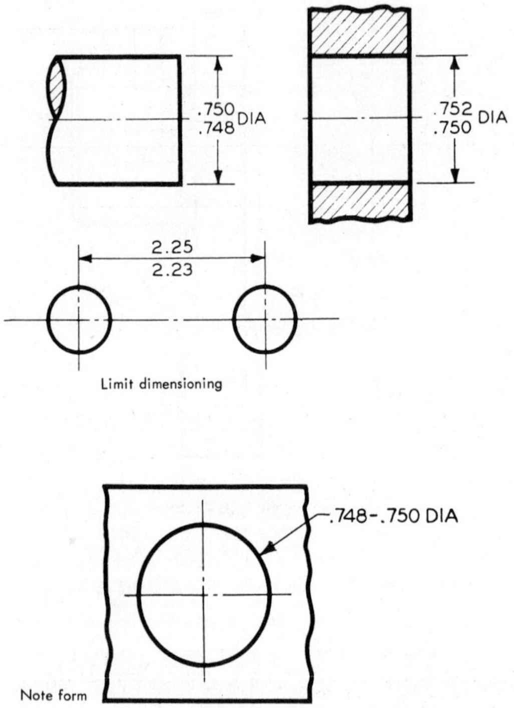

Figure 7-15
One method of specifying limits.
ASA Y14.5-1957

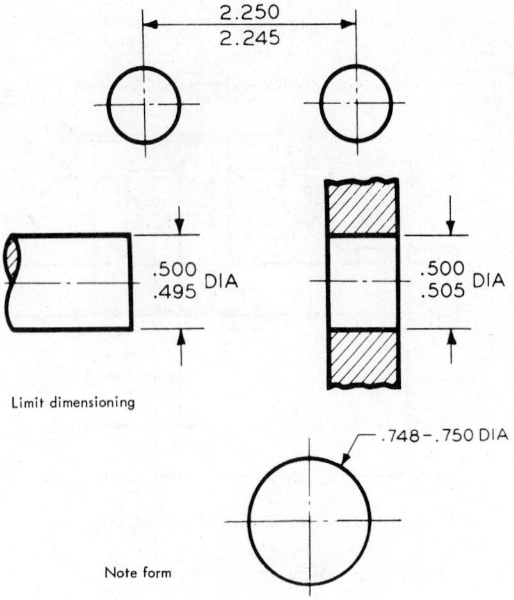

Figure 7-16
A second method of specifying limits.
ASA Y14.5-1957

Different methods are used to indicate the amount of variation allowed for any given dimension. The practices recommended by the American Standards Association are:[3]

1 Two tolerance numerals are specified, one plus and one minus if the plus variation differs from the minus variation. See Fig. 7-13.

2 A combined plus and minus size followed by a single tolerance numeral if the plus variation is equal to the minus variation. See Fig. 7-14.

In designating the maximum and minimum limits of a size, the numerals should be arranged in one of two ways (both arrangements should never be used on the same drawing):

1 The high limit is placed above the low limit where dimensions are given directly. The low limit precedes the high limit where dimensions are given in note form. See Fig. 7-15.

2 For location dimensions given directly, the high limit is placed above, the low limit below. For size dimensions given directly, the

3. Extracted from *American Drafting Standards Manual, ASA Y14.5 — 1957* (New York: The American Society of Mechanical Engineers, 1957).

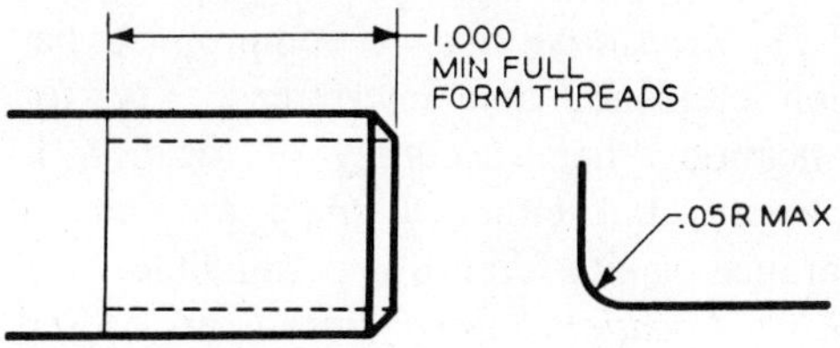

Figure 7-17
The abbreviation MIN or MAX is sometimes used when only one limit is important. ASA Y14.5-1957

limit representing the maximum material condition is placed above, the minimum material condition limit below. Where limits are given in note form, the numeral that otherwise would be above shall precede the other. See Fig. 7-16.

The abbreviation *MIN* or *MAX* is sometimes placed after a numeral when only one limit is important. This technique is often used when dimensioning depths of holes, length of threads, chamfers, etc. See Fig. 7-17.

7.4 Unilateral and bilateral tolerance system[4]

A *unilateral* system of tolerances allows variations in only one direction from a design size. This way of stating a tolerance is often helpful where a critical size is approached as material is removed during manufacture. See Fig. 7-18A. For example, close-fitting holes and shafts are often given unilateral tolerances.

A *bilateral* system of tolerances allows variations in both directions from a design size. Bilateral variations are generally given with locating dimensions, or with any dimension that can be allowed to vary in either direction. See Fig. 7-18B.

7.5 Standard fits[5]

To insure precision interchangeability of parts, certain types of fits have been established. The type of fit used is governed by the service required from the equipment being designed. The common accepted standard fits are:

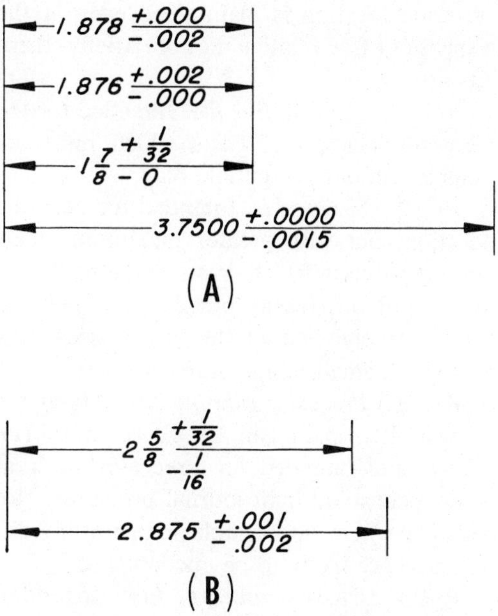

Figure 7-18
Unilateral and bilateral tolerance system.

RC	Running and Sliding Fit
LC	Locational Clearance Fit
LT	Transition Locational Fit
LN	Locational Interference Fit
FN	Force and Shrink Fit

These letter symbols are used in conjunction with numbers representing the class of fit; thus *"FN4"* represents a class 4 force fit. Each of the symbols (two letters and a number) represent a complete fit. Generally these symbols are not shown on manufacturing drawings; instead sizes are specified.

7.6 Description of fits[6]

Running and sliding fits. Running and sliding fits are intended to provide a similar running performance, with suitable lubrication allowance throughout the range of sizes. The clearances for the first two classes, used chiefly as slide fits, increase more slowly with diameter than the other classes, so that

4. *Ibid.*

5. Extracted from *Preferred Limits and Fits for Cylindrical Parts, ASA B4.1—1955* (New York: The American Society of Mechanical Engineers, 1955).

6. *Ibid.*

accurate location is maintained even at the expense of free relative motion. Briefly, these fits are:

RC 1 *Close sliding fits*. Intended for the accurate location of parts which must assemble without perceptible play.

RC 2 *Sliding fits*. Intended for accurate location, but with greater maximum clearance than class RC 1. Parts made to this fit move and turn easily but are not intended to run freely, and in the larger sizes may seize with small temperature changes.

RC 3 *Precision running fits*. About the closest fits which can be expected to run freely, and intended for precision work at slow speeds and light journal pressures. Not suitable where appreciable temperature differences are likely to be encountered.

RC 4 *Close running fits*. Intended chiefly for running fits on accurate machinery with moderate surface speeds and journal pressures, where accurate location and minimum play is desired.

RC 5/*RC* 6 *Medium running fits*. Intended for higher running speeds or heavy journal pressure, or both.

RC 7 *Free running fits*. Intended for use where accuracy is not essential, or where large temperature variations are likely to be encountered, or under both these conditions.

RC 8/*RC* 9 *Loose running fits*. Intended for use where materials such as cold-rolled shafting and tubing, made to commercial tolerances are involved.

Locational fits. Locational fits are fits intended to determine only the location of the mating parts; they may provide rigid or accurate location, as with interference fits, or provide some freedom of location, as with clearance fits. Accordingly they are divided into three groups: *clearance fits, transition fits*, and *interference fits*. These fits are:

LC *Locational clearance fits*. Intended for parts which are normally stationary, but which can be freely assembled or disassembled. They run from snug fits for parts such as spigots, to the looser fastener fits where freedom of assembly is of prime importance.

LT *Transition fits*. A compromise between clearance and interference fits, for application where accuracy of location is important, but either a small amount of clearance or interference is permissible.

LN *Locational interference fits*. Used where accuracy of location is of prime importance, and for parts requiring rigidity and alignment with no special requirements for bore pressure. Such fits are not intended for parts designed to transmit frictional loads from one part to another by virtue of the tightness of fit, as these conditions are covered by force fits.

Force fits. Force or shrink fits constitute a special type of interference fit, normally characterized by maintenance of constant bore pressures throughout the range of sizes. The interference therefore varies almost directly with diameter, and the difference between its minimum and maximum value is small, maintaining the resulting pressures within reasonable limits. Briefly, these fits are:

FN 1 *Light drive fits*. Require light assembly pressures and produce more or less permanent assemblies. They are suitable for thin sections or long fits, or in cast iron external members.

FN 2 *Medium drive fits*. Suitable for ordinary steel parts, or for shrink fits on light sections. They are about the tightest fits that can be used with high-grade cast-iron external members.

FN 3 *Heavy drive fits*. Suitable for heavier steel parts or for shrink fits in medium sections.

FN 4/*FN* 5 *Force fits*. Suitable for parts which can be highly stressed, or for shrink fits where the heavy pressing forces required are impractical.

7.7 Dimensioning for fits[7]

For interchangeable manufacture, the tolerances on dimensions must be such that an acceptable fit will result from assembly of

7. Extracted from *American Drafting Standards Manual, ASA Y14.5 — 1957* (New York: The American Society of Mechanical Engineers, 1957).

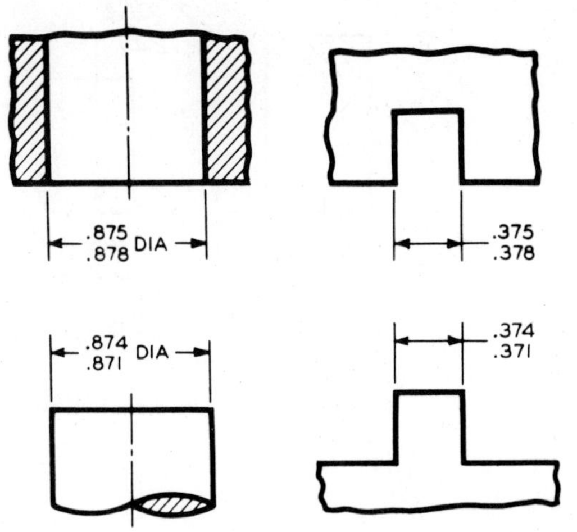

Figure 7-19
Indicating dimensions of surfaces that are to fit closely. ASA Y14.5-1957

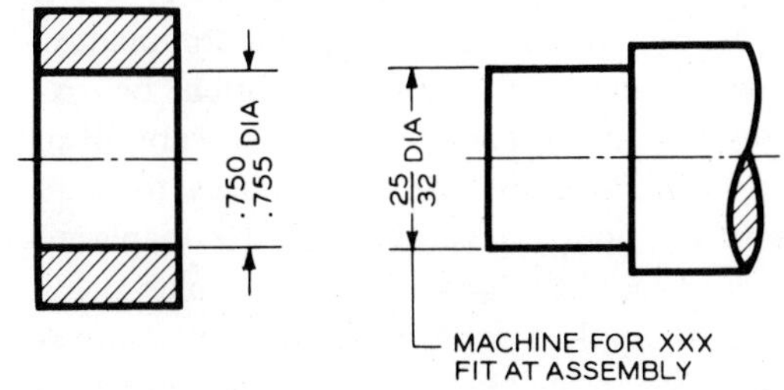

Figure 7-20
Dimensioning non-interchangeable parts that are to fit closely.
ASA Y14.5-1957

parts having any combination of actual sizes that are within the tolerances. See Fig. 7-19. The method of dimensioning mating parts that must fit one another when they do not need to be interchangeable is shown in Fig. 7-20. The size of one part need not be held to a close tolerance, because it is to be modified at assembly to the size that is necessary for the desired fit.

To specify the dimensions and tolerances of an internal and external cylindrical surface so that they will fit together as desired, it is necessary to begin calculations by assuming either the minimum hole size or the maximum shaft size. This procedure is based on what is known as the *basic hole system* or *basic shaft system.*

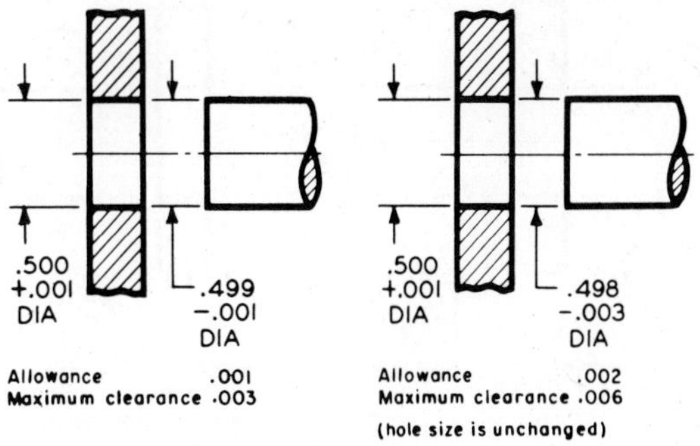

Figure 7-21
Basic hole fits. ASA Y14.5-1957

Basic hole system. A basic hole system is a system of fits in which the design size of the hole is the basic size and the allowance is applied to the shaft. Limits for a fit in the basic hole system are determined by (1) specifying the minimum hole size, (2) determining the maximum shaft size by subtracting the desired allowance (minimum clearance) from the minimum hole size for a clearance fit, or adding the desired allowance (maximum interference) for an interference fit, and (3) adjusting the hole and shaft tolerance to obtain the desired maximum clearance or minimum interference. See Fig. 7-21. Tooling economies can often be realized by calculating from the basic hole size, providing the size selected can be produced by a standard tool (reamer, broach, etc.) or gaged with a standard plug gage.

Basic shaft system. A basic shaft system is a system of fits in which the design size of the shaft is the basic size and the allowance is applied to the hole. Limits for a fit in the basic shaft system are determined by (1) specifying the maximum shaft size, (2) determining the minimum hole size by adding the desired allowance (minimum clearance) to the maximum shaft size for a clearance fit, or subtracting for an interference fit, and (3) adjusting hole and shaft tolerances to obtain the desired maximum clearance or minimum interference. See Fig. 7-22. The basic shaft method is recommended only if there is a particular reason for it; for example, where a standard size of shafting can be used.

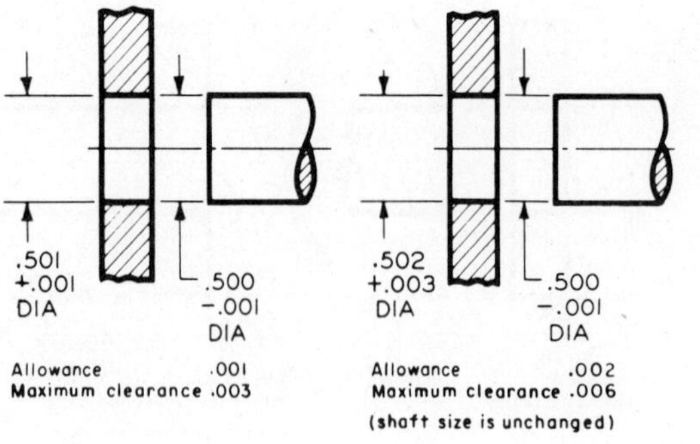

Figure 7-22
Basic shaft fit.
ASA Y14.5-1957

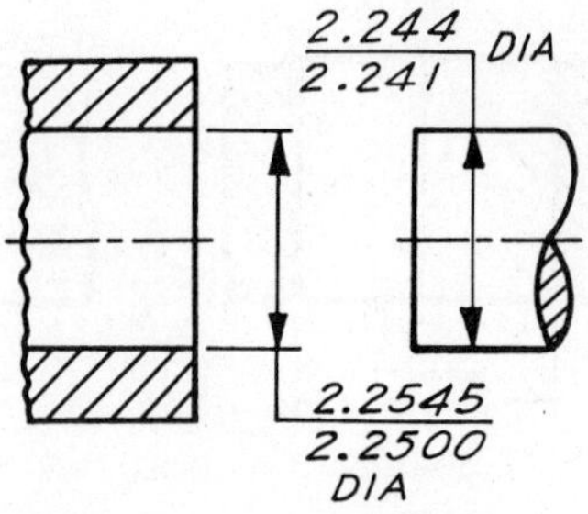

Figure 7-23
Computing hole and shaft size.

7.8 Selecting the correct fit

Assume that a component must be designed wherein a 2-1/4 in. diameter shaft having a class *RC*8 fit is to slide in a hole with a nominal diameter of 2-1/4 inches. (See Fig. 7-23.) Since most limit dimensions are computed on the basic hole system, the limits for the example above can be determined by converting the nominal size to the basic hole size and adding to or subtracting from the basic size the standard limits specified for hole and shaft sizes. For the illustration shown in Fig. 7-23 the procedure would be:

1 Locate the nominal size range of the hole and shaft in Table II, which is 1.97-3.15.

2 Under the column class *RC*8, the limit range for the hole size runs from .000″ to plus .0045″, and for the shaft a minus .006″ to a minus .009″.

3 Since the nominal hole and shaft size is 2–1/4 inches, the hole may therefore range from 2.250″ to 2.2545″ and the shaft from 2.244″ to 2.241″, and is expressed in inches as:

$$\text{Limits on hole: } \frac{2.250 \text{ plus } .0045 = 2.2545}{2.250 \text{ plus } .000 \quad = 2.2500}$$

$$\text{Limits on shaft: } \frac{2.250 \text{ minus } .006 = 2.244}{2.250 \text{ minus } .009 = 2.241}$$

Table III shows *clearance locational fits*. Table IV shows *transition locational fits*, Table V shows *interference locational fits*, and Table VI shows *force and shrink fits*.

7.9 Positional tolerances[8]

In the past, the coordinates used to locate holes or other features have been shown with individual tolerances predominantly. The engineering intent can often be expressed more precisely if locations are given as *True Positions*, with tolerances to state how far actual positions can be displaced from True Positions. Positional tolerancing may be applied for the location of features by stating in the note the allowable tolerance.

Features such as holes and bosses may be allowed to vary from the specified position in any direction from the true position axis while other features such as slots may be allowed to vary from the specified position on either side of the true position plane. Therefore, there are two methods for applying positional tolerancing (see Fig. 7-24):

1 Where features are located by dimensions to their axes and where the location may be allowed to vary in any direction, the zone of tolerance, which in this case is a cylinder, shall be specified by giving either the diameter of the circle or its radius, with either of these typical forms:

6 HOLES LOCATED AT TRUE POSITION WITHIN .010 DIA

or

6 HOLES LOCATED WITHIN .005 R OF TRUE POSITION

8. *Ibid.*

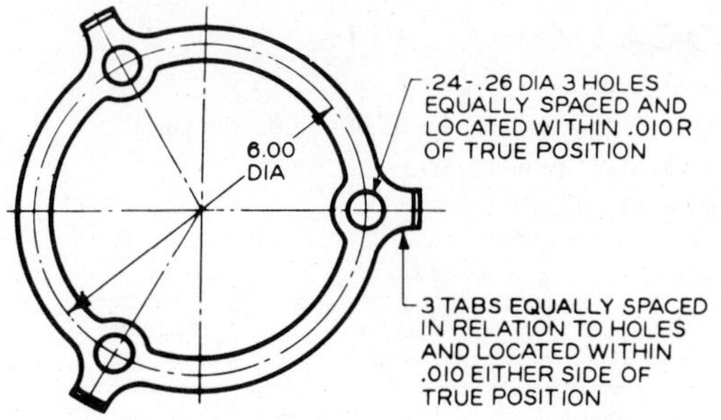

Figure 7-24
True position dimensioning. ASA Y14.5-1957

TABLE II RUNNING AND SLIDING FITS

Limits are in thousandths of an inch.

Limits for hole and shaft are applied algebraically to the basic size to obtain the limits of size for the parts.

Data in bold face are in accordance with ABC agreements.

Symbols H5, g5, etc., are Hole and Shaft designations used in ABC System.

Nominal Size Range Inches	Class RC 1			Class RC 2			Class RC 3			Class RC 4		
	Limits of Clearance	Standard Limits		Limits of Clearance	Standard Limits		Limits of Clearance	Standard Limits		Limits of Clearance	Standard Limits	
Over To		Hole H5	Shaft g4		Hole H6	Shaft g5		Hole H6	Shaft f6		Hole H7	Shaft f7
0.04– 0.12	0.1 0.45	+0.2 0	− 0.1 − 0.25	0.1 0.55	+ 0.25 0	− 0.1 − 0.3	0.3 0.8	+ 0.25 0	− 0.3 − 0.55	0.3 1.1	+ 0.4 0	− 0.3 − 0.7
0.12– 0.24	0.15 0.5	+0.2 0	− 0.15 − 0.3	0.15 0.65	+ 0.3 0	− 0.15 − 0.35	0.4 1.0	+ 0.3 0	− 0.4 − 0.7	0.4 1.4	+ 0.5 0	− 0.4 − 0.9
0.24– 0.40	0.2 0.6	+0.25 0	− 0.2 − 0.35	0.2 0.85	+ 0.4 0	− 0.2 − 0.45	0.5 1.3	+ 0.4 0	− 0.5 − 0.9	0.5 1.7	+ 0.6 0	− 0.5 − 1.1
0.40– 0.71	0.25 0.75	+0.3 0	− 0.25 − 0.45	0.25 0.95	+ 0.4 0	− 0.25 − 0.55	0.6 1.4	+ 0.4 0	− 0.6 − 1.0	0.6 2.0	+ 0.7 0	− 0.6 − 1.3
0.71– 1.19	0.3 0.95	+0.4 0	− 0.3 − 0.55	0.3 1.2	+ 0.5 0	− 0.3 − 0.7	0.8 1.8	+ 0.5 0	− 0.8 − 1.3	0.8 2.4	+ 0.8 0	− 0.8 − 1.6
1.19– 1.97	0.4 1.1	+0.4 0	− 0.4 − 0.7	0.4 1.4	+ 0.6 0	− 0.4 − 0.8	1.0 2.2	+ 0.6 0	− 1.0 − 1.6	1.0 3.0	+ 1.0 0	− 1.0 − 2.0
1.97– 3.15	0.4 1.2	+0.5 0	− 0.4 − 0.7	0.4 1.6	+ 0.7 0	− 0.4 − 0.9	1.2 2.6	+ 0.7 0	− 1.2 − 1.9	1.2 3.6	+ 1.2 0	− 1.2 − 2.4
3.15– 4.73	0.5 1.5	+0.6 0	− 0.5 − 0.9	0.5 2.0	+ 0.9 0	− 0.5 − 1.1	1.4 3.2	+ 0.9 0	− 1.4 − 2.3	1.4 4.2	+ 1.4 0	− 1.4 − 2.8
4.73– 7.09	0.6 1.8	+0.7 0	− 0.6 − 1.1	0.6 2.3	+ 1.0 0	− 0.6 − 1.3	1.6 3.6	+ 1.0 0	− 1.6 − 2.6	1.6 4.8	+ 1.6 0	− 1.6 − 3.2

Nominal Size Range Inches	Class RC 5			Class RC 6			Class RC 7			Class RC 8			Class RC 9		
	Limits of Clearance	Standard Limits		Limits of Clearance	Standard Limits		Limits of Clearance	Standard Limits		Limits of Clearance	Standard Limits		Limits of Clearance	Standard Limits	
Over To		Hole H7	Shaft e7		Hole H8	Shaft e8		Hole H9	Shaft d8		Hole H10	Shaft c9		Hole H11	Shaft
0.04– 0.12	0.6 1.4	+ 0.4 0	− 0.6 − 1.0	0.6 1.8	+ 0.6 0	− 0.6 − 1.2	1.0 2.6	+ 1.0 0	− 1.0 − 1.6	2.5 5.1	+ 1.6 0	− 2.5 − 3.5	4.0 8.1	+ 2.5 0	− 4.0 − 5.6
0.12– 0.24	0.8 1.8	+ 0.5 0	− 0.8 − 1.3	0.8 2.2	+ 0.7 0	− 0.8 − 1.5	1.2 3.1	+ 1.2 0	− 1.2 − 1.9	2.8 5.8	+ 1.8 0	− 2.8 − 4.0	4.5 9.3	+ 3.0 0	− 4.5 − 6.0
0.24– 0.40	1.0 2.2	+ 0.6 0	− 1.0 − 1.6	1.0 2.8	+ 0.9 0	− 1.0 − 1.9	1.6 3.9	+ 1.4 0	− 1.6 − 2.5	3.0 6.6	+ 2.2 0	− 3.0 − 4.4	5.0 10.7	+ 3.5 0	− 5.0 − 7.2
0.40– 0.71	1.2 2.6	+ 0.7 0	− 1.2 − 1.9	1.2 3.2	+ 1.0 0	− 1.2 − 2.2	2.0 4.6	+ 1.6 0	− 2.0 − 3.0	3.5 7.9	+ 2.8 0	− 3.5 − 5.1	6.0 12.8	+ 4.0 0	− 6.0 − 8.8
0.71– 1.19	1.6 3.2	+ 0.8 0	− 1.6 − 2.4	1.6 4.0	+ 1.2 0	− 1.6 − 2.8	2.5 5.7	+ 2.0 0	− 2.5 − 3.7	4.5 10.0	+ 3.5 0	− 4.5 − 6.5	7.0 15.5	+ 5.0 0	− 7.0 − 10.5
1.19– 1.97	2.0 4.0	+ 1.0 0	− 2.0 − 3.0	2.0 5.2	+ 1.6 0	− 2.0 − 3.6	3.0 7.1	+ 2.5 0	− 3.0 − 4.6	5.0 11.5	+ 4.0 0	− 5.0 − 7.5	8.0 18.0	+ 6.0 0	− 8.0 − 12.0
1.97– 3.15	2.5 4.9	+ 1.2 0	− 2.5 − 3.7	2.5 6.1	+ 1.8 0	− 2.5 − 4.3	4.0 8.8	+ 3.0 0	− 4.0 − 5.8	6.0 13.5	+ 4.5 0	− 6.0 − 9.0	9.0 20.5	+ 7.0 0	− 9.0 − 13.5
3.15– 4.73	3.0 5.8	+ 1.4 0	− 3.0 − 4.4	3.0 7.4	+ 2.2 0	− 3.0 − 5.2	5.0 10.7	+ 3.5 0	− 5.0 − 7.2	7.0 15.5	+ 5.0 0	− 7.0 − 10.5	10.0 24.0	+ 9.0 0	− 10.0 − 15.0
4.73– 7.09	3.5 6.7	+ 1.6 0	− 3.5 − 5.1	3.5 8.5	+ 2.5 0	− 3.5 − 6.0	6.0 12.5	+ 4.0 0	− 6.0 − 8.5	8.0 18.0	+ 6.0 0	− 8.0 − 12.0	12.0 28.0	+ 10.0 0	− 12.0 − 18.0

ASME

TABLE III CLEARANCE LOCATIONAL FITS

Limits are in thousandths of an inch.

Limits for hole and shaft are applied algebraically to the basic size to obtain the limits of size for the parts.

Data in bold face are in accordance with ABC agreements.

Symbols H6, h5, etc., are Hole and Shaft designations used in ABC System.

Nominal Size Range Inches		Class LC 1			Class LC 2			Class LC 3			Class LC 4			Class LC 5		
		Limits of Clearance	Standard Limits		Limits of Clearance	Standard Limits		Limits of Clearance	Standard Limits		Limits of Clearance	Standard Limits		Limits of Clearance	Standard Limits	
Over	To		Hole H6	Shaft h5		Hole H7	Shaft h6		Hole H8	Shaft h7		Hole H9	Shaft h9		Hole H7	Shaft g6
0.04–	0.12	0 0.45	+ 0.25 − 0	+ 0 −0.2	0 0.65	+ 0.4 − 0	+ 0 − 0.25	0 1	+ 0.6 − 0	+ 0 − 0.4	0 2.0	+ 1.0 − 0	+ 0 − 1.0	0.1 0.75	+ 0.4 − 0	− 0.1 − 0.35
0.12–	0.24	0 0.5	+ 0.3 − 0	+ 0 −0.2	0 0.8	+ 0.5 − 0	+ 0 − 0.3	0 1.2	+ 0.7 − 0	+ 0 − 0.5	0 2.4	+ 1.2 − 0	+ 0 − 1.2	0.15 0.95	+ 0.5 − 0	− 0.15 − 0.45
0.24–	0.40	0 0.65	+ 0.4 − 0	+ 0 −0.25	0 1.0	+ 0.6 − 0	+ 0 − 0.4	0 1.5	+ 0.9 − 0	+ 0 − 0.6	0 2.8	+ 1.4 − 0	+ 0 − 1.4	0.2 1.2	+ 0.6 − 0	− 0.2 − 0.6
0.40–	0.71	0 0.7	+ 0.4 − 0	+ 0 −0.3	0 1.1	+ 0.7 − 0	+ 0 − 0.4	0 1.7	+ 1.0 − 0	+ 0 − 0.7	0 3.2	+ 1.6 − 0	+ 0 − 1.6	0.25 1.35	+ 0.7 − 0	− 0.25 − 0.65
0.71–	1.19	0 0.9	+ 0.5 − 0	+ 0 −0.4	0 1.3	+ 0.8 − 0	+ 0 − 0.5	0 2	+ 1.2 − 0	+ 0 − 0.8	0 4	+ 2.0 − 0	+ 0 − 2.0	0.3 1.6	+ 0.8 − 0	− 0.3 − 0.8
1.19–	1.97	0 1.0	+ 0.6 − 0	+ 0 −0.4	0 1.6	+ 1.0 − 0	+ 0 − 0.6	0 2.6	+ 1.6 − 0	+ 0 − 1	0 5	+ 2.5 − 0	+ 0 − 2.5	0.4 2.0	+ 1.0 − 0	− 0.4 − 1.0
1.97–	3.15	0 1.2	+ 0.7 − 0	+ 0 −0.5	0 1.9	+ 1.2 − 0	+ 0 − 0.7	0 3	+ 1.8 − 0	+ 0 − 1.2	0 6	+ 3 − 0	+ 0 − 3	0.4 2.3	+ 1.2 − 0	− 0.4 − 1.1
3.15–	4.73	0 1.5	+ 0.9 − 0	+ 0 −0.6	0 2.3	+ 1.4 − 0	+ 0 − 0.9	0 3.6	+ 2.2 − 0	+ 0 − 1.4	0 7	+ 3.5 − 0	+ 0 − 3.5	0.5 2.8	+ 1.4 − 0	− 0.5 − 1.4
4.73–	7.09	0 1.7	+ 1.0 − 0	+ 0 −0.7	0 2.6	+ 1.6 − 0	+ 0 − 1.0	0 4.1	+ 2.5 − 0	+ 0 − 1.6	0 8	+ 4 − 0	+ 0 − 4	0.6 3.2	+ 1.6 − 0	− 0.6 − 1.6

Nominal Size Range Inches		Class LC 6			Class LC 7			Class LC 8			Class LC 9			Class LC 10			Class LC 11		
		Limits of Clearance	Standard Limits		Limits of Clearance	Standard Limits		Limits of Clearance	Standard Limits		Limits of Clearance	Standard Limits		Limits of Clearance	Standard Limits		Limits of Clearance	Standard Limits	
Over	To		Hole H8	Shaft f8		Hole H9	Shaft e9		Hole H10	Shaft d9		Hole H11	Shaft c11		Hole H12	Shaft		Hole H13	Shaft
0.04–	0.12	0.3 1.5	+ 0.6 − 0	− 0.3 − 0.9	0.6 2.6	+1.0 − 0	−0.6 −1.6	1.0 3.6	+1.6 − 0	− 1.0 − 2.0	2.5 7.5	+2.5 − 0	−2.5 −5.0	4 12	+ 4 − 0	− 4 − 8	5 17	+ 6 − 0	− 5 − 11
0.12–	0.24	0.4 1.8	+ 0.7 − 0	− 0.4 − 1.1	0.8 3.2	+1.2 − 0	−0.8 −2.0	1.2 4.2	+1.8 − 0	− 1.2 − 2.4	2.8 8.8	+3.0 − 0	−2.8 −5.8	4.5 14.5	+ 5 − 0	−4.5 −9.5	6 20	+ 7 − 0	− 6 − 13
0.24–	0.40	0.5 2.3	+ 0.9 − 0	− 0.5 − 1.4	1.0 3.8	+1.4 − 0	−1.0 −2.4	1.6 5.2	+2.2 − 0	− 1.6 − 3.0	3.0 10.0	+3.5 − 0	−3.0 −6.5	5 17	+ 6 − 0	− 5 − 11	7 25	+ 9 − 0	− 7 − 16
0.40–	0.71	0.6 2.6	+ 1.0 − 0	− 0.6 − 1.6	1.2 4.4	+1.6 − 0	−1.2 −2.8	2.0 6.4	+2.8 − 0	− 2.0 − 3.6	3.5 11.5	+4.0 − 0	−3.5 −7.5	6 20	+ 7 − 0	− 6 − 13	8 28	+ 10 − 0	− 8 − 18
0.71–	1.19	0.8 3.2	+ 1.2 − 0	− 0.8 − 2.0	1.6 5.6	+2.0 − 0	−1.6 −3.6	2.5 8.0	+3.5 − 0	− 2.5 − 4.5	4.5 14.5	+5.0 − 0	−4.5 −9.5	7 23	+ 8 − 0	− 7 − 15	10 34	+ 12 − 0	− 10 − 22
1.19–	1.97	1.0 4.2	+ 1.6 − 0	− 1.0 − 2.6	2.0 7.0	+2.5 − 0	−2.0 −4.5	3.0 9.5	+4.0 − 0	− 3.0 − 5.5	5 17	+6 − 0	− 5 − 11	8 28	+ 10 − 0	− 8 − 18	12 44	+ 16 − 0	− 12 − 28
1.97–	3.15	1.2 4.8	+ 1.8 − 0	− 1.2 − 3.0	2.5 8.5	+3.0 − 0	−2.5 −5.5	4.0 11.5	+4.5 − 0	− 4.0 − 7.0	6 20	+7 − 0	− 6 − 13	10 34	+ 12 − 0	− 10 − 22	14 50	+ 18 − 0	− 14 − 32
3.15–	4.73	1.4 5.8	+ 2.2 − 0	− 1.4 − 3.6	3.0 10.0	+3.5 − 0	−3.0 −6.5	5.0 13.5	+5.0 − 0	− 5.0 − 8.5	7 25	+9 − 0	− 7 − 16	11 39	+ 14 − 0	− 11 − 25	16 60	+ 22 − 0	− 16 − 38
4.73–	7.09	1.6 6.6	+ 2.5 − 0	− 1.6 − 4.1	3.5 11.5	+4.0 − 0	−3.5 −7.5	6 16	+6 − 0	− 6 −10	8 28	+10 − 0	− 8 − 18	12 44	+ 16 − 0	− 12 − 28	18 68	+ 25 − 0	− 18 − 43

ASME

TABLE IV TRANSITION LOCATIONAL FITS

Limits are in thousandths of an inch.

Limits for hole and shaft are applied algebraically to the basic size to obtain the limits of size for the mating parts.

Data in bold face are in accordance with ABC agreements.

"Fit" represents the maximum interference (minus values) and the maximum clearance (plus values).

Symbols H8, j6, etc., are Hole and Shaft designations used in ABC System.

Nominal Size Range Inches	Class LT 1			Class LT 2			Class LT 3			Class LT 4			Class LT 6			Class LT 7		
	Fit	Standard Limits		Fit	Standard Limits		Fit	Standard Limits		Fit	Standard Limits		Fit	Standard Limits		Fit	Standard Limits	
Over To		Hole H7	Shaft j6		Hole H8	Shaft j7		Hole H7	Shaft k6		Hole H8	Shaft k7		Hole H8	Shaft m7		Hole H7	Shaft n6
0.04– 0.12	−0.15 +0.5	+0.4 − 0	+0.15 −0.1	−0.3 +0.7	+0.6 − 0	+0.3 −0.1							−0.55 +0.45	+0.6 − 0	+0.55 +0.15	−0.5 +0.15	+0.4 − 0	+0.5 +0.25
0.12– 0.24	−0.2 +0.6	+0.5 − 0	+0.2 −0.1	−0.4 +0.8	+0.7 − 0	+0.4 −0.1							−0.7 +0.5	+0.7 − 0	+0.7 +0.2	−0.6 +0.2	+0.5 − 0	+0.6 +0.3
0.24– 0.40	−0.3 +0.7	+0.6 − 0	+0.3 −0.1	−0.4 +1.1	+0.9 − 0	+0.4 −0.2	−0.5 +0.5	+0.6 − 0	+0.5 +0.1	−0.7 +0.8	+0.9 − 0	+0.7 +0.1	−0.8 +0.7	+0.9 − 0	+0.8 +0.2	−0.8 +0.2	+0.6 − 0	+0.8 +0.4
0.40– 0.71	−0.3 +0.8	+0.7 − 0	+0.3 −0.1	−0.5 +1.2	+1.0 − 0	+0.5 −0.2	−0.5 +0.6	+0.7 − 0	+0.5 +0.1	−0.8 +0.9	+1.0 − 0	+0.8 +0.1	−1.0 +0.7	+1.0 − 0	+1.0 +0.3	−0.9 +0.2	+0.7 − 0	+0.9 +0.5
0.71– 1.19	−0.3 +1.0	+0.8 − 0	+0.3 −0.2	−0.5 +1.5	+1.2 − 0	+0.5 −0.3	−0.6 +0.7	+0.8 − 0	+0.6 +0.1	−0.9 +1.1	+1.2 − 0	+0.9 +0.1	−1.1 +0.9	+1.2 − 0	+1.1 +0.3	−1.1 +0.2	+0.8 − 0	+1.1 +0.6
1.19– 1.97	−0.4 +1.2	+1.0 − 0	+0.4 −0.2	−0.6 +2.0	+1.6 − 0	+0.6 −0.4	−0.7 +0.9	+1.0 − 0	+0.7 +0.1	−1.1 +1.5	+1.6 − 0	+1.1 +0.1	−1.4 +1.2	+1.6 − 0	+1.4 +0.4	−1.3 +0.3	+1.0 − 0	+1.3 +0.7
1.97– 3.15	−0.4 +1.5	+1.2 − 0	+0.4 −0.3	−0.7 +2.3	+1.8 − 0	+0.7 −0.5	−0.8 +1.1	+1.2 − 0	+0.8 +0.1	−1.3 +1.7	+1.8 − 0	+1.3 +0.1	−1.7 +1.3	+1.8 − 0	+1.7 +0.5	−1.5 +0.4	+1.2 − 0	+1.5 +0.8
3.15– 4.73	−0.5 +1.8	+1.4 − 0	+0.5 −0.4	−0.8 +2.8	+2.2 − 0	+0.8 −0.6	−1.0 +1.3	+1.4 − 0	+1.0 +0.1	−1.5 +2.1	+2.2 − 0	+1.5 +0.1	−1.9 +1.7	+2.2 − 0	+1.9 +0.5	−1.9 +0.4	+1.4 − 0	+1.9 +1.0
4.73– 7.09	−0.6 +2.0	+1.6 − 0	+0.6 −0.4	−0.9 +3.2	+2.5 − 0	+0.9 −0.7	−1.1 +1.5	+1.6 − 0	+1.1 +0.1	−1.7 +2.4	+2.5 − 0	+1.7 +0.1	−2.2 +1.9	+2.5 − 0	+2.2 +0.6	−2.2 +0.4	+1.6 − 0	+2.2 +1.2

ASME

TABLE V INTERFERENCE LOCATIONAL FITS

Limits are in thousandths of an inch.

Limits for hole and shaft are applied algebraically to the basic size to obtain the limits of size for the parts.
Data in bold face are in accordance with ABC agreements.

Symbols H7, p6, etc., are Hole and Shaft designations used in ABC System.

Nominal Size Range Inches	Class LN 2			Class LN 3		
	Limits of Interference	Standard Limits		Limits of Interference	Standard Limits	
Over To		Hole H7	Shaft p6		Hole H7	Shaft r6
0.04– 0.12	0 0.65	+ 0.4 − 0	+ 0.65 + 0.4	0.1 0.75	+ 0.4 0	+ 0.75 + 0.5
0.12– 0.24	0 0.8	+ 0.5 − 0	+ 0.8 + 0.5	0.1 0.9	+ 0.5 0	+ 0.9 + 0.6
0.24– 0.40	0 1.0	+ 0.6 − 0	+ 1.0 + 0.6	0.2 1.2	+ 0.6 − 0	+ 1.2 + 0.8
0.40– 0.71	0 1.1	+ 0.7 − 0	+ 1.1 + 0.7	0.3 1.4	+ 0.7 − 0	+ 1.4 + 1.0
0.71– 1.19	0 1.3	+ 0.8 − 0	+ 1.3 + 0.8	0.4 1.7	+ 0.8 − 0	+ 1.7 + 1.2
1.19– 1.97	0 1.6	+ 1.0 − 0	+ 1.6 + 1.0	0.4 2.0	+ 1.0 − 0	+ 2.0 + 1.4
1.97– 3.15	0.2 2.1	+ 1.2 − 0	+ 2.1 + 1.4	0.4 2.3	+ 1.2 − 0	+ 2.3 + 1.6
3.15– 4.73	0.2 2.5	+ 1.4 − 0	+ 2.5 + 1.6	0.6 2.9	+ 1.4 − 0	+ 2.9 + 2.0
4.73– 7.09	0.2 2.8	+ 1.6 − 0	+ 2.8 + 1.8	0.9 3.5	+ 1.6 − 0	+ 3.5 + 2.5

ASME

TABLE VI FORCE AND SHRINK FITS

Limits are in thousandths of an inch.

Limits for hole and shaft are applied algebraically to the basic size to obtain the limits of size for the parts.

Data in bold face are in accordance with ABC agreements.

Symbols H7, s6, etc., are Hole and Shaft designations used in ABC System.

Nominal Size Range Inches		Class FN 1			Class FN 2			Class FN 3			Class FN 4			Class FN 5		
		Limits of Interference	Standard Limits		Limits of Interference	Standard Limits		Limits of Interference	Standard Limits		Limits of Interference	Standard Limits		Limits of Interference	Standard Limits	
Over	To		Hole H6	Shaft		Hole H7	Shaft s6		Hole H7	Shaft t6		Hole H7	Shaft u6		Hole H7	Shaft x7
0.04–	0.12	0.05	+0.25	+ 0.5	0.2	+ 0.4	+ 0.85				0.3	+ 0.4	+ 0.95	0.5	+ 0.4	+ 1.3
		0.5	– 0	+ 0.3	0.85	– 0	+ 0.6				0.95	– 0	+ 0.7	1.3	– 0	+ 0.9
0.12–	0.24	0.1	+0.3	+ 0.6	0.2	+ 0.5	+ 1.0				0.4	+ 0.5	+ 1.2	0.7	+ 0.5	+ 1.7
		0.6	– 0	+ 0.4	1.0	– 0	+ 0.7				1.2	– 0	+ 0.9	1.7	– 0	+ 1.2
0.24–	0.40	0.1	+0.4	+ 0.75	0.4	+ 0.6	+ 1.4				0.6	+ 0.6	+ 1.6	0.8	+ 0.6	+ 2.0
		0.75	– 0	+ 0.5	1.4	– 0	+ 1.0				1.6	– 0	+ 1.2	2.0	– 0	+ 1.4
0.40–	0.56	0.1	+0.4	+ 0.8	0.5	+ 0.7	+ 1.6				0.7	+ 0.7	+ 1.8	0.9	+ 0.7	+ 2.3
		0.8	– 0	+ 0.5	1.6	– 0	+ 1.2				1.8	– 0	+ 1.4	2.3	– 0	+ 1.6
0.56–	0.71	0.2	+0.4	+ 0.9	0.5	+ 0.7	+ 1.6				0.7	+ 0.7	+ 1.8	1.1	+ 0.7	+ 2.5
		0.9	– 0	+ 0.6	1.6	– 0	+ 1.2				1.8	– 0	+ 1.4	2.5	– 0	+ 1.8
0.71–	0.95	0.2	+0.5	+ 1.1	0.6	+ 0.8	+ 1.9				0.8	+ 0.8	+ 2.1	1.4	+ 0.8	+ 3.0
		1.1	– 0	+ 0.7	1.9	– 0	+ 1.4				2.1	– 0	+ 1.6	3.0	– 0	+ 2.2
0.95–	1.19	0.3	+0.5	+ 1.2	0.6	+ 0.8	+ 1.9	0.8	+ 0.8	+ 2.1	1.0	+ 0.8	+ 2.3	1.7	+ 0.8	+ 3.3
		1.2	– 0	+ 0.8	1.9	– 0	+ 1.4	2.1	– 0	+ 1.6	2.3	– 0	+ 1.8	3.3	– 0	+ 2.5
1.19–	1.58	0.3	+0.6	+ 1.3	0.8	+ 1.0	+ 2.4	0.8	+ 1.0	+ 2.6	1.5	+ 1.0	+ 3.1	2.0	+ 1.0	+ 4.0
		1.3	– 0	+ 0.9	2.4	– 0	+ 1.8	2.4	– 0	+ 2.0	3.1	– 0	+ 2.5	4.0	– 0	+ 3.0
1.58–	1.97	0.4	+0.6	+ 1.4	0.8	+ 1.0	+ 2.4	1.2	+ 1.0	+ 2.8	1.8	+ 1.0	+ 3.4	3.0	+ 1.0	+ 5.0
		1.4	– 0	+ 1.0	2.4	– 0	+ 1.8	2.8	– 0	+ 2.2	3.4	– 0	+ 2.8	5.0	– 0	+ 4.0
1.97–	2.56	0.6	+0.7	+ 1.8	0.8	+ 1.2	+ 2.7	1.3	+ 1.2	+ 3.2	2.3	+ 1.2	+ 4.2	3.8	+ 1.2	+ 6.2
		1.8	– 0	+ 1.3	2.7	– 0	+ 2.0	3.2	– 0	+ 2.5	4.2	– 0	+ 3.5	6.2	– 0	+ 5.0
2.56–	3.15	0.7	+0.7	+ 1.9	1.0	+ 1.2	+ 2.9	1.8	+ 1.2	+ 3.7	2.8	+ 1.2	+ 4.7	4.8	+ 1.2	+ 7.2
		1.9	– 0	+ 1.4	2.9	– 0	+ 2.2	3.7	– 0	+ 3.0	4.7	– 0	+ 4.0	7.2	– 0	+ 6.0
3.15–	3.94	0.9	+0.9	+ 2.4	1.4	+ 1.4	+ 3.7	2.1	+ 1.4	+ 4.4	3.6	+ 1.4	+ 5.9	5.6	+ 1.4	+ 8.4
		2.4	– 0	+ 1.8	3.7	– 0	+ 2.8	4.4	– 0	+ 3.5	5.9	– 0	+ 5.0	8.4	– 0	+ 7.0
3.94–	4.73	1.1	+0.9	+ 2.6	1.6	+ 1.4	+ 3.9	2.6	+ 1.4	+ 4.9	4.6	+ 1.4	+ 6.9	6.6	+ 1.4	+ 9.4
		2.6	– 0	+ 2.0	3.9	– 0	+ 3.0	4.9	– 0	+ 4.0	6.9	– 0	+ 6.0	9.4	– 0	+ 8.0
4.73–	5.52	1.2	+1.0	+ 2.9	1.9	+ 1.6	+ 4.5	3.4	+ 1.6	+ 6.0	5.4	+ 1.6	+ 8.0	8.4	+ 1.6	+ 11.6
		2.9	– 0	+ 2.2	4.5	– 0	+ 3.5	6.0	– 0	+ 5.0	8.0	– 0	+ 7.0	11.6	– 0	+ 10.0
5.52–	6.30	1.5	+1.0	+ 3.2	2.4	+ 1.6	+ 5.0	3.4	+ 1.6	+ 6.0	5.4	+ 1.6	+ 8.0	10.4	+ 1.6	+ 13.6
		3.2	– 0	+ 2.5	5.0	– 0	+ 4.0	6.0	– 0	+ 5.0	8.0	– 0	+ 7.0	13.6	– 0	+ 12.0

ASME

2 Where features are located by dimensions to a center plane or to one surface of the feature, positional tolerancing shall be applied by the use of either of these typical forms:

6 SLOTS LOCATED AT TRUE POSITION WITHIN .010 WIDE ZONE

or

6 SLOTS LOCATED WITHIN .005 EITHER SIDE OF TRUE POSITION

7.10 Positional tolerance related to feature size[9]

Since all features have allowable variations of size, it must be clear at what condition of size the true position tolerances apply. Since the least favorable assembly relationship between the mating parts exists when the mating parts are at their maximum material condition, it is usually necessary that the true position tolerance apply only to this maximum material condition.

Maximum material condition of a part is that condition where the part contains the maximum material; e.g., minimum hole size and maximum shaft size. Where the requirements of the maximum material condition (*MMC*) apply, it shall be stated in one of these ways:

1 By the use of a general note.

2 By adding the abbreviation *"MMC"* to each applicable size specification.

9. *Ibid.*

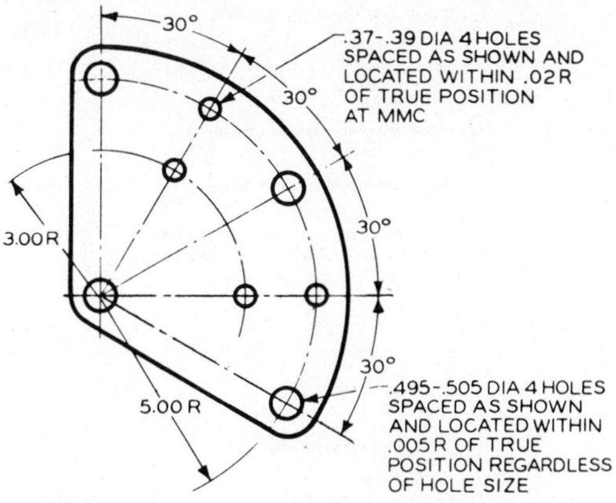

Figure 7-25
True position dimensioning.
ASA Y14.5-1957

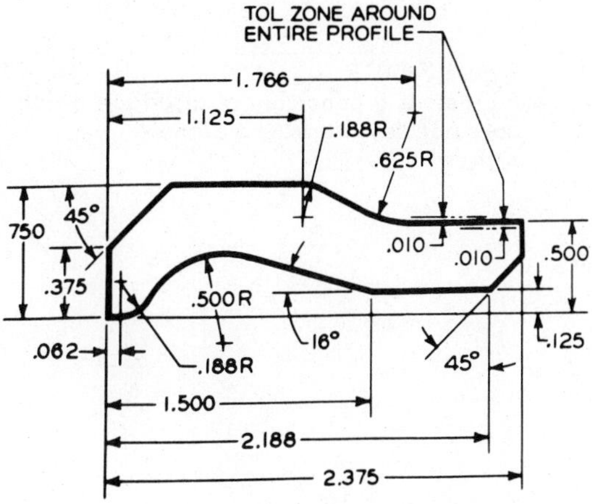

Figure 7-26
Zone tolerance around an entire contour. ASA Y14.5-1957

3 By suitable coverage in a specification which is referenced on the drawing.

Where maximum material condition is not used, the true position tolerance applies regardless of feature size. The following shall be added to the drawing note: "REGARDLESS OF FEATURE SIZE". See Fig. 7-25. Example:

6 HOLES LOCATED AT TRUE POSITION WITHIN .010 DIA REGARDLESS OF HOLE SIZE

or

6 HOLES LOCATED WITHIN .005 R OF TRUE POSITION REGARDLESS OF HOLE SIZE

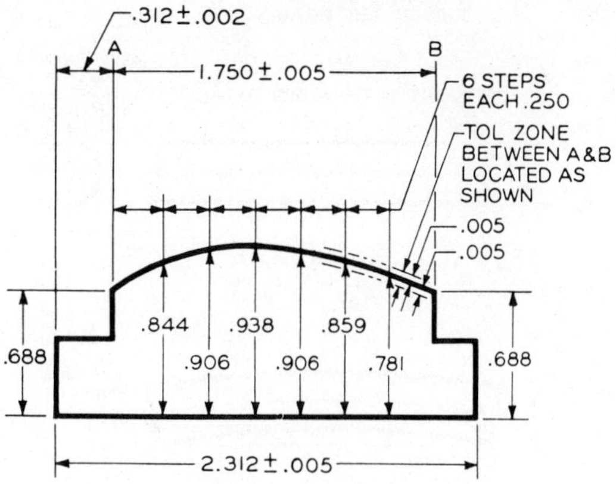

Figure 7-27
A zone tolerance between two points on a contour. ASA Y14.5-1957

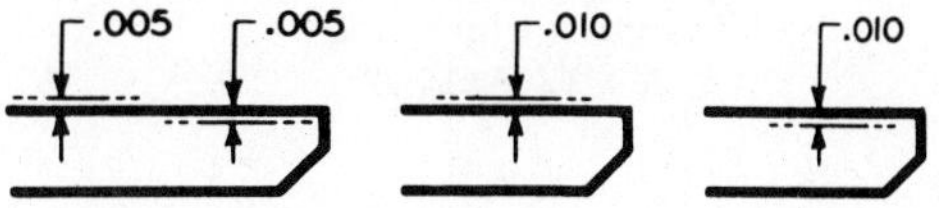

Figure 7-28
Bilateral and unilateral zone tolerance. ASA Y14.5-1957

7.11 Zone tolerance for contours[10]

A zone tolerance may be given where a uniform amount of variation can be permitted along a contour. The drawing is constructed to show the desired contour fully defined by dimensions without tolerances. Information must be included specifying that the general tolerances do not apply to the dimensions establishing the desired contour. At a conspicuous place along the contour, one or two phantom lines are drawn with dimension lines and arrowheads to indicate the location of the tolerance zone. The value of the tolerance is given by note. See Figs. 7-26 and 7-27. If some limits on a drawing are expressed by a zone tolerance and others by a general tolerance, the extent of the zone tolerance must be clearly indicated as in Fig. 7-27. The zone may be symmetrical around the desired contour, or it may be entirely plus or entirely minus. See Fig. 7-28.

10. *Ibid.*

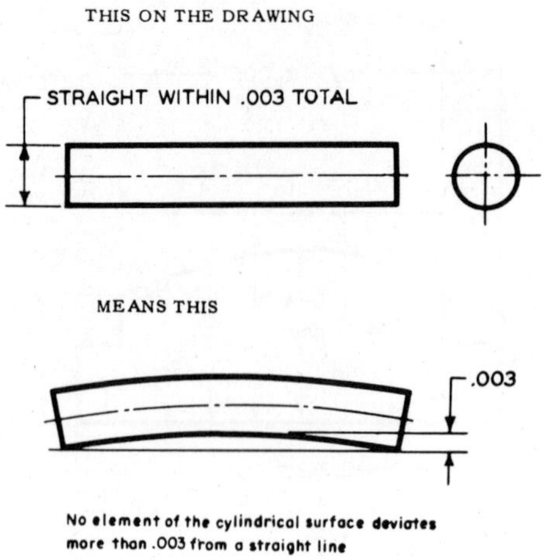
THIS ON THE DRAWING
STRAIGHT WITHIN .003 TOTAL
MEANS THIS
.003
No element of the cylindrical surface deviates more than .003 from a straight line

Figure 7-29
Straightness is a condition where an element of a surface does not deviate from a straight line.
ASA Y14.5-1957

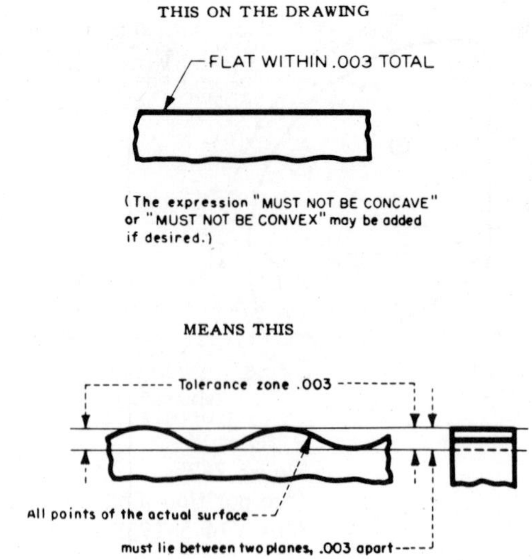
THIS ON THE DRAWING
FLAT WITHIN .003 TOTAL
(The expression "MUST NOT BE CONCAVE" or "MUST NOT BE CONVEX" may be added if desired.)
MEANS THIS
Tolerance zone .003
All points of the actual surface
must lie between two planes, .003 apart

Figure 7-30
Flatness is a condition of a surface which does not deviate from a plane.
ASA Y14.5-1957

7.12 Geometric tolerancing

A geometric tolerance is the permissible variation in the specified form of an individual feature of a part. Shapes or forms into which material is fabricated are defined by the use of geometric terms, such as a plane, a cylinder, a cone, a square, or a hexagon. The geometric definition assumes a perfect form, but because a perfect form cannot be produced, variations must be restricted if a specified quality is to be maintained. Geometric tolerances should be specified where appropriate for all requirements critical to functioning and interchangeability.

Tolerances of form. Tolerances of form define conditions of straightness, flatness, parallelism, squareness, angularity, roundness, concentricity and symmetry. These tolerances specify the maximum permissible variation from the desired form and apply to all points on the designated surface or line unless otherwise specified. Tolerances of form are indicated by notes or supplemental specifications. Figs. 7-29 through 7-36 illustrate first how to specify tolerances of form on drawings by means of standardized abbreviated notes; second, the meaning is shown with the interpretation of the tolerance. The requirement of most designs for interchangeable parts are that the specified tolerance of form applies regardless of the feature size. Therefore, where tolerances of form are expressed as shown in these figures, they are observed regardless of the actual finished sizes of the features concerned.

THIS ON THE DRAWING

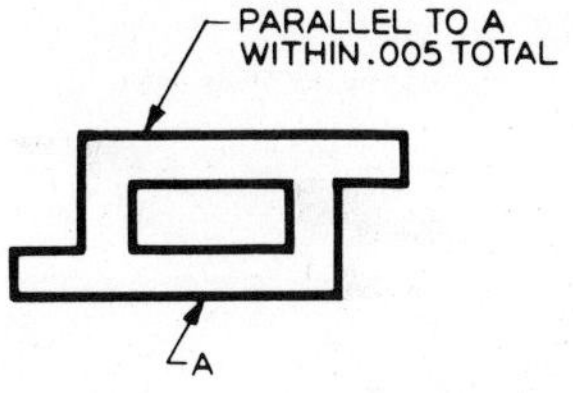

MEANS THIS

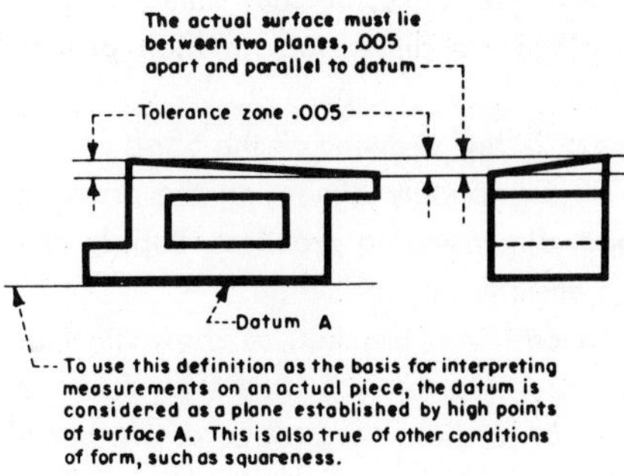

Figure 7-31
Parallelism is a condition wherein two or more planes or straight lines extend in the same direction and are equidistant at all points. ASA Y14.5-1957

THIS ON THE DRAWING

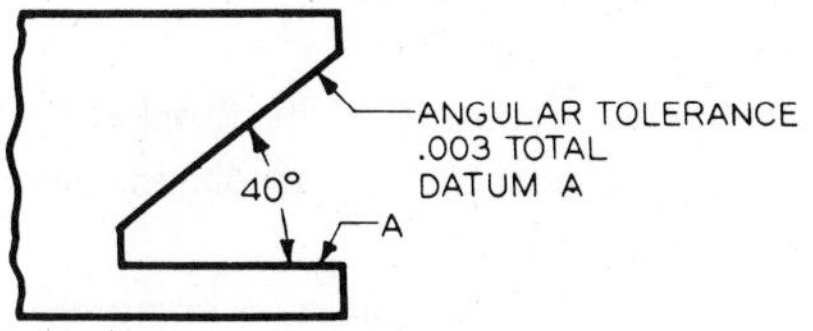

MEANS THIS

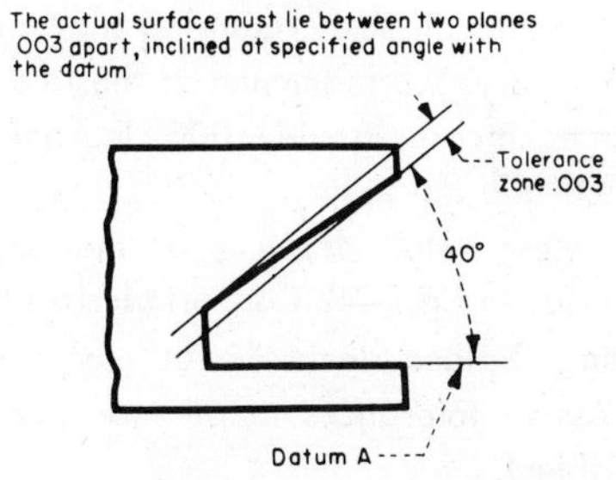

Figure 7-32
Angularity is the condition of surfaces or lines which are at an angle to each other. ASA Y14.5-1957

THIS ON THE DRAWING

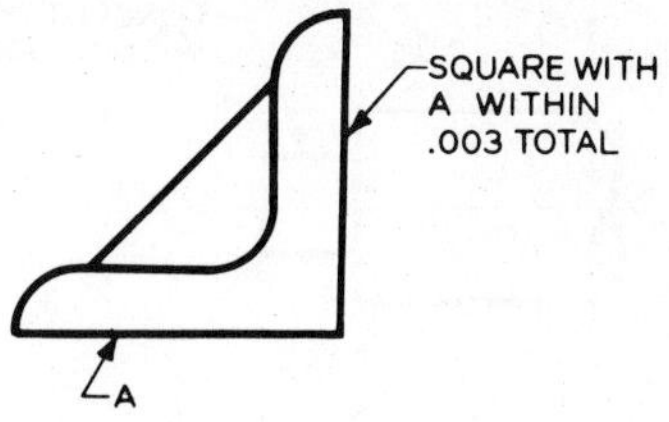

MEANS THIS

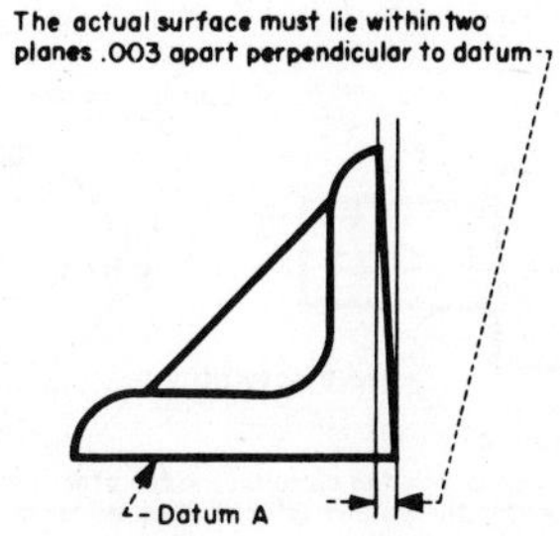

Figure 7-33
Squareness is the condition of surfaces or lines which are at right angles to each other. ASA Y14.5-1957

THIS ON THE DRAWING

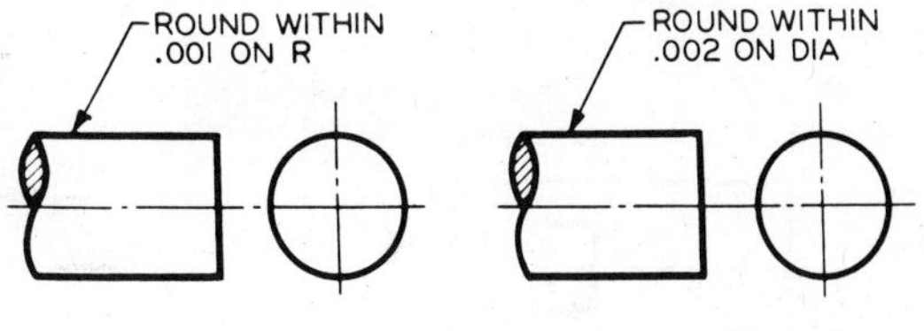

MEANS THIS

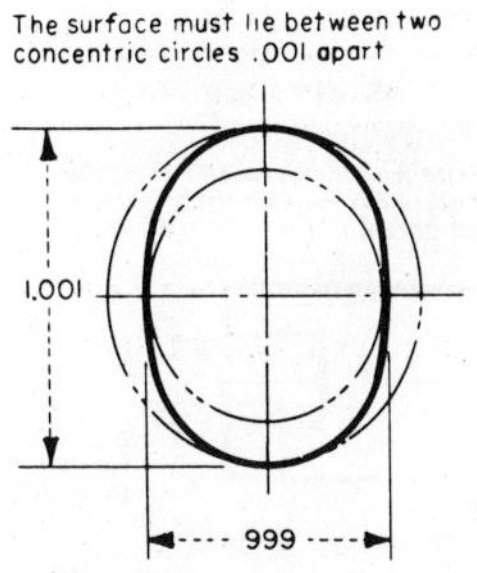

Figure 7-34
Roundness is a condition on a surface of revolution such as a cylinder or cone, where all points, on a plane normal to the axis, are equidistant from the center. ASA Y14.5-1957

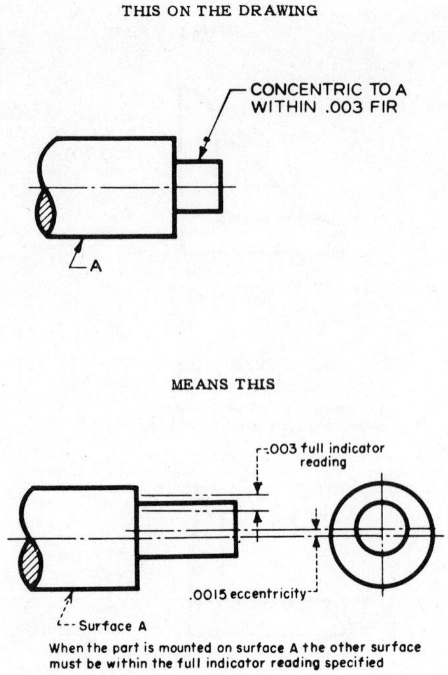
THIS ON THE DRAWING
CONCENTRIC TO A
WITHIN .003 FIR
A
MEANS THIS
.003 full indicator reading
.0015 eccentricity
Surface A
When the part is mounted on surface A the other surface must be within the full indicator reading specified

Figure 7-35
Concentricity is a condition where the center of one cylindrical surface coincides with the center of another. ASA Y14.5-1957

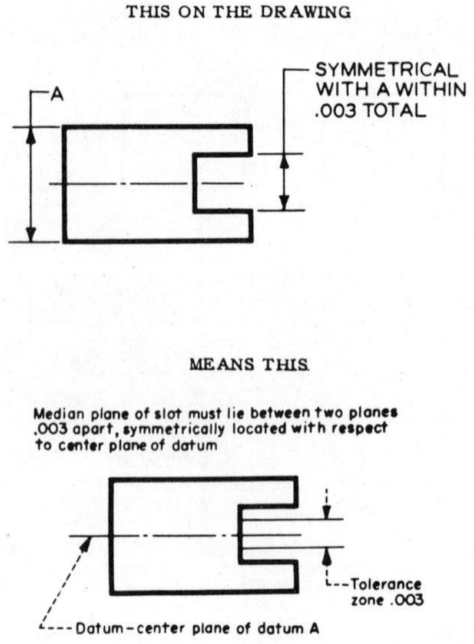
THIS ON THE DRAWING
A
SYMMETRICAL
WITH A WITHIN
.003 TOTAL
MEANS THIS
Median plane of slot must lie between two planes .003 apart, symmetrically located with respect to center plane of datum
Tolerance zone .003
Datum-center plane of datum A

Figure 7-36
Symmetry is a condition in which a part or feature is the same on opposite sides of a center plane. ASA Y14.5-1957

Problems, section 7

1 Using the Tables for Fits (Tables II-VI), determine the shaft and bore limits for each of the cases of Table VII. Make sketches similar to Fig. 7-23 and place the dimensions in their proper locations.

2 Prepare a 2-view drawing of the Shaft shown in Fig. 7-37. Completely dimension the drawing using proper dimensioning practices. Supply any design dimensions not indicated.

3 Design a cast iron Bracket, as shown in Fig. 7-38, for mounting a 1/2 diameter shaft to run free in 15/16 diameter bronze sleeve bearings which are to be pressed into the bracket. The base width of the bracket is 4 inches. Place four conveniently located clearance holes for 3/8 diameter bolts. Provide a completely dimensioned 3-view drawing of the bracket and 2-views of the bearing. Use standard fits and supply all design sizes not indicated.

4 Make a multiview drawing of the Guide shown in Fig. 7-39 and change all dimensions from fractional to decimals.

5 Make a multiview drawing of the Bracket illustrated in Fig. 7-40 and change all dimensions from fractions to decimals.

6 Using decimal dimensions, make a complete drawing of the Piercing Punch and Die shown in Fig. 7-41. Use Tables II through VI for determining the proper limits for the fits specified. Assign tolerances to all sizes requiring machining from Table I. Use the maximum of the tolerance range in each case. Provide .006 clearance between punch and die hole.

7 Make a 2-view detail drawing of the cast steel Flanged Hub in Fig. 7–42. Convert all sizes to decimals, using 2-place decimals for cast surfaces only. Assign tolerances to all machining sizes from Table I.

8 Make a 2-view drawing of the 1/2 x 2–3/4 x 4 steel Jig Plate in Fig. 7-43. Determine hole sizes and tolerances. Use limits for all dimensions.

TABLE VII

Case	Nominal shaft and hole size		Class of fit
1	1-1/4	DIA	RC 2
2	1-15/16	DIA	RC 4
3	1-7/16	DIA	LC 3
4	4-11/16	DIA	LC 5
5	2-1/4	DIA	LT 7
6	1-7/8	DIA	LN 2
7	5/8	DIA	LN 3
8	3/16	DIA	FN 2
9	3/8	DIA	FN 5
10	2-11/16	DIA	FN 4

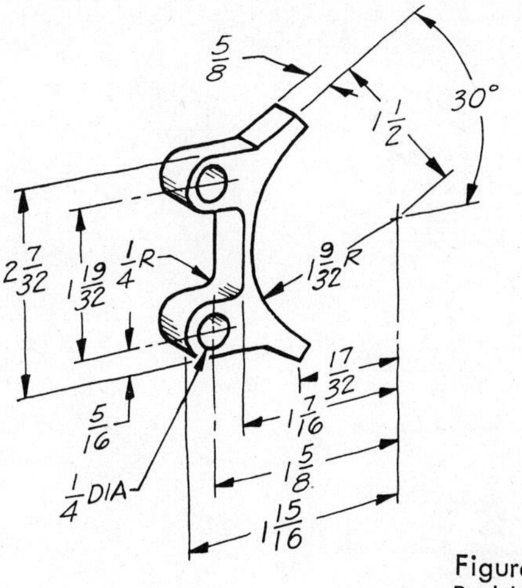

Figure 7-39
Problem 4.

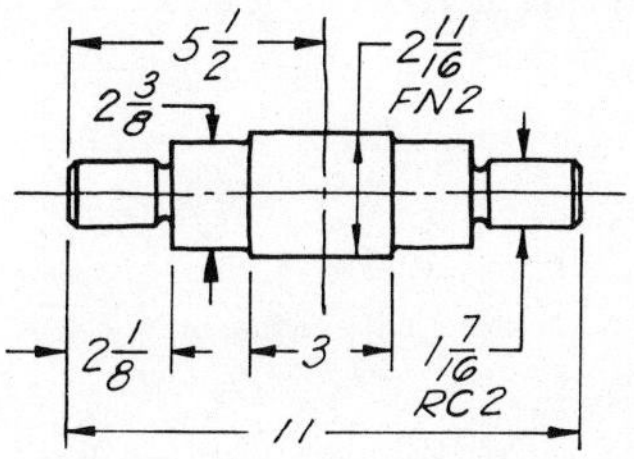

Figure 7-37
Problem 2.

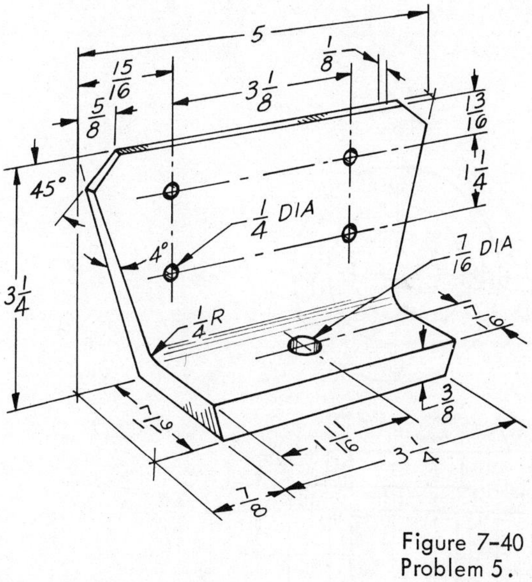

Figure 7-40
Problem 5.

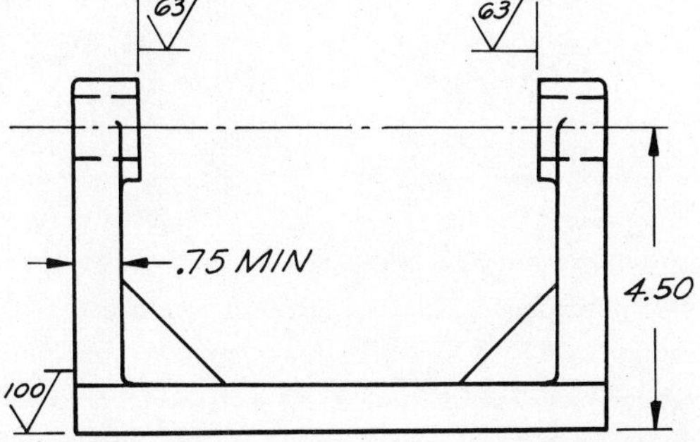

Figure 7-38
Problem 3.

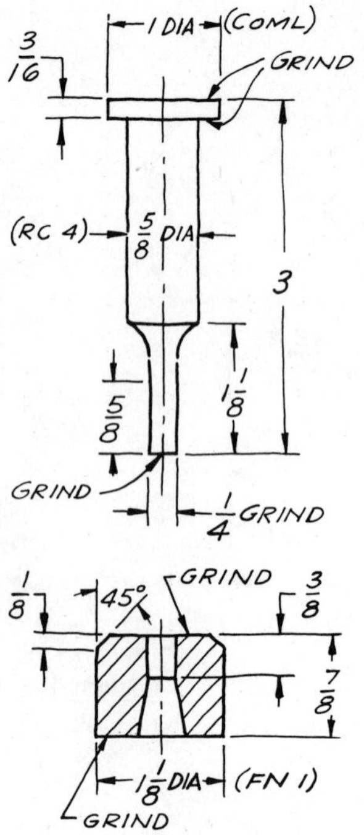

Figure 7-41
Problem 6.

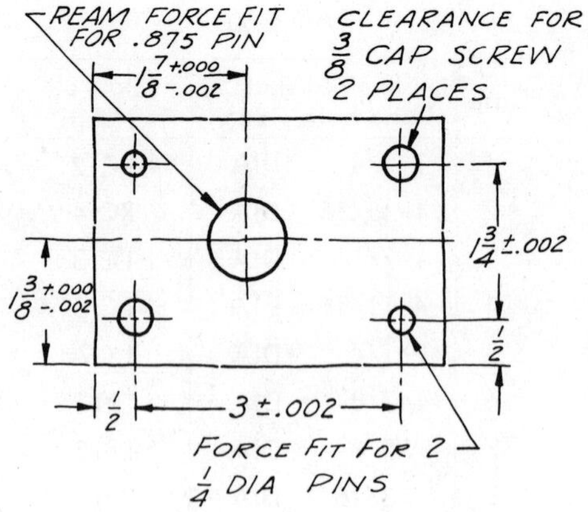

Figure 7-43
Problem 8.

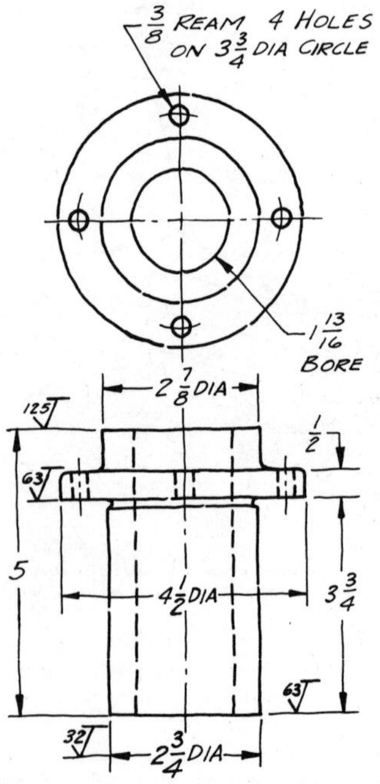

Figure 7-42
Problem 7.

ectional views 8

For objects which are comparatively simple in design, the problem of showing complete construction details can be achieved by the usual orthographic representation of views. Many objects, however, have internal shapes which are so complicated in nature that it is virtually impossible to show their true shape without employing numerous confusing hidden lines. See Fig. 8-1. In situations where intermediate or interior construction cannot be clearly shown in exterior views, the draftsman resorts to the use of one or more sectional views. A sectional view not only reveals the actual internal shape of an object but it also retains the significant outline of the external contour. The process of drawing sectional views is described in this section.

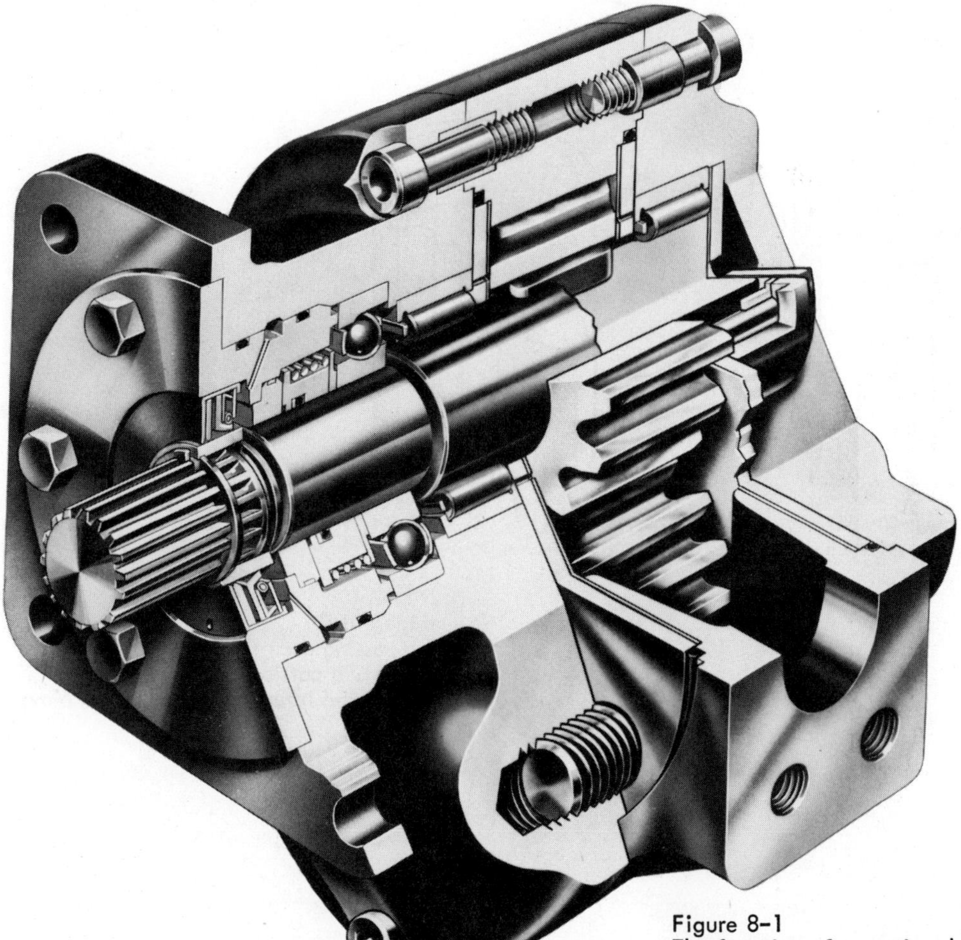

Figure 8-1
The function of a sectional view is to show the internal construction of an object. New York Air Brake Co.

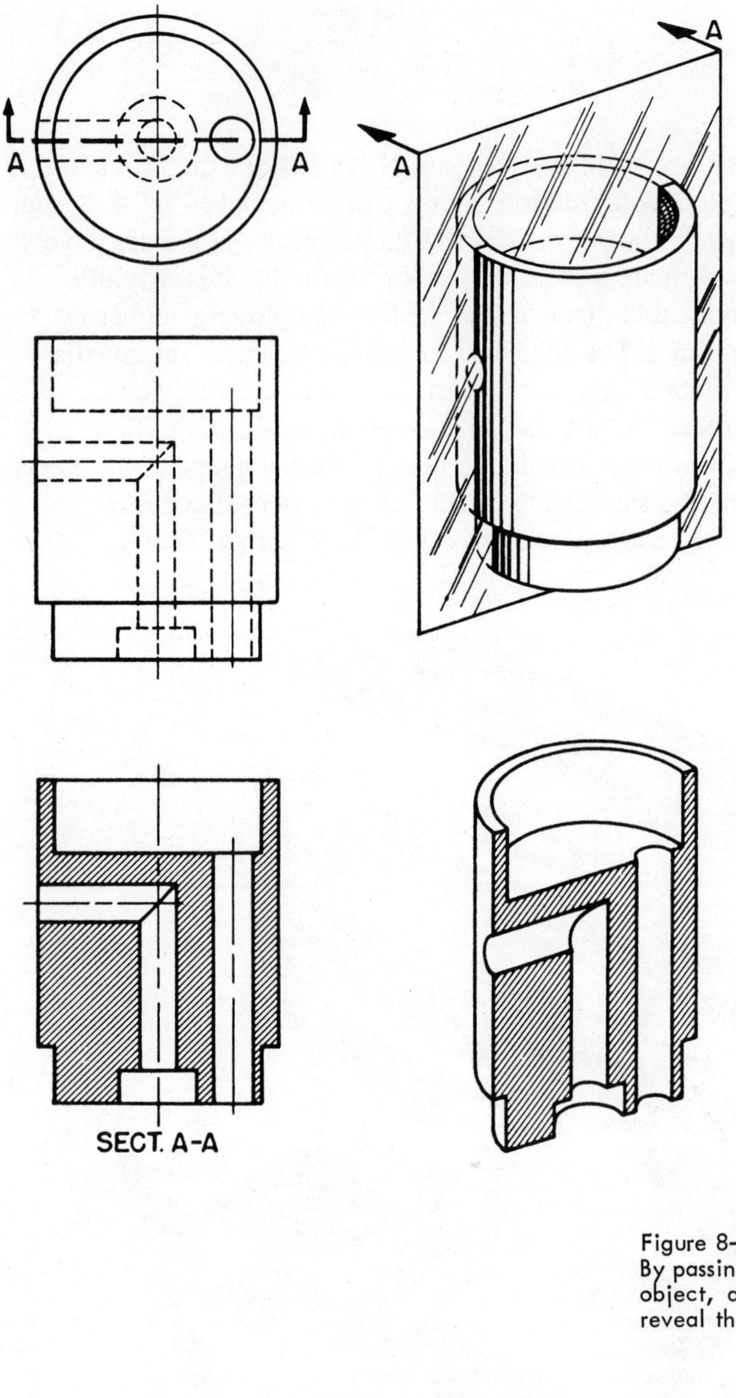

Figure 8–2
By passing a cutting plane through the object, a portion can be removed to reveal the internal shape. U.S. Navy

8.1 Sectional view

A sectional view is one wherein a cross-section of an object is obtained by passing an imaginary cutting plane through the object. The cutting plane is assumed to pass through at some selected portion of the object and the cut part is removed. See Fig. 8-2.

There are various types of sectional views, such as full section, half section, offset section, broken-out section, revolved section, removed section, auxiliary section and thin section. In each case the view produced is referred to as a *sectional view*.

8.2 Cutting plane line

The cutting plane is shown on the regular view by means of a cutting plane line. Two forms of cutting plane lines may be used. See Fig. 8-3. The first consists of alternating long dashes and pairs of short dashes. The long dashes may vary from 3/4 inch to 1–1/2 inches or more, depending on the size of the drawing, and the short dashes approximately 1/8 inch long with 1/16 inch spaces. The second form is made of equal dashes about 1/4 inch long or slightly longer on large drawings. The ends of both types of lines are bent at 90° and terminate with bold arrowheads. The arrowheads should point in the direction of sight in which the object is viewed when the sectional view is made. See Fig. 8-4.

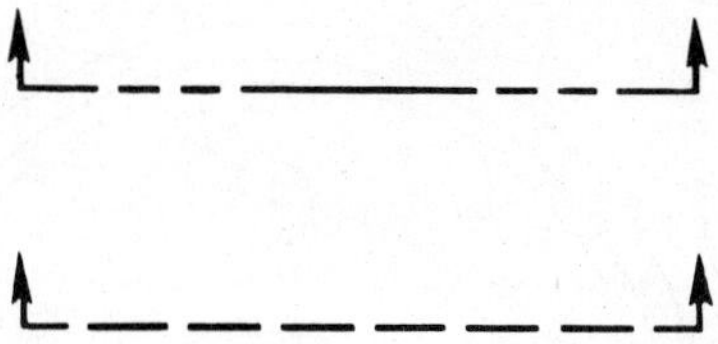

Figure 8–3
Use these lines to indicate the location of the cutting plane.

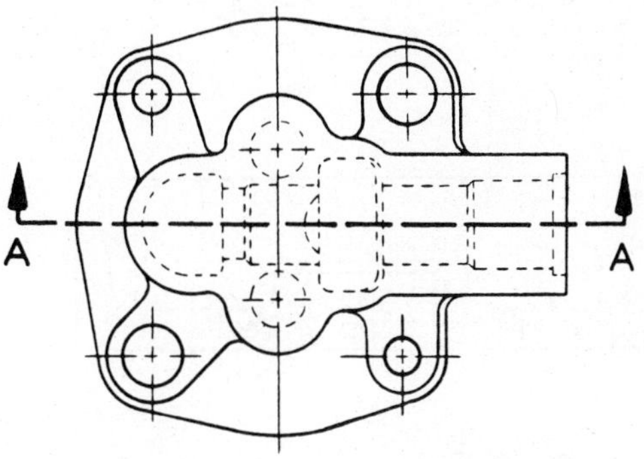

Figure 8–4
The arrows should always point away from the removed portion of the object. General Motors Corp.

Capital letters such as *A-A, B-B, C-C,* etc., are used when it is necessary to identify the section. The letters should be made to read horizontally, should not be underlined, and should be located behind the arrowheads wherever possible. A notation is also placed under the view as *SECTION A-A*. The letters should be approximately 1/4 to 3/8 inch high. See Fig. 8-5.

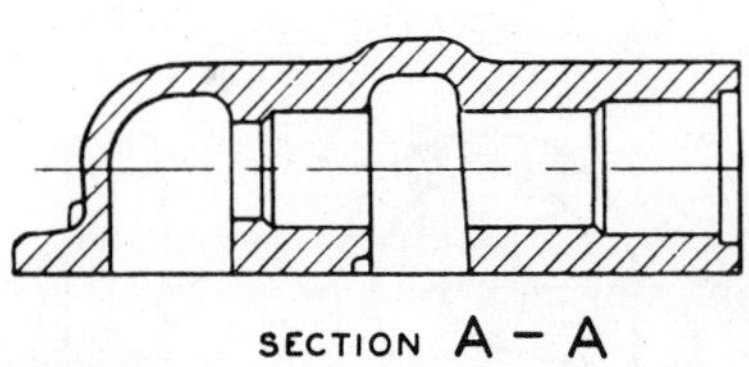

Figure 8–5
This is how a sectional view is identified. General Motors Corp.

On objects having one major center line in which the cutting plane is assumed to pass through the axis of symmetry, the practice is to omit the cutting plane line since its position is already clear that the section is taken along that center line. See Fig. 8-6.

The cutting plane line may be bent or offset if by this means the construction can be shown more clearly or thoroughly. The cutting plane line preferably should be shown through an exterior and not through a sectional view.

8.3 Full section

When the cutting plane passes entirely across the object, the result is a full section. Notice

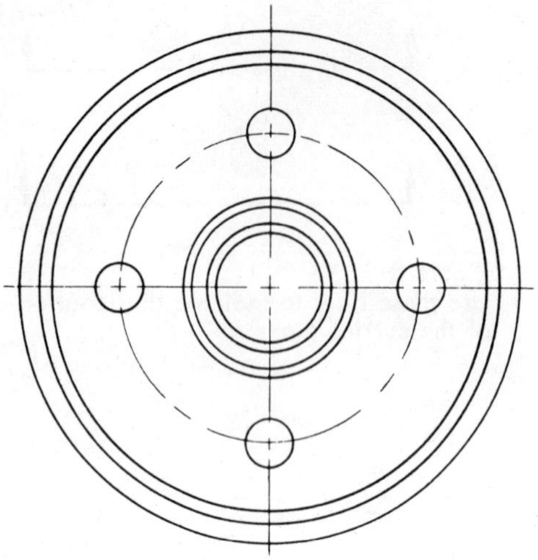

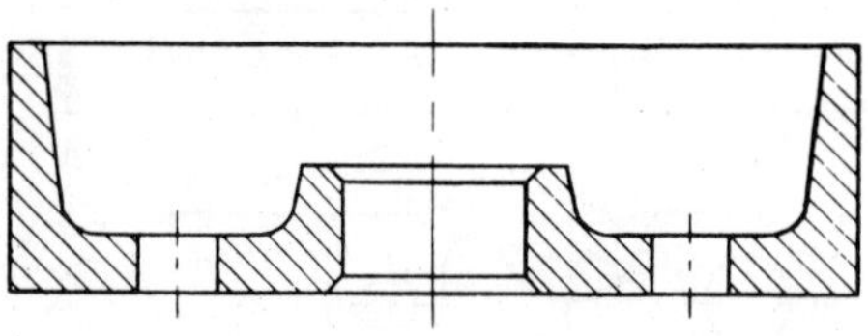

Figure 8-6
On objects having a major centerline, the cutting plane may be omitted if the section is taken along that center line. Chrysler Corp.

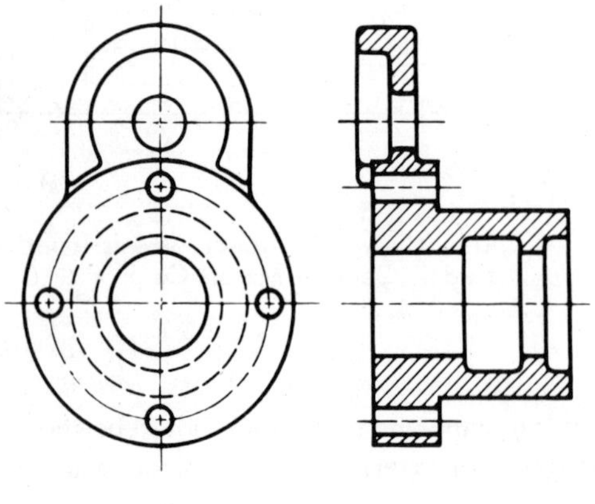

Figure 8-7
By cutting through the entire object a full section is obtained.
ASA Y14.2-1957

in Fig. 8-7 that half of the object which is between the observer and the cutting plane is considered to be removed and the remaining half (in full section) exposed to view.

8.4 Half section

A half section results when two cutting planes are passed at right angles to each other along the center lines or symmetrical axes. As shown in Fig. 8-8, passage of the cutting planes in this manner permits the removal of one-quarter of the object and a half section of the interior is exposed to view.

A half section has the advantage of showing the interior of the object and at the same time maintaining the shape of the exterior. Its usefulness is limited to symmetrical objects. Because it is often difficult to completely dimension the internal shape of a half section, this type of sectional view is not widely used in detail drawings (drawings of single parts). Its greatest value is in assembly drawings where it is necessary to show both internal and external construction on the same view.

Either a visible line or a center line may be used to separate the sectioned half from the unsectioned half. It is generally conceded that a center line is much more realistic for this purpose because the removal of a quarter of the object is imaginary only and the actual edge as implied by a solid line does not exist. See Fig. 8-9.

8.5 Offset section

It is often necessary to change the direction of the cutting plane line from along the main axis in order to include features which are not located in a straight line. The cutting plane is therefore offset to pass through these features and the resulting section is called an *offset section*. Note in Fig. 8-10, that by offsetting the cutting plane in several places it exposes the shape of the openings and recess which normally would not be seen if a regular full section were utilized. In making an offset sectional view, the offsets are not included in the sectional view but only in the view showing the cutting-plane line.

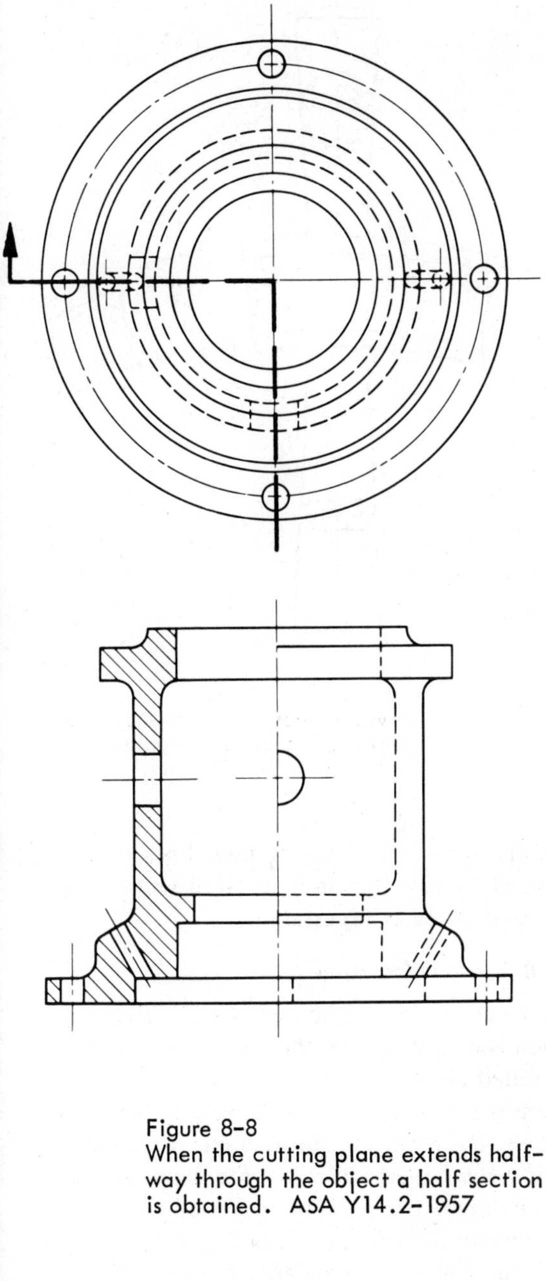

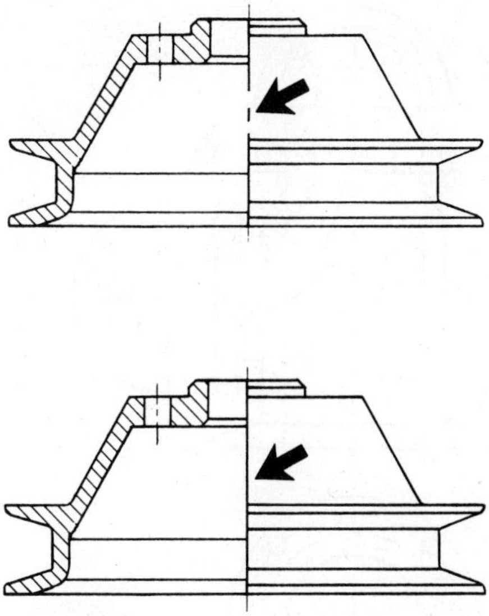

Figure 8-9
A visible or center line may be used to divide the sectioned parts in a half sectional view, but the center line is preferable.

Figure 8-8
When the cutting plane extends halfway through the object a half section is obtained. ASA Y14.2-1957

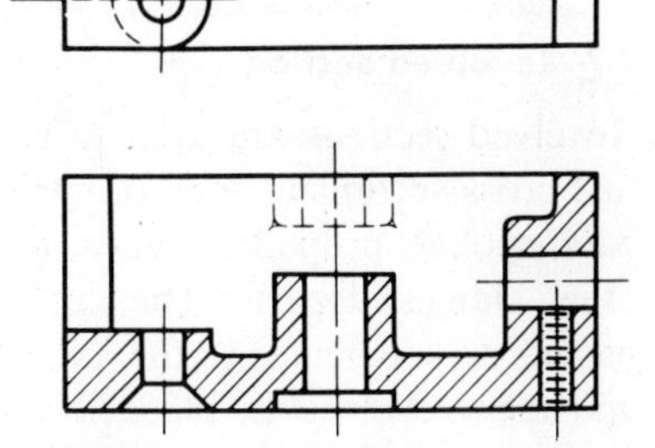

Figure 8-10
In an offset section, the cutting plane line is offset to pass through features not located in a straight line. ASA Y14.2-1957

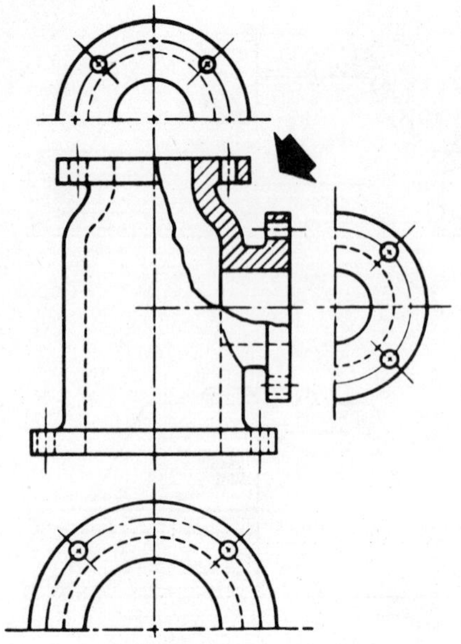

Figure 8-11
A broken-out section is used to show only a desired feature of the object. No cutting plane line is necessary. ASA Y14.2-1957

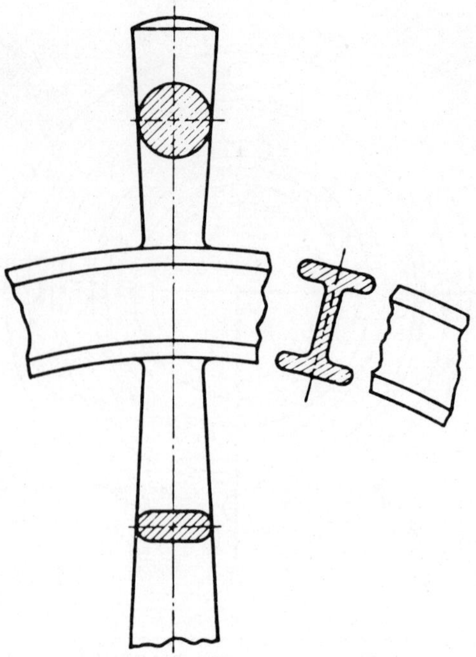

Figure 8-12
A revolved section is used to show the cross sectional shape of elongated objects. ASA Y14.2-1957

8.6 Broken-out section

For certain types of objects, the removal of only a small portion is necessary to show the interior construction. In this instance the cutting plane is assumed to pass through the desired feature and the interior exposed to view. The sectioned area is outlined by a breakline and the resulting part is known as a *broken-out section.* Observe in Fig. 8-11 that in the broken-out sectional view the symbolic cutting plane line is not shown.

8.7 Revolved section

Revolved sections are used to show the actual cross sectional shape of such objects as bars, spokes, propeller blades, arms, ribs or other elongated parts. The cutting plane is passed perpendicular to the axis of the piece and then revolved in place through 90 degrees into the plane of the sheet. See Fig. 8-12. The visible lines on each side of the adjacent view may be removed and broken lines used so as to leave the revolved section clear. The true shape of the exposed revolved section should always be retained regardless of the direction of the contour lines of the object. Notice that in a revolved section no cutting plane is necessary.

8.8 Removed section

Greater clarity is often achieved if the section is detached from the projected view and located elsewhere on the sheet. Such a section is known as a removed section. See Fig. 8-13. By removing the section, the regular view can be left intact and the removed section drawn to a larger scale to facilitate more complete dimensioning. See Fig. 8-14.

The American Standards Association recommends the following practices regarding removed sections:[1]

1 A removed section should be labeled in bold lettering, as **SECTION B-B,** to identify it with the cutting-plane line which is designated with corresponding letters at the ends. See Fig. 8-14.

1. Extracted from *American Drafting Standards Manual, ASA Y14.2 — 1957* (New York: The American Society of Mechanical Engineers, 1957).

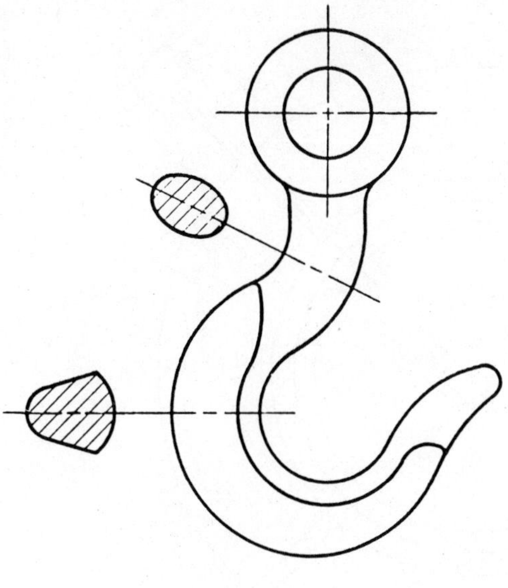

Figure 8-13
For greater clarity, place the removed section elsewhere on the sheet. ASA Y14.2-1957

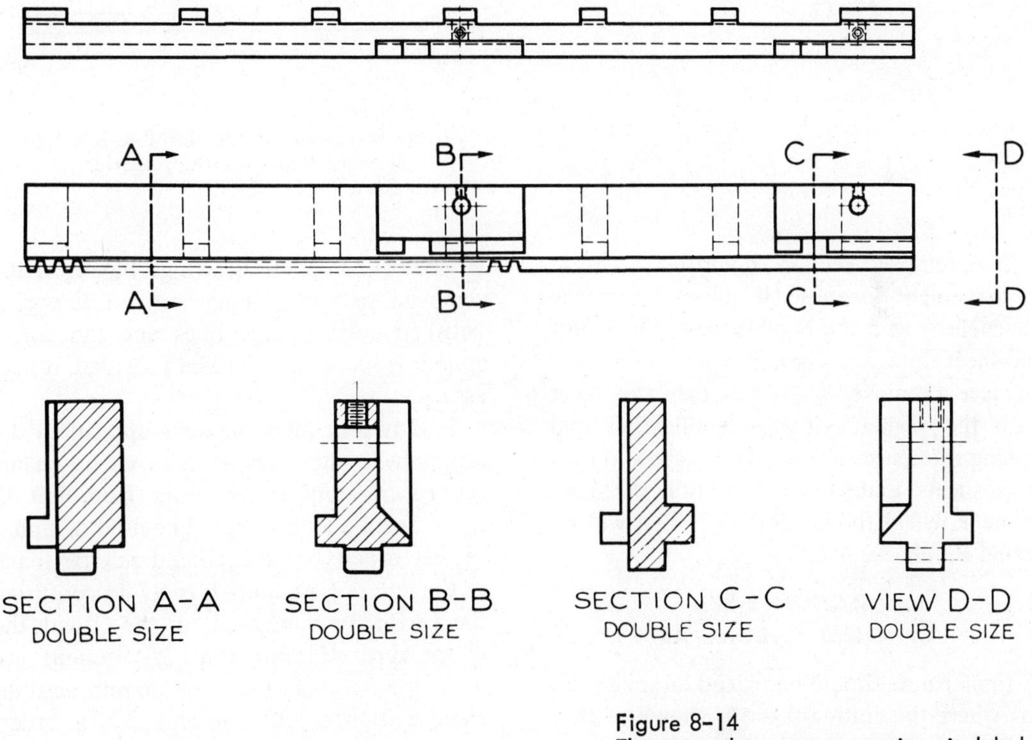

Figure 8-14
These are the correct practices in labeling removed sections. ASA Y14.2-1957

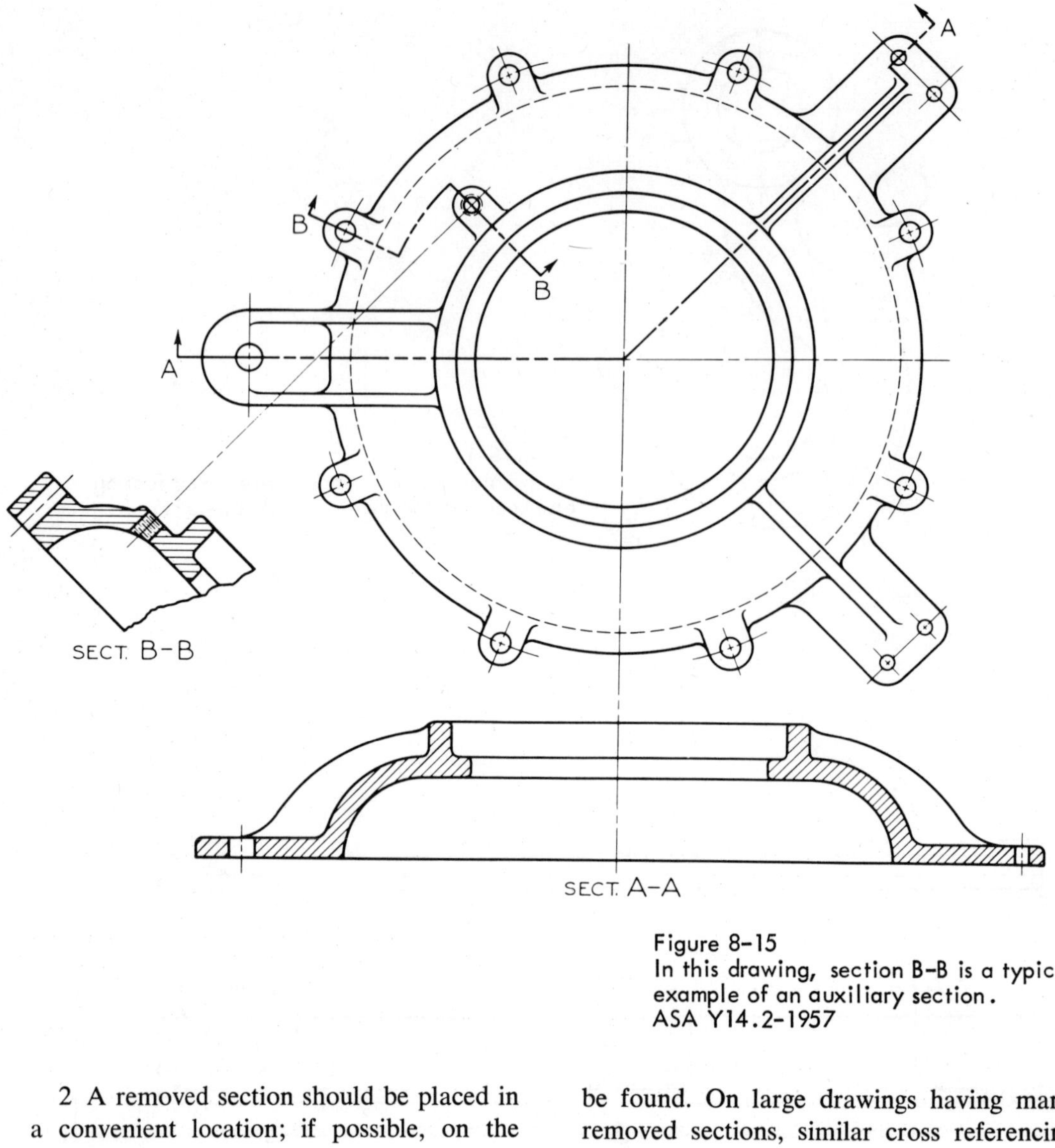

Figure 8-15
In this drawing, section B-B is a typical example of an auxiliary section.
ASA Y14.2-1957

2 A removed section should be placed in a convenient location; if possible, on the same sheet with the regular view. On multiple-sheet drawings where it is not practicable to place a removed section on the same sheet with the regular views, identification and zoning references should be indicated on related sheets. Below the section title, the sheet number where the cutting-plane line will be found should be given as:

SECTION B-B
ON SHEET 4, ZONE A3

A similar note should be placed on the drawing where the cutting-plane is shown, with a leader pointing to the cutting-plane, referring to the sheet where the section will be found. On large drawings having many removed sections, similar cross referencing between cutting-plane lines and the corresponding sections should be provided, if necessary.

3 If two or more sections appear on the same sheet, they should, if possible, be arranged in alphabetical order from left to right. Section letters should be used in alphabetical order, but use should not be made of the letters *I*, *O*, and *Q*, to avoid confusing the *I* with the numeral 1, or the *O* with the *Q*, or zero. If more than 23 sections are used, the additional sections should be indicated by double letters in alphabetical order, *AA-AA*, *BB-BB*, etc.

4 A removed section may be drawn to a

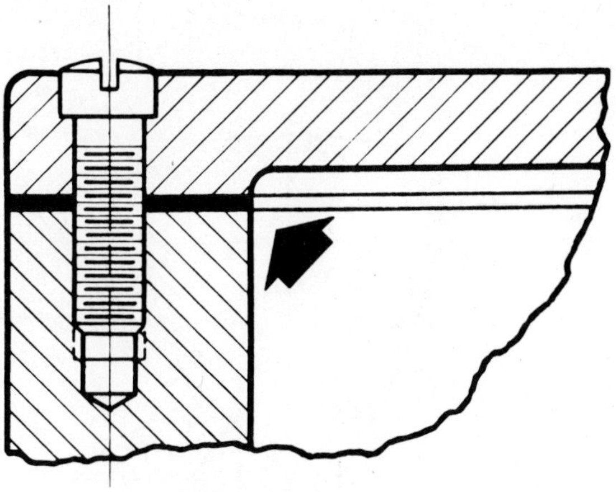

Figure 8-16
Thin material should be cross-sectioned in solid black. ASA Y14.2-1957

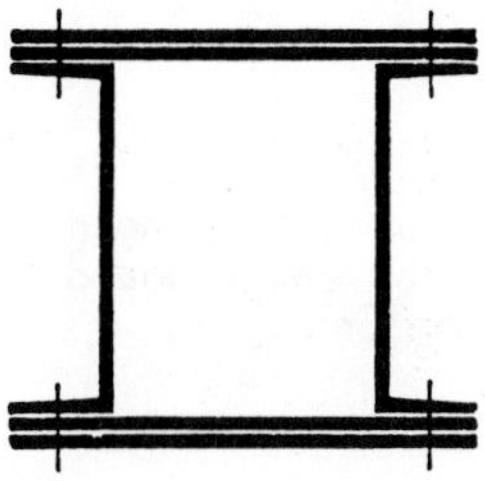

Figure 8-17
This is another method of sectioning thin parts.

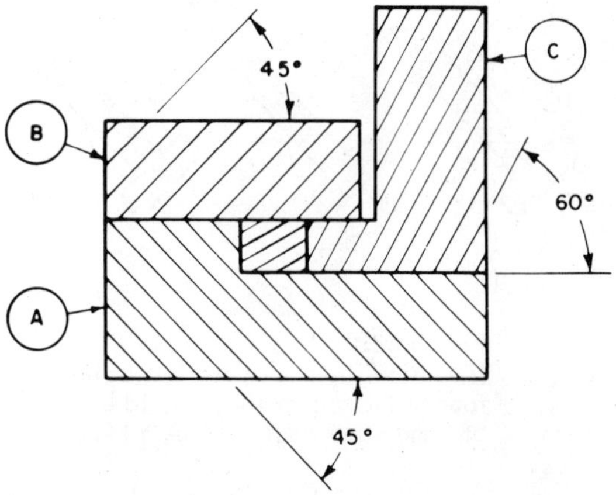

Figure 8-18
The cut surfaces of adjacent parts in sectional views should be shown with section lines drawn in this manner. ASA Y14.2-1957

larger scale if necessary, in which case the scale should be shown under the section title. See Fig. 8-14.

5 A removed section should not be rotated on the sheet when this would diminish the clearness of the drawing; that is, its edges or center lines should be parallel to the corresponding lines in the normal projected position.

6 Removed sections may be placed on center lines extended from the section cuts.

8.9 Auxiliary sections

Occasionally it is necessary to show a sectional view that is not one of the principal planes. This view is called an *auxiliary section.* Complete description of auxiliary views will be found in Section 9. An auxiliary section may be full, half, broken out, removed or revolved. The section should be shown in its normal auxiliary position and clearly identified with a cutting plane and appropriate letters. Fig. 8-15 illustrates a partial section at *B-B*.

8.10 Thin sections

Material such as sheet metal, gaskets, packing and other thin substances cannot be shown by the ordinary cross-sectioning convention. Cross sections of material of this kind are drawn in solid black. See Fig. 8-16. If two or more pieces are adjacent to each other, a white space is left to separate the sections. See Fig. 8-17.

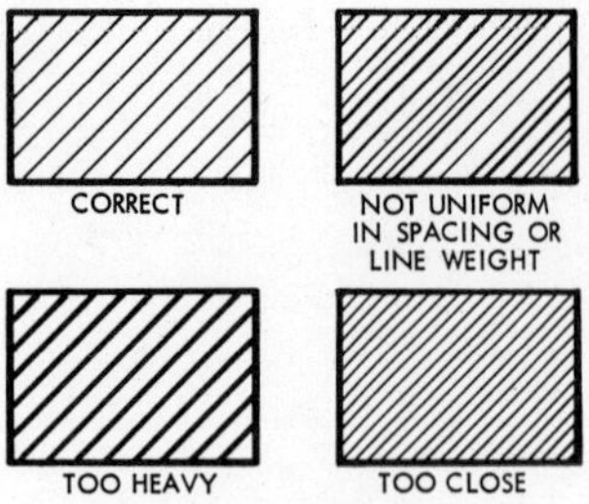

Figure 8-19
These are some of the common faults that should be avoided in drawing sectional lines.

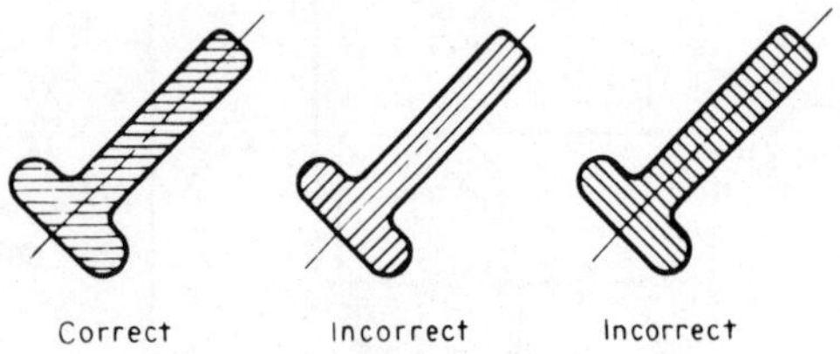

Figure 8-20
If section lines are parallel to the contour of the object they should be drawn at some other angle. ASA Y14.2-1957

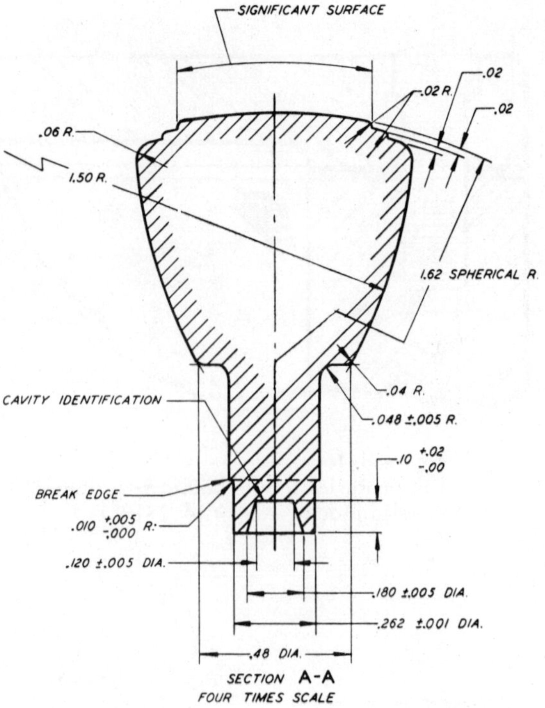

Figure 8-21
On large sections, section lines need be drawn only near the outside boundary. General Motors Corp.

Some industries specify that where two or more adjacent thin sections are used, they shall be shown solid, but an additional exploded view of that portion shall be included to properly define the arrangement of parts.[2]

8.11 Section lining

To clearly define the surfaces of a section, thin lines are drawn across the cut area at a 45° angle with the horizontal. See Fig. 8-18. If the section consists of two adjacent parts, such as in an assembly drawing, the section lines should run in opposite directions in order to provide contrast. When three parts form the section, the third part adjacent to the first two should have lines sloping at 30° or 60° with the main outline of the view. For additional adjacent parts, the lines may be drawn at any suitable angle just so each part stands out separately and clearly.

All lines should be uniformly spaced from approximately 1/32 to 1/8 inch or more apart. The actual spacing depends on the size of the drawing. However, to save time, care should be taken to avoid spacing lines too closely. The spacing should not be measured but judged by eye. Equally important is not to get the lines too heavy. The essential consideration is to preserve the unity and contrast of sectional areas. See Fig. 8-19.

If the shape or portion of a sectional area is such that the section lines would be parallel or nearly perpendicular to the dominant visible lines of the section, the section lines must be drawn to some other angle. See Fig. 8-20.

In sectioning very large areas, it is permissible to use section lines only near the adjacent boundary of the sectioned area with the interior portion left clear. See Fig. 8-21.

2. *Drafting Standards* (Waltham, Mass.: Raytheon Manufacturing Co.).

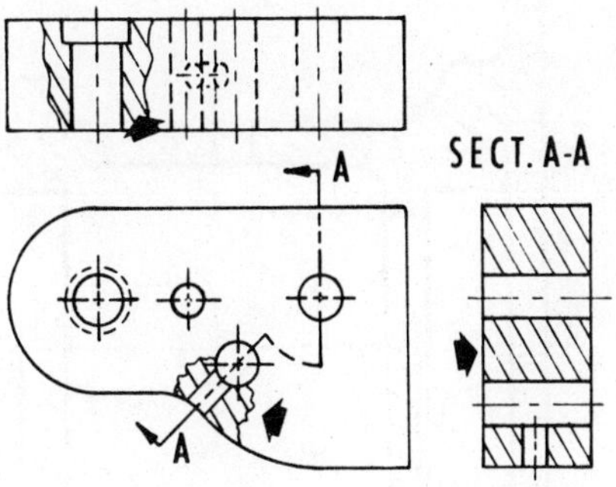

Figure 8-22
If more than one view is sectioned, all section lines must be drawn parallel.

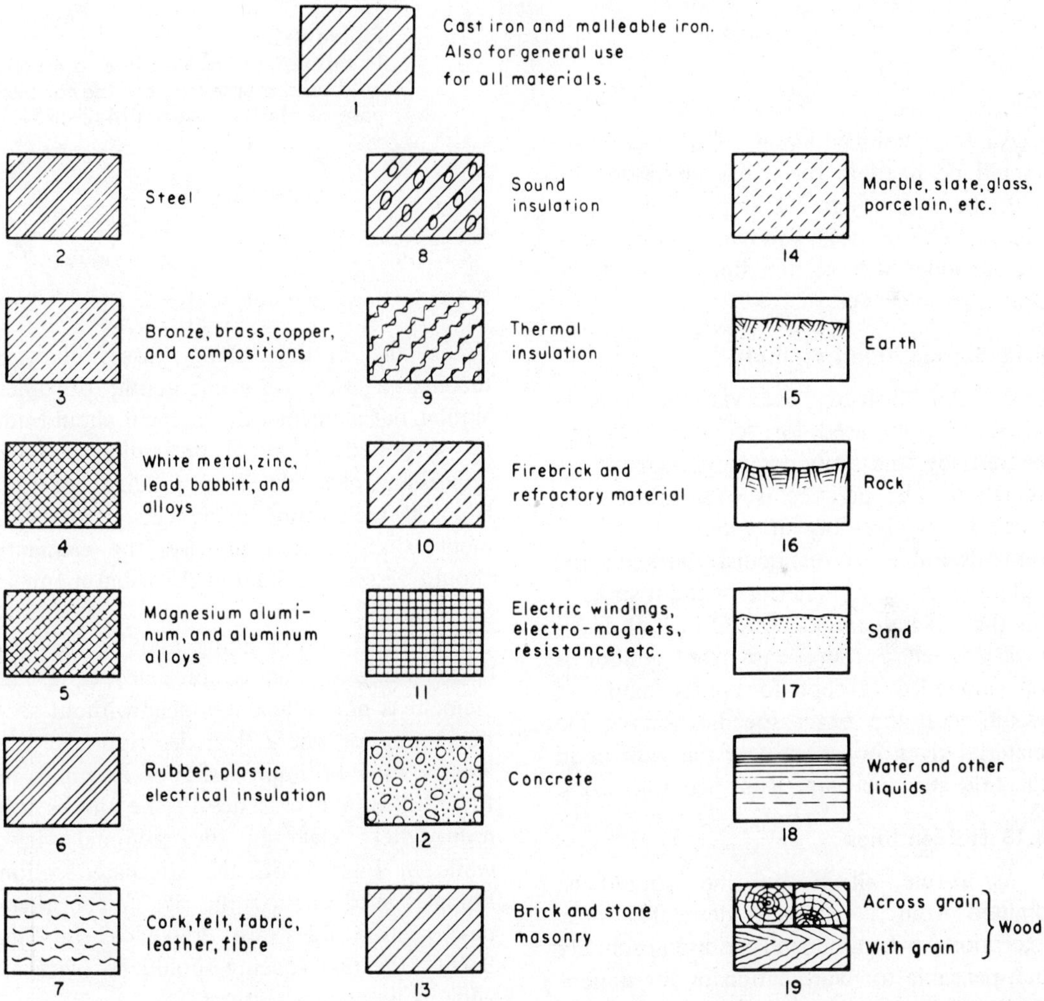

Figure 8-23
These are the standard code symbols for section lining. ASA Y14.2-1957

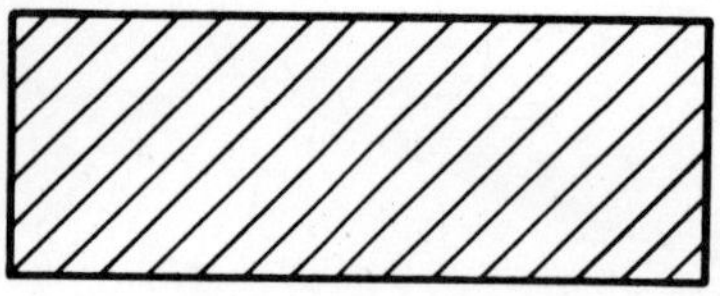

Figure 8-24
On detail drawing, (single drawing) this "all purpose symbol" is used for section lining with a note near the view. Instead of a note, the kind of material can be shown in the title strip or parts lists.

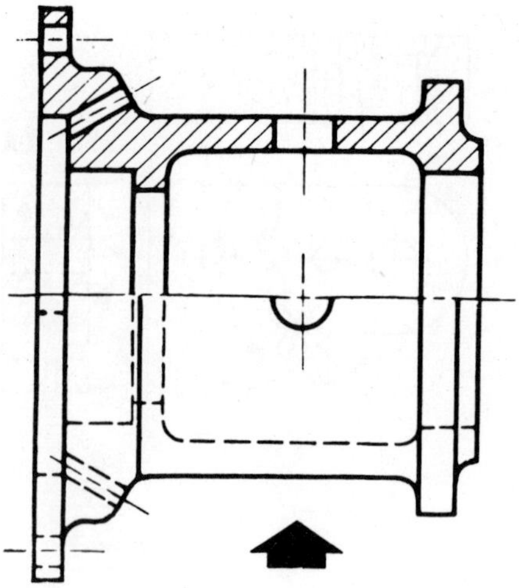

Figure 8-25
In this object, hidden lines are used only on the unsectioned side for purpose of clarity. ASA Y14.2-1957

All the sectioned areas of a single part should be lined in the same direction and with the same angle of slope. Thus if an object has three views and two or more views are sectioned, the section lines must all be drawn parallel. See Fig. 8-22.

8.12 Section lining symbols

Fig. 8-23 illustrates the various symbols which may be used for sectioning as approved by the American Standards Association. The practice is to employ these symbols on assembly drawings where it is only desirable to distinguish between the different classes of materials without specifying their exact composition. On detail drawings, the all purpose cast iron symbol is recommended, except for parts made of wood, with the exact specification of the material given in a note near the view or in the title strip or parts lists. See Fig. 8-24.

8.13 Hidden lines

As a rule, all hidden lines should be omitted from a sectional view. The only exception is when hidden lines are absolutely indispensable for clarification or for dimensioning. In half sections, hidden lines should be used only on the unsectioned side, providing they are necessary for dimensioning or clarity. See Fig. 8-25.

8.14 Sections through webs or ribs[3]

When the cutting plane passes flatwise through a web, rib, gear tooth, or other similar flat elements, the element should not be sectioned to avoid presenting a false impression of thickness or solidity. See Fig. 8-26. If the cutting plane cuts across elements that are not flatwise, the elements should be section-lined in the usual manner. See Fig. 8-27.

Alternate section lining may be used in cases where the actual presence of a flat element is not sufficiently clear without section lining, or where clear description of the feature may be improved. For example, in Fig. 8-26B, the presence of the ribs is not immediately clear in the sectional view; while in Fig. 8-26C the alternate section lining is used to show the ribs. When alternate section lines are drawn, as in Fig. 8-26C, the line spacing should be twice as wide as in normal sections.

3. Extracted from *American Drafting Standards Manual, ASA Y14.2 — 1957* (New York: The American Society of Mechanical Engineers, 1957).

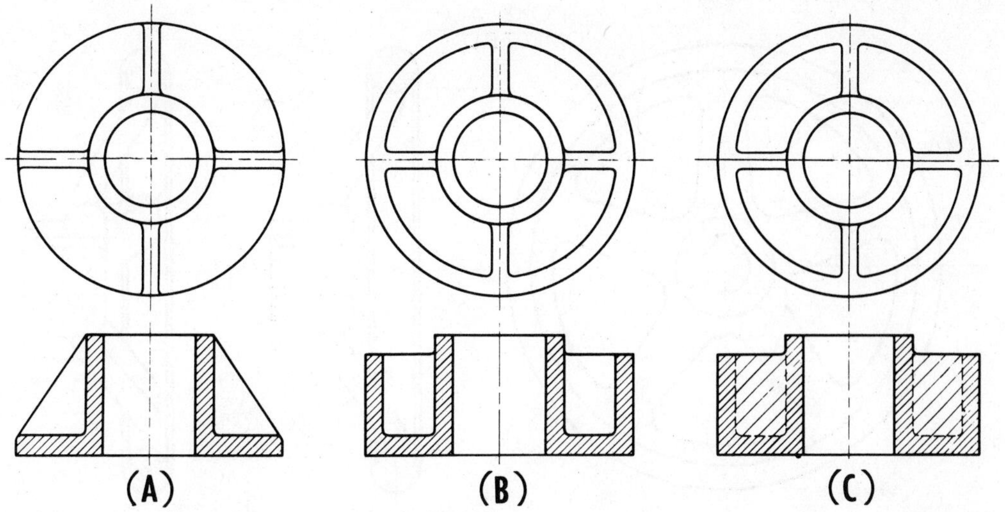

Figure 8-26
Method of sectioning if a cutting plane passes flatwise through a web, rib, or gear tooth.

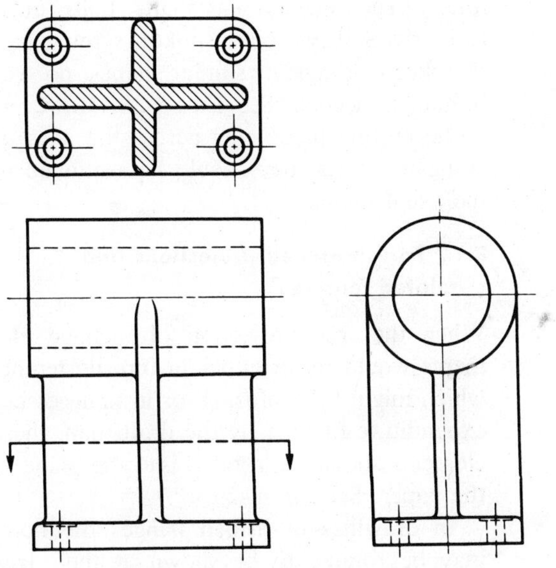

Figure 8-27
If a cutting plane passes across elements that are not flatwise, section lines should be used.

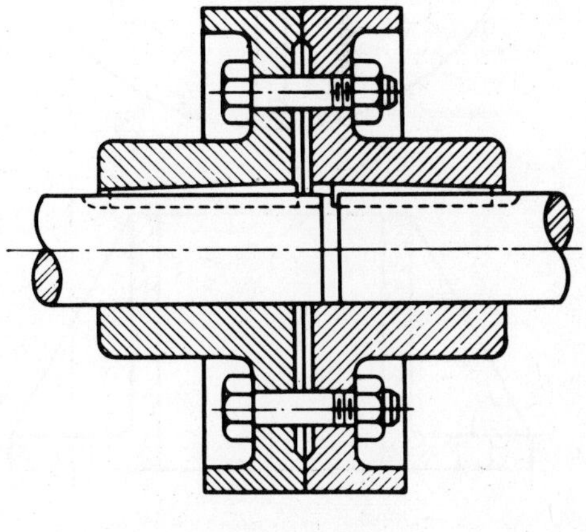

Figure 8-28
Elements such as bolts, screws, pins, etc., should not be sectioned.

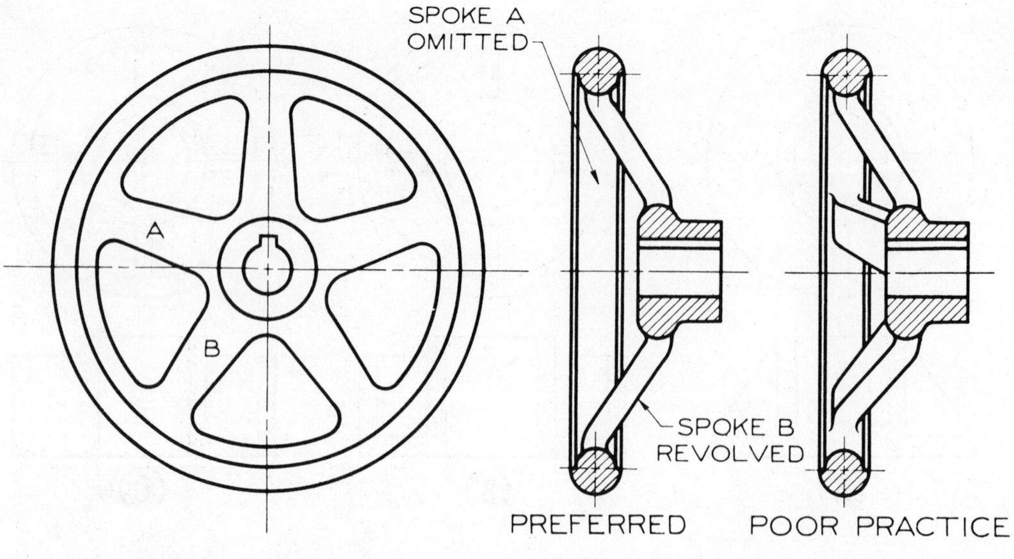

Figure 8-29
Parts which normally include foreshortened elements should be drawn like this.

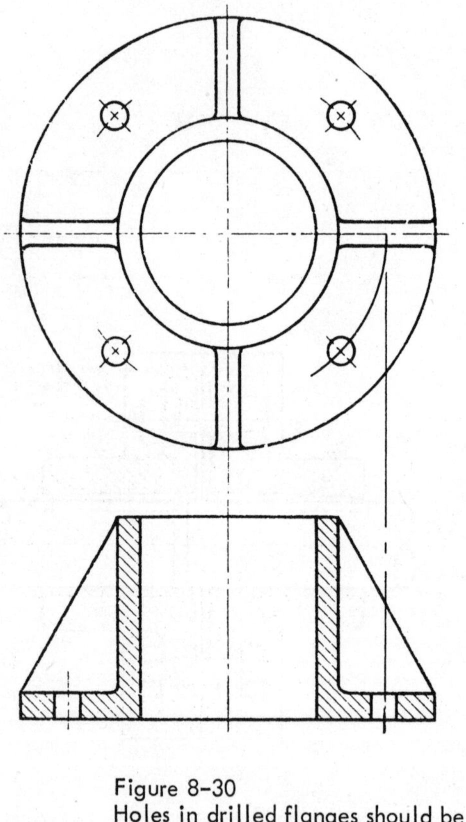

Figure 8-30
Holes in drilled flanges should be rotated so their true distance from the center is shown.

8.15 Sections through shafts, bolts, pins[4]

When the cutting plane contains the center lines of such elements as shafts, bolts, nuts, rods, rivets, keys, pins, spokes, screws, ball or roller bearings, or similar shapes, no sectioning is needed. See Fig. 8-28. However, if the cutting plane cuts across the axes of elongated parts they should be sectioned in the usual manner.

8.16 Foreshortened projections and related features[5]

When the true projection of inclined elements would result either in foreshortening, which might be confusing, or in unnecessary expenditure of time by the draftsman, these elements should be rotated into the plane of the paper. See Fig. 8-29.

In drawings of drilled flanges the holes may be rotated to be shown at their true distance from the center rather than in true projection, if clearness is promoted. See Fig. 8-30.

In order to include features not located along a straight line, the plane may be bent or changed in direction to pass through these features and the sections drawn as if they

4. *Ibid.*

5. *Ibid.*

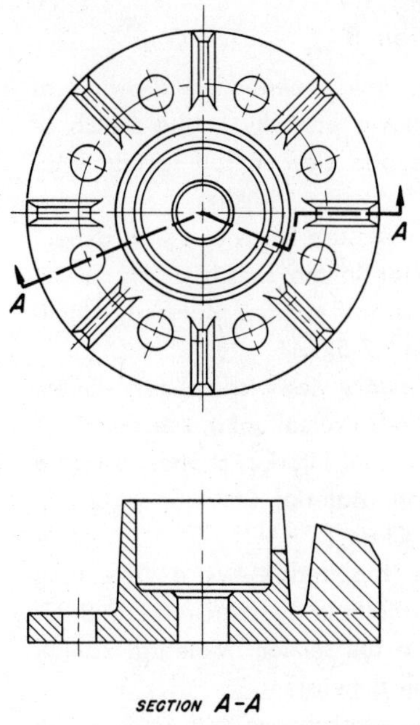

Figure 8-31
Aligned sections should be drawn in this manner.

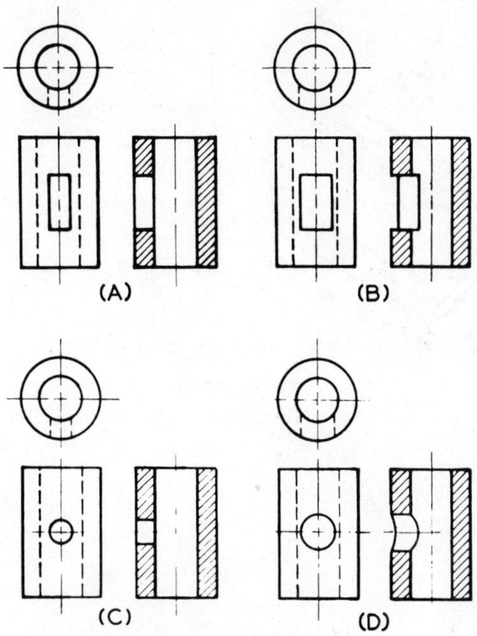

Figure 8-32
Here is how intersections in sections should be drawn.

were rotated into a plane. See Fig. 8-31. Such sections are called *aligned sections,* whether features are rotated into the cutting plane or the cutting plane is bent to pass through them.

8.17 Intersections in section[6]

When a section is drawn through an intersection in which the exact figure or curve of intersection is small or of no consequence, the figure or curve of intersection may be simplified as in A and C of Fig. 8-32, or approximated by circular arcs as at D in Fig. 8-32.

8.18 Conventional breaks

It is sometimes impossible or inconvenient to draw elongated objects to their required size. The practice in these cases is to shorten the view by using break lines. Notice in Fig. 8-33 how break lines are drawn for round and rectangular shaped parts.

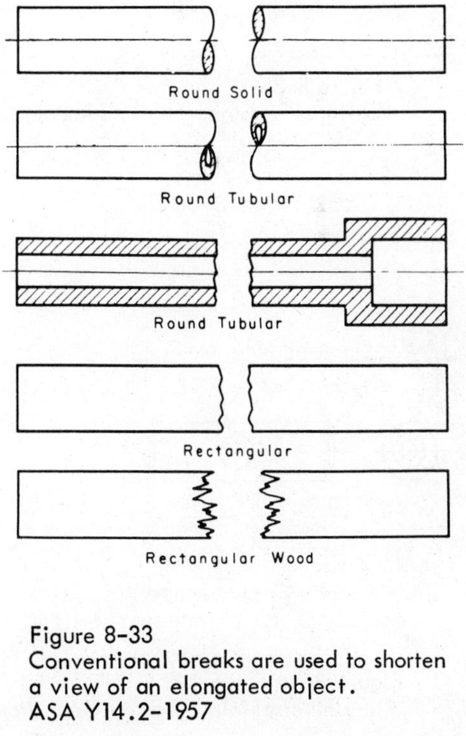

Figure 8-33
Conventional breaks are used to shorten a view of an elongated object.
ASA Y14.2-1957

6. *Ibid.*

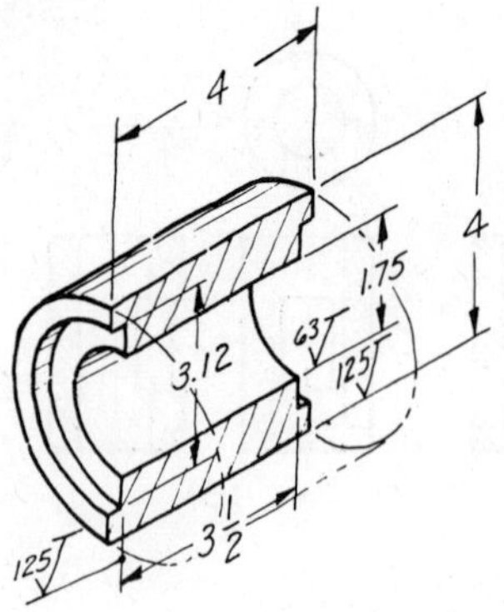

Figure 8–34
Idler roll. Johns-Manville

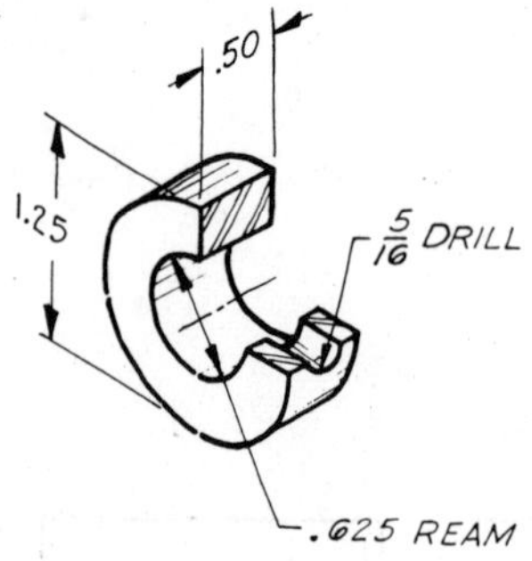

Figure 8–35
Collar. Firestone Tire and Rubber Co.

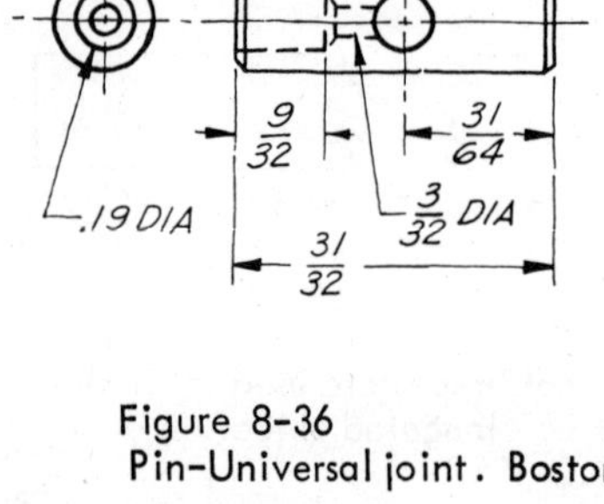

Figure 8–36
Pin-Universal joint. Boston Gear Works

Problems, section 8

1 Make a two view dimensioned drawing of the Idler Roll shown partially in the sketch of Fig. 8-34. Make one view in full section. Material: Steel.

2 Produce the necessary two views with dimensions of the Collar in the sketch of Fig. 8-35. Make one view a half section. Material: Aluminum, Spec. ASTM A7-52T.

3 Make the necessary views, completely dimensioned, of the Pin-Universal Joint, see sketch of Fig. 8-36. Show the interior shapes using a broken-out section. Material: Steel, Spec. QQ-S-770, Cond. QT, Class 1.

4 Construct the required views of the Ring Jacket shown partially in the sketch of Fig. 8-37. Make one view a full section. Material: Zamak No. 8. Include all dimensions.

5 Provide the necessary views with sizes of the Bracket Armature shown in the sketch of Fig. 8-38. Make one view in full section. Material: Brass, Spec. ASTM B 16, half hard. Finish: Cadmium Plate.

6 Draw the necessary views, complete with sizes of the cylindrical Shaft Housing, partially shown in the sketch of Fig. 8-39. Make one view a half section. Material: Steel Casting, SAE 030. Choose suitable fillet radii.

7 From the sketch of Fig. 8-40 of the Shaft-Transition Drum, produce the necessary views with dimensions. Make one view a full section to show interior. Assume any sizes not furnished. Material: Aluminum Bar, Spec. QQ-A-268, Temper T4. All machined surfaces to be 125 microinches.

8 Using the sketch of Fig. 8-41, construct two views of the steel Sprocket Blank complete with dimensions. Show one view as a half section.

9 Construct the necessary views of the cast Bracket, see sketch of Fig. 8-42, making one view a full section. Show all sizes. Material: Steel, Spec. SAE 050-080.

10 Make the necessary views with dimensions of the steel Sprocket Adapter shown in the sketch of Fig. 8-43. Show one view in full section.

11 Construct the required views with complete sizes of the Filter Connector, see sketch of Fig. 8-44. Material: Brass, Spec. QQ-B-626, Comp. 22.

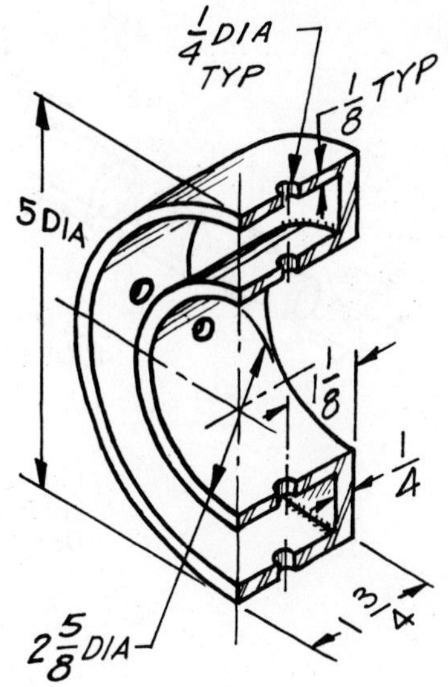

Figure 8-37
Ring jacket.

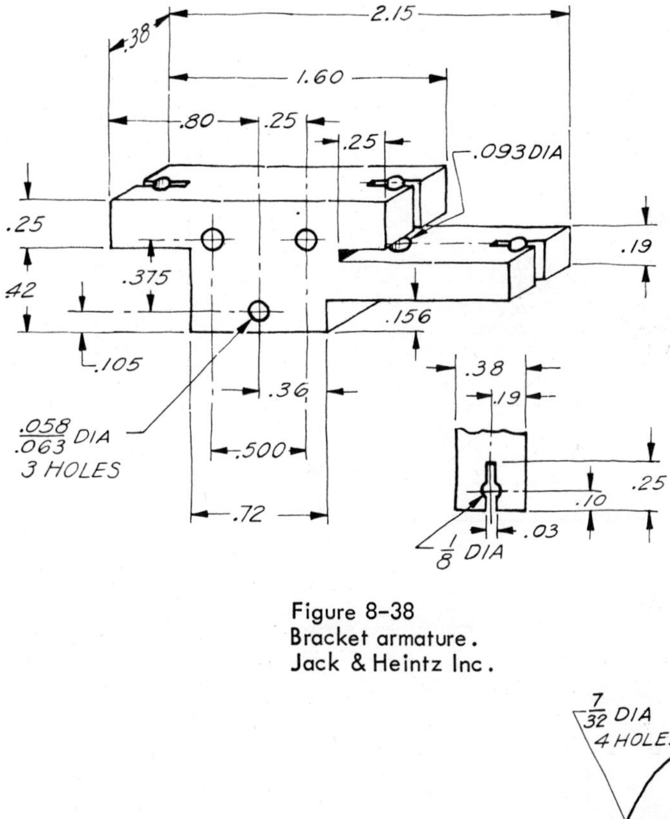

Figure 8-38
Bracket armature.
Jack & Heintz Inc.

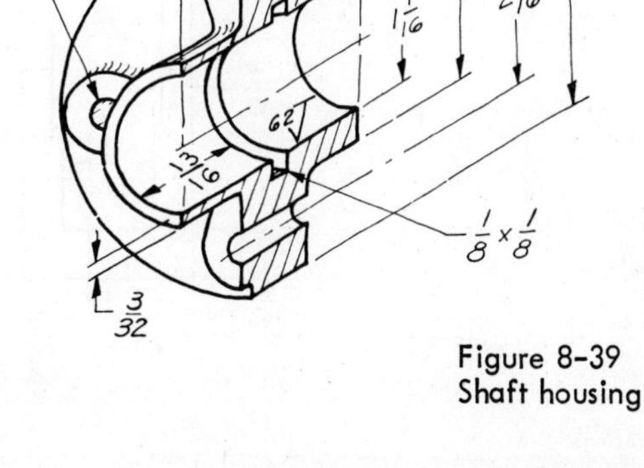

Figure 8-39
Shaft housing.

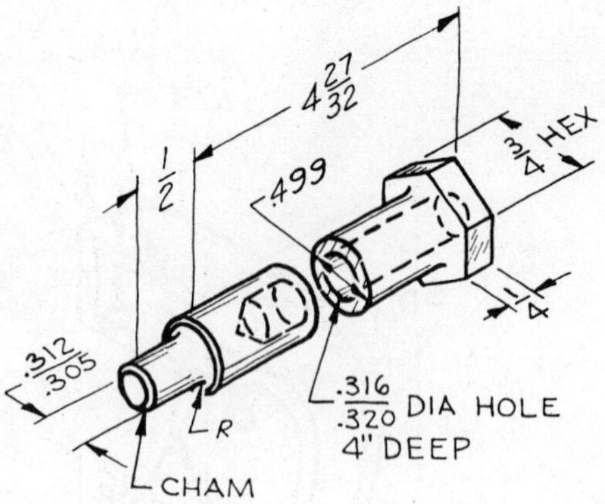

Figure 8-40
Shaft-transition drum.
Douglas Aircraft Co.

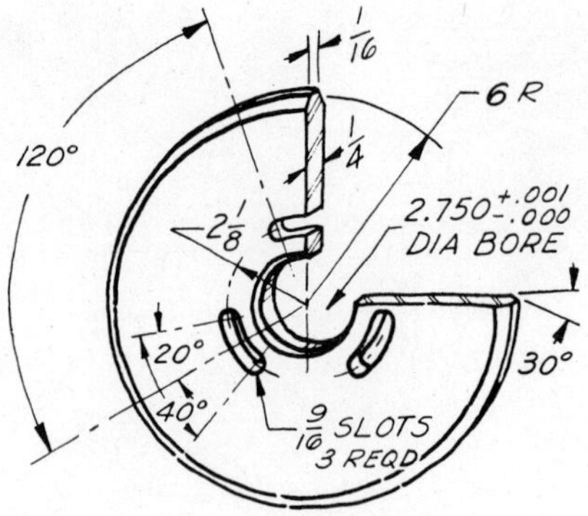

Figure 8-41
Steel sprocket blank.
Johns-Manville

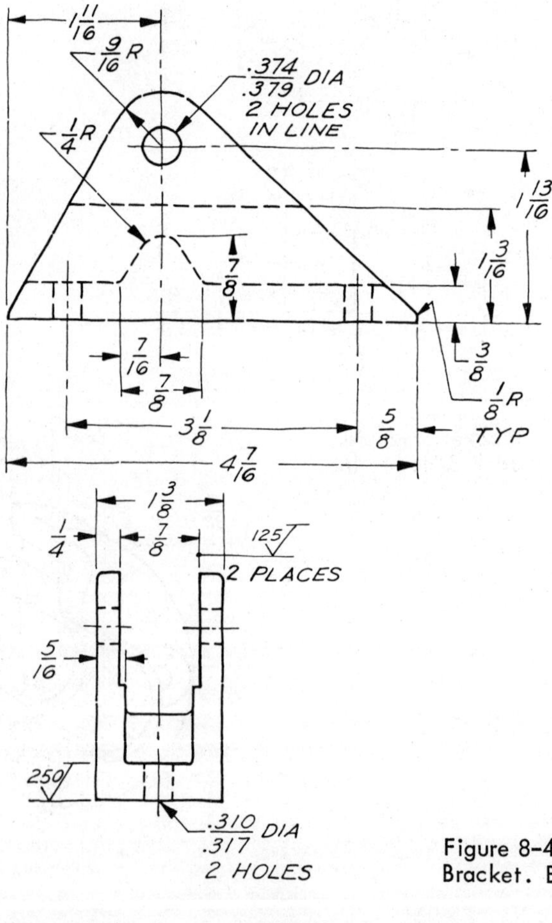

Figure 8-42
Bracket. Borg-Warner Corp.

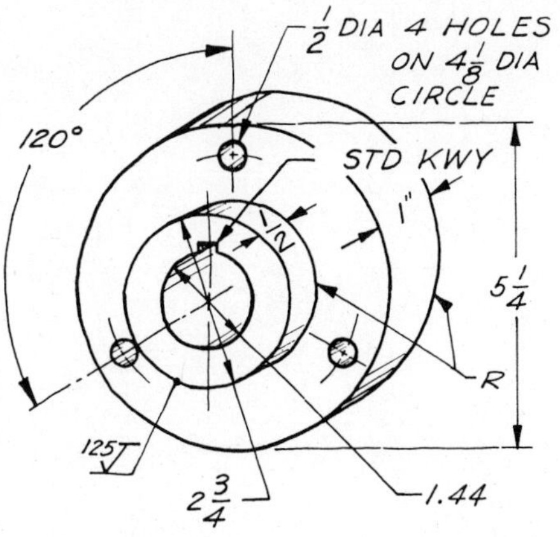

Figure 8-43
Sprocket adapter.
Johns-Manville

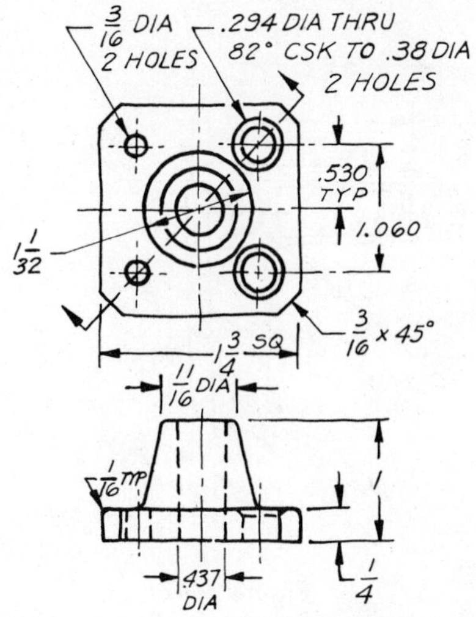

Figure 8-44
Filter connector.
Borg-Warner Corp.

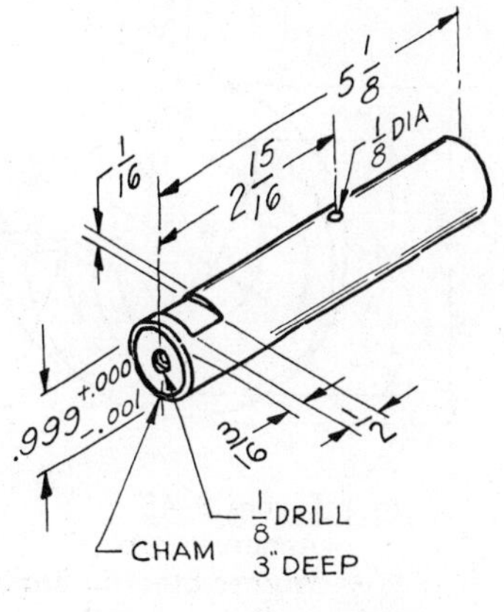

Figure 8-45
Pin. Johns-Manville

12 Draw two views of the Pin, shown in sketch of Fig. 8-45, with one view a broken-out section to show interior; include all sizes. Material: C.F. Steel.

13 Construct the proper views of the Spectrophotometer Drum, shown in sketch of Fig. 8-46. Include a full section. Show all dimensions. Material: Brass.

14 Construct the necessary views of the Bellcrank shown in the sketch of Fig. 8-47. Include dimensions. Show a revolved section of one arm. Material: Aluminum, 2014-T6.

15 Make a two view dimensioned drawing of the Armature Hub shown in sketch of Fig. 8-48. Make one view a full section. Material: Meehanite, Type GA.

16 Draw the appropriate views of the Base shown in the sketch of Fig. 8-49. Material: Cast Iron. Show all sizes and make one view a full offset section.

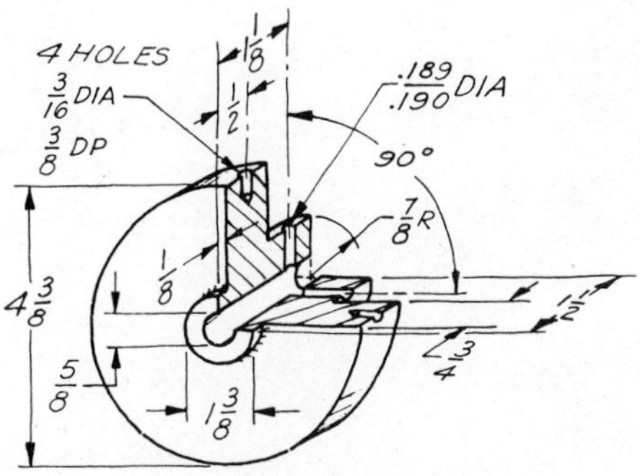

Figure 8-46
Spectrophotometer drum.
Bausch & Lomb Optical Co.

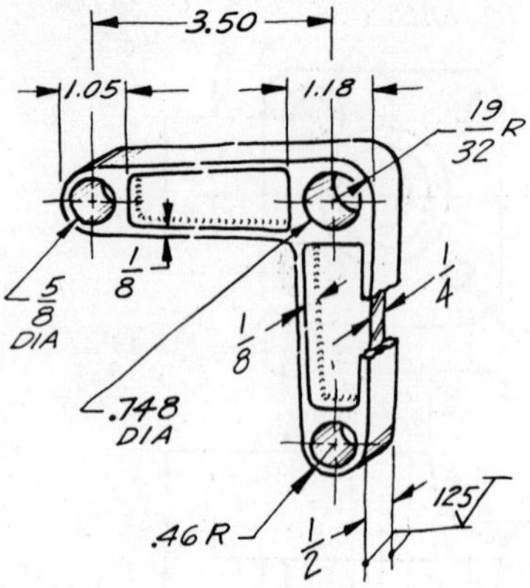

Figure 8-47
Bellcrank. Boeing Airplane Co.

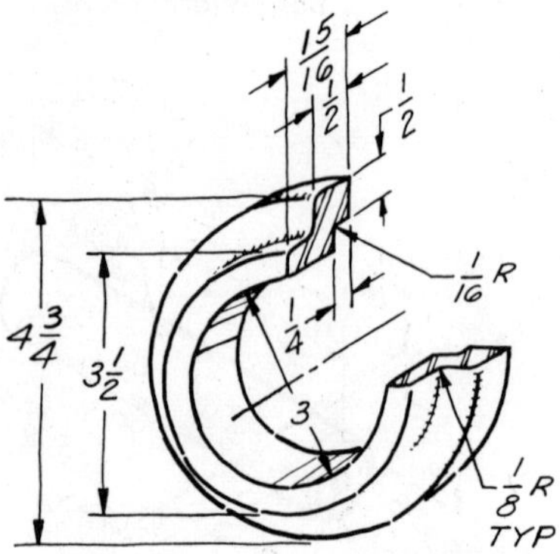

Figure 8-48
Armature hub.
Warner Electric Brake & Clutch Co.

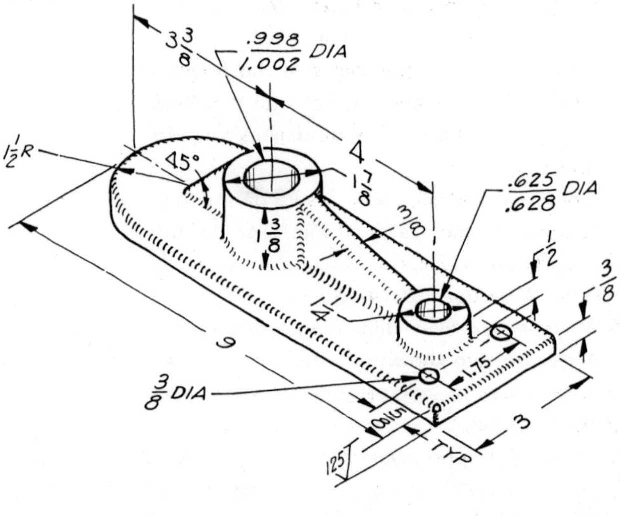

Figure 8-49
Base.

Auxiliary views 9

Section 5 described the method of presenting the principal views of an object on a drawing. For the most part, that section dealt with objects in which their true shape could be projected to the three principal planes of projection. However, some objects have inclined surfaces and consequently their true shapes cannot always be shown in the regular planes of projection. Since a drawing to be complete must portray the exact shape of all essential surfaces, it becomes obvious that other means are necessary to describe inclined surfaces. The views employed for such purposes are know as *primary* and *secondary auxiliary views*. How these views are drawn is described in this section.

9.1 Primary auxiliary view

A primary auxiliary view is one which is projected to a plane that is perpendicular to one of the three principal planes and inclined to the other two. Thus as shown in Fig. 9-1, the inclined surface is perpendicular to the front plane and inclined to the top and side planes. The true shape of the slanted surface is obtained only by passing a plane parallel to the inclined surface. This auxiliary plane is then considered to be hinged to the plane to which it is perpendicular and revolved into the front plane in much the same way the other views are rotated to their principal planes of projection. Notice in Fig. 9-2 the position the auxiliary view assumes when it is revolved in the front plane.

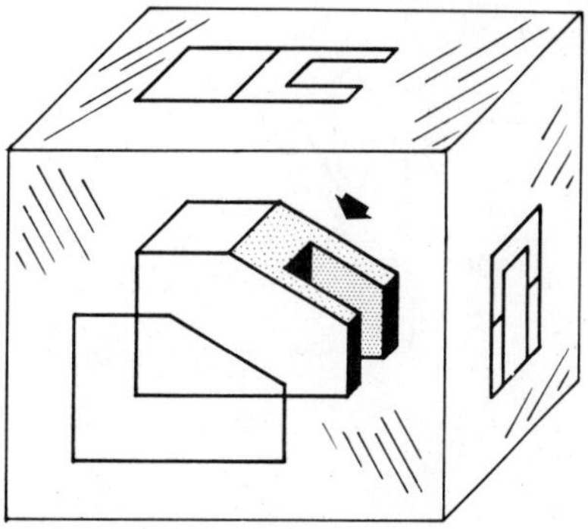

Figure 9-1
A primary auxiliary view is perpendicular to one plane and inclined to the other two.

9.2 Auxiliary partial view

In making an auxiliary view, the practice is to show the actual contour of only the inclined surface. The projection of the entire view usually adds very little to the shape description. More often than not the additional lines needed to present a complete view detracts from the true intent of the auxiliary. Notice in Fig. 9-3 how much clearer the true shape of the auxiliary surface is than when the entire view is drawn as in Fig. 9-4.

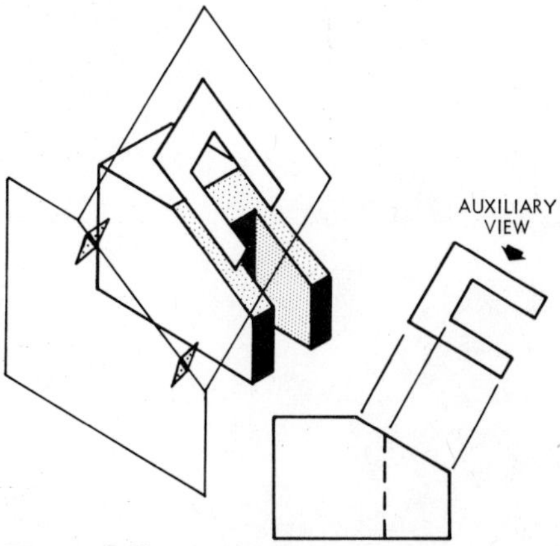

Figure 9-2
This is the position of the auxiliary view when the inclined surface is revolved into the frontal plane.

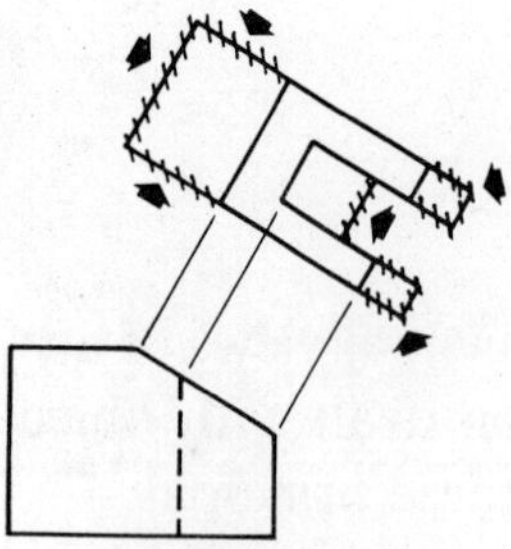

Figure 9-3
Only the shape of the slanted surface needs to be shown in the auxiliary view.

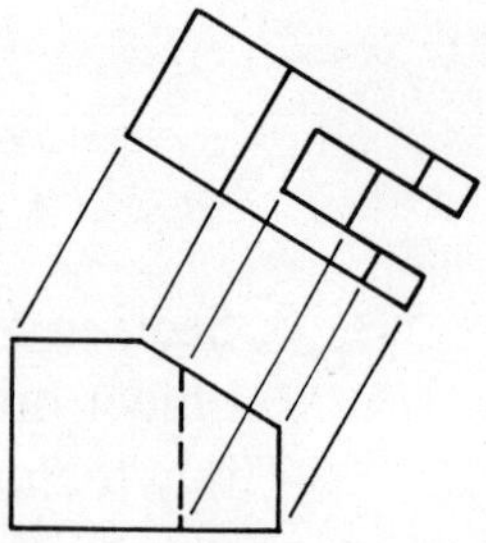

Figure 9-4
A complete auxiliary is often confusing and requires more time to draw.

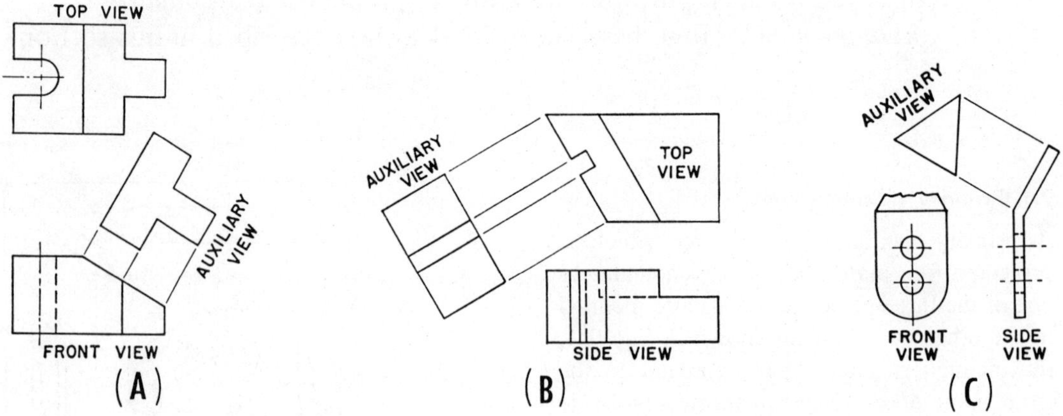

Figure 9-5
Primary auxiliary views are classified according to the plane to which the auxiliary view is hinged.

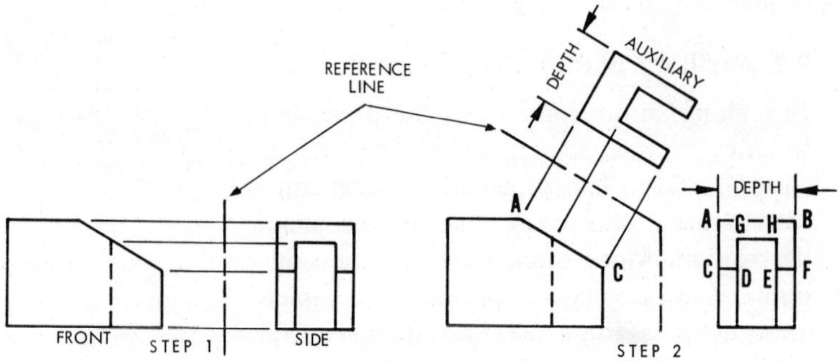

Figure 9-6
Steps in drawing an auxiliary view.

9.3 Types of primary auxiliary views

Generally, primary auxiliary views may be classified into three groups—*front auxiliary, top auxiliary,* and *side auxiliary.* The views are determined according to the plane to which the auxiliary surface is hinged. A front auxiliary view is one where the inclined surface is perpendicular to the frontal plane and is assumed to be hinged to the frontal plane. See Fig. 9-5A. A top auxiliary view is one where the inclined surface is perpendicular to the top plane and is hinged to the top plane. See Fig. 9-5B. A side auxiliary view is one where the inclined surface is perpendicular to the side plane and is considered to be hinged to the side plane. See Fig. 9-5C.

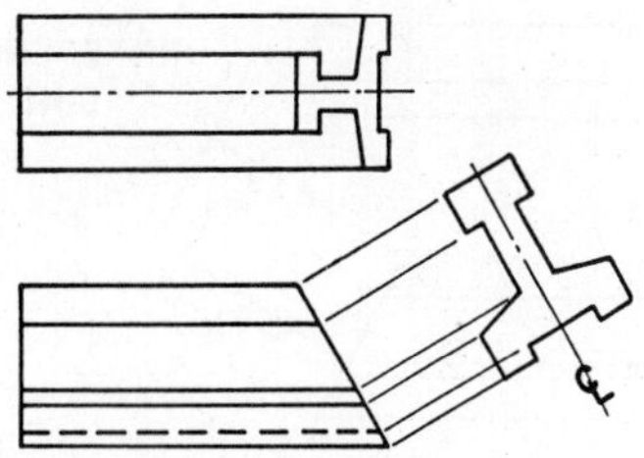

Figure 9-7
In a symmetrical auxiliary, the view is worked from the right and left of the reference line.

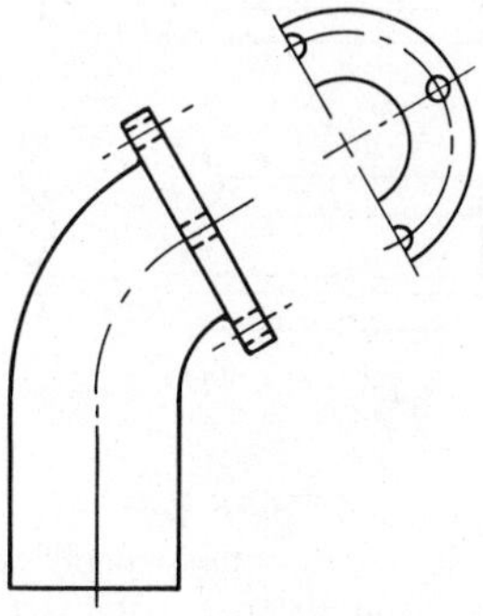

Figure 9-8
Drawing time is saved if only half of a symmetrical auxiliary is made.

9.4 Drawing a primary auxiliary view

Fig. 9-6 illustrates the general procedure for constructing any primary auxiliary view. The basic steps are as follows:

1 Draw two related principal views of the object, such as the front and side views. One of the principal views must always include the edge line of the inclined surface. See Step 1 of Fig. 9-6. Here the edge line *AC* of the inclined surface appears in the front view.

2 Draw a reference line parallel to the edge line of the inclined plane. This reference line is assumed to be the hinge line which connects the auxiliary view with the frontal plane. The reference line should be located at some convenient distance from the line of projection so the auxiliary view falls in a clear space on the drawing sheet. See Step 2 of Fig. 9-6.

3 From the principal view containing the edge line of the inclined surface, extend perpendiculars to the reference line.

4 With compass or dividers secure the necessary depth dimensions and transfer them to the auxiliary view. For example, the depth dimensions of the auxiliary view in Fig. 9-6 are obtained from the side view. Thus the length of lines *AB, CD,* and *EF* are all transferred from the side view to the auxiliary view.

5 Since both the front and side views of the object shown in Fig. 9-6 contain all the necessary dimensions, no top view is required. A top view in this instance would simply cause an overlapping of projections.

6 Hidden lines as a rule are omitted from an auxiliary view unless they are needed for clarity.

The same procedure is also followed in projecting an auxiliary view from the top or side view. In all three types of auxiliary views the shape description of the slanted surface is projected from the view that shows the surface as an oblique line. The distances for the auxiliary are then taken from the other principal views that contain the common sizes for the slanted surface.

9.5 Symmetrical auxiliary view

If an auxiliary view is symmetrical, the reference line can serve as a center line, and the auxiliary view worked from the right and left of this line. See Fig. 9-7.

To save drawing time, the practice is to include only half of the view. Thus in the flange shown in Fig. 9-8, only the one half

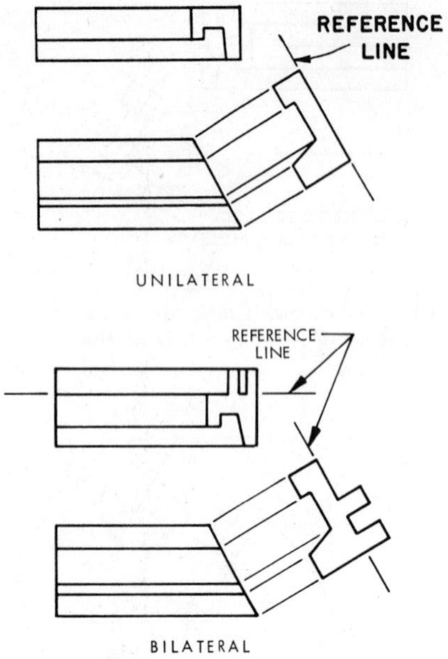

Figure 9-9
A non-symmetrical auxiliary is considered either unilateral or bilateral.

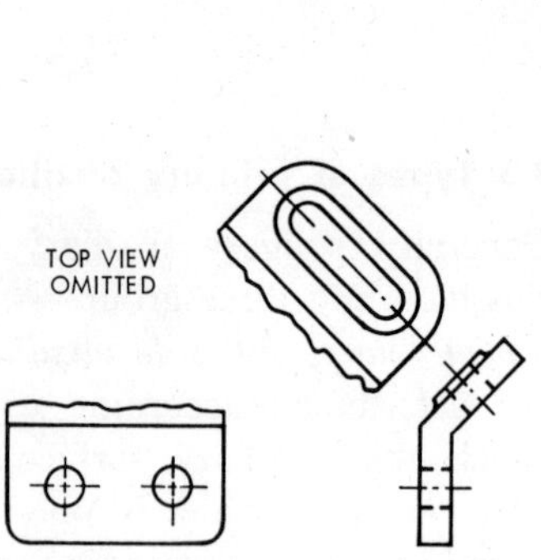

Figure 9-10
An auxiliary often eliminates the need for one of the principal views.

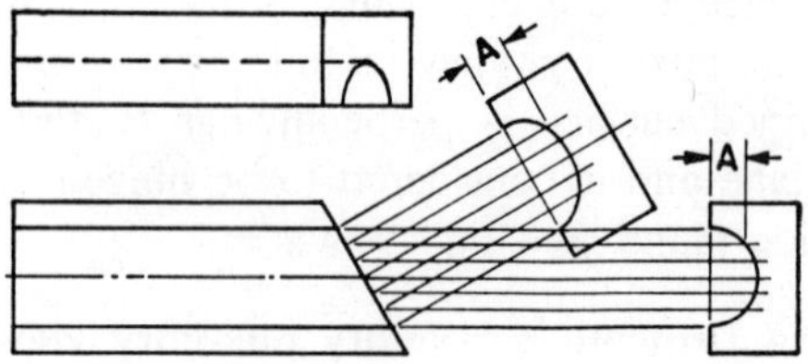

Figure 9-11
This is how a curved line auxiliary view is drawn.

is drawn since the other portion is simply a duplication of the part shown.

9.6 Unsymmetrical auxiliary view

An unsymmetrical auxiliary is considered to be *unilateral* or *bilateral.* A unilateral auxiliary is drawn entirely on one side of the reference line. A bilateral view is projected on both sides of the reference line. See Fig. 9-9.

9.7 Elimination of principal views

Frequently an auxiliary view permits the elimination of one of the principal views; that is, top, front or side views. The general rule is to eliminate a principal view whenever the auxiliary provides sufficient description for a complete understanding of the shape of the part. Thus in Fig. 9-10, the auxiliary furnishes enough information without having to include a top view. Observation of this practice simplifies the readability of the drawing and reduces considerable drawing time.

9.8 Drawing auxiliary views having curved surfaces

Fig. 9-11 illustrates the necessary steps in drawing an auxiliary view having a curved surface. A side view of the curved surface is drawn first and the curve divided into any number of equal parts. These points are projected across to the slanted edge of the front view. From the front view the points are projected to the reference line of the auxiliary view. Each distance shown as *A* in the side view of Fig. 9-11 is taken and spaced off on the auxiliary view.

9.9 Double auxiliary view

The majority of engineering drawings usually involve the preparation of views that are in conventional planes of projection. However, there are instances when the true shape of the object cannot be shown in the ordinary planes of projection. For such objects a *double auxiliary view,* sometimes referred to as a *secondary auxiliary view,* is necessary. A double auxiliary view may be de-

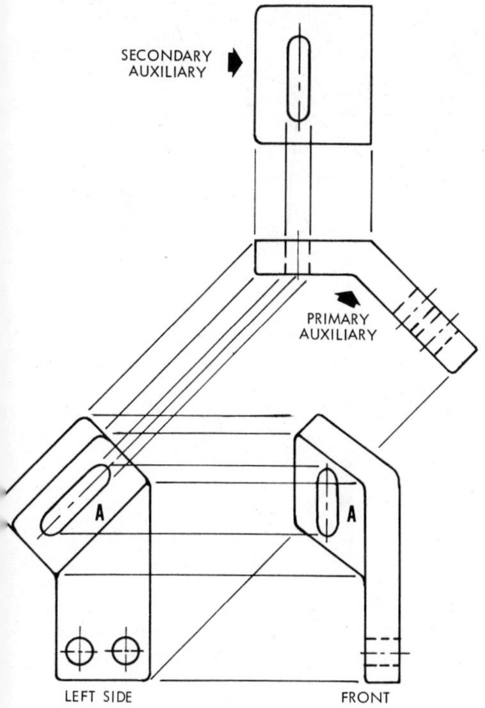

Figure 9-12
To show the true shape of this object a secondary auxiliary view is necessary.

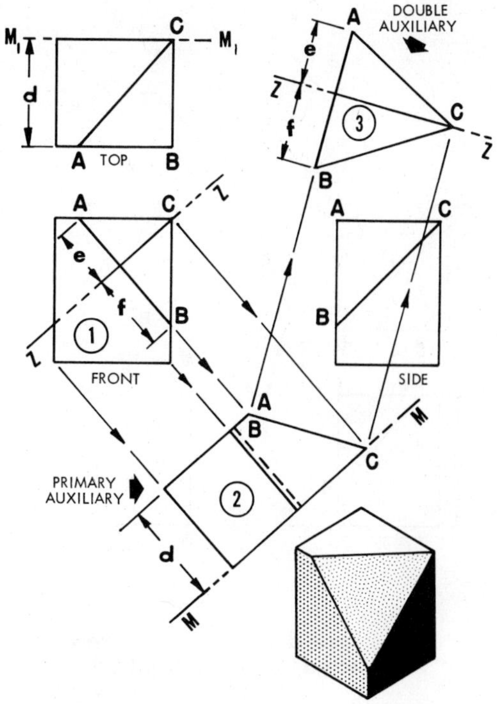

Figure 9-13
Preparing a double auxiliary view which is projected from a front auxiliary view.

fined as a projection that lies obliquely to all of the principal views. Whereas a primary auxiliary view is always projected from a principal view, a double auxiliary view is always projected from a primary auxiliary view.

The object illustrated in Fig. 9-12 is an example of the need for a double auxiliary view. Notice that the true shape of surface *A* cannot be shown in either the front, side, or primary auxiliary view. The actual shape of the object can be produced only by first drawing a primary auxiliary view from the side view and then projecting a double auxiliary view from the primary auxiliary view.

A double or secondary auxiliary view may be projected from a front, top, or side auxiliary view.

9.10 Double auxiliary view projected from a front auxiliary view

The procedure for drawing a double auxiliary view which is to be projected from a front auxiliary view is as follows:

1 Draw a primary auxiliary view by projecting lines parallel to line *AB* from points in the front view. See Fig. 9-13. Establish a reference plane *MM* at some convenient distance so it is perpendicular to lines drawn from the front view. Complete the outline of the primary auxiliary view with the distance *d* taken from the top view. Surface *ABC* now appears as line *BC* in the primary auxiliary view.

2 To show the true shape of surface *ABC*, construct the double auxiliary view by projecting parallel lines from the edge view *BC* in the primary auxiliary view. These lines should be perpendicular to edge *BC* and reference plane *ZZ* which is placed in some convenient position. Locate reference plane *ZZ* in the front view so it is perpendicular to line *AB*. Distances such as *e* and *f* are then transferred from the front view to the double auxiliary view which together with the parallel lines extending from the primary auxiliary view will furnish the necessary points to complete the view.

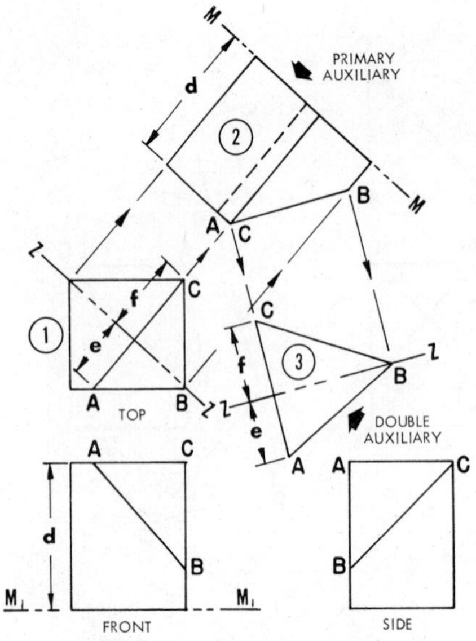

Figure 9-14
Preparing a double auxiliary view which is projected from a top auxiliary view.

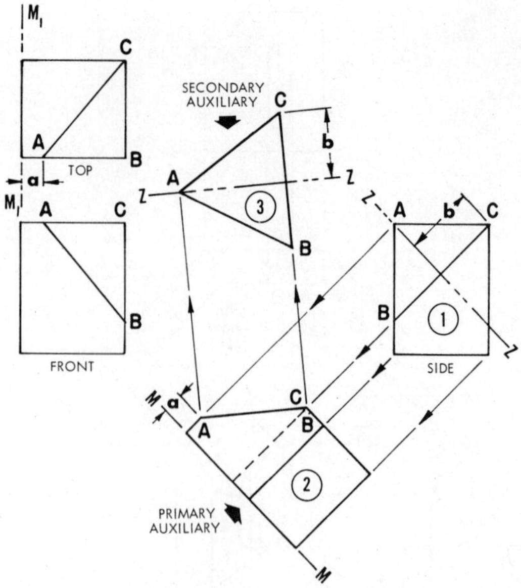

Figure 9-15
Preparing a double auxiliary view which is projected from a side auxiliary view.

9.11 Double auxiliary view projected from a top auxiliary view

If the arrangement of the view is such that a primary auxiliary view must be projected from a top view as shown in Fig. 9-14, the double auxiliary view is constructed as follows:

1 Draw a primary auxiliary view by projecting lines parallel to line *AC* in the top view. Locate reference plane *MM* so it is perpendicular to the projectors from the top view. Distances such as *d* are taken from the front view.

2 Construct the double auxiliary view by projecting parallel lines from the edge *CB* in the primary auxiliary view perpendicular to the reference plane *ZZ*. Draw reference plane *ZZ* in the top view perpendicular to line *AC*. Transfer distances such as *e* and *f* in the top view to the double auxiliary view.

9.12 Double auxiliary views projected from a side auxiliary view

The procedure for drawing a double auxiliary view which is to be projected from a side auxiliary view is essentially the same as described in Sub-sections 9.10 and 9.11. The primary auxiliary view is completed first and the double auxiliary view then projected from this view. See Fig. 9-15. For additional information regarding double auxiliary view solutions see Section 21.

9.13 Engineering representation of auxiliary views

In actual engineering drawings the representation of an auxiliary view will include only such principal views as are necessary to complete the auxiliary view. For most objects two principal views usually are sufficient. The complete details of the true shape of the inclined surfaces are then shown on the auxiliary views. Fig. 9-16 (A and B) is a typical example of how primary and secondary auxiliary views are actually prepared for objects having inclined surfaces which are oblique to principal planes of projection.

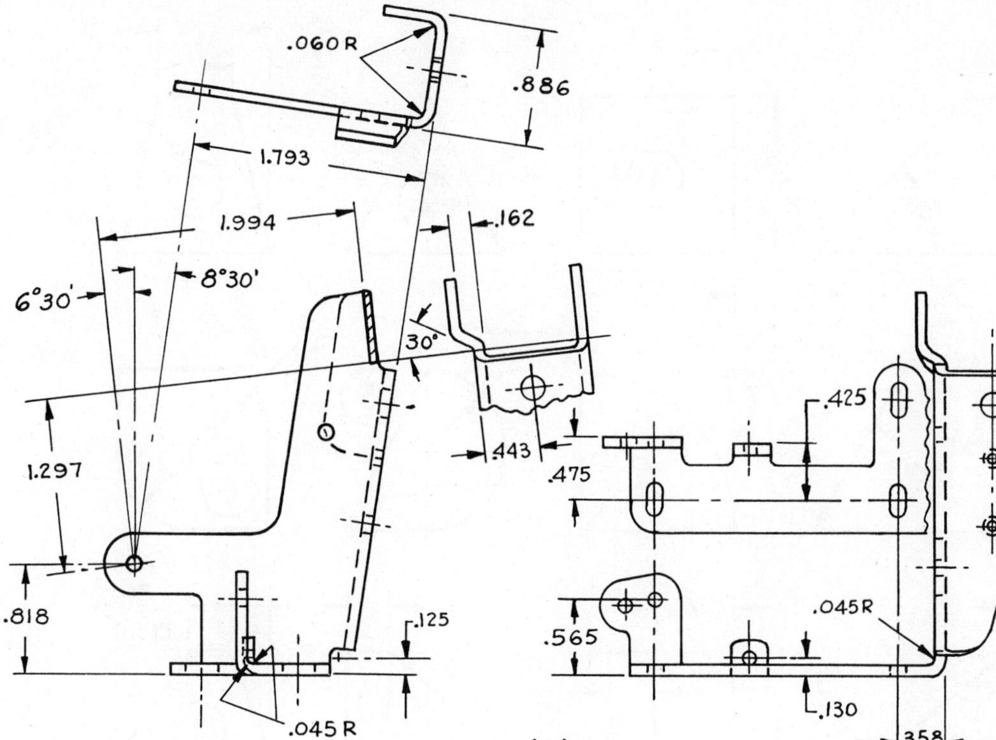

(A)

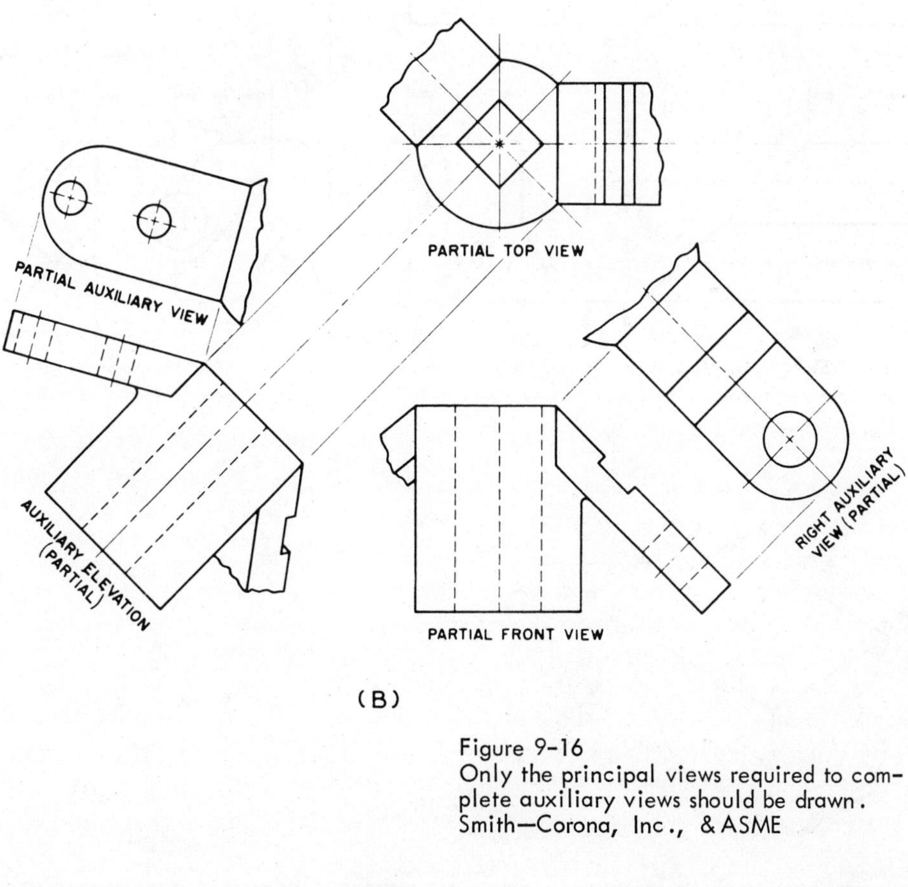

(B)

Figure 9-16
Only the principal views required to complete auxiliary views should be drawn.
Smith—Corona, Inc., & ASME

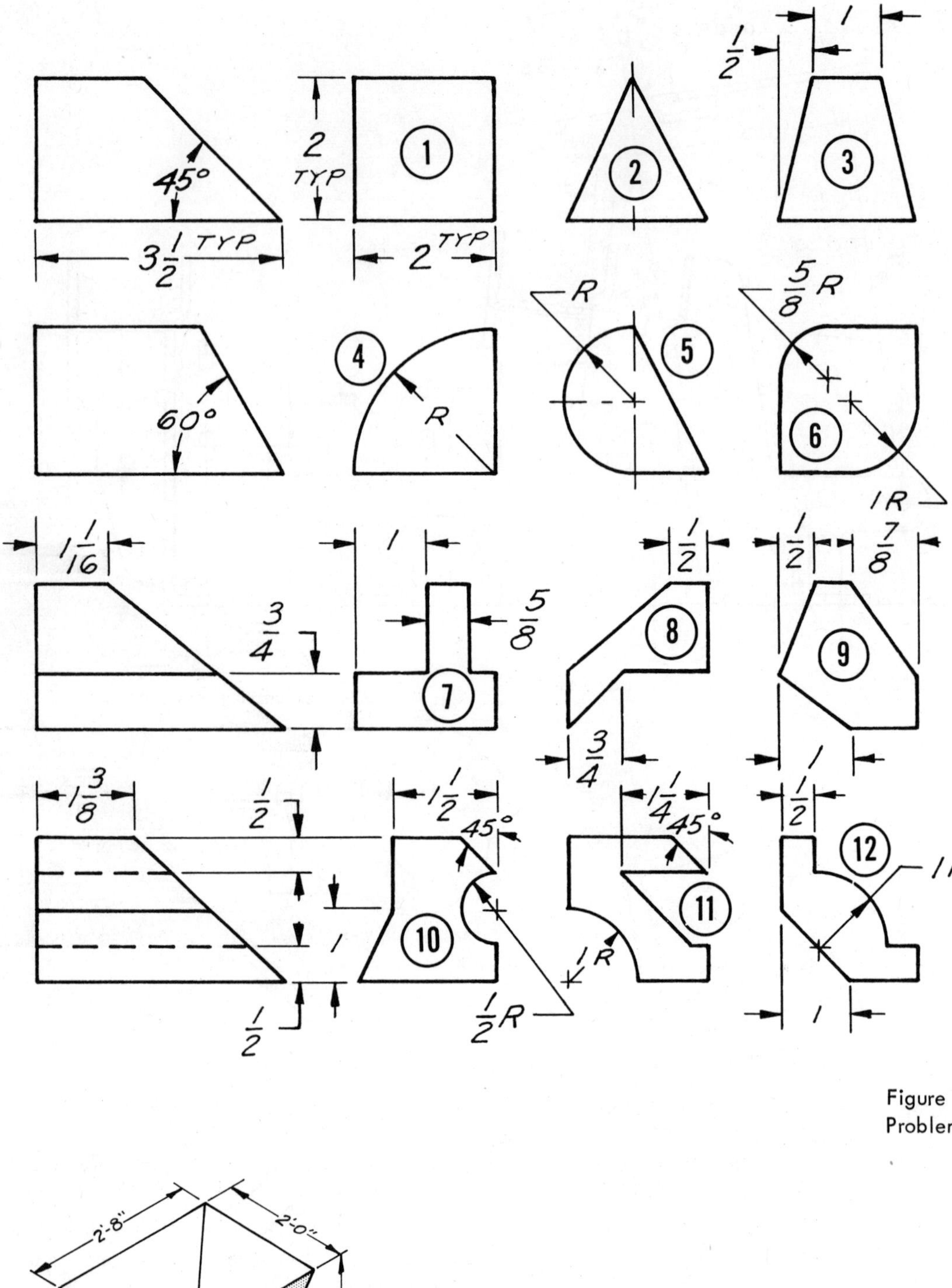

Figure 9–17
Problems 1–12.

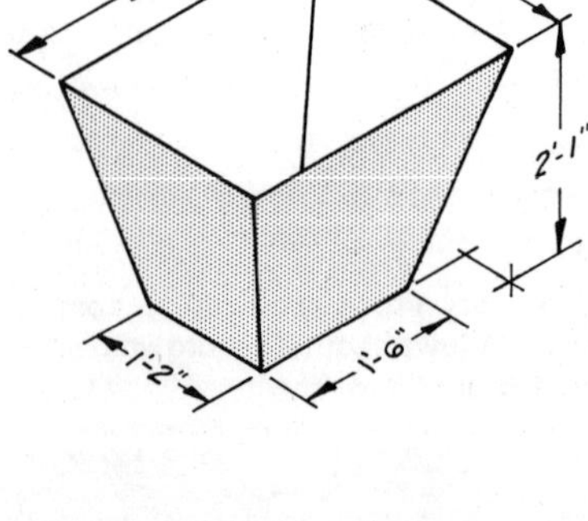

Figure 9–18
Hopper.

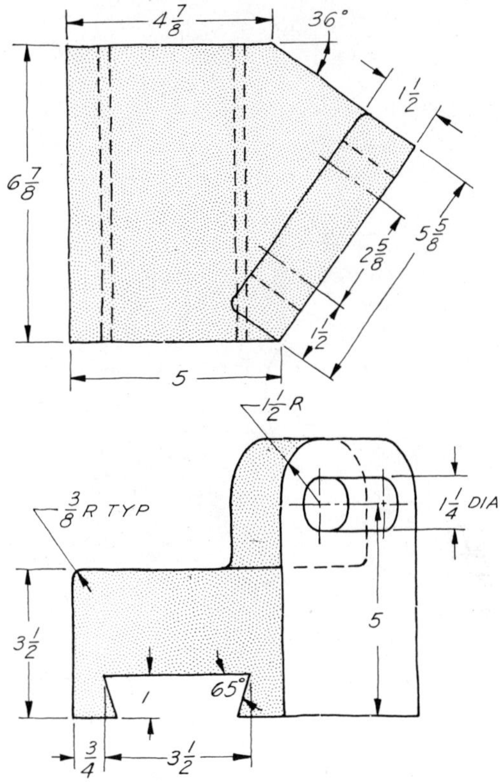

Figure 9–19
Cross slide bracket.

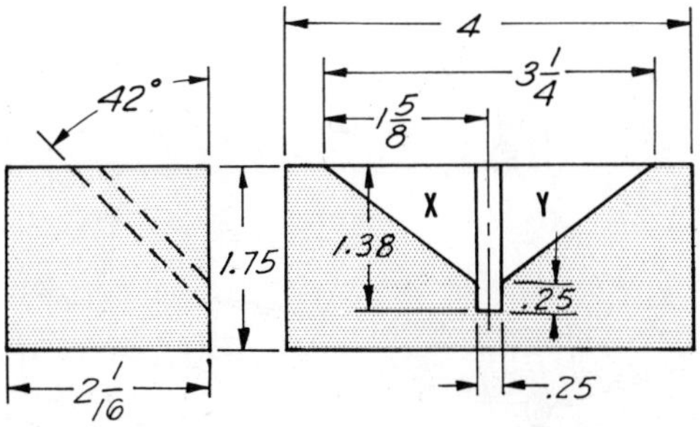

Figure 9–20
Guide block.

Problems, section 9

1-12 Draw the given front and right side views and add an auxiliary view of each of the problems shown in Fig. 9-17.

13 By means of auxiliary views, determine the true shapes of the inclined plates of the Hopper shown in Fig. 9-18. Dimension the auxiliary views as well as the principal views. All material: 1/4" steel plate.

14 Draw the top and front views of the Cross Slide Bracket shown in the sketch of Fig. 9-19. Add an auxiliary view of the inclined face. Dimension completely. Material: Cast steel, Spec. SAE 030.

15 Draw front, left side and a complete auxiliary view of the Guide Block shown in Fig. 9-20. Material: Tool Steel. Make another auxiliary view to show the true angle between surfaces **X** and **Y.**

16 Prepare the necessary principal and auxiliary views of the Angle Bracket included in the sketch of Fig. 9-21. Show dimensions.

17 Make a dimensioned drawing of the Rod Guide in the sketch of Fig. 9-22, showing the necessary principal and auxiliary views.

18 Prepare the necessary views with dimensions of the Pulley Support in the sketch of Fig. 9-23. Material: 2020-T4 Clad Aluminum, .090 thick.

19 Construct the necessary views of the Angle Support shown in the sketch of Fig. 9-24. Dimension properly. Material: Meehanite, grade GB.

20 Make a complete dimensioned drawing of the Bracket in the sketch of Fig. 9-25. Material: Magnesium, Spec. QQ-M-56, Comp. AZ 63, Temp. T6.

21-24 Draw the necessary views including a secondary auxiliary of each problem shown in Fig. 9-26. Refer to Par. 21.9, p. 611.

25 Prepare the necessary views including a secondary auxiliary view of the Mounting shown in the sketch of Fig. 9-27. Material: Zamak No. 8.

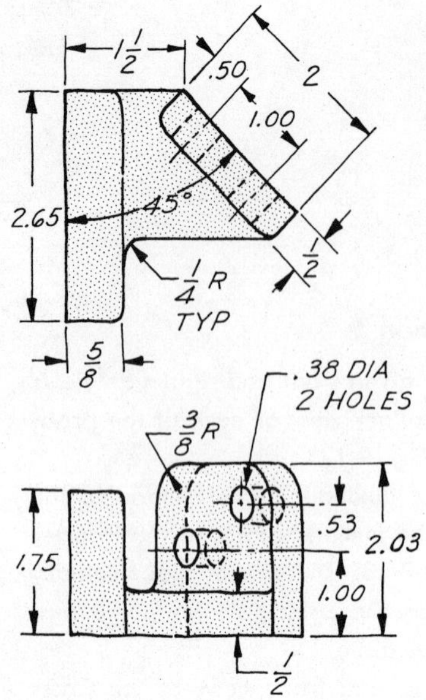

Figure 9-21
Angle bracket.

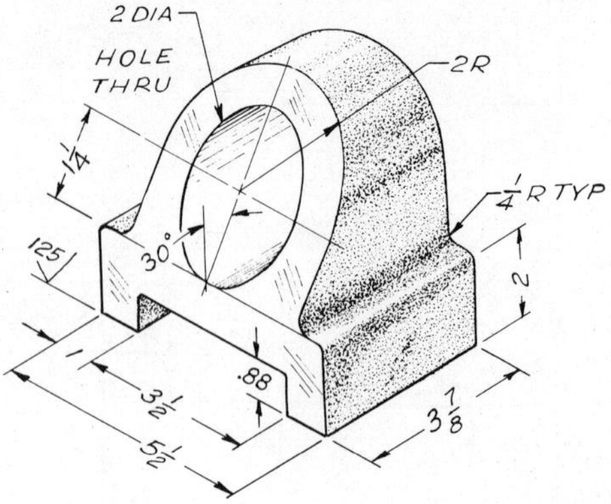

Figure 9-22
Rod guide.

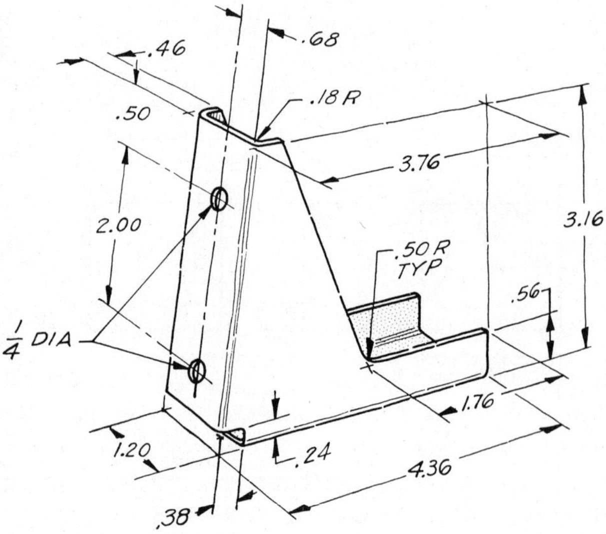

Figure 9-23
Pulley support.

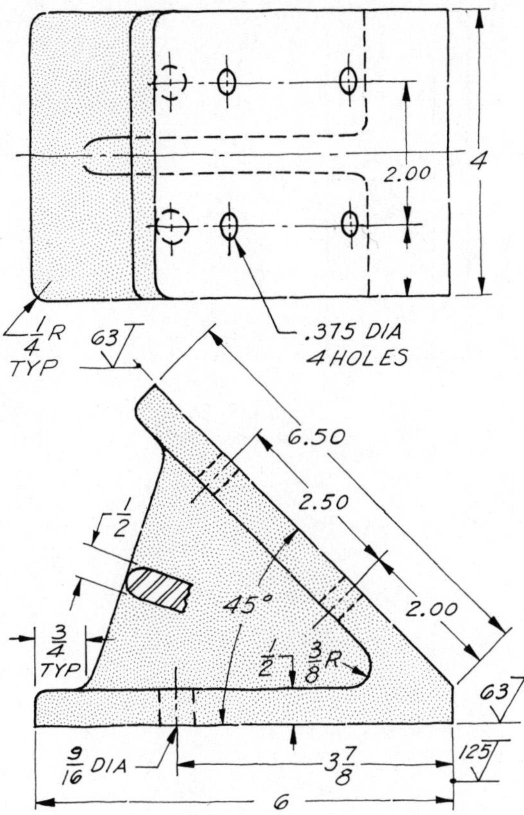

Figure 9-24
Angle support.

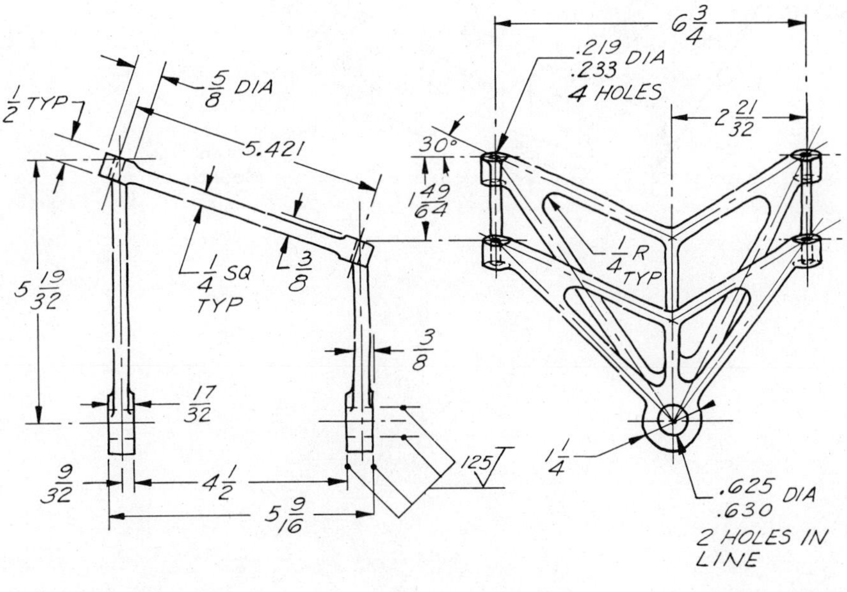

Figure 9-25
Bracket.

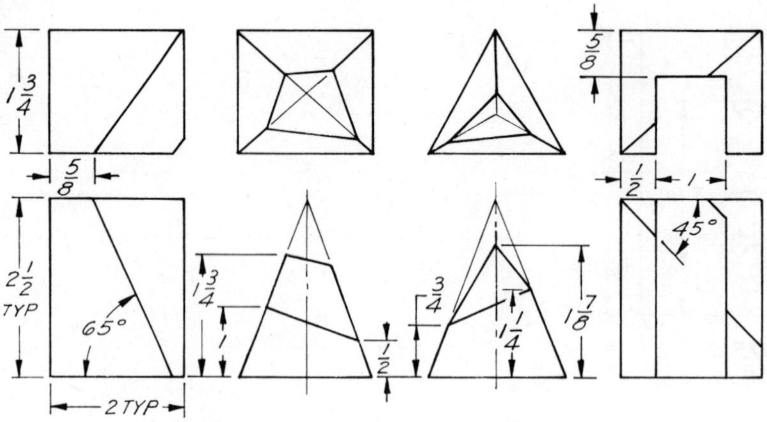

Figure 9-26
Problems 21-24.

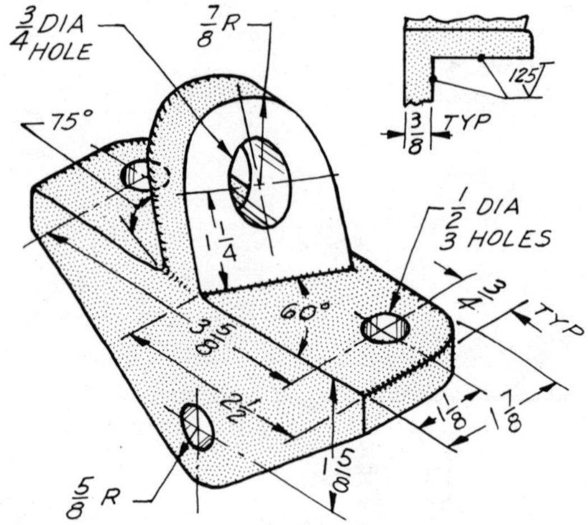

Figure 9-27
Mounting.

Fasteners 10

In the manufacture of any structural assembly, various means are used to fasten parts together. The kind of fastener employed is governed by such factors as method of fabrication, kind and strength of materials, as well as the function of the assembly itself.

While designing a component, the engineer must not only determine what types of fastening devices will best serve the purpose but he must also specify them correctly in the assembly drawing. Therefore, it becomes obvious that he needs to have a thorough understanding of different fastening processes. The basic information covering fasteners in general is included in this section.

10.1 Classification of fasteners

All fastening devices may be classified into two main groups. One group includes fasteners which are intended to join parts permanently together. Permanent fasteners are rivets, nails and wood screws. Welding can be considered as falling into this classification, since any welding process will permanently fasten sections together. See *Section 11.*

The second group of fasteners are those which permit parts to be disassembled whenever necessary. In this category are such devices as bolts, machine screws, cap screws, set screws, keys and pins. See Fig. 10-1.

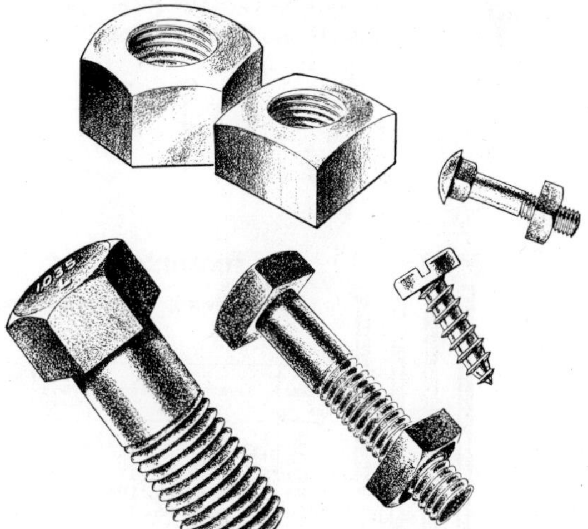

Figure 10-1
Threaded fasteners play an important role in the fabrication of industrial products. Lamson & Sessions

10.2 Nails

See Fig. 10-2. When parts are fastened with nails, no special convention is used to represent nails on a drawing. If necessary, the draftsman simply specifies the size and type by means of a note.

The most commonly used nails are known as *common, box, casing,* and *finishing nails,* and *tacks. Common nails* have larger diameters and wider heads than other types and are used mostly in rough carpentry. *Box nails* also have wide heads but are not as large in diameter as common nails. They are used extensively in box construction and in many types of carpentry where common nails would be unsuitable. *Casing nails* are smaller in diameter and head size than box nails and are especially designed for blind nailing of flooring, ceilings, and cabinet work where large heads are undesirable. *Finishing nails* have the smallest diameters and the smallest heads. Their chief use is in cabinet work and furniture construction where it is often necessary to sink the heads below the surface of the wood.

COMMON NAILS

20d 16d 12d 10d 9d 8d 7d 6d

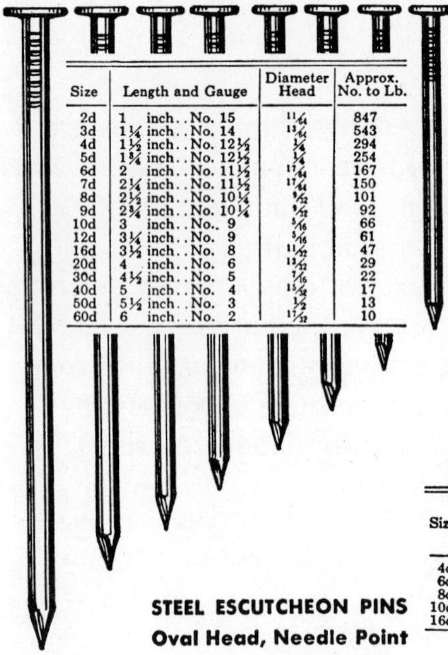

Size	Length and Gauge	Diameter Head	Approx. No. to Lb.
2d	1 inch..No. 15	11/64	847
3d	1¼ inch..No. 14	13/64	543
4d	1½ inch..No. 12½	¼	294
5d	1¾ inch..No. 12½	¼	254
6d	2 inch..No. 11½	17/64	167
7d	2¼ inch..No. 11½	17/64	150
8d	2½ inch..No. 10¼	9/32	101
9d	2¾ inch..No. 10¼	9/32	92
10d	3 inch..No.. 9	5/16	66
12d	3¼ inch..No. 9	5/16	61
16d	3½ inch..No. 8	11/32	47
20d	4 inch..No. 6	13/32	29
30d	4½ inch..No. 5	7/16	22
40d	5 inch..No. 4	15/32	17
50d	5½ inch..No. 3	½	13
60d	6 inch..No. 2	17/32	10

SMOOTH BOX NAILS

Large Flat Head, Diamond Point

Size	Length and Gauge	Diameter Head	Approx. No. to Lb.
3d	1¼ inch...No. 14½	7/32	588
4d	1½ inch...No. 14	7/32	453
5d	1¾ inch...No. 14	7/32	389
6d	2 inch...No. 12½	17/64	225
7d	2¼ inch...No. 12½	17/64	200
8d	2½ inch...No. 11½	19/64	136
10d	3 inch...No. 10½	5/16	90
16d	3½ inch...No. 10	11/32	69
20d	4 inch...No. 9	3/8	50

CASING NAILS

Deep Countersunk Head, Diamond Point

4d 6d 8d 10d 16d

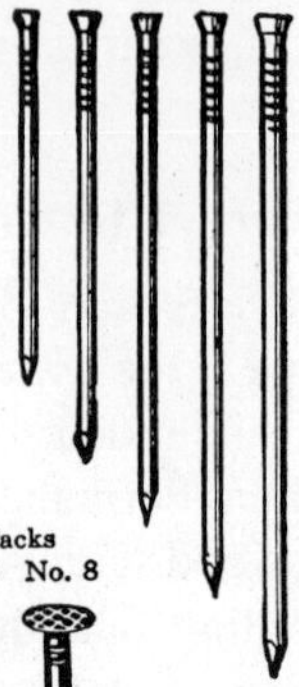

Size	Length and Gauge	Degree of Countersunk	Dia. Head Ga.	Ap. No. to Lb.
4d	1½ inch..No. 14	32	11	489
6d	2 inch..No. 12½	32	9½	244
8d	2½ inch..No. 11½	32	8½	147
10d	3 inch..No. 10½	32	7½	96
16d	3½ inch..No. 10	32	7	73

STEEL ESCUTCHEON PINS

Oval Head, Needle Point

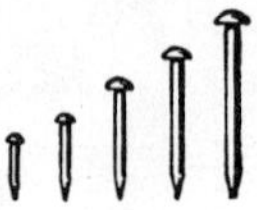

Carpet Tacks

No. 4 No. 6 No. 8

FINISHING NAILS

Brad Head, Diamond Point

8d 6d 4d 3d

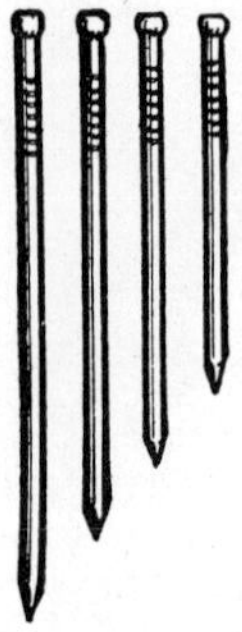

Size	Length and Gauge	Dia. Head Gauge	Approx. No. to Pound
3d	1¼ inch. .No. 15½	12½	880
4d	1½ inch. .No. 15	12	630
6d	2 inch. .No. 13	10	288
8d	2½ inch. .No. 12½	9½	196
10d	3 inch. .No. 11½	8½	124

Upholsterer Tacks

No. 4 No. 6 No. 8

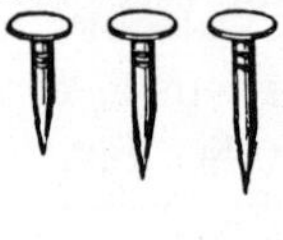

Double Pointed Tacks

No. 8 No. 9 No. 10

Figure 10-2
These are the most common types of nails, brads, and tacks.

Sizes of nails are designated by the term *penny* (symbol *d*), with a number as a prefix such as 4*d*, 10*d*. The term penny refers to the weight of the nails per thousand in quantity. Thus a 6*d* nail means that the nails weigh six pounds per thousand. The weight has a direct relationship to the size.

Brads are the smallest type of finishing nails. The sizes of brads are indicated by the length in inches and the diameter by the gage number of the wire. The higher the gage number the smaller the diameter.

Tacks are used mostly for fastening material to some wooden surface. The several different shapes of tacks are illustrated in Fig. 10-2. Sizes of tacks are indicated by a gage number which in turn governs their length.

On a drawing nails, brads or tacks are shown as

8*d* FINISHING NAIL
1″–NO. 20 BRAD
NO. 4 CARPET TACK

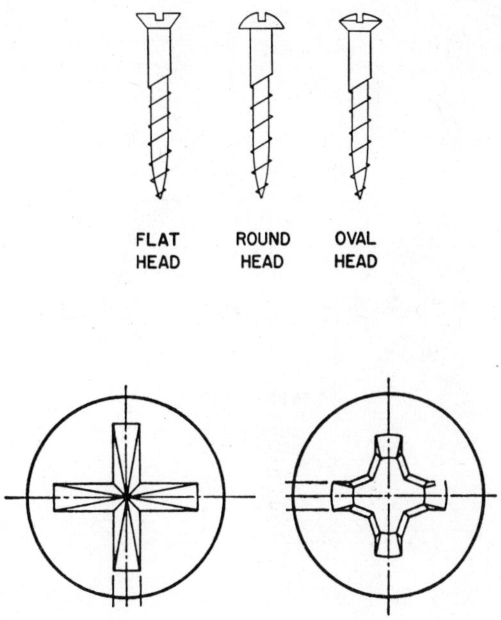

Figure 10–3
Common types of wood screws.

10.3 Wood screws

Wood screws are made of steel, brass, bronze and aluminum alloy. They are available in three types of heads: flat, oval, and round. See Fig. 10-3. The steel flat head and oval head screws are usually sold in a bright finish and the round head in a blue finish, or they may be plated. Screws are available either with slotted or recessed-type heads.

The sizes of wood screws are designated by the length and wire gage number. On a drawing screws should be indicated as

3/4–NO. 6 FH WOOD SCREW–STEEL
1-1/4–NO. 10 RH WOOD SCREW–BRASS

10.4 Tapping screws

Tapping screws are used in assemblies of sheet metal parts, plastics and soft castings. They form their own mating threads as they are driven into the material. Their use eliminates time consuming threading operations and tightening of nuts.

Tapping screws are manufactured with a plain steel finish or with a plated finish of brass, zinc, nickel or cadmium. They are available with slotted or Phillips driving recesses in eight basic head shapes: flat, oval, round, fillister, truss, pan, hex, and hex washer. These screws come in a variety of types and sizes. A few of the more common types are shown in Fig. 10-4. Type *A* have pointed ends and coarse threads for ease in assembling. Type *B* have blunt ends with slightly finer pitches than type *A* and are intended for joining thicker metal where a sharp point would be objectionable. Type *C* are utilized for joining thicker material than used for type *A* or *B*. Types *D, F, G,* and *T* have machine screw threads and blunt points and are employed in sheetmetal, structural steel, cast iron, die castings, brass, bronze and plastics when holding power is more critical. Types *BF, BG,* and *BT* have blunt points and spaced threads, and are intended primarily for very thin sections, brittle plastics, die castings and other non-metallic materials.

The sizes of tapping screws are designated by the length and wire gage number. On a

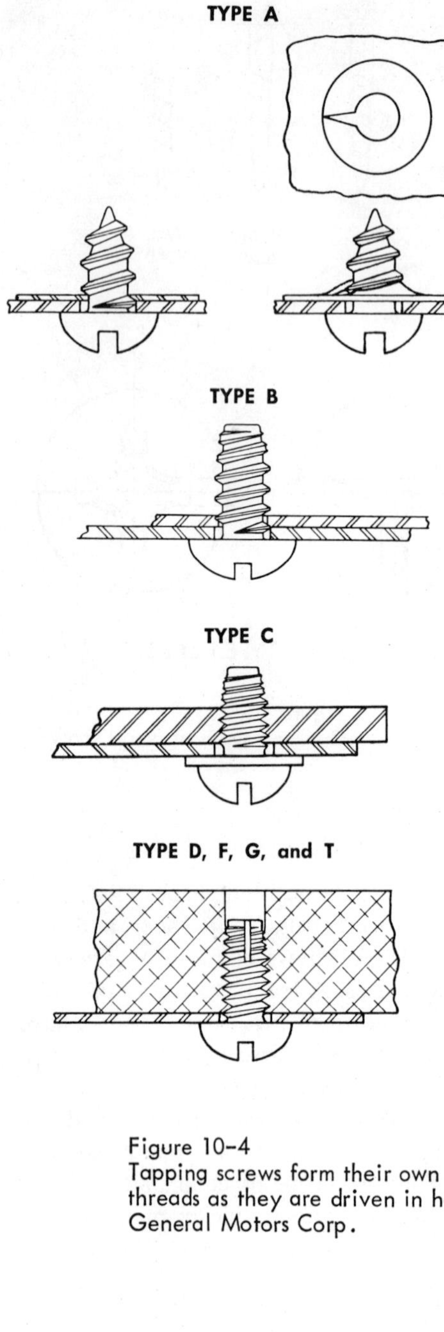

Figure 10-4
Tapping screws form their own mating threads as they are driven in holes. General Motors Corp.

drawing, tapping screws are indicated by a note as

3/8–NO. 4 TYPE *A*–RH TAPPING SCREW–NICKEL FINISH

10.5 Rivets

Rivets are considered as permanent fastening devices and are used in joining parts constructed of sheetmetal or steel plate. They are made of many different kinds of metal. The most common are wrought-iron, steel, copper, brass and aluminum.

Rivets are available in various head shapes such as cone, button, truss, countersunk, pan and flat. See Fig. 10-5. The sizes of rivets are usually indicated by the diameter and length of the stem.

The type of rivet used will depend on the nature of the structure, location of the joint, and appearance of the finished product. When shear is the only stress involved, a rivet head that enhances the appearance is a primary factor. On the other hand, if the rivet is subject to tension, a relatively high head rivet such as the cone, button, or pan is necessary.

The two principal types of joints used in riveting are the *butt* and *lap*. Rivets may be driven in either single, double, triple or even quadruple rows on these joints. The number of rows generally depends on the strength requirements of the joint. See Fig. 10-6.

Selection of rivet size is governed by the thickness of the sheet or plate and the stresses encountered. As a rule, rivet diameter should range from the thickness to three times the thickness of the thickest plate. Minimum pitch or spacing of rivets should be about three times the rivet diameter, whereas maximum spacing should be limited to eight times the thickness of the heaviest plate.

On a drawing rivets are represented by circle symbols designating the riveting process and the location. For fabrication in the shop, the symbols are left open, whereas for field riveting the symbols are made solid. See Fig. 10-7 and Fig. 10-8. When necessary to specify a rivet on a drawing, a note stating the size, type of head, and the length of the rivet is given.

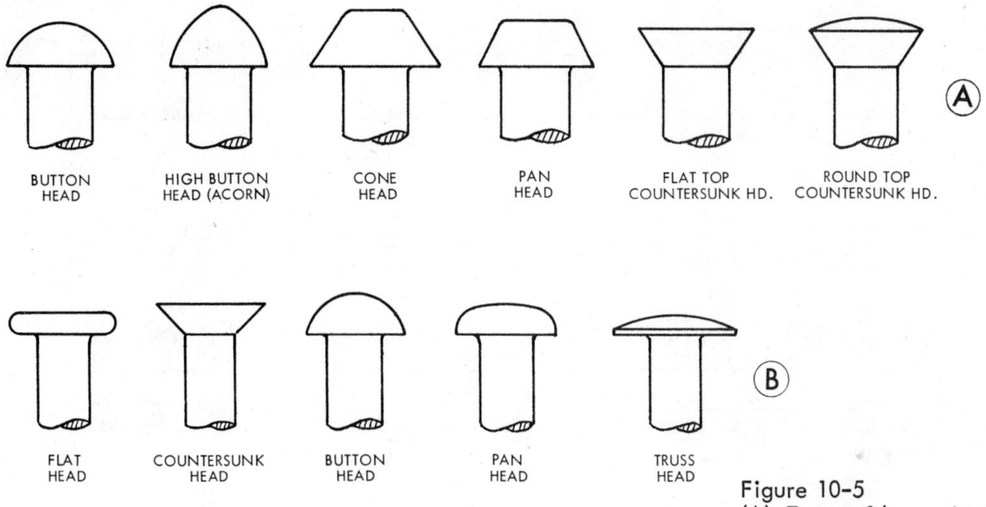

Figure 10-5
(A) Types of large rivet heads.
(B) Types of small rivet heads.

10.6 Screw Threads[1]

A screw thread is a ridge of uniform section in the form of a helix on the internal or external surface of a cylinder, or in the form of a conical spiral on the internal or external surface of a cone or frustrum of a cone. A thread formed on a cylinder is known as a *straight* or *parallel thread,* to distinguish it from a *taper thread* which is formed on a cone or frustrum of a cone.

Threads are used for three basic purposes: fastening, adjusting, and transmitting power. Since threads perform a very important function in numerous fabricating processes, a study of the following terms will facilitate a better understanding of threads in general (see Fig. 10-9):

Terms relating to
types of screw threads

External thread. A thread on the external surface of a cylinder or cone.

Internal thread. A thread on the internal surface of a hollow cylinder or cone.

Right hand thread. A thread is a right hand thread if, when viewed axially, it winds in a clockwise and receding direction.

Left hand thread. A thread is a left hand thread if, when viewed axially, it winds in a

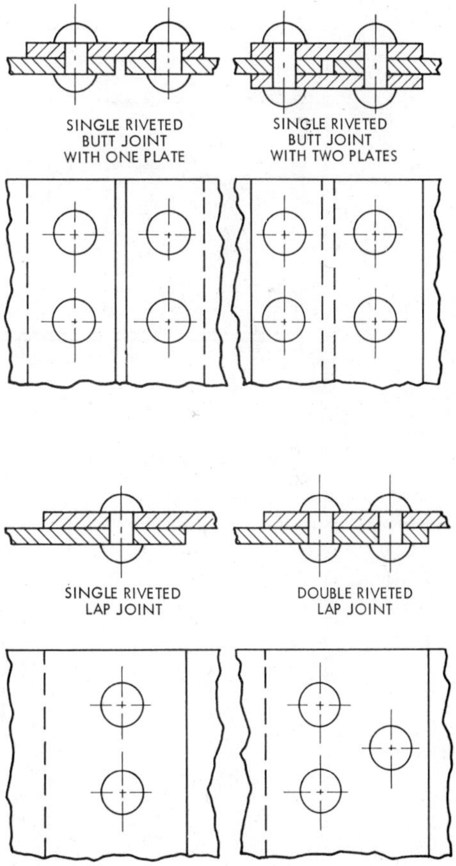

Figure 10-6
Types of riveted joints.

1. *ASME Screw Thread Manual* (New York: The American Society of Mechanical Engineers, 1953).

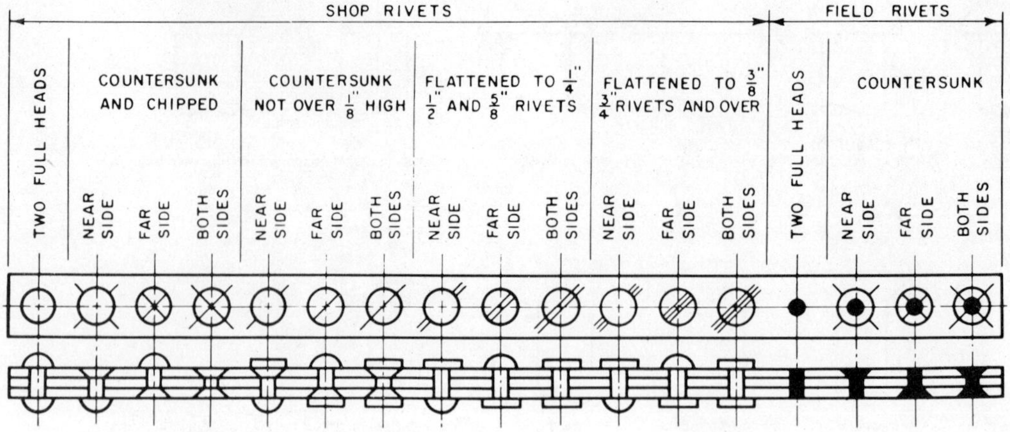

Figure 10–7
On a drawing rivets may be indicated by symbols which show the process as well as where the process takes place. ASA Y14.14

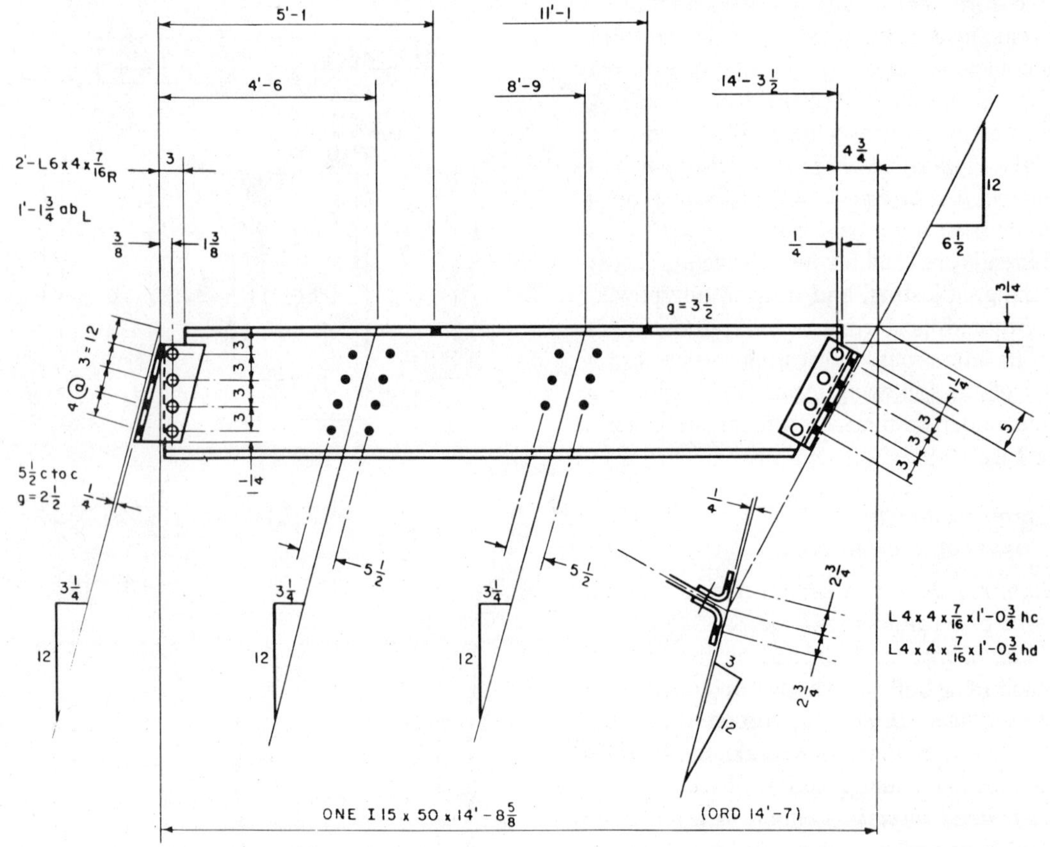

Figure 10–8
This is a typical structural member in which riveted joints are to be used. ASA Y14.14

counterclockwise and receding direction. All left hand threads are designated *LH*.

Single thread. A thread having a lead equal to the pitch; also called *single start thread.*

Multiple thread. A thread in which the lead is an integral multiple of the pitch; also called *multiple start* thread.

Classes of threads. Classes of threads are distinguished from each other by the amount of tolerance or tolerance and allowance specified.

Terms relating to geometrical elements of screw threads

Axis of a thread. The axis of the thread's pitch cylinder or cone.

Pitch line. A generator of the imaginary cylinder or cone specified in the definition of pitch diameter.

Form of thread. The thread's profile in an axial plane for a length of one pitch.

Basic form of thread. The theoretical profile of the thread for a length of one pitch in an axial plane, on which the design forms of the threads for both the external and internal threads are based.

Design form of thread. The maximum metal forms permitted for the external and internal threads.

Fundamental triangle. The triangle whose corners coincide with three consecutive intersections of the extended flanks of the basic form.

Flank (or side) of a thread. Either surface connecting the crest with the root, the intersection of which, with an axial plane, is a straight line.

Leading flank of a thread. The flank which, when the thread is about to be assembled with a mating thread, faces the mating thread.

Following flank of a thread. The flank which is opposite to the leading flank.

Pressure flank. The flank which takes the thrust or load in an assembly. The term is used particularly in relation to buttress and other similar threads.

Clearance (or trailing) flank. The flank which does not take the thrust or load in an assembly.

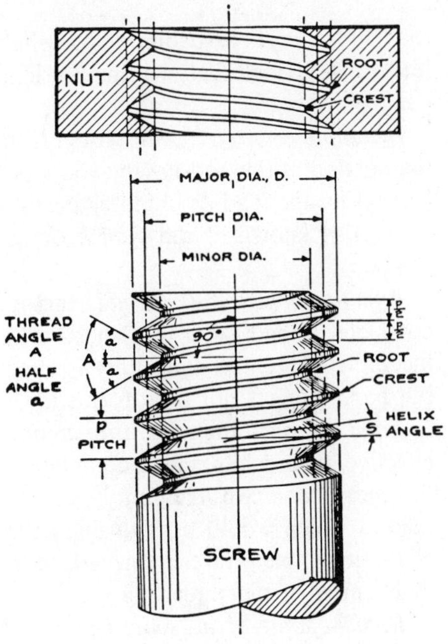

Figure 10-9
Illustration of thread terms.

Crest of a thread. The surface that joins the flanks of the thread and is farthest from the cylinder or cone from which the thread projects.

Root of a thread. The surface that joins the flanks of adjacent thread forms and is identical in position with or immediately adjacent to the cylinder or cone from which the thread projects.

Sharp crest (or crest apex). The apex formed by the intersection of the flanks of a thread when extended, if necessary, beyond the crest.

Sharp root (or root apex). The apex formed by the intersection of the flanks of adjacent thread forms when extended, if necessary, beyond the root.

Base of a thread. The section of the thread which coincides with the cylinder or cone from which the thread projects.

Complete (or full) thread. The part of the thread having full form at both crest and root. When there is a chamfer at the start of the thread not exceeding two pitches in length, it is included within the length of complete thread.

Incomplete thread. On straight threads, the portion at the end having roots not fully formed by the lead or chamfer on threading tools; also known as the *vanish* or *washout thread.*

Effective (or useful) thread. Includes the complete thread and that portion of the incomplete thread having fully formed roots but having crests not fully formed.

Total thread. Includes the complete or effective thread and the incomplete thread.

Vanish cone. An imaginary cone, the surface of which would pass through the roots of the incomplete thread formed by the lead or chamfer of the threading tool.

Vanish point of an external thread. The intersection of a generator of the vanish cone with a generator of the cylinder of the largest major diameter of the thread.

Blunt start. Designates the removal of the partial thread at the entering end of thread. This is a feature of threaded parts which are repeatedly assembled by hand, such as hose couplings and thread plug gages, to prevent cutting of hands and crossing of threads, and which was formerly known as a *Higbee cut.*

Terms relating to dimensions of screw threads

Pitch. The distance, measured parallel to the thread's axis, between corresponding points on adjacent thread forms in the same axial plane and on the same side of the axis.

Lead. The distance a threaded part moves axially, with respect to a fixed mating part, in one complete rotation.

Threads per inch. The reciprocal of the pitch in inches.

Turns per inch. The reciprocal of the lead in inches.

Included angle of a thread (or angle of thread). The angle between the flanks of the thread measured in an axial plane.

Flank angle. The angles between the individual flanks and the perpendicular to the axis of the thread, measured in an axial plane. A flank angle of a symmetrical thread is commonly termed the *half-angle of thread.*

Lead angle. On a straight thread, the angle made by the helix of the thread at the pitch line with a plane perpendicular to the axis. On a taper thread at a given position, the angle made by the conical spiral of the thread at the pitch line with the plane perpendicular to the axis at that position.

Thickness of thread. The distance between the flanks of the thread measured at a specified position and parallel to the axis.

Height of fundamental triangle of a thread. The distance, measured perpendicular to the axis, between the major and minor cylinders or cones, respectively; also is the height of a *sharp-V thread.*

Height (or depth) of thread. The distance, measured perpendicular to the axis, between the major and minor cylinders or cones, respectively.

Addendum of an external thread. The distance, measured perpendicular to the axis, between the major and pitch cylinders or cones, respectively.

Addendum of an internal thread. The distance, measured perpendicular to the axis, between the minor and pitch cylinders or cones, respectively.

Dedendum of an external thread. The distance, measured perpendicular to the axis, between the pitch and minor cylinders or cones, respectively.

Dedendum of an internal thread. The distance, measured perpendicular to the axis, between the major and pitch cylinders or cones, respectively.

Crest truncation of a thread. The distance, measured perpendicular to the axis, between the sharp crest (or crest apex) and the cylinder or cone which bounds the crest.

Root truncation of a thread. The distance, measured perpendicular to the axis, between the sharp root (or root apex) and the cylinder or cone which bounds the root.

Major diameter. On a straight thread, the diameter of the imaginary co-axial cylinder which bounds the crest of an external thread or the root of an internal thread. On a taper thread at a given position on the thread axis, the diameter of the major cone.

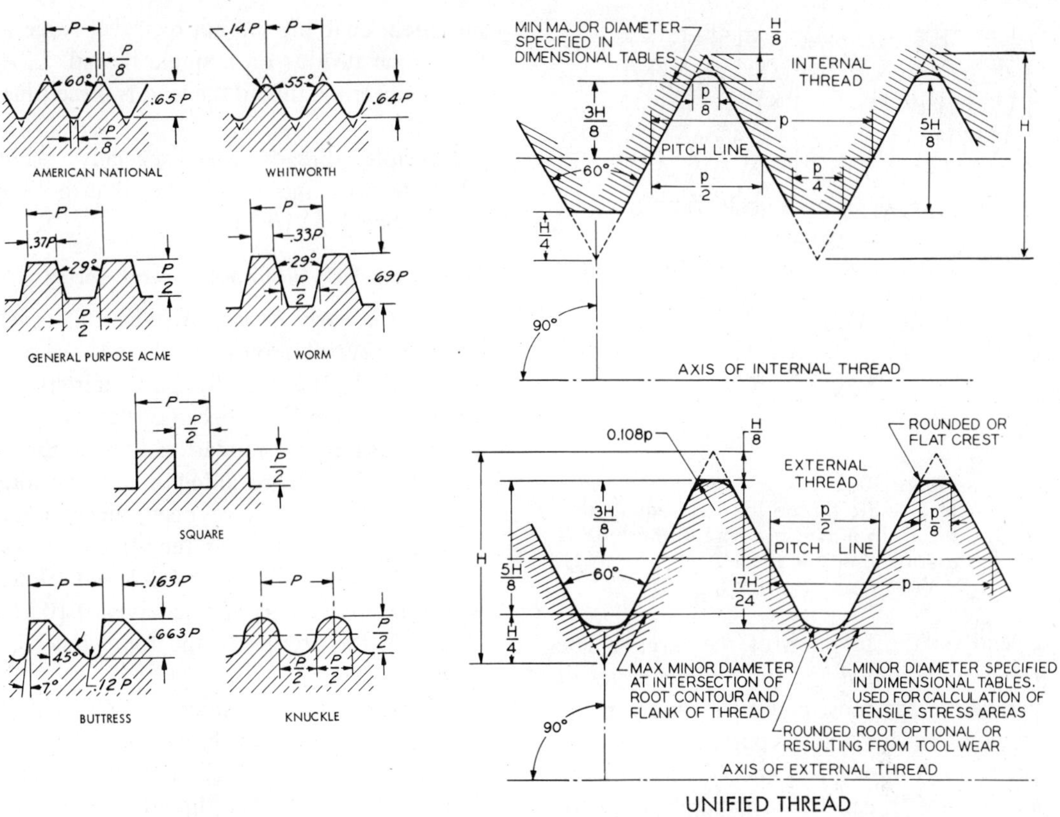

Figure 10-10
The profile of threads used is governed by the intended function of the thread.

Minor diameter. On a straight thread, the diameter of the imaginary co-axial cylinder which bounds the root of an external thread or the crest of an internal thread. On a taper thread at a given position on the thread axis, the diameter of the minor cone at that position.

Pitch diameter (or simple effective diameter). On a straight thread, the diameter of the imaginary co-axial cylinder, the surface of which would pass through the thread profiles at such points as to make the width of the groove equal to one-half of the basic pitch. On a perfect thread this occurs at the point where the widths of the thread and groove are equal. On a taper thread at a given position on the thread axis, the diameter of the pitch cone at that position.

Effective size (or virtual effective diameter). The diameter derived by adding to the pitch diameter in the case of an external thread, or subtracting from the pitch diameter in the case of an internal thread, the cumulative effects of pitch and angle errors.

Depth of thread engagement. Between two mating threads, the distance, measured perpendicular to the axis, by which their thread forms overlap each other.

Length of thread engagement. The distance between the extreme points of contact on the pitch cylinders or cones of two mating threads, measured parallel to the axis.

Crest clearance. In a thread assembly, the distance, measured perpendicular to the axis, between the crest of a thread and the root of its mating thread.

10.7 Thread profiles

See Fig. 10-10. The shape or profile of threads used will, to a considerable extent,

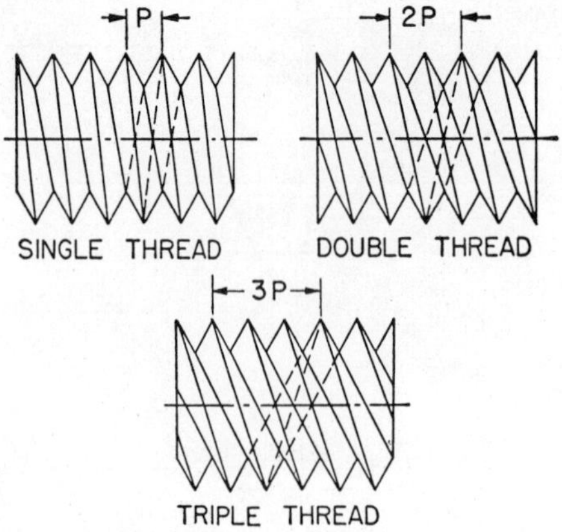

Figure 10-11
In a single thread the lead equals the pitch; in a multiple thread the lead is greater than the pitch.

depend on the function of the thread. The *American National* and the *Unified* series of threads are the most commonly used in the United States for holding parts together. The *American National* is a modification of the old sharp-V thread which is rarely used today. The *Whitworth thread* is principally a British thread and serves the same purpose as the American National does in the United States.

The *Knuckle thread* is a cast or rolled thread with a rounded profile and is commonly found on incandescent lamps and plugs. The *Square, Acme,* and *Brown & Sharpe worm threads* are designed primarily for transmitting power. The *Buttress thread* is particularly adapted for transmitting power in one direction only, such as on breech mechanisms of large guns and airplane propeller hubs. The *Standard Pipe Thread* in either the straight or tapered form is used to join pipe sections.

10.8 Single and multiple threads

A thread that consists of a single continuous ridge is known as a single thread and its lead is equal to the pitch.

A multiple thread consists of two or more ridges cut side by side, thereby producing a lead that is always greater than the pitch. Thus in a double thread, the lead is twice the pitch, enabling the nut to travel twice as far in one turn as on a single thread. Likewise, on a triple thread the lead is three times the pitch.

Multiple threads are especially useful where travel is more important than holding power. See Fig. 10-11.

10.9 American national thread series

During the early period of industrial development, several groups of threads were in existence. As the need for part interchangeability increased, it became necessary to bring about some standardization of thread design. Today the prevailing threads for holding parts together have been incorporated into one group known as the *American National Thread* and *Unified Thread Series,* which is covered in Sub-section 10.10. Included in the group are the following basic types:

American National coarse (NC). This is the old U.S. Standard thread with the addition of the numbered sizes 1 to 12 below 1/4 inch diameter. The thread is coarse and recommended for all general purpose work. It is particularly adaptable for cast iron, soft metals or plastics, and for applications requiring rapid assembly or disassembly.

American National fine (NF). This is the old SAE thread with the addition of the numbered sizes 0 to 12 below 1/4 inch diameter. It is a fine thread and is used where greater resistance to vibration is required or where greater strength is mandatory.

The 8-pitch American National thread (8*N*). The 8-pitch thread series has 8 threads per inch. Originally it was intended for high pressure joints but is now widely used as a substitute for the coarse thread series requiring diameters larger than 1 inch.

The 12-pitch American National thread (12*N*). This thread has 12 threads per inch for diameters larger than 1-1/2 inches. It is used extensively in machine construction, boiler work, and other similar places where thin nuts on shafts and sleeves are required.

The 16-pitch American National thread (16*N*). The 16-pitch thread series has 16 threads per inch and is intended for diam-

UNIFIED AND AMERICAN SCREW THREAD STANDARD SERIES.

Size	Basic Major Dia.	Threads Per Inch: Coarse (UNC or NC)	Fine (UNF or NF)	Extra Fine (UNEF or NEF)	8 Thread Series (N)	12 Thread Series (UN or N)	16 Thread Series (UN or N)	Size
0	0.0600	-	80	-	-	-	-	0
1	0.0730	64	72	-	-	-	-	1
2	0.0860	56	64	-	-	-	-	2
3	0.0990	48	56	-	-	-	-	3
4	0.1120	40	48	-	-	-	-	4
5	0.1250	40	44	-	-	-	-	5
6	0.1380	32	40	-	-	-	-	6
8	0.1640	32	36	-	-	-	-	8
10	0.1900	24	32	-	-	-	-	10
12	0.2160	24	28	32	-	-	-	12
1/4	0.2500	20	28	32	-	-	-	1/4
5/16	0.3125	18	24	32	-	-	-	5/16
3/8	0.3750	16	24	32	-	-	-	3/8
7/16	0.4375	14	20	28	-	-	-	7/16
1/2	0.5000	13	20	28	-	12	-	1/2
9/16	0.5625	12	18	24	-	12	-	9/16
5/8	0.6250	11	18	24	-	12	-	5/8
11/16	0.6875	-	-	24	-	12	-	11/16
3/4	0.7500	10	16	20	-	12	16	3/4
13/16	0.8125	-	-	20	-	12	16	13/16
7/8	0.8750	9	14	20	-	12	16	7/8
15/16	0.9375	-	-	20	-	12	16	15/16
1	1.0000	-	14		-	-	-	1
1	1.0000	8	12	20	8	12	16	1
1-1/16	1.0625	-	-	18	-	12	16	1-1/16
1-1/8	1.1250	7	12	18	8	12	16	1-1/8
1-3/16	1.1875	-	-	18	-	12	16	1-3/16
1-1/4	1.2500	7	12	18	8	12	16	1-1/4
1-5/16	1.3125	-	-	18	-	12	16	1-5/16
1-3/8	1.3750	6	12	18	8	12	16	1-3/8
1-7/16	1.4375	-	-	18	-	12	16	1-7/16
1-1/2	1.5000	6	12	18	8	12	16	1-1/2
1-9/16	1.5625	-	-	18	-	-	16	1-9/16
1-5/8	1.6250	-	-	18	8	12	16	1-5/8
1-11/16	1.6875	-	-	18	-	-	16	1-11/16
1-3/4	1.7500	5	-	16	8	12	16	1-3/4
1-13/16	1.8125	-	-	-	-	-	16	1-13/16
1-7/8	1.8750	-	-	-	8	12	16	1-7/8
1-15/16	1.9375	-	-	-	-	-	16	1-15/16
2	2.0000	4-1/2	-	16	8	12	16	2
2-1/16	2.0625	-	-	-	-	-	16	2-1/16
2-1/8	2.1250	-	-	-	8	12	16	2-1/8
2-3/16	2.1875	-	-	-	-	-	16	2-3/16
2-1/4	2.2500	4-1/2	For diameters over 1-1/2 inches, use 12 Thread Series	For diameters over 2 inches, use 16 Thread Series	8	12	16	2-1/4
2-5/16	2.3125	-			-	-	16	2-5/16
2-3/8	2.3750	-			-	12	16	2-3/8
2-7/16	2.4375	-			-	-	16	2-7/16
2-1/2	2.5000	4			8	12	16	2-1/2
2-5/8	2.6250	-			-	12	16	2-5/8
2-3/4	2.7500	4			8	12	16	2-3/4
2-7/8	2.8750	-			-	12	16	2-7/8
3	3.0000	4			8	12	16	3
3-1/8	3.1250	-			-	12	16	3-1/8
3-1/4	3.2500	4			8	12	16	3-1/4
3-3/8	3.3750	-			-	12	16	3-3/8
3-1/2	3.5000	4			8	12	16	3-1/2
3-5/8	3.6250	-			-	12	16	3-5/8
3-3/4	3.7500	4			8	12	16	3-3/4
3-7/8	3.8750	-			-	12	16	3-7/8
4	4.0000	4			8	12	16	4
4-1/4	4.2500	-			8	12	16	4-1/4
4-1/2	4.5000	-			8	12	16	4-1/2
4-3/4	4.7500	-			8	12	16	4-3/4
5	5.0000	-	-	-	8	12	16	5
5-1/4	5.2500	-	-	-	8	12	16	5-1/4
5-1/2	5.5000	-	-	-	8	12	16	5-1/2
5-3/4	5.7500	-	-	-	8	12	16	5-3/4
6	6.0000	-	-	-	8	12	16	6

Figure 10-12
The Unified Thread Series are those which conform in both series and class with British and Canadian practices and are similar to the American National Series.

eters larger than 2 inches. It is designed chiefly for adjusting collars and bearing retaining nuts.

Extra fine thread (NEF). The extra fine thread has the same form as the American National thread but with more threads per inch for all small diameters. Sizes above 1-3/4 inch are the same as the 16-thread series. The extra fine thread is better adapted to meet the needs of the automotive industry, particularly where parts are subjected to serious vibrations or must withstand highly stressed conditions.

10.10 Unified screw thread

The first agitation for unification of thread standards started as a result of experiences in repairing equipment during World War I. However, it was not until 1948 that general accord was reached. In November of that year, an agreement was signed by representatives of governments and industries of Great Britain, Canada, and the United States legalizing certain basic requirements for the general interchangeability of threaded products. The result produced the currently known Unified Thread Series.

The threads that make up these series are similar to the American National threads except that they have slightly more rounded roots and crests on the external threads and slightly flatter crests and roots on the internal threads.

The Unified Thread Series are used for essentially the same purposes as the American National Series. See table in Fig. 10-12. They are designated as follows:

Coarse thread—UNC
Fine thread—UNF
Extra-fine thread—UNEF
The 12 and 16 thread series—
12UN, 16UN.

10.11 Thread classes

The class of a thread refers to the amount of tolerance or the amount of tolerance and allowance as applied to pitch diameter. In the past, class was commonly called *fit of a thread* which actually described the degree of *looseness* or *tightness* between two mating threaded parts. Originally this designation was applied to four classes of fits known as Class 1, Class 2, Class 3 and Class 4. Class 1 has now been eliminated in the new Unified and American Standard. Classes 2 and 3, because of their long and wide usage, have been retained to cover the period of change-over to the new standard

The new Unified and American Screw Thread Standards specify three classes. External threads are classified as *1A, 2A, 3A,* and internal threads as *1B, 2B, 3B.* Application of these classes are as follows:

Classes 1A and 1B. Replace the old Class 1 of the previous American Standard. These classes are for exceptional applications requiring frequent and rapid assembly and disassembly with a minimum of binding.

Classes 2A and 2B. For general purpose threads on bolts, nuts, and screws. They provide standard allowances to ensure minimum clearance between external and internal threads which minimize galling and seizing in high cycle wrench assembly. Because of their realistic tolerances, classes 2*A* and 2*B* are widely used in mass production industries.

Classes 3A and 3B. Suitable for applications requiring closer tolerances than those provided by classes *2A* and *2B.* The maximum diameters of the *3A* external thread and the minimum diameters of the *3B* internal threads are basic, affording no allowance or clearance for assembly of maximum metal components.[2]

The requirements for screw thread fits depend on their end use. Whenever possible threads in the Standard thread series should be selected. Combination of thread classes for components is possible. For example, a Class 2A external thread may be used with a Class 1B, 2B, 3B, 2 or 3 internal thread.

10.12 Thread representation[3]

There are three conventions in general use for depicting screw threads on drawings:

2. Extracted from *Screw Threads, ASA Y14.6—1957* (New York: The American Society of Mechanical Engineers, 1957).
3. *Ibid.*

the detailed, the schematic and the simplified. End purpose and use of drawings, general workmanship, drafting time, etc., influence the selection and use of the conventions. For clarity of representation where good judgment dictates, all three conventions may be used on a single drawing. See Fig. 10-13.

The *detailed representation* is a close approximation of the actual appearance of screw threads. See Fig. 10-14. The form of the thread is simplified by showing the normal helices as straight slanting lines and the truncated crests and roots as sharp *V*'s. While the detailed rendering is comparatively difficult and time consuming, its use is sometimes justified by such considerations as permanency of drawing, general workmanship of the drafting project, and the necessity for avoiding any confusion which might result from a less realistic thread representation.

The *schematic representation* is nearly as effective as the pictorial and is much easier to draw. See Fig. 10-15. The staggered lines, symbolic of the thread crests and roots, may be perpendicular to the axis of the thread or slanted to the approximate angle of the thread helix. This construction should not be used for hidden internal threads or sections of external threads.

The *simplified representation,* on the grounds of economy and ease of rendering, is the most commonly used method for showing screw threads on drawings. See Fig. 10-16. It is particularly useful for indicating hidden internal threads. The simplified representation should be avoided where there is any possibility of confusion with other drawing details.

In rare instances where threads are shown as a portion of a greatly enlarged detail, the representation of exact thread geometry might be justified. See Fig. 10-17.

10.13 Designating screw threads[4]

A screw thread is designated on a drawing by a note with a leader and arrow pointing to the thread. See Fig. 10-18. The minimum of information required in all notes is (1)

4. *Ibid.*

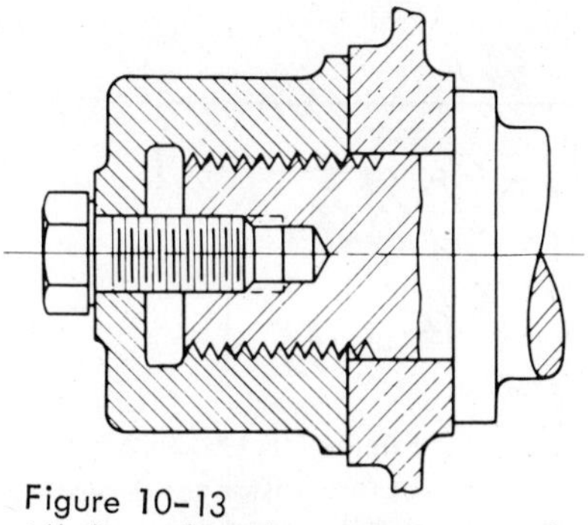

Figure 10-13
All three thread conventions may be used on a single drawing.

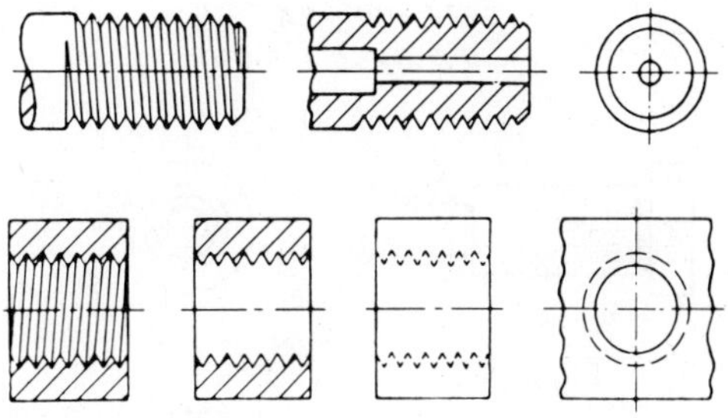

Figure 10-14
Detailed representation of screw threads.

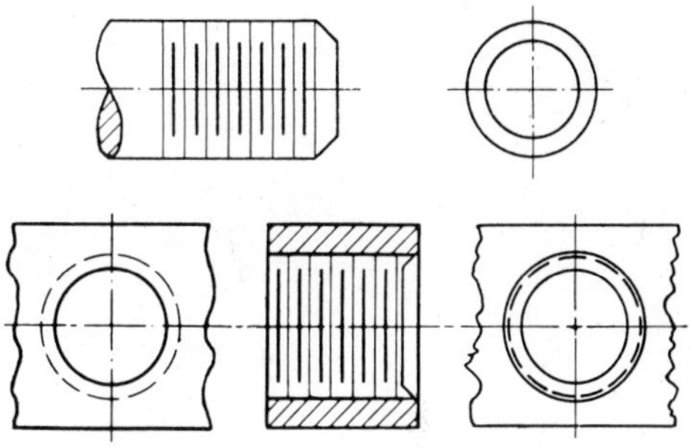

Figure 10-15
Schematic representation of screw threads.

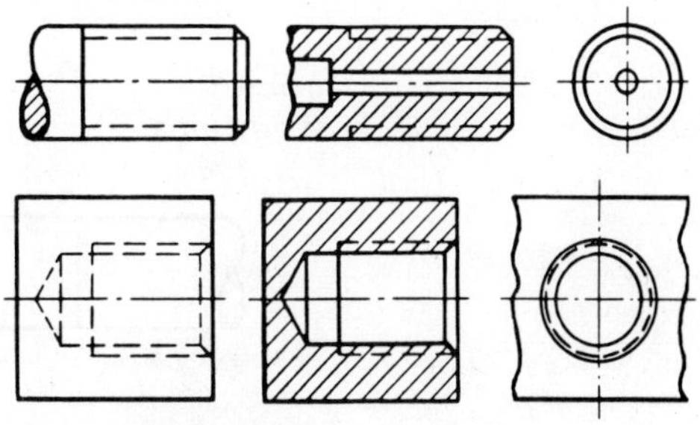

Figure 10-16
The simplified representation of screw threads is the most commonly used.

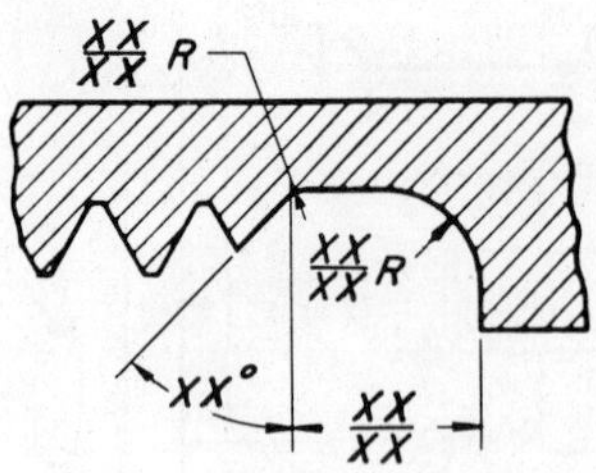

Figure 10-17
In rare instances a representation of exact thread geometry may be used.

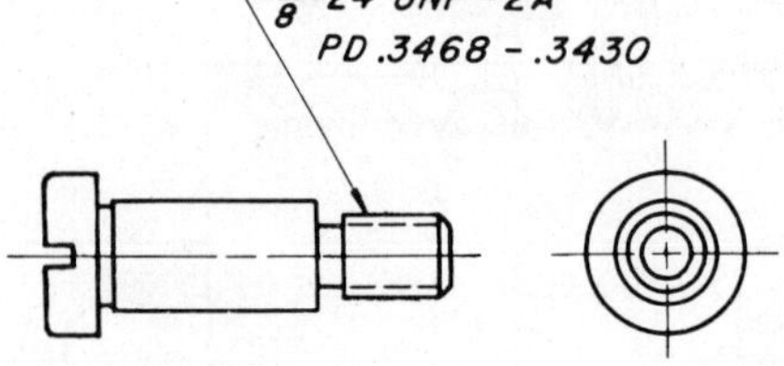

Figure 10-18
A screw thread is designated on a drawing by a note with a leader pointing to the thread.

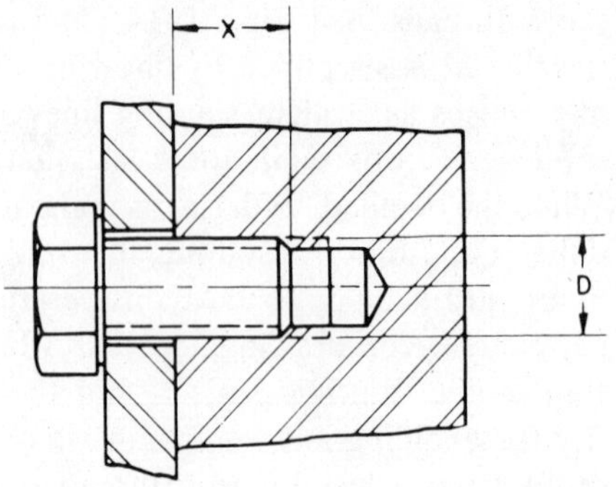

Figure 10-19
The length of engagement depends on the function and material of the threaded component.

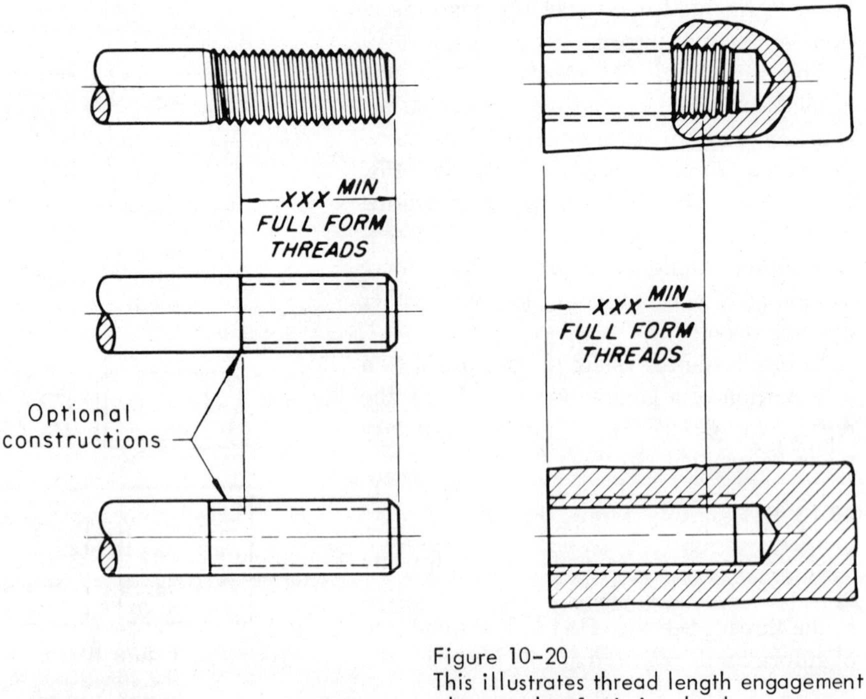

Figure 10-20
This illustrates thread length engagement where a chamfer is involved.

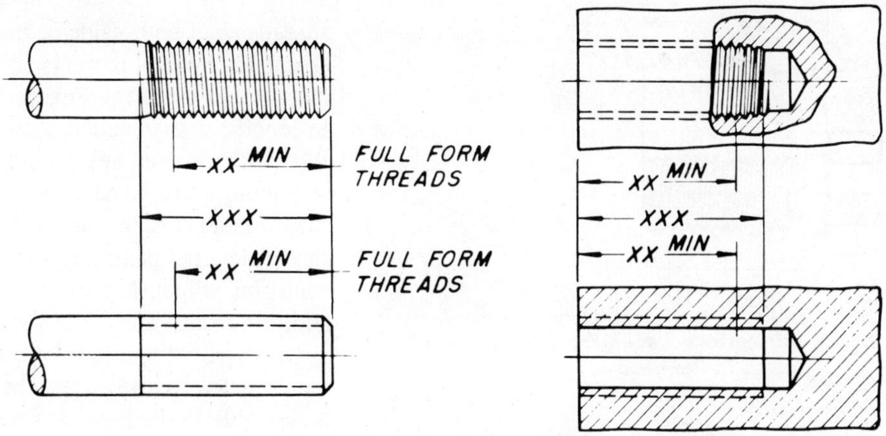

Figure 10-21
When the number of partial threads are to be limited, the threaded section is dimensioned in this manner.

the specification in sequence of the nominal size (or screw number), (2) number of threads per inch, (3) thread series symbol, and (4) the thread class number, supplemented optionally by the pitch diameter limits. Example:

1/4-20UNC-2A
- 2A — Class of screw thread
- UNC — Thread series
- 20 — Number of threads per inch
- 1/4 — Nominal size (dia., in in.)

or

1/4-20UNC-2A
PD 0.2164-0.2127 (Optional)

or

1/4-20UNC-2A-LH

Unless otherwise specified, threads are right hand and single lead. Left hand threads are designated by the letters *LH* following the class symbol. Double or triple lead threads are designated by the words *DOUBLE* or *TRIPLE* preceding the pitch diameter limits.

For coated Class 2*A* external threads, the pitch diameter limits should be followed by the words *BEFORE COATING* and the basic pitch diameter should be specified as the maximum pitch diameter followed by the words *AFTER COATING*. Example:

1/4 – 20 UNC – 2*A*
PD .2164—.2127 BEFORE COATING
MAX PD .2175 AFTER COATING

10.14 Dimensioning[5]

The length of engagement required by the threaded components should be the first consideration in determination and specification of thread lengths. For fastenings and other general purpose applications, engagement may be derived from an empirical formula based on the nominal diameter of the thread and the material of the internal threaded component. Referring to Fig. 10-19, the engagement length *X* when both components are steel, is equal to the nominal diameter *D* of the thread. For steel external threads assembling into cast iron, brass or bronze, *X* is equal to 1-1/2 *D;* and when assembled into aluminum, zinc or plastic, *X* is equal to 2*D*.

The thread length dimension on the drawing shall be the gaging length or the length of threads having full form, i.e., the partial

5. *Ibid.*

threads shall be outside or beyond the length specified. Where there is a chamfer at the start of the thread not exceeding two pitches in length, it is included within the length of full form thread. See Fig. 10-20.

Should there be reason to control or limit the number of partial threads, the overall thread length, including the partial threads, shall be dimensioned on the drawing in addition to full form threads. See Fig. 10-21.

On short bolts, screws or other parts where the objective is to run the thread as close as practicable to the head or shoulder, the maximum permissible distance from the head or shoulder to the nearest thread of full form may be dimensioned on the drawing instead of the thread length. See Fig. 10-22.

If a definite length of unthreaded and unscored body or shank of a threaded part is a critical functional requirement, it should be dimensioned on the drawing. See Fig. 10-23.

The number of partial threads (called *runout*) should not be restricted unnecessarily as it has considerable bearing on production efficiency and the life of threading tools. In general practice, allowance should be made for at least two or three partial threads on externally threaded parts.

The runout of milled or ground external threads is very abrupt as shown in Fig. 10-24. The partial threads are only a fraction of one thread in length, and full formed threads can be run to within one thread length from a shoulder. However, milled and ground threads are costly as compared to die cut or rolled threads.

Thread cutting dies are usually chamfered two or more threads, producing an equivalent runout of partial threads on the product as shown in Fig. 10-25. The number of partial threads on the product can be reduced to 1-1/2 threads by using a die with shorter chamfer or by a second operation with a chaser die having a small chamfer.

Thread rolling dies have a minimum chamfer or lead which seldom exceeds one thread in length, producing an equivalent runout on the product as shown in Fig. 10-26. On unthreaded blanks, where the body

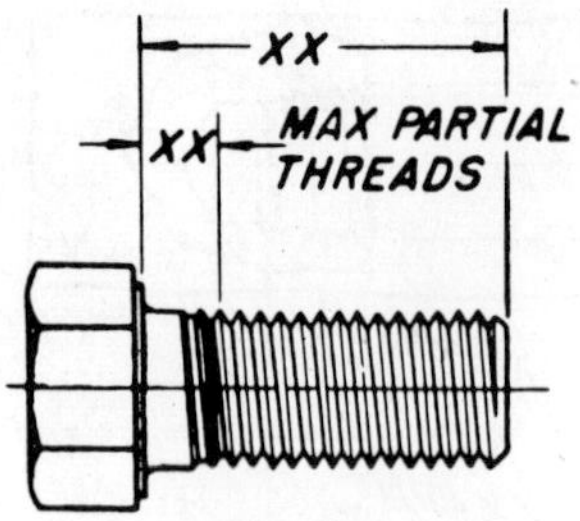

Figure 10-22
This is the way a threaded section is dimensioned when the thread must run close to the head.

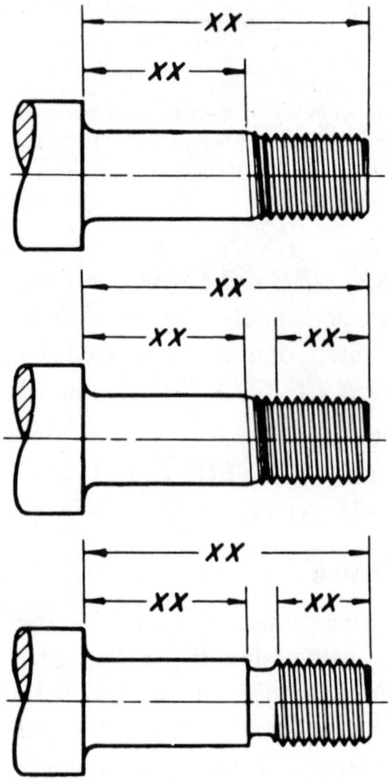

Figure 10-23
If an unthreaded length is critical it must be dimensioned.

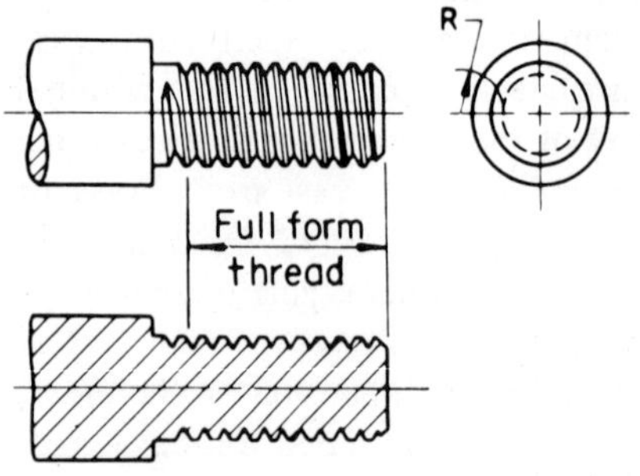

Figure 10-24
Milled or ground threads can be run to within one thread from a shoulder.

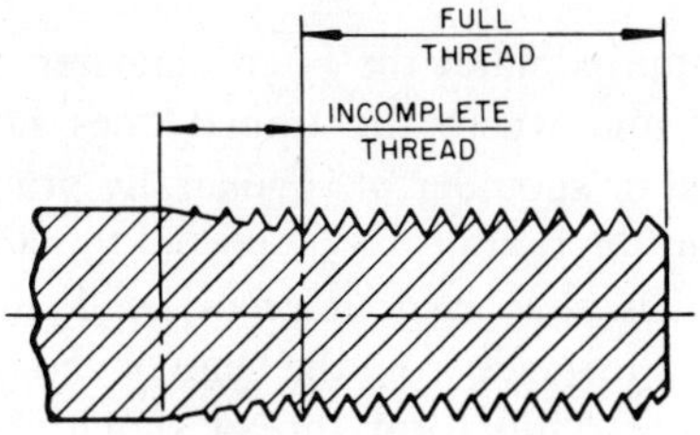

Figure 10-25
Die cut threads have a runout equal to about two or more threads.

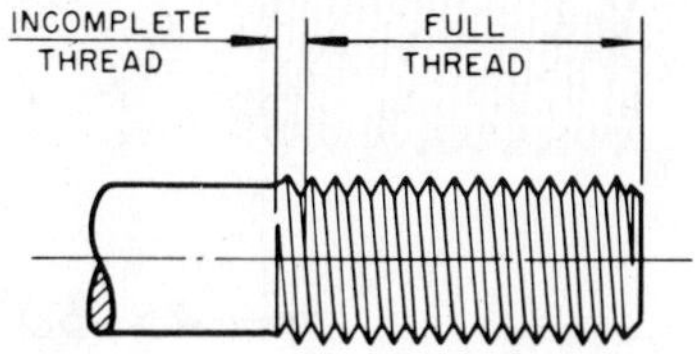

Figure 10-26
A rolled thread usually has a runout of one thread.

THREADS PER INCH	LENGTH OF RELIEF FOR PITCH OR THREAD INTERVAL							RELIEF CONSTANT	
	1 p	1-1/2 p	2 p	2-1/2 p	3 p	5 p	6 p	INT. THD. A	EXT. THD. B
80	.012	.019	.025	.031	.038	.062	.075	.005	.020
72	.014	.021	.028	.035	.042	.069	.083	.006	.022
64	.016	.023	.031	.039	.047	.078	.094	.006	.024
56	.018	.027	.036	.045	.054	.089	.107	.007	.027
48	.021	.031	.042	.052	.062	.104	.125	.007	.032
44	.023	.034	.045	.057	.068	.114	.136	.008	.034
40	.025	.038	.050	.062	.075	.125	.150	.008	.037
36	.028	.042	.056	.069	.083	.139	.167	.009	.041
32	.031	.047	.062	.078	.094	.156	.188	.010	.046
28	.036	.054	.071	.089	.107	.179	.214	.011	.053
24	.042	.062	.083	.104	.125	.208	.250	.013	.061
20	.050	.075	.100	.125	.150	.250	.300	.014	.072
18	.056	.083	.111	.139	.167	.278	.333	.016	.081
16	.062	.094	.125	.156	.188	.312	.375	.018	.090
14	.071	.107	.143	.179	.214	.357	.429	.020	.103
13	.077	.115	.154	.192	.231	.385	.462	.022	.110
12	.083	.125	.167	.208	.250	.417	.500	.023	.120
11	.091	.136	.182	.227	.273	.455	.545	.025	.130
10	.100	.150	.200	.250	.300	.500	.600	.027	.143
9	.111	.167	.222	.278	.333	.556	.667	.030	.158
8	.125	.188	.250	.312	.375	.625	.750	.033	.178
7	.143	.214	.286	.357	.429	.714	.857	.038	.203
6	.167	.250	.333	.417	.500	.833	1.000	.044	.237
5	.200	.300	.400	.500	.600	1.000	1.200	.052	.283
4-1/2	.222	.333	.444	.556	.667	1.111	1.333	.058	.314
4	.250	.375	.500	.625	.750	1.250	1.500	.064	.353

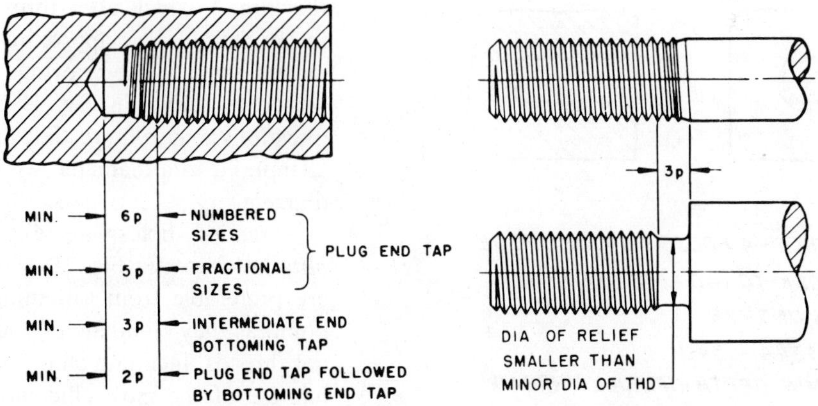

Figure 10-27
This table specifies the allowance that can be provided between thread and shoulder when method of manufacture is not provided.

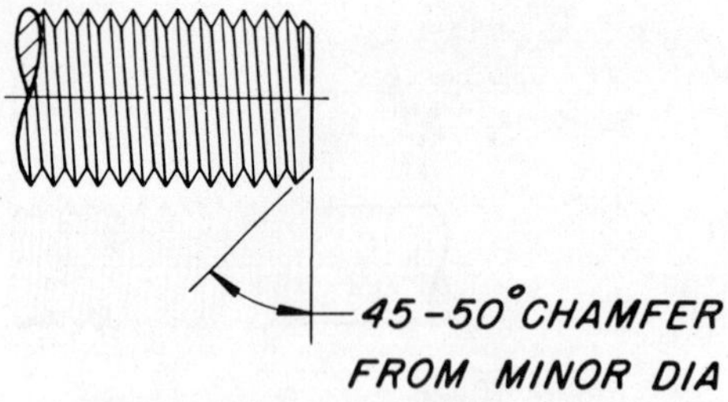

Figure 10-28
The external thread blanks before threading should be chamfered 45° to 50°.

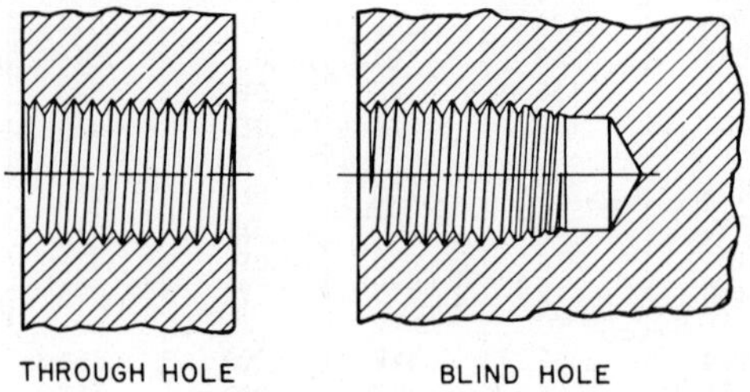

Figure 10-29
Threaded holes are either through or blind.

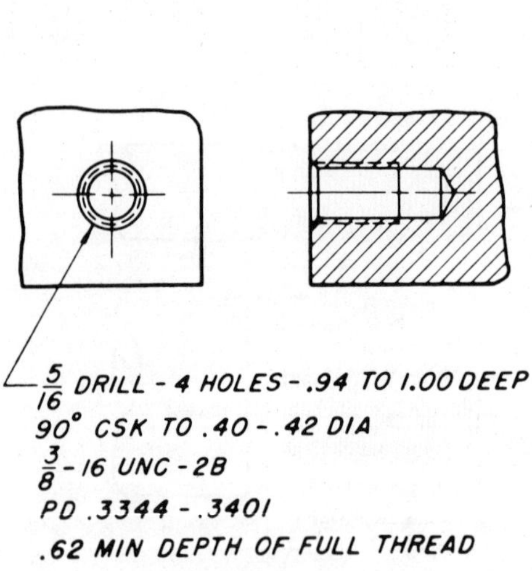

Figure 10-30
Typical drawing designation of an internal thread.

diameter approximates the pitch diameter of the thread and where the thread does not abut a head or shoulder, it is generally practical to limit the runout to one partial thread. If the threads abut a shoulder or head, the distance or allowance from the head or shoulder to the first full form thread should be equivalent to the length of two threads.

On unthreaded blanks, where the body diameter approximates the major or outside diameter of the thread and where the thread is rolled on a reduced portion of the blank equivalent in diameter to the pitch diameter of the thread, the runout may be limited to 1-1/2 partial threads, providing the threads do not abut a head or shoulder. If the threads abut a head or shoulder, a clearance equivalent to the length of one thread is necessary to avoid kissing the die, and the total distance or allowance to the first full form thread should be equivalent to the length of 2-1/2 threads.

When information is not available as to the method of manufacture, it is advisable in order not to limit the manufacturing process to provide an allowance between thread and the shoulder or unthreaded shank, not less than that shown in Fig. 10-27.

For cut or ground threads, the external thread blanks before threading should be chamfered 45-50° to the minor diameter of the thread. For rolled threads the blanks before threading should be chamfered 60-65° (included angle) to the minor diameter of the thread, which after threading will result in a chamfer of approximately 90° (included angle). The drawings may be dimensioned as shown in Fig. 10-28. Certain applications may require that finished parts be chamfered to a diameter less than the minor diameter.

Threaded holes are either *through* or *blind* as shown in Fig. 10-29. Through holes are preferable from a manufacturing standpoint, as they eliminate consideration of partial threads, facilitate chip disposal, and permit use of the most efficient taps.

Design permitting, through holes should be tapped their full length except where holes are considerably deeper than the thread

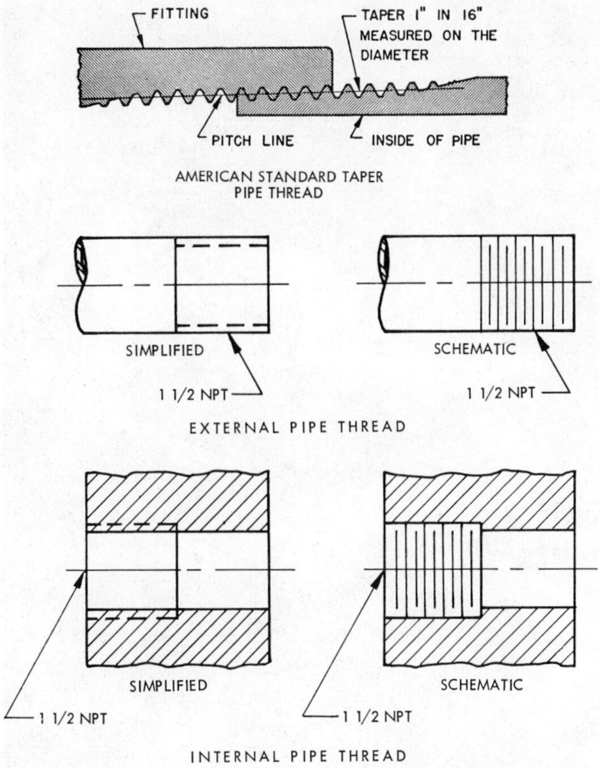

Figure 10-31
Pipe thread is shown on a drawing by the conventional simplified representation with a note.

length required. They should break out squarely on a surface normal to the axis of the drill and not into a fillet or side wall. They should not be used in castings where removal of objectionable chips would create a problem.

The depths of drill holes for blind tapped holes should not be unnecessarily restricted. The holes should be considerably deeper than the required length of thread to (1) afford chip clearance, (2) speed up the tapping operation, (3) minimize the possibility of tap breakage, and (4) permit the use of the same taps and tapping technique as for through holes. The allowance for tool chamfer, partial threads and tap clearance at the bottom of the holes should not be less than that shown in Fig. 10-27. Where hole depth is restricted by design it should be remembered that in order to produce internal threads of full form to within one thread of the bottom of a hole, the use of a bottoming tap is necessary, involving in some cases a second operation.

It is usual to countersink holes before threading although this may be unnecessary if the holes are tapped with a taper tap. The included angle of countersinks should be 90° and the diameter should be 1/64 larger than the nominal diameter of the thread with a plus tolerance of 1/64. See Fig. 10-30 for a typical drawing designation of an internal thread.

10.15 American standard pipe thread

The American Standard pipe thread has a 60° angle and is in two forms, straight and tapered. Both have the same number of threads per inch. The tapered thread is used to insure a tight joint.

Pipe threads are shown on a drawing by means of the simplified symbolic representation. As a rule, the taper is not included unless this feature must be emphasized. The fact that the thread is tapered is indicated by a note. If the taper is shown, then it should be exaggerated on the sheet. As shown in Fig. 10-31, the thread note should

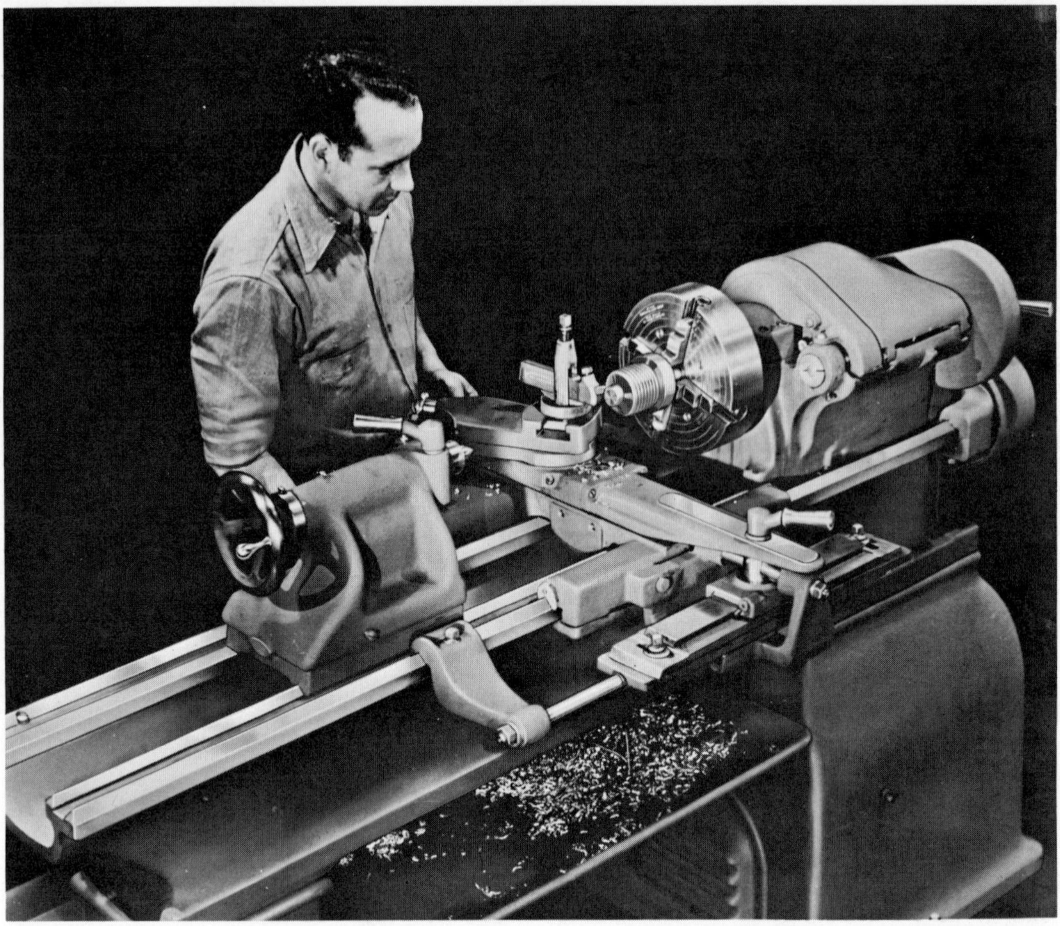

Figure 10-32
Cutting a thread with a tool bit in lathe.
South Bend Lathe, Inc.

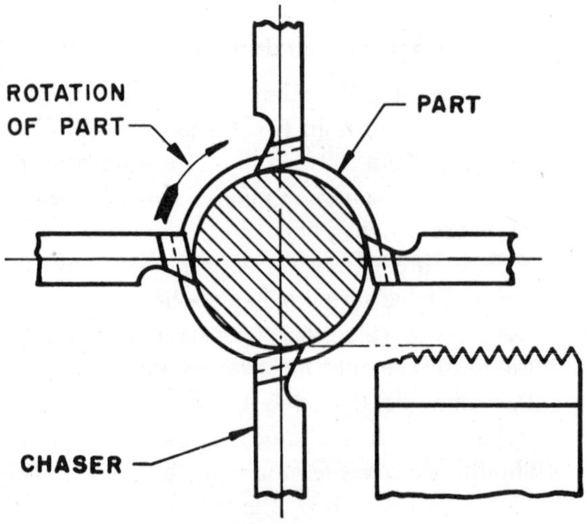

Figure 10-33
Threads may be cut with a chaser.

include the nominal diameter of the thread followed by the letters *NPT* (National Pipe Taper) or *NPS* (National Pipe Straight). See Appendix for data on various pipe thread sizes.

10.16 Methods of producing screw threads[6]

There are three general processes for the production of screw threads, namely: *cutting, rolling,* and *grinding.* Threads may be cut with a single point threading tool, thread chaser, tap, die, or by thread milling with single or multiple cutters. Some threads may be rolled by either flat or cylindrical rolling dies. Certain threads are ground with a grinding wheel dressed to conform with the shape of the thread groove. A brief description of the various cutting methods follows.

Cutting threads with a tool bit. Cut threads may be produced on a machine lathe by traversing a tool bit in an axial plane along the unthreaded blank. A tool bit is a single point threading tool shaped to correspond with the space between threads. Longitudinal motion is imparted to the tool by a lead screw so geared that the rate of rotation of the blank and the traverse of the tool will produce a thread of the desired lead. See Fig. 10-32.

Cutting a thread with a chaser. Cut threads may be produced on a machine lathe by successively traversing a multiple type threading tool known as a *chaser* along the part to be threaded, each tooth of the tool following in the thread in the same manner as the single point threading tool. Chasers are well adapted to roughing out threads because they cut rapidly and may be used for finishing threads accurately if the teeth of the chasers are ground after hardening. See Fig. 10-33.

Cutting threads with tap and die. Threads may be produced internally by *taps* and externally by *dies.* Tools, available in a variety of commercial designs, usually consist of multiple point cutters or chasers arranged circumferentially. See Fig. 10-34. By their use a thread is generally finished by one passage of the tool although a second or finishing cut is sometimes made to assure accuracy.

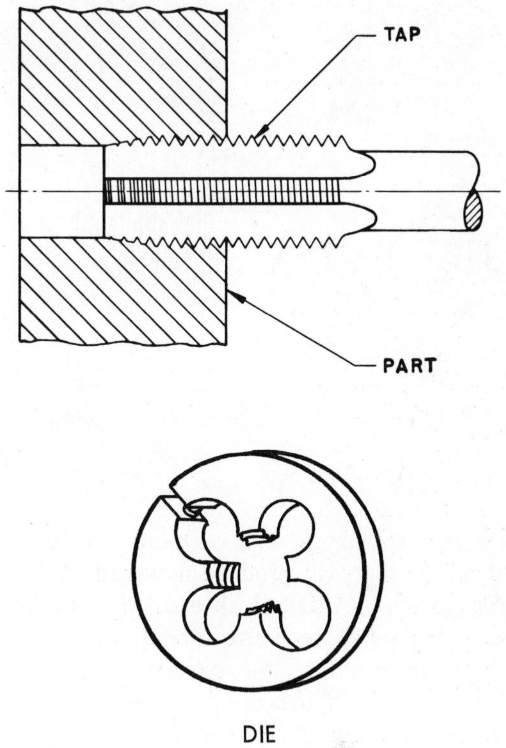

Figure 10-34
Threads may be cut with taps and dies.

Cutting threads with milling cutter. Cut threads may be produced on a milling machine by feeding a rapidly revolving single or multiple tooth milling cutter into the work to the depth of the thread and then traversing the cutter along the slower revolving work blank at a rate that will produce a thread of the desired lead. The multiple milling cutter or thread hob is an integral tool with annular rows of teeth forming a series of single point threading tools. See Fig. 10-35.

Cutting threads with a grinding wheel. Screw threads may be ground on a grinding wheel by a process similar to that of milling a thread. The profile of the periphery of the grinding wheel is dressed to conform to the shape of the thread groove in an axial plane. The rapidly revolving wheel is fed into the work and traversed along the slower revolv-

6. *Alcoa Engineering Drafting Standards* (Pittsburgh: Aluminum Company of America).

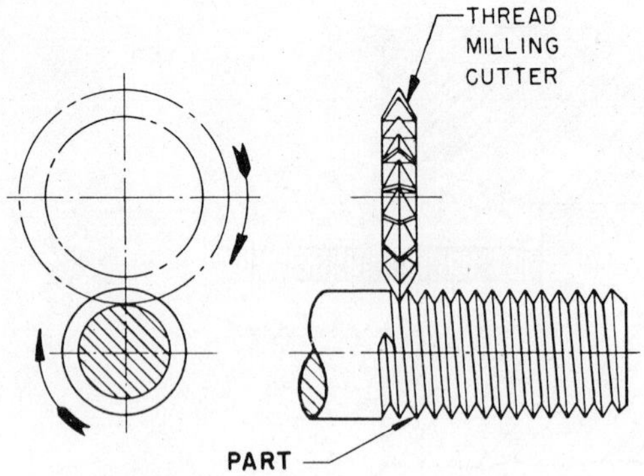

Figure 10-35
Cutting threads on a milling machine.

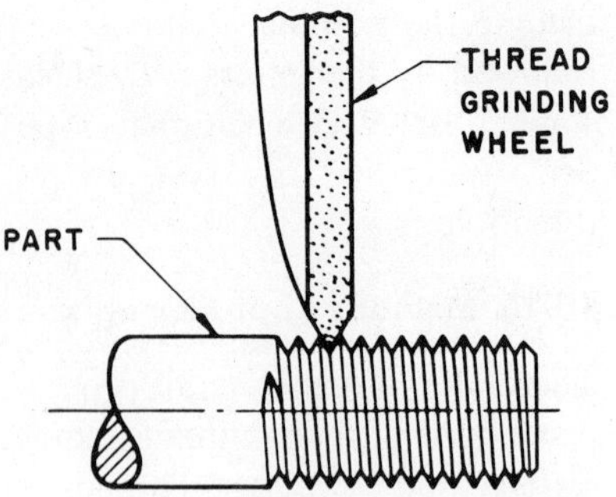

Figure 10-36
Grinding screw threads.

ing work blank for one or more light cuts at a rate that will produce a thread of the desired lead. Although threads are ground from the solid, the entire thread being produced by grinding, the process is applied principally as a finishing operation to correct distortion in hardened screw threads. See Fig. 10-36.

Rolling screw threads. Rolling of screw threads is essentially a forging process whereby threads are formed by forcing a threaded rolling die into the work to displace metal and conform it to the contours of the die. The unthreaded blank is rolled between the dies, which may be flat or cylindrical in form. The action of flat thread rolling dies and the action of circular rolling dies is illustrated in Fig. 10-37.

10.17 Bolts

See Fig. 10-38. The American Standards Association has approved two series of square and hexagon head bolts known as *regular* and *heavy*. The regular bolts are recommended for general purpose work and the heavy for use where greater bearing surface is necessary. These bolts are also classified as *finished, semifinished,* and *unfinished.* The term finished refers to the quality of manufacture and the closeness of tolerance. Both the semifinished and finished bolts may be obtained with a washer face. The washer face is approximately 1/64 inch thick and serves as a bearing in place of a regular washer.

The type and size of bolts to be used is determined by the engineer or designer and is largely governed by the strength requirement of the assembled unit. Hexagon bolts are the most common since they often require less head clearance. A typical application of a hexagon head bolt is shown in Fig. 10-39. Hexagon bolts are available with either plain or slotted heads.

Bolts come in a variety of sizes. Their length is measured from the bearing surface of the head to the extreme point. In selecting thread pitches for various bolt diameters, it should be remembered that the fine thread bolt is usually much stronger than the coarse thread bolt and has an advantage where length of engagement is limited, where vibration may be excessive or thin walls may be encountered. The class of fit is also important. For general application class 2A threads are used. With automotive assemblies such as connecting rods, main bearings, etc., Class 3A threads are generally recommended.

On a drawing, the specifications of a bolt should include diameter, number of threads per inch, series, class, type of finish, type of head, name and length, as

3/8 – 16 UNC – 2*A* x 2-1/2
SEMI-FIN HEX HD BOLT

To draw a bolt head and nut, obtain the dimensions from the tables in the Appendix and lay out as shown in Fig. 10-40.

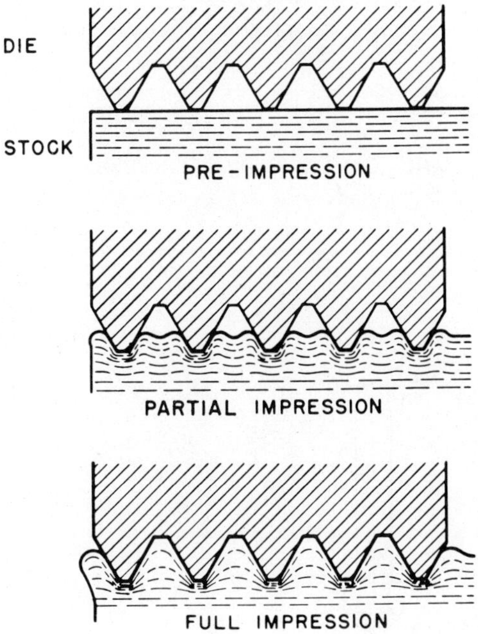

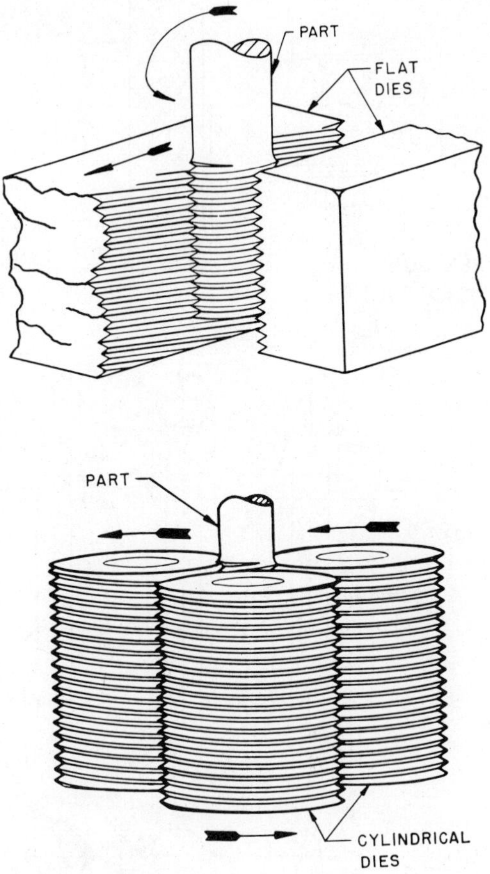

Figure 10-37
Action of dies in rolling of screw threads.

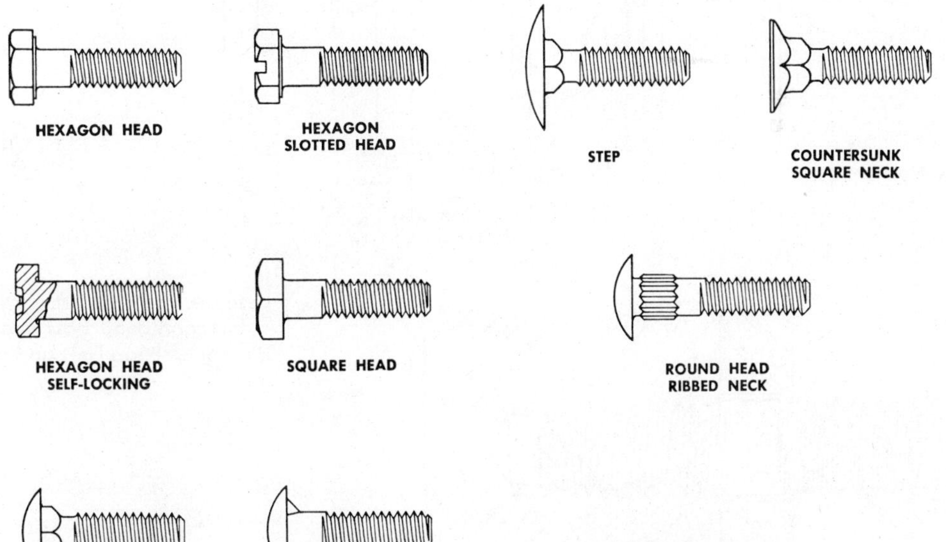

Figure 10-38
Common types of bolts.
General Motors Corp.

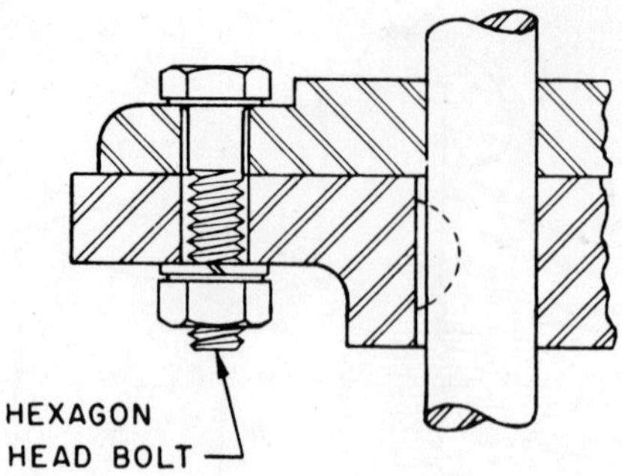

Figure 10-39
Hexagon head bolts are the most common type of bolts used.

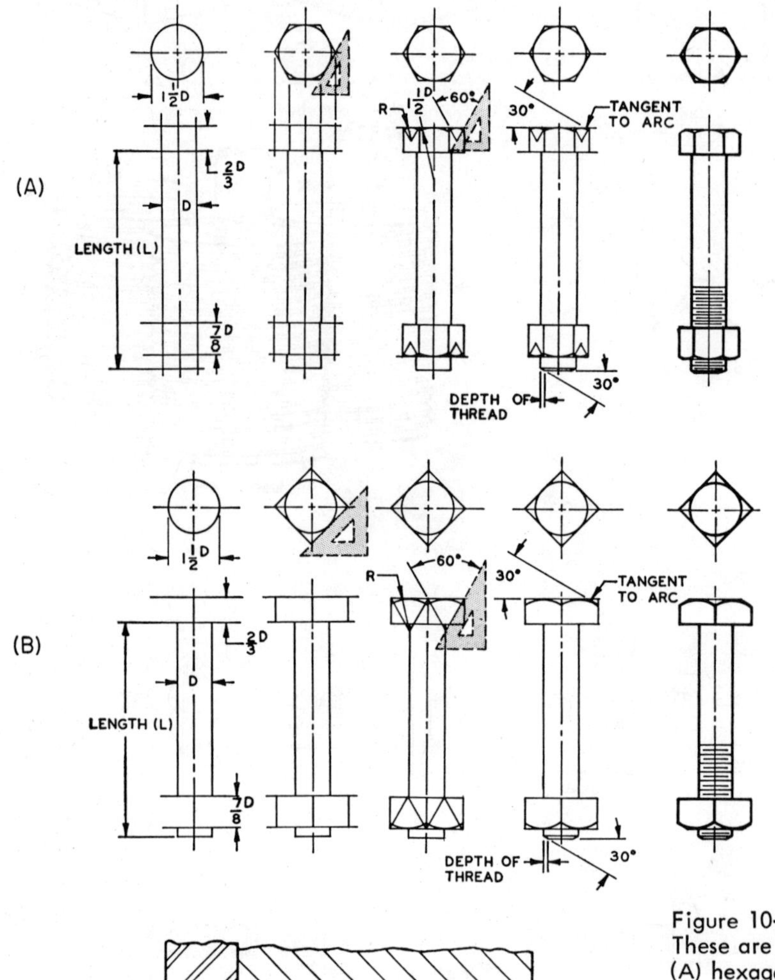

Figure 10-40
These are the steps in drawing a (A) hexagon head bolt and nut, and (B) a squarehead bolt and nut.

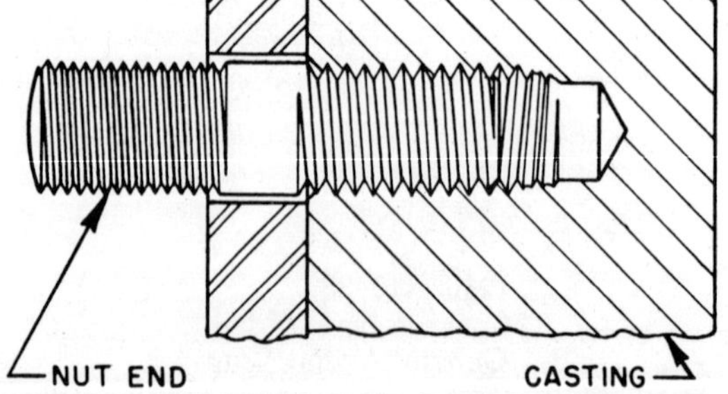

Figure 10-41
This is how a stud is used.

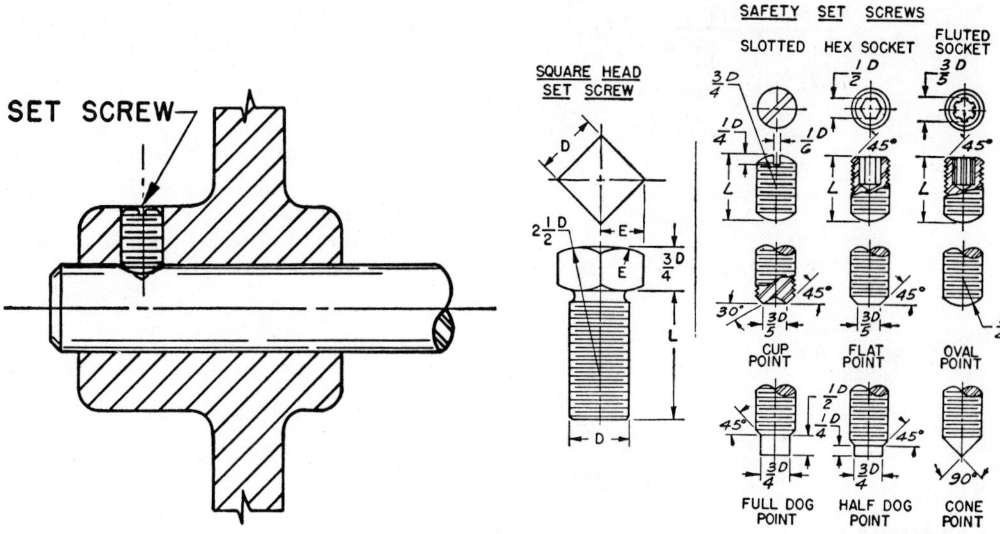

Figure 10-42
Types of set screws and how they are used.

10.18 Studs

A stud or stud bolt is a rod threaded on both ends. It is used when regular bolts are not suitable, especially on parts that must be removed frequently, such as cylinder heads. One end of the stud is screwed into a threaded or tapped hole, and the other end fits into the removable piece of the structure. A nut is used on the projecting end to hold the parts together. See Fig. 10-41. Ordinarily, a stud is made with coarse threads on the stud end and fine threads on the nut end.

On a detailed drawing, a stud is dimensioned to show the length of thread for both ends along with an overall length. The specification is given by a note. On an assembly drawing the specifications of the stud are included in the parts list or bill of material. The specifications of a stud should be given as

3/8 – 16 UNC – 2*A* x 2-1/2 STUD

10.19 Set screws

The function of a set screw is to prevent rotary motion between two parts, such as the hub of a pulley and shaft, as shown in Fig. 10-42. It is also used to make slight adjustments between mating parts. In all cases, the set screw is driven into one piece so that its point bears firmly against the other part. As a rule, a set screw is rarely used where the fixed parts are subjected to heavy stresses.

Set screws are available in the following types: headless slotted, hexagon socket, fluted socket and square head. Each of these can be obtained with these points: cup point, flat point, oval point, cone point, full dog point and half dog point. Because the projecting heads often produce a dangerous situation, set screws with heads are being used less frequently; instead the socket or safety headless type is more universally recommended. The safety type has either a slotted end or an end with a fluted or hexagonal hole to receive a tightening wrench. Specifications for set screws should include diameter, number of threads per inch, series, class of fit, type of head, type of point, and length. Example:

1/4 – 20 UNC – 2*A* x 1/2
SLOTTED CONE PT SET SCR

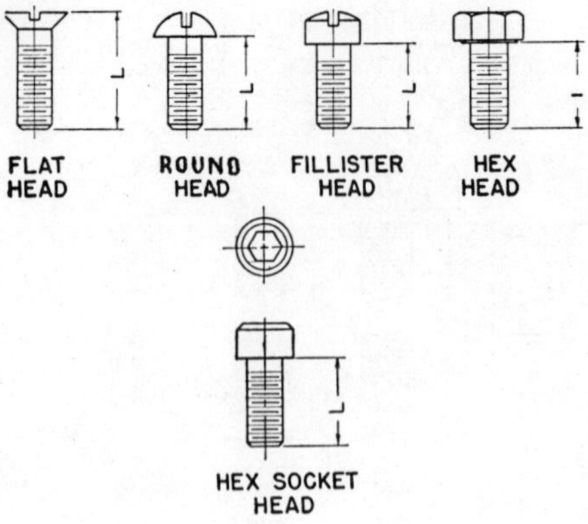

Figure 10-43
Here are examples of various types of cap screws.

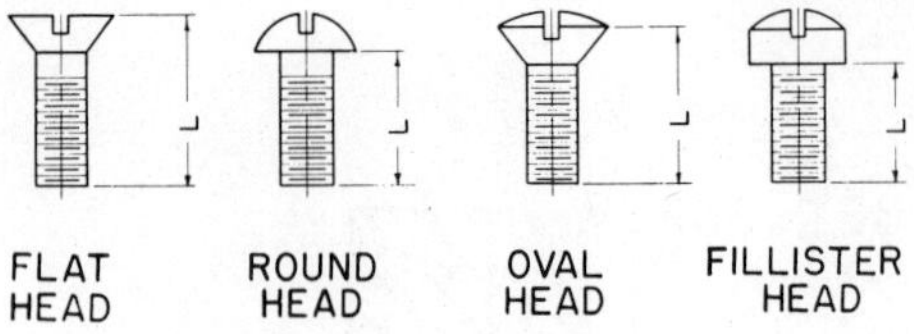

Figure 10-44
Examples of different types of machine screws.

10.20 Cap screws

A cap screw passes through a clearance hole in one member of the structure and screws into a threaded or tapped hole in the other. They range in diameter from 1/4 to 1-1/4 inches and are made with five types of heads: hexagon, round, flat, fillister, and socket. See Fig. 10-43. The length of cap screws is not standardized; the length is measured from the largest diameter of the bearing surface of the head to the extreme point of the screw. The point of a cap screw is chamfered 45° to the flat surface.

A cap screw is available with either the American National and Unified Coarse or Fine threads. The specifications of a cap screw should be given as

1/2 – 13 UNC – 2*A* x 1
ROUND HD CAP SCR

10.21 Machine screws

Machine screws are similar to cap screws except that they are smaller and are used chiefly on small work having thin sections. See Fig. 10-44. Below 1/4″ size, machine screws are specified by numbers from 2 to 12. Above 1/4″ the size is indicated by diameter. They are available in either the American National and Unified Coarse or Fine thread series. On a drawing machine screws are shown as

No. 10 – 24 UNC – 2*A* x 3/8
RD HD MACH SCR

10.22 Nuts[7]

As shown in Fig. 10-45, there are many types of nuts available to satisfy specific requirements. The most common are:

Hexagon nuts. Made to fit the various types of hexagon bolts. They are classified into three principal groups: regular, heavy and light. Just as hexagon bolts, they are available in the finish, semifinish and regular finish quality.

Slotted hexagon nuts (with cotter pins or wire). Used where there is danger of the nuts coming off due to vibration or other causes.

Jam hexagon nuts. Used where height is restricted or as a means of locking the working nut.

Square nuts. Rough unfinished nuts most frequently used in conjunction with square neck bolts and square head bolts. Square nuts may be used with machine screws if the screws are to be driven through the head; otherwise, it is advisable to use hexagon machine screw nuts.

Lock nuts. Nuts which have a special means for gripping a threaded member or bearing surface so that relative back off rotation between the nut and the threaded companion member is impeded. Prevailing torque type lock nuts employ a self-contained locking feature such as deformed or undersize

7. *General Motors Drafting Standards Manual* (Detroit: General Motors Corp.).

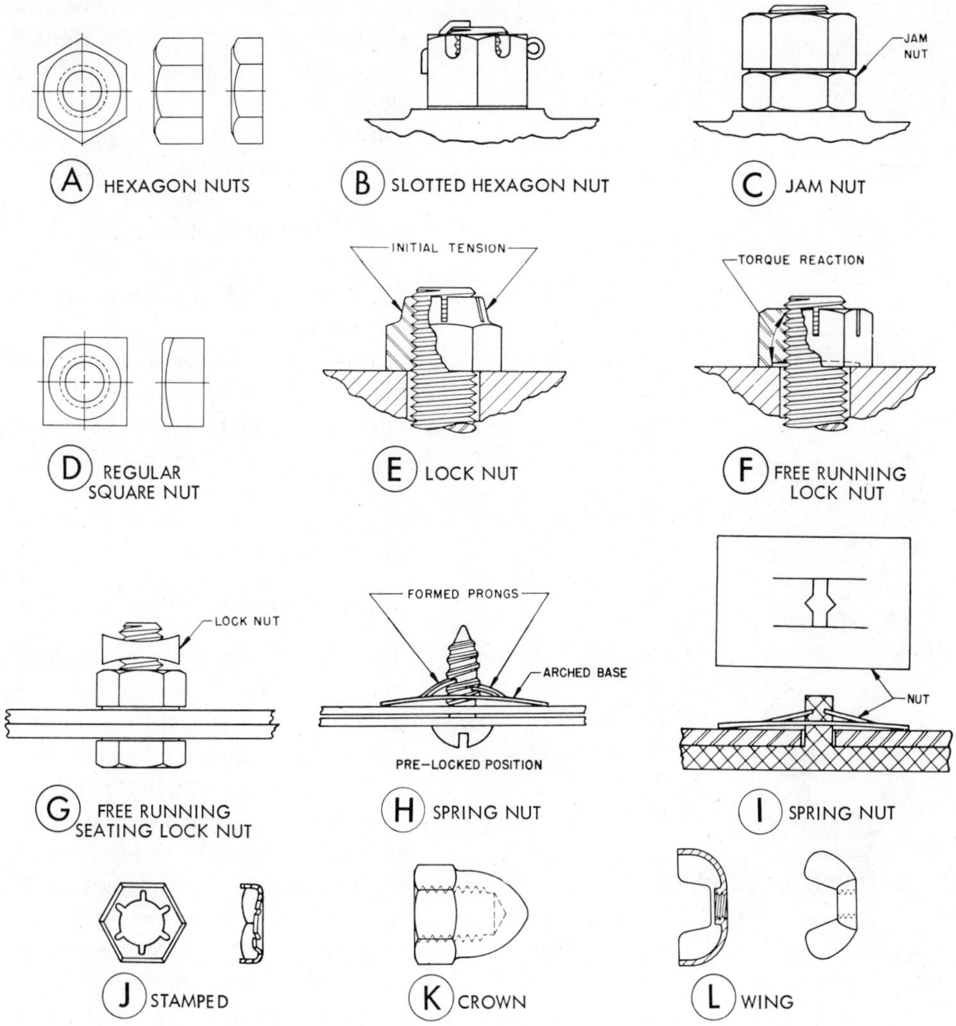

Figure 10-45
Common types of nuts.

threads, variable lead angle, plastic or fiber washers, or plug inserts. This type of nut resists screwing on, as well as unscrewing, and does not depend on bolt load for locking.

Free running lock nuts. Develop their locking action after the nut has been seated by reactive spring force against the threads or by friction against the bearing surface.

Free running seating lock nuts. Applied over hexagon nuts, the concave surface of this type nut, in contacting the top of the hexagon nut, tends to flatten, thereby deflecting the nut threads from their true helix and causing them to bind on the bolt or screw thread.

Spring nuts. Made of thin spring metal; have arched prongs or formed embossments to fit a single lead of a screw thread. Used extensively for sheet metal construction where high torque is not required. A type of spring nut is available which can be used with rivets, tubing, nails and other unthreaded parts. It is pushed on and provides a positive bite that grips securely even on very smooth surfaces.

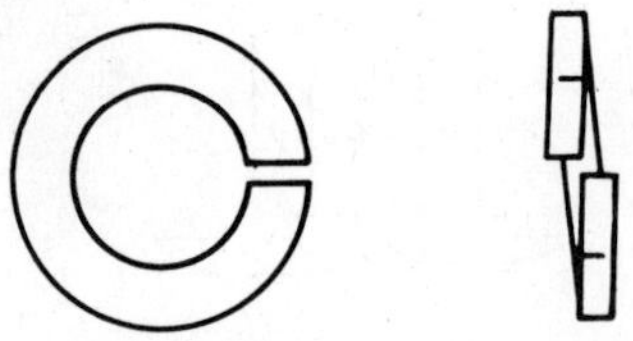

Figure 10-46
Spring lock washers are split and helical in shape.

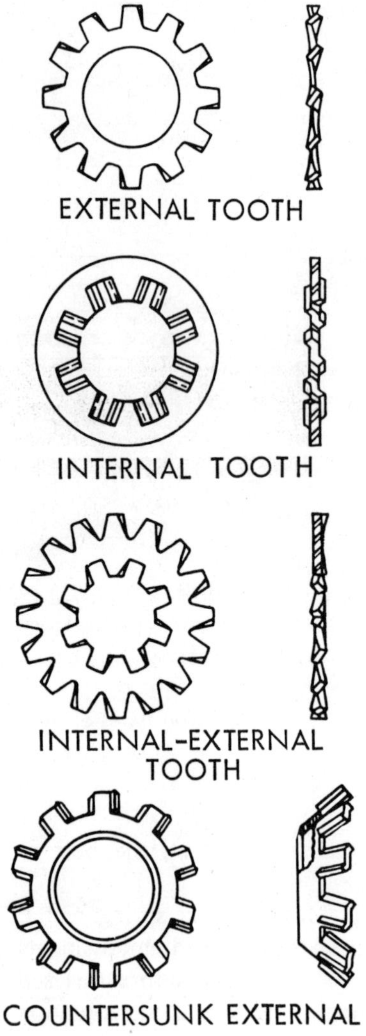

Figure 10-47
The various types of tooth lock washers have teeth that are offset to bite or grip the bolt or nut and the work surface.

Stamped nuts. Usually made of thin spring steel; have arched prongs formed to fit a single lead of a thread. Have the same functional usage as a spring nut with an additional advantage of having tightening provisions by means of hexagon flanges.

Crown nuts. Generally used where the end of the external threaded part should be hidden. The crown on top of the nut provides a suitable surface to be finished for appearance.

Wing nuts. As the name implies, are provided with two wings to facilitate hand tightening and loosening. Used where high torque is not required and where the nuts are to be tightened and loosened frequently. Available in a stamped, cast or forged form in either brass or steel.

10.23 Washers[8]

The three basic types of washers are: the *plain,* the *spring lock* and the *tooth lock.* All three types are available in standard sizes to suit standard bolts and screws.

Plain washers. Annular shaped parts, usually flat. They are used for two principal purposes: under the head of a screw or bolt, or under a nut to spread a load over a greater area. They are also used to prevent the marring of the parts during assembly as a result of the turning of the screw, bolt or nut.

Spring lock washers. Made of steel that is capable of being hardened or of bronze or aluminum alloys. They are split on one side and are helical in shape as shown in Fig. 10-46. They have the dual function of: (1) springing take-up devices to compensate for developed looseness and the loss of tension between component parts of an assembly, and (2) acting as hardened thrust bearings to facilitate assembly and disassembly of bolted fastenings by decreasing the frictional resistance between the bolted surface and the bearing face of the bolt head or nut.

Tooth lock washers. Made in three types as shown in Fig. 10-47: the *external,* the *internal* and the *internal-external.* The hardened teeth of these washers are twisted offset to bite or grip both the bolt head or the nut

8. *Ibid.*

and the respective work surface to help prevent the loosening of the assembly due to vibration. They also make good electrical contacts. Unlike the spring lock washers, they do not provide spring action to counteract wear or stretch in the parts of an assembly.

The external tooth lock washer is the most commonly used of the tooth type lock washers, but the internal tooth lock washer is generally used where it is necessary to consider appearance and to insure engagement of teeth with the bearing surface of the fastener.

Where additional locking ability is required or where there is need for a large bearing surface, such as over a clearance hole, the internal-external tooth lock washer may be used. Countersunk external tooth lock washers are used with flat head and oval head machine screws.

There are many variations of special washers for specific applications. The more common of these special washers are the *finish washer* and the *grip washer*. See Fig. 10-48. Finish washers are used under the heads of countersunk and oval head screws to provide proper seating of the screw heads and at the same time eliminate countersinking of the work face. The finish washers, as the name implies, enhance the appearance of the product. Grip washers, both square and round, are used under bolt heads against wood. They provide a solid seat for the bolt head and prevent depressing or scoring of the wood.

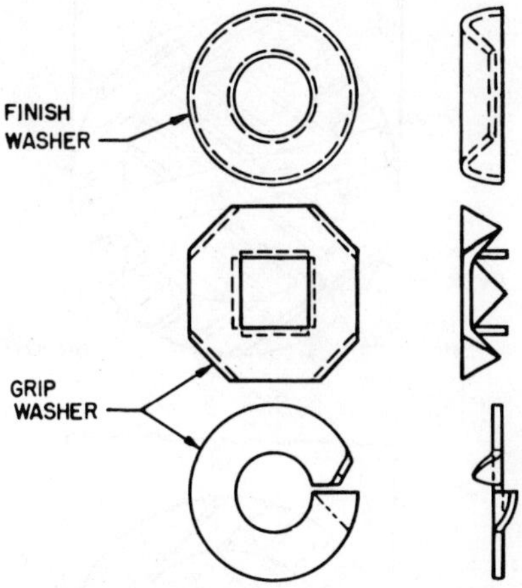

Figure 10-48
These special washers are for specific applications such as under bolt heads against wood.

10.24 Pins[9]

Cotter pins, groove pins, taper pins and clevis pins are used to lock parts of an assembly in position.

Cotter pins. Used for retaining or locking slotted nuts, ball sockets, movable links or rods, etc., as shown in Fig. 10-49.

Groove pins. Straight pins made of cold drawn steel. They have longitudinal grooves rolled or pressed into the body to provide a locking effect when the pin is driven into a drilled hole. This type of pin eliminates

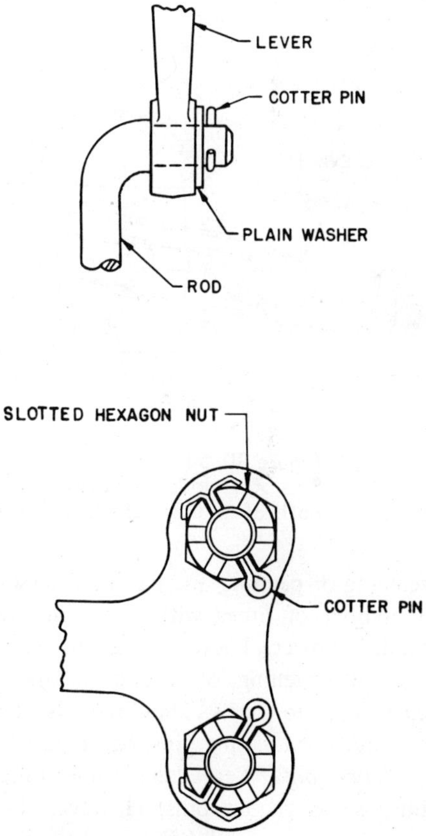

Figure 10-49
Cotter pins are used to lock slotted nuts, rods, or moveable links.

9. *Ibid.*

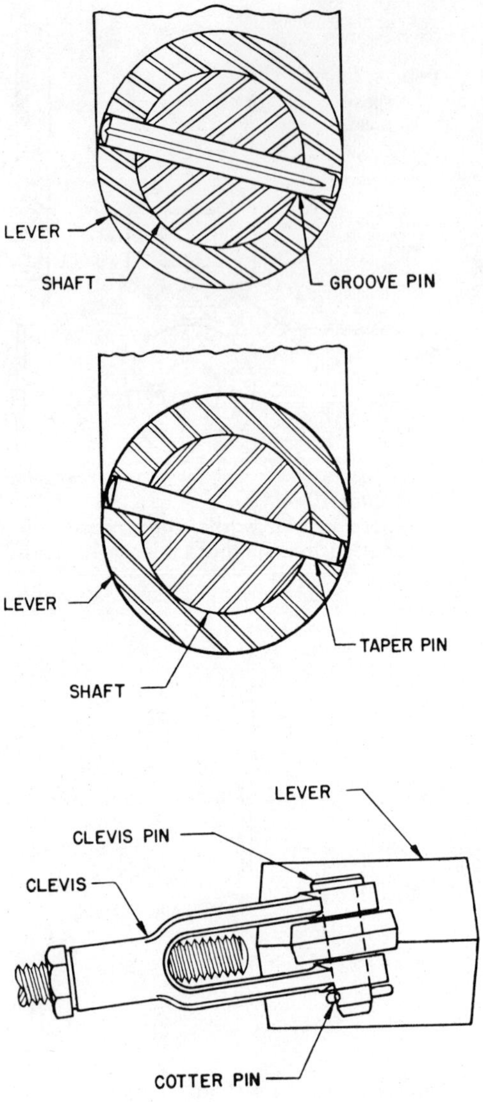

Figure 10-50
Pins of various sorts are used to lock parts of an assembly in position.

reaming or peening and can be disassembled a number of times without serious loss of holding power. They are used for semi-permanent fastening of levers, collars, gears, cams, etc., to shafts. They may also be used as guides or locating pins. See Fig. 10-50.

Taper pins. Serve the same functional purpose as groove pins. However, they require taper reamed holes at assembly and depend only on taper locking which can totally disengage when minor displacement occurs. See Fig. 10-50.

Clevis pins. Used to attach clevises to rod ends and levers and to serve as bearings. They are held in place by cotter pins as shown in Fig. 10-50.

10.25 Keys

Keys are used to prevent parts attached to shafts, wheels, cranks, etc., from rotating. Fig. 10-51 illustrates some of the more common types of keys. When force is not too severe either a flat key or round key is used. On heavier work the rectangular key is more suitable. The Pratt and Whitney and square keys are probably more popular for most machine designs. The gib-head key is designed so the head protrudes far enough from the hub to allow the insertion of a drift pin to remove the key. Another frequently used key is known as the Woodruff key. This key consists of a flat segmental disc with a flat or round bottom.

On drawings, flat, taper, square, and gib-head keys are specified by a note giving the width, height and length. Pratt and Whitney keys are shown by a number. Woodruff keys are also specified by a number with the last two digits representing the nominal diameter in eighths of an inch, and the preceding digits indicating the width in thirty-seconds of an inch. (See Appendix for sizes of different keys.) The information for keys should be listed as

3/16 x 1-1/4 SQUARE KEY
1/4 x 3/16 x 1-1/4 FLAT KEY
No. 12 PRATT & WHITNEY KEY
No. 304 WOODRUFF KEY

Keys are usually not drawn except when some special key having other than standard limits must be shown. The practice is often to dimension keyways on shafts or internal members. The procedure for dimensioning such keyways is illustrated in Fig. 10-52.

10.26 Springs

Springs are not actually fasteners but they are included in this section since their method of representation closely resembles screw thread representations. Springs in reality are devices which store energy when dis-

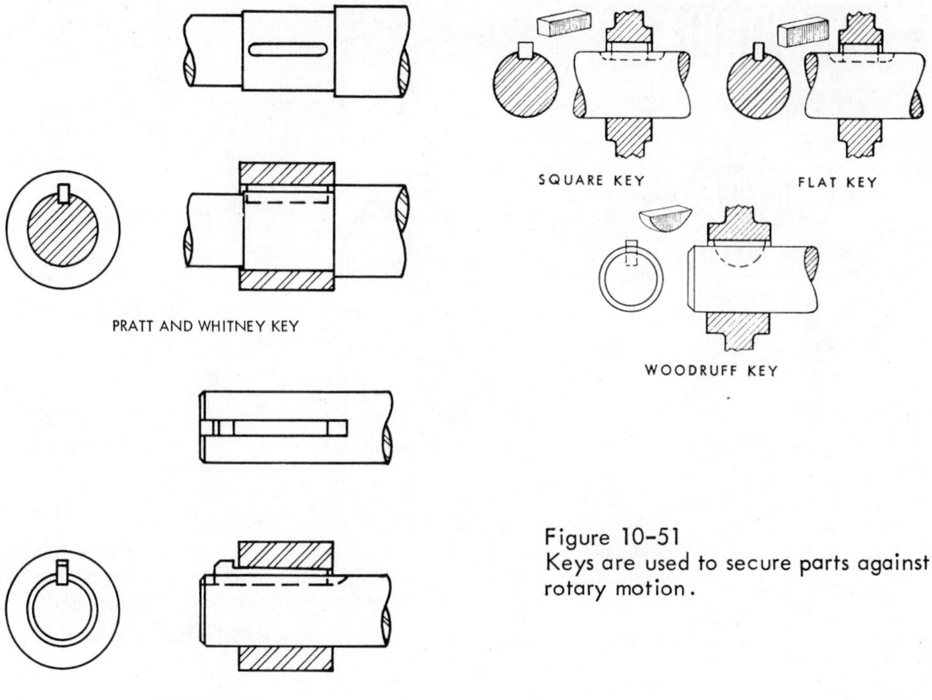

Figure 10-51
Keys are used to secure parts against rotary motion.

torted and then return an equivalent amount of energy upon their release. They are very important units in the operation of numerous mechanical and electrical components.

Springs are classified into three main groups: *controlled action, variable action* and *static*. Controlled action springs have a regulated range of action such as in valve or switch springs. Variable action springs are those which vary in their range of movement such as may be used on clutches or brakes. Static springs exert a constant pressure or tension between several parts. The various types of springs in each of the three main groups are illustrated and described in Fig. 10-53.

In order to properly designate springs in a drawing, a draftsman should have an understanding of these terms[10] (see Figs. 10-54 and 10-58):

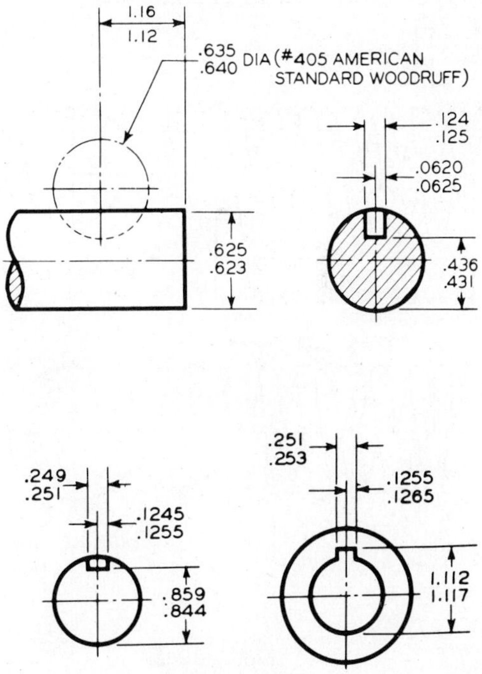

Figure 10-52
Keyways are dimensioned in this manner. ASA Y14.5-1957

10. *Ibid.*

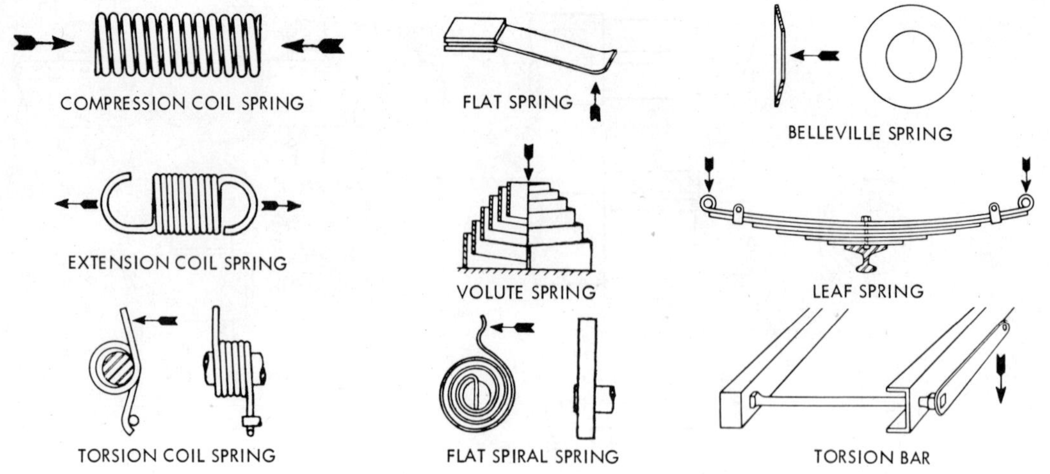

Figure 10-53
Springs are elastic bodies designed to perform predetermined functions involving pressure and movement. General Motors Corp.

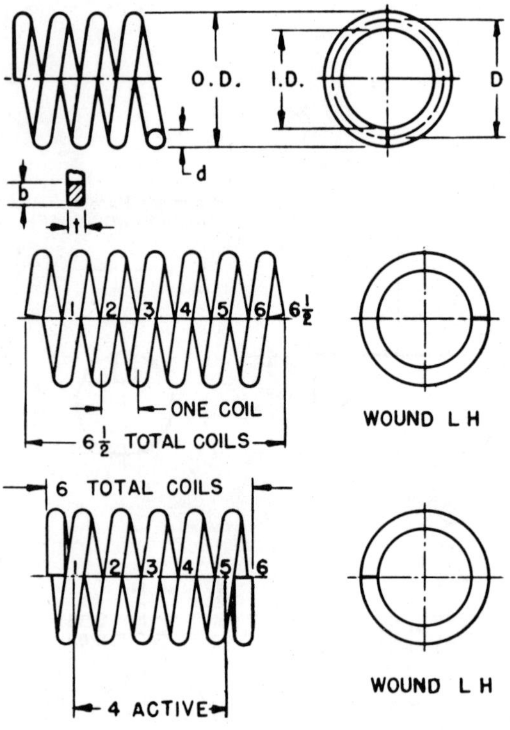

Figure 10-54
Illustration of spring terms.

Free length. The length of a coil spring measured parallel to its axis in the unloaded or free condition. The measurement is taken overall on a compression spring, but is usually taken inside the hooks on an extension spring, and should be specified *APPROX,* when not important.

Loaded length. The length of a spring under a given load.

Solid length. The length of a compression spring when completely compressed; that is, with all the coils completely closed upon each other.

Rate. The ratio of change in load of a spring to the corresponding change in deflection.

Outside diameter (O.D.). The diameter of a coil spring, measured on the outside of the wire, normal to the axis of the spring.

Inside diameter (I.D.). The diameter of a coil spring, measured on the inside of the wire, normal to the axis of the spring.

Wire size (d). The cross sectional diameter of round wire used in forming the spring.

Mean diameter (D). The theoretical diameter of a spring, for design purposes, measured to the center of the wire section *(O.D. — d).*

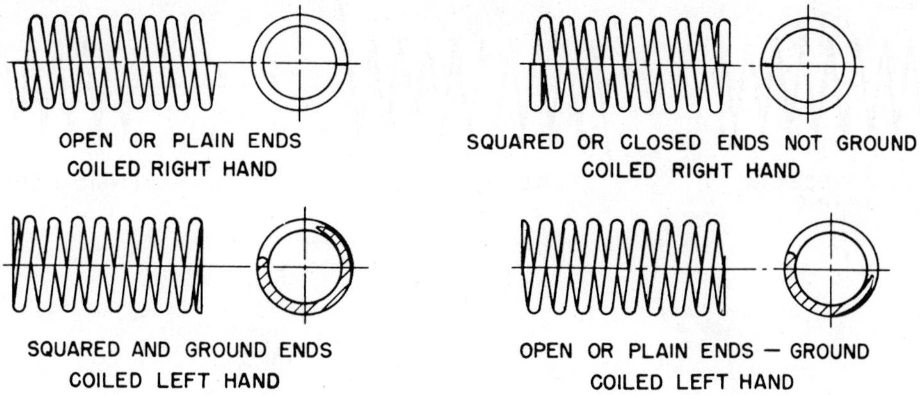

Figure 10-55
These are the ends commonly specified on compression springs.

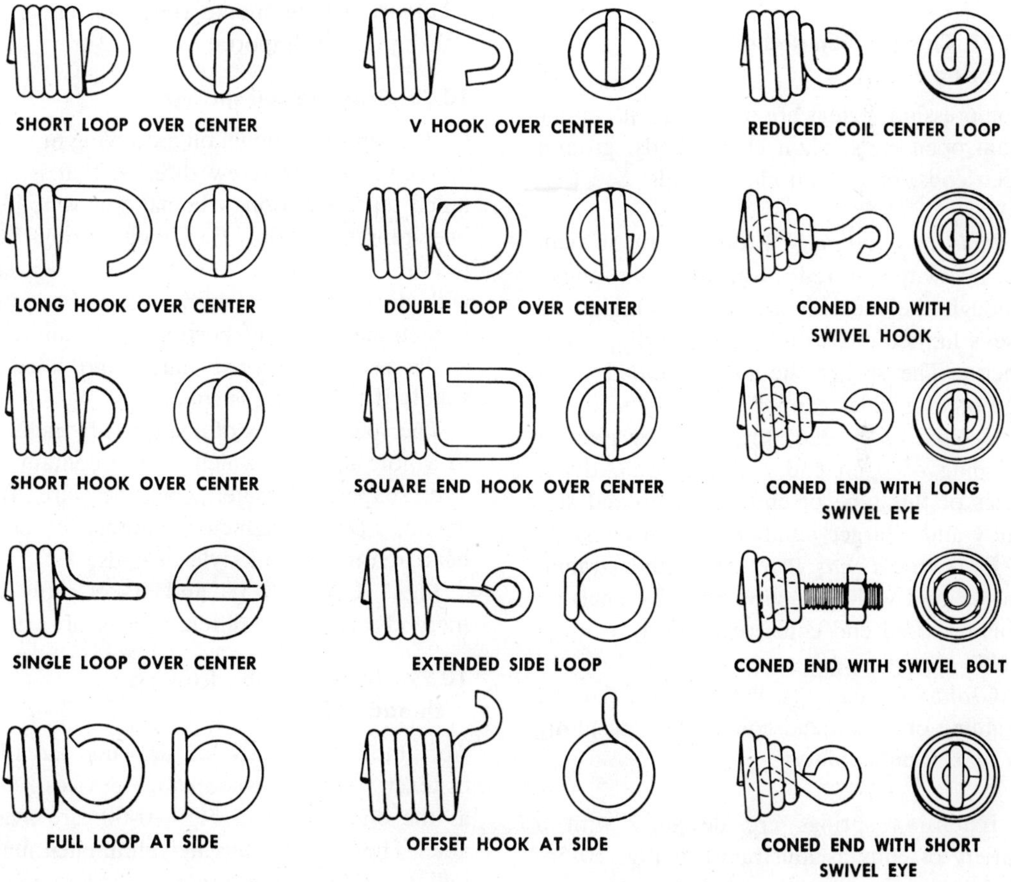

Figure 10-56
Types of ends used on extension springs.

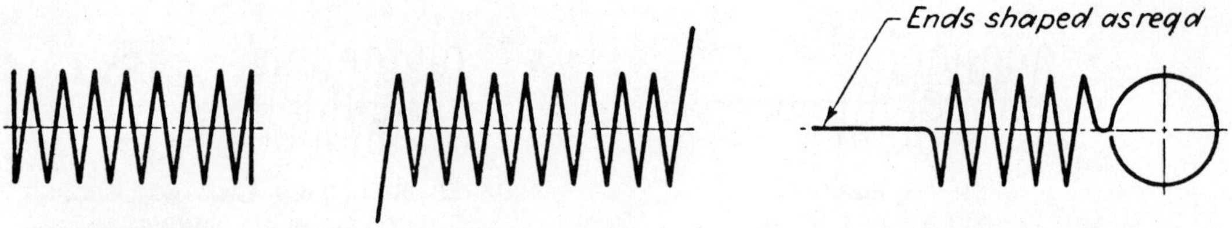

Figure 10-57
Springs may be represented with single line symbols.

Coil. One complete convolution or turn of the wire about the axis of the spring.

Total coils. The total number of complete and portions of coils.

Active coils (N). The total number of coils less those rendered inactive by the nature of design or application of the spring.

10.27 Compression and extension spring ends[11]

Compression springs are designed with either plain open ends, plain closed ends, ground open ends, or ground closed ends. See Fig. 10-55.

Plain or open ends. Produced by straight cut-off with no reduction of helix angle. Though the most economical to make, its use is limited due to inherent buckling tendencies. The spring should be guided on a rod or in a hole to operate satisfactorily.

Ground open ends. Produced by parallel grinding of open end coil springs. Advantages of this type of end are improved stability and a larger number of total coils.

Plain closed ends. Produced with a straight cut-off and with reduction of helix angle to obtain closed end coils, resulting in a more stable spring.

Ground closed ends. Produced by parallel grinding of closed end coil springs, resulting in maximum stability.

Extension springs are designed with a variety of ends as illustrated in Fig. 10-56. Different types of ends can be used on the same spring. The relative position of the two ends should be specified if important, otherwise a note should state that end relationship is not important.

11. *Ibid.*

10.28 Drawing coil springs

Coil springs are shown on a drawing in much the same way as screw threads; that is, detailed representation, schematic or simplified line representation. For long springs the practice is to show a few turns on each end with ditto marks between. When the spring is sectioned, the cut portion is section-lined if the representation is large and filled in solidly if the spring is small.

The specifications of a spring are included in a note or table which should contain the size, shape and material of the wire, free length, outside diameter, number of coils, heat treatment, and style of ends.

Figs. 10-57, 10-58, and 10-59 show the methods of drawing different types of springs.

10.29. Templates for drawing threaded fasteners

To simplify the task of drawing threaded fasteners, several commercial devices, such as the one shown in Fig. 10-60, are available. The use of templates eliminates many tedious and time consuming tasks and consequently should be employed by the draftsman whenever possible.

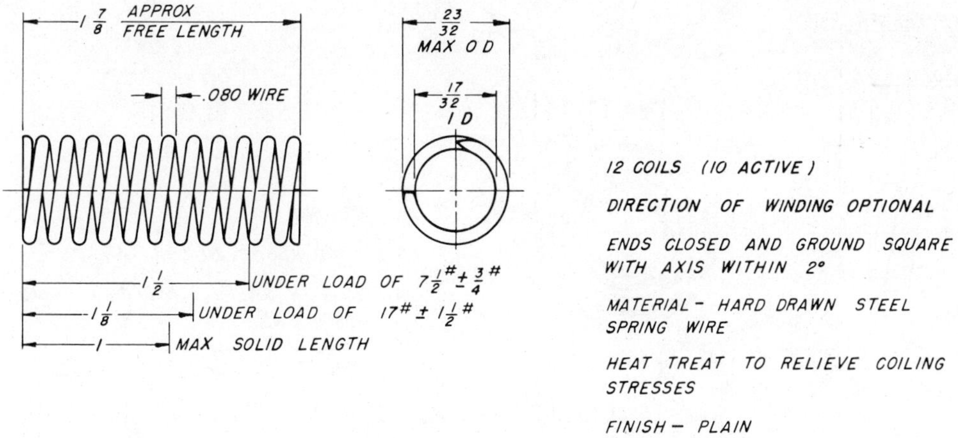

COMPRESSION COIL SPRING

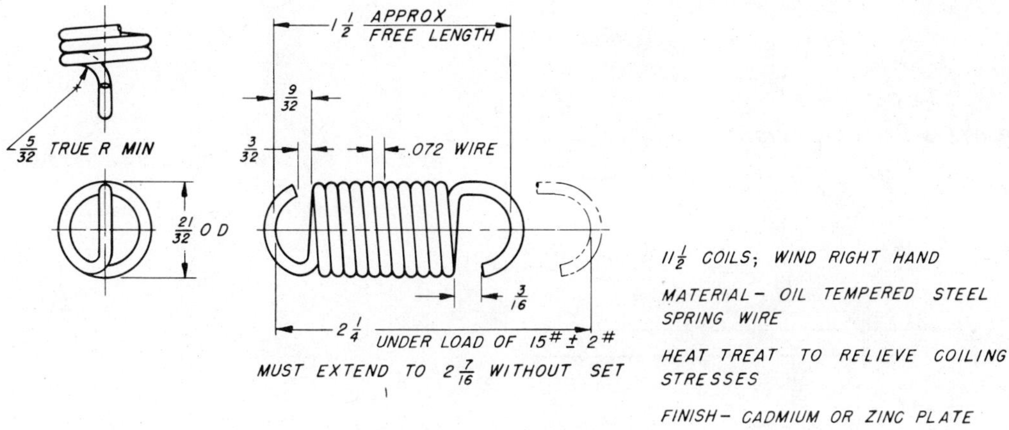

EXTENSION COIL SPRING

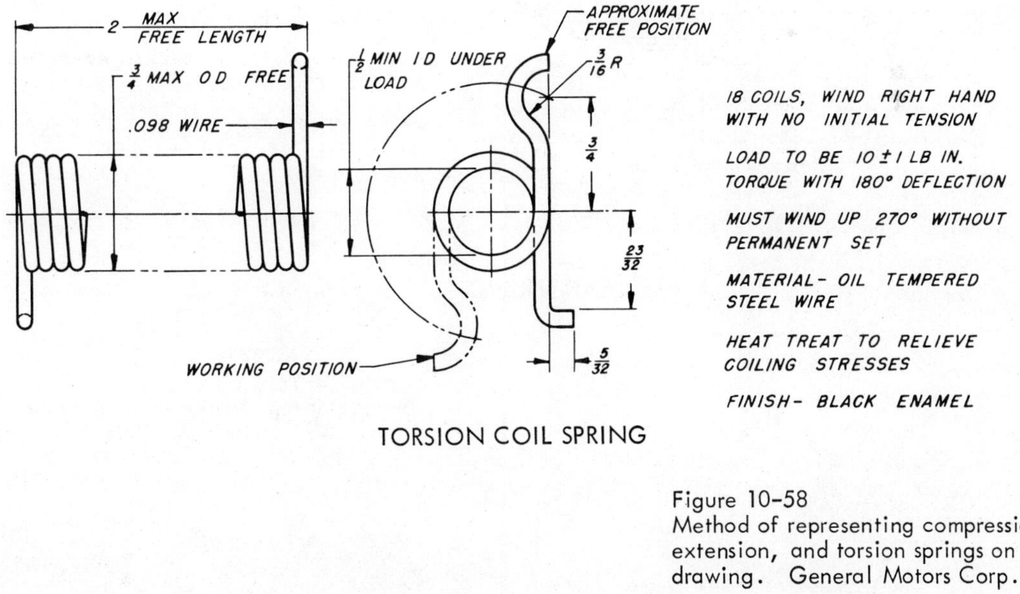

TORSION COIL SPRING

Figure 10-58
Method of representing compression, extension, and torsion springs on a drawing. General Motors Corp.

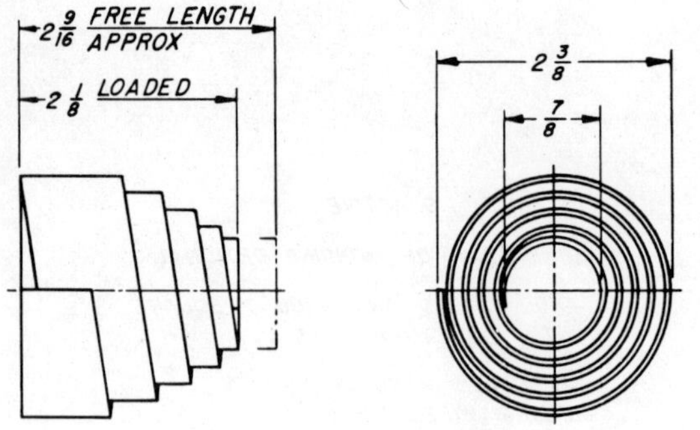

5 TOTAL COILS ENDS CLOSED AND GROUND

LOAD – 180 LBS. ± 20 LBS. AT 2 1/8

MATERIAL – C R SPRING STEEL S A E 1080.
THICKNESS – .062
WIDTH – 1 1/16
HEAT TREAT ROCKWELL C 40-50

VOLUTE SPRING

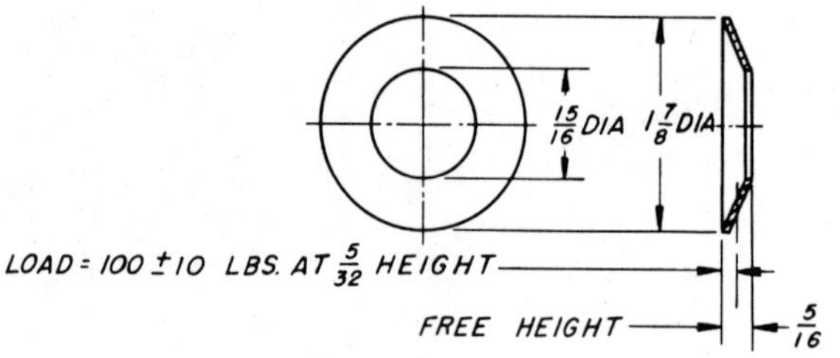

MATERIAL – C R SPRING STEEL S A E 1370
THICKNESS – .062
HEAT TREAT ROCKWELL C 38 – 43

BELLEVILLE SPRING

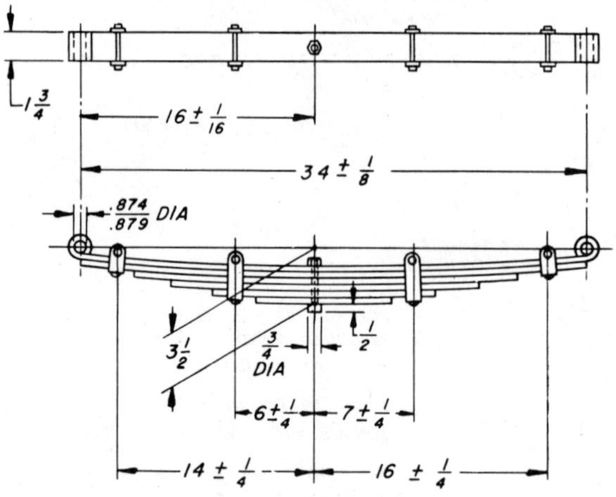

6 LEAVES 3/16 THICK

MATERIAL – H R SPRING STEEL S A E 9260
HEAT TREAT BRINELL 375 – 444

SHOWN UNDER 700 ± 50 LBS LOAD
INSTALLED RATE 230 LBS PER INCH APPROX

FOR CLIPS, BOLTS, AND LEAF DIMENSIONS SEE DETAILS

LEAF SPRING

Figure 10-59
Method of representing volute, belleville, and leaf springs on a drawing.

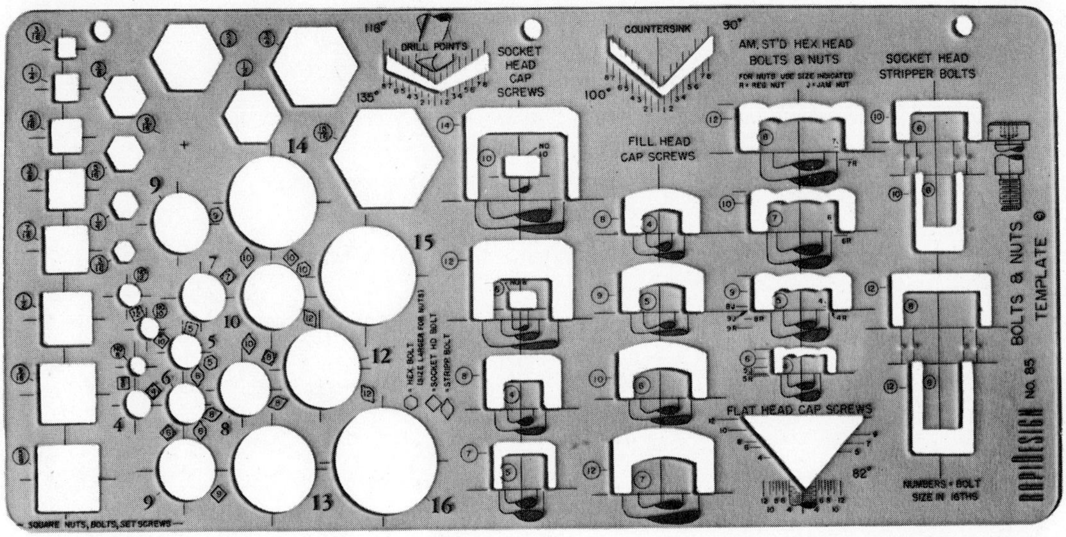

Figure 10-60
Templates simplify the drawing of threaded fasteners. RapiDesign

Problems, section 10

1 Make a 2-view drawing of a ¾″ dia. steel Shaft, 10″ long, having a 1/2-13 UNC-2A threaded section on one end 2–1/4″ long, and a 3/4-10 UNC-3A threaded section 1–1/2″ long on the opposite end. Show threads using schematic representation. Include dimensions with proper thread callouts.

2 Make a 2-view dimensioned drawing of a steel Tapping Pad, 1/2″x 2-1/2″x6″, showing two holes, threaded 5/8-18 UNF-2B on centerline spaced 1–1/2″ from end and 3″ between centers. Dimension completely including tap drill size.

3 Make 2-view drawings of the following standard fasteners, showing thread representations as assigned by the instructor. Include correct nomenclature.

(a) 3/4-10 UNC-2A Semi-finished Hex Head Bolt 4″ long, with assembled spring lockwasher and hex nut.

(b) 1″-8NC Square Head Bolt 4″ long with plain washer and square nut.

(c) 3/8-24 UNF-3A Hex Socket Head Cap Screw 2″ long.

(d) 1/4-20 UNC-2A Round Head Machine Screw, 1–1/2″ long.

(e) 1/2-20 UNF-2A Slotted Set Screw, 1–1/2″ long.

(f) 3/4-10 NC-2 Flat Head Cap Screw, 2″ long.

4 Make a drawing of a 10″ long threaded Lead Screw, Spec. SAE 1115, having a 1″-5 general purpose Acme thread with a double lead. Leave a 3/4″ dia. × 1–1/8″ long unthreaded section at each end. Show 5 threads by detailed representation at each end of the threaded section using ditto lines between.

5 Make two views of a cast steel Collar 4″ O.D.x2″ long having a 2.502″/2.498″ bore. Show a keyway for a standard square key for this size bore. Show a 5/8-18 UNF-2A Square Head Set Screw centered on collar opposite the keyway. Rounds 1/4″ R. Include all dimensions.

6 Make a 2-view drawing of a Steel Shaft 1–1/2″ dia., 18″ long, having 1/8x45° chamfered ends. Show a keyway for a #608 Woodruff key located 3–1/2″ from one end. Include a hole for a #6 taper pin positioned 3–1/2″ from the opposite end, and in line with the keyway.

7 Make a 2-view drawing of a coil compression Spring to these specifications:

O.D.: 1–1/4 in.
Free length: 3–1/2 in.
No. of coils: 6
Type of ends: Plain ground
Material: #5 ga (.207) steel spring wire

8 Make a 2-view drawing of a coil compression Spring having 10 active coils, 2–3/4″ free length, closed and ground ends, 1–1/8″ O.D. of .105″ hard drawn steel spring wire.

Welding drawings 11

Welding performs an important function in the fabrication of metal products since it is one of the most effective processes in joining metal sections. In many instances, welding not only produces more permanent joints and simplifies production operations, but it also increases the strength and improves the appearance of the finished structure.

In the preparation of drawings of welded components, the draftsman is frequently required to indicate the type of joint, and the location and size of the welds. To eliminate time consuming details, the American Welding Society has developed a set of welding symbols to supply the needed welding information on a drawing. These symbols and other pertinent welding data are discussed and illustrated in this section.

11.1 Types of joints

There are five basic joints used in welding—butt, corner, tee, lap and edge. These joints and the type of welds by which members are joined are shown in Fig. 11-1.

Selection of joints for various purposes is governed by four factors:

1 Magnitude of the load.
2 Characteristic of the load; that is, whether the load is in compression or tension.
3 Application of the load; that is, whether it is steady, variable, or sudden.
4 Cost of preparing and welding the joint.

11.2 Welding processes

There are many different welding methods. The type used depends on the kind of material to be joined, operating cost, shape and size of components to be welded, strength and appearance of the seam. A brief description of various welding processes is included here for general familiarization purposes. The draftsman may need to consult other welding references for more specific welding data.

11.3 Oxyacetylene welding

The oxyacetylene process is a form of welding in which fusion of metal is achieved by a gas flame burning a mixture of oxygen and acetylene. Combustion of these two gases produces a temperature of approximately 6300° F. which can melt and effect fusion of weldable metals. Most commercial metals can be welded by the oxyacetylene process.

The welding operation is performed by directing a lighted torch over the seam of a joint. See Fig. 11-2. As the metal melts, filler rod is added to the molten puddle to strengthen the weld and form a bead of the required shape and size.

11.4 Metallic arc welding

In the metallic arc process, an electric arc formed between the work and the electrode liberates the necessary heat to effect fusion of the joint. The arc is produced by a specially designed generator or transformer. The intense heat that is developed by the arc instantly brings to a melting point a small portion of the work to be welded. The tip of the metallic electrode is simultaneously melted and the tiny globules of molten metal are deposited into the molten pool of the parent metal. See Fig. 11-3.

11.5 Carbon arc welding

Carbon arc welding is somewhat similar to oxyacetylene welding in that a flame is used to bring about fusion of the parent metal and filler rod. Whereas the oxyacetylene flame is produced by burning a mixture of

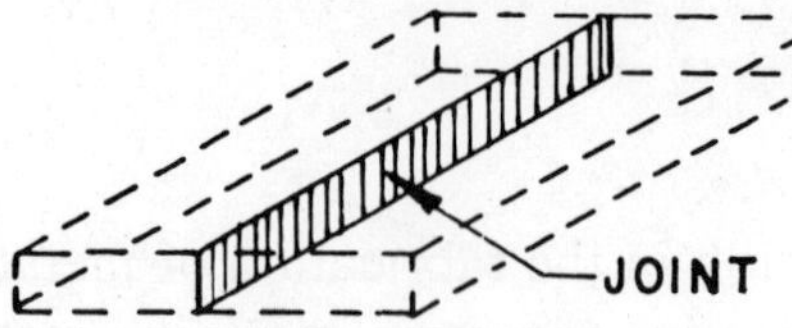

APPLICABLE WELDS

Square-Groove
V-Groove
Bevel-Groove
U-Groove
J-Groove
Flare-V-Groove
Flare-Bevel-Groove
Melt-Thru
Edge-Flange
Flash
Upset

(A) **BUTT JOINT**

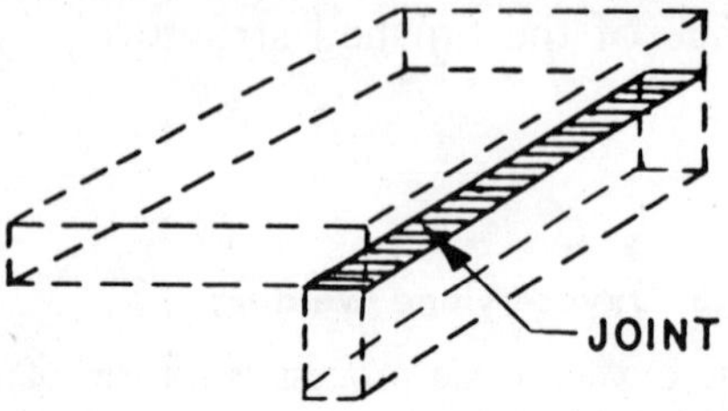

APPLICABLE WELDS

Fillet
Arc-Spot
Arc-Seam
Square-Groove
V-Groove
Bevel-Groove
U-Groove
J-Groove
Flare-V-Groove
Flare-Bevel-Groove
Melt-Thru
Edge-Flange
Corner-Flange
Resistance-Spot
Projection
Resistance-Seam
Flash

(B) **CORNER JOINT**

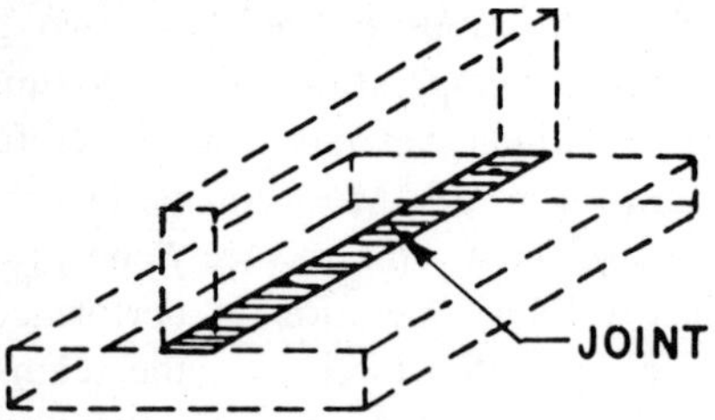

APPLICABLE WELDS

Fillet
Plug
Slot
Arc-Spot
Arc-Seam
Bevel-Groove
J-Groove
Flare-Bevel-Groove
Melt-Thru
Resistance-Spot
Projection
Resistance-Seam
Flash

(C) **TEE JOINT**

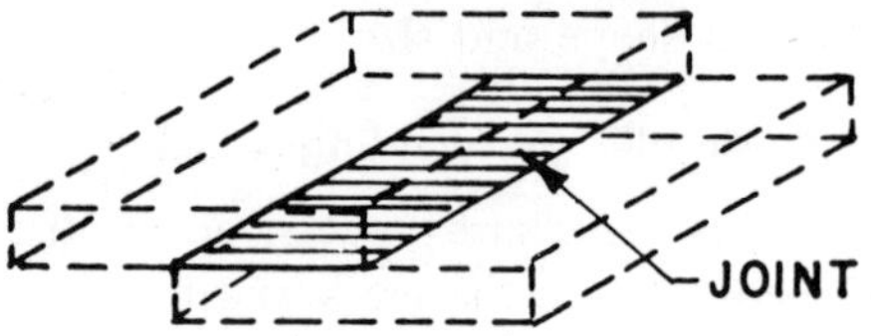

APPLICABLE WELDS

Fillet
Plug
Slot
Arc-Spot
Arc-Seam
Bevel-Groove
J-Groove
Flare-Bevel-Groove
Resistance-Spot
Projection
Resistance-Seam

(D) **LAP JOINT**

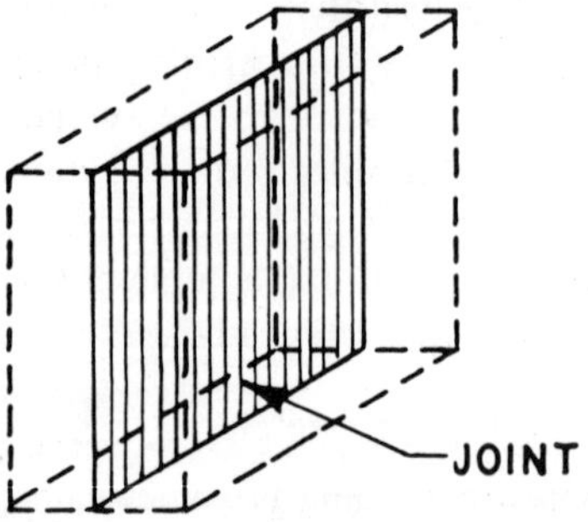

APPLICABLE WELDS

Plug
Slot
Arc-Spot
Arc-Seam
Square-Groove
Bevel-Groove
V-Groove
U-Groove
J-Groove
Edge-Flange
Corner-Flange
Resistance-Spot
Projection
Resistance-Seam

(E) **EDGE JOINT**

Figure 11-1
These are the basic joints used in welding. American Welding Society

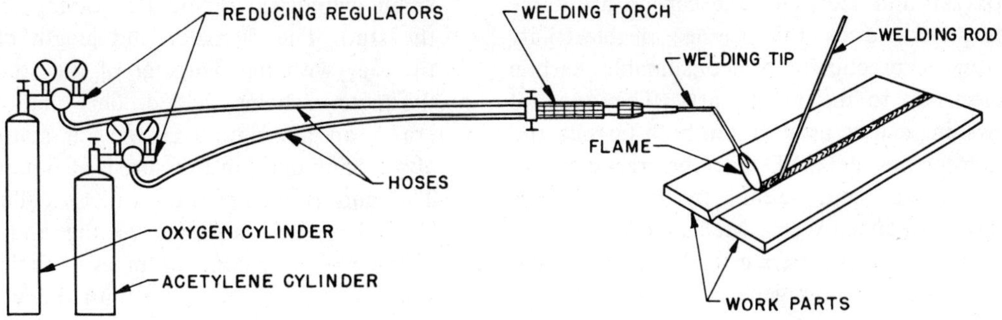

Figure 11-2
Most commercial metals can be welded successfully by the oxyacetylene process. General Motors Corp.

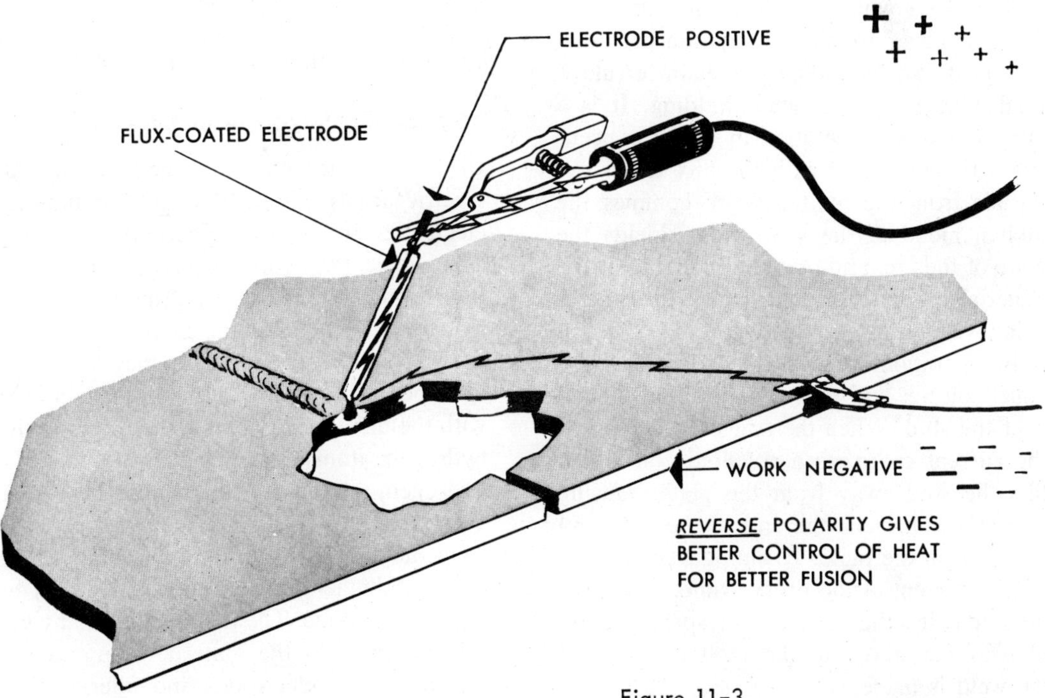

Figure 11-3
The metallic arc is probably the most extensively used manual welding process for joining structural parts of countless products ranging from small metal boxes to huge locomotives, tractors, and steamships. Republic Steel Corp.

oxygen and acetylene, the carbon arc flame is generated by the passage of electricity from a practically nonconsumable carbon electrode to the work parts. This type of welding can be used to join both ferrous and non-ferrous metals. Due to the erratic nature of the arc, hand welding by this method is not used extensively. Mechanical or automatic methods provide better control and therefore are most generally employed.

11.6 Stud welding[1]

Stud welding is a form of electric arc welding. At present there have been two methods developed, each with a different principle of operation. One of these is recognized by the use of a flux and a ceramic ferrule. Equipment consists of a gun, a timing device which controls the DC welding current, the specially designed studs and ceramic ferrules. Studs are available in a wide variety of shapes, sizes and types to meet a variety of purposes. These studs have a recess in the welding end which contains the flux. The flux acts as an arc stabilizer and a deoxidizing agent. An individual porcelain ferrule is used with each stud when welding. It is a vital part of the operation in that it concentrates the heat, acts with the flux to restrict the air from the molten weld, confines the molten metal to the weld area, shields the glare of the arc, and prevents charring of the material (if any) through which the stud is being welded.

In operation, a stud is loaded into the chuck of the gun and a ferrule positioned over the stud. When the trigger is depressed the current energizes a solenoid coil which lifts the stud away from the plate, causing an arc which melts the end of the stud and the area on the plate. A timing device shuts off the current at the proper time. The solenoid releases the stud and a spring action plunges the stud into the molten pool and the weld is made.

Another method is characterized by a small cylindrical tip on the joining face of the stud. The diameter and length of this tip vary with the diameter of the stud and the material being welded. This method operates on alternating current; a source of about 85 pounds air pressure is also required. The gun is air-operated with a collet (to hold the stud) attached to the end of a piston rod. Constant air pressure holds the stud away from the metal until the weld is ready to be made, then air pressure drives the stud against the work. When the small tip touches the workpiece, a high amperage, low voltage discharge results, creating an arc which melts the entire area of the stud and the corresponding area of work. The stud is driven at a velocity of about 31 inches per second and the explosive action as it meets the workpiece cleanses the area to be welded. A minimum thickness of the workpiece of 0.02 inches is desired, particularly if no marking on the reverse side is required.

Both methods of stud welding are adaptable to welding of most ferrous and also non-ferrous metals, their alloys, and any combinations thereof. See Fig. 11-4.

11.7 Atomic hydrogen welding

In the atomic hydrogen method, an AC electric arc is placed between two tungsten electrodes in an atmosphere of hydrogen. The molecular hydrogen (H_2), when passing through the arc, transforms into atomic hydrogen (H), absorbing energy in the form of heat in the process. As they leave the influence of the arc and come in contact with the metal being joined, these very active hydrogen atoms reassociate into molecular hydrogen, giving up their absorbed heat. Thus the two combined sources of heat, from the arc and from the molecular action, result in higher temperatures than from an electric arc alone. The presence of the hydrogen gas protects the material being welded as well as the electrodes and filler rod (if used) from oxidation, thus coated rods or fluxes are not required. At the same time the hot hydrogen envelope reduces any oxides that may be present in the metal. See Fig. 11-5.

1. *Welding, Brazing, Soldering and Hot Cutting Republic Stainless Steels* (Cleveland: *Republic Steel* Corp., 1952).

STUD WELDING
(Nelson Method)

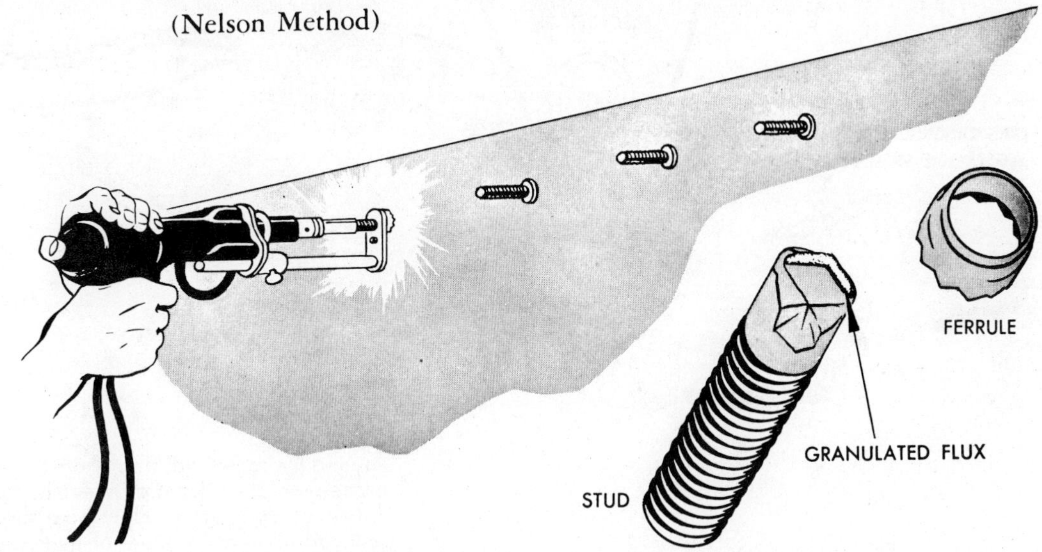

STUD WELDING
(Graham Method)

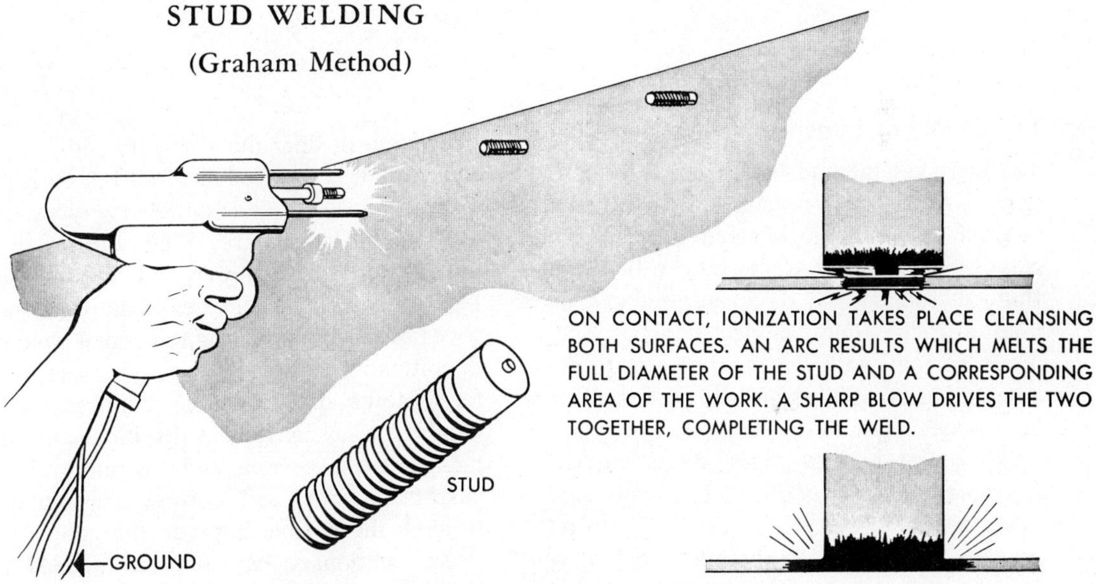

Figure 11–4
Stud welding is a form of arc welding used in fastening studs to various metal components. Republic Steel Corp.

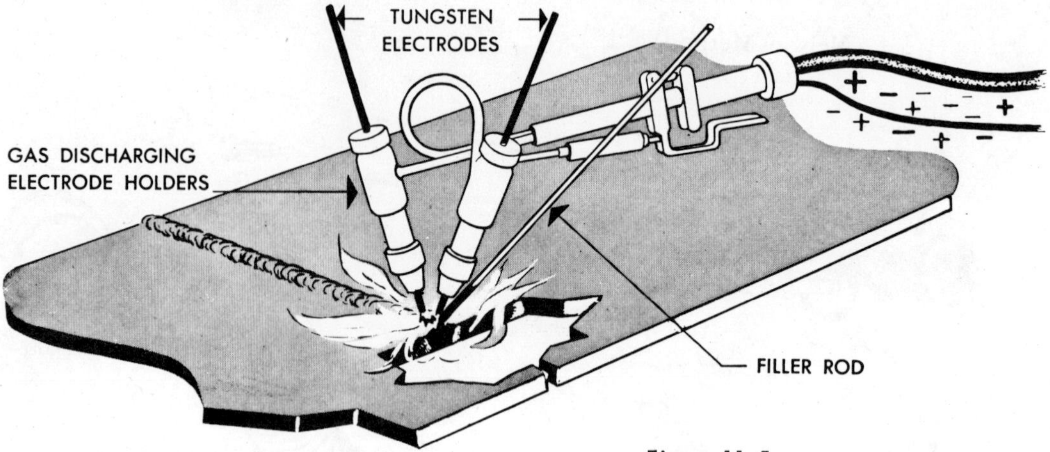

Figure 11-5
Atomic hydrogen welding is a welding process which utilizes an electric arc between two tungsten electrodes surrounded in an atmosphere of hydrogen. Republic Steel Corp.

11.8 Inert gas (argon or helium) welding

The inert gas method uses a specially constructed torch which dispenses a monotomic, inert gas around a single electrode. Either a carbon or a tungsten electrode can be used. Both alternating and direct current can be used with the tungsten electrode but only direct current with the carbon electrode. Alternating current is generally preferred for light gages because it provides better arc stability. For heavier gages, direct current is favored because of the deeper and narrower weld beads. The work must be grounded, and the arc between the work and the electrode is constantly surrounded by an atmosphere of inert gas. Under these conditions, no flux is needed because the gas protects the weld. Argon or helium may be used; however, helium, with its high rate of dispersion, is generally being replaced with heavier and purer argon.

Automatic methods of inert gas welding are also available. These automatic methods have similar welding characteristics as those just described, their only difference being in the use of a consumable electrode. The deposition of filler metal is very rapid, consequently it is supplied in wire form on reels.

Both portable and stationary types are available. The portable type consists of a gun attached to a power and feed unit by flexible hoses, the gun being the only part necessary to move during the actual welding operation. The unit contains the wire reel, feed motor and electrical controls. It is carried to a convenient location and attached to the current and gas supply. The gas, filler wire, and current are supplied through the flexible hoses to the gun.

The stationary type of machine can be used only for flat or horizontal fillet welding. In some instances the work remains stationary and the machine travels; in others, this is reversed.

Still another process which makes use of the protective qualities of argon gas is that known as the *inert gas-shielded arc spot welding method.* It is a combination of inert gas welding and spot welding. The equipment consists of a very light gun equipped with a water cooled copper cup which bears against the workpiece. A tungsten electrode

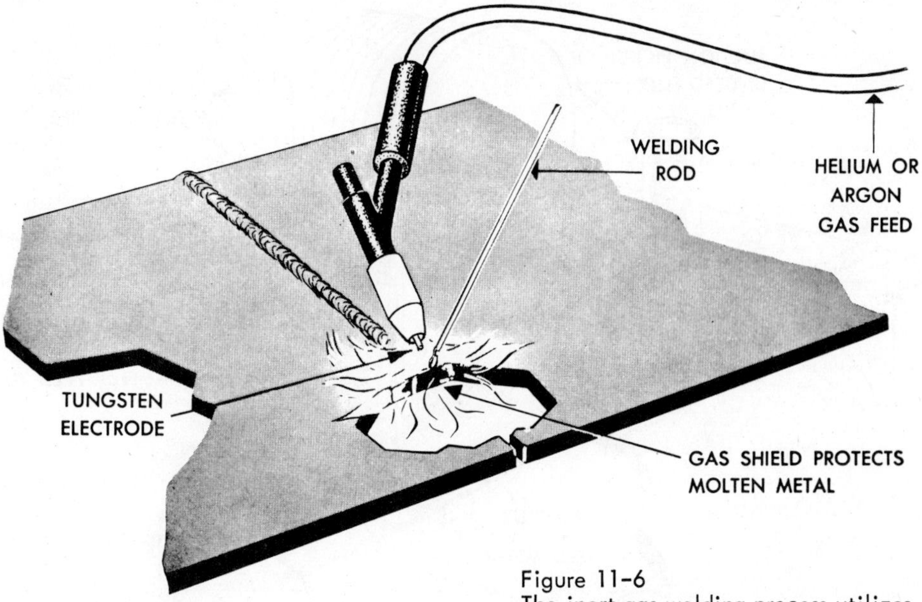

Figure 11-6
The inert gas welding process utilizes an arc which is completely surrounded by an inert gas such as argon.
Republic Steel Corp.

is located so as to be in the center of the cup and about 3/32 of an inch from the work surface. (The distance varies with the material being welded.) Argon gas enters the cup when the trigger is pulled and timing devices initiate the electric arc required for the weld shortly afterwards. At the proper time, the arc is extinguished and the argon flow is continued until the electrode and the fluid puddle have cooled. See Fig. 11-6.

11.9 Submerged arc welding

In this method, an AC or DC electric arc, buried in a protective layer of granular mineral material, provides the heat of welding. Filler metal serves as the electrode; the work is grounded. Automatically controlled mechanisms must be used in this type of welding. See Fig. 11-7.

Essentially the operation consists of a unit which moves at a controlled speed over the weld area. This unit contains a feeding hopper which deposits the granulated flux ahead of the filler rod. The filler rod, which is also the electrode, is automatically fed into the flux so as to maintain a constant distance between the melting end of the electrode and the pool of molten metal. That portion of the granular flux immediately around the arc fuses and covers the molten metal. A means of reclaiming the unused flux—usually with a suction tube—follows this.

The arc is not visible since it is buried in the flux, thus there is no flash; neither is there any splatter.

Due to the nature of this operation, welding must be done on a horizontal, or nearly horizontal, plane. In some setups, the welding head moves and the work remains stationary. In others, the head is stationary and the work moves, such as in joining sections of large diameter pipe which can be rotated under the welding head.

11.10 Thermit welding

This type of welding is accomplished by igniting a mixture of iron oxide and finely divided aluminum in a crucible. The two materials react exothermically, forming a superheated molten metal and a slag of molten aluminum oxide. The molten metal is poured into a heated form or mold con-

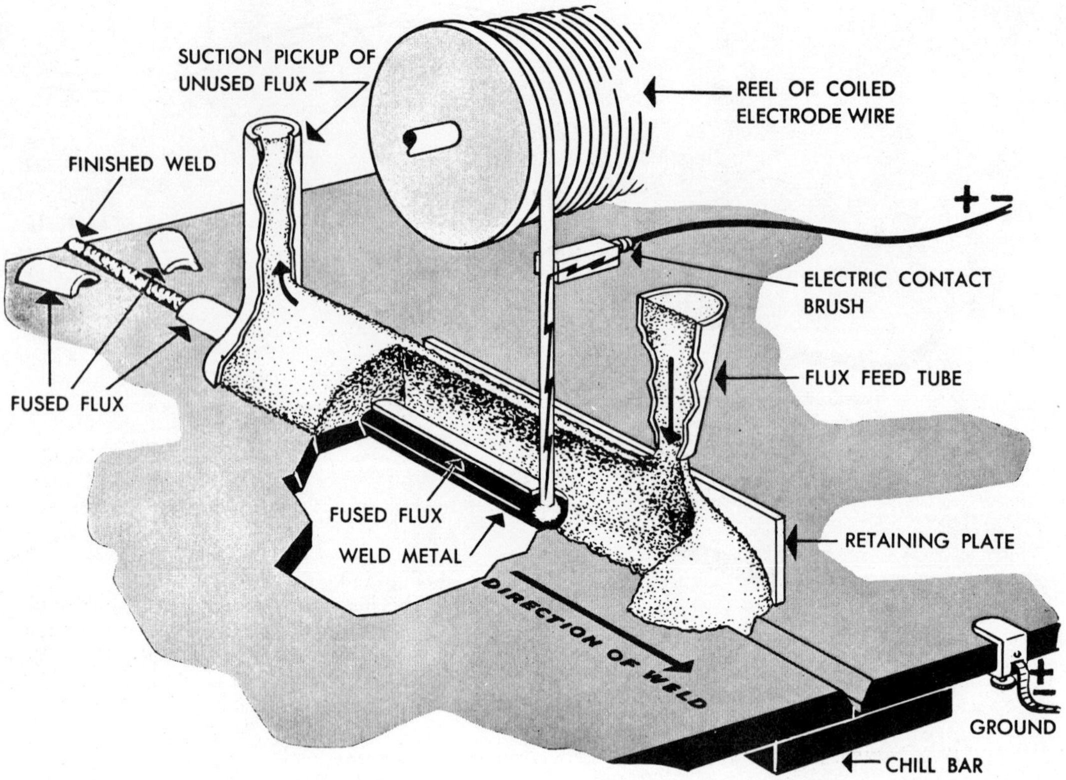

Figure 11-7
Submerged arc welding is an automatic welding process in which heat is provided by an arc buried in a protective layer of granular mineral material. Republic Steel Corp.

taining the materials to be welded much the same as pouring a casting. The superheated metal thoroughly unites with, and joins, the parts to be welded. This method is not commonly used throughout the industry.

11.11 Spot welding

This method, and its various forms, is probably the most common and generally used of the resistance welding methods. Two or more layers of material can be joined simultaneously. These layers are placed between two electrodes and pressure is applied, a quick "shot" of electricity is sent from one electrode through the material to the other, the pressure is continued momentarily, and the weld is completed. The method is adaptable to material as thick as one inch. See Fig. 11-8.

There are three separate stages to the actual process of making a spot weld. First, the electrodes are brought against the material and pressure applied before the current is turned on. This minimizes the possibilities of arcing and is sometimes referred to as "squeeze" time. Second, the current is turned on momentarily; third, the current is turned off but the pressure contin-

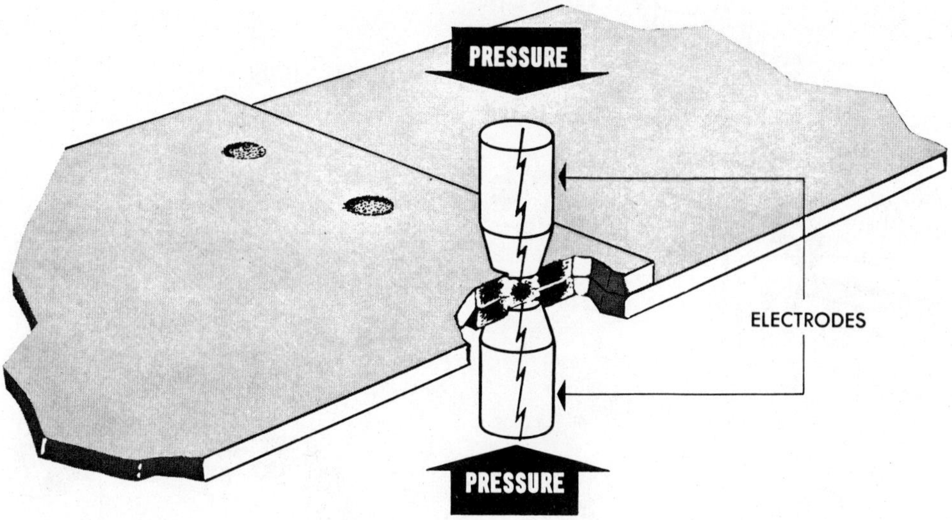

Figure 11-8
Spot welding is a form of resistance welding in which two layers of material are placed between two electrodes, a shot of electricity is sent through, and a small spot of fusion occurs as pressure is applied momentarily. Republic Steel Corp.

ued, which is called "hold time." This allows complete formation of the weld and cools the weld as much as possible.

Spot welding machines are also designed with multiple sets of electrodes in which the current is passed through each set separately and in rotation, providing a multiple number of spot welds with one setting operation.

11.12 Pulsation welding

Pulsation welding is merely a form of spot welding in which the current is regulated to go on and off a given number of times during the making of one weld. It is claimed to have advantages over straight spot welding in that (1) welding of thicker materials is possible, (2) electrode life is increased since the interrupted current tends to keep the electrodes cooler, thus minimizing electrode distortion, and (3) there is less tendency of the weld to spit or spark.

11.13 Projection welding

This method is similar to the spot method except that projections are formed on one of the sheets being welded (usually on the thicker sheet when sizes vary). The two electrodes contact the material in line with the projection, the projection itself acting as a sharp-pointed electrode which localizes the heat. Other characteristics of the welding procedure are the same as for spot welding.

Projection welding can be set up in such a manner as to complete more than one "spot" at a time. See Fig. 11-9.

11.14 Seam welding

Two types of setups are common to seam welding, the *lap* and the *line methods.* In both cases, rolling electrodes are used.

In lap seam welding, which is most frequently used on flat pieces, the materials

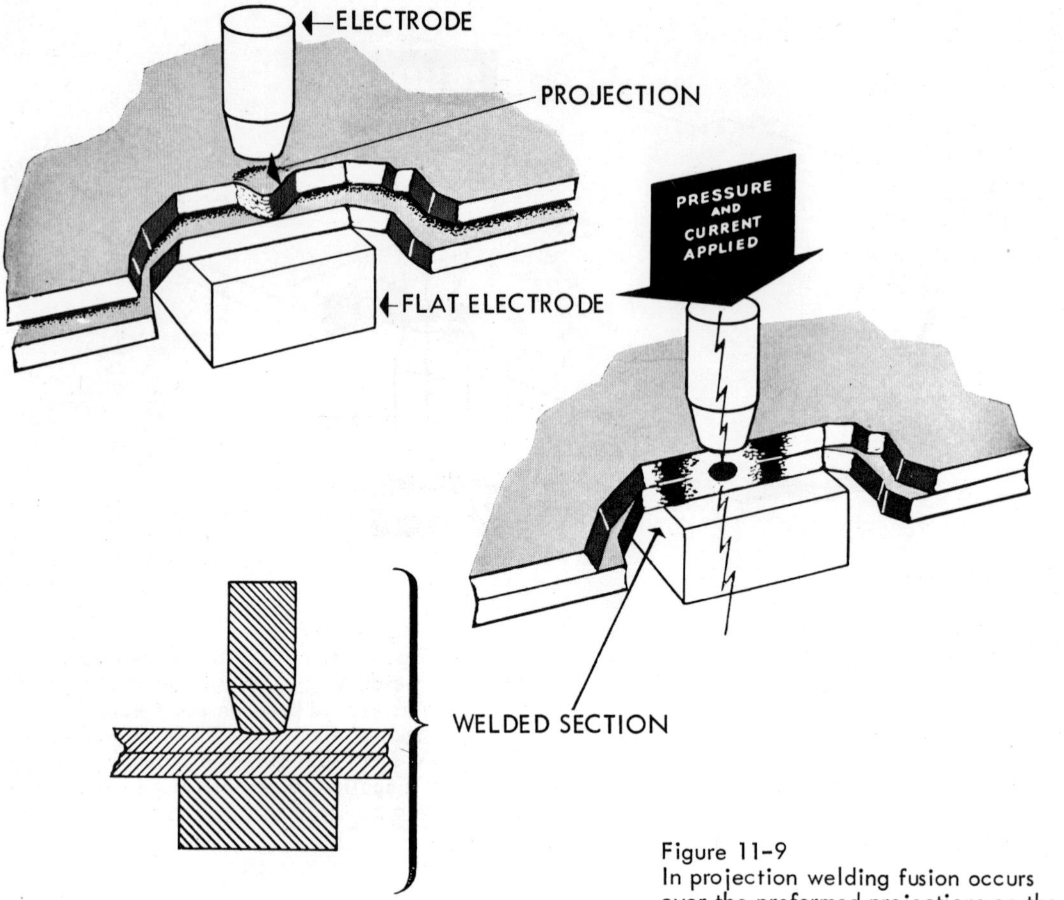

Figure 11-9
In projection welding fusion occurs over the preformed projections on the sheet. Republic Steel Corp.

are placed one on top of the other with a roller type electrode on opposite sides. As the work is fed between these rollers, a controlled timing of the current flow produces a series of spot welds. The faster the cycle of current flow (or the slower the work moves), the closer the spot welds. Watertight seams are possible by controlling the process so that each weld slightly overlaps the former. Naturally, the slower the cycle (or the faster the work moves), the farther apart will be the spacing of each weld.

In line seam welding (generally employed in welding tubing) pressure rolls force the two edges of the tube together. Two roller type electrodes contact the work on each side of the seam, as shown in Fig. 11-10. The current cycle and speed of work feed can be adjusted similar to that in lap seam welding to produce a watertight weld. In both cases the constantly rolling electrodes and moving work leave less contact time between the electrodes and hot weld, thus less cooling effect is realized from the electrode and plenty of coolant is required.

11.15 Butt welding

This form of welding is frequently used for joining bars, rods or wire, end to end. The two ends are butted together by use of clamps which also serve as electrodes. See Fig. 11-11. Pressure is applied and a high

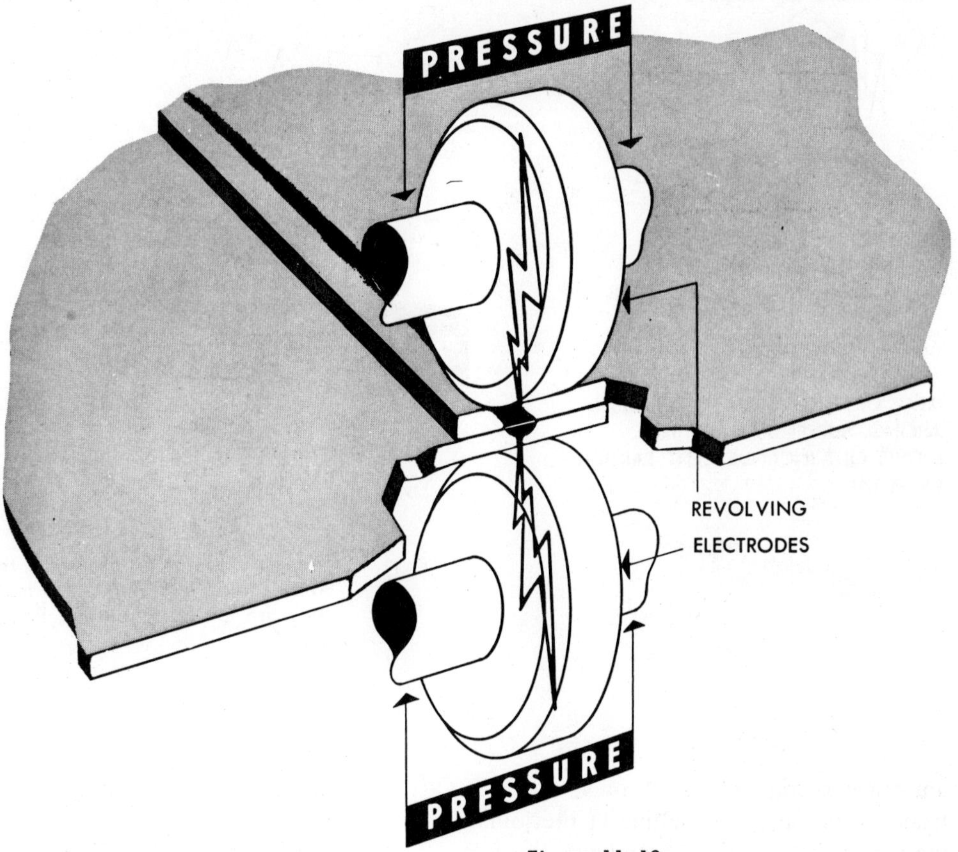

Figure 11-10
Seam welding is a production type welding process in which the work to be welded is fed between two revolving electrodes. Republic Steel Corp.

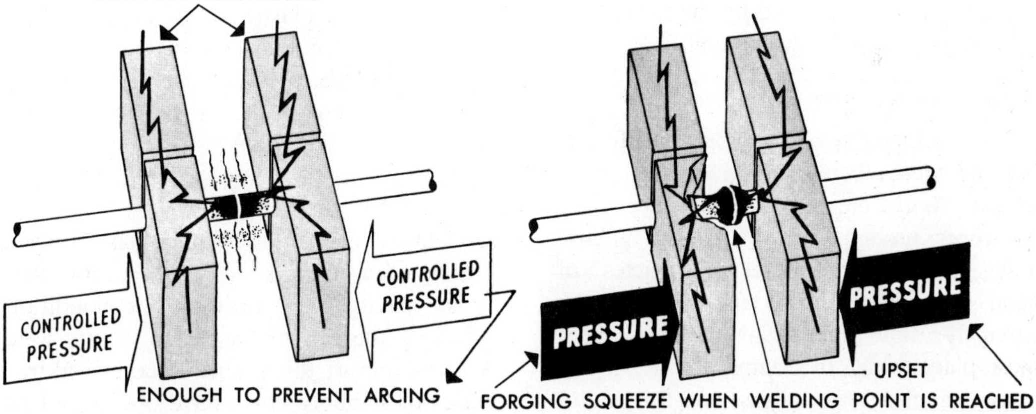

Figure 11-11
Butt welding is used to join bars, rods, or wire end to end. Republic Steel Corp.

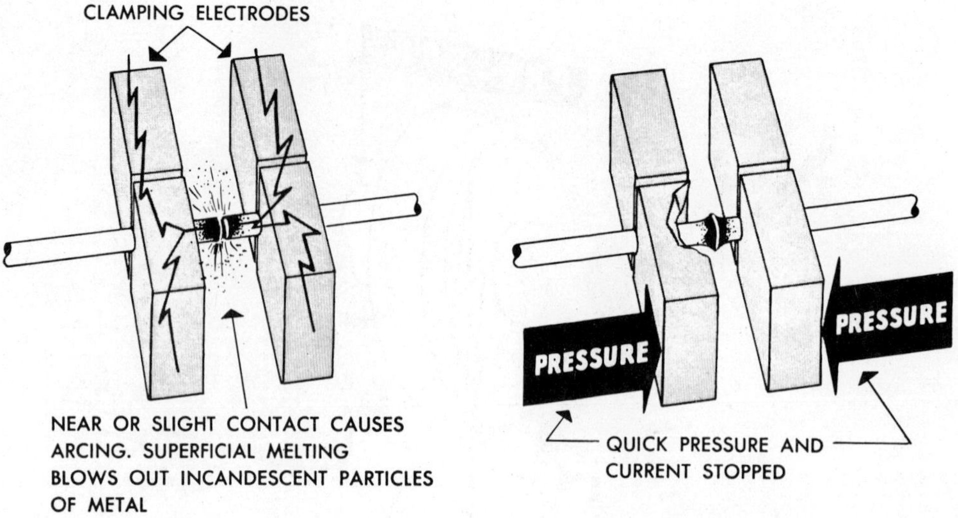

Figure 11-12
In flash welding an arc melts the edges to be joined and while in a molten state they are forced together. Republic Steel Corp.

amperage current passes through one electrode to the other. A melting at the joining faces results and the continuous pressure forces any oxidized metal out of the joint and provides the necessary pressure for fusion of the two ends when the proper temperature is reached.

There is, of course, no arcing, thus no flash or weld splatter. Even so, this method is largely being supplanted by the faster, less power consuming, flash welding.

11.16 Flash welding

Flash welding differs from butt welding in that the pieces being joined do not touch initially. As the current is turned on and the two edges brought into proximity, intense arcing occurs. Incandescent particles of metal are blown out of the joint by the extremely rapid superficial melting which takes place, thus the name *flash.* At the proper moment, the edges are forced together and the molten metal, slag and impurities are forced out of the joint and a very solid weld is produced between the two plastic edges. See Fig. 11-12.

11.17 Forge welding method

This method of joining two pieces of metal was used hundreds of years ago. It was the first known method for completely uniting two metals into one homogeneous unit and it is still very much in use today. It is a process in which areas to be joined are heated to the plastic state, superimposed, and by repeated blows from a hammer, or by tremendous pressure, are worked into complete union. Both manual and machine methods are adaptable.

11.18 Welding symbols

To ensure that the workman has sufficient information to make a weld, a draftsman must specify on a drawing the conditions affecting the proper execution of the weld. Information of this nature is conveyed by a series of symbols which have been standardized by the American Welding Society and adopted by the American Standards Association. A general explanation of welding symbols is presented here.

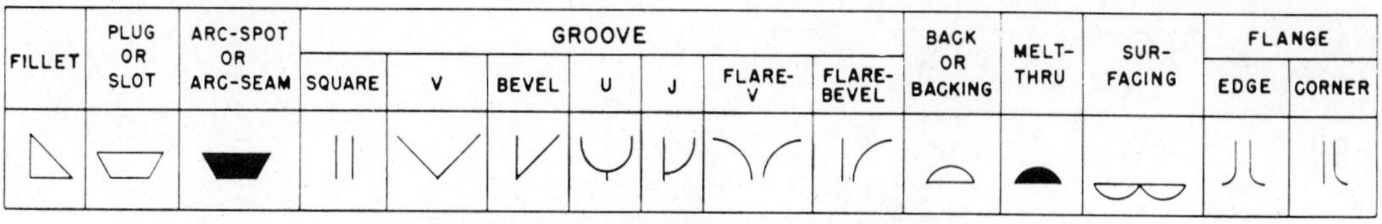
FILLET
PLUG OR SLOT
ARC-SPOT OR ARC-SEAM
GROOVE
SQUARE
V
BEVEL
U
J
FLARE-V
FLARE-BEVEL
BACK OR BACKING
MELT-THRU
SUR-FACING
FLANGE
EDGE
CORNER

BASIC ARC AND GAS WELD SYMBOLS

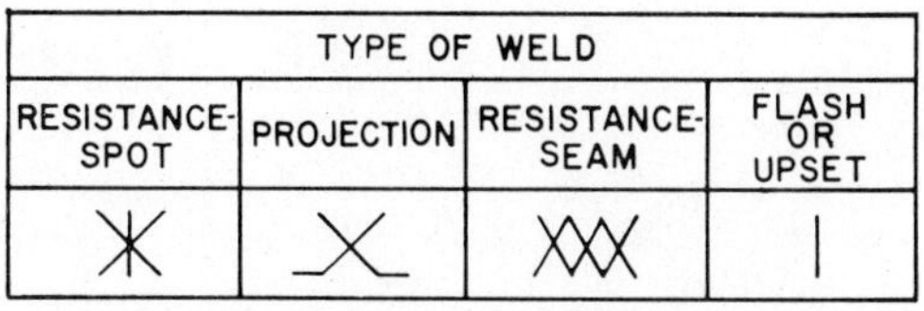
TYPE OF WELD
RESISTANCE-SPOT
PROJECTION
RESISTANCE-SEAM
FLASH OR UPSET

BASIC RESISTANCE WELD SYMBOLS

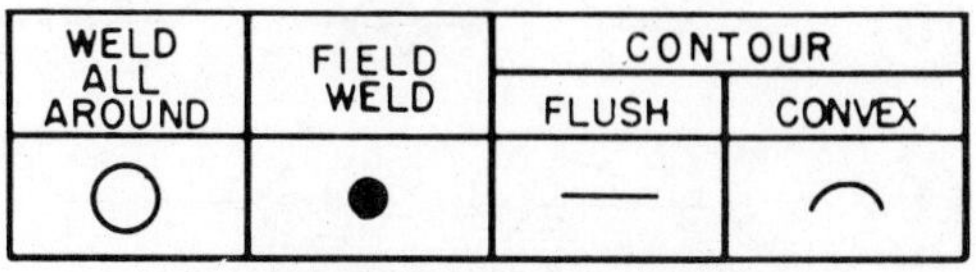
WELD ALL AROUND
FIELD WELD
CONTOUR
FLUSH
CONVEX

SUPPLEMENTARY SYMBOLS

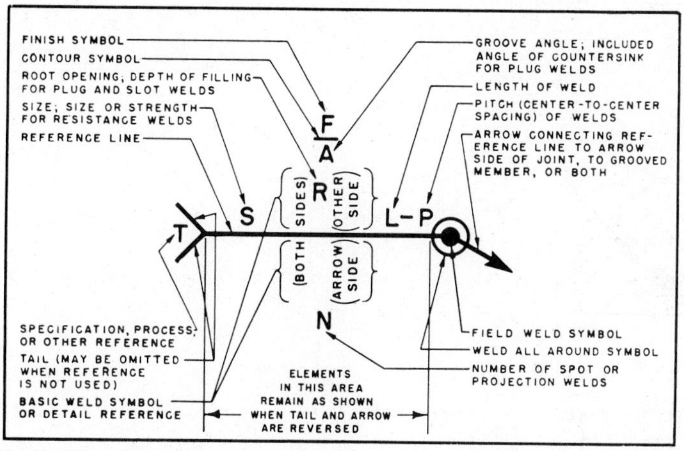

STANDARD LOCATION OF ELEMENTS OF A WELDING SYMBOL

Figure 11-13
Basic welding symbols.
American Welding Society

11.19 General explanation of welding symbols[2]

The main base of the symbol consists of an arrow. Other symbols representing various welding details are arranged around the arrow. See Fig. 11-13.

1 Location significance of arrow

(a) In the case of fillet, groove, flange, and flash or upset welding symbols, the arrow shall connect the welding symbol reference line to one side of the joint, and this side shall be considered the *arrow side* of the joint. The side opposite the arrow side of the joint shall be considered the *other side* of the joint.

(b) In the case of plug, slot, arc-spot, arc-seam, resistance-spot, resistance-seam and projection welding symbols, the arrow shall connect the welding symbol reference

2. Reproduced from *Standard Welding Symbols Manual* (New York: The American Welding Society, 1958).

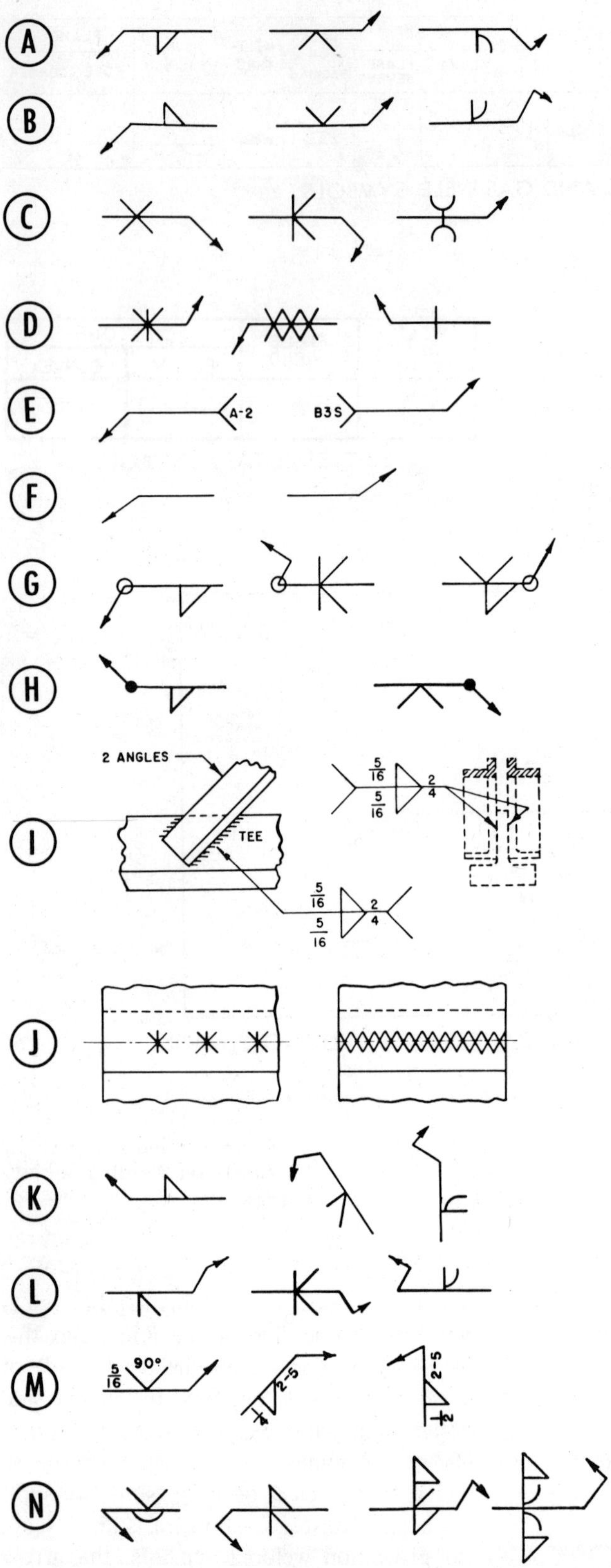

Figure 11-14
Meaning of various welding symbols.

line to the outer surface of one of the members of the joint at the centerline of the desired weld. The member to which the arrow points shall be considered the *arrow-side* member. The other member of the joint shall be considered the *other-side* member.

(c) When a joint is depicted by a single line on the drawing and the arrow of a welding symbol is directed to this line, the arrow side of the joint shall be considered as the near side of the joint in accordance with the usual conventions of drafting.

(d) When a joint is depicted as an area parallel to the plane of projection in a drawing and the arrow of a welding symbol is directed to that area, the *arrow-side* member of the joint shall be considered as the near member of the joint in accordance with the usual conventions of drafting.

2 Location of weld with respect to joint

(a) Welds on the arrow side of the joint shall be shown by placing the weld symbol on the side of the reference line toward the reader. See Fig. 11-14A.

(b) Welds on the other side of the joint shall be shown by placing the weld symbol on the side of the reference line away from the reader. See Fig. 11-14B.

(c) Welds on both sides of the joint shall be shown by placing weld symbols on both sides of the reference line, toward and away from the reader. See Fig. 11-14C.

(d) Resistance-spot, resistance-seam, flash and upset weld symbols have no arrow-side or other-side significance in themselves, although supplementary symbols used in conjunction therewith may have such significance. Resistance-spot, resistance-seam, flash and upset weld symbols shall be centered on the reference line. See Fig. 11-14D.

3 Location of specification, process or other references

(a) When a specification, process or other reference is used with a welding symbol, the reference shall be placed in the tail. See Fig. 11-14E.

(b) When no specification, process or other reference is used with a welding symbol, the tail may be omitted. See Fig. 11-14F.

4 Use of symbols without references

When desired, symbols may be used without specification, process or other references in the following instances:

(a) When a note such as the following appears on the drawing: "Unless otherwise designated, all welds are to be made in accordance with Specification No. ———."

(b) When the welding procedure to be used is prescribed elsewhere.

5 Use of general notes

When desired, general notes such as the following may be placed on a drawing to provide detailed information pertaining to the predominating welds, and this information need not be repeated on the symbols:

"Unless otherwise indicated, all fillet welds are 5/16 inch size."

"Unless otherwise indicated, root openings for all groove welds are 3/16 inch."

6 Use of weld-all-around symbol

Welds extending completely around a joint shall be indicated by means of the weld-all-around symbol. See Fig. 11-14G.

7 Use of field weld symbol

Field welds (welds not made in a shop or at the place of initial construction) shall be indicated by means of the field weld symbol. See Fig. 11-14H.

8 Extent of welding denoted by symbols

(a) Symbols apply between abrupt changes in the direction of the welding or to the extent of hatching or dimension lines, except when the weld-all-around symbol is used.

(b) The welding on hidden joints may be covered as shown in Fig. 11-14I when welding of the hidden joint is the same as that of the visible joint. In this case, a section is desirable but is not necessary. The drawing shall indicate the presence of hidden members. If the welding on the hidden joint is different from that of the visible joint, specific information for the welding of both shall be given.

9 Finishing of welds

Finishing of welds, other than cleaning, shall be indicated by suitable contour and finish symbols.

10 Location of weld symbols

(a) Weld symbols, except resistance-spot and resistance-seam, shall be shown only on the welding symbol reference line and not on the lines of the drawing.

(b) Resistance-spot and resistance-seam weld symbols may be placed directly on drawings at the locations of the desired welds. See Fig. 11-14J.

11 Construction of symbols

Fillet, bevel- and J-groove, flare-bevel-groove and corner-flange weld symbols shall be shown with the perpendicular leg *always* to the left. See Fig. 11-14K.

12 Use of break in arrow of bevel- and J-groove welding symbols

When a bevel- or J-groove weld symbol is used, the arrow shall point with a definite break toward the member which is to be chamfered. See Fig. 11-14L. (In cases where the member to be chamfered is obvious, the break in the arrow may be omitted.)

13 Reading of information on welding symbols

Information on welding symbols shall be placed to read from left to right along the reference line in accordance with the usual conventions of drafting. See Fig. 11-14M.

14 Combined weld symbols

For joints having more than one weld, a symbol shall be shown for each weld. See Fig. 11-14N.

11.20 Fillet weld symbols[3]

1 General

(a) Dimensions of fillet welds shall be shown on the same side of the reference line as the weld symbol. See Fig. 11-15*A*.

(b) When no general note governing the dimensions of fillet welds appears on the drawing, the dimensions of fillet welds on both sides of the joint shall be shown as follows:

(1) When both welds have the same dimensions, one or both may be dimensioned. See Fig. 11-15*B*.

(2) When the welds differ in dimensions, both shall be dimensioned. See Fig. 11-15*C*.

(c) When there appears on the drawing a general note governing the dimensions of fillet welds, such as "All fillet welds 5/16 in. size unless otherwise noted," the dimensions of fillet welds on both sides of the joint shall be indicated as follows:

(1) When both welds have dimensions governed by the note, neither need be dimensioned. See Fig. 11-15*D*.

(2) When the dimensions of one or both welds differ from the dimensions given in the general note, both welds shall be dimensioned. See Fig. 11-15*E*.

2 Size of fillet welds

(a) The size of a fillet weld shall be shown to the left of the weld symbol. See Fig. 11-15*F*.

(b) The size of a fillet weld with unequal legs, shall be shown in parentheses to the left of the weld symbol, as shown in Fig. 11-15*G*. Weld orientation is not shown by the symbol and shall be shown on the drawing when necessary.

3 Length of fillet welds

(a) The length of a fillet weld, when indicated on the welding symbol, shall be shown to the right of the weld symbol. See Fig. 11-15*H*.

(b) When fillet welding extends for the full distance between abrupt changes in the direction of the welding no length dimension need be shown on the welding symbol.

(c) Specific lengths of fillet welding may be indicated by symbols in conjunction with dimension lines. See Fig. 11-15*I*.

4 Extent of fillet welding

(a) When it is desired to show the extent of fillet welding graphically, one type of hatching with or without definite end lines shall be used. See Fig. 11-15*J*.

(b) Fillet welding extending beyond abrupt changes in the direction of the welding shall be indicated by means of additional arrows pointing to each section of the joint to be welded except when the weld-all-around symbol is used.

5 Dimensioning of intermittent fillet welding

(a) The pitch (center-to-center spacing) of intermittent fillet welding shall be shown as the distance between centers of increments on *one* side of the joint.

(b) The pitch (center-to-center spacing)

3. *Ibid.*

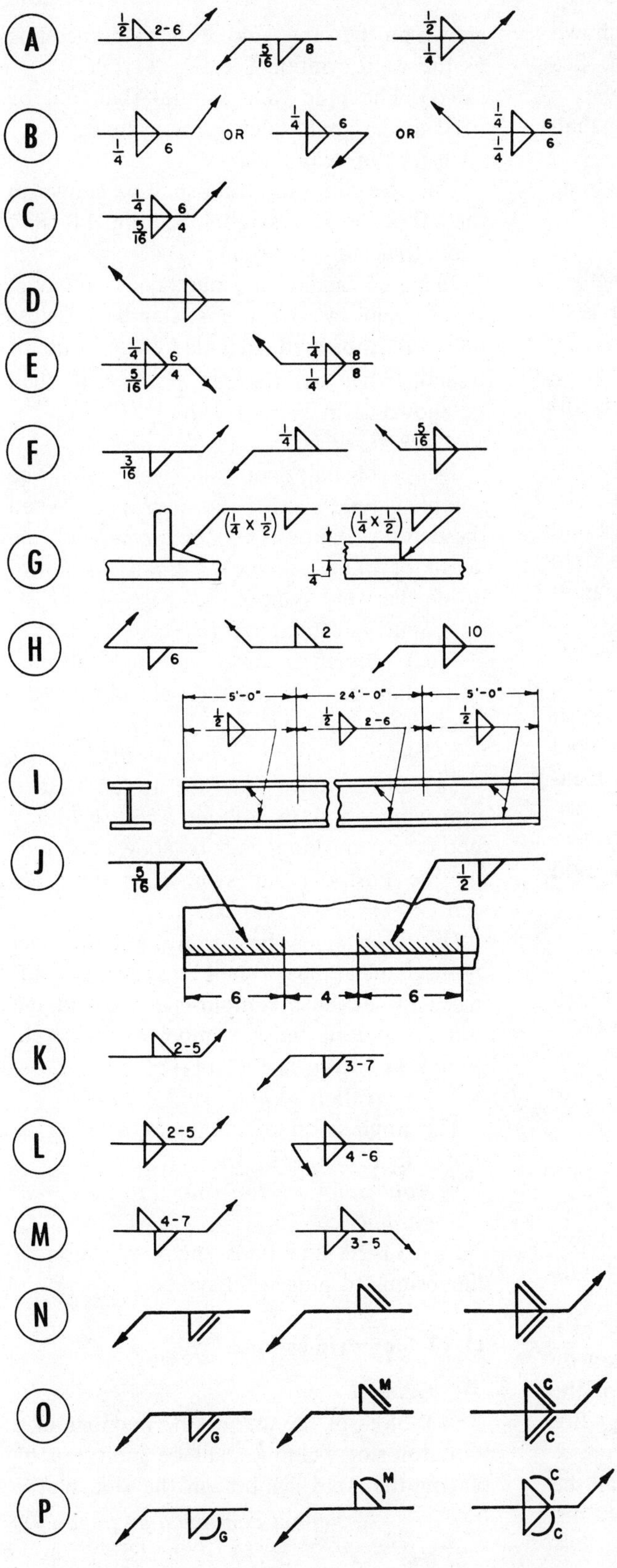

Figure 11-15
Meaning of symbols as they apply to fillet welds.

of intermittent fillet welding shall be shown to the right of the length dimension. See Fig. 11-15*K*.

(c) Chain intermittent fillet welding shall be shown as in Fig. 11-15*L*.

(d) Staggered intermittent fillet welding shall be shown as in Fig. 11-15*M*.

6 Surface contour of fillet welds

(a) Fillet welds that are to be welded approximately flat-faced without recourse to any method of finishing shall be shown by adding the flush-contour symbol to the weld symbol, observing the usual location significance. See Fig. 11-15*N*.

(b) Fillet welds that are to be made flat-faced by mechanical means, shall be shown by adding both the flush-contour symbol and the user's standard finish symbol to the weld symbol, observing the usual location significance. See Fig. 11-15*O*.

(c) Fillet welds that are to be mechanically finished to a convex contour, shall be shown by adding both the convex-contour symbol and the user's standard finish symbol to the weld symbol, observing the usual location significance. See Fig. 11-15*P*.

7 Application of fillet weld symbols

Fig. 11-16 illustrates a typical fillet weld and the application of weld symbols.

8 Application of dimensions to fillet welding symbols

The method of applying dimensions to fillet welding symbols is shown in Fig. 11-17.

11.21 Plug weld symbols[4]

1 General

(a) Holes in the arrow-side member of a joint for plug welding shall be indicated by placing the weld symbol on the side of the reference line toward the reader. See Fig. 11-18*A*.

(b) Holes in the other-side member of a joint for plug welding shall be indicated by placing the weld symbol on the side of the reference line away from the reader. See Fig. 11-18*B*.

(c) Dimensions of plug welds shall be shown on the same side of the reference line as the weld symbol. See Fig. 11-18*C*.

(d) The plug weld symbol shall not be used to designate fillet welds in holes.

2 Size of plug welds

The size of a plug weld shall be shown to the left of the weld symbol. See Fig. 11-18*D*.

3 Angle of countersink

Included angle of countersink of plug welds shall be the user's standard unless otherwise indicated. Included angle of countersink, when not the user's standard, shall be shown as in Fig. 11-18*E*.

4 Depth of filling

Depth of filling of plug welds shall be complete unless otherwise indicated. When the depth of filling is less than complete, the depth of filling, in inches, shall be shown inside the weld symbol. See Fig. 11-18*F*.

5 Spacing of plug welds

Pitch (center-to-center spacing) of plug welds shall be shown to the right of the weld symbol, as shown in Fig. 11-18*G*.

6 Surface contour of plug welds

(a) Plug welds that are to be welded approximately flush without recourse to any method of finishing shall be shown by adding the flush-contour symbol to the weld symbol. See Fig. 11-18*H*.

(b) Plug welds that are to be made flush by mechanical means shall be shown by adding both the flush-contour symbol and the user's standard finish symbol to the weld symbol as shown in Fig. 11-18*I*.

7 Application of plug weld symbols

The application of plug weld symbols is shown in Fig. 11-19.

8 Application of dimensions to plug weld symbols

Fig. 11-20 illustrates the application of dimensions to plug weld symbols.

11.22 Slot weld symbols[5]

1 General

(a) Slots in the arrow-side member of a joint for slot welding shall be indicated by placing the weld symbol on the side of the

(Text continued on page 252)

4. *Ibid.*

5. *Ibid.*

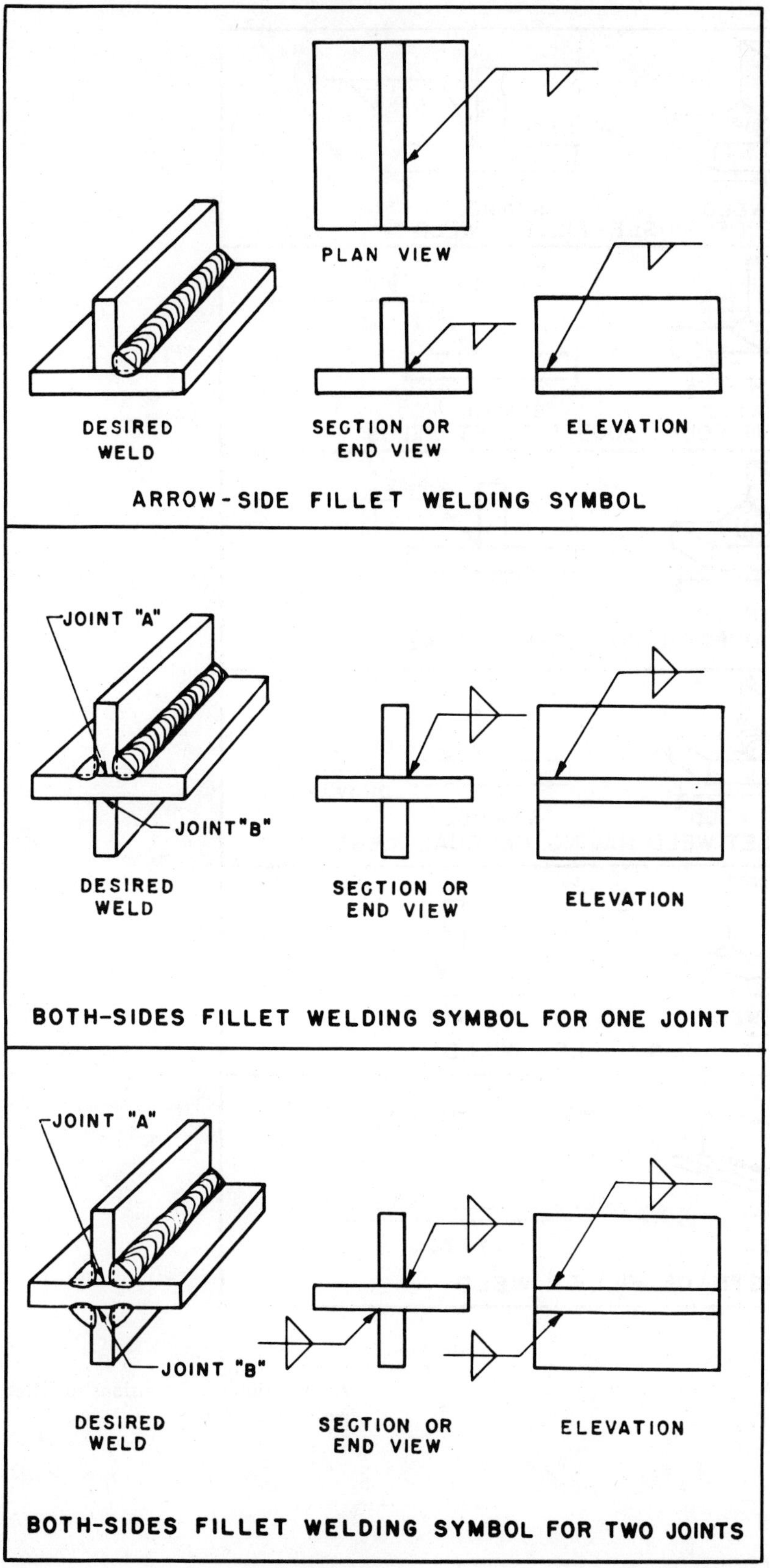

Figure 11-16
Application of fillet weld symbols.

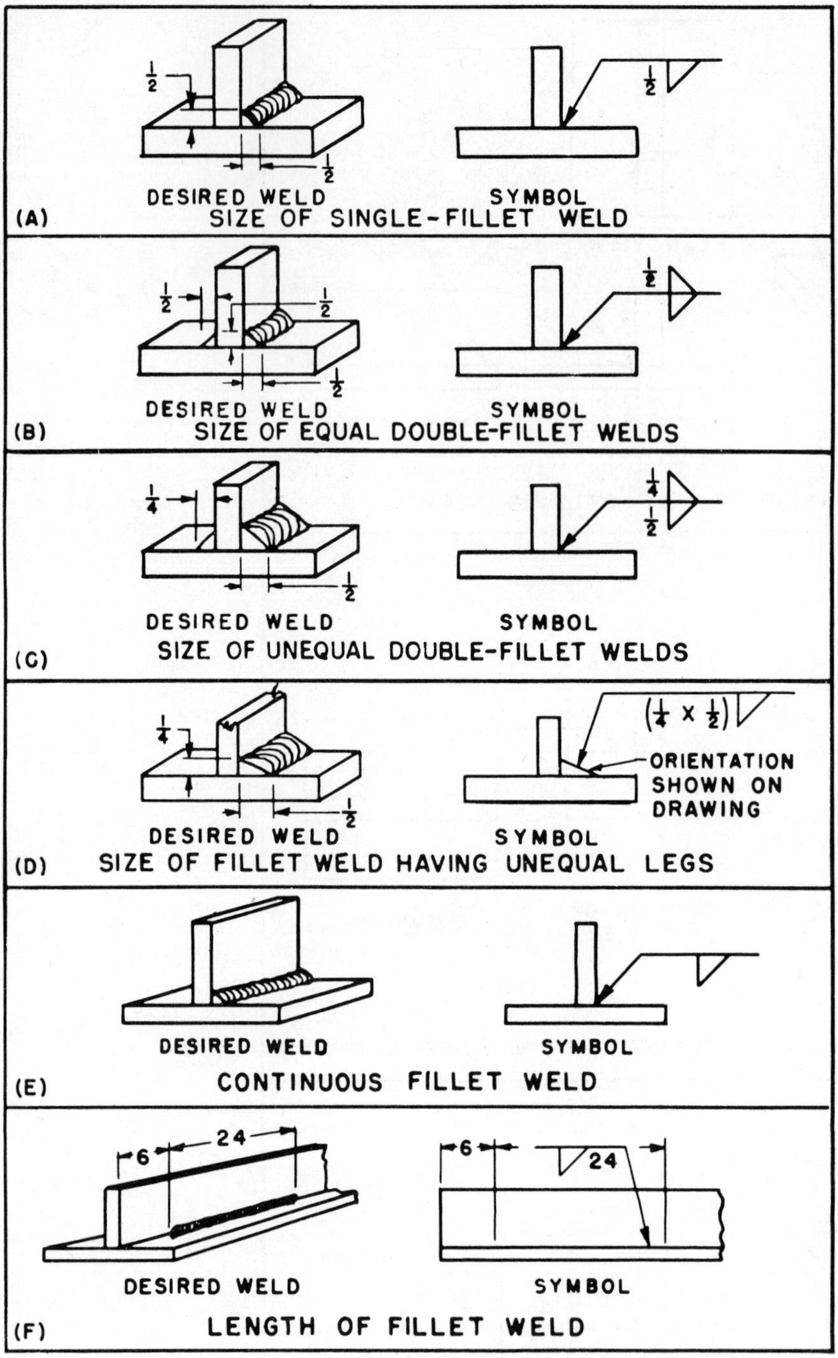

Figure 11-17
Application of dimensions to fillet welding symbols.

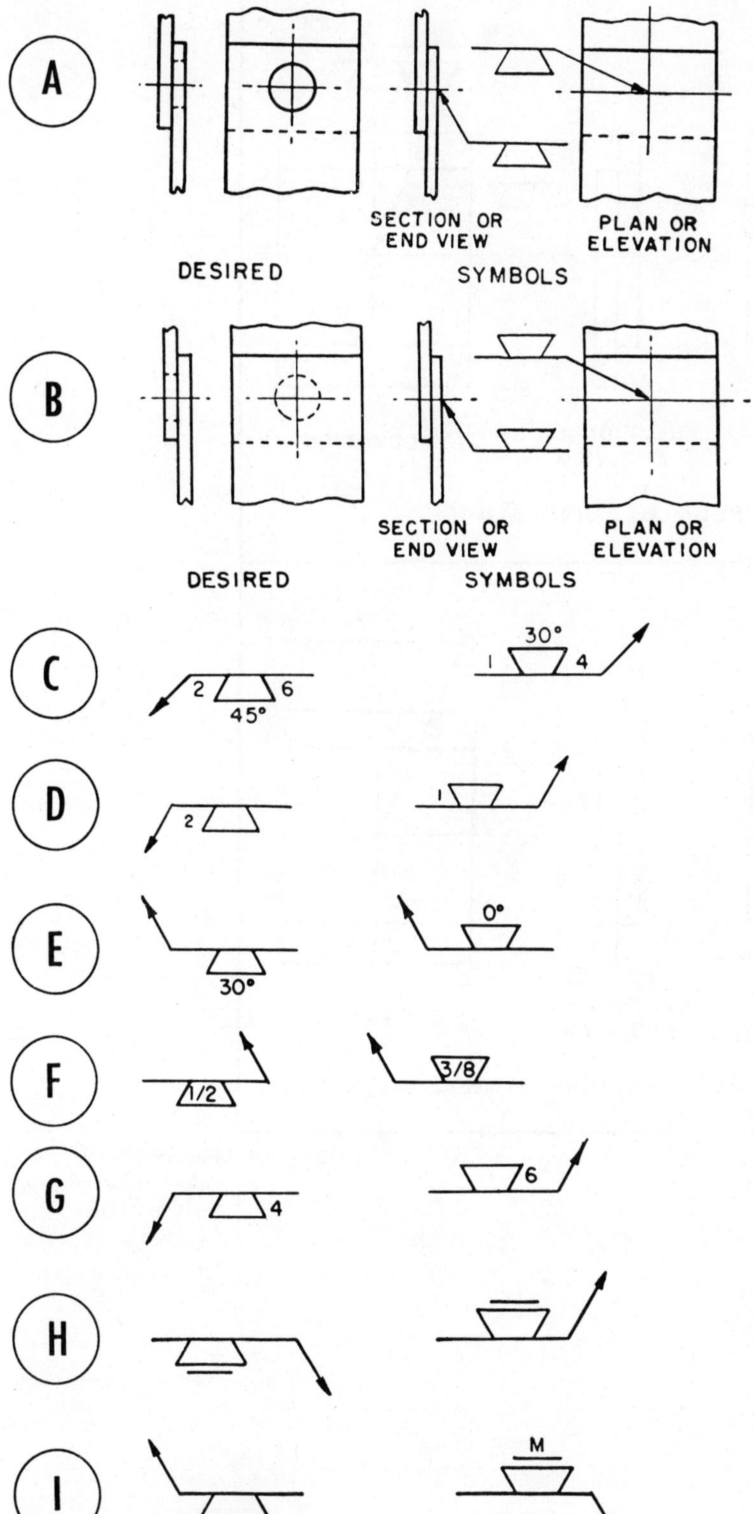

Figure 11-18
Meaning of symbols as they apply to plug welds.

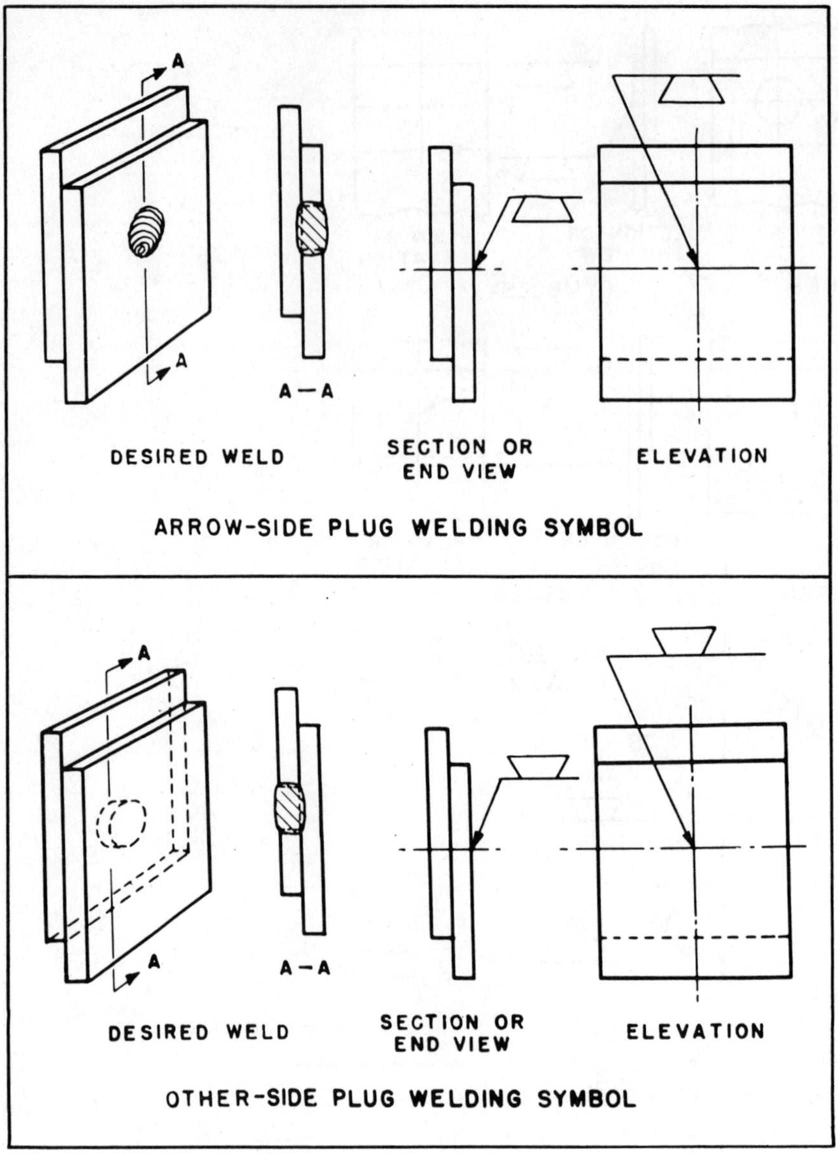

Figure 11-19
Application of plug weld symbols.

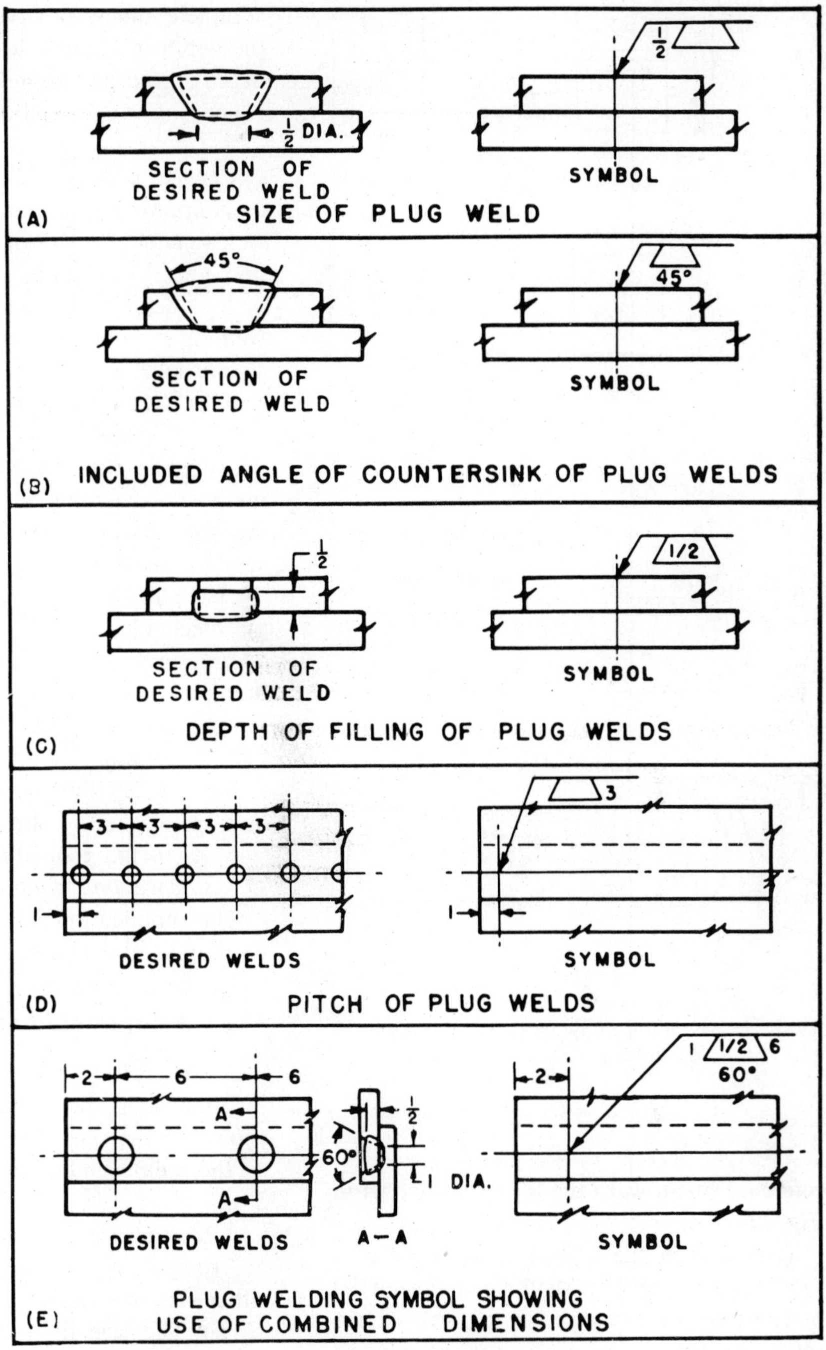

Figure 11-20
Application of dimensions to plug welding symbols.

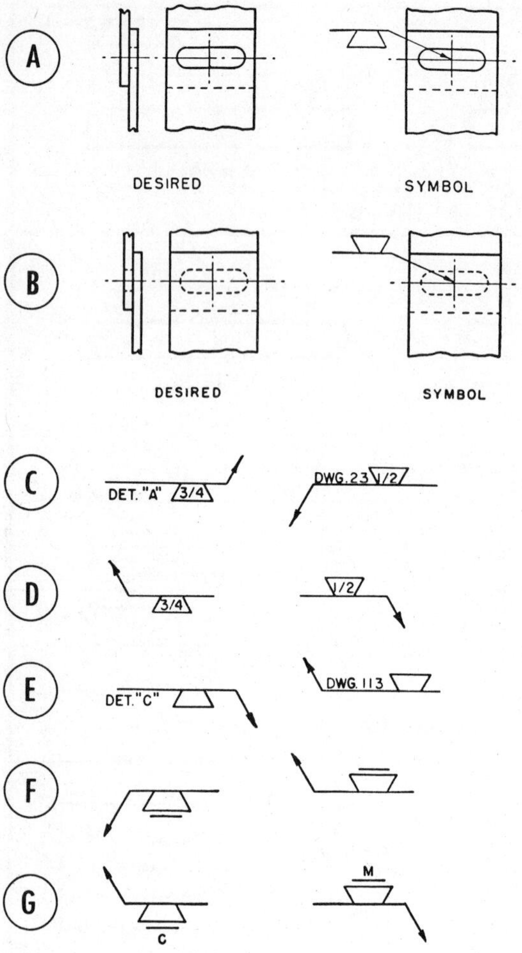

Figure 11-21
Meaning of symbols as they apply to slot welds.

reference line toward the reader as shown in Fig. 11-21*A*.

(b) Slots in the other-side member of a joint for slot welding shall be indicated by placing the weld symbol on the side of the reference line away from the reader, as shown in Fig. 11-21*B*.

(c) Dimensions of slot welds shall be shown on the same side of the reference line as the weld symbol, as shown in Fig. 11-21*C*.

(d) The slot weld symbol shall not be used to designate filler welds in slots.

2 Depth of filling

Depth of filling of slot welds shall be complete unless otherwise indicated. When the depth of filling is less than complete, the depth of filling, in inches, shall be shown inside the weld symbol. See Fig. 11-21*D*.

3 Details of slot welds

Length, width, spacing, included angle of countersink, orientation and location of slot welds cannot be shown on the welding symbol. This data shall be shown on the drawing or by a detail with a reference thereto on the welding symbol, observing the usual location significance, as shown in Fig. 11-21*E*.

4 Surface contour of slot welds

(a) Slot welds that are to be welded approximately flush without recourse to any method of finishing shall be shown by adding the flush-contour symbol to the weld symbol. See Fig. 11-21*F*.

(b) Slot welds that are to be made flush by mechanical means shall be shown by adding both the flush-contour symbol and the user's standard finish symbol to the weld symbol. See Fig. 11-21*G*.

5 Application of slot weld symbols

Fig. 11-22 illustrates how welding symbols are applied to slot welds.

6 Application of dimensions to slot welding symbols

The application of dimensions to slot welding symbols is shown in Fig. 11-23.

11.23 Arc-spot weld symbols[6]

1 General

Dimensions of arc-spot welds shall be shown on the same side of the reference line as the weld symbol, as shown in Fig. 11-24*A*.

2 Size of arc-spot welds

Arc-spot welds shall be dimensioned by either size or strength, as follows:

(a) The size of arc-spot welds shall be designated as the diameter of the weld expressed in fractions or decimally in hundredths of an inch, and shall be shown with or without inch marks to the left of the weld symbol. See Fig. 11-24*B*.

(b) The strength of arc-spot welds shall be designated as the minimum acceptable

6. *Ibid.*

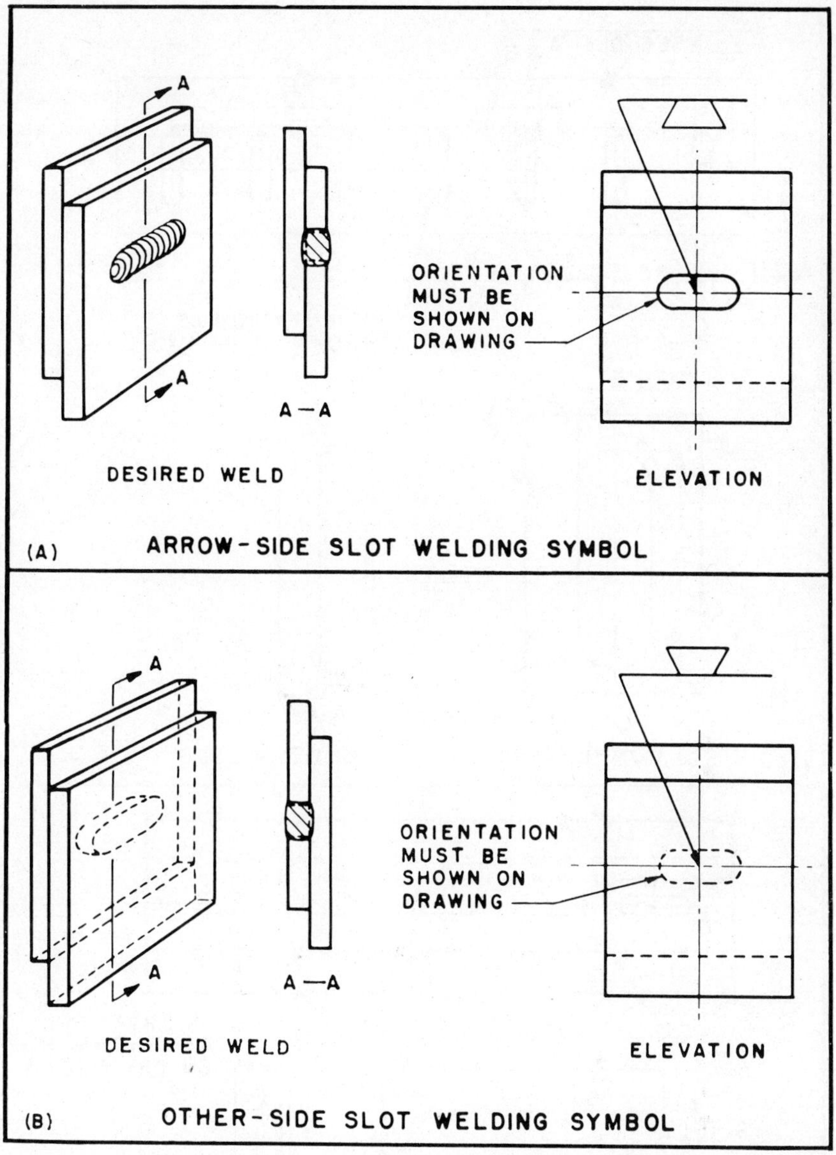

Figure 11-22
Application of slot weld symbols.

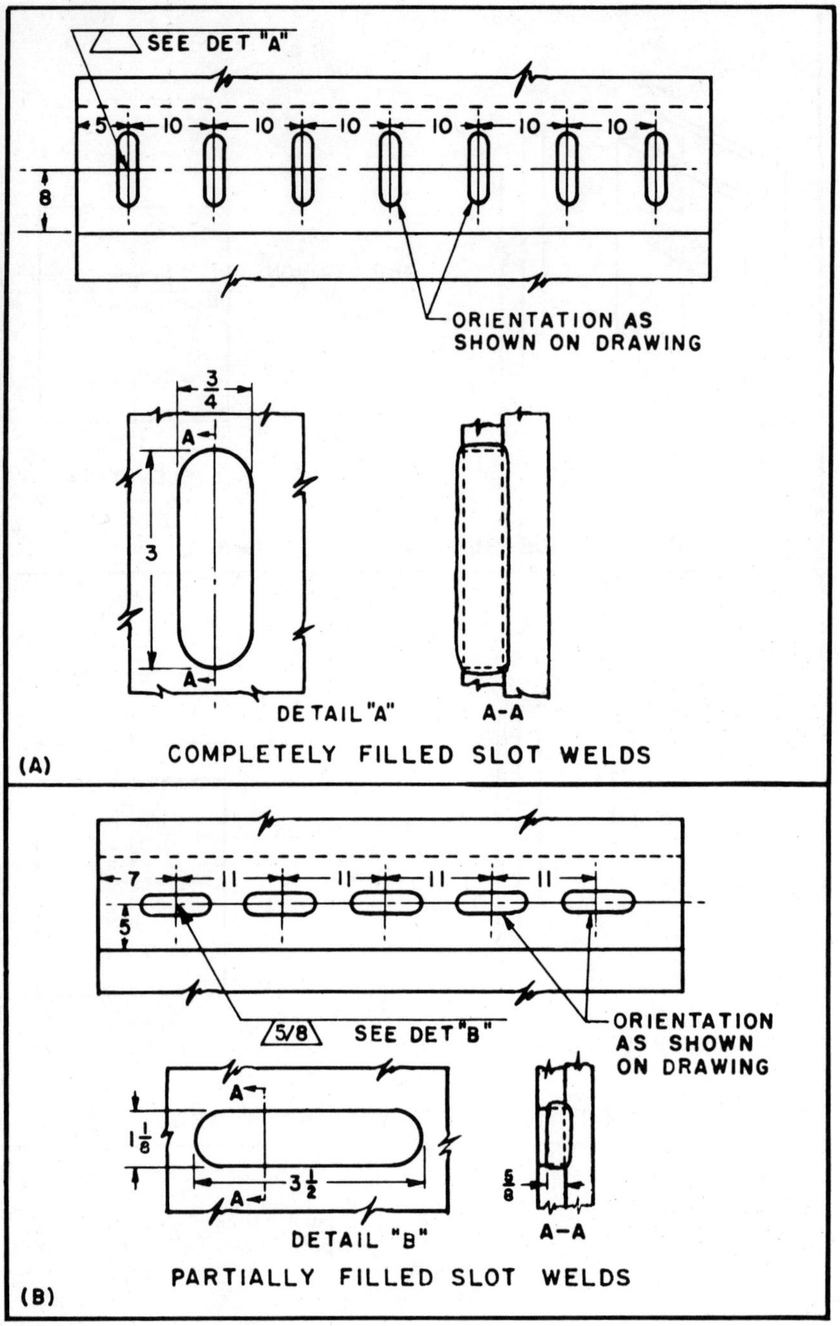

Figure 11-23
Application of dimensions to slot welding symbols.

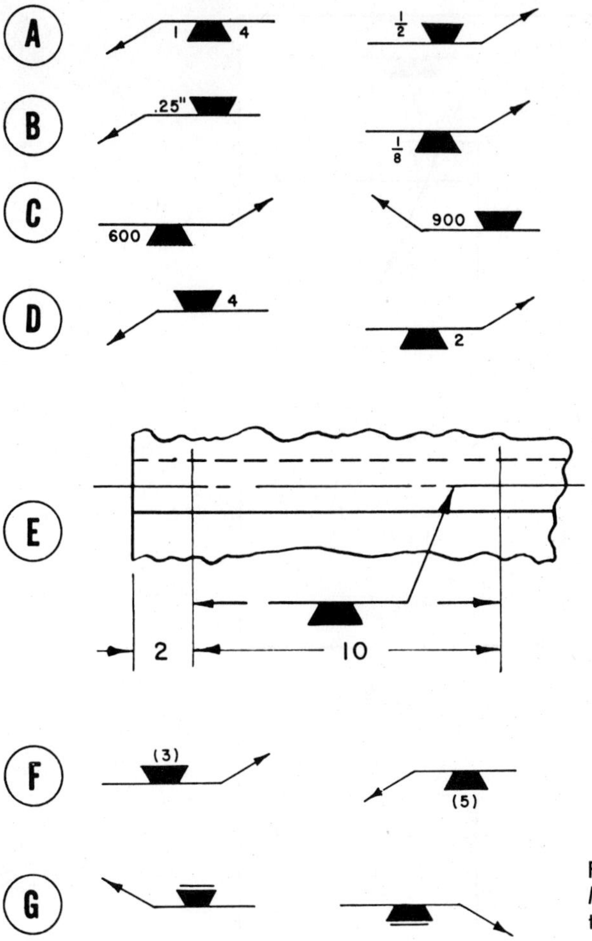

Figure 11-24
Meaning of symbols as they apply to arc-spot welds.

shear strength in pounds per spot, and shall be shown to the left of the weld symbol, as shown in Fig. 11-24*C*.

3 Spacing of arc-spot welds

The pitch (center-to-center spacing) of arc-spot welds shall be shown to the right of the weld symbol. See Fig. 11-24*D*.

4 Extent of arc-spot welding

When arc-spot welding extends less than the distance between abrupt changes in the direction of the welding, or less than the full length of the joint, the extent shall be dimensioned. See Fig. 11-24*E*.

5 Number of arc-spot welds

When a definite number of arc-spot welds is desired in a certain joint, the number shall be shown in parentheses either above or below the weld symbol, as shown in Fig. 11-24*F*.

6 Flush arc-spot-welded joints

When the exposed surface of one member of an arc-spot-welded joint is to be flush, that surface shall be indicated by adding the flush-contour symbol to the weld symbol, observing the usual location significance, as shown in Fig. 11-24*G*.

7 Application of arc-spot weld symbols

The method of applying symbols to arc-spot welds is shown in Fig. 11-25.

8 Application of dimensions to arc-spot welding symbols

The application of dimensions to arc-spot welding symbols is shown in Fig. 11-26.

11.24 Arc-seam weld symbols[7]

1 General

Dimensions of arc-seam welds shall be

7. *Ibid.*

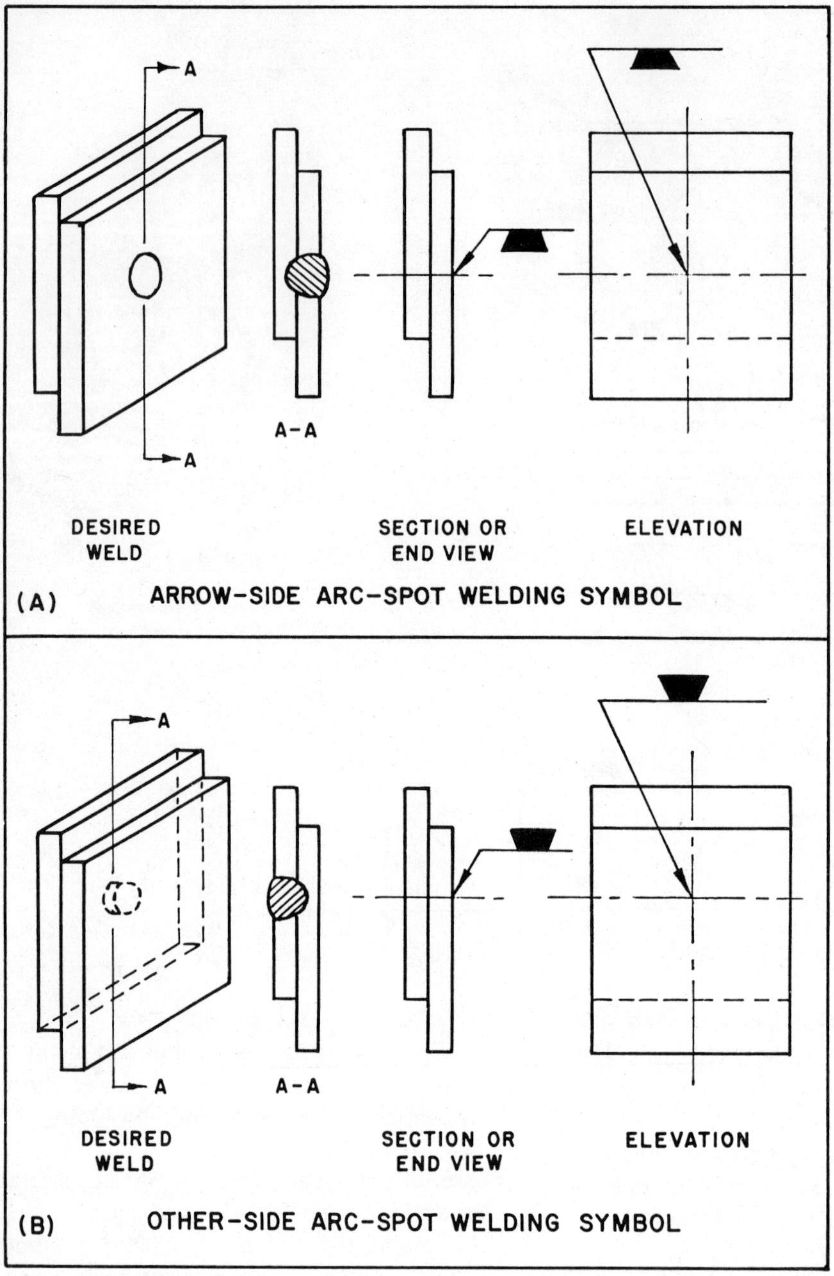

Figure 11-25
Application of arc-spot weld symbols.

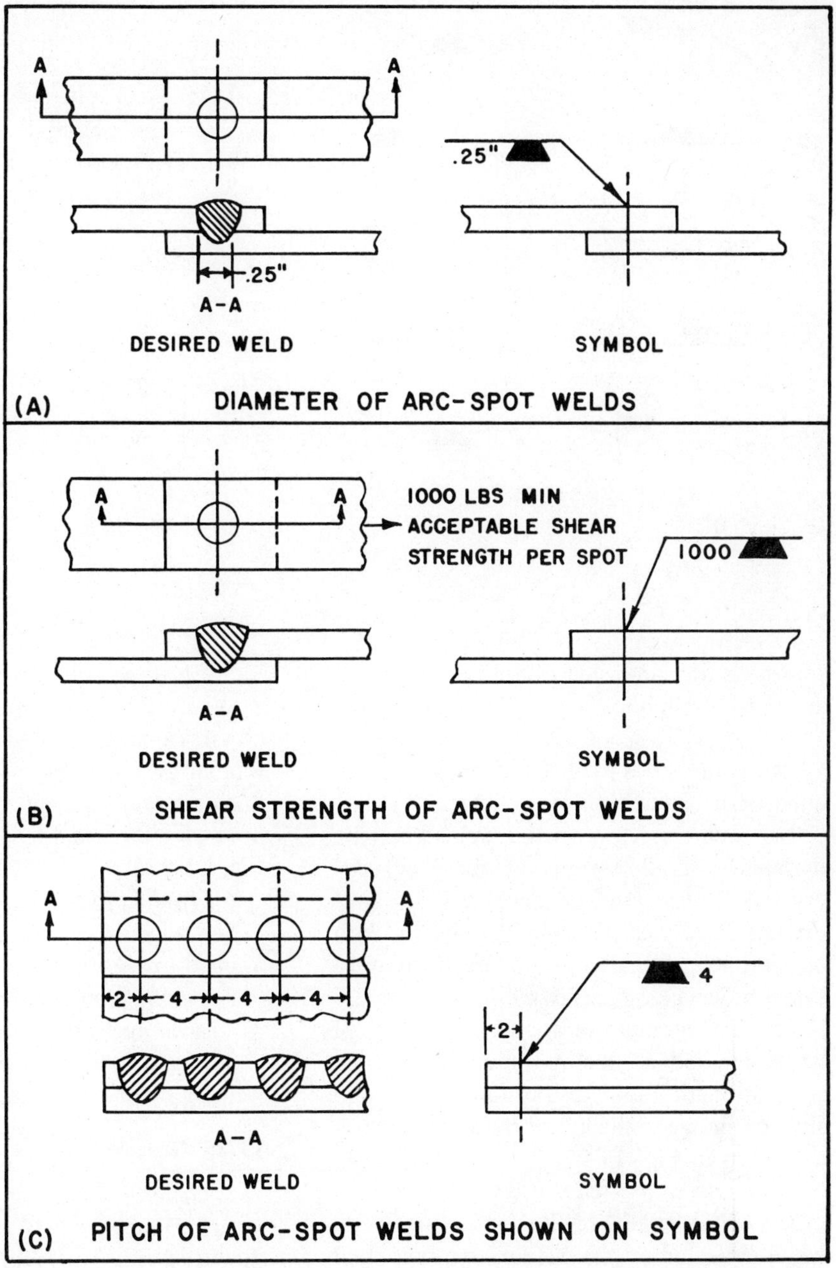

Figure 11-26
Application of dimensions to arc-spot welding symbols.

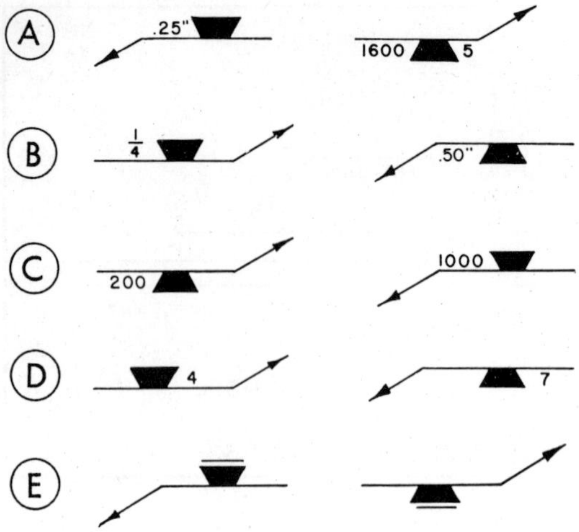

Figure 11-27
Meaning of symbols as they apply to arc-seam welds.

shown on the same side of the reference line as the weld symbol. See Fig. 11-27*A*

2 Size of arc-seam welds

Arc-seam welds shall be dimensioned by either size or strength, as follows:

(a) The size of arc-seam welds shall be designated as the width of the weld expressed in fractions or decimally in hundredths of an inch, and shall be shown, with or without inch marks to the left of the weld symbol. See Fig. 11-27*B*.

(b) The strength of arc-seam welds shall be designated as the minimum acceptable shear strength in pounds per linear inch, and shall be shown to the left of the weld symbol, as shown in Fig. 11-27*C*.

3 Length of arc-seam welds

(a) The length of an arc-seam weld, when indicated on the welding symbol, shall be shown to the right of the weld symbol, as shown in Fig. 11-27*D*.

(b) When arc-seam welding extends for the full distance between abrupt changes in the direction of the welding no length dimension need be shown on the welding

4 Details of arc-seam welds

Spacing, extent, orientation and location of arc-seam welds cannot be shown on the welding symbol. This data shall be shown on the drawing.

5 Flush arc-seam-welded joints

When the exposed surface of one member of an arc-seam-welded joint is to be flush, that surface shall be indicated by adding the flush-contour symbol to the weld symbol, observing the usual location significance. See Fig. 11-27*E*.

6 Application of arc-seam weld symbols

See Fig. 11-28 as to how symbols are applied to arc-seam welds.

7 Application of dimensions to arc-seam welding symbols

The application of dimensions to arc-seam welding symbols is shown in Fig. 11-29.

11.25 Groove weld symbols[8]

1 General

(a) Dimensions of groove welds shall be shown on the same side of the reference line as the weld symbol, as in Fig. 11-30*A*.

(b) When no general note governing the dimensions of groove welds appears on the drawing, the dimensions of double-groove welds shall be shown as follows:

(1) When both welds have the same dimensions, one or both may be dimensioned. See Fig. 11-30*B*.

(2) When the welds differ in dimen-

(Text continued on page 262)

8. *Ibid.*

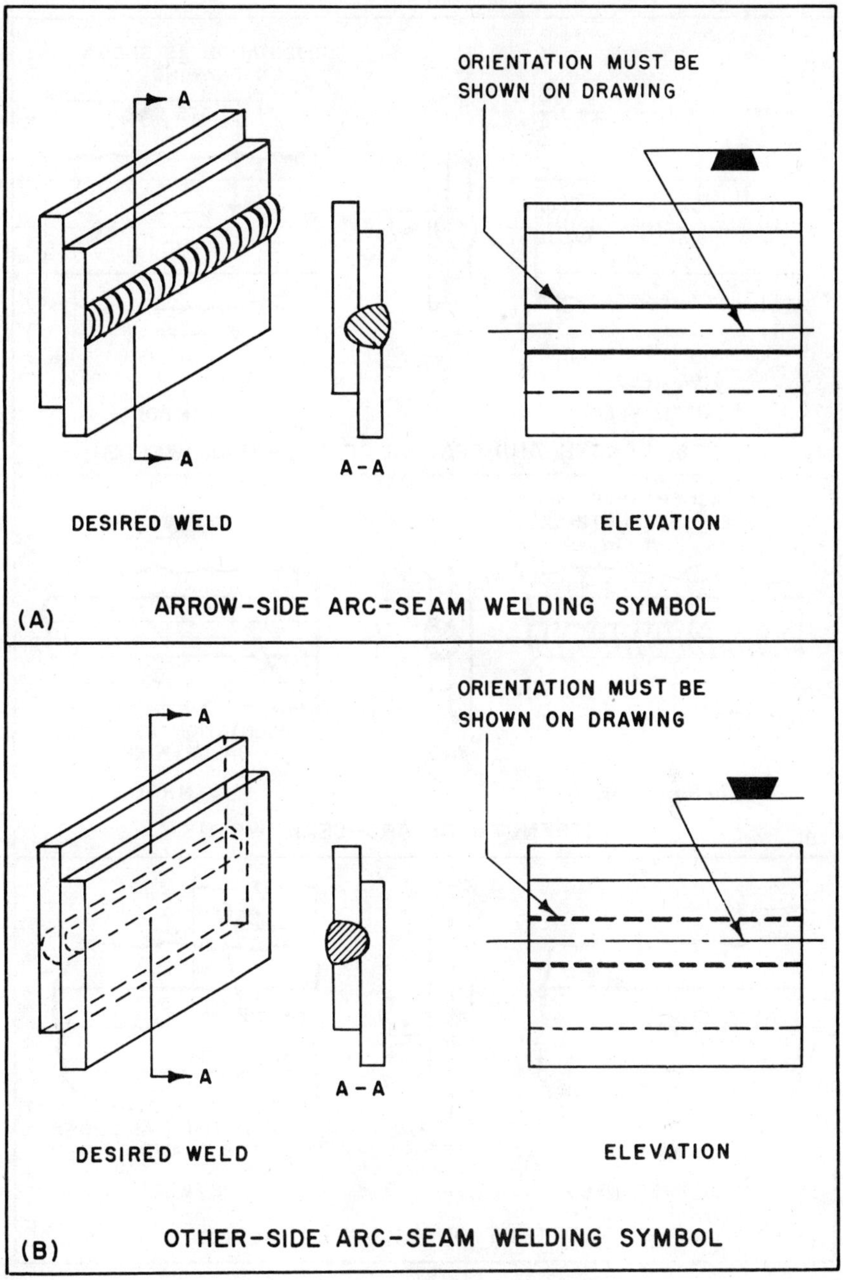

Figure 11-28
Application of arc-seam weld symbols.

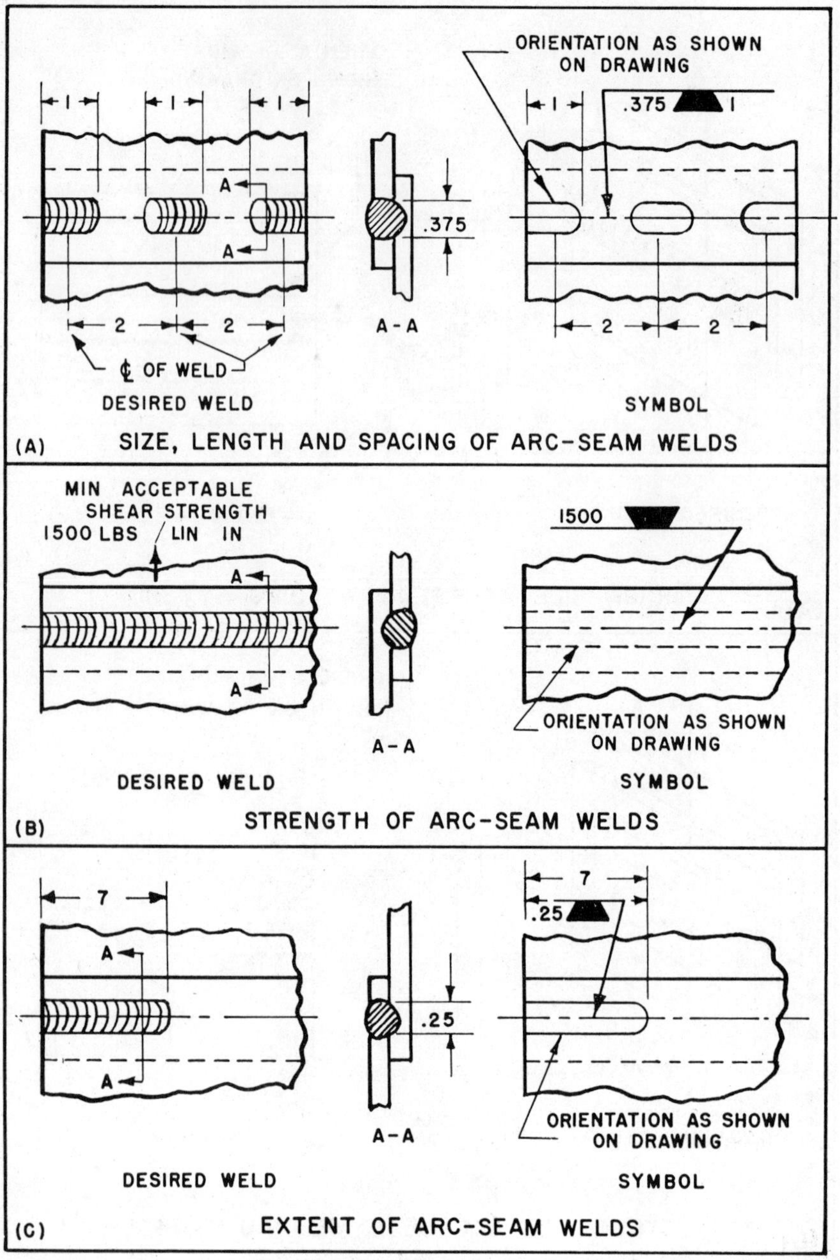

Figure 11-29
Application of dimensioning to arc-seam welding symbols.

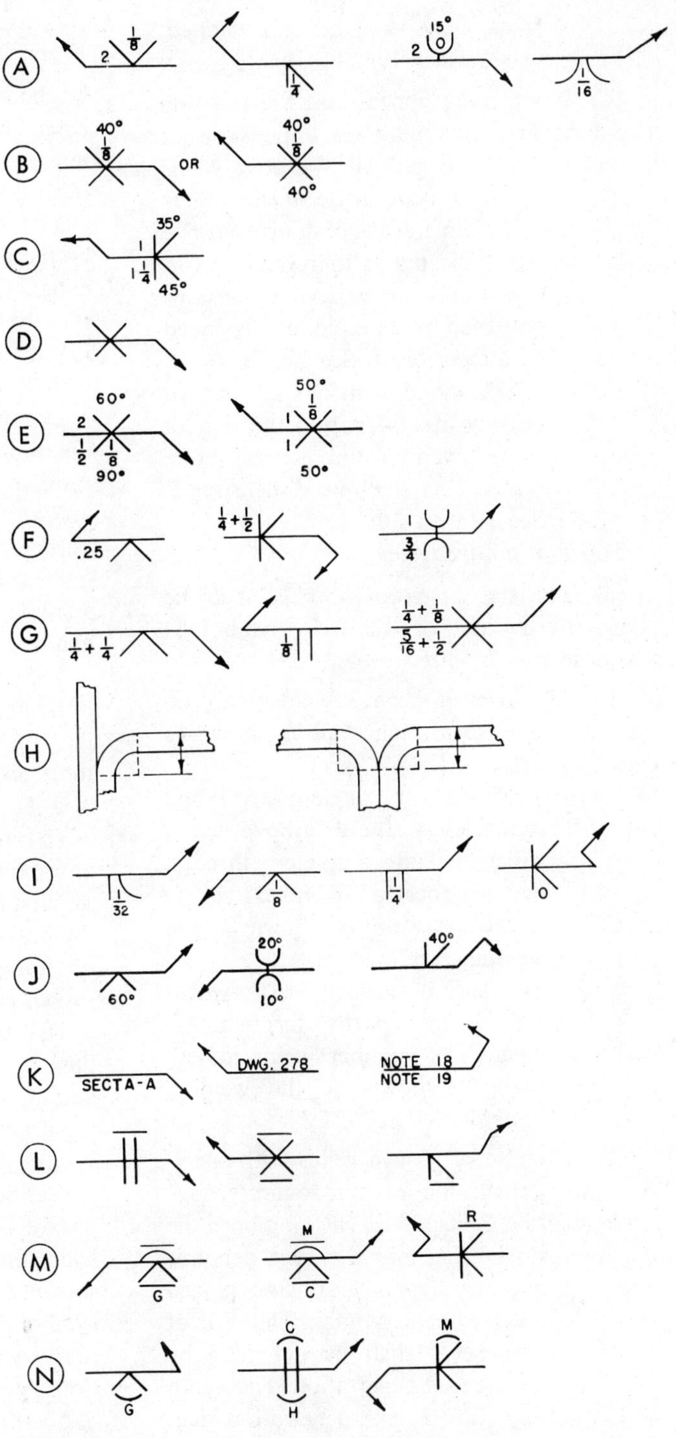

Figure 11-30
Meaning of symbols as they apply to groove welds.

sions, both shall be dimensioned, as shown in Fig. 11-30*C*.

(c) When there appears on the drawing a general note governing the dimensions of groove welds, such as "All V-groove welds shall have a 60° groove angle unless otherwise noted," the dimensions of double-groove welds shall be indicated as follows:

(1) When both welds have dimensions governed by the note, neither need be dimensioned. See Fig. 11-30*D*.

(2) When the dimensions of one or both welds differ from the dimensions given in the general note, both welds shall be dimensioned. See Fig. 11-30*E*.

2 Size of groove welds

(a) The size of groove welds shall be shown to the left of the weld symbol as shown in Fig. 11-30*F*.

(b) The size of groove welds with no specified root penetration shall be shown as follows:

(1) The size of single-groove and symmetrical double-groove welds which extend completely through the member or members being joined, need not be shown on the welding symbol.

(2) The size of groove welds which extend only partly through the member or members being joined, shall be shown on the welding symbol.

(c) The size of groove welds with specified root penetration except square-groove welds shall be indicated by showing both the depth of chamfering and the root penetration, separated by a plus mark and placed to the left of the weld symbol. The size of square-groove welds shall be indicated by showing only the root penetration. The depth of chamfering and the root penetration shall read in that order from left to right along the reference line, as shown in Fig. 11-30*G*.

(d) The size of flare-groove welds is considered as extending only to the tangent points as indicated in Fig. 11-30*H* by dimension lines.

3 Groove dimensions

(a) Root opening of groove welds shall be the user's standard unless otherwise indicated. Root opening of groove welds, when not the user's standard, shall be shown inside the weld symbol. See Fig. 11-30*I*.

(b) Groove angle of groove welds shall be the user's standard, unless otherwise indicated. Groove angle of groove welds, when not the user's standard, shall be shown as in Fig. 11-30*J*.

(c) Groove radii and root faces of U- and J-groove welds shall be the user's standard unless otherwise indicated. When groove radii and root faces of U- and J-groove welds are not the user's standard, the weld shall be shown by a cross section, detail or other data, with a reference thereto on the welding symbol, observing the usual location significance. See Fig. 11-30*K*.

4 Designation of back and backing welds

Bead-type back and backing welds of single-groove welds shall be shown by means of the back or backing weld symbol.

5 Surface contour of groove welds

(a) Groove welds that are to be welded approximately flush without recourse to any method of finishing shall be shown by adding the flush-contour symbol to the weld symbol, observing the usual location significance, as shown in Fig. 11-30*L*.

(b) Groove welds that are to be made flush by mechanical means shall be shown by adding both the flush-contour symbol and the user's standard finish symbol to the weld symbol, observing the usual location significance. See Fig. 11-30*M*.

(c) Groove welds that are to be mechanically finished to a convex contour shall be shown by adding both the convex-contour symbol and the user's standard finish symbol to the weld symbol, observing the usual location significance, as shown in Fig. 11-30*N*.

6 Application of groove weld symbols

Fig. 11-31 illustrates how symbols are applied to groove welds.

7 Application of dimensions to groove welding symbols

The method of applying dimensions to groove weld symbols is shown in Fig. 11-32.

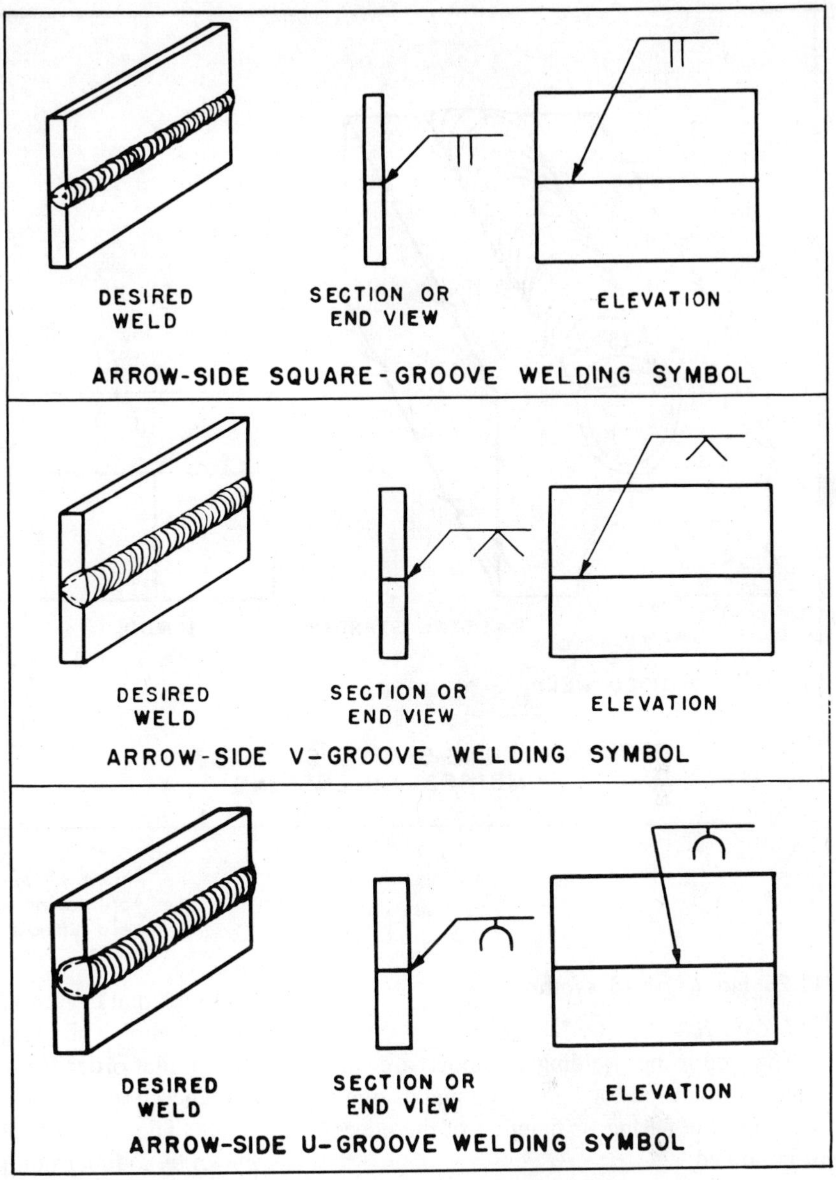

Figure 11-31
Application of groove weld symbols.

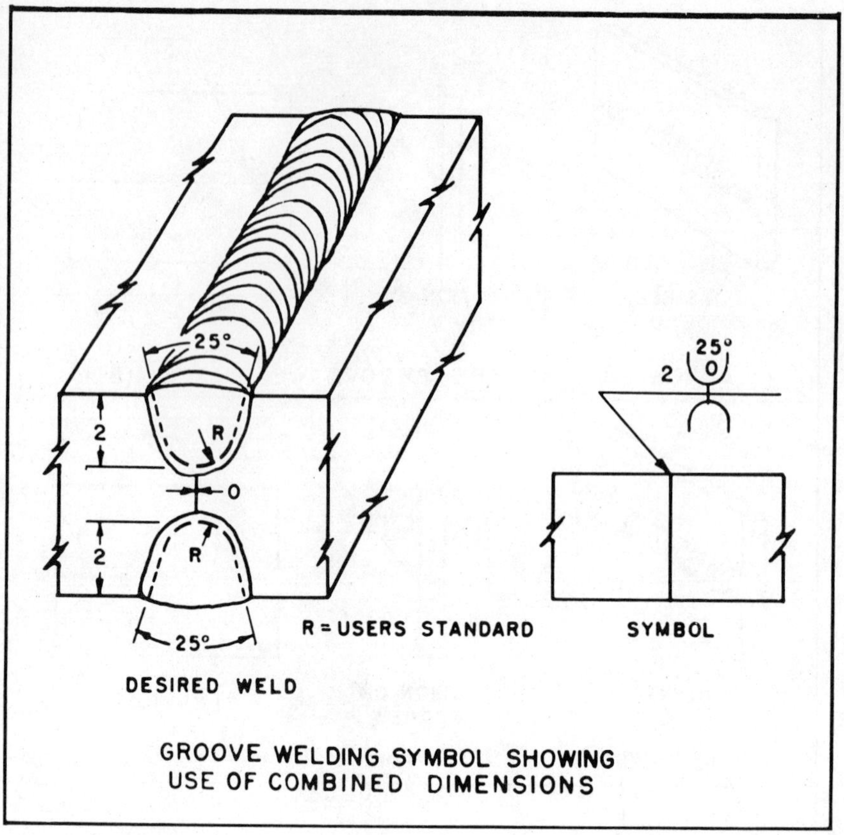

Figure 11-32
Application of dimensions to groove weld symbols.

11.26 Flange weld symbols[9]

1 General

The following welding symbols are intended to be used for light gage metal joints involving the flaring or flanging of the edges to be joined:

(a) Edge-flange welds shall be shown by the edge-flange weld symbol. See Fig. 11-33*A*.

(b) Corner-flange welds shall be shown by the corner-flange weld symbol. See Fig. 11-33*B*.

2 Dimensions of flange welds

(a) Dimensions of flange welds shall be shown on the same side of the reference line as the weld symbol. See Fig. 11-33*C*.

(b) The radius and the height above the point of tangency shall be indicated by showing both the radius and the height separated by a plus mark, and placed to the left of the weld symbol. The radius and the height shall read in that order from left to right along the reference line, as shown in Fig. 11-33*D*.

(c) The size of flange welds shall be shown by a dimension placed outward of the flange dimensions, as shown in Fig. 11-33*E*.

(d) Root opening of flange welds shall not be shown on the welding symbol. If it is desired to specify this dimension, it shall be shown on the drawing.

3 Multiple joint flange welds

For flange welds, when one or more pieces are inserted between the two outer pieces, the same symbol as for the two outer pieces shall be used regardless of the number of pieces inserted, as shown in Fig. 11-33*F*.

4 Application of flange weld symbols

Fig. 11-34 designates the method of how symbols are applied to flange welds.

9. *Ibid.*

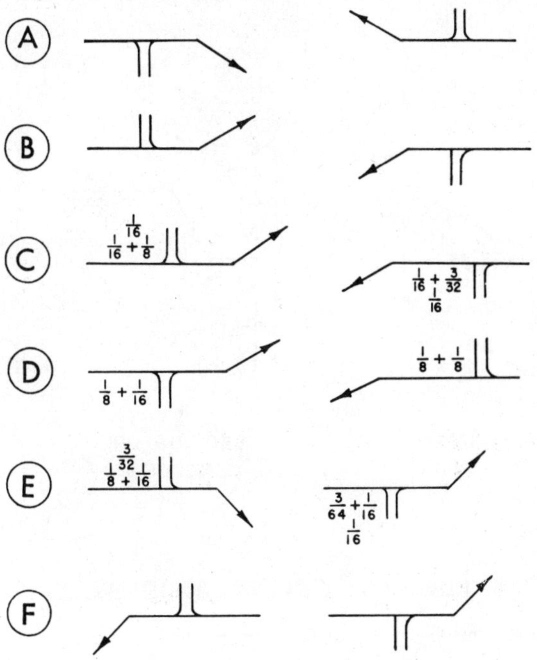

Figure 11-33
Meaning of symbols as they apply to flange welds.

11.27 Resistance-spot weld symbols[10]

1 General

(a) Resistance-spot weld symbols have no arrow- or other-side significance in themselves, although supplementary symbols used in conjunction therewith may have such significance. Resistance-spot weld symbols shall be centered on the reference line.

(b) Dimensions of resistance-spot welds may be shown on either side of the reference line.

2 Size of resistance-spot welds

Resistance-spot welds shall be dimensioned by either size or strength, as follows:

(a) The size of resistance-spot welds shall be designated as the diameter of the weld expressed in fractions or decimally in hundredths of an inch, and shall be shown, with or without inch marks, to the left of the weld symbol. See Fig. 11-35*A*.

(b) The strength of resistance-spot welds shall be designated as the minimum acceptable shear strength in pounds per spot, and shall be shown to the left of the weld symbol. See Fig. 11-35*B*.

3 Spacing of resistance-spot welds

(a) The pitch (center-to-center spacing) of resistance-spot welds shall be shown to the right of the weld symbol. See Fig. 11-35*C*.

(b) When resistance-spot weld symbols are shown directly on the drawing, spacing shall be shown by dimensions.

4 Extent of resistance-spot welding

When resistance-spot welding extends less than the distance between abrupt changes in the direction of the welding, or less than the full length of the joint, the extent shall be dimensioned, as shown in Fig. 11-35*D*.

5 Number of resistance-spot welds

10. *Ibid.*

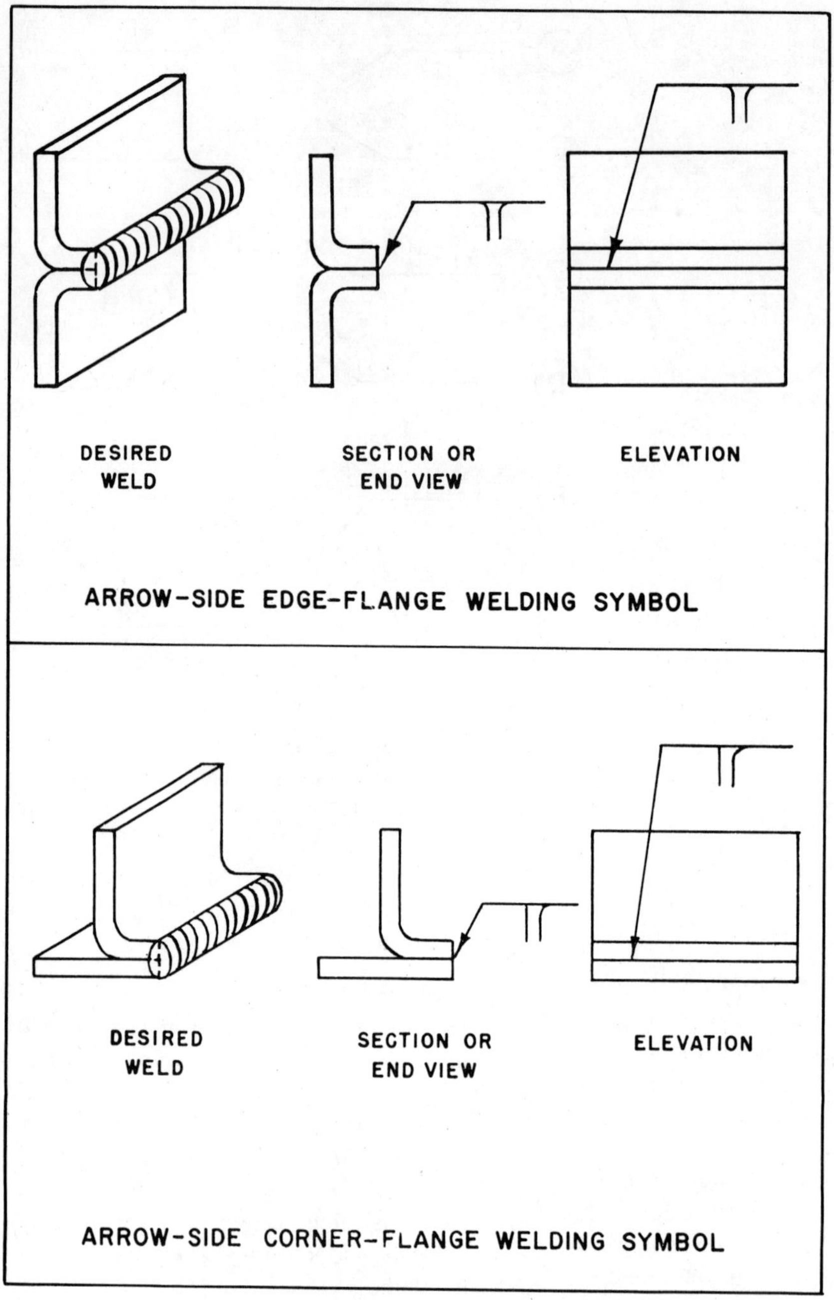

Figure 11-34
Application of flange weld symbols.

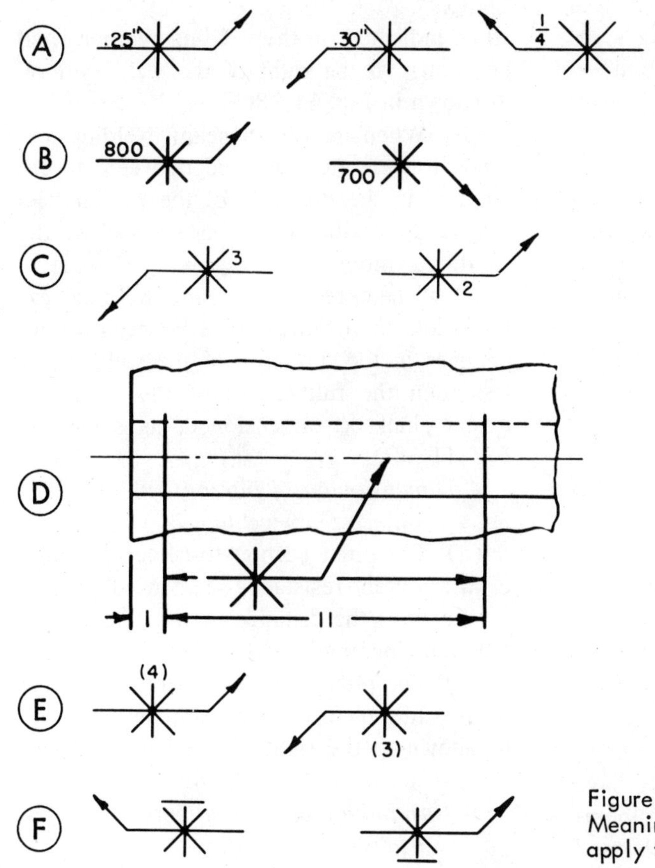

Figure 11-35
Meaning of symbols as they apply to resistance-spot welds.

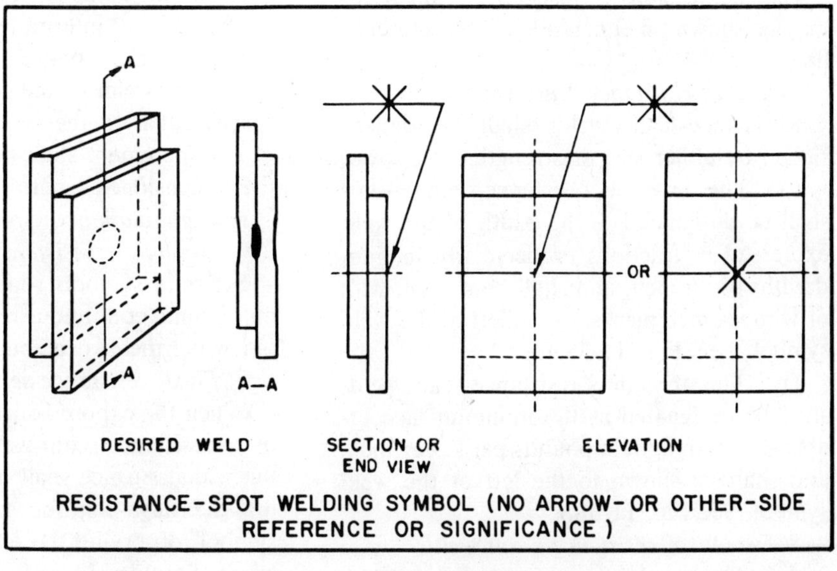

Figure 11-36
Application of resistance-spot weld symbols.

When a definite number of resistance-spot welds is desired in a certain joint, the number shall be shown in parentheses either above or below the weld symbol, as shown in Fig. 11-35*E*.

6 Flush resistance-spot-welding joints

When the exposed surface of one member of a resistance-spot-welded joint is to be flush, that surface shall be indicated by adding the flush-contour symbol to the weld symbol, observing the usual location significance, as shown in Fig. 11-35*F*.

7 Application of resistance-spot weld symbols

Fig. 11-36 indicates the application of symbols to resistance-spot welds.

8 Application of dimensions to resistance-spot welding symbols

Application of dimensions to resistance-spot welding symbols is shown in Fig. 11-37.

11.28 Resistance-seam weld symbols[11]

1 General

(a) Resistance-seam weld symbols have no arrow- or other-side significance in themselves, although supplementary symbols used in conjunction therewith may have such significance. Resistance-seam weld symbols shall be centered on the reference line.

(b) Dimensions of resistance-seam welds may be shown on either side of the reference line.

2 Size of resistance-seam welds

Resistance-seam welds shall be dimensioned by either size or strength as follows:

(a) The size of resistance-seam welds shall be designated as the width of the weld expressed in fractions or decimally in hundredths of an inch, and shall be shown, with or without inch marks, to the left of the weld symbol. See Fig. 11-38*A*.

(b) The strength of resistance-seam welds shall be designated as the minimum acceptable shear strength in pounds per linear inch, and shall be shown to the left of the weld symbol. See Fig. 11-38*B*.

3 Length of resistance-seam welds

(a) The length of a resistance-seam weld, when indicated on the welding symbol, shall be shown to the right of the weld symbol, as shown in Fig. 11-38*C*.

(b) When resistance-seam welding extends for the full distance between abrupt changes in the direction of the welding, no length dimension need be shown on the welding symbol.

(c) When resistance-seam welding extends less than the distance between abrupt changes in the direction of the welding, or less than the full length of the joint, the extent shall be dimensioned, as shown in Fig. 11-38*D*.

4 Dimensioning of intermittent resistance-seam welding

(a) The pitch (center-to-center spacing) of intermittent resistance-seam welding shall be shown as the distance between centers of the weld increments.

(b) The pitch (center-to-center spacing) of intermittent resistance-seam welding shall be shown to the right of the length dimension, as shown in Fig. 11-38*E*.

5 Termination of intermittent resistance-seam welding

(a) When intermittent resistance-seam welding is used by itself, the symbol indicates that increments shall be located at the ends of the dimensioned length.

(b) When intermittent resistance-seam welding is used between continuous resistance-seam welding, the symbol indicates that spaces equal to the pitch minus the length of one increment shall be left at the ends of the dimensioned length.

6 Combination of intermittent and continuous resistance-seam welding

Separate symbols shall be used for intermittent and continuous resistance-seam welding when the two are used in combination.

7 Flush resistance-seam-welded joints

When the exposed surface of one member of a resistance-seam-welded joint is to be flush, that surface shall be indicated by adding the flush-contour symbol to the weld symbol, observing the usual location significance. See Fig. 11-38*F*.

8 Application of resistance-seam weld symbols

11. *Ibid.*

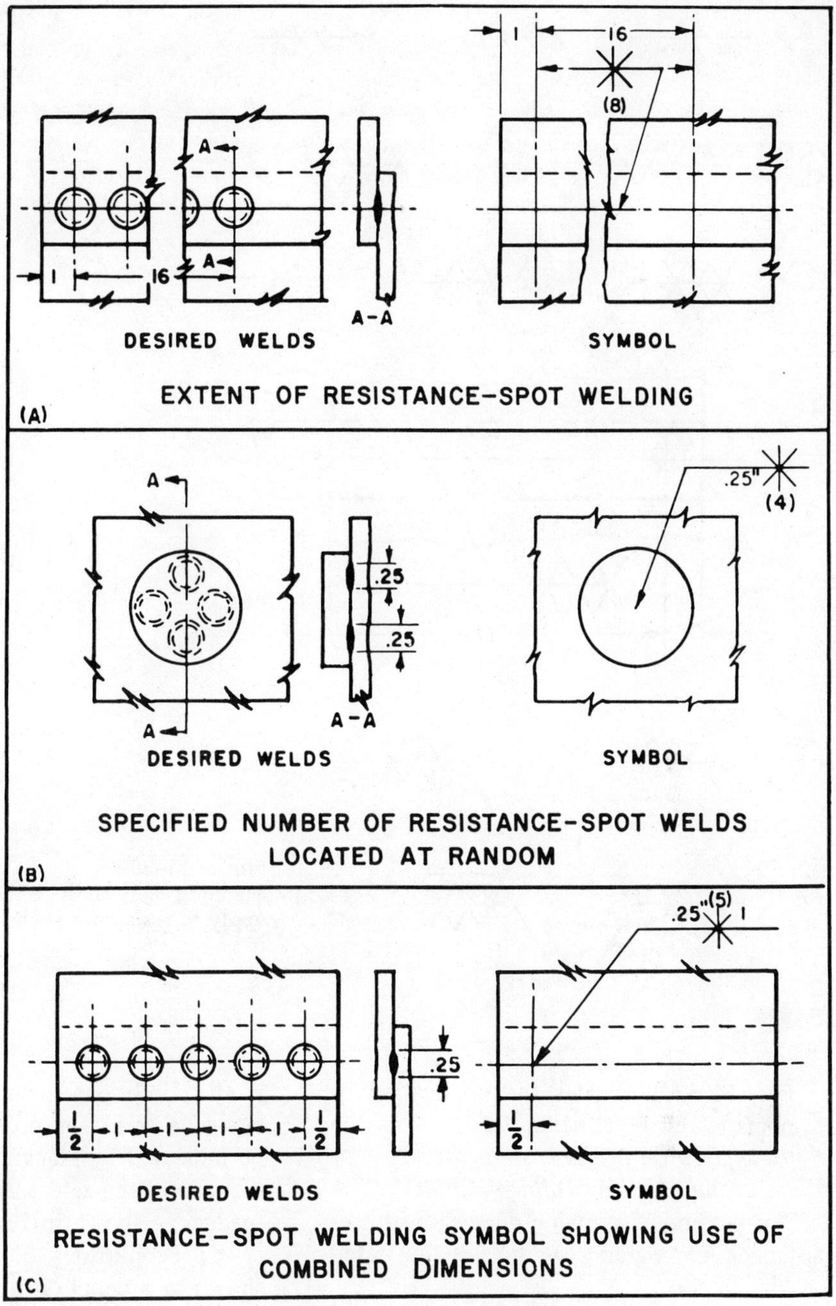

Figure 11-37
Application of dimensions to resistance-spot welding symbols.

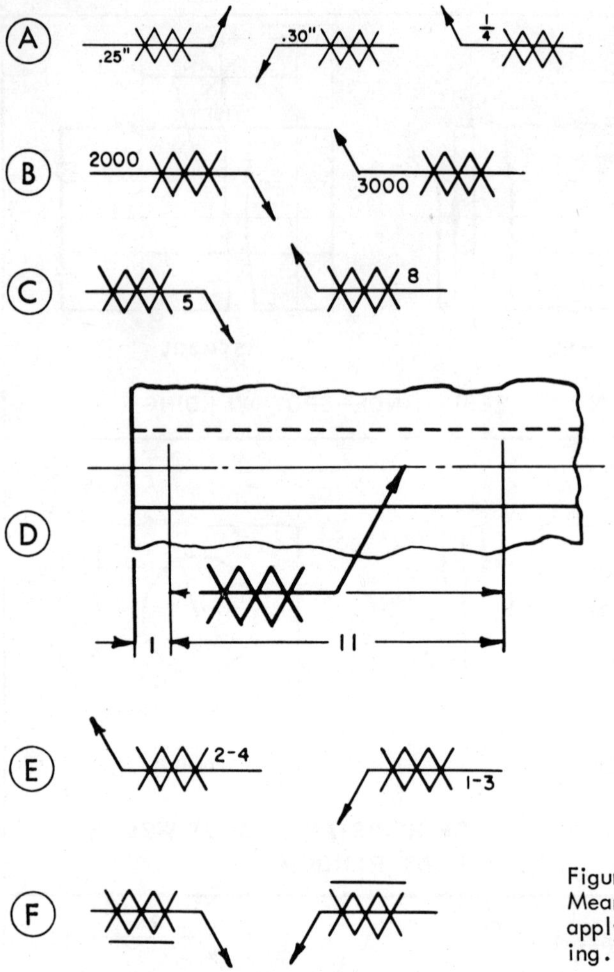

Figure 11-38
Meaning of symbols as they apply to resistance-seam welding.

Fig. 11-39 illustrates the application of symbols to resistance-seam welds.

9 Application of dimensions to resistance-seam welding symbols

The method of applying dimensions to resistance-seam welding symbols is illustrated in Fig. 11-40.

11.29 Projection weld symbols[12]

1 General

(a) Embossments on the arrow-side member of a joint for projection welding shall be indicated by placing the weld symbol on the side of the reference line toward the reader, as shown in Fig. 11-41*A*.

12. *Ibid.*

(b) Embossments on the other-side member of a joint for projection welding shall be indicated by placing the weld symbol on the side of the reference line away from the reader, as shown in Fig. 11-41*B*.

(c) Proportions of projections shall be shown by a detail or other suitable means.

(d) Dimensions of projection welds shall be shown on the same side of the reference line as the weld symbol. (Fig. 11-41*C*.)

2 Size of projection welds

Projection welds shall be dimensioned by strength. Circular projection welds may be dimensioned by size.

(a) The size of circular projection welds shall be designated as the diameter of the weld expressed in fractions or decimally in

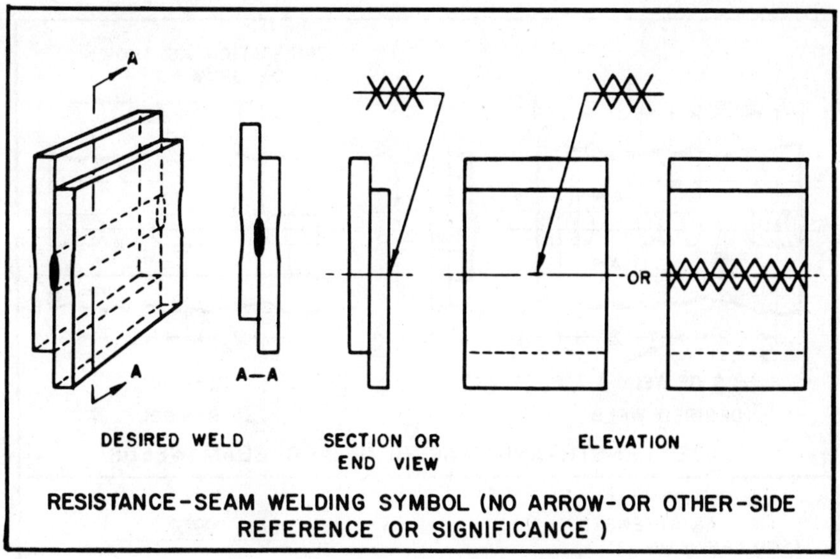

Figure 11-39
Application of resistance-seam weld symbols.

hundredths of an inch, and shall be shown, with or without inch marks, to the left of the weld symbol. See Fig. 11-41*D*.

(b) The strength of projection welds shall be designated as the minimum acceptable shear strength in pounds per weld, and shall be shown to the left of the weld symbol. See Fig. 11-41*E*.

3 Spacing of projection welds

The pitch (center-to-center spacing) of projection welds shall be shown to the right of the weld symbol, as shown in Fig. 11-41*F*.

4 Extent of projection welding

When projection welding extends less than the distance between abrupt changes in the direction of the welding, or less than the full length of the joint, the extent shall be dimensioned, as shown in Fig. 11-41*G*.

5 Number of projection welds

When a definite number of projection welds is desired in a certain joint, the number shall be shown in parentheses, as shown in Fig. 11-41*H*.

6 Flush projection-welded joints

When the exposed surface of one member of a projection welded joint is to be made flush, that surface shall be indicated by adding the flush-contour symbol to the weld symbol, observing the usual location significance. See Fig. 11-41*I*.

7 Application of projection welding symbols

Fig. 11-42 illustrates the application of symbols to projection welds.

8 Application of dimensions to projection weld symbols

Dimensions to projection weld symbols are applied as shown in Fig. 11-43.

11.30 Flash or upset weld symbols[13]

1 General

(a) Flash or upset weld symbols have no arrow-side or other-side significance in themselves although supplementary symbols used in conjunction therewith may have such significance. Flash or upset weld symbols shall be centered on the reference line.

(b) Dimensions of flash or upset welds shall not be shown on the welding symbol.

2 Surface contour of flash or upset welds

(a) Flash or upset welds that are to be made flush by mechanical means shall be shown by adding both the flush-contour symbol and the user's standard finish symbol to

(Text continued on page 276)

13. *Ibid.*

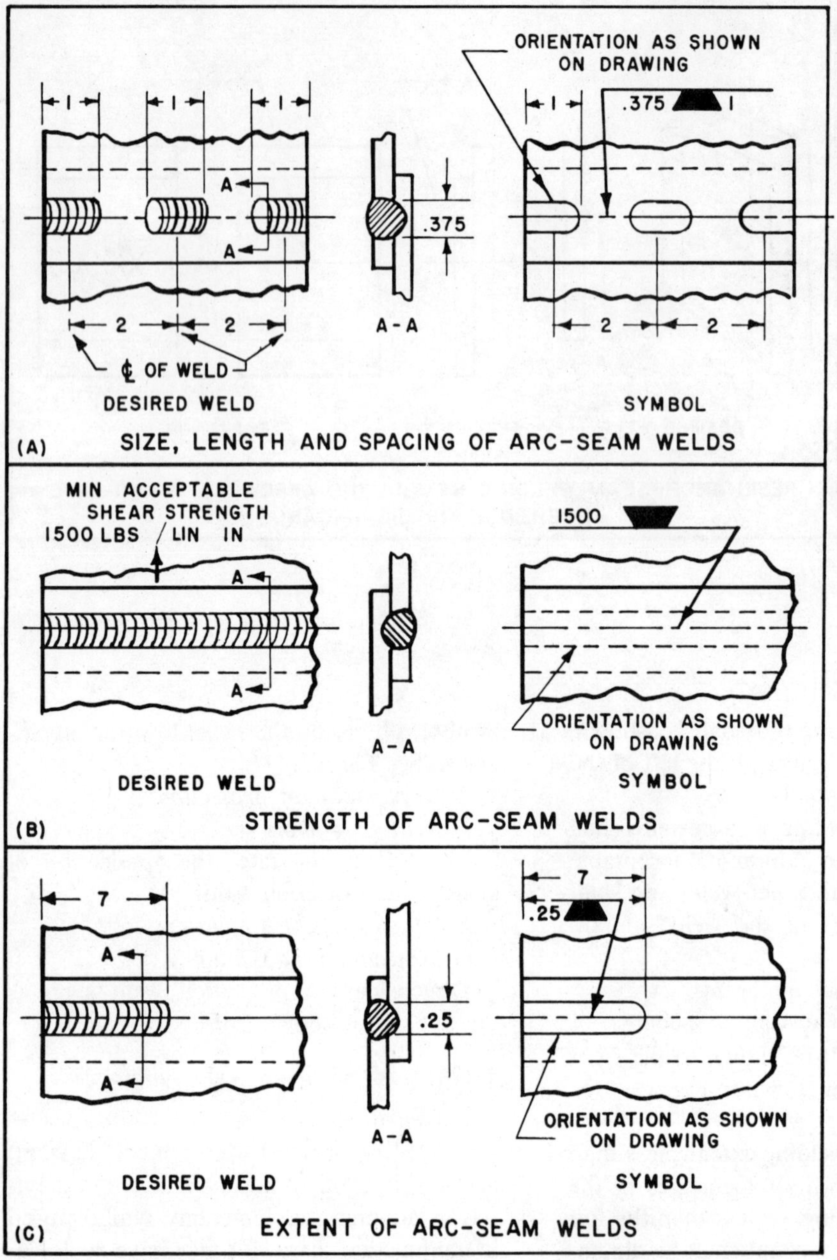

Figure 11-40
Application of dimensions to arc-seam welding symbols.

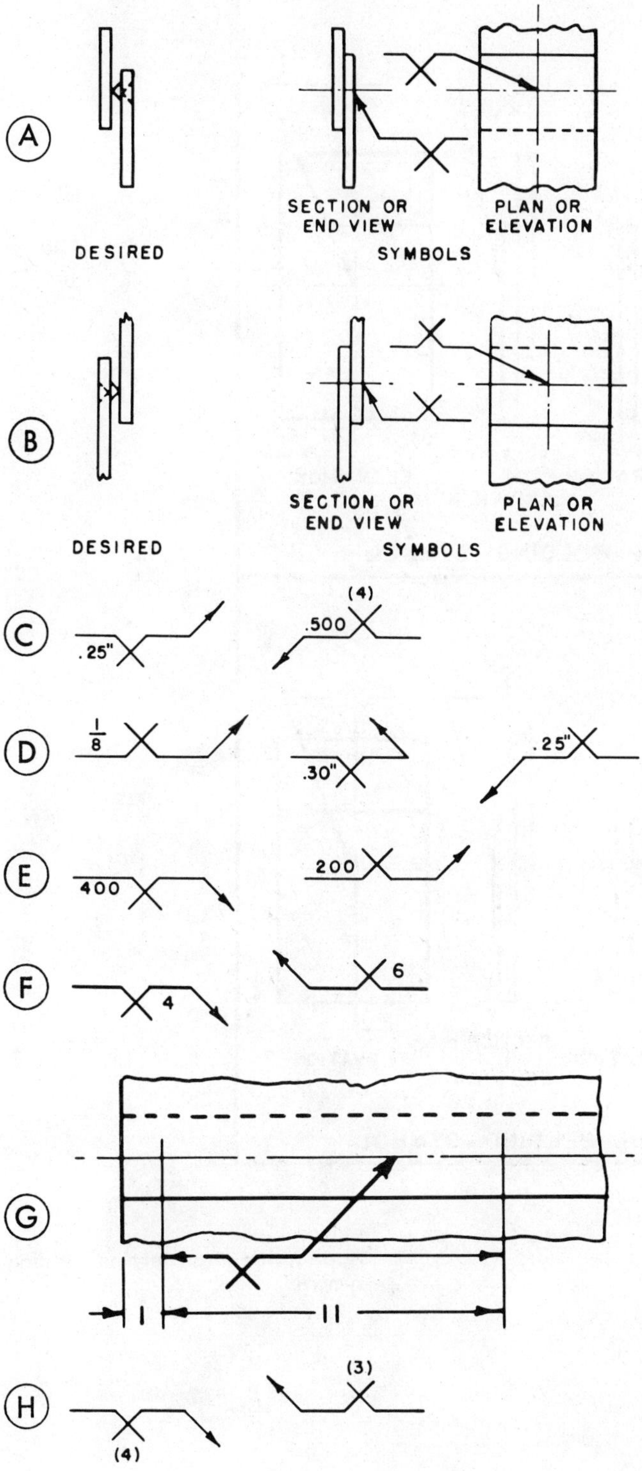

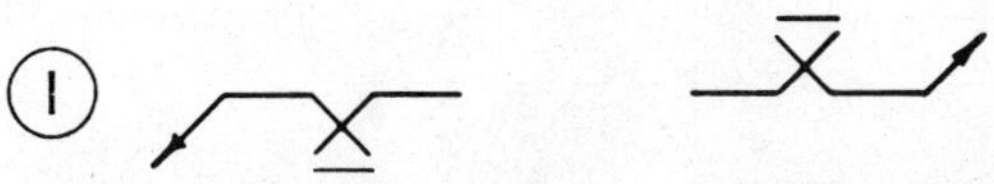

Figure 11-41
Meaning of symbols as they apply to projection welds.

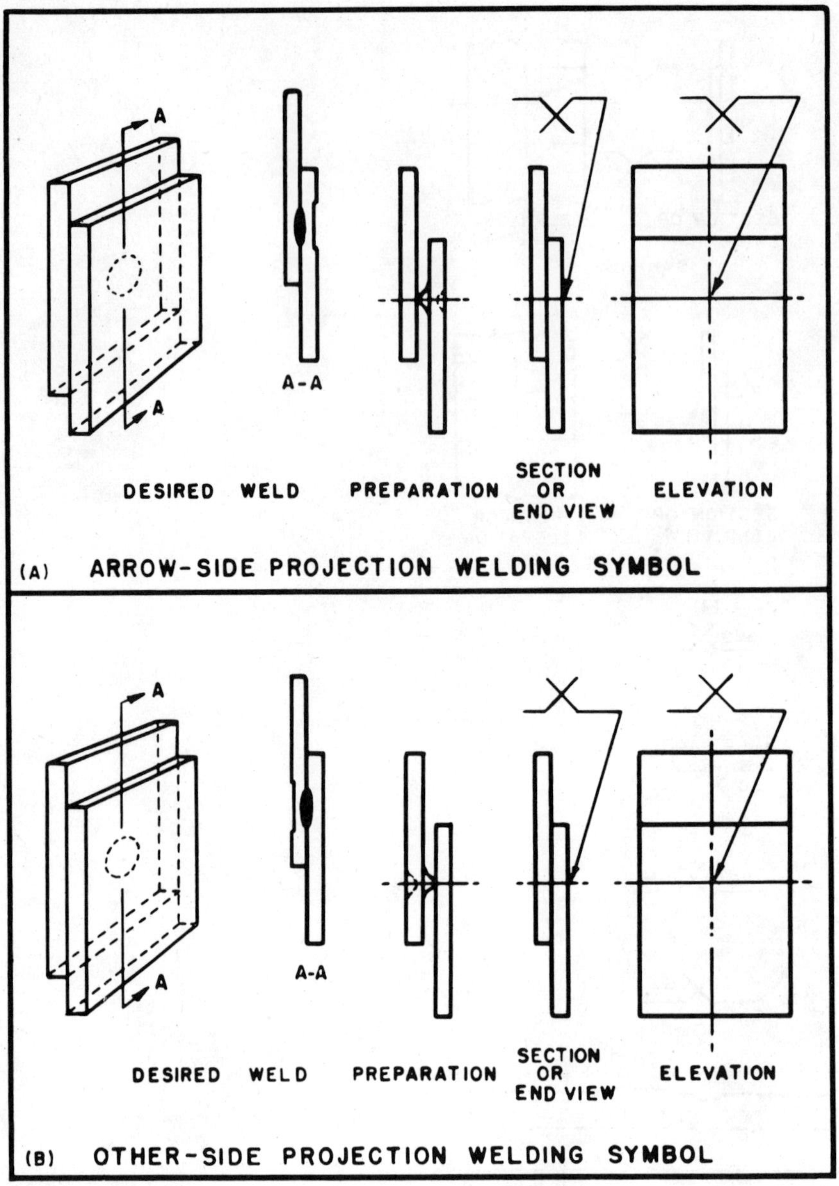

Figure 11-42
Application of projection welding symbols.

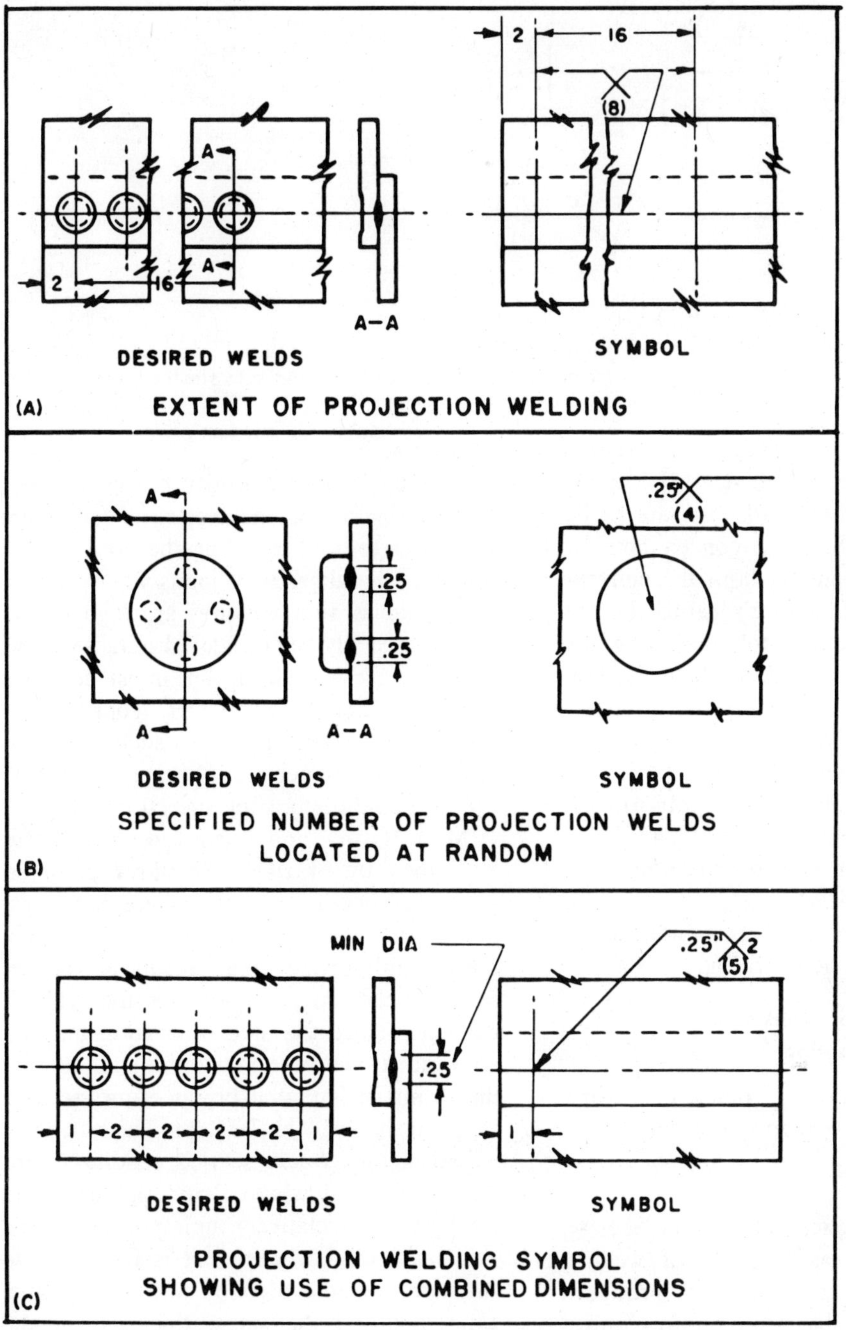

Figure 11-43
Application of dimensions to projection welds.

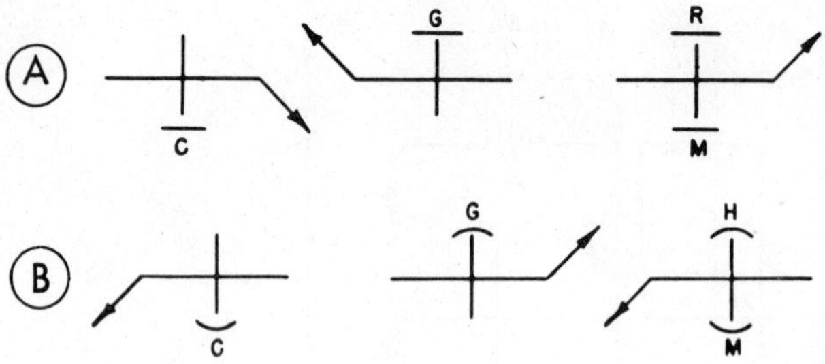

Figure 11-44
Meaning of symbols as they apply to flash or upset welds.

the weld symbol, observing the usual location significance. See Fig. 11-44*A*.

(b) Flash or upset welds that are to be mechanically finished to a convex contour shall be shown by adding both the convex-contour symbol and the user's standard finish symbol to the weld symbol, observing the usual location significance, as shown in Fig. 11-44*B*.

3 Application of flash or upset welding symbols

The use of symbols as they apply to flash or upset welds is shown in Fig. 11-45.

4 Use of welding symbols to indicate the welding of studs

The use of welding symbols to indicate the welding of studs is shown in Fig. 11-46.

11.31 Illustration of weld symbols in a finished drawing[14]

Fig. 11-47 shows how a complete drawing looks when proper welding symbols are used.

11.32 Brazing[15]

According to the American Welding Society, *brazing* is defined as a group of welding processes wherein coalescence is produced by heating to suitable temperatures above 800° F. and by using a nonferrous filler metal having a melting point below that of the base metals. It differs from regular welding in that the base metal is not melted but heated only to the point where the nonferrous material flows evenly between the closely fitted surfaces of the joint by capillary attraction.

Brazing is used considerably in automotive, refrigeration, and electrical equipment industries to hold parts together and to provide liquid and gas tight joints where service temperatures and pressures are higher than would normally be considered suitable if soft soldering were utilized. The most common brazing materials are silver, copper, and copper alloys. Brazing alloys such as aluminum-silicon, copper-phosphorous and others are available for brazing special metals.

Most ferrous and nonferrous metals can be joined by brazing. The three common joints for brazing operations are lap, butt, and scarf. The joint used depends on the design and service requirements of the assembly. The lap joint provides the greatest efficiency since the area of overlap may be adjusted to yield the maximum strength. Its disadvantage is that it produces an increase in metal thickness at the joint. The butt joint is satisfactory where service conditions are not severe and where liquid tightness and strength are relatively unimportant. Scarf joints are used whenever it is necessary to increase the area of bond and at the same time maintain the single thickness of the base metal. Although scarf joints provide more area, they are often difficult to hold in alignment during the brazing operations. Fig. 11-48 illustrates typical brazing joints.

A flux must be used in performing a brazing operation (1) to prevent oxidation of the filler metal and surfaces of the joint, (2) to dissolve oxides which may form during

(Text continued on page 280)

14. *Ibid.*

15. *Ibid.*

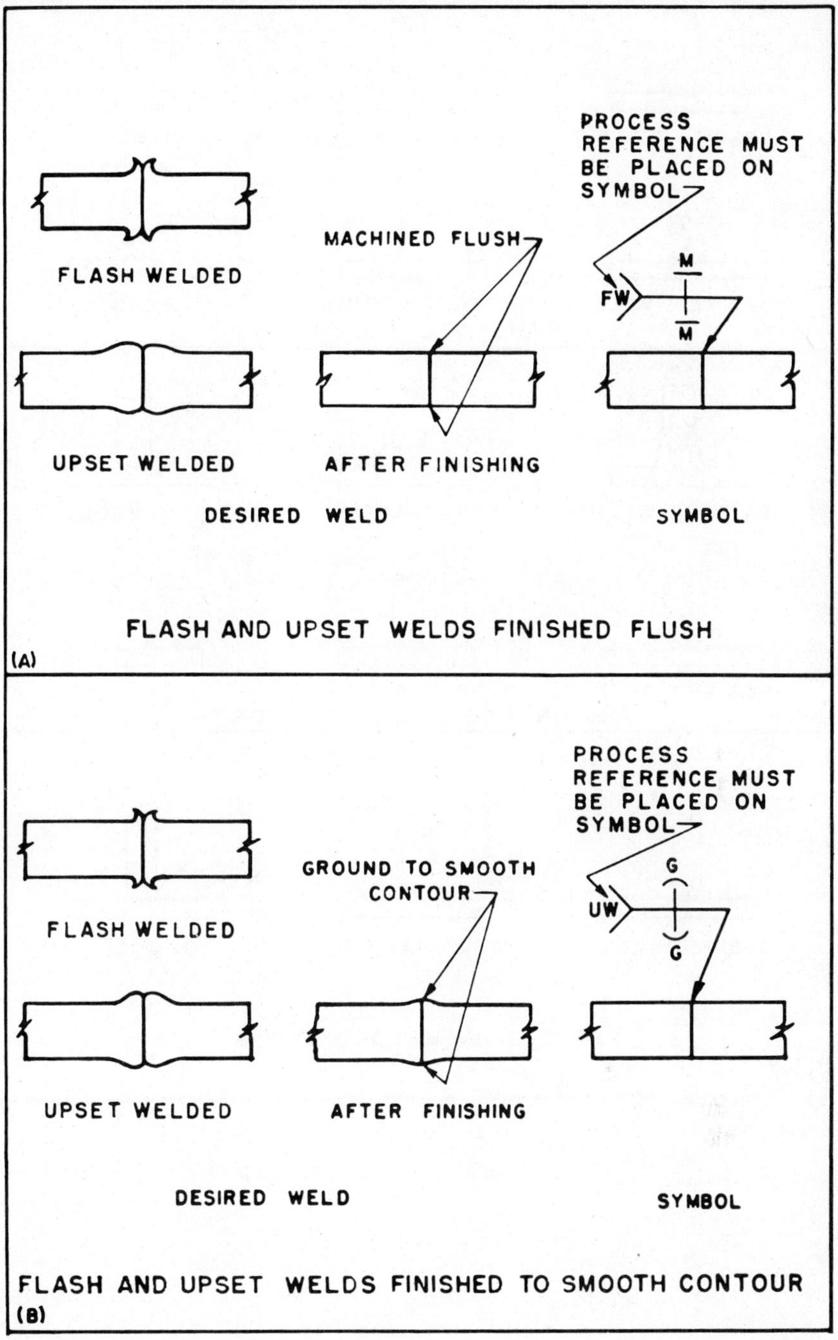

Figure 11-45
Application of flash and upset welding symbols.

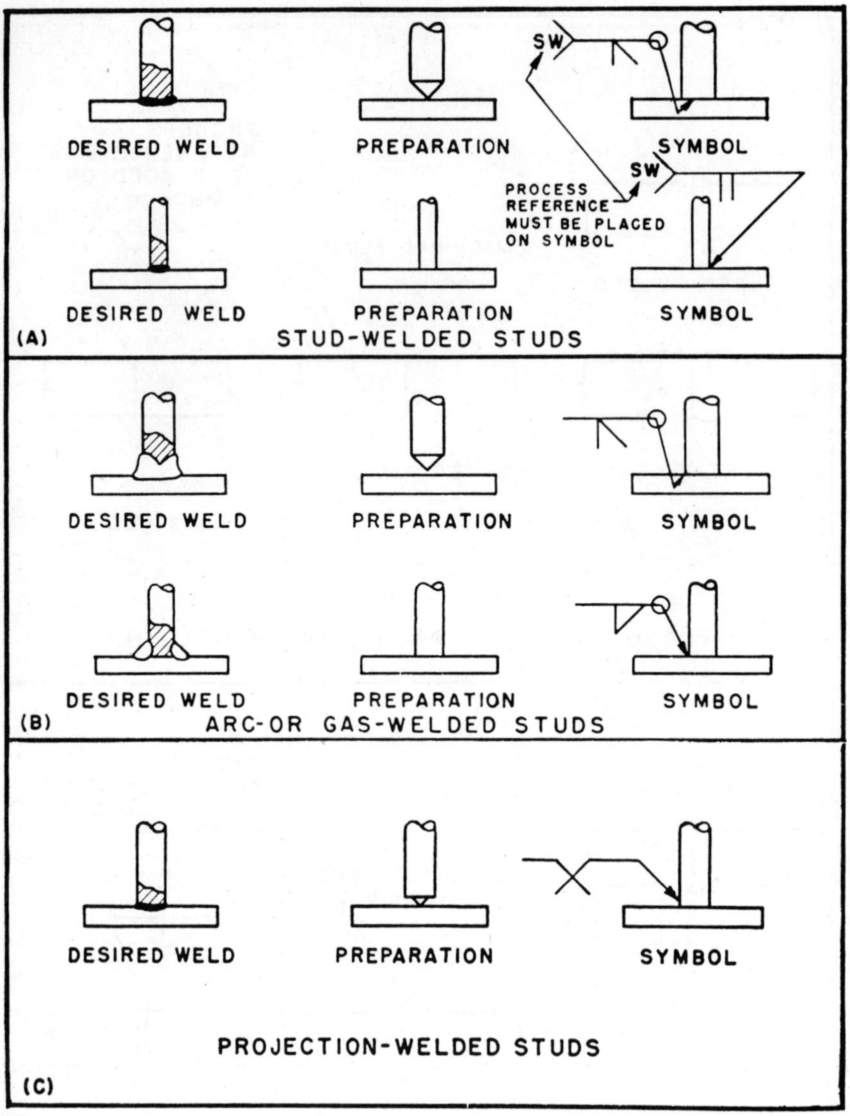

Figure 11-46
Application of symbols to stud welding.

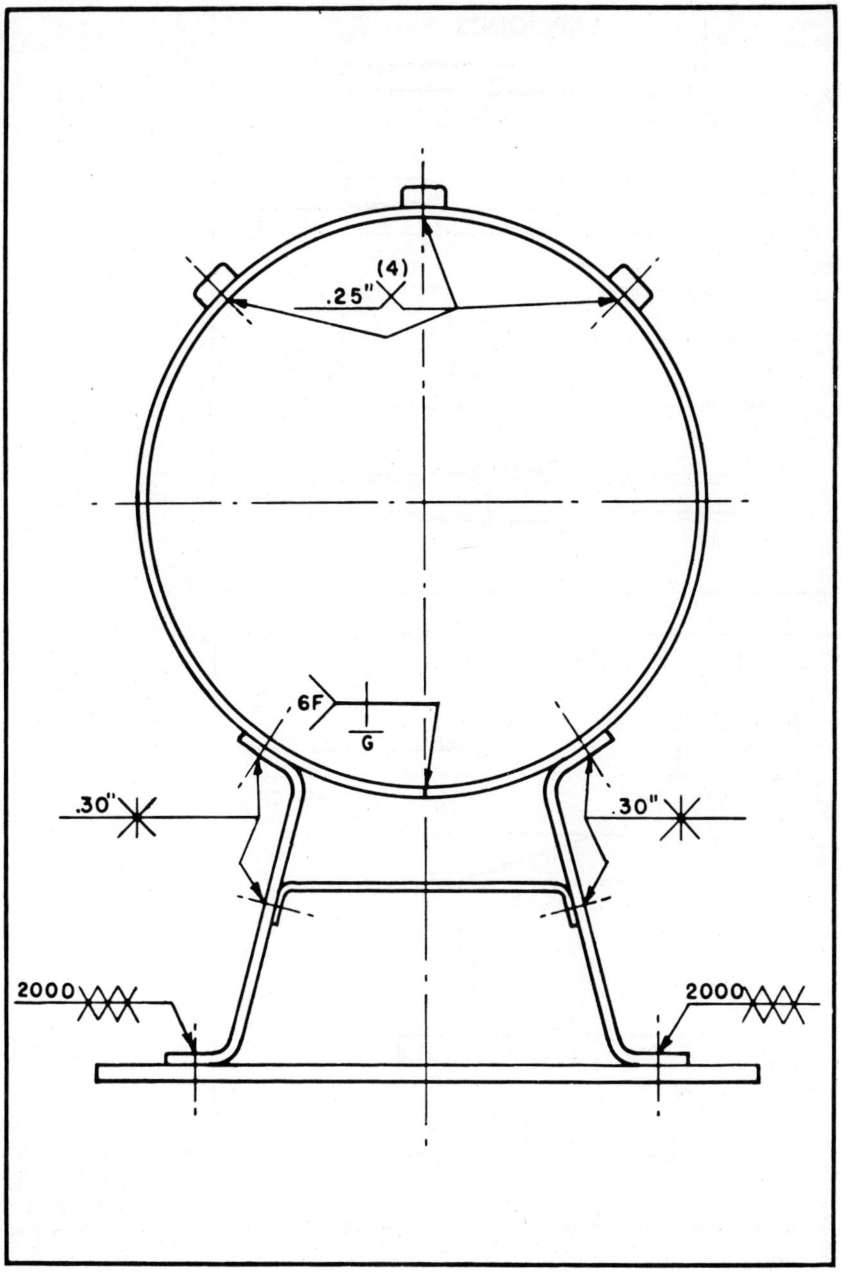

Figure 11-47
Use of resistance welding symbols on sheetmetal fabrication drawing.

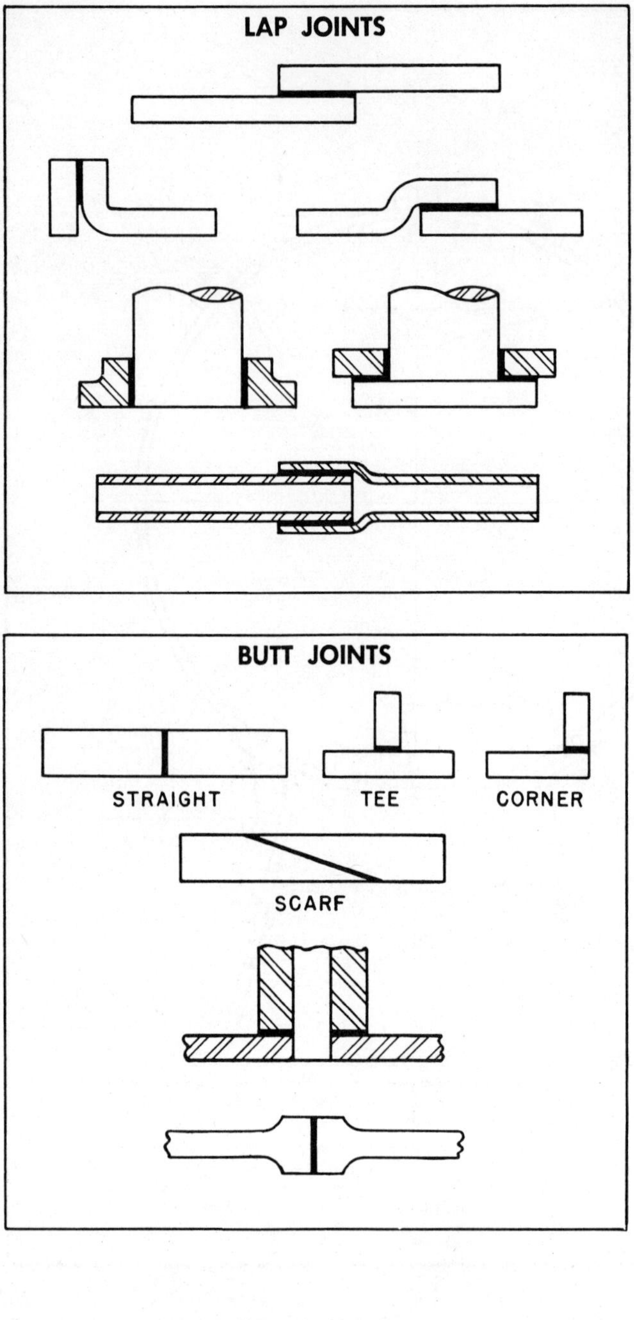

Figure 11-48
These joints are satisfactory for most brazing operations providing there is an extremely tight fit.
General Motors Corp.

heating, and (3) to promote the free flow of the filler material. The actual brazing operation may be conducted in one of the following ways:

Torch brazing using air-gas, air-acetylene, or oxyacetylene is probably the most common, especially for joining ferrous and nonferrous metals in production or maintenance work. Silver brazing, sometimes referred to as hard soldering, is particularly adaptable for joining dissimilar metals by this process.

Furnace brazing is used extensively for mass production of relatively small assemblies. The brazing material is applied near or at the joint and the assembly moved into a furnace having heating and cooling chambers with automatic temperature controls.

Induction brazing is used in many indus-

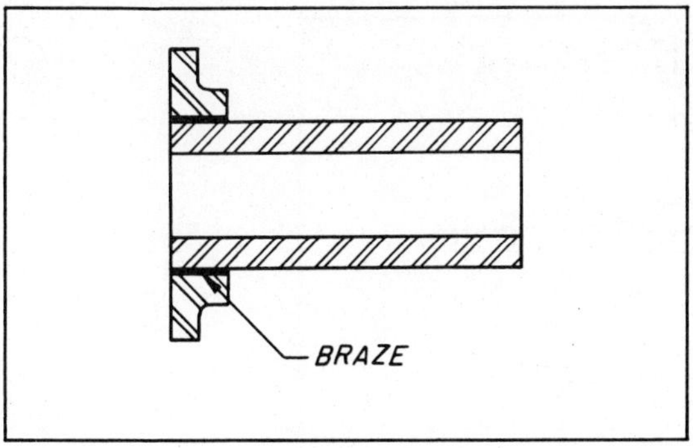

Figure 11-49
Brazed joints in a drawing may be designated by a solid line with an accompanying note. General Motors Corp.

tries instead of furnace brazing because of the small amount of space required and the added feature of having the work visible at all times. The parts to be brazed are brought near a coil carrying an electric current.

Resistance brazing is adaptable for joining small parts usually of dissimilar metals. The parts in this case are assembled between electrodes and current flowing from the electrodes provides the heat to effect the brazing operation.

Dip brazing is frequently used by refrigeration and other industries where parts to be joined can be assembled and jigged. The assembled pieces with the pre-placed filler metal are dipped into a hot chemical bath which provides the heat to braze the joint properly. Another dipping process consists of dipping the parts in a bath of molten brazing alloy. This method is limited to joining small parts such as ends of wire.

11.33 Designating brazed joints on a drawing

Brazed joints may be shown graphically on a drawing by a heavy black line with a note, as illustrated in Fig. 11-49. Standard symbols shown in Fig. 11-50 may also be used to identify such joints.

11.34 Soft soldering

Soft soldering is a process of joining metals in which bonding is achieved by means of a metal that melts at temperatures below the melting point of the base metal and in all instances is less than 800° F. Soldering is used in assemblies where parts are not subjected to any severe stress, where strength of the joint is not critical, but where liquid tightness is necessary.

The principal solders consist of tin and lead except for joining aluminum which requires a solder made of tin and zinc. A special flux is needed in soldering to dissolve any presence of oxides and to better facilitate the flow of the solder. Fluxes are either of the acid or noncorrosive type. Zinc chloride is the most common acid flux and rosin the chief ingredient of the noncorrosive flux.

The soldering operation is conducted with a hand soldering copper which is either heated electrically or in a special gas furnace. For rapid work, the joint is often heated by an open flame from a blow torch or welding torch and the solder applied to the heated surface. Induction heating and resistance heating are also used. Dipping of assembled parts in a bath of molten solder is frequently employed for joining small parts. The wiping process is basically a means of joining and sealing sections of lead pipe with brass, bronze and copper fittings. The solder while in a plastic state is poured slowly over the joint, which supplies the required heat to the base metal. A cloth is held under the joint and used to work the solder into the joint and to wipe off any excess.

11.35 Designating soldered joints on a drawing

Soldered joints on a drawing are shown graphically by a heavy black line with the accompanying word *solder,* as shown in Fig. 11-51.

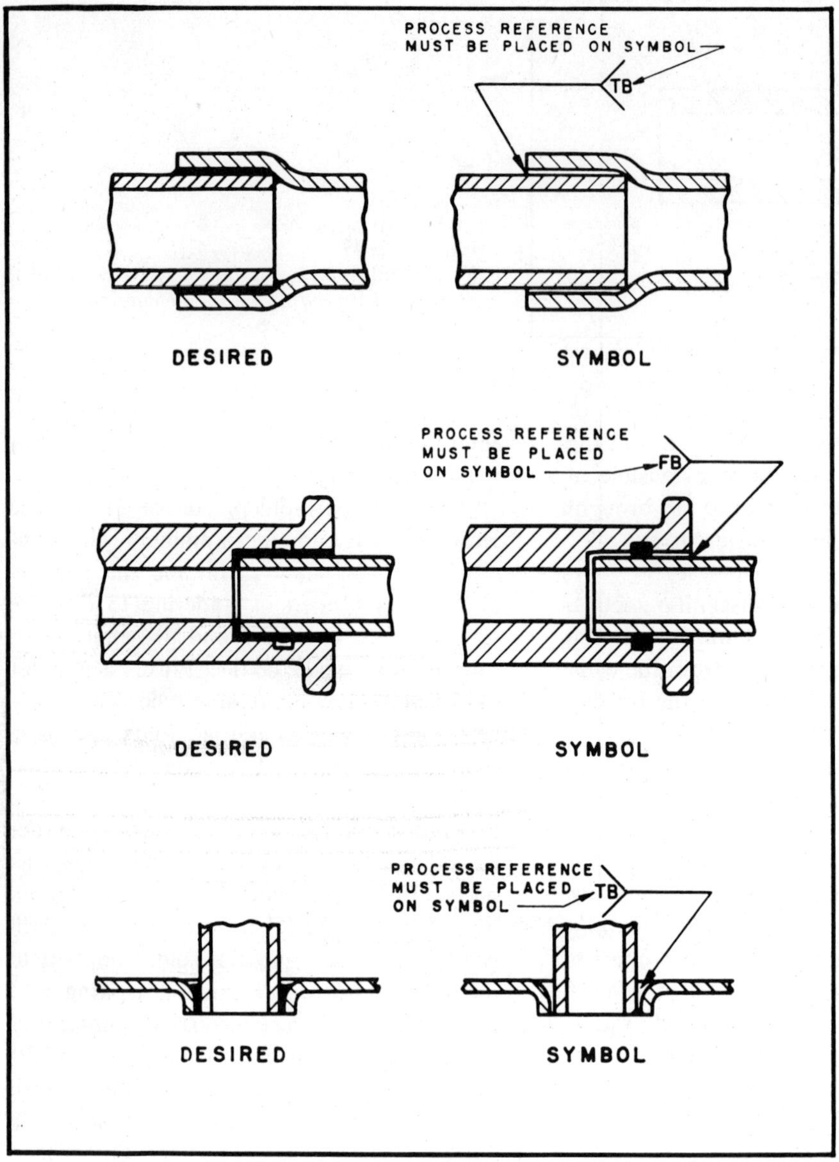

Figure 11-50
Brazed joints in a drawing may also be designated by means of standard brazing symbols. American Welding Society

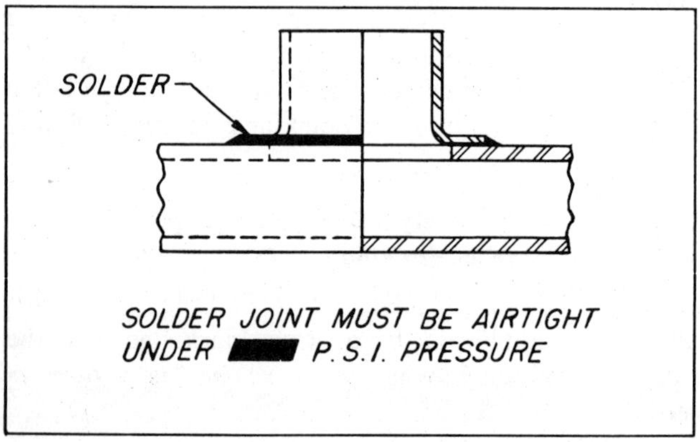

Figure 11-51
Soldered joints are shown on a drawing by means of a heavy black line and with a note. General Motors Corp.

Problems, section 11

1 Make the necessary views of the Anchor Collar shown in the sketch of Fig. 11-52. Weld all joints using fillet welds. Material: SAE 1020 Steel. Show all dimensions.

2 Make a 2-view drawing of the Angle Bracket in the sketch of Fig. 11-53. Material: Steel plate. Choose appropriate welded joints. Dimension completely.

3 Make a 2-view drawing of the Cover and Hasp assembly in the sketch of Fig. 11-54. Spot weld as needed. Show all weld symbols. Assume all sizes not given.

4 Make a dimensioned drawing of the Jig Lid shown in the sketch of Fig. 11-55. Use 1/2″ DIA cold rolled steel shafting for hinge and 1/4″ mild steel for lid. Choose proper welded joints.

5 Make a dimensioned drawing of the welded Machine Base as sketched in Fig. 11-56. Provide tabs for anchoring base with 3/4″ DIA bolts. Show symbols for all welds.

6 Make a welded assembly joining the two Latch Pins together as shown in the sketch of Fig. 11-57.

7 Design a Caster Wheel Bracket as in the sketch of Fig. 11-58. Show all dimensions and weld symbols. Choose appropriate weld joints. Material: SAE 1020 steel.

8 Make a 2-view weldment drawing of an Eccentric shown in the sketch of Fig. 11-59. Material: C.R. steel shafting and mild steel plate.

9 Make a welded assembly drawing of the Lever Arm in the sketch of Fig. 11-60. Use steel tubing having a 1/8″ wall, and mild steel plate. Choose welds.

10 Design a wheel to be fabricated by welding from steel shafting and H.R. steel bar stock having the following specifications:

Hub: 2″ DIA x 3″ long
Bore: 3/4″ DIA with standard keyway for square key
Spokes: 3/8″ x 1-1/2″ flat bar stock, 6 required
Rim: 3/8″ x 2″ flat bar stock

11 Redesign the forged steel Link in the sketch of Fig. 11-61 for welded fabrication. Use H.R. steel bar and steel shafting.

12 Make a dimensioned weldment drawing of the Brace shown in the sketch of Fig. 11-62.

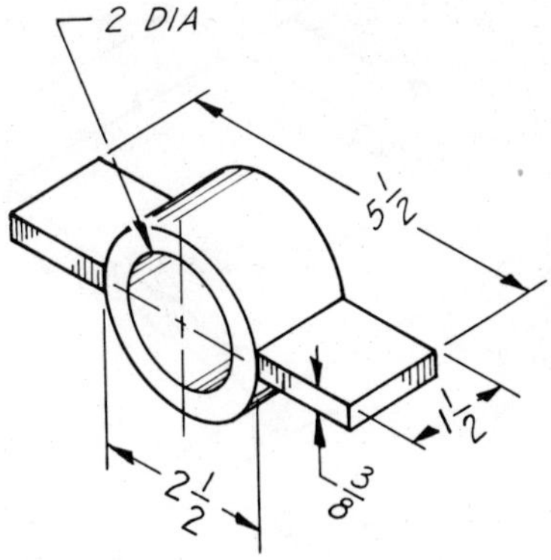

Figure 11-52
Anchor collar.

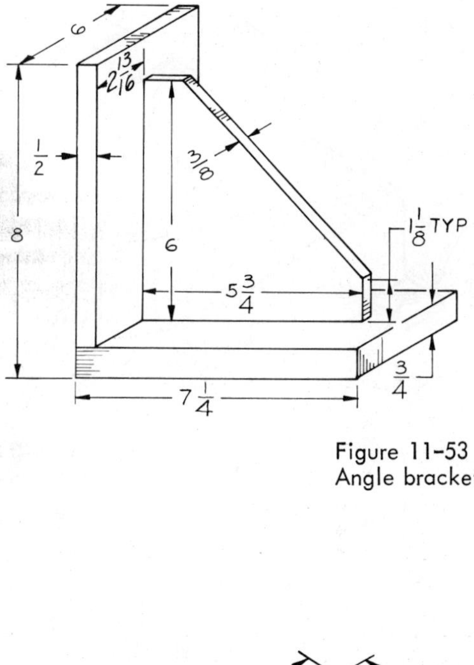

Figure 11-53
Angle bracket.

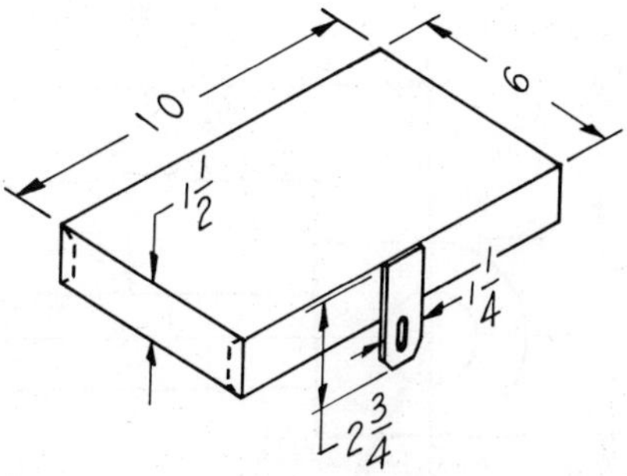

Figure 11-54
Cover and hasp.

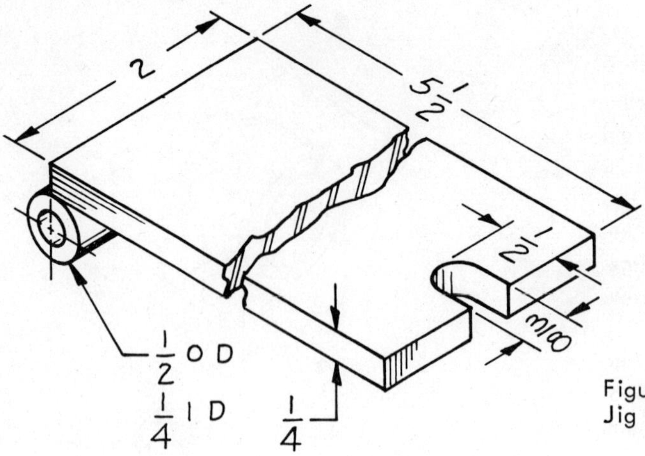

Figure 11-55
Jig lid.

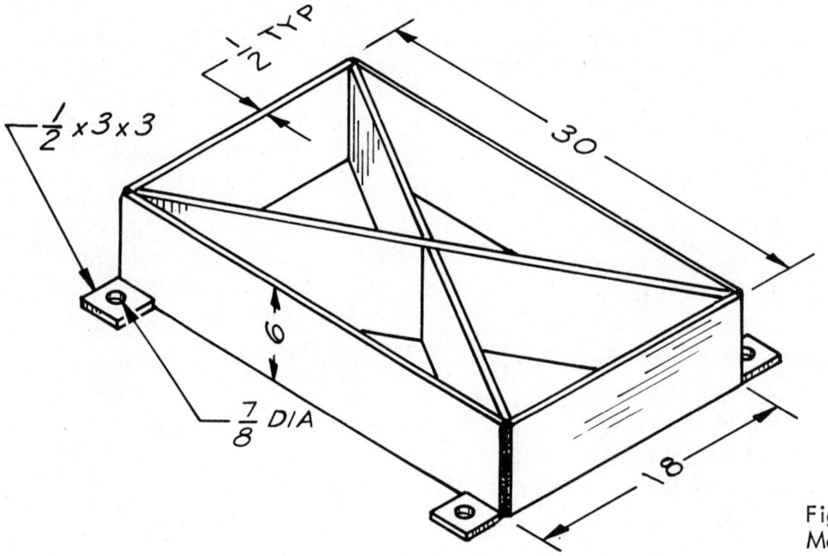

Figure 11-56
Machine base.

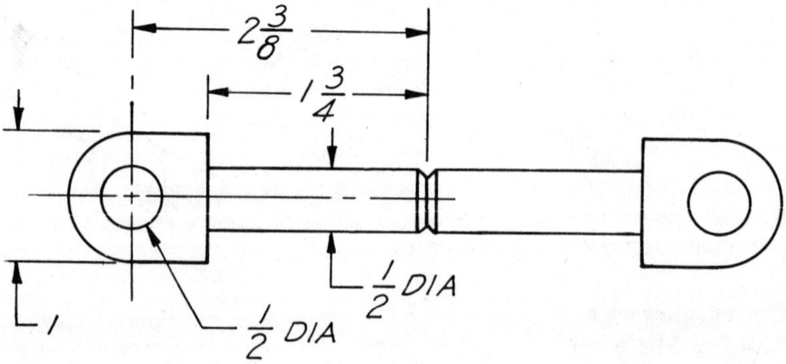

Figure 11-57
Latch pins.

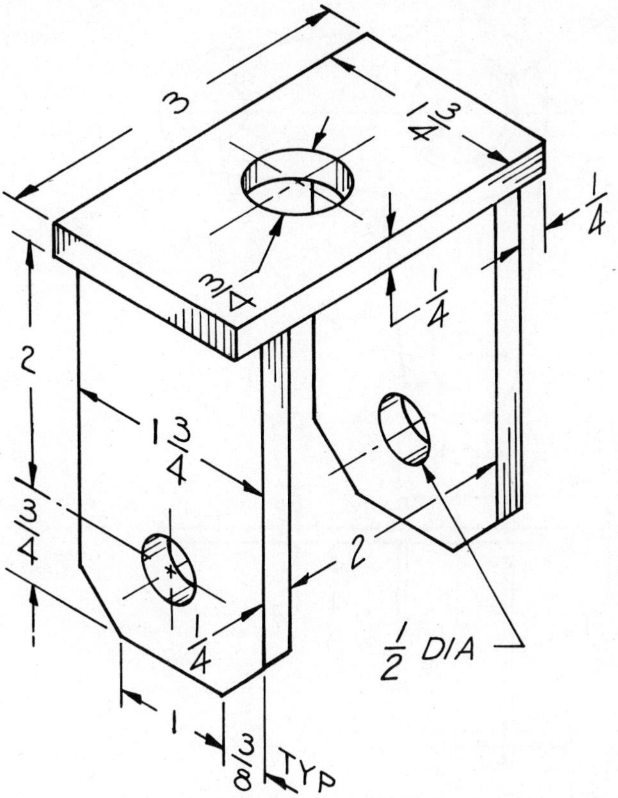

Figure 11-58
Caster wheel bracket.

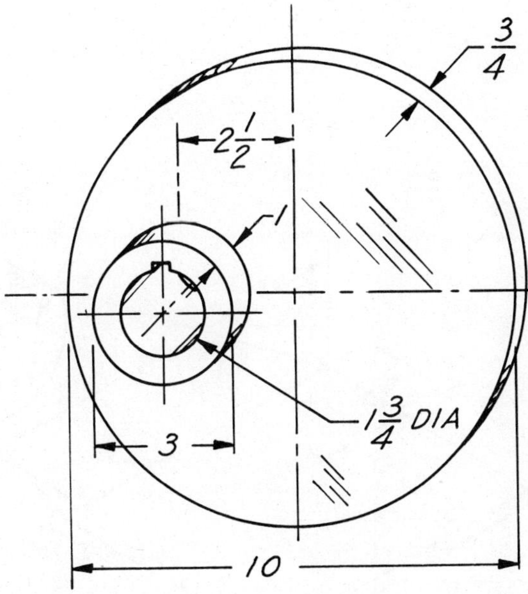

Figure 11-59
Eccentric.

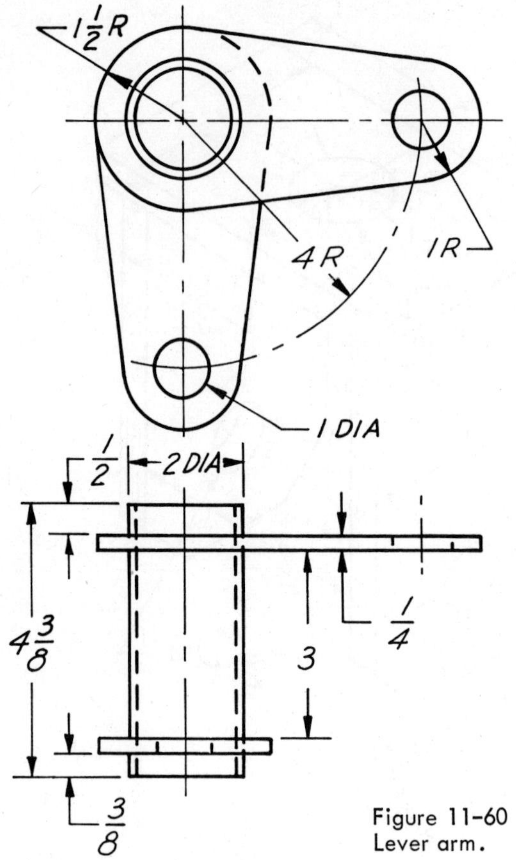

Figure 11-60
Lever arm.

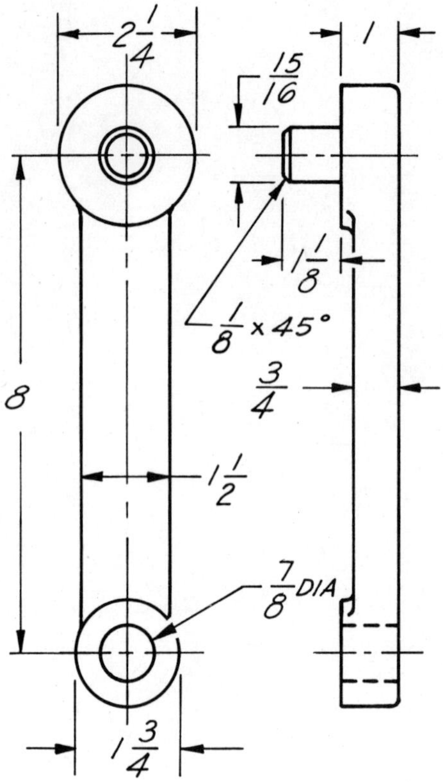

Figure 11-61
Link.

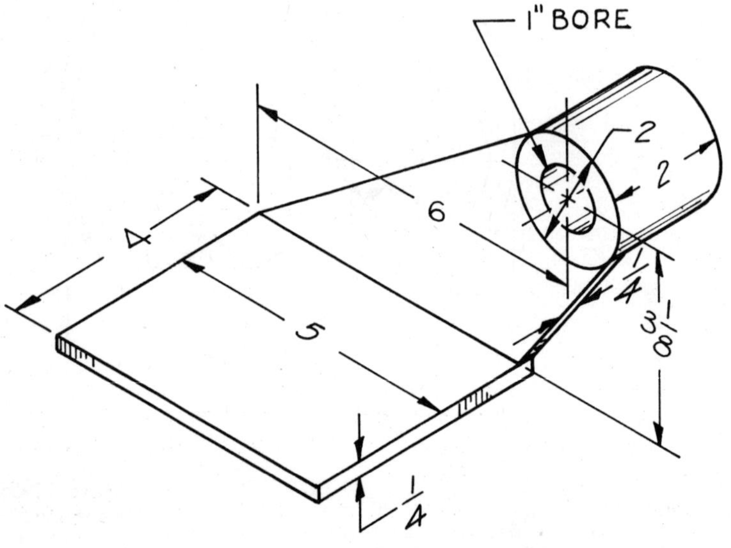

Figure 11-62
Brace.

Production drawings and operations 12

In the fabrication of any structure or mechanism, two types of drawings are required—detail and assembly. A *detail drawing* is one that contains all of the essential views and dimensions necessary to construct a component of the designed product. An *assembly drawing* shows how the various components of the product are put together. These two types of drawings are commonly referred to as *working drawings*. The essential features, specific functions, and the preparation of detail and assembly drawings are described in this section.

While preparing working drawings a draftsman must rely on considerable technical information dealing with pattern making, casting, stamping, forging, heat treating, and machining. Some of the basic elements of these industrial operations are also covered in this section.

PRODUCTION DRAWINGS

12.1 Design layout drawing

The development of a new tool, fixture, machine, device, appliance, or consumer product, or the improvement of an existing structural or mechanical unit generally starts as an idea in the mind of a designer. This idea is then placed on paper in the form of a freehand sketch. Once the basic idea sketch is completed, other sketches may be prepared and calculations made to determine further the suitability of the design.

The preliminary sketches are followed by a design layout drawing, which is accurately made and is usually full scale to produce the entire effects of part proportions and sizes. Some of the design details may be worked out but no attempt is made to include the full size description of all the intricate parts. Only a limited number of key dimensions are shown. The emphasis is placed primarily on how the parts go together and operate. Section and auxiliary views are used only if further clarity is necessary. Notes are included either on the layout itself or on separate sheets to stipulate general specifications such as materials, finishes, heat treatment, clearances, use of standard parts, etc.

While preparing the design layout, particular attention is given to clearances of moving parts, assembly methods, serviceability of the unit and functional value in terms of production costs. Fig. 12-1 illustrates a typical design layout drawing.

12.2 Detail drawings

When a design layout is approved, draftsmen proceed to make the necessary production drawings. The first task involves the drawing of each individual part to be produced. These drawings are called detail drawings and they furnish all of the essential shape and size descriptions and specifications required for their construction.

If the machine or product component is small and consists of only a few parts, the details of each piece are often grouped together on one large sheet. Sometimes these details are even placed with the assembly drawing. The practice in many industries is to draw each detail on a separate sheet.

Industries involved in large quantity production usually follow the multiple system of detail drawing; that is, separate drawings are prepared to cover each specific manufacturing process. Thus there may be a pattern drawing, a forging drawing, a machine drawing, a welding drawing and a stamping drawing. Each drawing will contain only

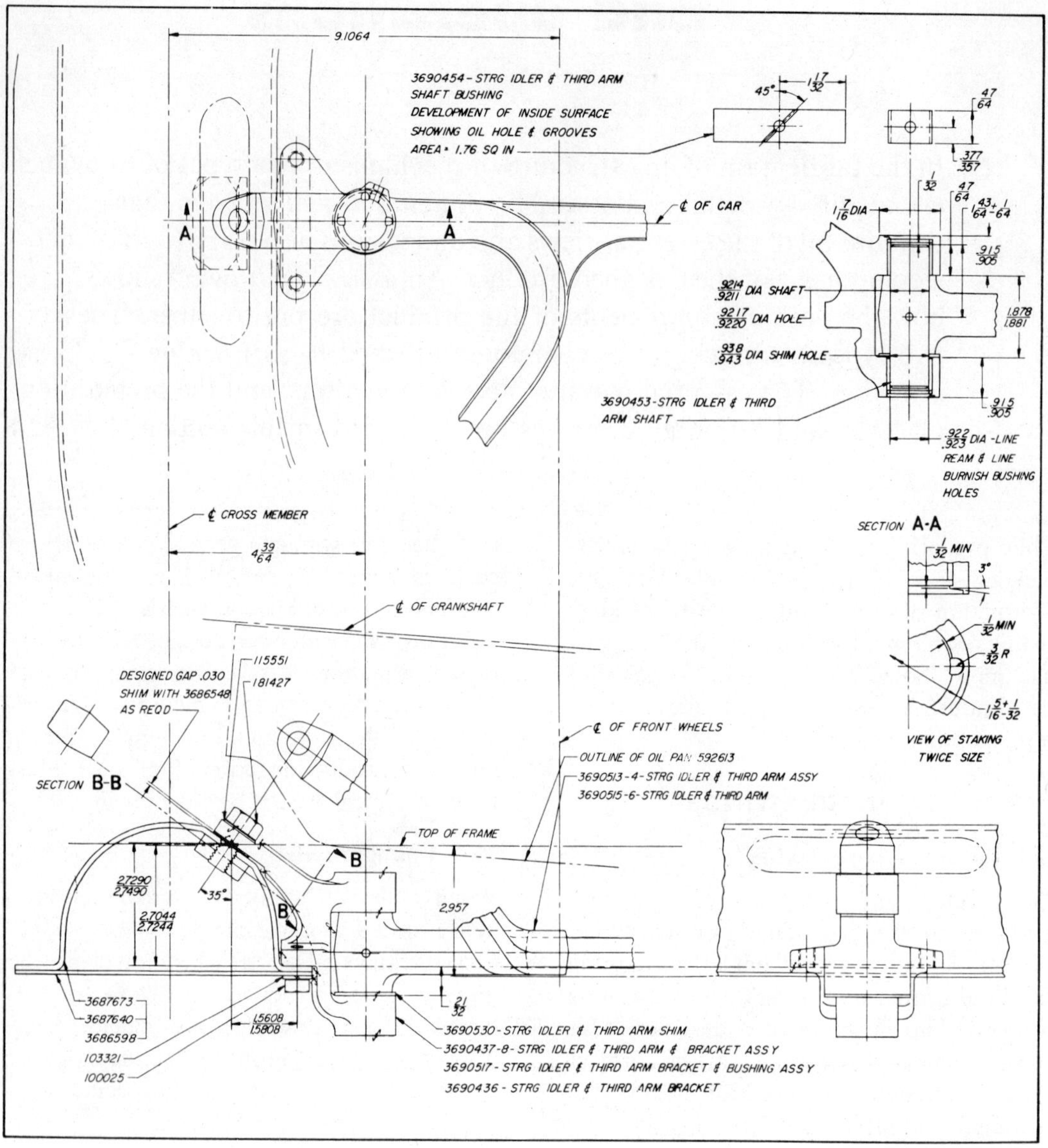

Figure 12-1
A design layout drawing presents the basic concept of a new part or machine. From this layout essential production drawings are prepared.
General Motors Corp.

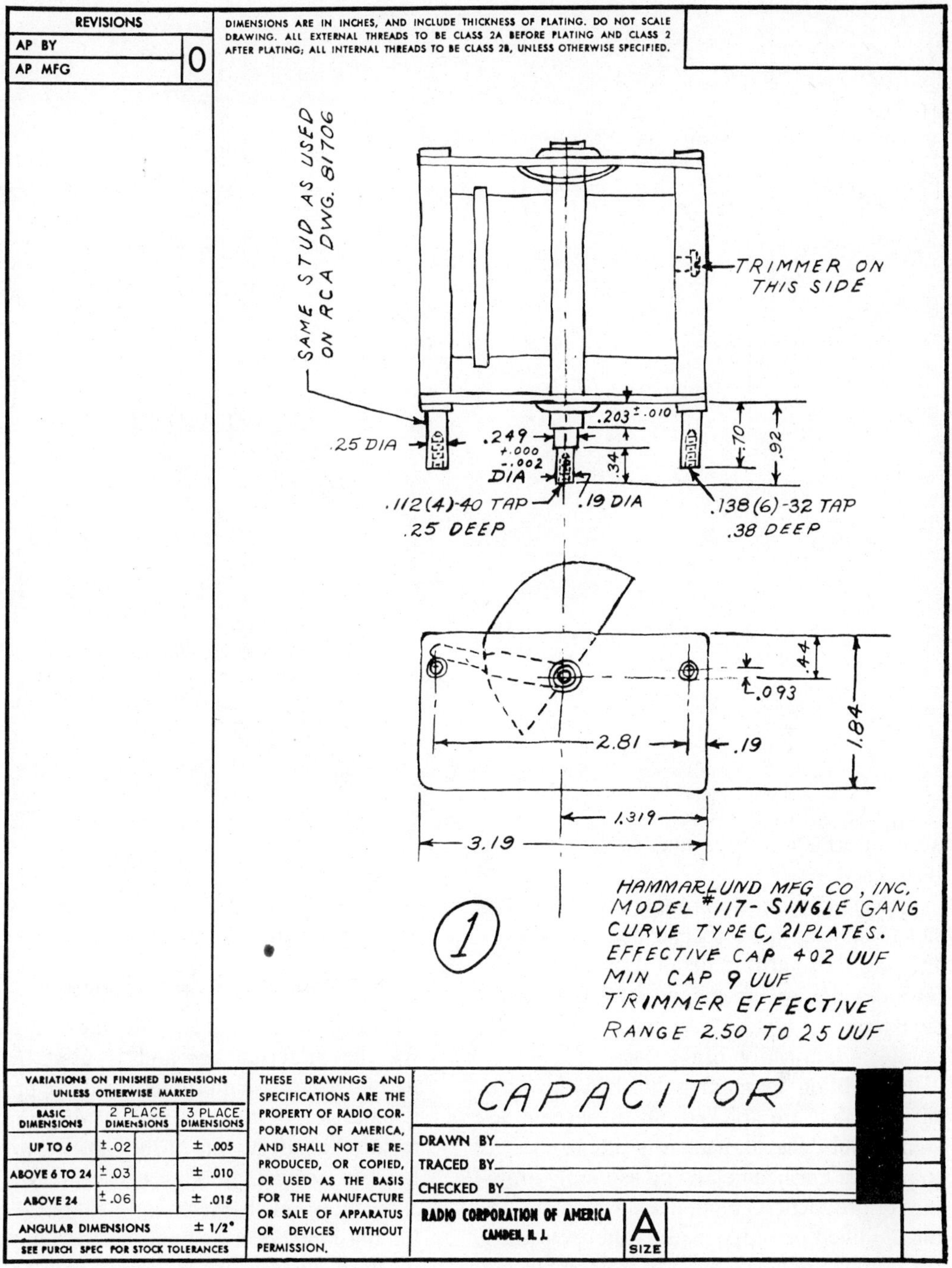

Figure 12-2
A draftsman often prepares finished drawings from rough freehand sketches.
Radio Corp. of America

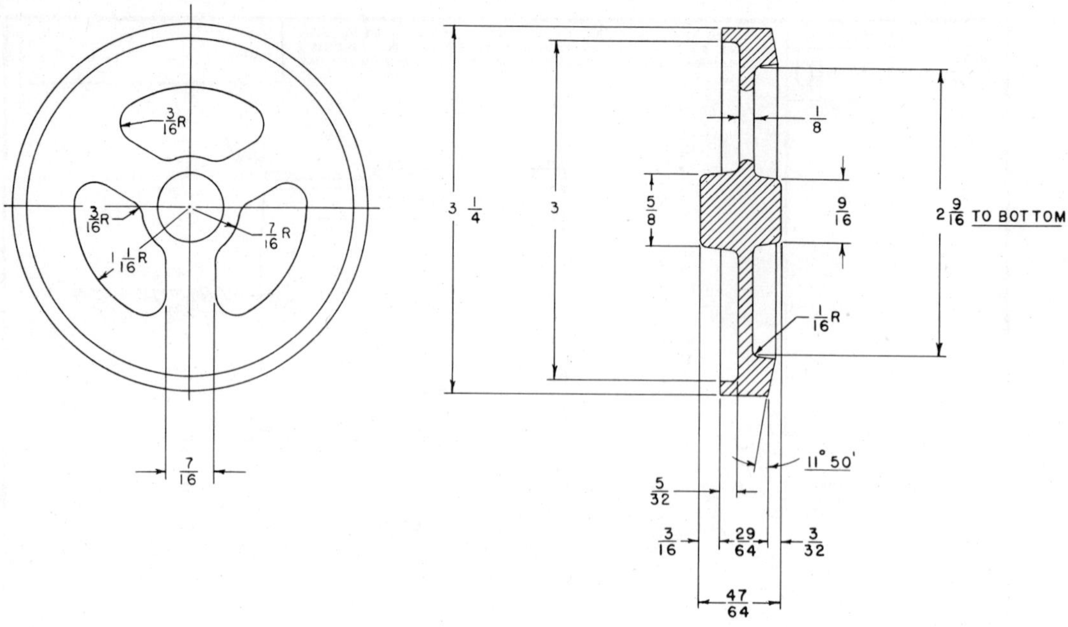

Figure 12-3
A pattern drawing is a special detail drawing used by the patternmaker in constructing the pattern required for producing a casting. Millers Falls Co.

such information as is needed by the shop concerned.

For small quantity production where it is not feasible to have special detail drawings, the single all-purpose detail drawing is used. This drawing will include all of the information required by the various shops for the complete fabrication of the part.

In addition to making finished drawings of parts that are "picked-off" from new design layouts, the draftsman is often required to prepare finished detail and assembly drawings of production components which are being modified or redesigned. Quite frequently the draftsman works directly from corrected prints or freehand sketches as shown in Fig. 12-2.

A detail drawing may show one or more views, depending on the shape description of the part. Section and auxiliary views are included if needed. The important consideration is to have sufficient views and enough dimensions so the workmen will understand the shape of the piece and the nature of the work involved.

12.3 Pattern shop detail drawing

The pattern shop detail drawing is intended for the patternmaker and is used by him in making the pattern required to produce a mold for casting. A pattern drawing will locate the parting line of the pattern, provide for the correct amount of shrinkage, and show how much material is to be allowed for finishing. It also stipulates the allowance for draft, the size of core prints, and the radii of fillets and rounds. See Fig. 12-3 and Sub-section 12.17.

On some pattern drawings the various allowances are often omitted, in which case the patternmaker determines the necessary calculations. In other instances, the engineering department makes the calculations and includes them on the drawing.

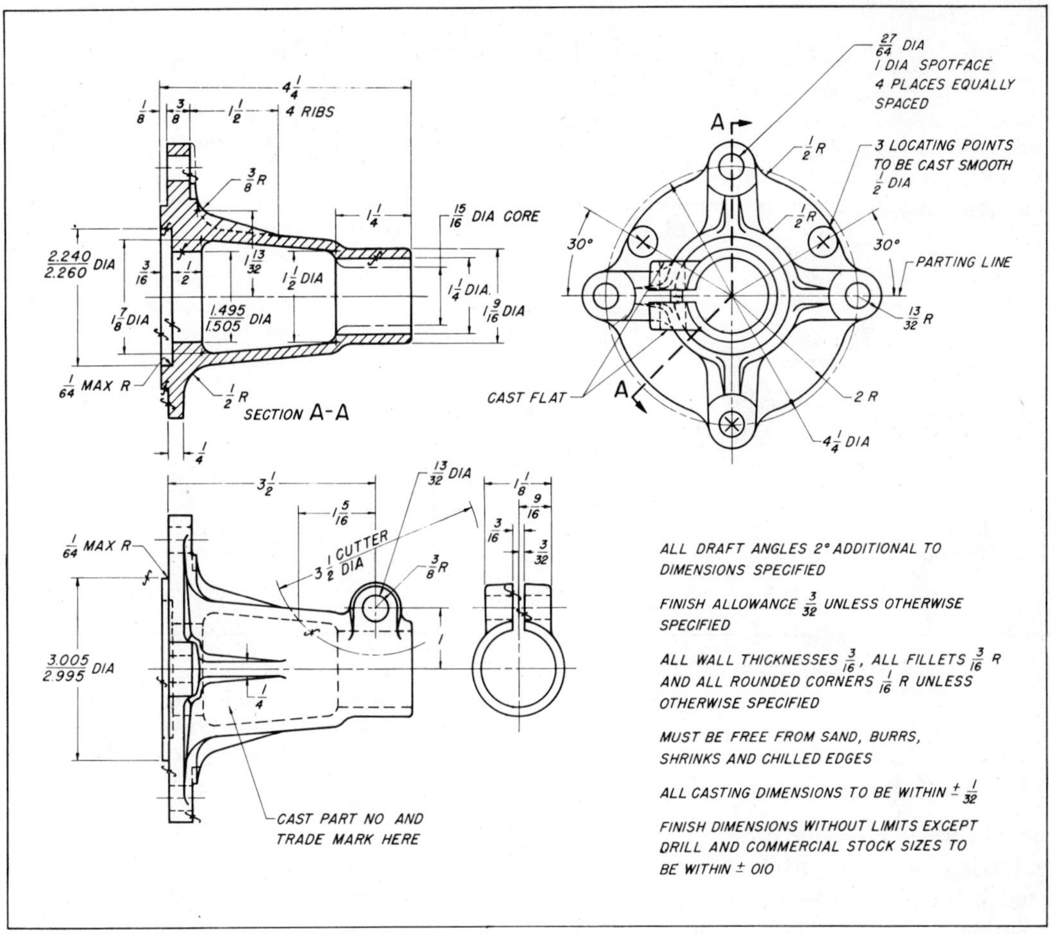

Figure 12-4
An example of a single casting and machining drawing showing all required information. General Motors Corp.

12.4 Casting drawings

A casting drawing shows the details of a casting. (See Sub-section 12.19) Two practices are followed in the preparation of casting drawings. In one method a composite is made showing the rough and finished machine part. See Fig. 12-4. The other method calls for separate drawings of the rough and finished casting. Both drawings are often included on a single sheet with a vertical line between them and the rough picture located to the left of the finished part.

A casting drawing should give complete information, including sectional and auxiliary views if necessary. On rough castings, dimensions should run to mold points of intersecting surfaces. Specifically a casting drawing should indicate:

- Allowances for machining
- Surface finish
- Draft angles
- Parting line
- Edge and corner radii
- Fillet radii
- Heat treating if required
- Essential notes

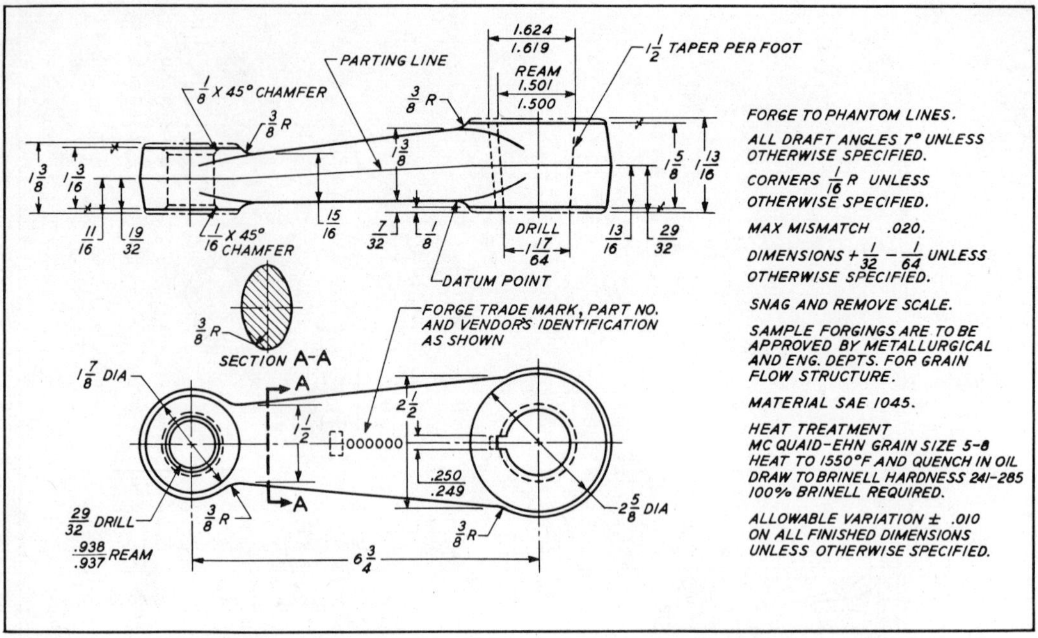

Figure 12-5
A typical single rough forging and machining drawing with the forging outline indicated by phantom lines over the finished part.
General Motors Corp.

12.5 Detail forging drawing

The function of a forging drawing is to show the forging operations involved in producing a rough forging. Two systems are used in preparing forging drawings. If the piece is not too complicated, the forging outline is shown in phantom lines over the finished part. See Fig. 12-5. When the part is so complicated that the outline of the rough forging cannot be clearly seen if placed on the finished drawing, a separate rough forging drawing is made. It is often the practice to place both the rough forging drawing and the machining drawing on one sheet with the forging drawing to the left. See Fig. 12-6.

A rough forging drawing should always show some surface of the finished part by phantom lines with a dimension that locates it to the forged surface. If both rough forging and machining drawings are included on one sheet the notations "Forging Drawing" and "Machining Drawing" are placed directly under their corresponding views. When separate sheets are used the notation "See Forging Drawing" is placed on the machining drawing and "See Machining Drawing" on the forging drawing.

In general, the following drafting conventions are observed in preparing forging drawings:[1]

1 Forging drawings should be located so the forging plane, in the main side view, is parallel to the bottom edge of the part.

2 The parting line must be shown and noted. On exterior views the parting line is shown as a solid line. On sectional views it is shown in phantom.

3 The forging plane must be defined when not parallel to the parting line.

4 Section views to aid visualization of the part should be used freely.

5 The desired grain direction must be indicated on all forging drawings. Direction arrows should be placed alongside the plan or top view.

6 Arcs showing a corner of a boss or curved flange of constant height should be

1. *Douglas Drafting Manual* (Santa Monica, Calif.: Douglas Aircraft Co.).

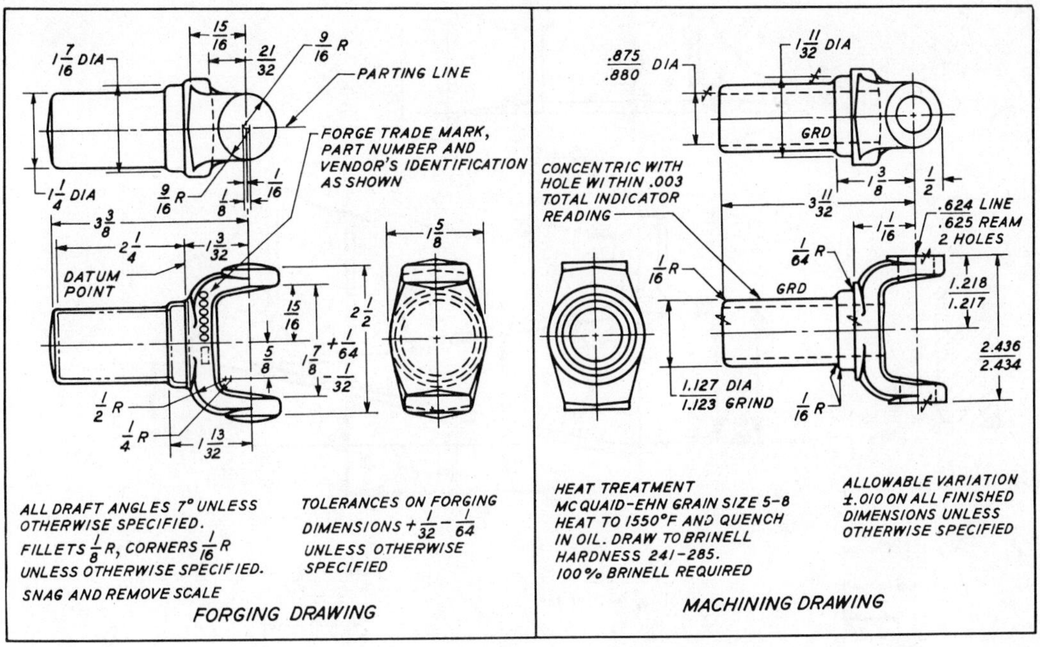

Figure 12-6
A rough forging drawing placed on the same sheet with a machining drawing. General Motors Corp.

drawn concentric to indicate constant draft angle on the sides of the boss or flange. See *A,* Fig. 12-7.

7 The forging blank must be dimensioned so that it can readily be checked with the machining drawing, to insure sufficient material.

8 In general, dimensions are given at the deepest points of the forging die; depths are dimensioned from the parting line. See *B,* Fig. 12-7.

9 Forgings should always be dimensioned to the intersection of the main heel lines except on full radius ribs where dimensions may be to either the center of rib or to the heel line. See *C,* Fig. 12-7.

10 Ribs intersecting at acute angles are dimensioned as in *D,* Fig. 12-7.

12.6 Machine detail drawing

The function of a machine detail drawing is to provide those dimensions, shape descriptions and specifications involved in machining a casting or forging. The machine work may consist of drilling, reaming, broaching or countersinking. Surfaces may have to be machined on a planer, shaper, milling machine, lathe or grinder. Finish symbols are included to designate the kind of surface finish required. Tolerances are shown as well as type of heat treatment necessary.

12.7 Stamping drawing

Stampings are products obtained by shaping sheet metal between members of a die that are under a pressure movement. Just as in other forms of detail drawings, a stamping drawing must accurately show how the part is to be fabricated. Some of the basic considerations involved in stamping design and stamping drawings are discussed in Sub-section 12.23. Fig. 12-8 illustrates a typical stamping drawing.

12.8 Welding drawing

A welding drawing is one that includes the essential information needed to construct a part when welding operations are involved. Welding information is designated on a drawing by symbols and notes as described

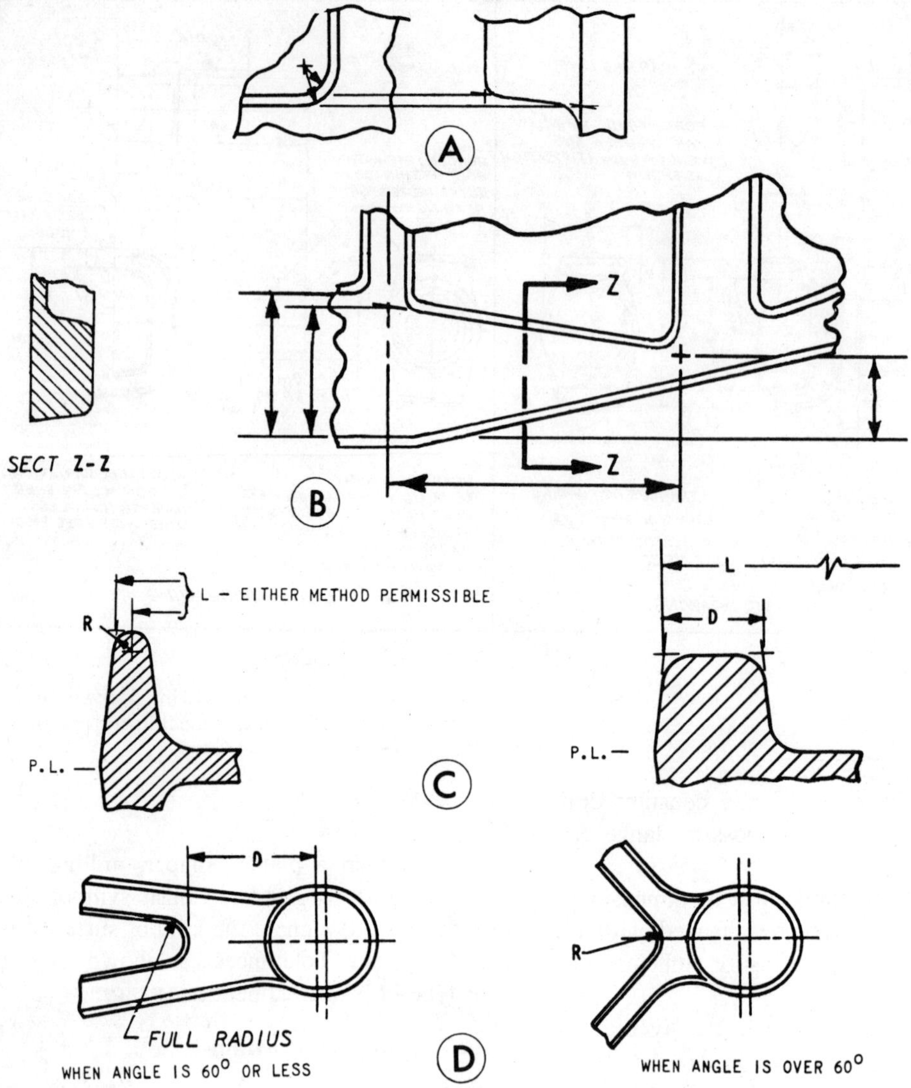

Figure 12-7
These drafting conventions are applicable to forging drawings.

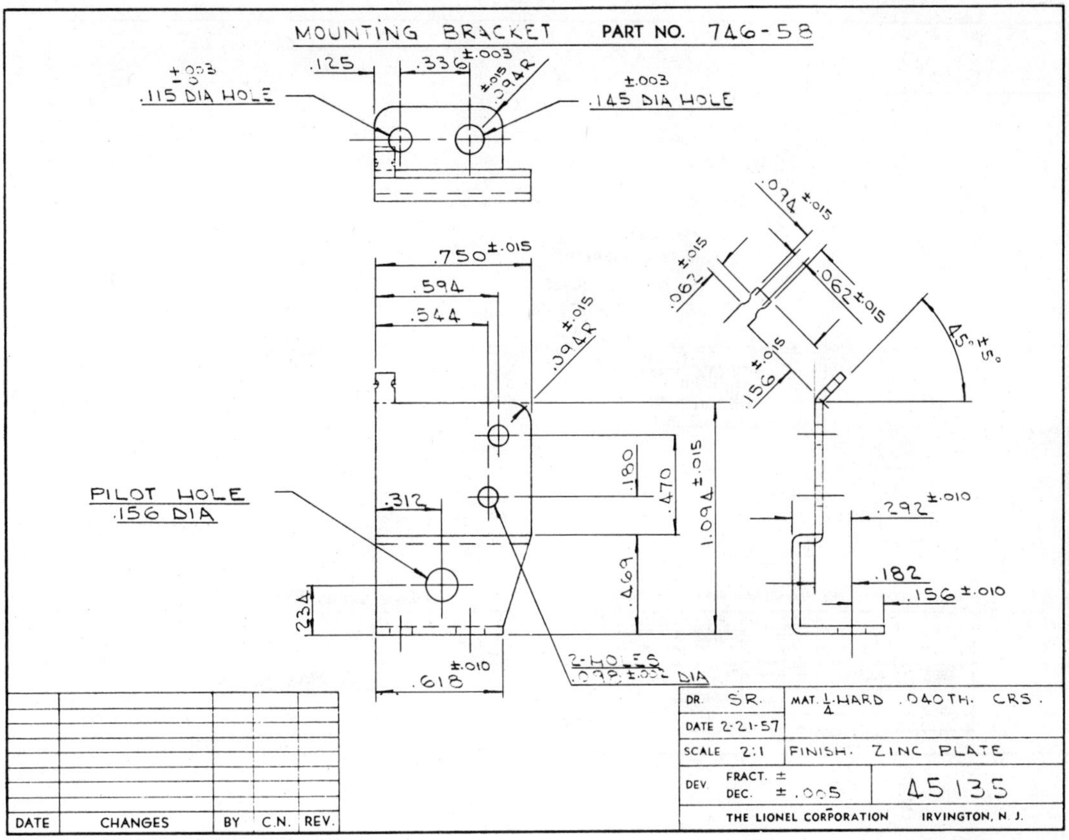

Figure 12-8
A stamping drawing. The Lionel Corp.

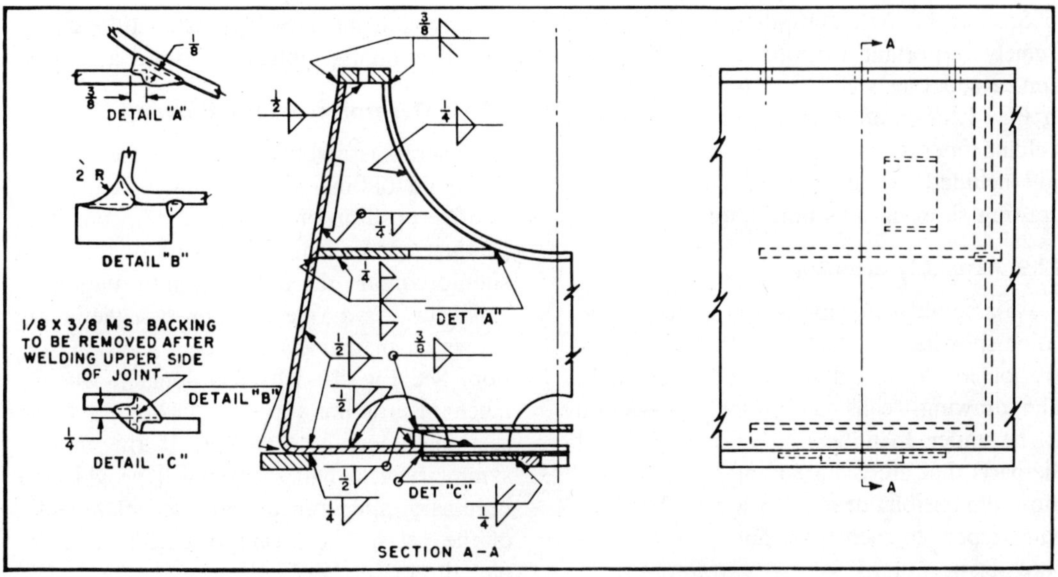

Figure 12-9
A typical welding drawing showing how various welding symbols are used.
American Welding Society

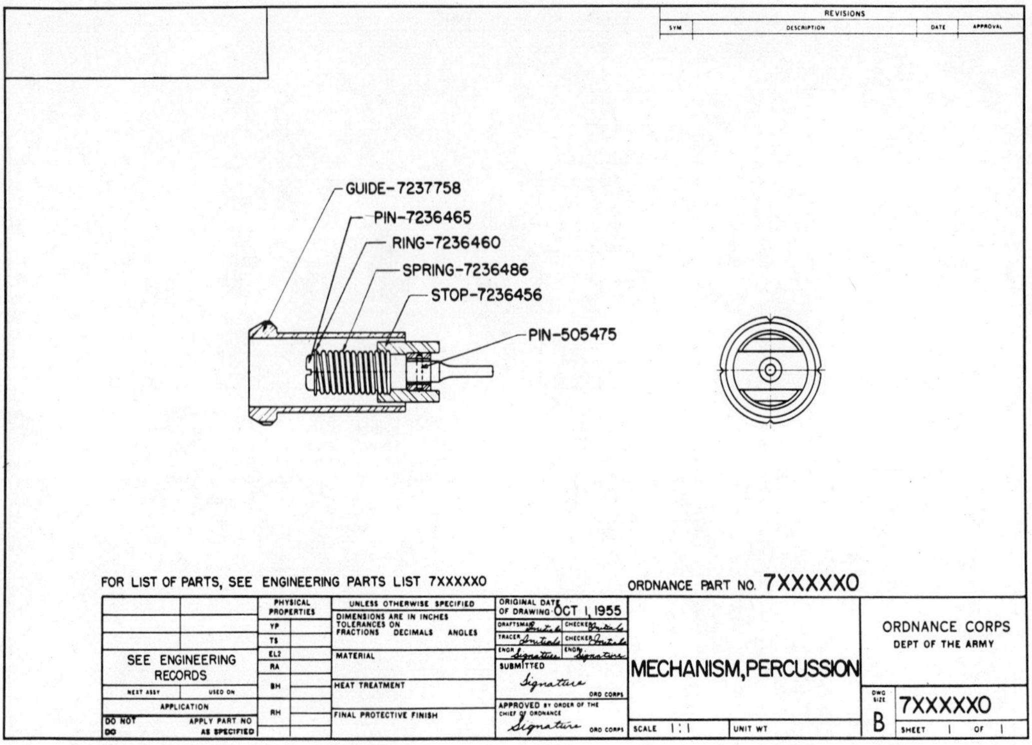

Figure 12–10
A general assembly drawing includes the outline of only the principal parts of a product. US Army Ordnance Corps

in Section 11. When welding plays an extremely important function in the fabrication, a separate welding drawing as shown in Fig. 12-9 is often prepared. For limited welding operations, the information is usually included on the single all-purpose detail drawing showing all information.

12.9 Assembly drawing

An assembly drawing is a graphic presentation showing how two or more detail parts are joined to form a sub or complete unit. The drawing "calls out" (see Sub-section 12.10 under Identification of parts) all of the parts that are required and includes only those dimensions needed to locate the parts with respect to each other and overall reference sizes.

There are several kinds of assembly drawings with each one serving a particular function. The principal types are: general assembly, detail assembly, installation assembly, diagram assembly, and display assembly.

12.10 General assembly drawing

A general assembly drawing presents only the main outline, primary movements, and relative position of all parts of a product or product component. A drawing of this kind should contain the following information:

Views. As a rule, one or two views are shown; a main view and/or a view in section. See Fig. 12-10. Occasionally, when a mechanism is not very complicated, a single sectional view is sufficient. If the unit is symmetrical, a half section will provide the necessary appearance and the relationship of the parts. The assembly usually is completed on one sheet.

Dimensions. Only principal dimensions such as overall height, width, length, essential center distances, and working height

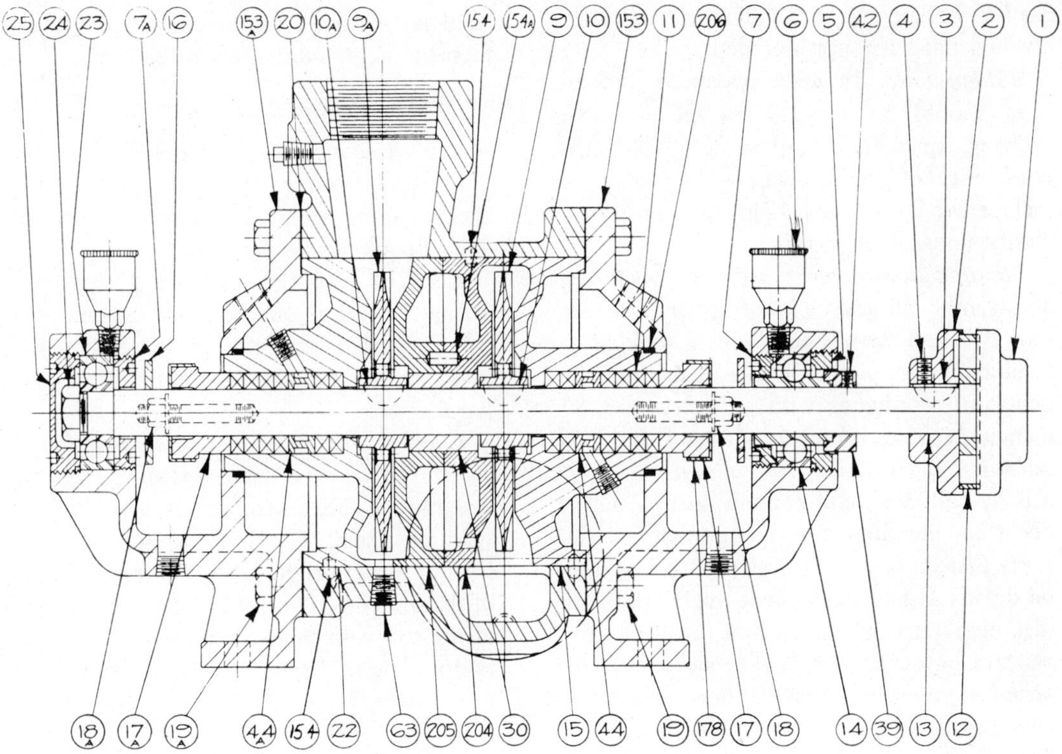

No.	Part	No.	Part	No.	Part
1	Coupling Motor Half	14	Ball Bearing	30	Spacer Bushing
2	Coupling Pump Half	15	Cover (Left)	34	Pipe Plug
3	Coupling Key	16	Water Slinger	39	Lock Collar
4	Setscrew	17	Gland	42	Lock Collar Setscrew
5	Adjusting Nut	18	Stud, Nut, & Washer	44	Lantern Rings
6	Grease Cup	19	Capscrews	63	Pipe Plug
7	Adjusting Nut	20	Gasket	153	Bearing Bracket
8	Shell	22	Cover (Right)	204	Spacer Half (Right)
9	Impeller	23	Ball Bearing	205	Spacer Half (Left)
10	Impeller Key	24	Jam Nut	206	Seal Ring
11	Packing	25	Adjusting Nut		
12	Coupling Insert	154	Lock Pin		
13	Shaft	29	Setscrews		

Figure 12-11
All parts of an assembly must be properly identified. Cutler-Hammer, Inc.

need to be shown. Detail dimensions of individual parts are not included.

Hidden lines. In most instances, hidden lines should be avoided on an assembly drawing, since they tend to complicate the readability of the drawing. They may be included only if they help to identify or clarify unusual details.

Identification of parts. All components of an assembly should be identified by a leader line with an arrowhead which touches a prominent part of the outline of the component and terminates with a circle. A 3/8″ diameter circle is generally used for this purpose. Each circle or *balloon,* as it is usually called, should contain an item number that identifies the component in the *Parts List* or *List of Materials.* Leaders may be drawn at any convenient angle from the identified part but must not obstruct any views or notes. They should be systematically arranged either in vertical or horizontal rows and not scattered all over the sheet. See Fig. 12-11.

While most industries use balloon *call-outs* on assembly drawings, it is also common practice to *call out* each part name and number with just a leader, thus avoiding a listing of the parts and supplies on the face of the drawing. In such cases, typewritten Parts Lists are executed and furnished with the assembly prints similar to that shown in Fig. 12-12.

To prevent leaders from becoming obscured by lines in an assembly drawing, especially on sectional views, draftsmen often resort to the use of curved line leaders to identify parts. These leaders should not blend in with the ordinary cross section line symbols.

While there are several methods of affixing numbers to the parts, two systems are commonly used. Some industries number the parts according to the size of the pieces; that is, the largest piece is labeled "1" with progressing higher numbers for smaller parts. The other practice is to number the parts according to the sequence in which they are handled by the worker in assembling the unit. Another method that is sometimes used is to list all purchased parts first and then the items fabricated in the plant.

12.11 List of materials

A *List of Materials* is a detailed list of subassemblies, parts, supplies, and process specifications required for one or more related or similar assemblies.

Lists of Materials will vary slightly in format, location on the drawing, and item columns. However, the one described here contains the typical requirements of most types.

Location and format. The List of Materials may be on the same drawing where the assembly is illustrated, or it may be on a separate sheet. The List of Materials may start at the top-right or the bottom-right side of the drawing. The column headings may be at the top with items numbered from top to bottom, or at the bottom with items numbered from bottom to top. Fig. 12-13 illustrates two formats for a List of Materials. The width of the columns and lines are usually adjusted to satisfy special requirements.

Items in the list of materials. The following information may be listed in a List of Materials for an assembly drawing:

1 Item number
2 Part name or description
3 Number of items required
4 Material specification
5 Remarks to provide additional information
6 Drawing number of drawing on which the part is detailed
7 Weight if required
8 Manufacturer (for purchased parts)
9 Drawing number

12.12 Detail assembly drawing

Simple mechanisms are often shown on one drawing which includes both the assembly arrangement as well as the entire construction details of the various parts. All dimensions, necessary views, notes, etc., are presented on this single drawing. See Fig. 12-14. This type of drawing is sometimes referred to as a *working assembly* or *detailed assembly drawing.*

ORDNANCE CORPS
ENGINEERING PARTS LIST - LIST OF PARTS

PARTS LIST NO. 8408945
SHEET 1 OF 4 SHEETS

IDENTITY
GUN, AUTOMATIC, 20 MM M39A1 (R.H. MODEL)

DRAWING NO.
F8408945

ITEM	ORDNANCE DRAWING NUMBER	PART NUMBER	NOMENCLATURE - DESCRIPTION	REQ'D PER UNIT	P.L	NOTES
1						
2	F8412332	8412332	Body, Drum Cradle	1		
3						
4	F8401744	8401744	Barrel Assy., Gun	1	X	
5						
6	C8413039	8413039	Drum & Bushing Assy.	1	X	
7						
8	D8412491	8412491	Shaft, Drum & Bushing	1		
9						
10	B8401878	8401878	Seal, Drum & Bushing	5		
11						
12	B8408578	8408578	Insert, Drum & Bushing Seal	1		
13						
14	A8408575	8408575	Retainer, Drum & Bushing Seal	1		
15						
16	B7184236	7184236	Roller, Drum	5		
17						
18	B7184237	7184237	Retainer, Drum Roller	5		
19						
20	B8412487	8412487	Plunger, Drum Shaft Latch	1		
21						
22	B8401772	8401772	Plunger, Gun Tube Latch	1		
23						
24	B8401774	8401774	Lock, Gun Tube Latch Plunger	1		
25						
26		(To secure Gun Tube Latch Plunger Lock)				
27	BFSX5	595150	Pin	2		
28						
29	A8401811	8401811	Lock, Gun Tube Latch Plunger	1		
30						
31	B8407343	8407343	Spring, Gun Tube Latch Plunger			
32			Lock Retaining	2		
33						
34	A8401812	8401812	Retainer, Gun Tube Latch Plunger			
35			Spring Lock	1		
36						
37	F8408977	8408977	Receiver Assy. (Welded & Riveted)	1	X	
38						
39	C8401758	8401758	Plate, Receiver End	1		
40						
41	F8401442	8401442	Feeder Assy. Disintegrating	1	X	

ORIGINAL DATE: Oct 1 PROCESSED BY: Detroit Arsenal

REV.	DATE	BY	REV.	DATE	BY	REV.	DATE	BY

SUBMITTED
Signature
ORD CORPS

APPROVED BY ORDER OF THE CHIEF OF ORDNANCE
Signature
ORD CORPS

Figure 12-12
Parts Lists are often prepared on a separate sheet. US Army Ordnance Corps

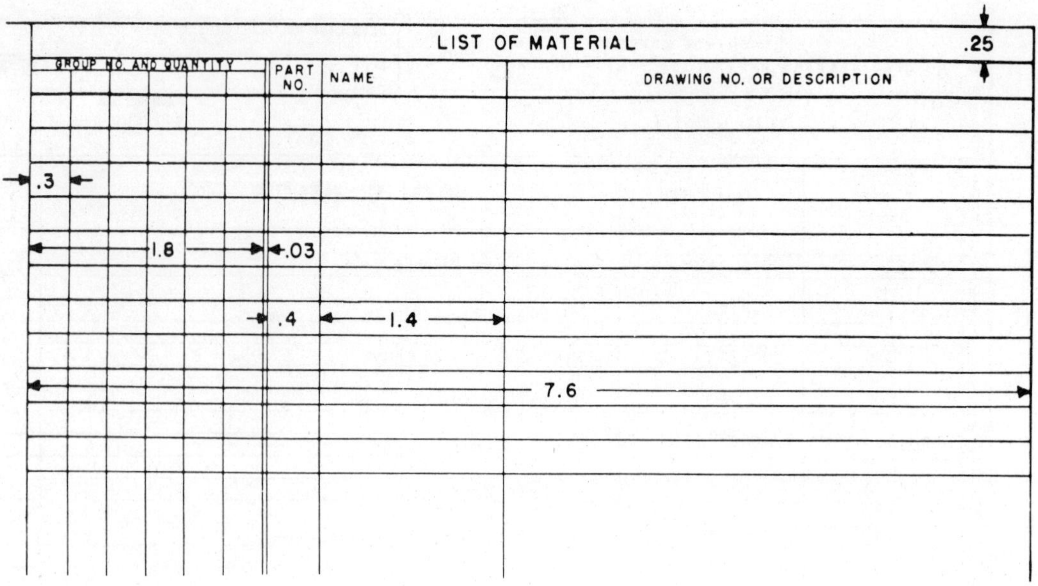

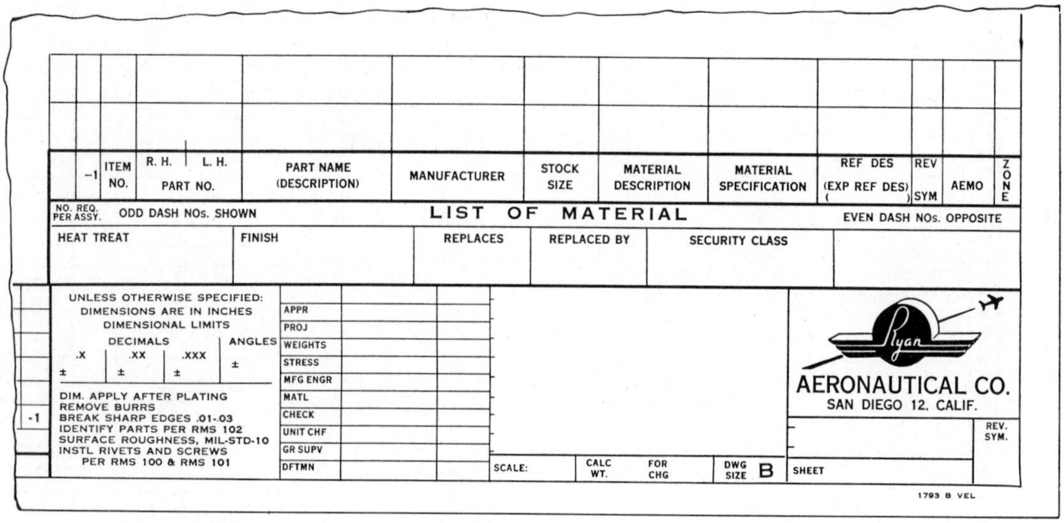

Figure 12-13
A List of Materials specifies the parts that are to be used in an assembly. ASA Y14.1-1957 and Ryan Aeronautical Co.

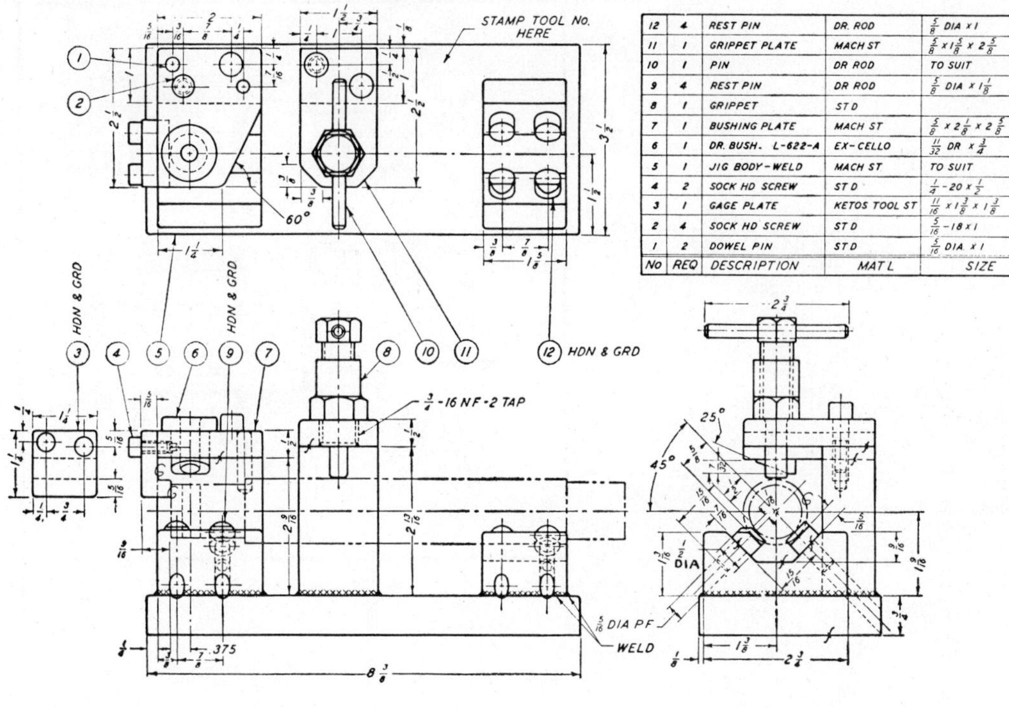

No	REQ	DESCRIPTION	MAT L	SIZE
12	4	REST PIN	DR. ROD	$\frac{5}{8}$ DIA x 1
11	1	GRIPPET PLATE	MACH ST	$\frac{5}{8} \times 1\frac{5}{8} \times 2\frac{5}{8}$
10	1	PIN	DR ROD	TO SUIT
9	4	REST PIN	DR ROD	$\frac{5}{8}$ DIA x $1\frac{1}{8}$
8	1	GRIPPET	STD	
7	1	BUSHING PLATE	MACH ST	$\frac{5}{8} \times 2\frac{1}{8} \times 2\frac{5}{8}$
6	1	DR. BUSH. L-622-A	EX-CELLO	$\frac{11}{32}$ DR x $\frac{3}{4}$
5	1	JIG BODY-WELD	MACH ST	TO SUIT
4	2	SOCK HD SCREW	STD	$\frac{1}{4}$-20 x $\frac{1}{2}$
3	1	GAGE PLATE	KETOS TOOL ST	$\frac{11}{16} \times 1\frac{3}{8} \times 1\frac{3}{8}$
2	4	SOCK HD SCREW	STD	$\frac{5}{16}$-18 x 1
1	2	DOWEL PIN	STD	$\frac{5}{16}$ DIA x 1

Figure 12-14
In a detail assembly drawing all of the construction details and assembly of parts are shown on one drawing.

12.13 Installation drawing

An outline or installation drawing is one where only the external contour of the structure is shown. Its primary function is to serve as a guide in erecting or installing an assembly. Usually only the over-all sizes are given. If the drawing is to be used for catalog or illustrative purposes, even the principal dimensions are omitted. Very often a chart is included which contains dimensional values that can be substituted for the reference letters shown on the drawing outline. See Fig. 12-15.

12.14 Diagram assembly drawing

A diagram assembly drawing is one that shows the erection or installation of equipment either in pictorial form or as a flat layout. The drawing is not made to any specific scale, and standard conventional symbols are used to represent various details. Such a drawing may illustrate, for example, the circuit of an electrical unit, a piping layout, a fuel flow system, etc. The only dimensions that are included are those which indicate distances between important points and are essential for installation. For more detailed information of this type of drawing see Section 19.

12.15 Display or exploded drawings

The display drawing is used principally for catalog or display purposes. It shows the actual shape of each part of a structure with all of the pieces placed in their proper assembly position. See Fig. 12-16. The parts are usually shaded to provide three-dimensional effects. Occasionally different colors are employed to make certain features stand out. Each piece is properly identified and descriptive notes are often added. Display

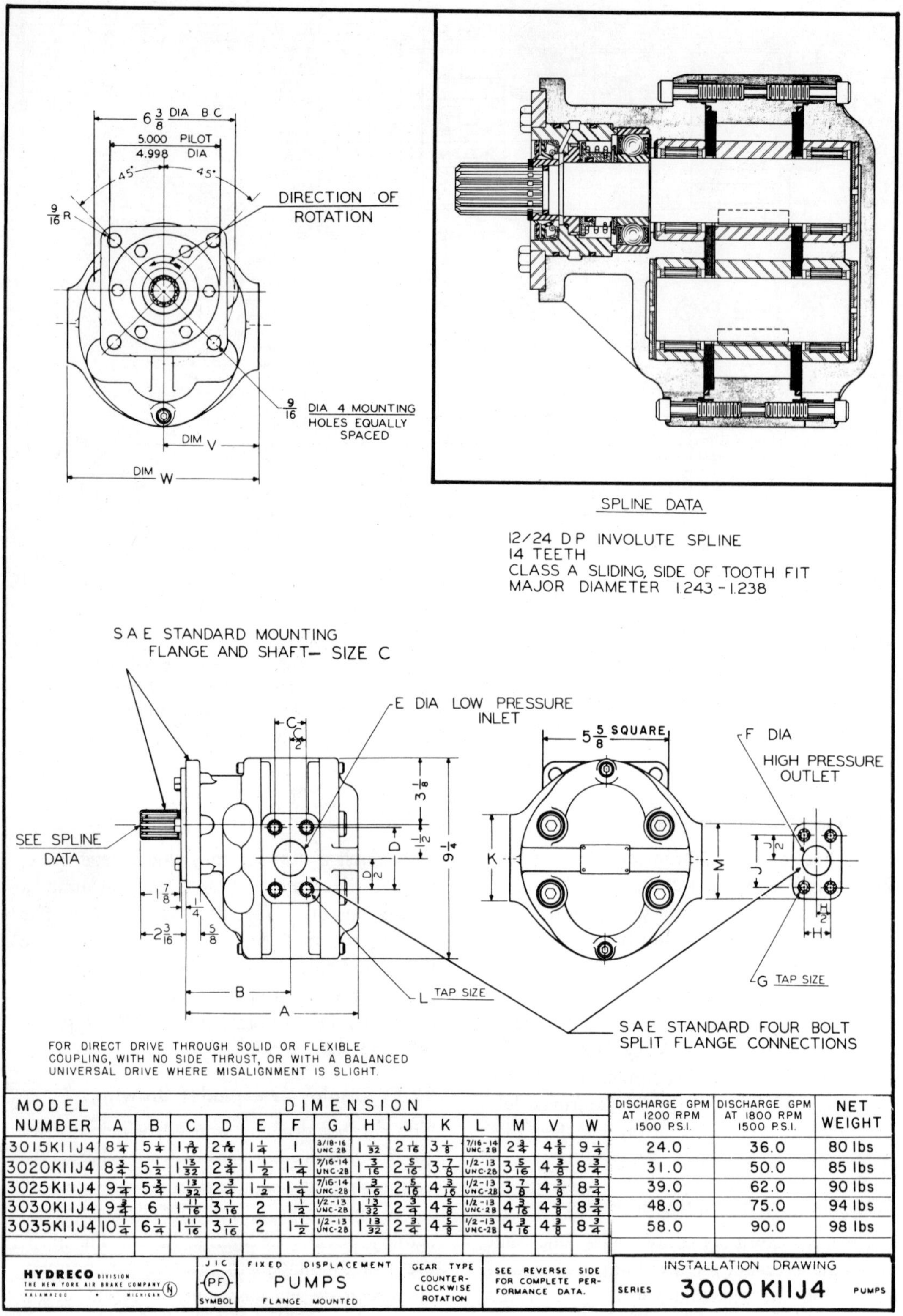

MODEL NUMBER	DIMENSION A	B	C	D	E	F	G	H	J	K	L	M	V	W	DISCHARGE GPM AT 1200 RPM 1500 P.S.I.	DISCHARGE GPM AT 1800 RPM 1500 P.S.I.	NET WEIGHT
3015K11J4	8 1/4	5 1/4	1 3/16	2 5/16	1 1/4	1	3/18-16 UNC 2B	1 1/32	2 1/16	3 1/8	7/16-14 UNC 2B	2 3/4	4 5/8	9 1/4	24.0	36.0	80 lbs
3020K11J4	8 3/4	5 1/2	1 13/32	2 3/4	1 1/2	1 1/4	7/16-14 UNC-2B	1 3/16	2 5/16	3 7/8	1/2-13 UNC-2B	3 5/16	4 3/8	8 3/4	31.0	50.0	85 lbs
3025K11J4	9 1/4	5 3/4	1 13/32	2 3/4	1 1/2	1 1/4	7/16-14 UNC-2B	1 3/16	2 5/16	4 3/16	1/2-13 UNC-2B	3 7/8	4 3/8	8 3/4	39.0	62.0	90 lbs
3030K11J4	9 3/4	6	1 11/16	3 1/16	2	1 1/2	1/2-13 UNC-2B	1 13/32	2 3/4	4 5/8	1/2-13 UNC-2B	4 3/16	4 3/8	8 3/4	48.0	75.0	94 lbs
3035K11J4	10 1/4	6 1/4	1 11/16	3 1/16	2	1 1/2	1/2-13 UNC-2B	1 13/32	2 3/4	4 5/8	1/2-13 UNC-2B	4 3/16	4 3/8	8 3/4	58.0	90.0	98 lbs

HYDRECO DIVISION THE NEW YORK AIR BRAKE COMPANY KALAMAZOO • MICHIGAN	J I C (PF) SYMBOL	FIXED DISPLACEMENT PUMPS FLANGE MOUNTED	GEAR TYPE COUNTER-CLOCKWISE ROTATION	SEE REVERSE SIDE FOR COMPLETE PERFORMANCE DATA.	INSTALLATION DRAWING SERIES 3000 K11J4 PUMPS

Figure 12-15
An installation assembly drawing is used as a guide in the installation of a mechanism. New York Air Brake Co.

BENCH DRILL-HEAD ASSEMBLY

1	Spindle stop collar	14	Spindle washer
2	Brass plug	15	Spindle
3	Headless set screw	16	Hexagon
4	Fillister head cap screw	17	Pinion
5	Driving flange	18	Taper pin
6	Spindle cone sleeve	19	Hand lever clutch
7	Spindle sleeve key	20	P & W key
8	Spindle cone bush	21	Spring
9	Spindle cone	22	Hand lever bracket
10	Spindle nut	23	Fillister head cap screw
11	Spindle sleeve	24	Hand lever
12	Head	25	Headless set screw
13	Spindle bushing	26	Hand lever shaft
		27	Straight pin

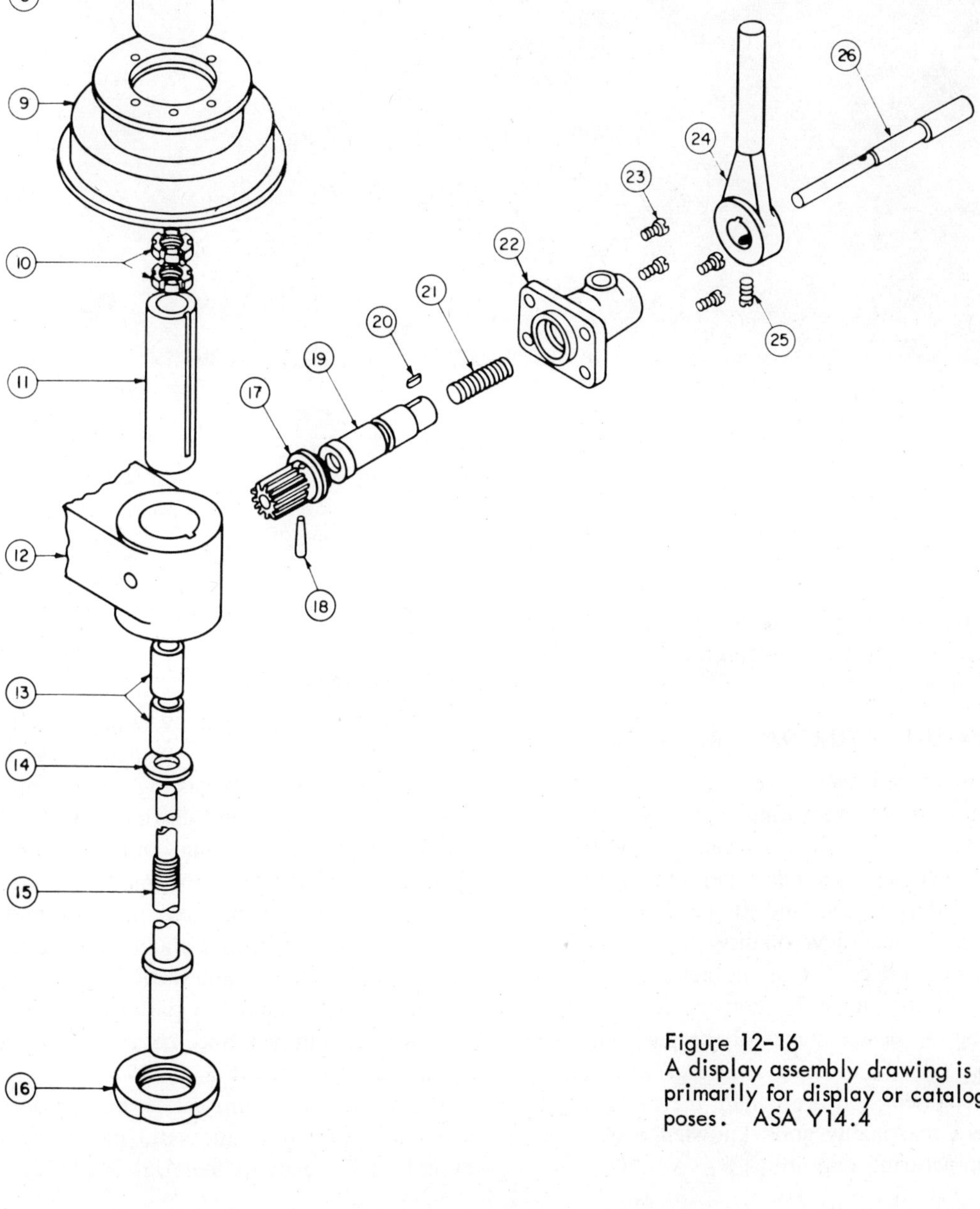

Figure 12-16
A display assembly drawing is used primarily for display or catalog purposes. ASA Y14.4

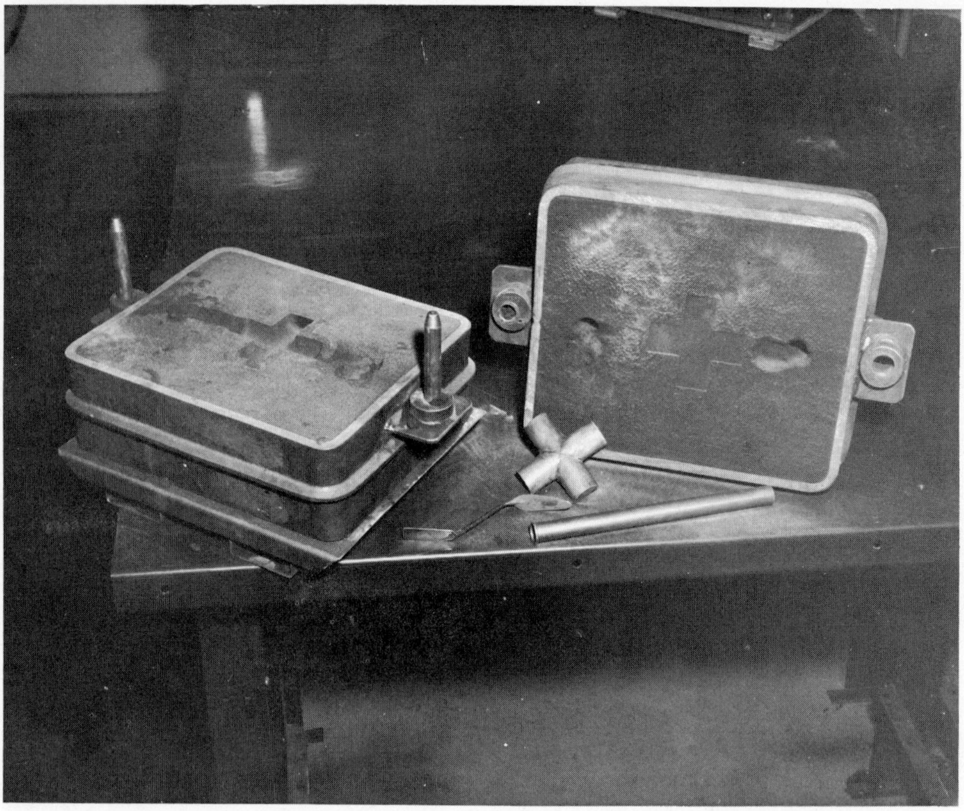

Figure 12-17
A sand mold is the form into which molten metal is poured to produce the casting.

drawings are prepared for the benefit of people who lack understanding of projection drawing.

MANUFACTURING PROCESSES

Manufactured parts are produced by one or more of the following methods: casting, machining, stamping, forging, or welding. The processes used will depend on construction material, size and shape of the part, degree of accuracy, quality of the finished product, and cost of manufacturing. All of these factors must be considered not only during the design stages of the part but also while various working drawings are made. The engineer and draftsman, therefore, must have a reasonably good knowledge of basic manufacturing operations.

12.16 Castings

A casting is a piece made by pouring molten metal into a mold. The principal casting methods are sand mold casting, plaster mold casting, permanent mold casting, investment casting, centrifugal casting, and die casting.

Sand mold casting. In this method a wood or metal pattern is used to make a mold. The mold is prepared by placing the pattern in a wood or metal frame called a flask and packing sand around the pattern. The pattern is then removed and metal poured into the mold cavity. See Fig. 12-17.

Plaster mold casting. The plaster mold process is similar to the sand mold casting except that the mold material is plaster or

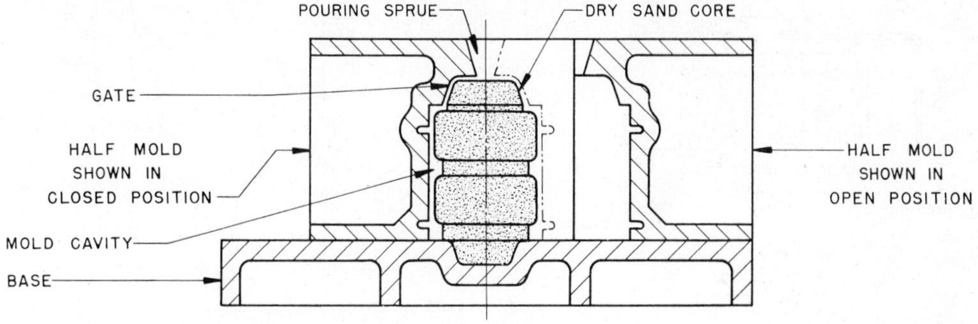

Figure 12-18
In permanent mold casting a metal mold is used to receive the molten metal.
General Motors Corp.

a combination of plaster and sand. This process is confined to the casting of nonferrous metals. Plaster mold castings have a smoother finish and greater dimensional accuracy than sand castings.

Permanent mold casting. Unlike the sand and plaster casting, where a new mold has to be prepared for each casting operation, the permanent mold process uses a metal mold which can be utilized repeatedly. Because of their greater precision, metal molds produce more accurate castings than the sand casting method. This type of casting is employed when high production warrants the additional cost of equipment. See Fig. 12-18.

Investment casting. Investment casting, sometimes referred to as the "lost wax" process is used to produce small and intricate parts requiring a high degree of surface smoothness and dimensional accuracy. This process is particularly adaptable in the production of parts for aircraft, ordnance and radar. The pattern is prepared by forcing molten wax or plastic into a metal die. The pattern is then used to make a sand mold after which the mold is fired at a high temperature to remove the wax or plastic. Molten metal is fed into the cavity either by centrifugal force or by gravity pouring.

Centrifugal casting. Centrifugal casting consists of a permanent mold which is rotated rapidly while a measured amount of molten metal is poured into the mold cavity. The process is applicable for cylindrical castings made either of ferrous or nonferrous metals. Centrifugal force holds the metal in the mold and the volume of metal poured controls the wall thickness of the casting. The advantage of centrifugal casting is that it produces smoother outside surfaces, thereby reducing a great deal of machining. See Fig. 12-19.

Die casting. Die casting is a process of forcing metal under pressure into metal dies. It is especially applicable for casting soft alloys of zinc, aluminum, magnesium and copper. Castings formed by this method are extremely accurate and require little or no machining. The process is adaptable to almost unlimited shapes without expensive supplementary operations.

Powder metallurgy. Although powder metallurgy is not an actual casting process, parts made by this method require the use of specially made dies. Metal powders are compressed into a form under extremely high pressures varying from 15,000 to 100,000 pounds per square inch. The powder metals most commonly used are copper and tin to produce bronze for bearings, and brass and iron for structural parts. The first opera-

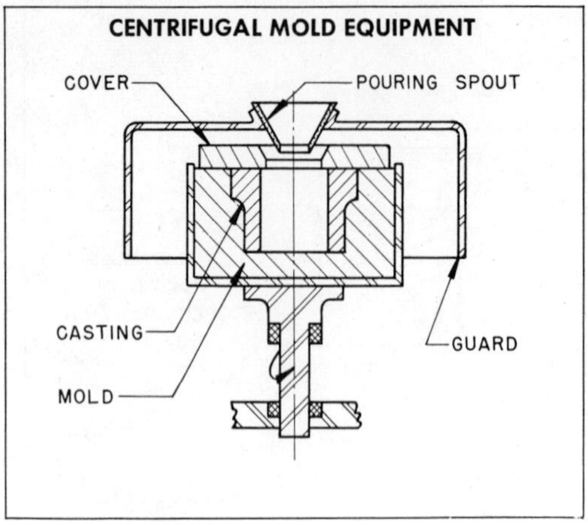

Figure 12-19
Centrifugal casting consists of a permanent mold that is rotated while a measured amount of molten metal is poured in the cavity. General Motors Corp.

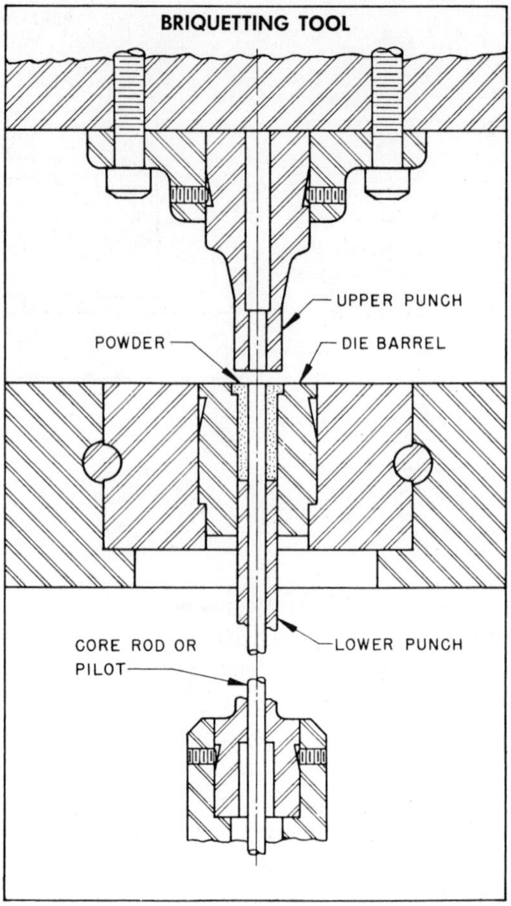

Figure 12-20
Powder metallurgy is a process of making parts by compacting powder metal into a form, heating the mixture, and subjecting the part to one or more finishing operations. The briquetting tool shown here is used to compact the powder into the die. General Motors Corp.

tion involves the mixing of the powders to obtain a homogeneous blend. The powder is then compressed into the form by means of briquetting tools with pressure supplied either by mechanical or hydraulic presses. See Fig. 12-20. The briquetted compacts are next passed through a furnace where heating bonds the particles firmly together. Upon cooling, the piece is ejected from the die and subjected to various treatments such as sizing, machining, or heat treatment.

12.17 Foundry shop

Before a sand casting can be produced a pattern, which is a duplicate of the part to be cast, is made. If only a few castings are required the pattern is constructed of wood; if a large number of castings are needed the pattern is generally made of metal. Here are some of the principal terms associated with patterns and the casting process:

Draft. Draft is the amount of taper incorporated in a pattern to permit its removal from the sand without tearing the walls of the mold. The amount of draft provided on a pattern is governed by the shape and size of the casting and method of production. Thus machine molding requires less draft than hand molding and interior surfaces often need more draft than exterior surfaces.

Parting line. The parting line represents the point where the pattern is divided for molding or that surface where sections of the mold separate. The location of the part-

Figure 12-21
The parting line divides the pattern for molding.

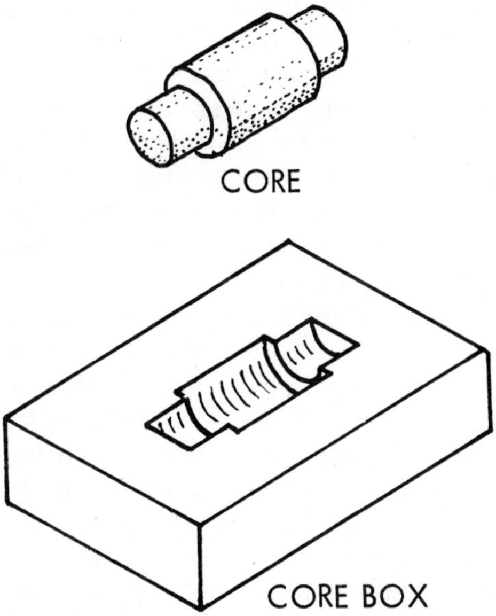

Figure 12-22
A core is made in a core box and is used to form the internal shape of a casting.

ing line on a pattern depends on the shape of the casting. In general, it is placed at the largest part of the pattern and where there are no projections or undercut faces. See Fig. 12-21.

Cores. When part of a casting is to be hollow, a form must be inserted in the mold to shape the interior. The place that occupies the hollow area is called a *core.* A core is made by packing sand in a core box having an impression of the internal shape to be produced. See Fig. 12-22. The sand is treated with a bonding agent to achieve cohesion. After the packing is completed the unit is baked or cured. This hardens the core so it can be handled and placed in the mold. The core is supported in the mold by projections known as core prints.

Shrinkage. When metal is poured into the mold and solidifies, a certain amount of contraction takes place. To obtain a casting of the required size, the pattern must be made slightly oversize to compensate for this shrinkage. The allowance is based on the shrinkage characteristics of the particular metal used. For example, if the casting were to be made of gray iron an allowance of 1/8 inch per foot would be provided.

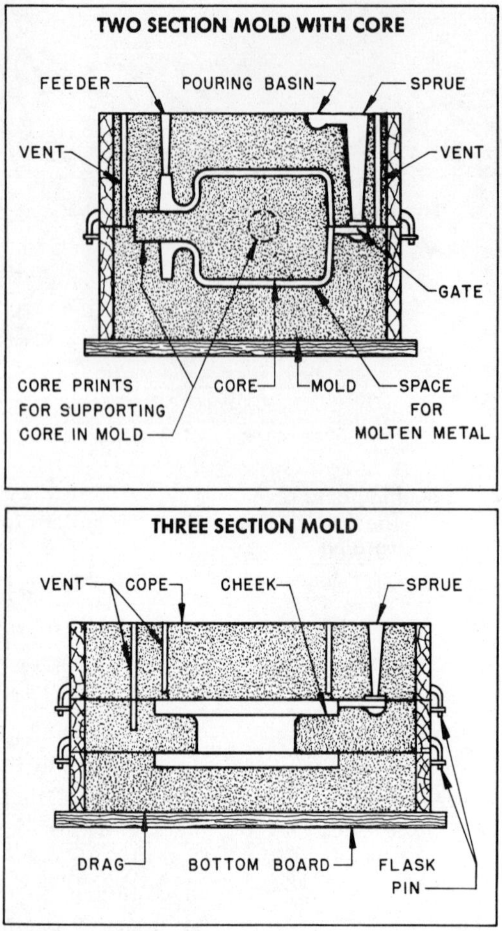

Figure 12-23
A mold is made by placing a pattern in a flask and packing sand around it. After the pattern is removed, molten metal is poured into the cavity through passages called sprues and gates.
General Motors Corp.

Machining allowances. A pattern must provide for certain finishing operations. The amount of machine-finish allowance depends upon the size and kind of casting, type of surface, method of machining, and the accuracy required of the finished product. This allowance will vary anywhere from 1/8 to 3/8 inch or more.

Flask. A flask is the container into which sand is packed to form the mold. See Fig. 12-23. It consists of two or more sections. The upper section is known as the *cope* and the lowest section as the *drag*. Intermediate sections called *cheeks* are sometimes placed between the cope and drag for complicated castings. Molten metal is poured into the mold cavity through vertical passages in the sand called *sprues*. From the sprue the metal flows into the cavity by horizontal passages called *gates*. A *feeder* or *runner* is an opening formed in the molding sand to supply additional metal to the casting during the cooling and shrinkage period to eliminate voids and hollows in the cast part. A small opening called a *vent* is provided through the sand to permit the escape of gases generated during the pouring process.

12.18 Casting methods[2]

The oldest and most generally used type of furnace for melting cast iron, and the most economical, is the cupola which is a continuously melting furnace. Fundamentally, it consists of a vertical steel cylinder lined with a refractory material and provided with openings for the air under pressure to enter the cylinder. Alternate charges of coke, iron and a suitable flux, generally limestone, are placed in the refractory-lined cylinder in properly predetermined quantities. Air forced through the charges causes combustion of the coke and melts the metal, which then drips down through the incandescent fuel to a hearth at the bottom of the cylindrical shaft. It is then withdrawn either continuously or as desired and poured into the molds.

The electric furnace is being used to an increasing extent in melting cast iron, because the composition can be controlled quite accurately and there is flexibility in the temperature control. However, its melting cost is normally higher than that of cupola melting, so that it is generally used only when special high-quality iron is desired.

The molten metal, when drawn from the furnace, is transferred in ladles to the molds where it is poured into the sprues. Where the mold material is a moist refractory sand and

2. *General Motors Drafting Standards* (Detroit: General Motors Corp.).

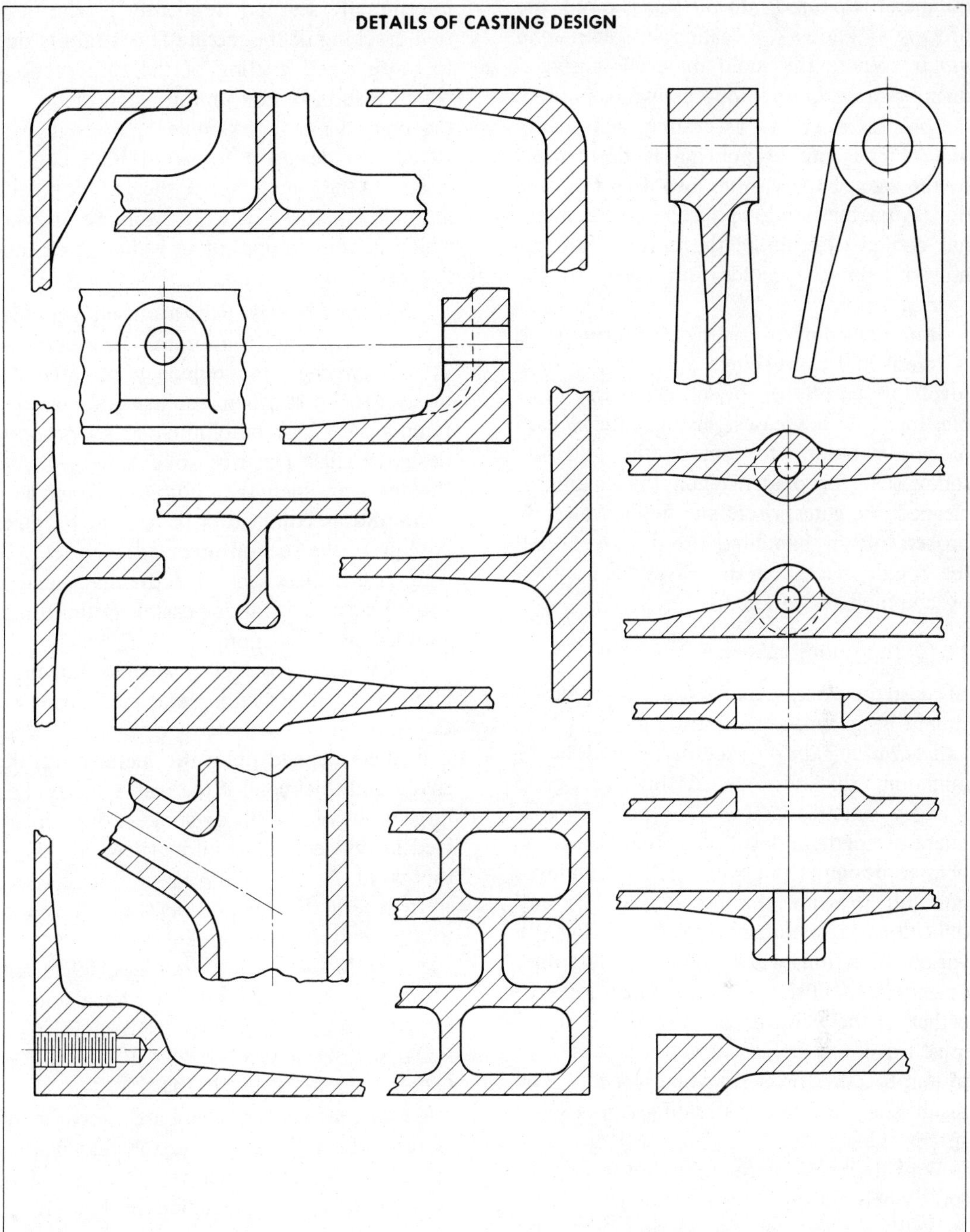

Figure 12-24
The above sections show some typical webs, clearances for machine cuts, and blending of sections of varying thicknesses.

the metal is poured into the moist mold, the process is known as casting in *green-sand molds*. Where the mold material is subsequently dried before the casting is poured, the process is known as casting in *dry-sand molds*. The rate of pouring is determined by the size of the casting and its metal section. After the mold is poured and the metal has cooled sufficiently, the castings are removed from the molds and taken to the cleaning room.

In the cleaning of castings, adhering sand is removed by brushing, or tumbling in a revolving barrel, or by abrasive or water blasting. In a few cases, castings are pickled in acid solutions to remove the adhering sandy scale or oxide. When the casting is cleaned, the gates, risers and fins not already broken off in handling, are removed and the rough places on the casting smoothed by chipping or grinding.

12.19 Designing castings[3]

In designing castings, particular attention should be given to the following:

Section thickness. Sections should be of minimum thickness consistent with good foundry practice and should provide adequate strength and stiffness. The least expensive design is one which is light enough, but still presents the fewest hazards and difficulties in manufacturing. Metal flows in various directions when entering a mold and, as the mold fills, this metal must join together. If the walls are too thin or the metal must travel too far, it will not be hot enough to join together properly when it meets. The result is a "cold shut", a seam giving a weak spot in the casting.

Wall thickness in castings should be uniform wherever the design permits.

Walls of gray iron castings and aluminum sand castings should not be less than 5/32″ thick. Walls of malleable iron and steel castings should be not less than 3/16″. Walls of brass, bronze, or magnesium castings should be not less than 5/32″ thick.

Sections of unequal size which do not blend gradually in thickness cause severe internal stresses and frequently produce actual cracking of the metal. This strain is due to more rapid cooling of the thin sections which results in non-uniform contraction of the poured metal. Example sections in Fig. 12-24 are designed to avoid high cooling strains in the metal. Notice the proper blending of thicknesses between walls and bosses which is very important in reducing casting stresses to a minimum.

Ribs and bosses. Ribs are used primarily as stiffeners and reinforcing members. In certain castings, the tendency of large flat areas to distort when cooling from casting temperature may be eliminated by properly designed ribs. The ribs solidify earlier than the section which they adjoin and act as a bond and as conductors of heat to promote cooling of the section involved. The relation of the rib or boss section to the main section should permit, as far as possible, a uniformly blended metal section.

Fillets and rounded corners. Adequate fillets at all intersections materially increase the strength and soundness of castings. Sizes and fillets depend upon the metal used, the shape and thickness of the wall section. Too large a fillet in a rib or spoke causes localized heavy sections resulting in weakness at this point.

In general, the fillet radius should be equal to the wall section thickness as shown in Fig. 12-25. On casting drawings, fillets and rounded corners are indicated by a note as follows: ALL FILLETS _R AND ALL ROUNDED CORNERS _R UNLESS OTHERWISE SPECIFIED.

Casting tolerances. There are a great many factors which contribute to the dimensional variations of castings. However, the standard drawing tolerances specified in Fig. 12-26 can be satisfactorily attained in the production of fairly simple castings. The somewhat closer tolerances specified in the normal minimum tolerance column may be applied to critical dimensions.

12.20 Forgings

Forging is a process of producing machine or structural parts that must withstand shock

3. *Ibid.*

or sudden impacts and cannot be fabricated by ordinary casting operations. Forgings are made by any one of the following methods (See Fig. 12-27):

Drop forging. Drop forging is the process of forming the desired shape by placing a heated bar or billet on the lower half of a forging die and pounding the top half of the die into the metal by means of a power driven machine called a drop hammer.

Press forging. In this process the heated billet is squeezed between dies. The pressure is applied by a forging press which completes the operation in a single stroke.

Rolling. Rolling involves the passing of a heated bar between revolving rolls which contain an impression of the required shape. It is a process designed chiefly to reduce short thick sections into long slender pieces.

Upsetting. Upsetting is the process of increasing the area of the forging metal by pressure applied between dies on a power driven machine called an upsetter or forging machine. This process is particularly applicable in the manufacture of bolts, forming cavities in the upset part of a forging or in piercing holes.

Extruding. Extruding consists of forcing metal under pressure through a die having the same cross section as the aperture in the die. The resulting shapes are then cut to their proper length, straightened, and heat treated if necessary.

12.21 Forging design[4]

A forged part should be designed as simply and practically as possible, and must serve its purpose in the assembly to the best advantage. To accomplish this function the following factors should be considered:

Draft angle. Draft is defined as the angle of taper given the side walls of the die impression in order to permit easy removal of the forging from the die. Draft must always be provided on parts produced by ordinary drop die forging. The normal amount of draft for exterior contours is 7°, and for interior contours 10°.

Die draft equivalent is the amount of off-

4. *Ibid.*

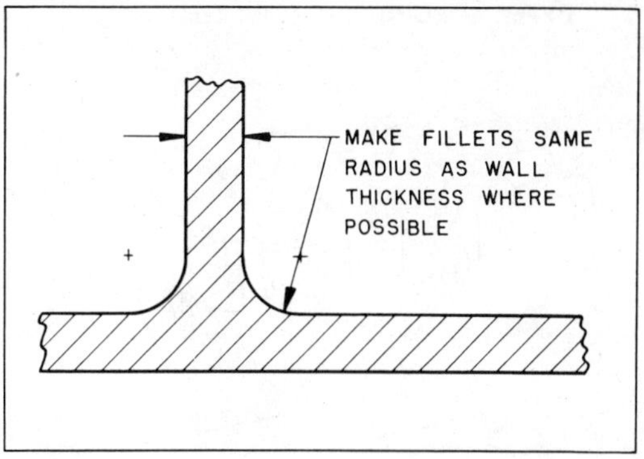

Figure 12-25
Fillet radius on a casting should be equal to the wall section thickness.

TYPE OF CASTING	STANDARD DRAWING TOLERANCE ±	NORMAL MINIMUM TOLERANCE ±
Sand Casting	1/32 Use normal min. tolerances for dimensions greater than 8″.	1/32 (Up to 8″) 3/64 (8″ to 16″) 1/16 (16″ to 24″)
Permanent Mold Casting (Semi-Permanent Mold)	1/32 Use normal min. tolerances for dimensions greater than 12″.	1/64 (Up to 5″) 1/32 (5″ to 12″) 3/64 (12″ to 24″)
Plaster Mold Castings	1/64 Use normal min. tolerances for dimensions greater than 8″.	.010 (Up to 4″) 1/64 (4″ to 8″) 1/32 (8″ to 12″)
Centrifugal Precision Castings	1/64	.005 (Up to 1/2″) .010 (1/2″ to 5″) .015 (over 5″)

Figure 12-26
These are some of the basic tolerances established for castings.

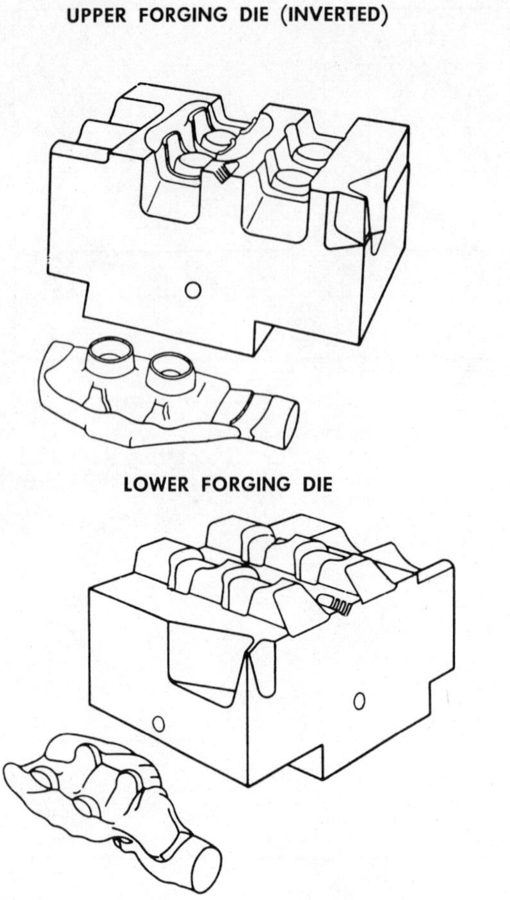

Figure 12-27
This illustration shows a hammer forging die which makes two pieces of a propeller shaft yoke at a time. General Motors Corp.

DIE DRAFT EQUIVALENT

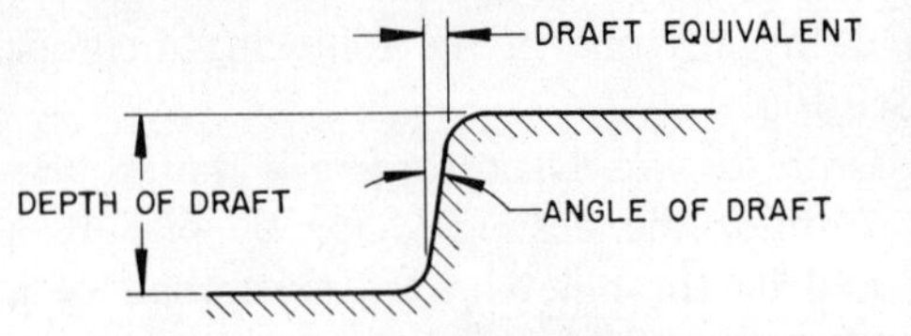

Depth of Draft	Draft Equivalent for Angle of 5°	7°	10°
1/32	.0027	.0038	.0055
1/16	.0055	.0077	.0110
3/32	.0082	.0115	.0165
1/8	.0109	.0153	.0220
5/32	.0137	.0192	.0276
3/16	.0164	.0230	.0331
7/32	.0192	.0268	.0386
1/4	.0219	.0307	.0441
9/32	.0246	.0345	.0496
5/16	.0273	.0384	.0551
11/32	.0301	.0422	.0606
3/8	.0328	.0460	.0661
13/32	.0355	.0499	.0716
7/16	.0383	.0537	.0771
15/32	.0410	.0576	.0827
1/2	.0438	.0614	.0882
9/16	.0492	.0691	.0992
5/8	.0547	.0767	.1102
11/16	.0601	.0844	.1212
3/4	.0656	.0921	.1322
13/16	.0711	.0998	.1433
7/8	.0766	.1074	.1543
1	.0875	.1228	.1763

Figure 12-28
Die draft equivalents are the offsets that result when draft is applied for a forging.

set that results when it is necessary to apply draft to a forging. See Fig. 12-28. Fig. 12-29 illustrates the manner in which draft may be applied to some of the more common sections of parts.

Parting line. The surfaces of dies that meet in forging are the striking surfaces. The line of meeting is the parting line. The parting line of the forging must be established in order to determine the amount of draft and its location.

The location and the type of parting as applied to simple forgings are shown in Fig. 12-30. The parting may be either flat, or locked where the dies have their faces in two or more planes. Flat partings are generally the most economical, but some forgings must be parted by locked partings.

Fillets and corner radii. An important problem of forging design is the use of correct radii where two surfaces meet. Corner and fillet radii on forgings should be as large as possible to assist the flow of metal for sound forgings, and to promote economical manufacture.

Stress concentrations due to abrupt changes in section thickness or direction are minimized by fillet and corner radii of the correct size. Any radius larger than recommended will increase die life. Any radius

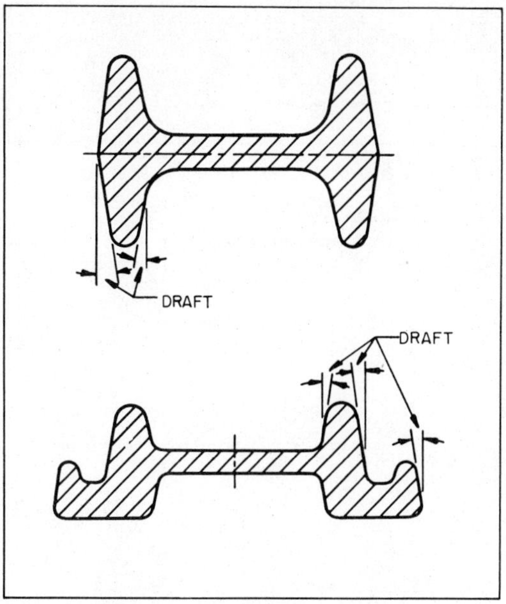

Figure 12-29
Draft for a forging may be applied as illustrated here.

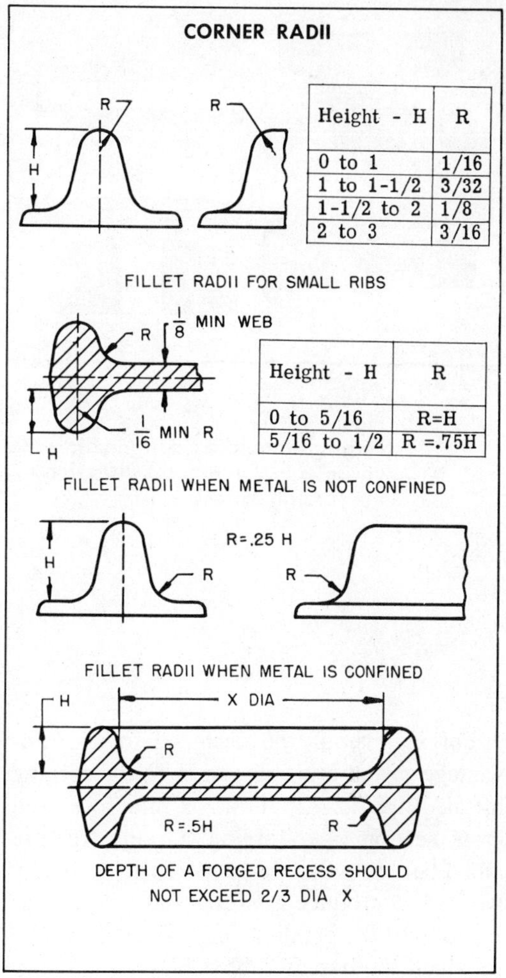

Figure 12-31
These corner radii are recommended for forgings.

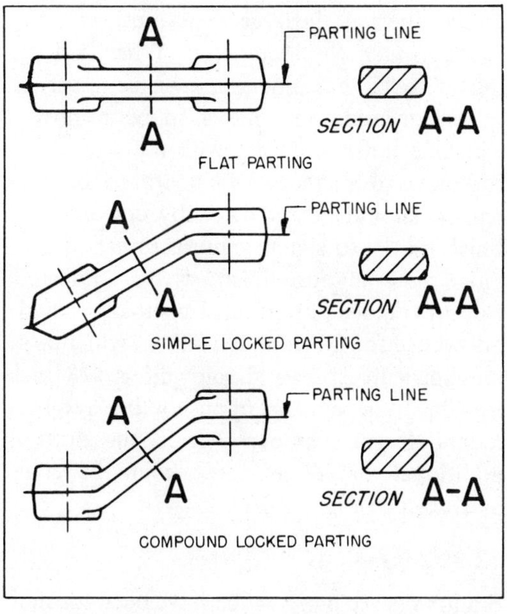

Figure 12-30
Typical location and type of parting lines for simple forgings are represented here.

smaller than recommended will decrease die life. See Fig. 12-31 for recommendations.

Grain direction. When considering the physical design of a part, grain direction offers one of the most important properties of forged metal. Grain or fiber direction is defined as the extension of alignment of metal grains in the direction of working. In forging, tests have shown that metal may be as much as five percent stronger in tension along the grain fibers than across them, and have the ability to resist shock and impact to a much greater degree than across grain direction.

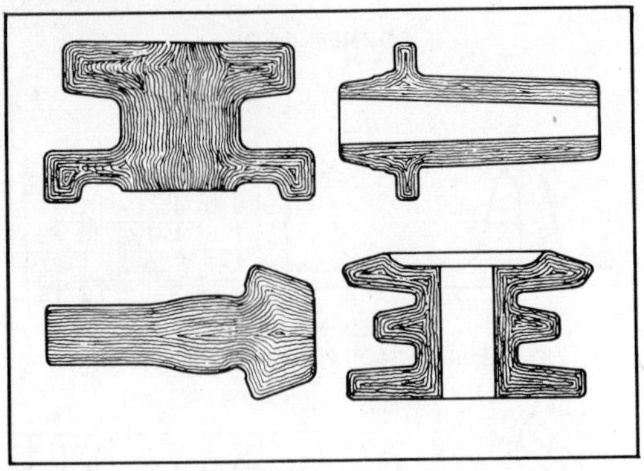

Figure 12-32
Forgings should be designed to take advantage of the grain direction of the forging metal.

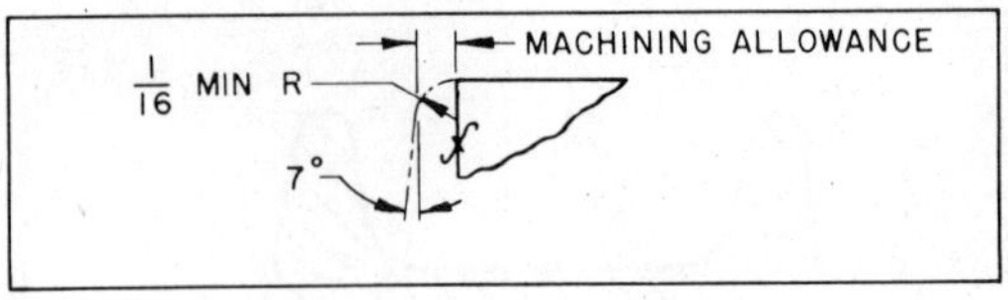

Figure 12-33
Allowance for machining and draft should be shown on a forging drawing.

Forgings should be designed to take advantage of the grain direction of the forging metal. Fig. 12-32 shows a macro-etched cross section of a forging. Grain structure and fiber direction have been directionally worked to produce a strong and tough forging to meet the bending and torsional stresses to which the part is subjected.

Tolerance. Due allowance must be made in the design of a forged part for variation in outline dimensions and weight of the finished part. These variations are caused by die wear and mismatch or lateral misalignment of the two halves of the die. Die wear causes the greatest variation in contours and planes that are parallel to the parting line. In many parts, variation in contours measured perpendicular to the parting line will cause large variations in weight, which is an important factor in the design of such parts as engine connecting rods. These variations can be corrected only by resinking the die. Since mismatch is a matter of die alignment, it can be controlled by set-up and general machine condition. It is very noticeable in the case of a gear forging with a web and rim design. Mismatch will cause one side of the rim to be eccentric to the other, making the finished part very difficult to balance dynamically. Therefore, tolerances for allowable variations in forging contours and mismatch should be clearly stated on the drawings of forged parts. These tolerances should be as generous as possible consistent with good design of the part. Close forging tolerances can be held, but only through increased die maintenance which adds to the cost of producing the part in large quantities.

Allowance for machining. When a forging is to be machined, allowance must be made for additional metal to be removed. Machine finish will vary with the size of the forging. All surfaces which are to be machined should be indicated by conventional finish marks to signal manufacturers to provide material for finish where indicated. Forging details of normal size should provide allowance for finish of 1/16 inch, while large and intricate shapes should allow 1/8 inch for finish depending upon tooling requirements. If surfaces carry draft, the draft is additional and dimensions should be given as shown in Fig. 12-33.

12.22 Stampings

Stampings are parts which have been formed, punched, or sheared from flat sheet metal stock. The following are the specific operations used in making stampings.

Blanking. Process of cutting out the de-

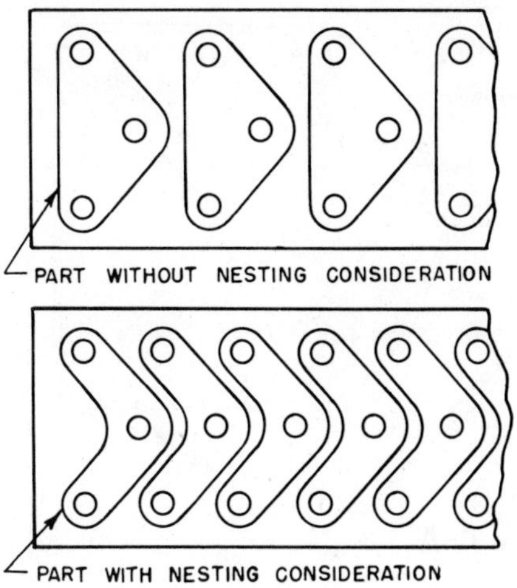

Figure 12-34
Blanks must be nested on a sheet to keep scrap to a minimum.

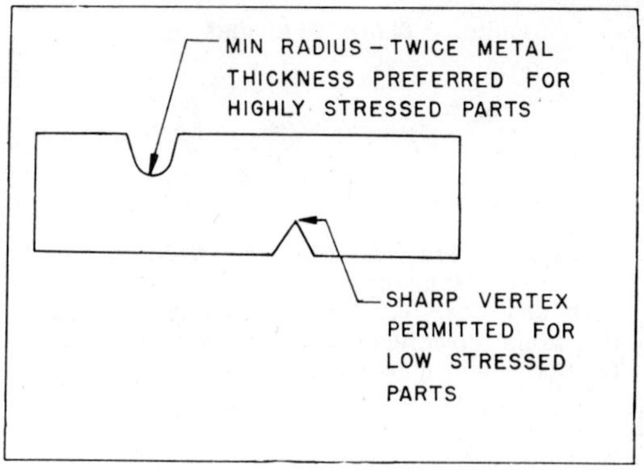

Figure 12-35
Notches in stampings are provided either to facilitate forming or for purposes of clearance, attachment or locating.

sired shape piece from flat stock.

Punching. Operation of forming a hole or opening in a sheet metal part.

Forming. Involves bending, flanging, folding, offsetting, or twisting metal to the needed shape.

Drawing. Process of stretching metal over a form to produce the required shape.

Trimming. Process of cutting off superfluous metal around the edges of drawn pieces or cutting strips of metal to produce blanks.

Coining. Process of forcing metal to flow from one area, which decreases its thickness, into an adjacent area which increases its thickness.

12.23 Stamping considerations

Dimensions. The general practice is to dimension stampings either on the punch side or die side and not by placing part of the dimension on one side and part on the other. Wherever possible dimensions should be given to intersection or tangent points instead of to a locus of a radius.

Nesting of blanks. Consideration must be given to the arrangement of the blanks on the sheet to minimize scrap. See Fig. 12-34.

Notches. "V" notches should never be used on highly stressed parts because the sharp vertex of the "V" might result in the starting point of a tear. Notches for stressed parts should be specified with a minimum of twice the metal thickness. Sharp notches may be used on lower stressed parts. See Fig. 12-35.

Design Hints.[5] The design hints in Figs. 12-36 to 12-40 illustrate some of the important points which should be considered by the draftsman in the design of stampings in order to promote the standardization of approved detail design.

12.24 Heat treatment of steels

Heat treatment is a heating and cooling process used to effect certain changes in the properties of steel. Principally heat treatment controls the grain structure which in turn changes the physical properties of the steel. Changes and refinements of the grain structure take place when the steel is heated to a temperature above its critical temperature range and then cooled. The basic heat treating operations for steel are as follows:

Annealing. Process of heating steel for a specified period either above or below its critical range and then allowing it to cool slowly. Annealing is used to soften metal, remove stresses, alter such characteristics as

(Text continued on page 321)

5. *Ibid.*

BEADS AND RIBS

Beads and ribs may often be used to impart rigidity to stampings which might otherwise be weak and flexible. Beads should be formed in the same direction as the outer flanges to facilitate die construction.

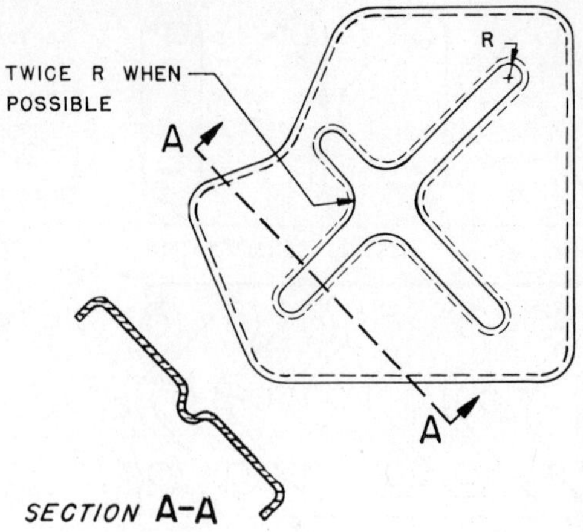

FLANGES

Tapered flanges should not be allowed to taper to the face of the metal, but should be cut off so that the narrowest section will be at least twice metal thickness but not less than .12 of an inch measured from the inside of metal.

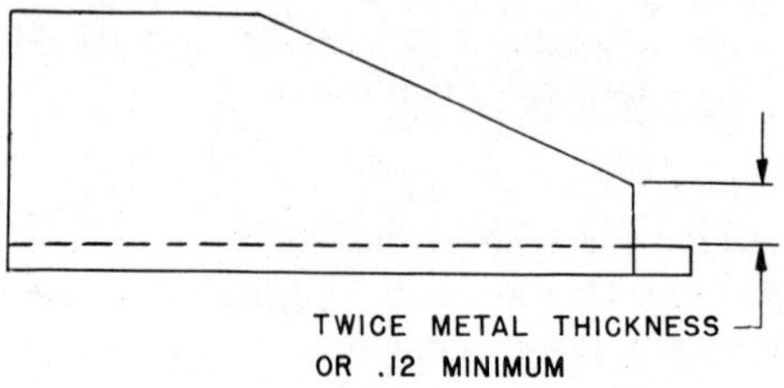

Outside flanges and flanges around openings should preferably have a height of at least twice the metal thickness or a minimum of .12 on thin stampings.

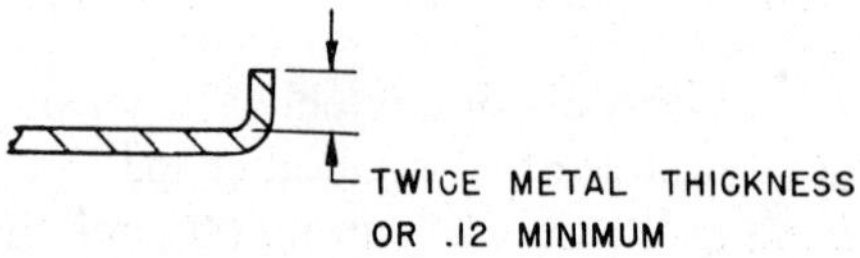

A hemmed edge should be notched at corners in order to eliminate gathering of metal in the flanging operation.

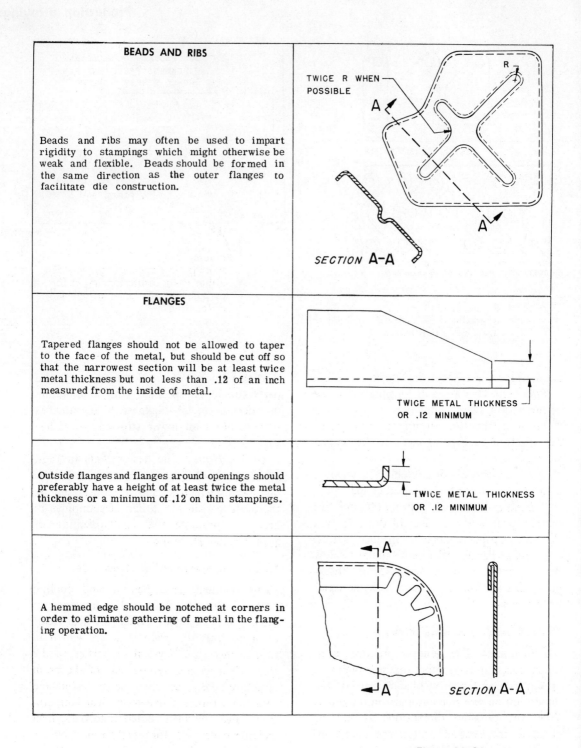

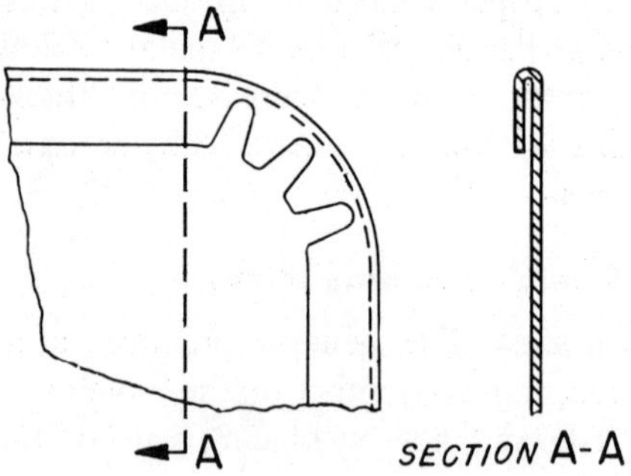

Figure 12-36
Design hints for stampings.

FLANGES In order to facilitate the trimming operation, the minimum flange width should be twice the metal thickness.	PREFERRED 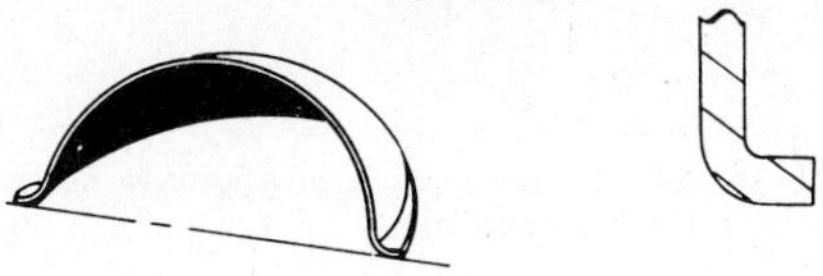
Permissible flange condition when a sharp edge is not objectionable.	PERMISSIBLE 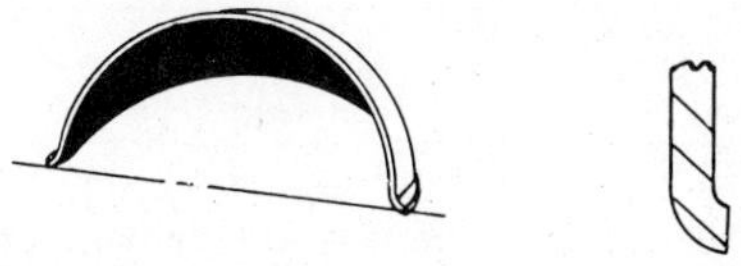
The absence of a flange requires expensive trim if X is maintained and the edge is held even, because the trimming must be done on a horizontal plane.	NOT RECOMMENDED 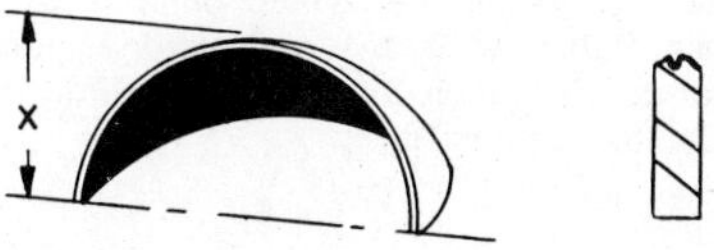
When flanges, that extend over only a portion of a part, are necessary in a highly stressed part, a notch or circular hole should be used in order to eliminate tearing of the metal. The circular hole, type A relief, is used when the maximum possible flange height is necessary. The notch, type B relief, is used when the flange can be shorter than the maximum possible height.	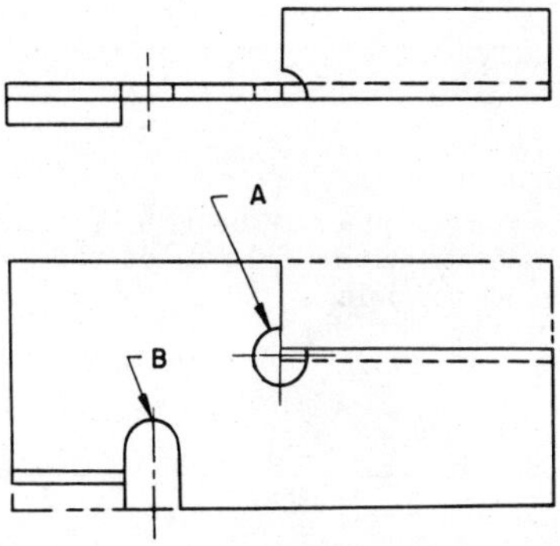
RADII Inside radii on stampings at bends should not be less than the thickness of metal, if possible. Larger radii facilitate production.	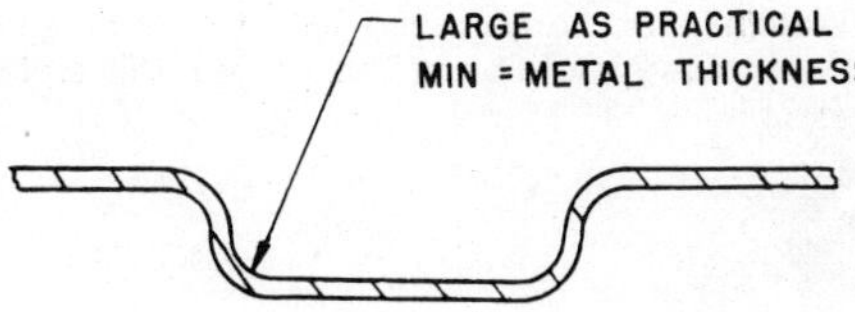

Figure 12-37
Design hints for stampings.

RADII The radii in the corners of rectangular holes should be as large as possible.	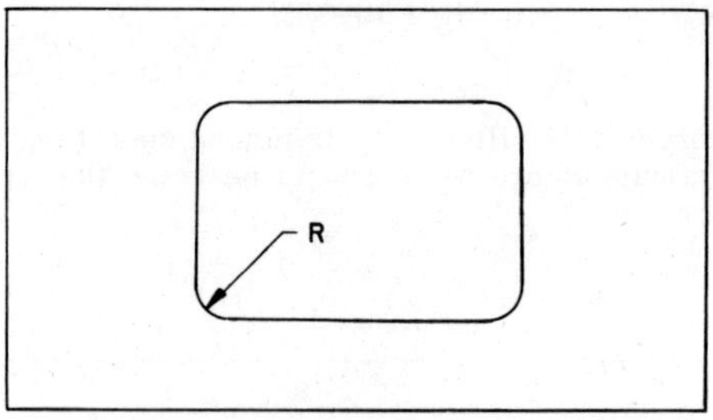
A radius which is four times metal thickness or greater at bottom of drawn stamping is preferable, as a small radius requires extra operations and extra dies. In using small radii on the punch of a die, the metal is very liable to fracture between punch and die, whereas if punch has large radius, the pinching action can be avoided.	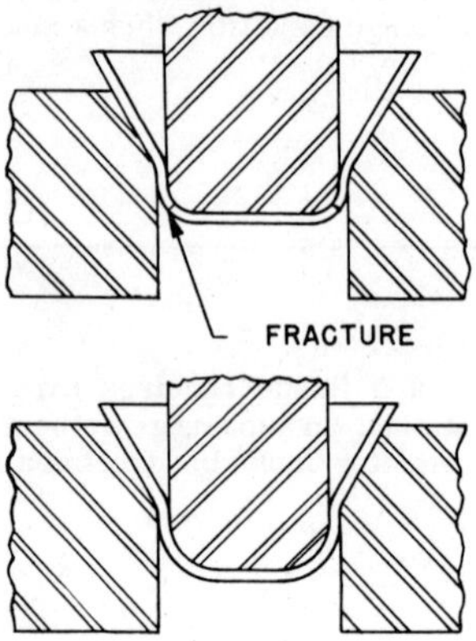
When a flanged piece is bent in the shape of an offset both the inside and outside radii should be as large as possible.	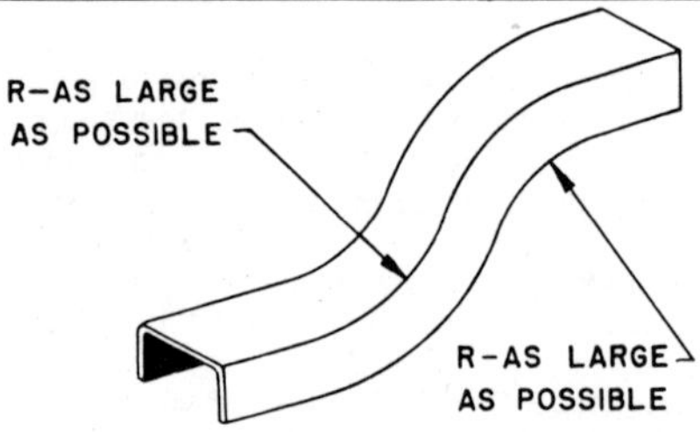
HOLES The distance from the edge of a hole to the tangent point of a radius should be at least twice the metal thickness.	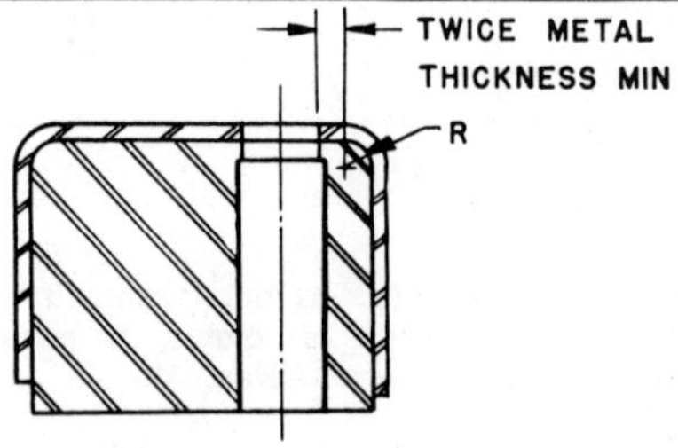

Figure 12-38
Design hints for stampings.

HOLES

The distance between holes or between a hole and the edge of a part should be large enough to prevent tearing of the metal and excessive die wear. The recommended minimum distances are shown.

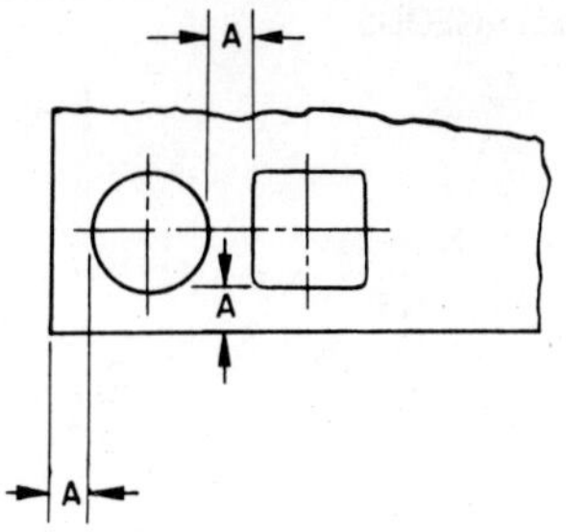

METAL THICKNESS	DISTANCE 'A' MIN
Up to .062	.125
Over .062	Two times Metal Thickness

MISCELLANEOUS

Feather edges should be avoided in shearing strip stock.

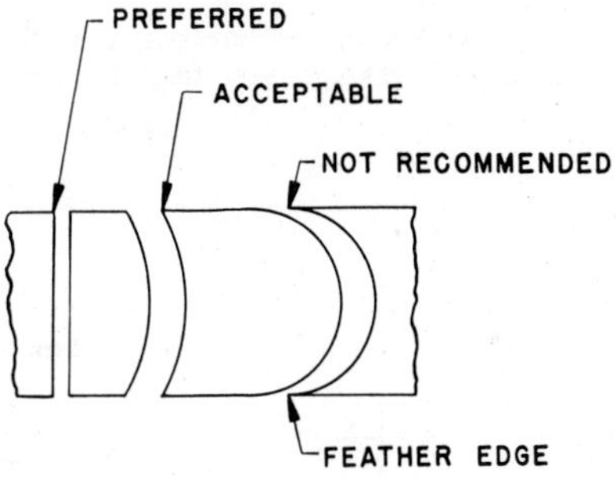

When designing parts to be cut from strip stock, the corners along the edge of the strip should be sharp corners and those not adjacent to the edge should be round, wherever possible.

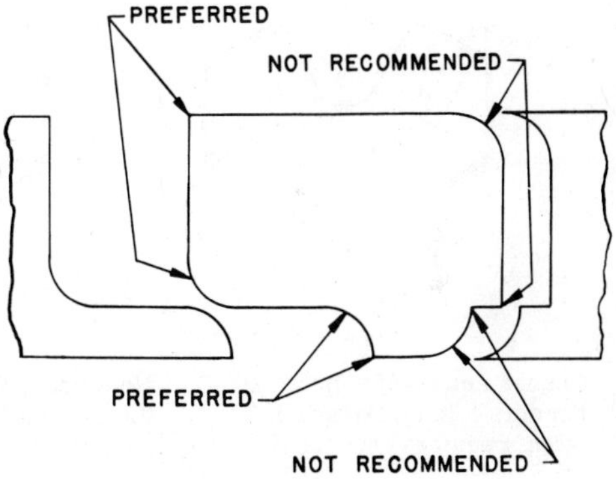

Figure 12-39
Design hints for stampings.

MISCELLANEOUS

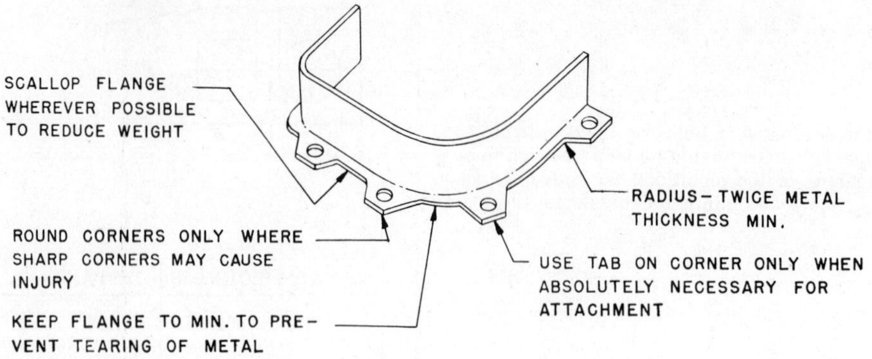

Wherever design permits make allowance for distortion and variation in tab shape and hole size to permit piercing and notching in blank.

When designing box shaped parts, if the strength of the part is not involved, it should be remembered that forming is less expensive than drawing.

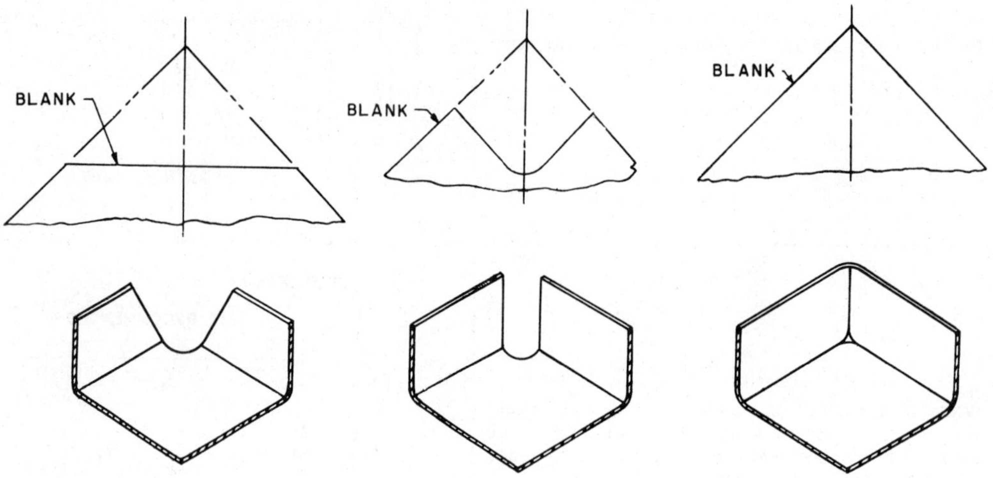

Corner cut at 45° in blank permits folding flanges and often requires no further trim.

Notching corners in blank has the same advantages as the 45° corners but often is more desirable for appearance.

Continuous flange as shown requires a draw operation.

Figure 12-40
Design hints for stampings.

ductility, toughness or magnetic properties, or produce a definite grain structure.

Normalizing. Practically the same as annealing except that cooling is done in still air instead of in the furnace. Normalizing usually produces slightly higher tensile strength and hardness than annealing.

Hardening. Process of heating a steel above its critical temperature for a given period of time and then quenching in liquids or gases. This action produces a metal that is extremely hard and brittle. Steels with a carbon content below .20 percent do not respond to this form of heat treatment.

Tempering. Process of reheating a steel that has been hardened below the critical range and then allowing it to cool. This treatment reduces the hardness, relieves stresses, decreases brittleness and at the same time increases the toughness and ductility of hardened steel.

Case hardening. Process of hardening only the outer surfaces of low carbon steels and leaving the interior soft. The result is a metal having a hard case to resist wear and abrasion and a tough core to withstand shock stresses. The common case hardening processes are carburizing, cyaniding, nitriding, induction hardening, and flame hardening—explained more fully as follows:

1 Carburizing. Process whereby a low carbon steel is heated above its critical range while in contact with carbonaceous material. The carbon either in the form of a liquid, gas, or solid diffuses into the steel to a depth governed by the nature of carburizing material, temperature, and heating period.

2 Cyaniding. Operation in which the low carbon steel is heated while in contact with a cyanide salt and then quenched. This process is used when only a very thin hard case is required.

3 Nitriding. Process in which a steel is heated in an atmosphere of ammonia vapor or is placed in contact with a nitrogenous material. No quenching follows the heating operation. Nitriding produces a harder case than carburizing with less distortion and cracking.

4 Induction hardening. Method of case hardening steel having not less than .35 percent carbon by placing it in a coil through which a high frequency current is passed. The high frequency current is induced in the surface of the steel which produces an almost instantaneous heating of the case to a depth of .010-.100 inch. The metal is then quenched in a water spray or oil bath. Induction hardening is used when certain hardened areas must be localized.

5 Flame hardening. Process of heating a metal by means of one or a series of gas burning torches to a specified temperature and then quenching. This process is used to harden local areas of such parts as gear teeth, shafts and rocker arms.

12.25 Heat treatment of nonferrous alloys[6]

Nonferrous alloys do not respond to the same type of heat treatment as do ferrous alloys. Some materials may not be hardened by any means except cold rolling or cold working. Other alloys respond to precipitation hardening, often called *aging.* This is a process wherein one or more constituents are precipitated from a solid solution, the size and distribution of the precipitate being such that a substantial increase in strength is obtained.

Precipitation hardening is generally accomplished by quenching from a temperature slightly below the temperature at which the material begins to melt followed by a hardening cycle ranging from room temperature to 900° F., depending upon the material being hardened. This treatment may be used to harden parts ranging from small springs to large die sections.

Aluminum. Alloys of aluminum respond to a small amount of cold working and to heat treatment. Commercially pure aluminum may be hardened by cold working alone. In some cases, both of these treatments are utilized to improve the physical properties of the alloys.

Heating aluminum alloys to 630-650° F. will anneal or remove the effects of cold

6. *Ibid.*

working and most of the heat treatment in case of heat treatable material.

The alloys which respond to solution treatment are heated to the required temperature, usually 950-1000° F., and held to obtain a homogeneous solid solution. They are then cooled rapidly to room temperature. In some alloys hardening begins immediately and is complete in a few hours at room temperature. It is necessary for other alloys to age at elevated temperatures for several hours in order to harden.

Copper alloys. In general, copper alloys may be hardened only by cold working to increase the tensile strength, yield strength, and elastic limit, and to reduce the elongation and reduction in area. Most annealed copper alloys are quite ductile and respond readily to cold work.

When the copper alloy is work hardened, annealing is required to soften it. Annealing consists of heating the metal above the recrystallization temperature. The most common range of annealing temperature is 800-1300° F.

12.26 Hardness testing[7]

The type of hardness test to be specified for any particular piece is governed by the type of material, hardness range, area where hardness test is to be made, surface condition of material to be tested, section size and permissible indenter impression size.

The following hardness testers and scales are commonly used (see Appendix for Table of Steel Hardness Number Conversions):

Brinell. A heavy load test, utilizing a 10 millimeter (mm) hardened steel ball indenter, that may be used on large parts, bar stock, large heavy wall tubing, forgings and castings where a large indenter impression is not objectionable. The Brinell is the best test for use on rough or non-homogeneous surfaces because the large impression is less sensitive to minor variations or imperfections. It is not generally used for hardness testing of finished parts. The following scales are employed:

1 3000 *Kilogram (Kg)* load may be used for hardness values up to 444 Bhn (Brinell hardness number). For hardness values between 444 and 745 Bhn, the Rockwell C test is generally used; however, it is permissible to use Brinell in this hardness range provided a tungsten-carbide ball penetrator is used. This scale is best adaptable on steels, but may be used for hard aluminum and copper alloys.

2 500 *Kilogram load.* Occasionally used for hardness values below 150 Bhn and restricted to nonferrous alloys.

3 1000 *Kilogram load.* Occasionally used with a 10 millimeter steel ball for copper alloys and soft steels where larger indentation is undesirable; with 9/16″ steel ball for aluminum alloys giving results numerically similar to those of the more common 500 kilogram load and 10 millimeter ball.

Rockwell standard. This test is rapid, accurate and has wide range of adaptability. By changing the scale (penetrator and/or major load; minor load is constant at 10 Kg) metals of most hardness ranges can be tested. The size of the indenter impression is fairly small, and decreases with increase in hardness of material tested and decrease in the major load of the Rockwell test. The Rockwell test is applicable, in many cases, to checking finished parts. The following scales are employed:

1 *Rockwell O.* (150 Kg major load, diamond Brale penetrator.) Should only be used for hardness range *RC* 20-65. It is generally used for determining hardness of through-hardened steels and core hardness of case hardened steels.

2. *Rockwell A.* (60 Kg major load, diamond Brale penetrator.) Generally used for checking case hardness of carburized steels. This test may be used for unusual requirements where a lighter load test than Rockwell *C* is required. Also it may be used in special cases for hard nonferrous alloys.

3 *Rockwell B.* (100 Kg major load, 1/16 inch steel ball penetrator.) Should not be used for hardness values greater than *RB* 100. It is generally used for soft steels and for

7. *Drafting Room Manual* (East Hartford, Conn.: Pratt and Whitney Aircraft, Division of United Aircraft Corporation).

nonferrous alloys.

4 *Rockwell F.* (60 Kg major load, 1/16 inch steel ball penetrator.) Generally used only on non-ferrous alloys, but for unusual requirements it may be used on soft steels where a lighter load test than Rockwell *B* is required.

Rockwell superficial. For hardness tests where only very shallow penetration is desirable or permissible and to determine the hardness very close to the surface of the specimen. By changing the scale (penetrator and/or major load; minor load is constant at 3 Kg) metals of most hardness ranges can be tested. This test may be used for checking case hardness of nitrided, cyanided and carburized steels, and thin ferrous and nonferrous sheet stock. Because of the shallow indentation of this test it is often applicable to finished parts and in many cases may be used for checking the hardness of the working surfaces of parts. The following scales are employed:

1 *Rockwell* 30*N*. (30 Kg major load, diamond Brale penetrator.) Generally used for checking case hardness of nitrided and cyanided steels, and may be used, if desired, for checking case hardness of carburized steels. It is also used for testing thin hard steels. It may be specified for finished parts when a test by a Rockwell Standard Scale is objectionable because of indentation produced.

2 *Rockwell* 15*N*. (5 Kg major load, diamond Brale penetrator.) Similar in scope to the Rockwell 30N, but the Rockwell 30N is usually preferred. It may be desirable to stipulate Rockwell 15N for unusual requirements where lighter load test than Rockwell 30N is required, such as checking working surfaces of finished carburized parts.

3 *Rockwell* 30*T*. (30 Kg major load, 1/16 inch steel ball penetrator.) Generally used for thin sections of nonferrous alloys or soft steel, or on finished soft steel or nonferrous alloy parts where small indentation is desirable.

4 *Rockwell* 15*T*. (15 Kg major load, 1/16 inch steel ball penetrator.) Lighter load test than Rockwell 30T, but similar in use.

NORMALIZE (OR ANNEAL) TO BRINELL [redacted]-[redacted]
OR (ROCKWELL C[redacted]-C[redacted]).

NORMALIZE. HARDEN AND TEMPER TO
BRINELL [redacted]-[redacted] OR (ROCKWELL C[redacted]-C[redacted]).

HARDEN AND TEMPER TO BRINELL [redacted]-[redacted]
OR (TEMPER TO ROCKWELL C[redacted]-C[redacted])

CARBURIZE. .[redacted]-.[redacted] FINISH CASE DEPTH.
HARDEN AND TEMPER TO ROCKWELL C[redacted] MIN.

CYANIDE .[redacted] DEEP.
HARDNESS ROCKWELL SUPERFICIAL [redacted].

INDUCTION (OR FLAME) HARDEN.
.[redacted]-[redacted] FINISH CASE DEPTH.
TEMPER TO ROCKWELL C[redacted] MIN.

CARBO-NITRIDE .[redacted]-.[redacted] CASE DEPTH.
ROCKWELL SUPERFICIAL [redacted] BEFORE TEMPERING.

CARBO-NITRIDE .[redacted]-.[redacted] CASE DEPTH
HARDNESS ROCKWELL SUPERFICIAL [redacted].

Figure 12-41
Type of heat treatment and hardness on a drawing are shown by means of a note. General Motors Corp.

Vickers diamond pyramid. For testing all metallic materials in any hardness range. It is not generally used as a production hardness tester but rather as a laboratory tool and therefore should not be indiscriminately specified on drawings. However, for unusual requirements it may be desirable to specify the Vickers test. The loads usually used with the Vickers test are 50, 30, 10, 5, and 1 Kg and the penetrator is a diamond pyramid.

Scleroscope. This test has been largely superseded by other tests using instruments which give more reproducible results. It should not be specified on drawings for current parts.

Heat treating notes. The various heat treatment and hardness requirements are shown on a drawing in note form as illustrated in Fig. 12-41.

12.27 Surface treatment

Most metal products when exposed to atmospheric conditions have a tendency to

CLEAN AND FINISH PER SPECIFICATION
[redacted] TO MATCH COLOR # [redacted]
OR APPROVED EQUIVALENT.

BARE METAL TREATMENT PER SPECIFICATION # [redacted].

PRIMER TREATMENT PER SPECIFICATION
[redacted].

FINISH PER SPECIFICATION # [redacted].

ALL PROCEDURES IN ACCORD WITH
SPECIFICATIONS # [redacted], [redacted],
[redacted] AND [redacted].

[redacted] CO. # [redacted] CLOISONNE
BLUE METALLIC BAKING DULUX OR
EQUIVALENT.

ALL PAINTS TO BE SUITABLY APPLIED
AND BAKED TO MEET ADHESIVE
SPECIFICATIONS.

PAINT ADHESION MUST BE SATISFACTORY
AFTER 24 HOURS EXPOSURE TO 100 %
RELATIVE HUMIDITY AT 100° F.

Figure 12-42
These are typical notes used on drawings to designate painting requirements. General Motors Corp.

corrode unless they are treated with some protective coating. There are a number of protective measures that can be used, depending on the base material and the results desired. The following are a few of the more common methods:

Electroplating. The immersion of an object in a solution containing metal or salts of metals to be deposited. As an electric current is passed through the solution, with the object to be coated serving as the negative electrode, the dissolved metal is deposited on the surface of the object. The thickness of the deposited film is governed by the amount of current, time of current flow and shape of the object. The metals commercially used for plating are brass, cadmium, chromium, copper, gold, lead, tin, nickel, silver and zinc.

Non-electric plating. Parts to be coated are left in a solution containing the coating material. The deposit is achieved through chemical electrolysis without the use of any external current. Such a process is used in tin plating aluminum pistons and coating steel parts with copper sulphate, nickel or cobalt. Its advantages are more uniform thickness of coating and better coating of internal surfaces and irregular shapes.

Hot dipping. Consists of dipping parts in a molten solution of the plating or coating materials such as zinc, lead or tin. This process is used chiefly to coat raw sheet stock.

Sherardizing. Iron or steel is embedded in zinc powder and heated to a temperature just below the melting point of zinc. Sherardizing is used principally in coating bolts and small castings.

Anodizing. An electrolytic process used almost exclusively for aluminum to produce a film of oxide on the metal. The film provides a transparent, protective, anti-corrosion coating that imparts a hard, wear-resistant surface. The process consists of passing an electric current between the aluminum and an electrolytic bath in which the metal is immersed as an anode. The electrolytic bath may be a solution of sulfuric acid, chromic acid, boric acid or phosphoric acid.

Parkerizing. A surface plating operation in which an iron phosphate coating is applied to iron or steel parts by immersing them in a hot solution of manganese dihydrogen phosphate.

Painting. Paint is used to provide a protective finish and serve as a decorative measure. Many different kinds of paints are employed. Selection of paint is based on such factors as kind and quality of finish desired, nature and function of the fabricated product, cost, color, etc.

Typical painting notes. Examples of paint notes used on a drawing are shown in Fig. 12-42.

12.28 Plating specifications on a drawing

A drawing of a part that requires a metallic coating must indicate pertinent information

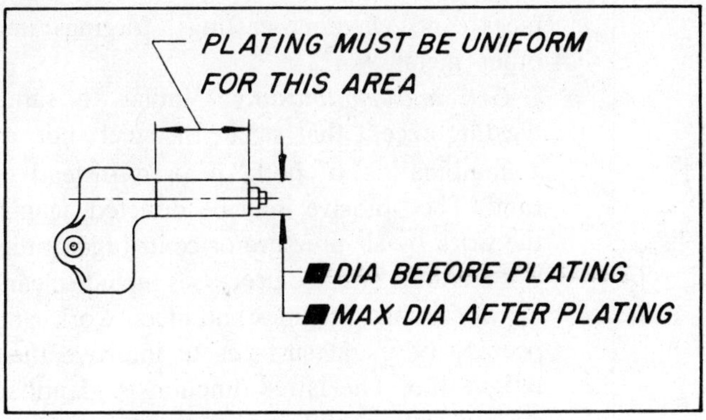

Figure 12-43
This is a common practice of specifying plating requirements on a drawing. General Motors Corp.

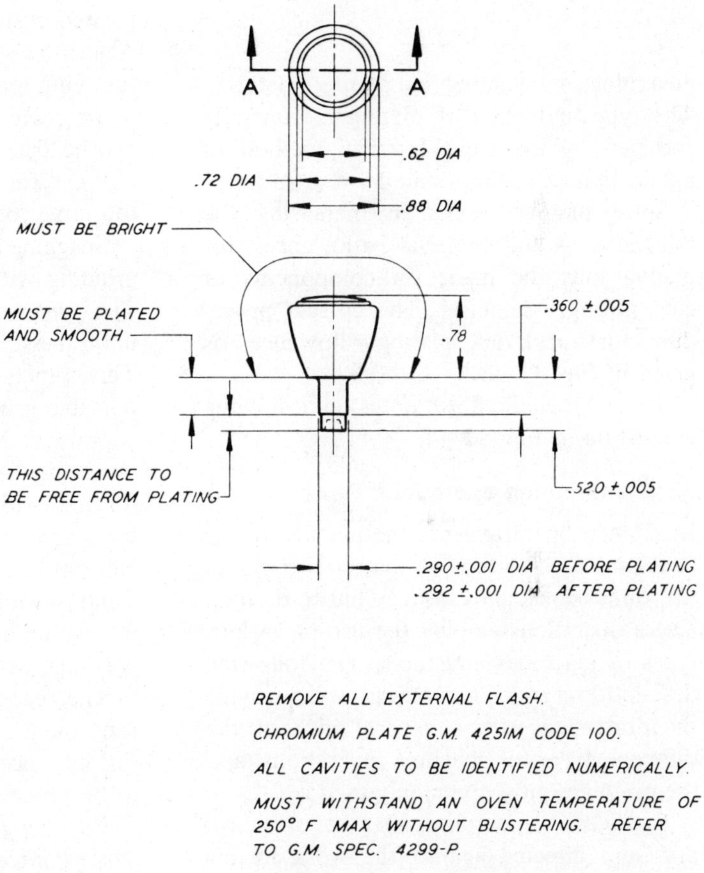

Figure 12-44
This illustration shows a typical drawing of a plated part with appropriate notes. General Motors Corp.

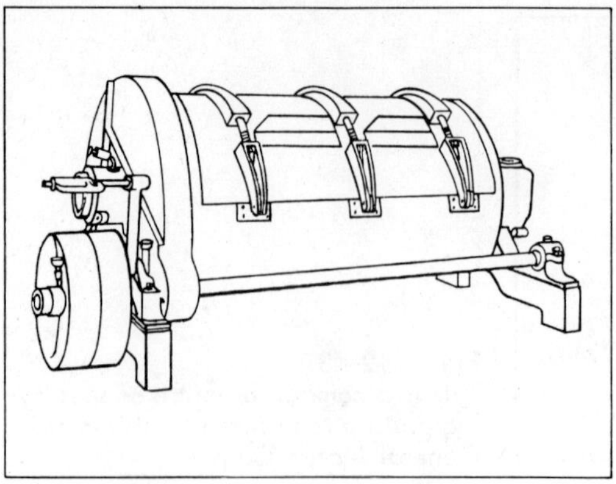

Figure 12-45
A tumbling machine is used to remove scale, fin projections, burrs, and tool marks from castings and metal parts.

governing the coating or plating material. The type and class of plating is generally specified by the engineer. The method of application is seldom stated.

Since plating results in increasing the thickness of the material, allowances for plating must be made on components of close fitting assemblies. The correct procedure for specifying plating allowances is given in Fig. 12-43.

Typical metallic finish notes on a drawing are shown in Fig. 12-44.

12.29 Machining operations[8]

Machining operations are the manufacturing processes used to remove material to obtain the dimensions and surface finish desired. These operations employ the use of various types of machines and tools. The following descriptions and illustrations will provide the draftsman with a general idea of the different types of machine operations and the machines most commonly used:

Sandblasting. Employs the use of sharp, dry sand directed against the work by air pressure. Functions of this process include removing surface oxidation, roughening metal surfaces to receive various coatings, removing hardened paint from metal surfaces, and cleaning castings, forgings and other metal work.

Grit and shotblasting. Similar to sandblasting except that steel grit, steel shot, or a combination of both, is used instead of sand. The abrasive may be directed against the work by air pressure or centrifugal force.

Functions of these processes include cleaning of castings, forgings and metal work, and peening of metal surfaces to improve their fatigue life. The latter function is identified entirely with shotblasting.

Tumbling. For removing scale, small external fins, projections, burrs and excessive tool marks from castings and metal parts. The work, together with the tumbling material, is placed in a closed drum which is then rotated at slow speed. The resulting agitation cleans the work. Fig. 12-45 shows a type of tumbling machine.

Snagging. For removing sprues, gates, risers, headers, large fins and projections from castings, forgings and raw materials which are too large for practical removal by tumbling.

Snagging is usually accomplished by rough grinding without precise limits of accuracy. The types of grinders used are dependent upon the size, shape and weight of the work. These include swing frame, pedestal and portable grinders.

Sawing. For cutting, shaping, slitting or removing material. This operation is performed with hacksaws, circular saws, or band saws. Circular sawing is considered an efficient and economical production method. Band sawing is a machine operation used for continuous rough outline cutting of irregular shaped contours.

The type of sawing, together with the arrangement of cutting teeth in the saw, is contingent upon the character of the material to be processed.

Burning or torch cutting. For cutting or shaping wrought iron, rolled steel, and steel castings by heating to extremely high temperature and simultaneously oxidizing or burning away metal with a hand operated or mechanically guided torch.

The torch is provided with two jets. One emits a flame combining a mixture of oxy-

8. *General Motors Drafting Standards* (Detroit: General Motors Corp.).

gen and acetylene for heating; the other introduces a large quantity of pure oxygen for oxidizing and burning away the metal to produce a rough cut.

Burning is used extensively on heavy work to produce irregular shapes, to cut extremely heavy steel plate or structural sections, and for general repair work.

Shaping. A surface machining process, for notching, key-seating, and facing. The cutting operation is performed by reciprocating motion of a cutting tool on a machine called a shaper.

There are two basic designs of shapers, the *conventional* and the *gear.* The conventional design of shaper, as shown in Fig. 12-46, is extremely flexible from the point of service but requires the guidance of an experienced operator. This machine is not readily adaptable to machining of production parts and is preferably a tool room, repair shop, or job shop machine.

The gear shaper is designed primarily for use on production items. This includes the cutting or generating of gear and sprocket teeth, splines, cams and plain or irregular outlines, both external and internal.

Planing. A process similar to shaping. It is primarily intended to produce large, flat, machined surfaces on metals. The work is mounted on a table which reciprocates under a tool that remains stationary except for either horizontal or vertical feed.

Planing is generally identified with heavy duty machines and is a comparatively slow operation. Therefore, planing cannot be regarded as a high production process.

Slotting. Removes material to provide a relieved longitudinal area, keyway, groove or opening in metal parts. The method of slotting may be accomplished in various ways depending on the type of slot required.

Machines used for slotting operations include shapers, keyseaters, broaching machines, spline mills and milling machines. Hence, cutting tools for producing slots include tool bits, broaches, milling cutters and saws.

Turning. For removing material to produce relatively smooth and dimensionally accurate external and internal surfaces of cylindrical, conical, shouldered or irregular form. Turning operations may be performed on metallic or non-metallic substances in the form of castings, forgings, moldings, bars, billets, etc. When such operations are performed internally, they are usually referred to as boring operations.

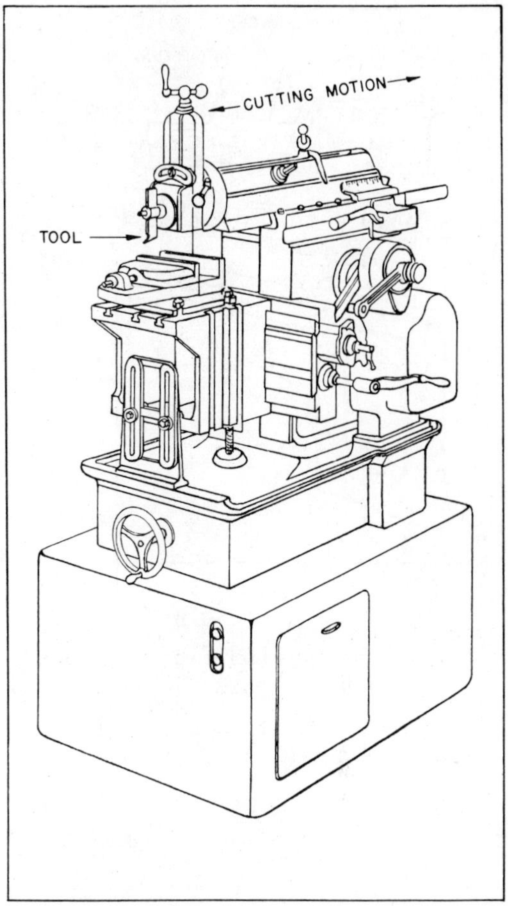

Figure 12-46
A shaper is used for surface machining, notching, key-setting and facing.

In performing turning operations, the work is rotated while the cutting tool is fed into or away from the work and is traversed along its axis of rotation. The work may be held in chucks or fixtures, or it may be supported on centers. The cutting tools are carried in cross slides or in a turret. Their movement may be controlled mechanically or manually.

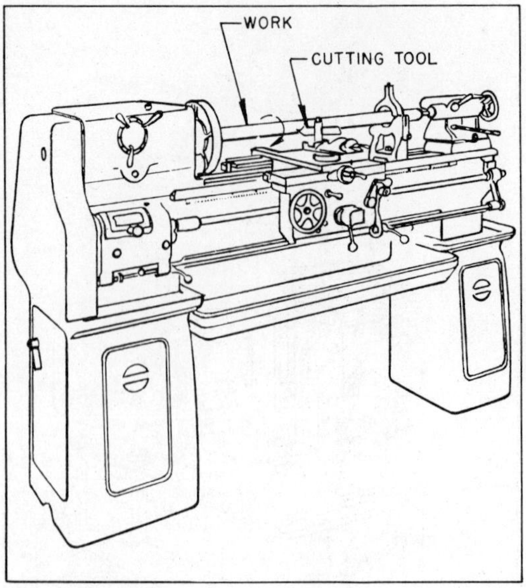

Figure 12-47
A lathe is used for a variety of turning operations.

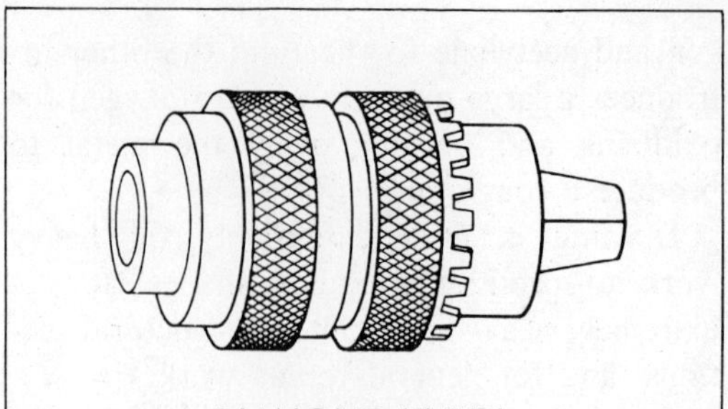

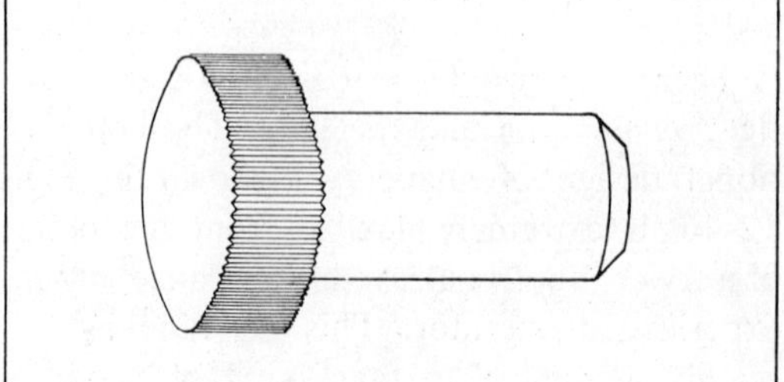

Figure 12-48
Knurling is a process of roughening a smooth surface to provide a better grip or to restrict a part from turning when in contact with a companion piece.

Turning may be performed on various types of lathes. They range from the single spindle tool room lathe, shown in Fig. 12-47, to the multiple spindle automatic screw machine and the universal turret lathe. The former is used for low volume or non-production work. The latter types are used for quantity production of interchangeable parts. The cutting tools vary in size, shape and nature of cutting edges, depending upon the material being turned and the nature of the surface required.

Knurling. A process whereby the smooth surface or periphery of a part is changed into uniform ridges and projections. The resulting uniformly roughened surface is known as a knurl. The purpose of the knurl is to provide a suitable finger or hand grip, or to restrict turning when assembled with a companion part.

The design of the knurl varies with the size and application of the part. The most common designs are the spiral and diamond shaped knurl of varying degrees of fineness.

Another knurl design is the straight tooth type which resembles a serration and runs parallel with the axis of the part. The dimensions and pitch of the knurl are dependent, to a large extent, on the size of the part and the type of material on which the knurl is applied. Examples of diamond and straight tooth types of knurling are shown in Fig. 12-48.

Milling. For removing material to produce internal or external machined surfaces of plain, complex, or irregular outline to close

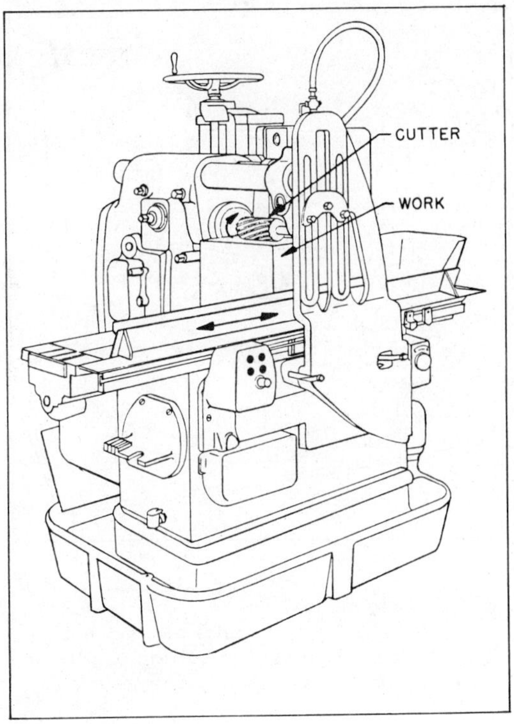

Figure 12-49
A milling machine is used to remove material to produce internal or external machined surfaces.

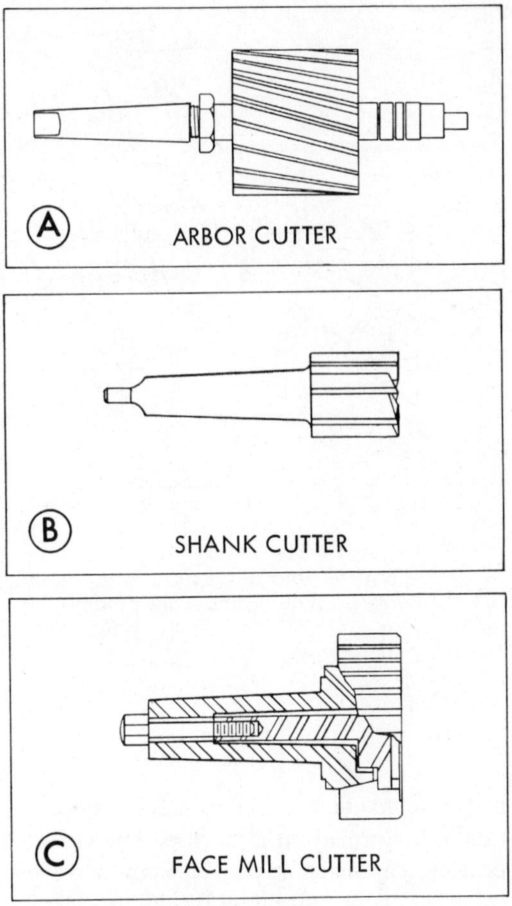

Figure 12-50
These are typical cutters used on a milling machine.

tolerances. The work is performed on a milling machine and the cutters are circular with multiple teeth. Each tooth removes a portion of the stock as the cutter rotates about its axis and the work travels back and forth.

The milling process combines the rotation of the cutter and the feeding of the work into the path of the cutter. The cutter is supported and driven by the spindle of the machine. The work is supported on the machine table, which may be either power or manually controlled. Milling machines are made with horizontal or vertical spindles and are identified as such. A typical horizontal production milling machine is shown in Fig. 12-49.

Milling cutters are made in a variety of sizes and shapes. They may also be of various types, including arbor cutters, shank cutters and face mills.

Arbor cutters are mounted on a spindle-driven arbor as shown in *A* of Fig. 12-50. Shank cutters have integral shanks designed to fit directly into the machine spindles. See *B* of Fig. 12-50. Face mills are designed to be attached directly to the end of the machine spindle or to a stub arbor as shown in *C* of Fig. 12-50.

Milling cutters may have their cutting edges on their periphery or on the face perpendicular to their axis of rotation. Obviously, the form of the milled surface is dependent on the form of the cutter.

Profiling. A form of two dimensional contour milling. The travel of the cutting tool across the work is controlled by means of a guide pin which follows the outline of a

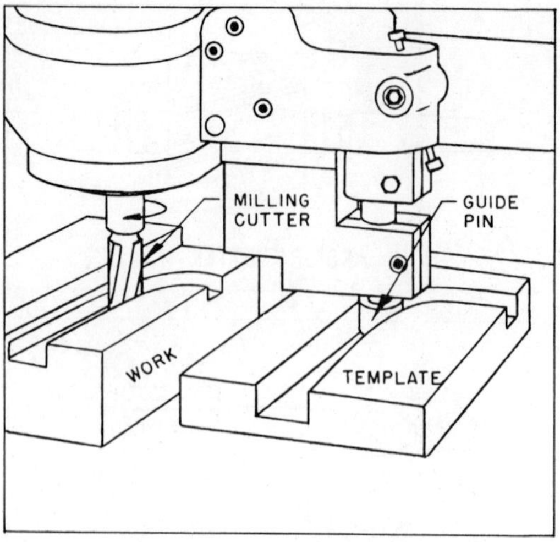

Figure 12-51
A profiler uses a template to guide the cutter in shaping the work pieces.

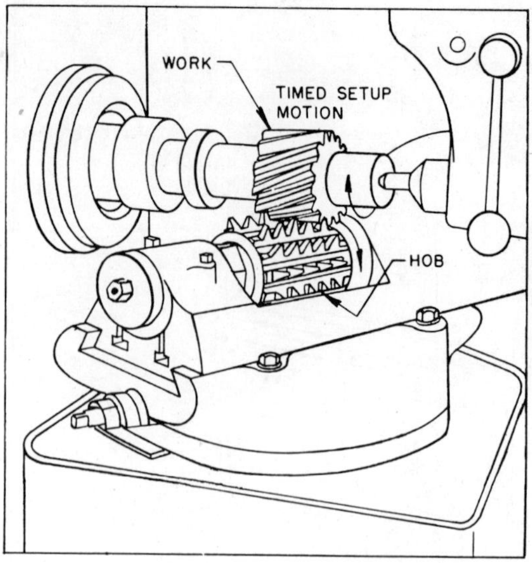

Figure 12-52
Hobbing is an automatic machining operation used in cutting gear teeth, threads, serrations, and splines.

master template. See Fig. 12-51. This operation is performed on a machine known as a profiler. The machine provides power driven spindles for the cutting tools and also blocks on which to mount the template follower guide pins. The spindle and follower guide blocks function as a unit and are mounted on cross slides which traverse on a cross rail. The work is held in a fixture provided with a template. This is secured to the machine table which traverses forward and backward. Both the cross slide and machine table are operated by suitable hand levers. By combining the directional travel of each, contours are machined as the guide pin, following the template, accurately guides the path of the cutter.

Hobbing. A continuous milling process. The cutter, known as a hob, and the work rotate in time relation to each other on individual spindles of a machine identified as a hobbing machine. In addition to the rotary motion, the hob traverses across the work, or the length of the area to be hobbed.

The scope of hobbing covers a generating method of machining various types of gear teeth, threads, serrations, splines and other special forms on external surfaces, as well as threads on internal surfaces. In fact, any form or shape that is uniformly spaced on a cylindrical surface may be hobbed, providing such form or shape is of sufficient width in proportion to height in order to permit a free rolling action of the hob.

The form of the cutting section of the hob is directly related to that of the finished gear tooth, spline or shape to be produced. The cutting process resembles that of a worm and worm gear in mesh, with the hob representing the worm, and the work representing the worm gear. Machining may be automatic, once set up, except for loading, unloading and starting of the machining cycle. Accordingly, hobbing is a production method of generating forms on parts of a high degree of accuracy. A typical hobbing operation is shown in Fig. 12-52.

Shaving. A finishing operation which supplements general machining to obtain a higher degree of finish, improved contour and greater accuracy of dimensions.

Shaving consists of removing a slight

amount of stock and may be applied to either exterior or interior surfaces. It may be performed in several ways, depending upon the design of the part and the nature of the surfaces to be shaved.

Similar to turning, shaving is commonly performed on lathes and automatic screw machines. The stock is revolved and the shaving tool is fed into the work.

Metal stampings are very often forced through shaving dies where accuracy of dimensions, surface finish and exacting contours are of prime importance.

Possibly the greatest application of independent shaving operations on production parts is in the final machine finishing of spur or helical gear teeth, and splines on shafts. Basically, gear and spline shaving is accomplished by means of a cutter having extremely accurate teeth conforming to the outline of the final gear tooth. Each cutter tooth is gashed or slotted at one or more points along its surface to provide multiple cutting surfaces.

This type of shaving may be accomplished by various methods which include:

1 Reciprocation of a rotary type cutter as it engages and drives the work.
2 A rotary type cutter in mesh with the work at crossed axes to provide an axial sliding motion.
3 By traverse of the work across a rack type cutter which reciprocates longitudinally with the work.

Each method results in the removal of minute particles of metal to achieve a high degree of accuracy and finish. A typical example of gear shaving is shown in Fig. 12-53.

Broaching. A production method of machining metal parts to a high degree of accuracy. The process employs the use of a machine operated cutter, known as a broach, which passes in a straight path through or over the stationary part to produce internal or external machined surfaces. These surfaces include holes of circular, square, or irregular outline, keyways, internal gear teeth, splines, and flat or varied external contours.

The broach, which is shown in *A* of Fig. 12-54, is provided with several cutting teeth. These teeth are graduated in size so each tooth removes a small amount of material as the broach is passed through or over the work.

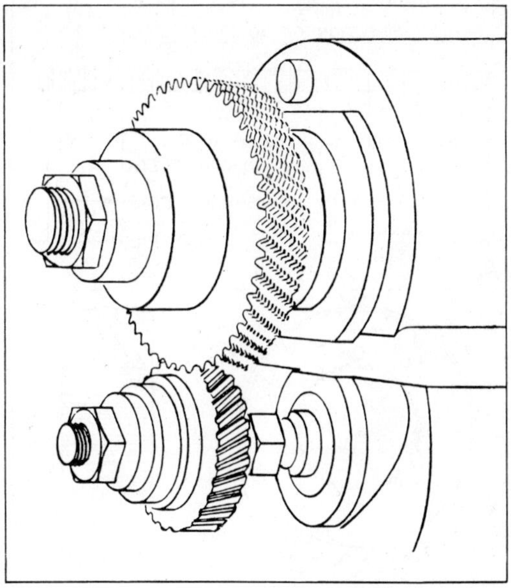

Figure 12-53
Shaving is a finishing operation used to remove small particles of metal.

Basically, there are two types of broaches: the *push type* and the *pull type*. The push type broach is forced through the work whereas the pull type is drawn through or over the work. Progressive broaching operations are sometimes necessary when the amount of stock to be removed exceeds the capacity of a single broach. A typical example of internal broaching is indicated in *B* of Fig. 12-54. An example of an external broach and broached part is shown in *C* of Fig. 12-54. The conventional broaching machines are made in two principal types, horizontal and vertical. Either type has one or more rams which actuate the broaches.

Drilling. A process of cutting round holes in material with a cutting tool known as a drill. The drilling operation is commonly performed on machines known as drill presses. The drills are held in a rotating spindle and fed into the work which is supported on the

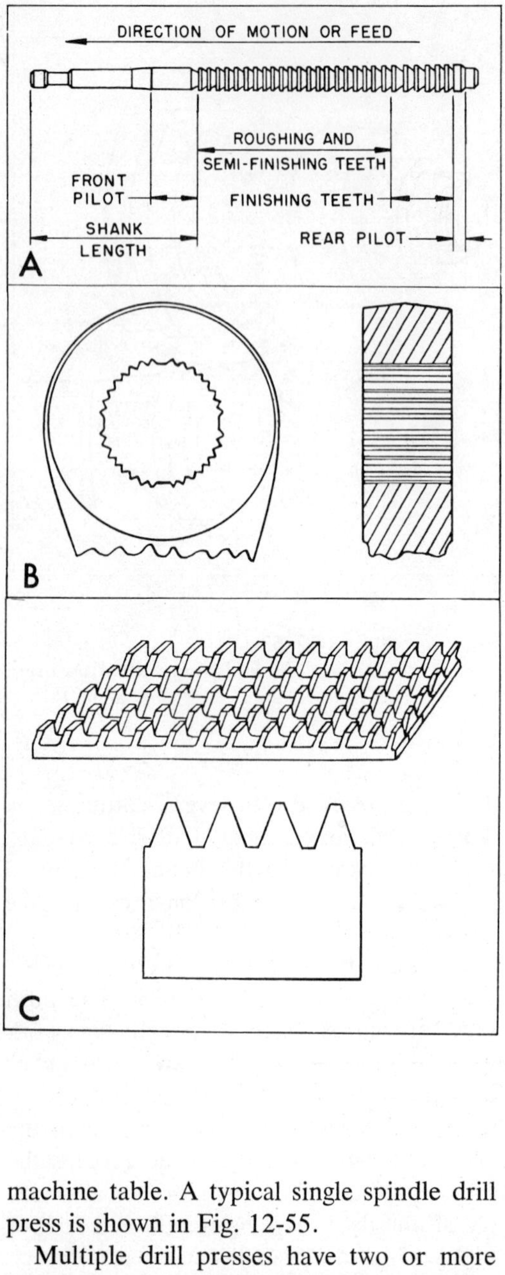

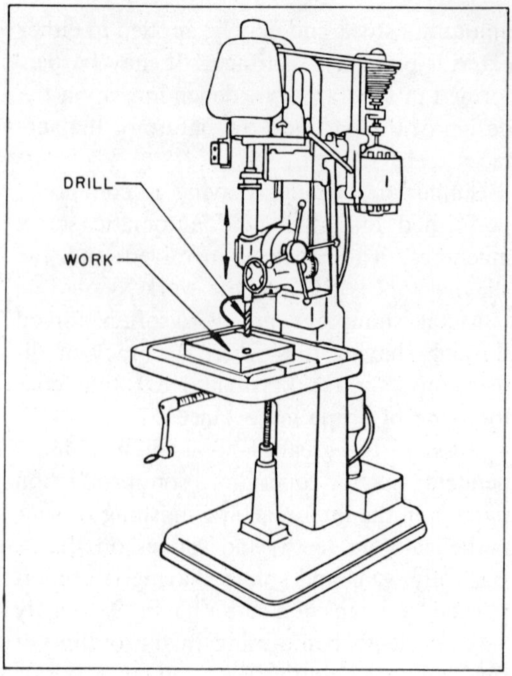

Figure 12-55
This is a typical single spindle drill press.

Figure 12-54
Broaching is used in cutting holes of circular, square, or irregular outlines, keyways, internal gear teeth, splines, and flat or varied external contours.

machine table. A typical single spindle drill press is shown in Fig. 12-55.

Multiple drill presses have two or more drills which are fed into the work simultaneously. A double spindle drill head is shown in Fig. 12-56.

Drilling is also done on lathes, automatic screw machines, and chucking machines. In this case the work is supported and rotated in chucking spindles and the drill is stationary except for feeding into the work.

Drilling can generally be classed as a roughing operation and is followed by reaming, boring, grinding, lapping, etc., to effect a finer finish and greater accuracy of hole size.

Counterdrilling. A drilling operation to enlarge a portion of a hole to a given depth that has previously been drilled.

In counterdrilling the shoulder formed at the junction of the two diameters is not square with the axis of the hole but takes the conical shape of the drill point. This shoulder is usually unimportant and not intended to be a seat or bearing for another part. A typical example of counterdrilling is shown in Fig. 12-57.

Countersinking. Removing of metal around the edge of a hole with a tool having conical

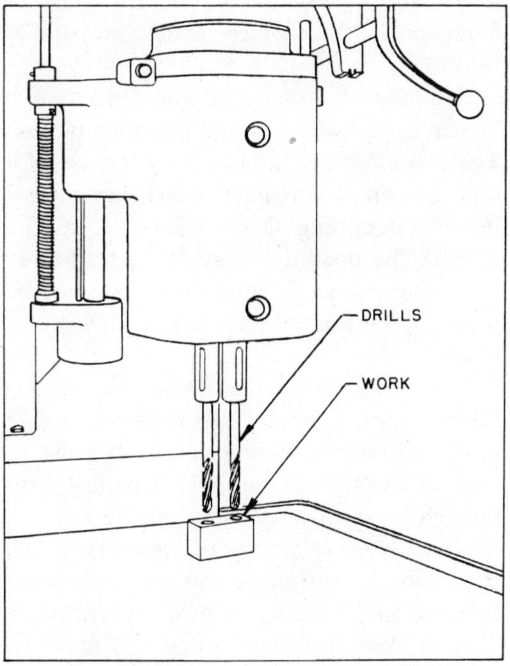

Figure 12-56
A double or multiple spindle drill head is frequently used in production work.

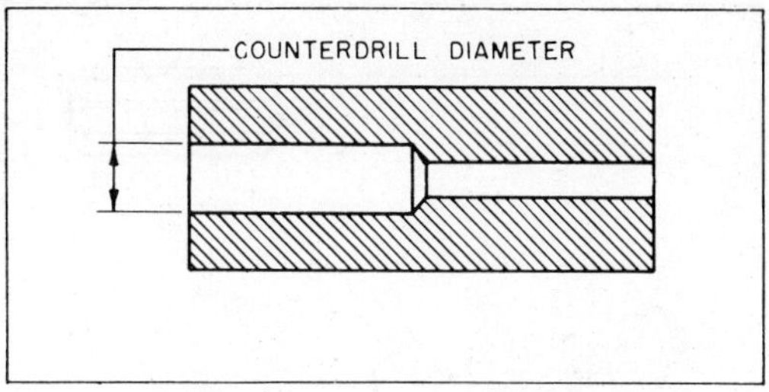

Figure 12-57
Counterdrilling is a process of enlarging a portion of a hole.

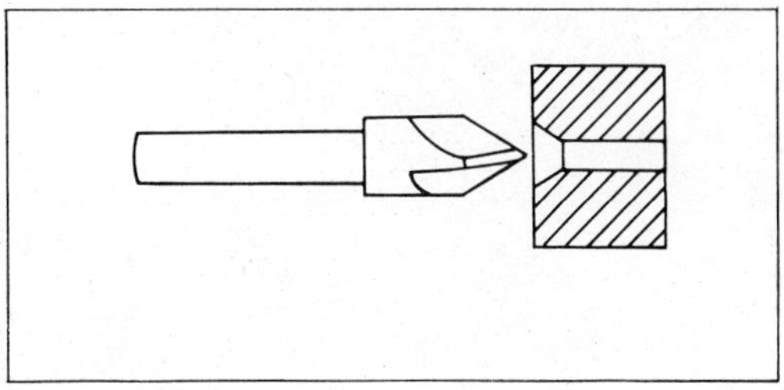

Figure 12-58
Countersinking is a process of removing metal around the edges of a hole to form a seat for screws, rivets, etc.

cutting flutes; may be performed similar to and on the same machines as for drilling. Its purpose is (1) to provide a seat for conical-shaped screw heads and rivets, (2) to provide, for subsequent operations, a seat for supporting the work on centers of machines such as the lathe and milling machine, or (3) to remove burrs and provide a chamfered hole. A typical example of a countersinking tool and the work produced are shown in Fig. 12-58.

Counterboring. Enlarging to a given depth a portion of a hole, which has previously been drilled or reamed, to accommodate a mating part having two or more diameters. The counterbore shoulder is made square with the axis of the hole to provide a seat or bearing surface for the mating part. A typical counterboring operation is shown in Fig. 12-59. The operation is performed similar to and on the same machines as those used for drilling.

The design of a counterboring tool, as shown in Fig. 12-59, embodies a shank for attachment to a collet or spindle, end cutting

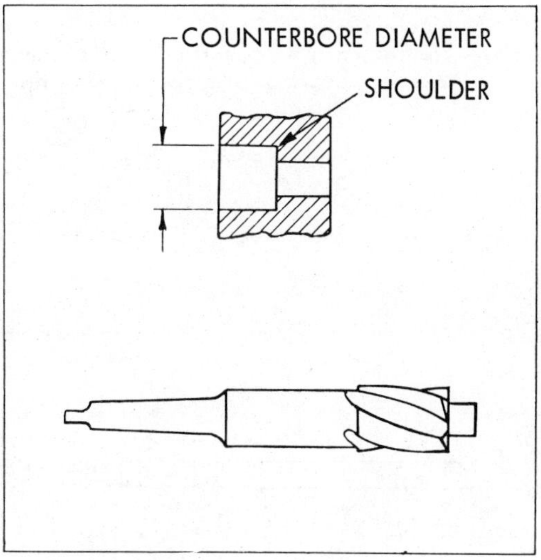

Figure 12-59
Counterboring is a process of enlarging a portion of a hole to accommodate a mating part having two or more diameters.

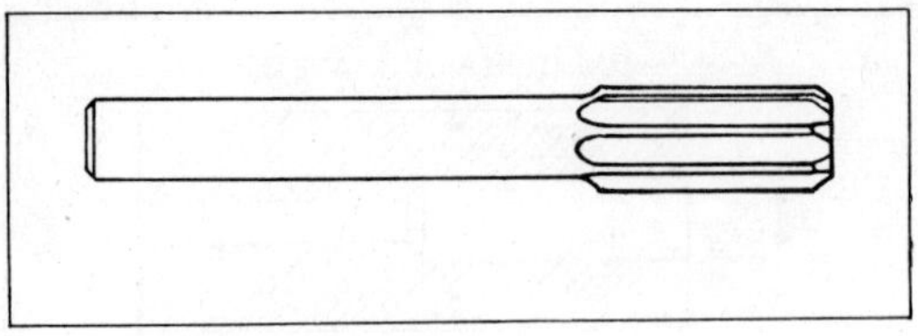

Figure 12-60
A reamer is used to enlarge a hole for greater accuracy.

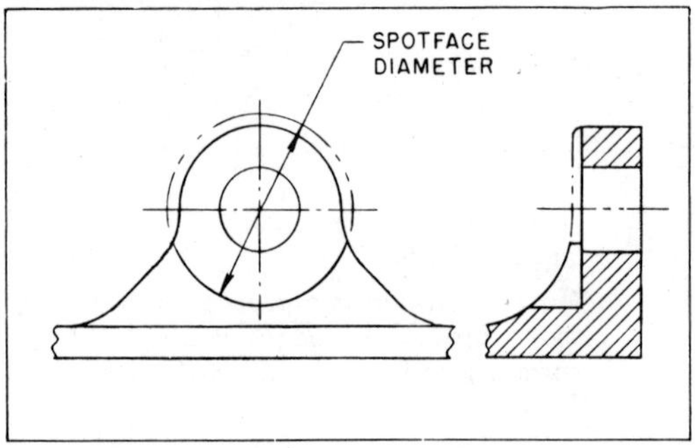

Figure 12-61
Spotfacing is an operation which forms a seat or bearing for a bolt head or nut.

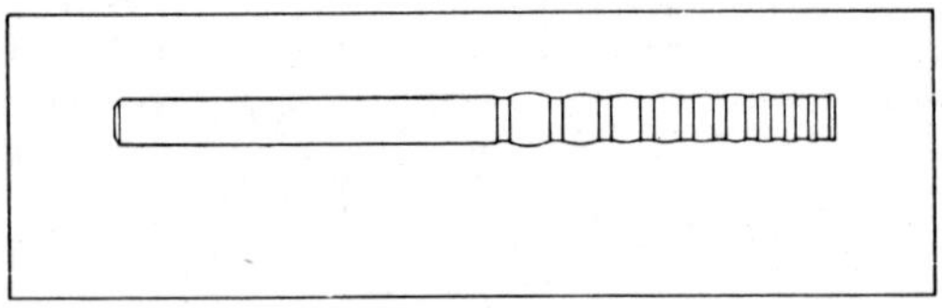

Figure 12-62
This burnishing tool is used to provide a high luster finish on a metal surface.

flutes, and a pilot which guides the path of the cut.

Reaming. Enlarging a hole to obtain a higher degree of finish and accuracy of size. The process is accomplished by the use of a tool, known as a reamer, which has several peripheral cutting flutes as shown in Fig. 12-60. The operation may be performed in the same manner as in drilling or it may be manually performed with the assistance of a wrench.

Spotfacing. A process similar to counterboring in which a square surface in a rough piece of work is provided as a bearing or seat for a bolt head, nut, etc. A typical spotfacing operation is shown in Fig. 12-61.

Burnishing. A process of finish sizing and producing an extremely smooth, high luster finish on metal surfaces previously machined. This process displaces, rather than removes, the minute surface irregularities produced with cutting tools and may be applied to internal or external surfaces.

The burnishing tool, shown in Fig. 12-62, is provided with several annular buttons, graduated in size, so that each button displaces a small amount of material as the tool is passed through the work. External burnishing is accomplished with the use of rolls and pressure and in some instances, where the design of the part will permit, the work is forced through a burnishing die.

Precision boring, facing, and turning. Strictly finishing processes whereby a small amount of stock is removed from metal parts to produce smooth, true, machined surfaces to a high degree of accuracy. These operations may be applied to internal, external or shouldered surfaces.

The process of precision boring is accomplished with a diamond or cemented-carbide-tipped tool bit supported in a boring bar revolved at high speed by the drive spindle. The work usually remains stationary except for feeding into and retracting from the tool. A typical boring operation is shown in Fig. 12-63.

The process of precision turning, facing, and shouldering differs slightly from precision boring. The work is held and rotated by the drive spindle at high speed while the tool bits, supported in the machine, feed into and retract from the work. A typical turning and facing operation is shown in Fig. 12-64.

Grinding. A process of removing material by means of a bonded abrasive wheel mounted on a suitable machine and rotated at high speed. Each abrasive grain on the wheel can be considered a very minute, sharp tool. As the wheel revolves, each grain cuts a small chip from the work, which may revolve or move transversely depending on the type of grinding operation to be performed.

Grinding wheels are classified according to abrasive material, grain size, and type of bond, the choice of which depends on the material to be worked and the surface finish required.

Grinding may be a roughing operation, as in the case of snagging; however, it is generally considered a finishing operation where applied to surfaces requiring accuracy and smooth finish. There are various classifications of grinding which include cylindrical, internal, centerless and surface grinding.

Honing. Another process of removing material from surfaces by means of bonded abrasives. It is generally applied to cylindrical surfaces, although other shapes may be honed with suitable equipment and operating methods.

The tool used on cylinder bores consists of a group of equally spaced abrasive stones supported in a holder. Each contacting abrasive grain cuts a small particle from the work. The tool works with a reciprocating and rotating motion while the work is stationary. A sectional view of a typical hone having multiple abrasive contact with the walls of a cylinder is shown in Fig. 12-65.

The tool or the work is permitted to float so that the bore and the tool may align themselves, thus maintaining the axial location of the hole. This is a contributing factor to the production of straight and round bores.

A typical floating type cylindrical hone is shown in Fig. 12-66.

The correction of inaccuracies in a bore sometimes necessitates removal of relatively large amounts of material. The usual eco-

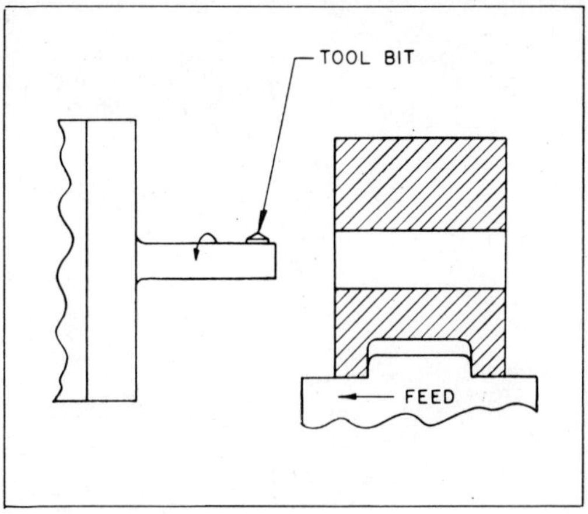

Figure 12-63
A precision boring operation.

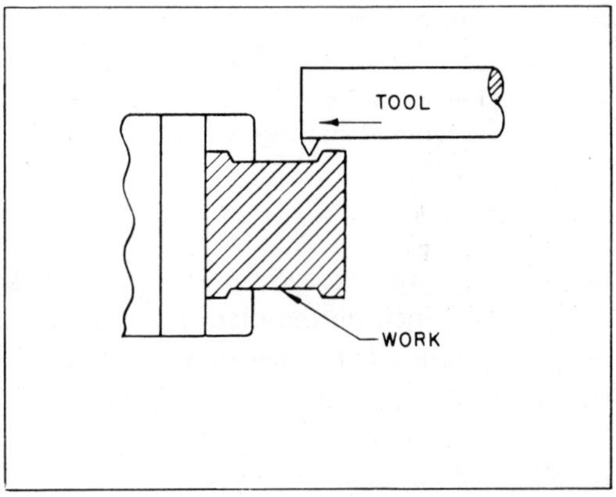

Figure 12-64
A precision turning and facing operation.

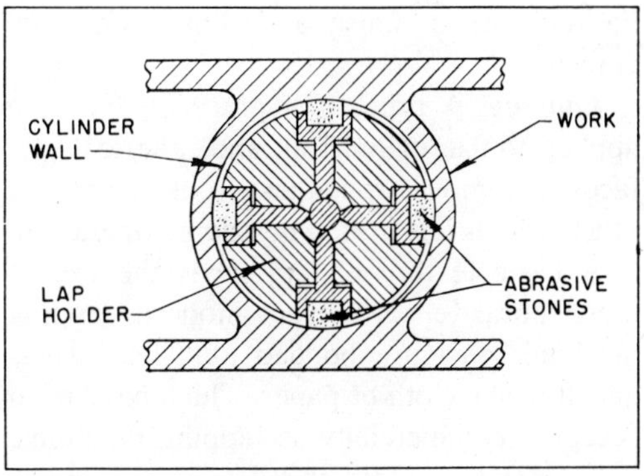

Figure 12-65
This is a sectional view of a hone with multiple abrasives.

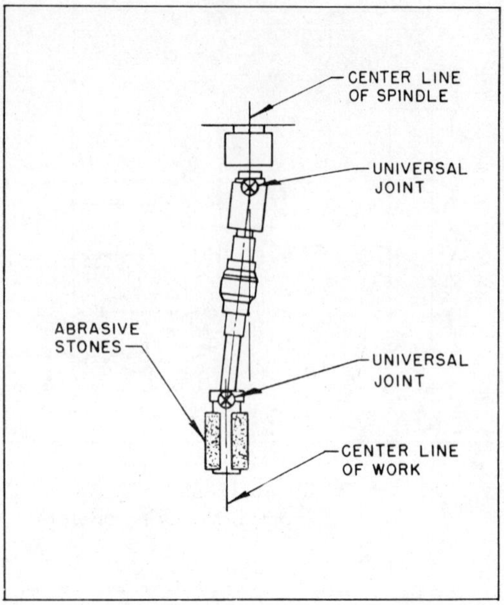

Figure 12-66
A typical floating type of cylindrical hone.

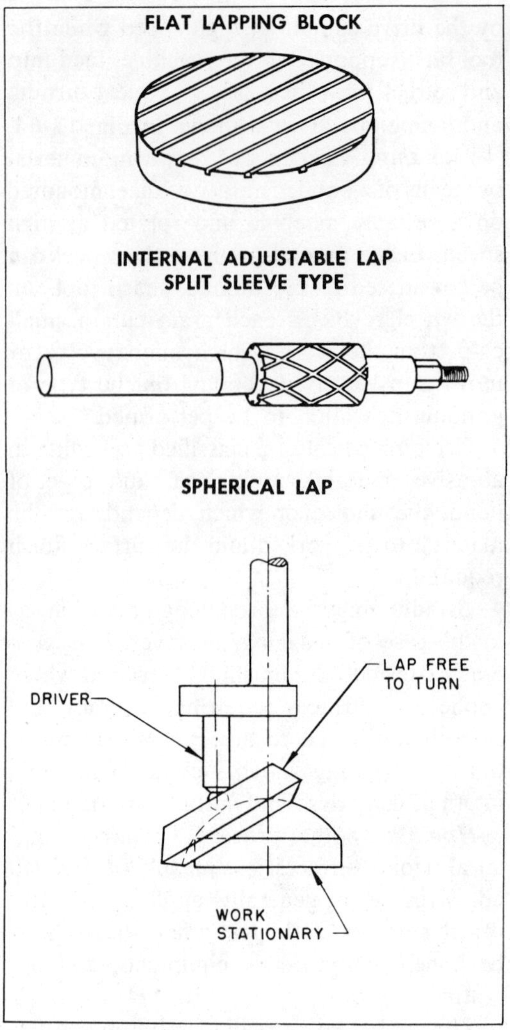

Figure 12-67
These lapping tools are used as a final surface finishing operation.

nomic range for average honing practice is .001 to .020 inch on the diameter. On parts honed for finish only, the amount of material necessary for removal of all marks left by previous operations may vary from .0002 to .001 inch on the diameter.

Honing is usually considered a precision machining operation. However, any or all of the following may be obtained: (1) rapid and economical removal of stock, (2) generation of straight, round bores, and (3) any desired surface finish and dimensional accuracy.

Lapping. A process of precision finishing applied to flat, cylindrical, and spherical surfaces. It removes roughness, tool marks and other defects left from a preceding operation.

A basic feature of lapping is the use of loose abrasive. However, modern lapping machines also use bonded abrasive wheels and abrasive cloth or paper, which have been accepted commercially as lapping mediums.

The abrasive cloth or paper is attached to the lap shoes, as in the case of crankshaft journal lapping. The loose abrasive is usually mixed with a lubricant and applied between the lap and the work. The laps are the tools used for the operation and are of various designs, shapes and sizes. Three typical designs are shown in Fig. 12-67.

Another feature of lapping is that fresh points of contact are made between the lap and the work through constantly changing relative movements. This feature is important when optical flatness or geometrical accuracy is required on the finished surface.

Lapping may be described as a final stock-

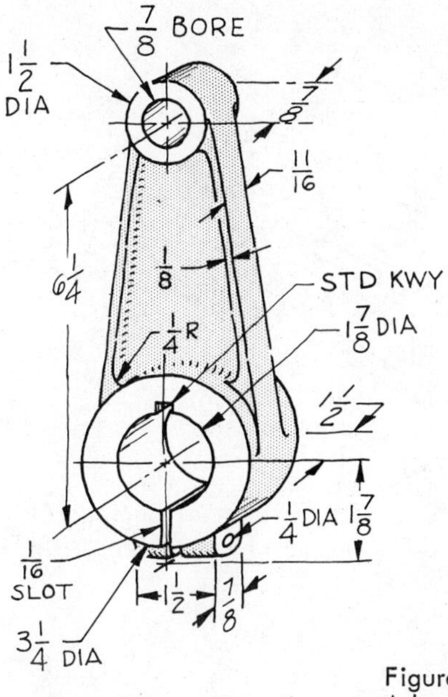

Figure 12-68
Arbor support.

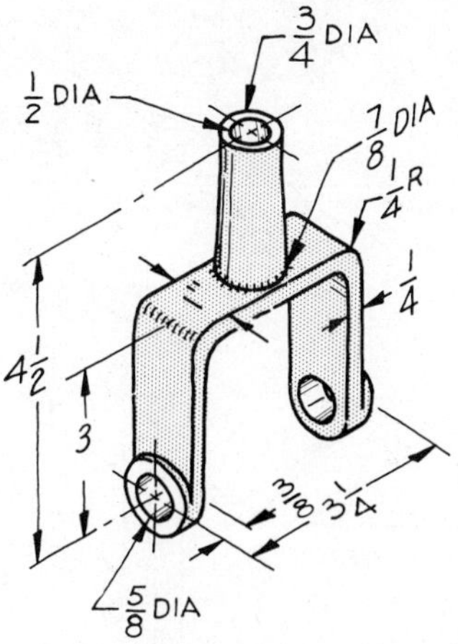

Figure 12-69
Aluminum rod yoke.

removing operation producing surface quality, geometric precision and dimensional accuracy, all of which add to the usefulness of the part or increase its wear life.

Polishing. A process sometimes referred to as "flexible grinding." It is used to smooth a surface by the cutting action of abrasive particles bonded to the surface of resilient wheels of wool, felt, leather, canvas or fabric. Sometimes the abrasive is bonded to belts operating over resilient wheels.

Polishing is generally a progressive operation performed with a set of wheels of different grain size, ranging from coarse grit to fine grit, and then followed by a buffing operation. Grain progression and the number of grain sizes used, depends on the work and the finish desired.

Metal polishing is usually performed for reasons of appearance rather than of accuracy. Polishing is also used on highly stressed machine parts to remove minute surface imperfections or to minimize wear on certain mating parts.

Problems, section 12

1 Make both a rough casting drawing and a finished machining drawing of the Arbor Support in the sketch of Fig. 12-68. Material: Steel, SAE 030. Web thickness to be 1/4".

2 Make a complete detail drawing of the die-cast aluminum Rod Yoke in the sketch of Fig. 12-69. Choose suitable fillets and rounds.

3 Prepare a forging drawing and a machining drawing for the steel Armature Mounting Hub shown in the sketch of Fig. 12-70. The spline is a standard SAE involute type. Finish to be 125√ all over except 63√ on splines.

4 Make a complete set of detail and assembly drawings of the Gear Puller in the sketch of Fig. 12-71. Use a straight knurl, medium pitch, on the screw knob. Choose appropriate materials.

5 Design a Drill Press Vise similar to that shown in the sketch of Fig. 12-72 and prepare complete detail and assembly drawings. Choose all design sizes not indicated. Provide hardened steel jaw plates as extra equipment. Specify materials.

6 Redesign the Pulley Bracket in the sketch of Fig. 12-73 for welded fabrication. Prepare a complete dimensioned weldment drawing.

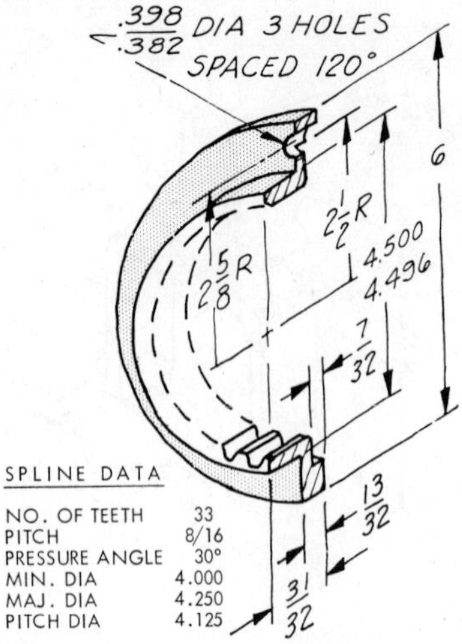

Figure 12–70
Armature mounting hub.

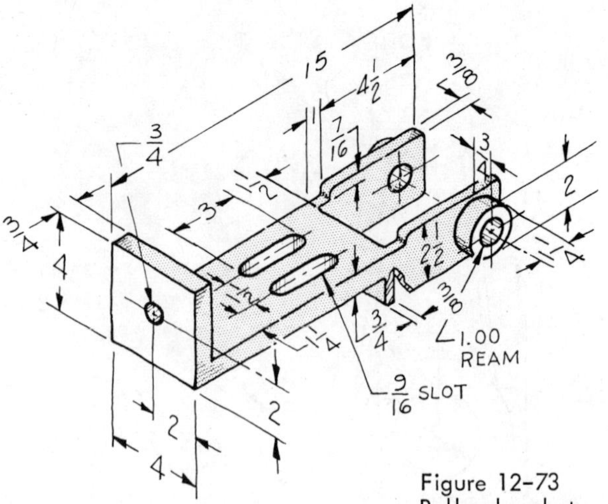

Figure 12–73
Pulley bracket.

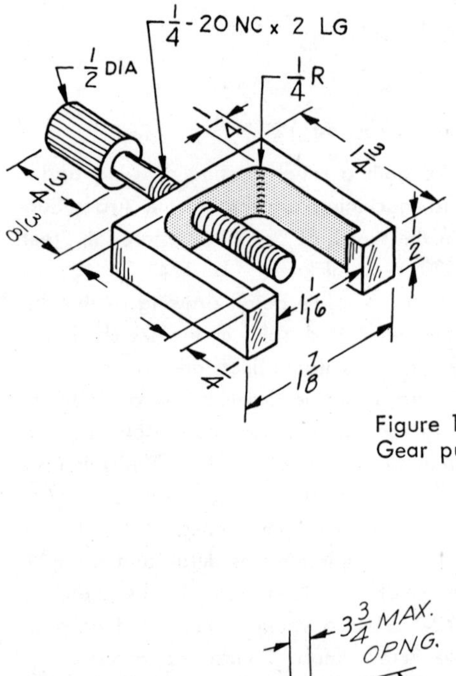

Figure 12–71
Gear puller.

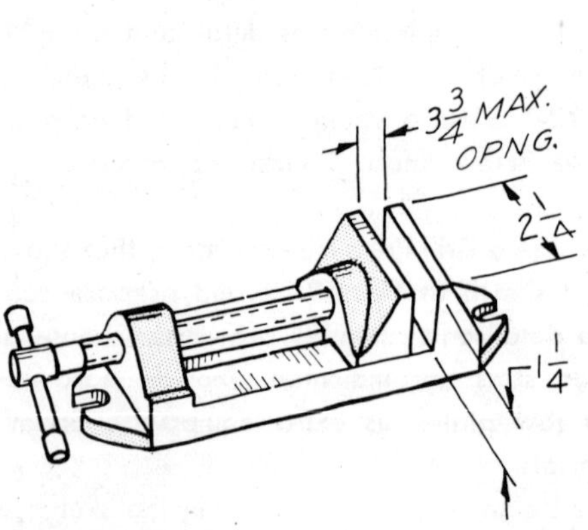

Figure 12–72
Drill press vise.

7 Make both a rough casting drawing and a finish machining drawing of the Wheel Arm in the sketch of Fig. 12-74. Material: Brass, SAE 40.

8 Make a complete detail drawing of the Valve Hanger shown in the sketch of Fig. 12-75. Determine and specify the flat blank size before forming. Material: .040″ 1/4 hard, cold rolled steel. Finish: Black Oxide.

9 Design a 12″ forged steel Wrench similar to that shown in the sketch of Fig. 12-76 having a capacity of 1-5/16″. Make complete detail and assembly drawings.

10 Design a Caster Assembly similar to the sketch of Fig. 12-77 including frame, mounting pad and bearing retainers for a 3″ DIA x 1-1/4″ wide caster wheel. Provide integral bearing races for ball bearings. Support caster on a 3/8″ DIA threaded shaft. Make a complete set of drawings for the job.

11 Design and prepare a set of drawings for a Universal Joint similar to the sketch of Fig. 12-78 capable of accommodating 13/16″ DIA shafts.

12 Design and prepare complete working drawings including assemblies of a Machinist's Vise, similar to the sketch of Fig. 12-79. Provide a jaw width of 3-1/2″, with a maximum opening of 5-5/8″. Use an Acme thread on the lead screw.

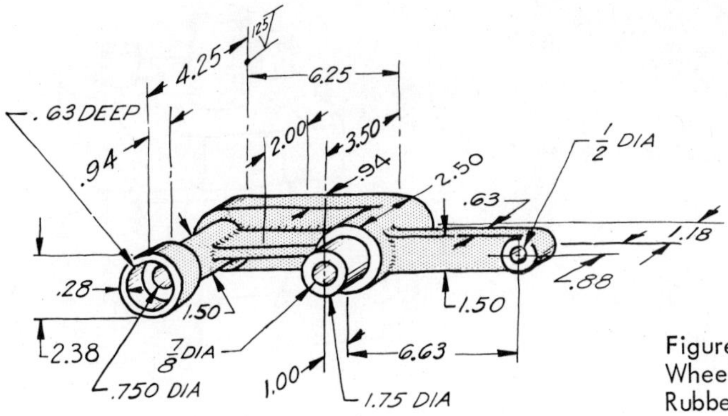

Figure 12-74
Wheel arm. Firestone Tire and Rubber Co.

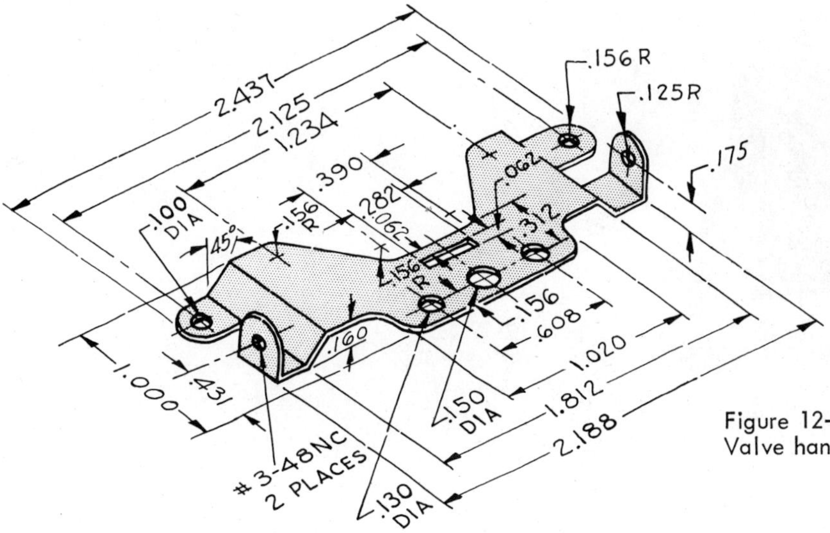

Figure 12-75
Valve hanger. The Lionel Corp.

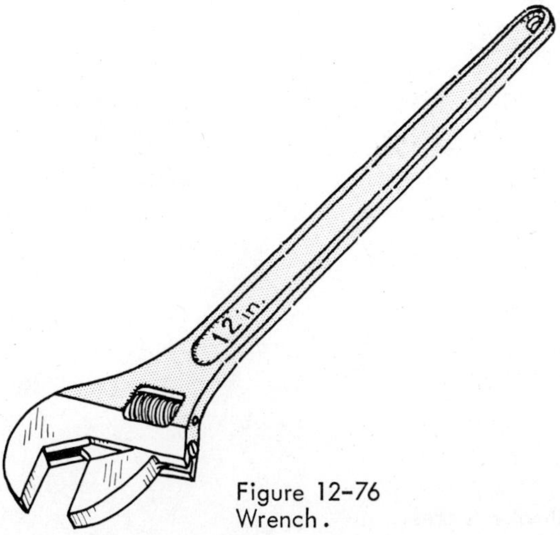

Figure 12-76
Wrench.

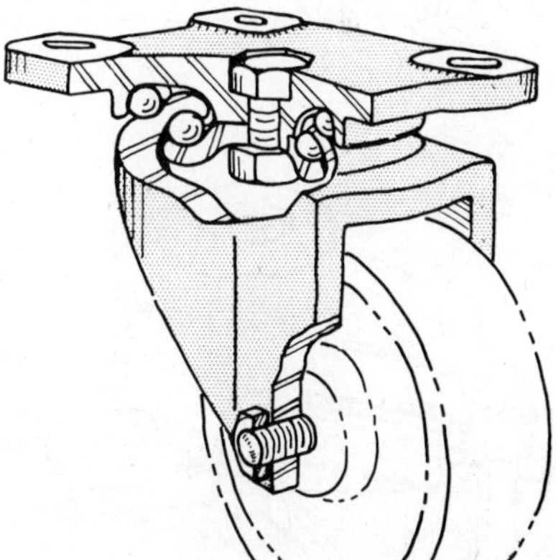

Figure 12-77
Caster assembly.

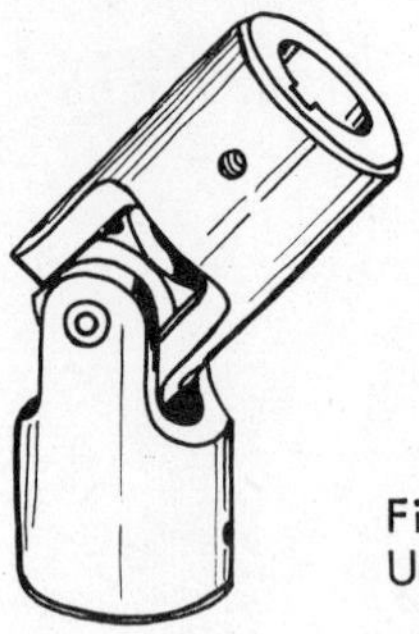

Figure 12-78
Universal joint.

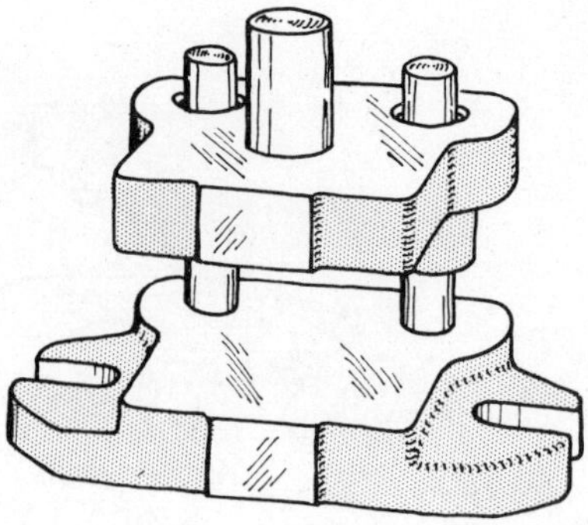

Figure 12-82
Die set.

Figure 12-79
Machinist's vise.

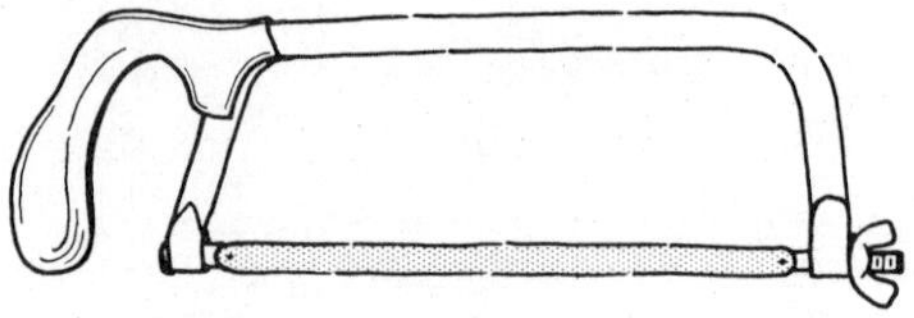

Figure 12-80
Hack saw frame.

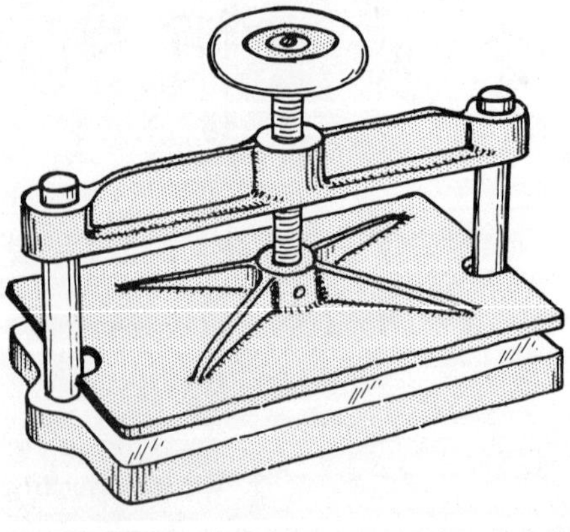

Figure 12-81
Modelmaker's press.

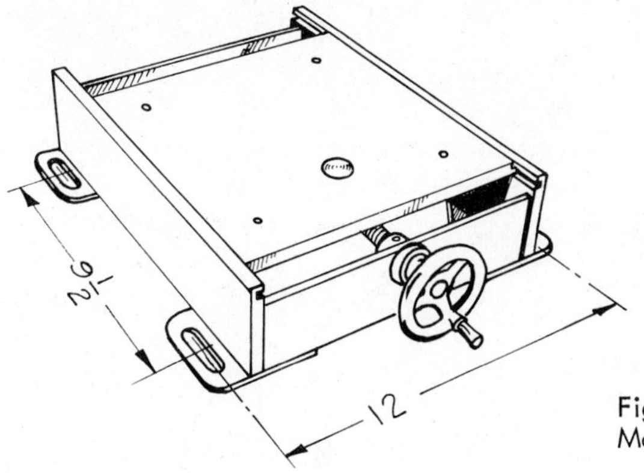

Figure 12-83
Motor base.

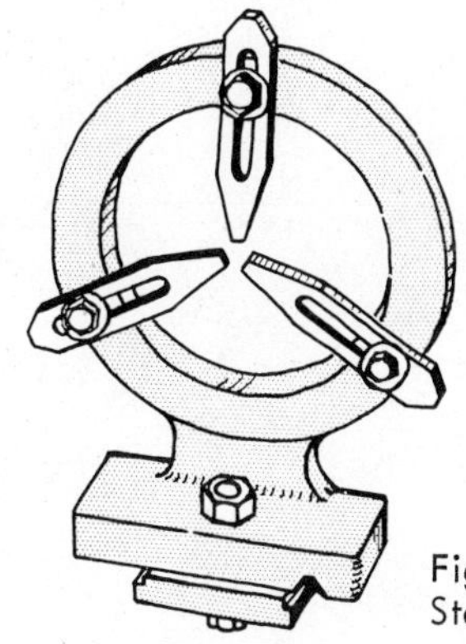

Figure 12-84
Steady rest.

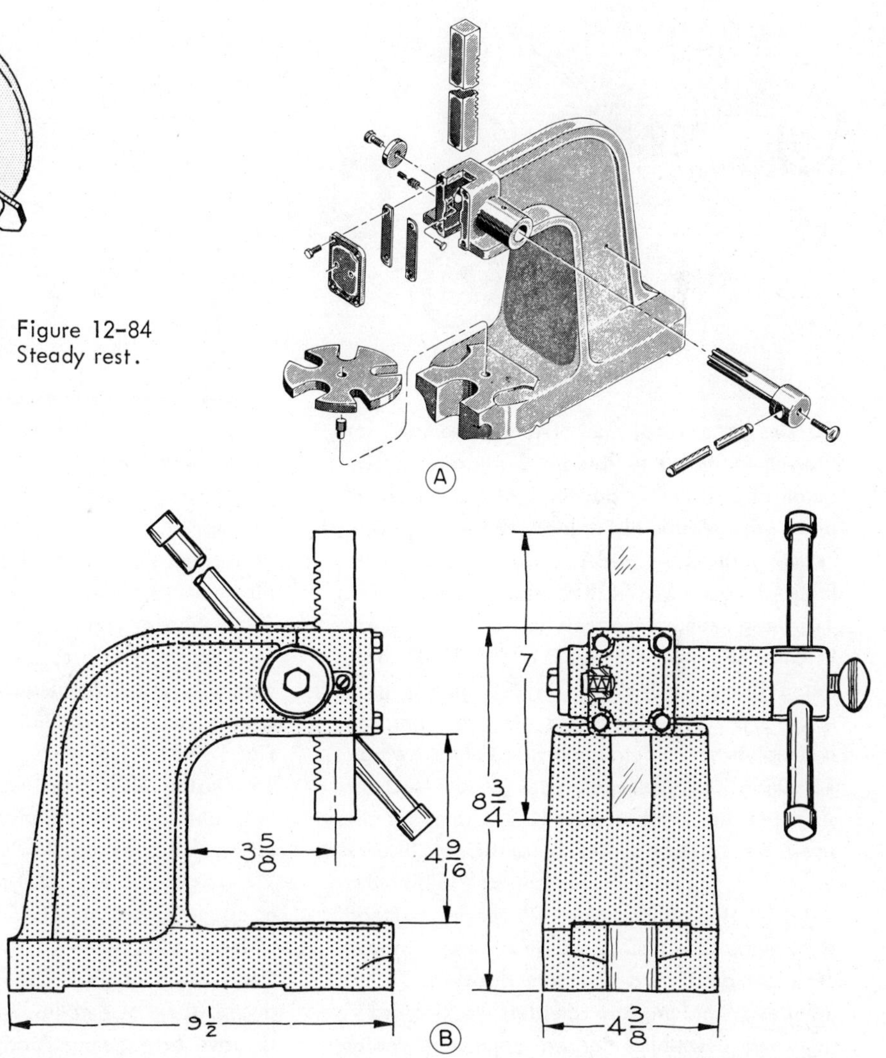

Figure 12-85
Arbor press.
Dake Engine Co.

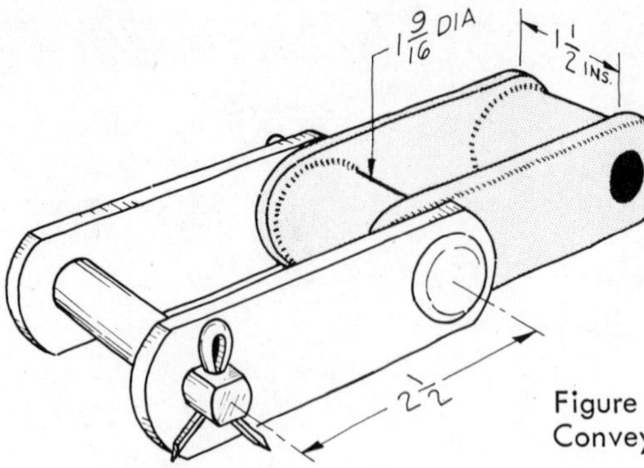

Figure 12–86
Conveyor chain.

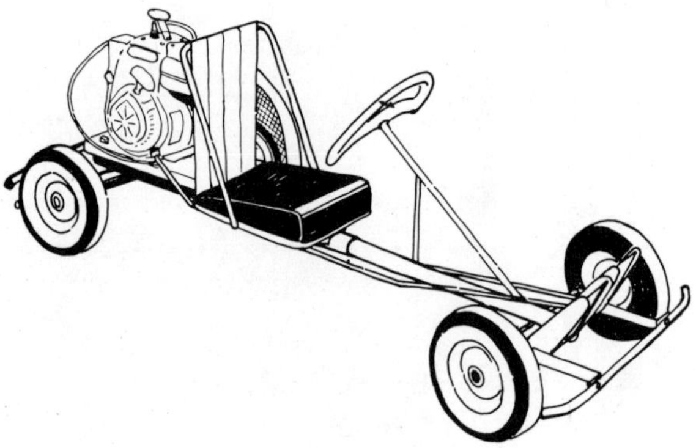
Figure 12–87
RACING KART

13 Design a Hack Saw Frame assembly for use with standard 10″ blades. Prepare complete detail and assembly drawings of the aluminum pistol grip, electrically welded frame and loops. Frame materials—3/16″ x 5/8″ C.R. Steel; loops—16 ga x 5/8″ C.R. Steel. See Fig. 12-80.

14 Design the components for a Modelmaker's Press, as shown in the sketch of Fig. 12-81, having a platen 6–3/8″ x 10–1/2″ and a lead screw 5/8″ DIA. All castings grey iron. Prepare a complete set of detail and assembly drawings.

15 Design a production-type Die Set such as shown in the sketch of Fig. 12-82, having a die space left to right of 4–1/2″ and front to back of 3–1/4″. Thickness of the semi-steel die holder is 1–1/4″, the punch holder 1″. Make hardened steel guide pins 1″ DIA x 5–1/2″ long. Prepare complete detail and assembly drawings.

16 Design and prepare complete working drawings and assemblies for an adjustable Motor Base, similar to that shown in Fig. 12-83. The motor base is to accommodate an electric motor having an NEMA frame #204. Make the welded base of steel plate 4-1/4″ high, 14″ long and 10-1/2″ wide with a 6″ adjustment for the slide plate.

17 Make complete detail and assembly drawings for a Steady Rest for a 9″ metalworking lathe. See the sketch of Fig. 12-84. Determine the measurements from a lathe in school machine shop or from a manufacturer's catalog.

18 Design and prepare complete detail and assembly drawings of an Arbor Press using the basic dimensions as indicated in the sketch of Fig. 12-85.

19 Design side links, cast malleable center link, and pin for a Conveyor Chain as shown in the sketch of Fig. 12-86.

20 (Group Project. Each member to work on a component.) Design a RACING KART, see sketch of Fig. 12-87, having a wheel base of 48″ and tread width of 29″. Choose commercially produced wheel assemblies, engine, etc. Select type of drive arrangement and brake mechanism to suit the design. Prepare complete detail, subassembly, and final assembly drawings together with Parts List for the complete vehicle.

Drafting department practices 13

Drafting departments in industry today vary in size from small departments employing only a few draftsmen to extremely large departments where several hundred may be employed. Obviously the organization of a small department is not nearly as extensive as that of a department where many people are involved. Regardless of size, however, each department must operate to insure efficiency in design, development, and rapid production of legible drawings.

In addition to an organizational plan which controls the flow of work, drafting departments also have certain rules and regulations which guide the draftsmen in the creation of uniform drawings.

The primary purpose of this section is not to describe all of the various organizational structures and departmental drafting procedures, but simply to bring to the attention of students some of the basic practices which are followed by most drafting departments.

13.1 Departmental organization

A newly employed draftsman is very early shown the organizational structure of the drafting department. Naturally, in a relatively small industry the organization will be comparatively simple; that is, a group working together and supervised by one of their number. Drafting departments of considerable size invariably are headed by a chief draftsman whose principal job is to direct all of the activities involving drafting services. Again, depending on the number of people employed, a department may be further divided into smaller groups headed by squad bosses or group leaders. Each group is responsible for certain types of work and in turn each draftsman is assigned a specific job to do.

As the newly employed draftsman assumes his duties, he should understand and appreciate the significance of the existing organizational structure, particularly since the organization was developed to produce the maximum efficiency in departmental work. To maintain this efficiency, each employee should recognize the proper lines of communication and carry out his assigned duties according to the specifications and instructions emanating from the authoritative sources.

13.2 Duties and responsibilities of the draftsman

The principal function of a draftsman is to express engineering ideas in the form of mechanical drawings. As such, he is required to produce drawings that are accurate and neat, and to complete them in the shortest possible time.

To insure the utmost degree of standardization of method and practice, certain rules and regulations governing drafting practices are often prescribed by industries. The newly employed draftsman has to familiarize himself with these practices and adhere to them as closely as possible. It is true that there is often more than one correct way to make and dimension a drawing. The adopted departmental drafting standard practices are not intended to stifle the draftsman's originality, but rather to provide an authoritative guide in the mechanics of drafting. By following these recommended drafting practices, the draftsman will make fewer mistakes and will produce more legible drawings.

The draftsman will have to keep himself informed of the latest specifications of materials, tools and processes that are applicable to his area of drafting. Although experienced checkers will make a final check of his drawings, each draftsman is expected to check his work so that a minimum of errors will be found by the checker. Above all, a draftsman must strictly follow all instructions given to him by his superior. Any deviation from these instructions may seriously impair the design intent of the product and cause unnecessary waste of time through costly delays. On the other hand, if the draftsman should discover an irregularity, he should discuss it with his superior before making any changes or corrections.

13.3 Employer-employee invention agreement

Draftsmen, engineers, and other individuals who in their jobs do creative work are usually required to sign an agreement form assigning all inventions to the company. It is the accepted practice that if such individuals, while carrying out company work, should discover some new process or device, these processes or devices rightfully belong to the company. See sample agreement in Fig. 13-1.

The agreement which employees sign also stipulates that they will not reveal to any other person or competing company their discoveries and that upon termination of their employment they will make no attempt to infringe on the patented process or device for a prescribed period of time.

Most companies usually do not make any promises that additional compensation will be given to the individual in the event he invents a new design or makes a new discovery. Nevertheless a company will generally recognize this invaluable service by proper adjustment of salary and advancement in the company. For information on patent drawings see Section 26.

13.4 Developing drafting efficiency

The need for standardization of drafting practices is fully recognized by industry. This is clearly emphasized in the introductory statement of *Drafting and Design Standards,* Chrysler Corporation, when it states: "Standardization of methods and practices in the drafting room has always been very necessary due to the dissemination and interchange of drawings and engineering information. Increasing competition is forcing products into a design field of closed limits of positional and decimal tolerancing. Direction toward such standardized drafting room practices cannot help but result in savings of a great deal of time, material and expense, not only in the engineering departments but throughout the entire organization."[1]

To a considerable extent, the standardization of drafting practices has been achieved over the years because of the efforts of standardizing agencies such as the American Standards Association (ASA) and the Society of Automotive Engineers (SAE); of industries such as the National Electrical Manufacturing Association (NEMA) and also the American Gear Manufacturers Association (AGMA); and of military committees such as Joint Army-Navy (JAN) and Military Standards (MIL). Most industrial drafting departments have gone even a step further to insure standardization by preparing their own drafting standards manuals. For the most part, a company's manual will contain those portions of ASA, SAE, JAN, or MIL standards that are of special significance to the work of the company. In addition, the manual will include many other items, such as company drafting policy, engineering data, specification of materials, and fabrication processes.

Every draftsman is expected to become familiar with his company's manual and to use it as the authoritative guide and source of reference whenever a question arises. Draftsmen who follow the manual usually make fewer mistakes, which simplifies the job of the checker and causes less confusion in the shop where the drawings are to be used.

Drafting department library. Besides the drafting standards manual, most modern drafting departments maintain a library consisting of reference books, manufacturer's catalogs, trade magazines, handbooks and standards. This fund of information is readily available to all draftsmen and is intended to

1. *Drafting and Design Standards* (Detroit: Chrysler Corp.).

INVENTION ASSIGNMENT AGREEMENT

In part consideration of my Employment by

____DIVISION,
BORG-WARNER CORPORATION, an Illinois Corporation, and for the wages now and hereafter paid to me by said Division, I agree in connection with any work assigned to me to use my skill and ability to discover, make and invent new and useful improvements and inventions relating to the art and business of said Division, and to assist other employees in so doing, and to communicate to my immediate superior or to the Patent Department of BORG-WARNER CORPORATION, during the term of my employment, any and all discoveries, improvements and/or inventions relating to said art and business of said Division: and

With respect to any and all such discoveries, improvements, and inventions which I may conceive or make during the term of my employment, and for six (6) months thereafter, either solely or jointly with others, which relate to the art or business of said Division; or relate to the art or business for which BORG-WARNER CORPORATION is wholly or in part equipped and growing out of my contact with said art or business; I agree to assign, and by these presents do hereby assign and transfer, all of my right, title and interest in and to such discoveries, improvements and inventions to BORG-W... of PORATION, its successors and assigns, and I agree, upon the request of sa... by appropri- deliver all documents and do all acts necessary to secure to BO... Patent Law and the cessors and assigns, or its nominee, the entire rig... on. provements and inventions, including appli... countries foreign ... or subsidiary of BORG-WARNER then I agree that said for Lett... may be included with or substituted for the above identified division and this agree- ... remain in full force and in effect until superseded by a new agreement or terminated by either party hereto.

This agreement shall be binding upon and the covenants and agreement herein contained shall inure to and be for the benefit of the parties hereto, their heirs, executors, administrators, legal representatives, nominees and assigns.

WITNESS:

____
Signature of Employee

____

DATED AT________________________ 19____

Figure 13-1
A draftsman while employed by a particular company will be required to sign an agreement relinquishing all rights to new inventions which he discovers or develops. Borg-Warner Corp.

help them keep constantly up-to-date.

Personal technical file. The conscientious engineer and draftsman often keep a personal file to maintain a current line of communication to new technical information in their field. The file is frequently in the form of a three-ring loose-leaf binder having suitable dividers. See Fig. 13-2. In this binder clippings from technical magazines, journals, and manufacturer's literature can be inserted. The loose-leaf file makes it easy to add or delete material and has the advantage of expandability and portability. By placing a tab on the divider leafs, each section of the file is readily accessible.

To make such a file really valuable, the draftsman or engineer should give considerable thought to the organization of the material. Divisions and sub-divisions should be selected that will best serve his need and interest. In every instance, simplicity of organization is the best measure of efficiency.

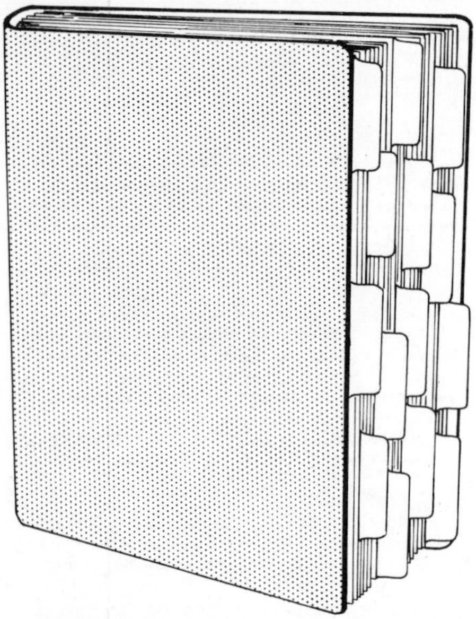

Figure 13-2
A personal technical file containing current clip sheets from magazines and other trade literature helps the draftsman keep up-to-date.

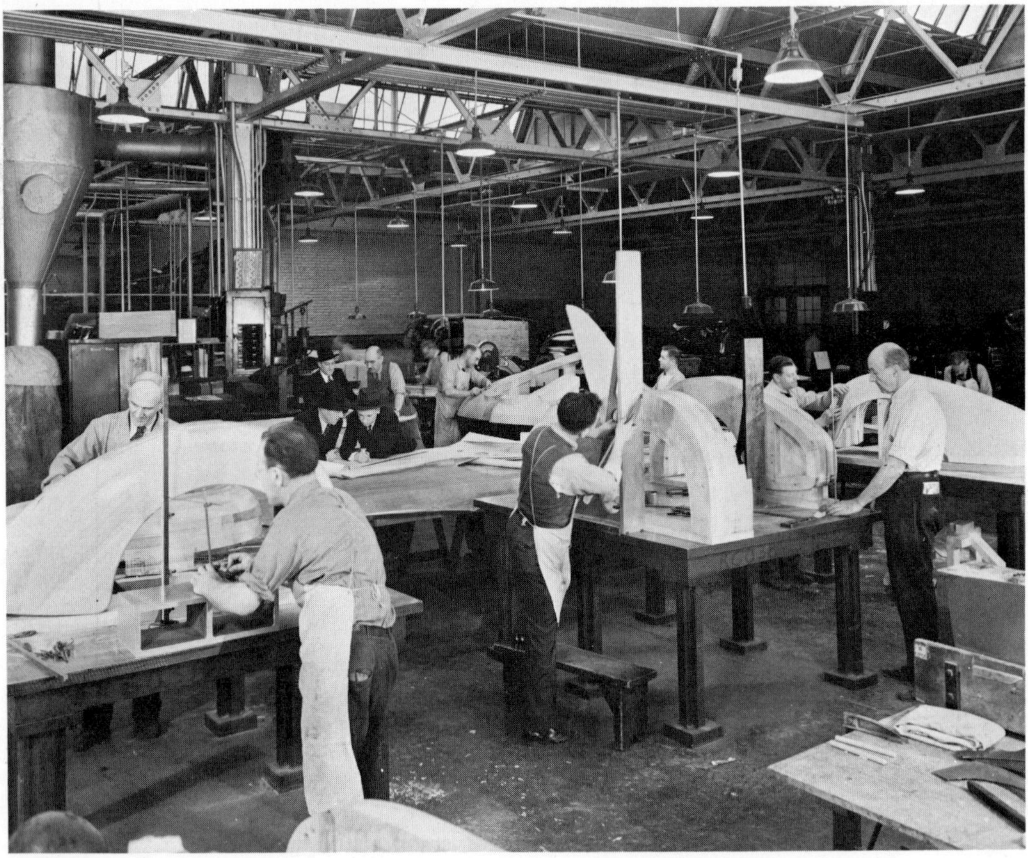

Figure 13-3
Model makers build models to check the accuracy of newly designed components. Chevrolet Motor Division, General Motors Corp.

Most draftsmen provide themselves with a single-drawer portable file for use at their reference desk. In this file they keep some of the material which is needed less frequently as well as catalogs and references which are too large to place in a binder.

13.5 Routing of drawings

The process of developing a new product from its design stages to final production consumes many manhours and involves many highly-trained specialists. Creation of a new design usually starts in the design office where experienced engineers and designers make preliminary sketches of the proposed product. The sketches are next turned over to the drafting department for preparation of preliminary layouts. From these layouts models, mockups, or a prototype of the product is constructed. See Fig. 13-3. The prototype is then tested and necessary design changes made.

After the design changes have been incorporated and the product accepted for production, the drafting department is called upon to prepare detailed production drawings. The chief draftsman with the help of his schedulers, analysts and supervisors breaks down the work into small blocks until each task involves an individual job. These jobs are assigned to draftsmen who work directly under a leader and prepare the required set of finished drawings.

As each drawing is completed, it is printed and a check print is passed on to a checker for its first "accuracy check." During this stage certain changes may become evident, changes which are not necessarily due to inaccuracies by the original draftsman but to design refinements in other parts or assemblies of the product. Here is where the draftsman assumes his true responsibility in bringing the drawings into final form. The "checker changes" must be made on the original drawings, and usually by the original draftsman. When these changes are completed, a second check print is sent to the checker for a final check. If the drawing is accepted by the checker, it is approved by the project engineer and becomes a production plan.

Work Order		Form 170		W.O. No.	
Machine type		Project No.		Date	
Order No.		Control No.		Issued by	
Customer or Engineering request by				Approved	
				Del. date prom.	
				Original Eng. promise	
Job Description				Present Eng. promise	Estimated hrs. to complete
Draftsmen	Est. hours	Scheduled to start	Completed	Prints issued	E. O.
Prototype					
Remarks					

Figure 13-4
Each work order identifies the job and is designed to keep an accurate check of its progress. Machine Design

13.6 Work orders, progress charts, individual work log

When a new task is undertaken, a record of its initiation and progress is maintained. A *work order* as shown in Fig. 13-4 is frequently used for this purpose. The work order may contain a description of the entire job or it may show one of several major divisions of the job. Thus the task may be broken down into such job components as electrical, structural and hydraulics.

Each work order includes the name of draftsmen assigned to the task, the estimated number of hours for completion, the date the work is scheduled to start, and the date the drawings are completed.

In addition to the work order, the chief draftsman or scheduler often keeps a *progress chart* which discloses the status of the total

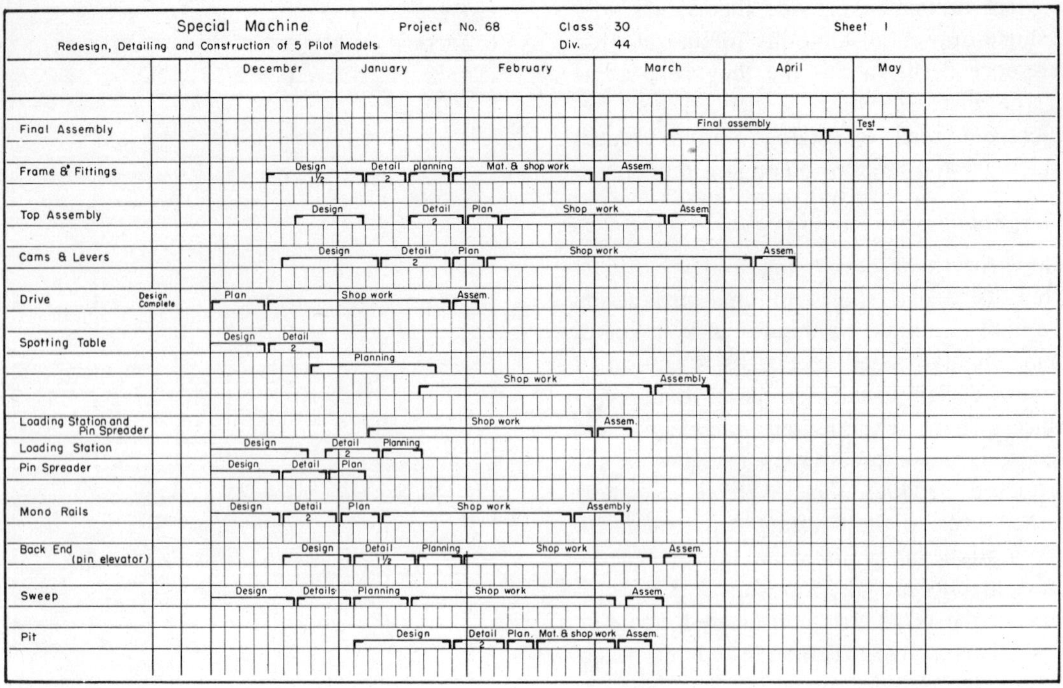

Figure 13-5
A progress chart shows the various stages of each drawing job and discloses whether or not the work is progressing according to the time schedule. Machine Design

drawing job. See Fig. 13-5. This progress chart is particularly valuable since it enables the chief draftsman to ascertain periodically if the work is proceeding according to the established time schedule.

Some firms often require their draftsmen to fill out a daily *time distribution card* as shown in Fig. 13-6. Note the type of information that is required in this record.

Another example is the draftsman's log reproduced in Fig. 13-7. This record is started at the assignment of each job and includes all data concerning decisions, sketches and calculations pertaining to it.

13.7 Checking drawings

Drafting departments retain one or more experienced draftsmen on their staff known as *checkers*. The principal job of a checker is to verify and examine all finished drawings to insure accuracy, completeness, and efficiency. Since the checker must certify to the correctness of the drawings before they are released, the importance of his job becomes very obvious.

To function effectively, a checker must be familiar with manufacturing practices and must have a thorough knowledge of drafting and drafting standards. He is required not only to check those dimensions and views which are shown on a drawing, but he also has to be constantly on the alert for omissions due to carelessness or lack of experience on the part of a detailer.

In most instances, a checker makes corrections on a print of the drawing rather than on the drawing itself. By using a print it avoids defacing the drawing and provides a clear record for the draftsman as well as the checker.

Checking routine. In a drawing, a checker uses the following questions as a guide:[2]

2. *Ibid.*

INGERSOLL KALAMAZOO DIVISION
BORG-WARNER CORPORATION
KALAMAZOO, MICHIGAN

DAILY TIME TICKET
DESIGN ENGINEERING

CLOCK NUMBER	NAME	DATE

CONTRACT NO.	PROJECT NUMBER	RECORD NUMBER	DESCRIPTION	HOURS	RATE	AMOUNT	ACCOUNT CHARGED
Remarks			Total				APPROVED BY

NO CARBON REQUIRED—MOORE BUSINESS FORMS, INC., ELMIRA, N. Y.—PAPER PAT. BY N. C. R. CO. DS-51-R-2

Figure 13-6
A draftsman often is required to record daily the progress of his work.
Borg-Warner Corp.

1 Does the general appearance of the drawing conform to the Drafting and Design Standards?
2 Is the part sufficiently strong and suitable for the function it has to perform?
3 Does the drawing represent the most economical method of manufacture?
4 Are all the necessary views and sections shown, and are they in proper relation to one another?
5 Are all necessary dimensions shown?
6 Do the dimensions agree with the layout and related parts, and are duplicate and unnecessary dimensions avoided?
7 Is the drawing to scale?
8 Is the drawing dimensioned to avoid unnecessary calculations in the shop?
9 Are stationary and operating clearances adequate?
10 Can the part or parts be assembled, disassembled, and serviced by the most economical methods?
11 Are proper limits or tolerances specified to produce the desired fits?
12 Have undesirable limit accumulations been avoided?
13 Are proper draft angles, fillets and corner radii specified?
14 Are all necessary symbols for finishing, grinding, etc., shown?
15 Are locating points and proper finish allowances provided?
16 Are sufficient notes, including concentricity, parallelism, squareness, flatness, etc., shown?
17 Is the approximate developed length shown?
18 Is the stock size specified?
19 Are material and heat treatment specifications given?
20 Are plating and painting specifications, either for protective or decorative purposes, given?
21 Are trademark, part number and manufacturer's identification shown according to requirements?

DRAFTSMAN'S DESIGN LOG	Sheet No. / of / Sheet
Detailed Description: Layout and details of new transmission low speed gear and mainshaft combination. Low speed gear to have I.D. of splines accurately ground with respect to gear teeth, and mainshaft to have three ground lands for mounting low speed gear on these surfaces.	Job no. 9344 - 97 Job name Trans. Mainshaft First and Reverse Gear Models 1950 Engineer Taylor Job started Job finished Layout numbers L - 35042

Job Objective: To eliminate selective fit on mating parts

References: L - 33827

Progress, Decisions and Authority:

-Messrs. Taylor and Gibson decided to change from a 22 tooth basic spline with 3 unevenly spaced lands to both a 24 tooth basic spline with 6 evenly spaced lands and a 24 tooth basic spline with 8 evenly spaced lands.

Engineers also requested study of a longer hub for 1st. and reverse gear to reduce runout.

After preliminary investigation Messrs. Taylor and Gibson decided to cancel the 8 lands construction and the elongated hub.

Mr. Gibson decided to have an additional layout made of a 22 tooth basic spline with alternating teeth and lands.

Calculations and sketches to be dated and attached.

Signature John R. Doe

Figure 13-7
Some drafting departments require that a draftsman keep a descriptive log of each drawing job. SAE

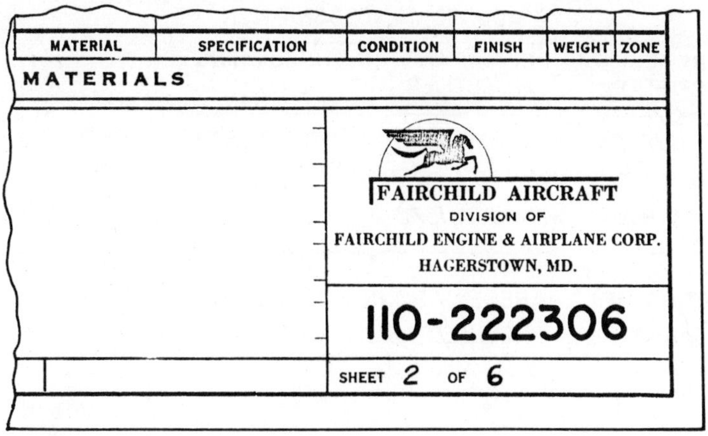

Figure 13-8
The drawing number in the title block identifies the drawing. Fairchild Aircraft

22 Has the title block been filled in with the correct information?
23 Has the date been entered?
24 Are primary and secondary part numbers identical?
25 Are necessary part numbers of detail parts and sub-assemblies shown on assembly drawings?
26 Have original lines and drawing information damaged by erasures been properly restored?
27 Are revisions properly recorded?
28 Have all related drawings been revised to conform?

13.8 Title block information

Although the arrangement of the required information in a title block may vary somewhat from one manufacturer to another, in general there will be included the following:

1 *Drawing number block.* All drawings are identified by a drawing number which appears in the drawing number block. Subsection 13.9 describes in more detail the structure of a numbering system. If a drawing is made up of two or more sheets, the first sheet is numbered 1 of so many and the additional sheets are numbered as sheet 2, 3, 4, etc., of the total number of sheets. See Fig. 13-8.

2 *Drawing title.* Should consist of a basic name and sufficient modifiers to properly establish a clear concept of the item. The basic name should be a noun or noun phrase which describes the part and the usage of the part, and not the material or method of fabrication. Thus the word "casting", "forging", or "weldment" would be improper. Instead the appropriate title would be BRACKET, SUPPORT BRACKET, or MIXING VALVE. The noun or noun phrase should be in singular form except where the only form of the noun is plural; e.g., TONGS, SCISSORS. Another exception: when multiple single items appear on the same drawing, such as FUSES, CONNECTORS. An ambiguous noun, or one which designates several classes of items, should not be used alone but as part of a noun phrase. Example:

Acceptable	Unacceptable
Running Board	Board, Running
Slide Rule	Rule, Slide
Soldering Iron	Iron, Soldering
Junction Box	Box, Junction
Cable Drum	Drum, Cable

A noun or noun phrase may require further clarification, in which case a modifier is added. A modifier may be a single word or a qualifying phrase. The first modifier is

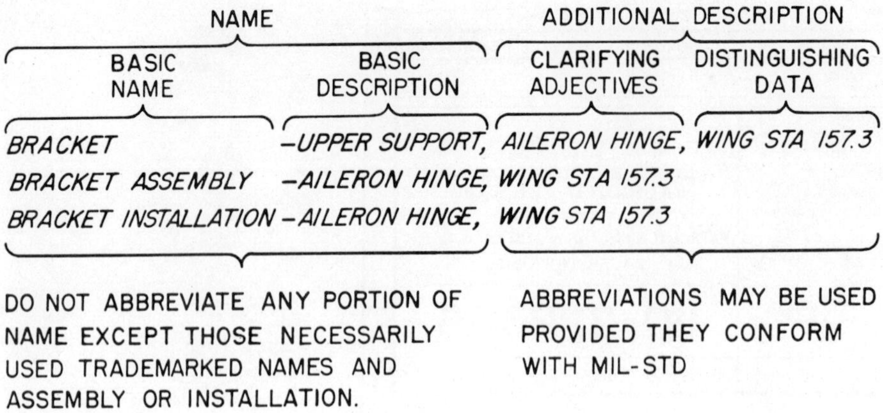

Figure 13-9
A drawing title should establish a clear concept of the item.

intended to narrow the area of concept established by the basic name. Succeeding modifiers must continue to narrow the item concept by expressing a different type of characteristic. A word directly qualifying a modifying word should precede the word it qualifies, thereby forming a modifying phrase; e.g., BRACKET, UTILITY LIGHT —ENGINEER'S COMPARTMENT. A modifier should be separated from the noun or noun phrase by a comma and from any preceding modifier by a comma. The first part of the title should be separated from the second part of the title by a dash. No abbreviation of any portion of the name (first part of the title) should be made, except those necessarily-used, trademarked names and the words ASSEMBLY (ASSY), SUBASSEMBLY (SUBASSY), or INSTALLATION (INSTL). Abbreviations may be used in the second part of the title, but in general abbreviations should be avoided.[3] See Fig. 13-9.

3. *Mil-STD-28,* U.S. Dept. of Defense, Government Printing Office, 1958.

3 *Signature.* Written in longhand; at least one initial and the last name is given, followed by the date.

4 *Scale block.* The scale to which the drawing has been laid out is shown in the scale block.

5 *Tolerance block.* Contains the variations in dimensional sizes which are permitted in fabricating the part. See Fig. 13-10.

6 *Heat treat block.* Provides the space for the specifications of the heat treatment required. See Fig. 13-11. A general note may be added to the face of the drawing giving additional heat treating information which cannot be shown in the heat treat block.

7 *Protective finish.* The specification of the protective finish required for the manufactured parts is included in the finish block. This information may if necessary be supplemented with a specific note on the face of the drawing.

8 *Replace block.* Shows what drawing, if any, has been replaced by a new drawing. When the replace block is inadequate, a general note is included and the note flagged

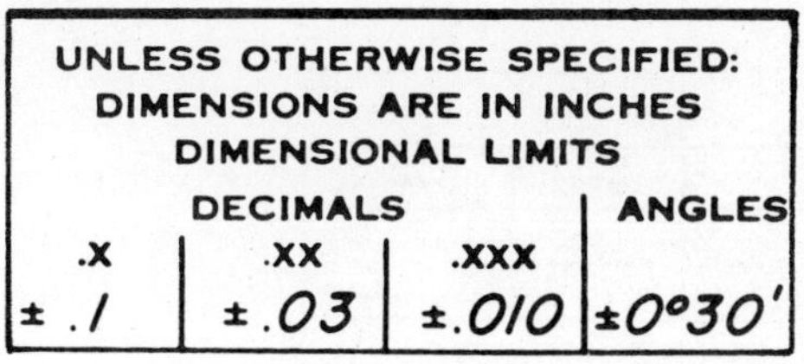

Figure 13-10
Tolerances should be indicated in the tolerance block. Ryan Aeronautical Co.

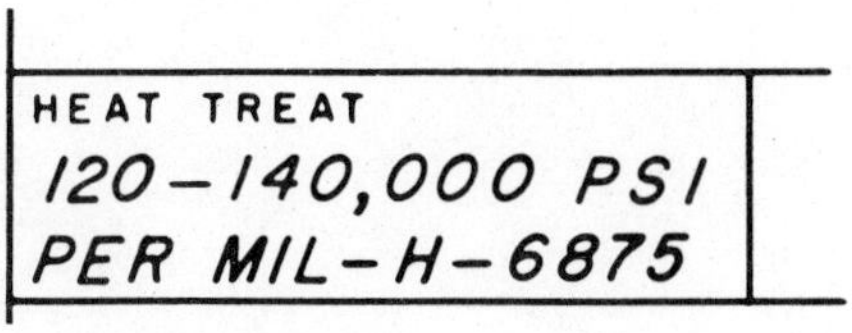

Figure 13-11
Example of a heat treat block. Ryan Aeronautical Co.

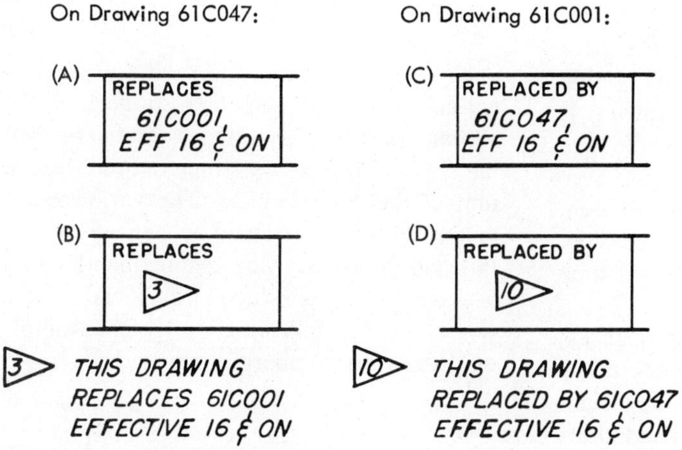

Figure 13-12
How replaced drawings are designated. Ryan Aeronautical Co.

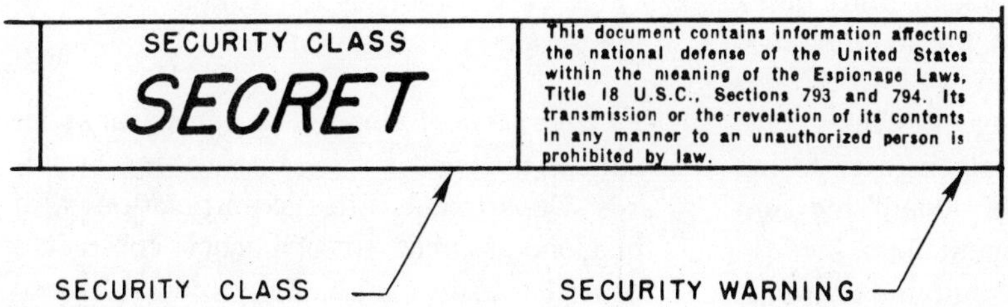

SECURITY CLASS
SECRET
This document contains information affecting the national defense of the United States within the meaning of the Espionage Laws, Title 18 U.S.C., Sections 793 and 794. Its transmission or the revelation of its contents in any manner to an unauthorized person is prohibited by law.
SECURITY CLASS
SECURITY WARNING

Figure 13-13
An example of a security block. Ryan Aeronautical Co.

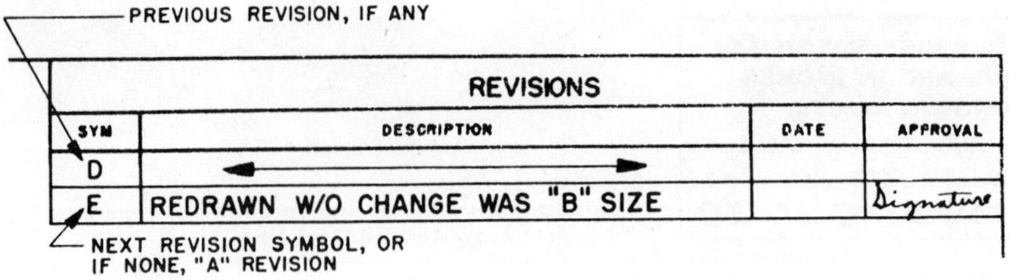

Figure 13-14
A revision block is used to indicate that a change in the drawing has been made.

to the replace block. See Fig. 13-12.

9 *Security class block*. Provides space for indicating the security classification within which the drawing falls. If the drawing is unclassified, the space remains blank. See Fig. 13-13.

10 *Revision block*. Identifies the revision, an important part of the drawing designation. The latest revision letter is added each time a change is made. See Fig. 13-14.

11 *Weight block*. When weight is an essential factor in the fabrication of the product, the weight must be entered in the weight block. The weight may be designated as estimated, calculated or actual.

13.9 Drawing numbering system

Countless drawings are required for the fabrication of any one product. Since most companies are involved in the manufacture of several products, it can well be appreciated that many, many drawings are necessary. To avoid misplacing or losing drawings, some system of identifying and recording them must be maintained.

No uniform system of identifying drawings is followed by all companies; each company has its own identification numbering system. Nevertheless, most numbering systems have certain principles in common. In general, the system consists of a block of numbers which has been selected by some administrative unit of the central office. The various allocated digits are designed to convey certain information. A drawing is thus identified by a series of digits which are placed in the title block. The following is a typical example of a drawing numbering system:[4]

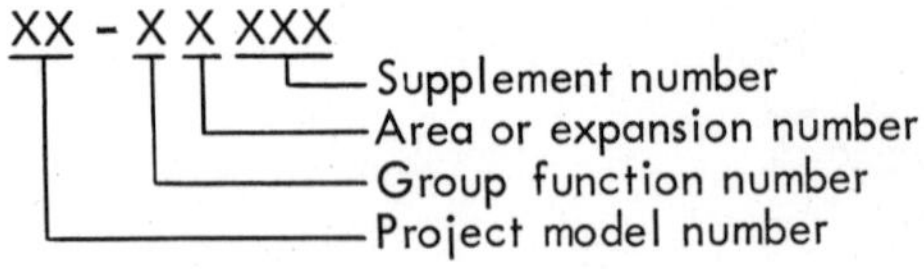

Project model number. A numerical serial number assigned by the Engineering Standards Department, after co-ordination with the General Office, to each article contracted to be designed, manufactured and delivered to the customer.

4. *Drafting Room Manual* (San Diego: Convair Division of General Dynamics Corp.).

DRAWING REVISION NOTIFICATION

DATE __________

Mr. ____________________ Please make revision to drawing as indicated below.

MACHINE

DRAWING No. PART No. PATT. No.

SO. No. SERIAL No. BLDG. No.

RECOMMENDED BY DEPT.

APPROVED BY

Make Sketch if Necessary

REASON FOR CHANGE

DRAWING REVISED BY ____________________ DATE __________

EP11251b **A 64706**

Form 43-12A SUPERIOR PRINTING CO.

FULLER MANUFACTURING CO.
KALAMAZOO, MICHIGAN

ENGINEERING CHANGE NOTICE

Part Name

COPIES TO	REC'D BY	Details of Change	Date
Supt.			
Inspection			
Planning			
Cost			
Purchasing			
Tool Design			
Western Dist.			
Expediter			
Service			
		Reason:	
		Change Goes Into Effect	
CUSTOMERS			

CHANGES	YES	NO	CHANGES	YES	NO
Is Pattern or Die to be changed?			Should work in process be stopped?		
Is New Pattern or New Die required?			Should finished stock be changed?		
Is Rough Stock on hand changed?			Does change affect Interchangeability?		
Can Present Rough Stock be used?			Does change affect shop tools?		

Approved ____________________ Signed ____________________

Figure 13-15
Before any change is made on an original drawing, forms similar to these must be issued by the engineering department.
Eastman Kodak Company,
Fuller Manufacturing Co.

Group function number. The article is divided into its structural and functional components, and applicable coded numbers are assigned. The following is a typical breakdown for an airplane:

0–General (General drawings, Mockup, Proposal, Study, Layout, and Specification control drawings)
1–Wing and Empennage
2–Power Plant and Nacelle
3–Electronics and Instruments
4–Controls and Mechanisms
5–Alighting Gear (Landing gear, Floats, Float braces, Skis)
6–Electrical
7–Body
8–Pneumatics, Heating, Ventilating, Pressurization, Anti-icing, Hydraulics
9–Furnishings and Handling Gear

Area or expansion number. A number which may be: (1) used for future expansion of Group Function (or Supplement) Number, (2) established as a code to represent major assembly components of the basic structural and functional components, or (3) established as a code to indicate the area or major assembly component into which the equipment is installed.

Supplement number. A number assigned in numerical order, as required, or preassigned into sets of reserved numbers for details, assemblies and installations or related units of structure, systems or equipment.

13.10 Revision of drawings

A draftsman is frequently required to revise a drawing either to correct errors, add or delete information, clarify design, or improve manufacturing methods. Definite procedures are established by engineering drafting departments for making drawing changes. One paramount rule that is in effect everywhere is that once a drawing has been released no changes whatsoever are to be undertaken without proper authorization and all revisions must be recorded. Authority for making changes usually is vested only in the engineering department. A drawing revision notification form similar to the ones shown in Fig. 13-15 is issued when requested changes are authorized.

Information concerning the revision of a drawing is placed in the revision block. This block is usually located in the upper right hand corner as shown in Fig. 13-16. It contains the necessary spaces to record the change symbols, dates, signatures and description of the changes. Drafting departments have their own particular revision symbols to designate drawing changes.

13.11 Procedure for revising drawings

The same procedure is followed in making changes for detail, assembly, and layout drawings. When the change is extensive, a print is made previous to the change and all changes or additions are indicated on it to facilitate checking. All changes are made to scale and with the least amount of erasing or moving of notes and dimensions. Views and sections affected by the change are brought up-to-date. Every effort is taken to match the new lettering with the original lettering. The effects of a detail part change on an assembly and layout drawing must be considered and these drawings revised where required.

Erasures. Erasing should be carried out very carefully and preferably in the following manner. On an ink tracing, use a soft eraser with the tracing lying on a flat, smooth, hard surface, such as a piece of flat glass or a draftsman's triangle. If proper care is taken, a number of erasures may be made in the same place without damage to the tracing. Use an erasing shield to eliminate unnecessary erasing. Avoid using a knife or razor blade unless it is done with extreme care and then only with the chief draftsman's permission. In making erasures on vellum, erase both sides of the paper.

Checkers' marks and notes. Checkers' marks and notes on the check print should not be removed by the draftsman unless requested to do so by the checker.

Change letters. All revisions, including those in the title block and revision column require a change letter. Change letters are usually consecutive except that letters I, O,

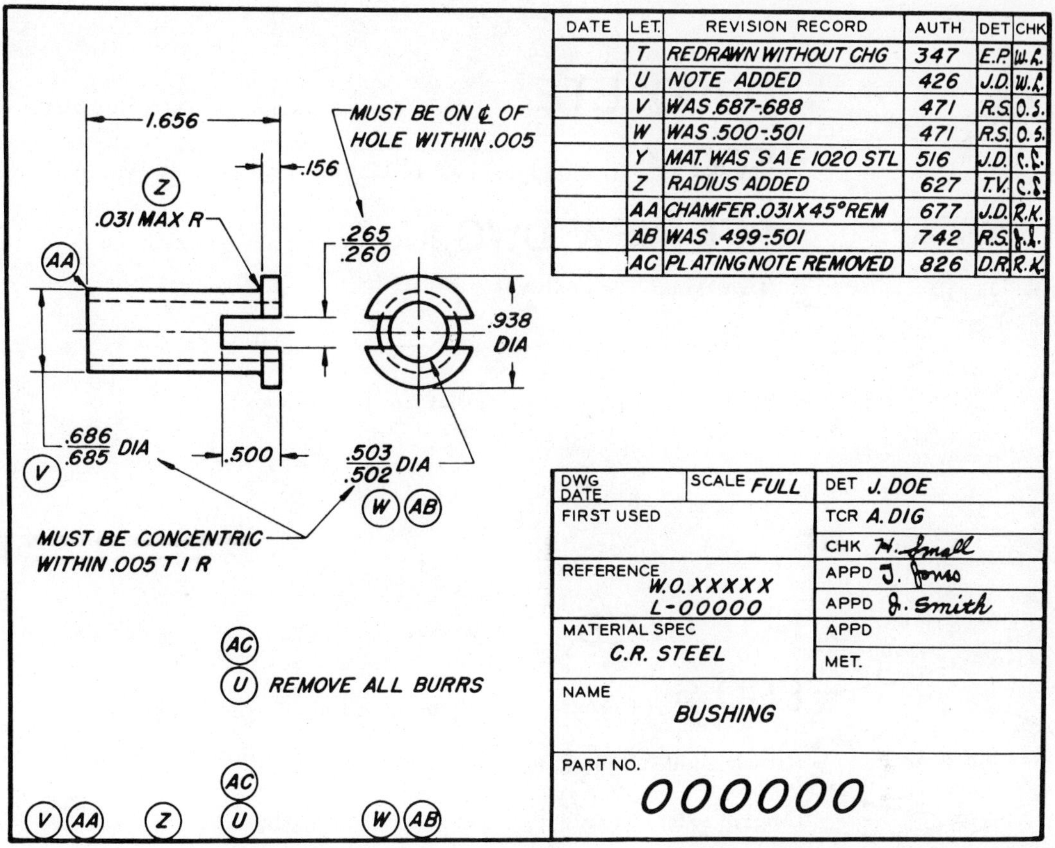

Figure 13–16
The revision block is used to record changes made in a drawing. SAE

Q, and X are omitted to avoid possible confusion. After the letter "Z" is used, additional revisions are identified with AA, AB, AC through AZ, then BA, BB and so forth.

The change letters are inclosed in a 5/16 to 3/8 inch circle and placed in the revision block and as close to the point of revision as practical but preferably not within the outlines of the part. Where a part view or a note is deleted, the revision letter is placed at or adjacent to its former location. When a change is to be made which replaces a previous change located in the original design, a new change letter is assigned and placed as close as possible to the old change letter.

Notes. If a note is removed it should be recorded in its entirety in the revision column whenever possible. Where it is impractical to do this, the record in the revision column should refer to the type of note involved; for example: PAINTING NOTE REMOVED or PAINTING NOTE REVISED, not merely NOTE REMOVED or NOTE REVISED. The note in its entirety is then recorded on the engineering change notice.

Redrawing. Where a large amount of erasing or a major change is required in revising a drawing, it is often more economical to prepare a new drawing. In such cases, all previous revisions, notations and change letters on the old drawing are omitted except the last change letter.

Retracings which do not incorporate a change should carry the notation TRACED together with the date, or the notation REDRAWN WITHOUT CHANGE. If changes are incorporated in the new drawing, the notation REDRAWN AND REVISED together with the date is entered in the appropriate revision block. See Fig. 13-16.

The original or superseded drawing should

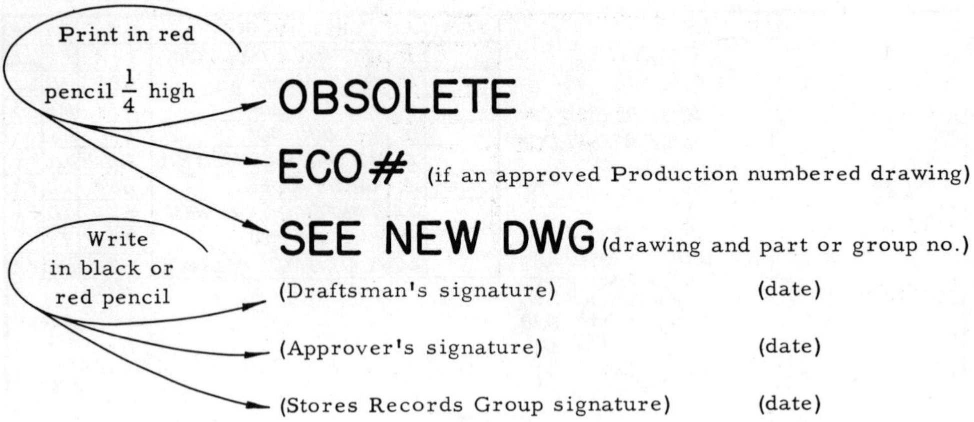

A

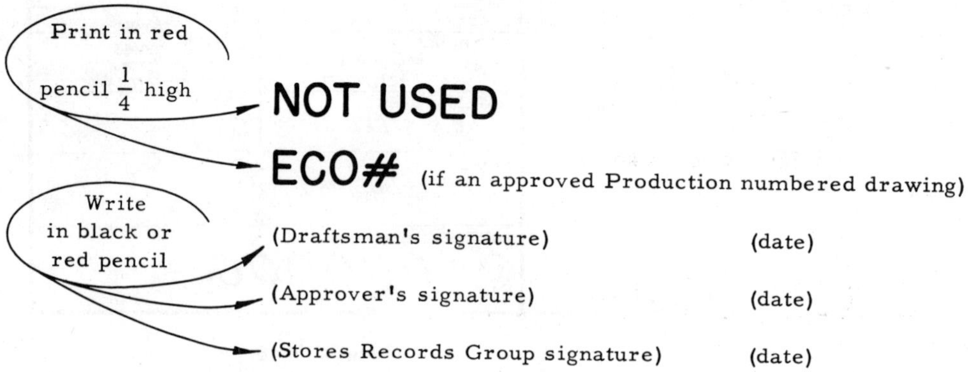

B

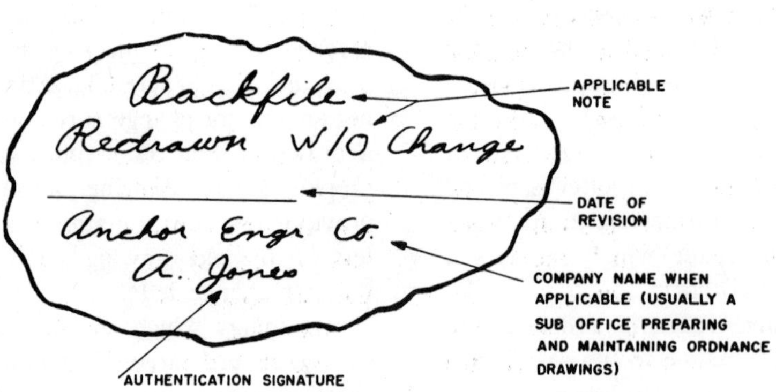

C

Figure 13-17
A drawing that is no longer used is said to be inactivated and is thereby properly identified and retired.
17A Raytheon
17B Raytheon
17C US Army Ordnance Corps

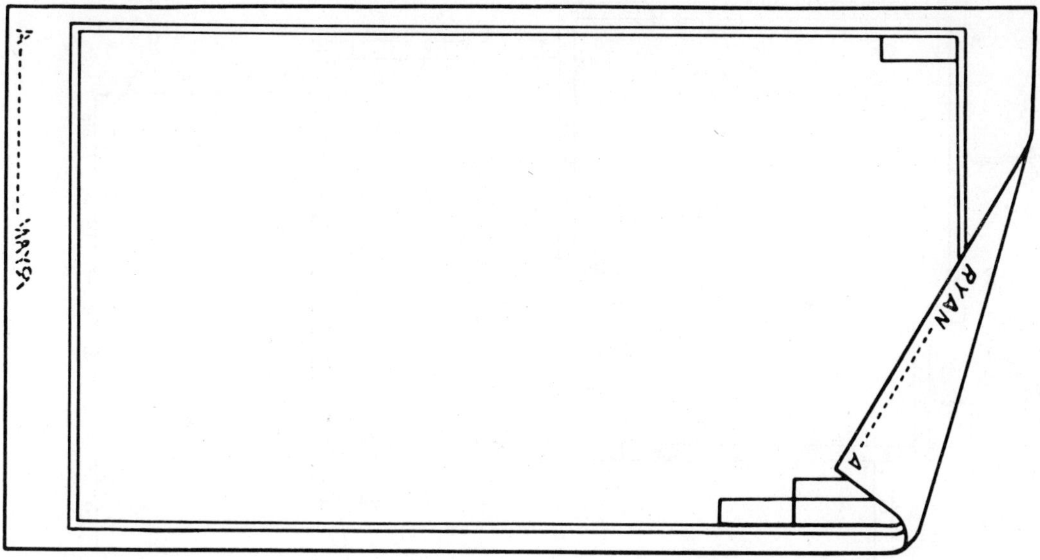

Figure 13-18
How the ends of roll drawings are identified. Ryan Aeronautical Co.

be suitably marked with the superseding date and authority and placed in the inactive or obsolete file for record purposes. The signatures and dates of those who signed the original drawing may be copied in plain printed letters or the drawing may be re-signed by authorized personnel.

13.12 Inactivation of drawings

A drawing that is no longer used in production or service is said to be inactive or backfiled, and a prescribed routine is followed to retire the drawing. The inactivation process deals with three sets of conditions: (1) drawings that have been redrawn with or without changes, (2) drawings that have been drawn but not released, and (3) drawings that have been replaced by other drawings.

Details of the procedure followed for inactivating a drawing will vary to some extent with different firms. Basically the first step is the issuance of an order requesting that a particular numbered drawing be inactivated. Authorization for inactivating drawings usually rests with the chief engineer.

A typical example of how an inactivated drawing is labeled is shown in Fig. 13-17. As illustrated here, a note is placed on the face of the drawing above or to the left of the title block but in such a manner that it does not obstruct any views or other notes. After the note is properly signed, the drawing is delivered to the record storage office.

13.13 Roll end marking

Some industries make it a practice to include the following information on the reverse side of each end of roll size drawings for ease in identification:

1 Name of company
2 Drawing number
3 Drawing title
4 Latest revision letter
5 Security classification when applicable
6 Sheet number when applicable.

This information is placed on diagonally opposite corners and so located that it may be read from the end of the drawing and seen without unrolling the drawing. See Fig. 13-18.

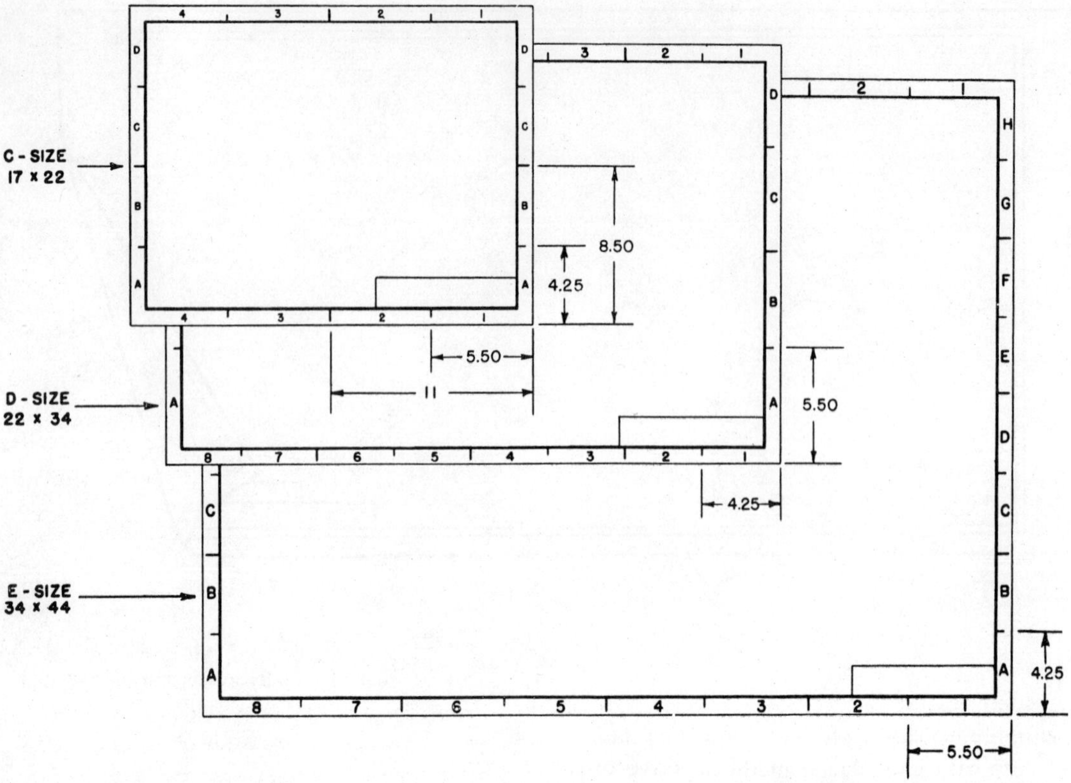

Figure 13-19
Zoning facilitates the location of particular information on a large drawing. Radio Corp. of America

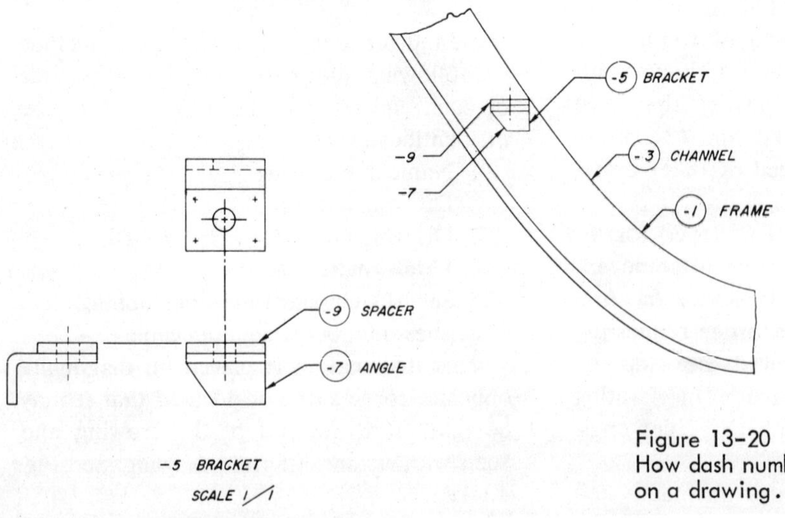

Figure 13-20
How dash number callouts are indicated on a drawing. Ryan Aeronautical Co.

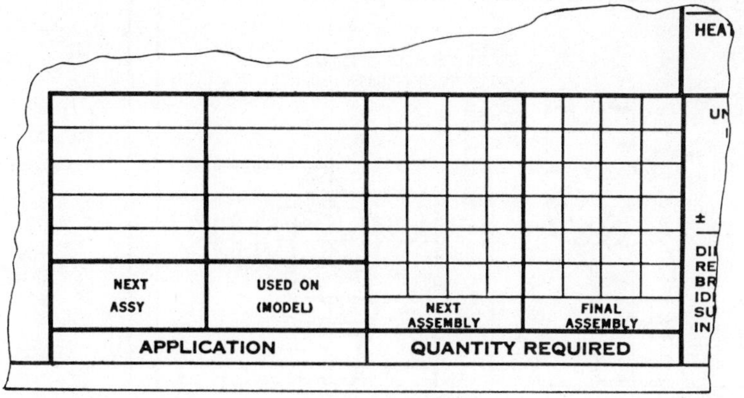

Figure 13-21
The application block serves as a record of the use of a part or parts. Ryan Aeronautical Co.

13.14 Zoning of drawings

Zoning is used on drawings of C-size and larger to facilitate the location of parts, details, sectional views, notes and changes in the same manner that numbers and letters on a map help to locate a particular area. It consists of regularly spaced blocks around the edges of the sheet. The upper and lower rows of horizontally spaced blocks are numbered consecutively from right to left. The vertical zone blocks on the right and left edges are designated by letters *A,B,C,* etc., reading upward. See Fig. 13-19.

13.15 Dash numbers[5]

The dash numbering system is used to save drawing time by showing the fabrication of more than one part on the same drawing. This eliminates the necessity for separate drawings to depict individual parts, subassemblies, or variations on assembly and installation drawings. The name *dash number* is derived from the fact that this number is a suffix added to the basic drawing number and is always preceded by a dash whether or not the basic number is shown. Thus all parts created in an assembly or installation drawing are assigned the number of the drawing on which they were created with a separate dash number suffixed to the drawing number for each part. Example:

36C942-1
DASH NUMBER
DRAWING NUMBER

5. *Ibid.*

Detail dash numbers are identifying numbers used on assembly and installation drawings to identify individual parts detailed thereon and on tabulated detail drawings to identify non-interchangeable variations. In all cases, the drawing number for a part assembly or installation is suffixed by odd dash numbers for left hand components and even dash numbers for opposite or right hand components.

Dash numbers, with the exception of major assembly dash numbers, must appear on the drawing in a circle with a leader line running from the circle to the outline of the part. The title of the dash number is placed adjacent to the circle. See Fig. 13-20.

13.16 Application block

The application block indicates which parts depicted on the drawings are used to make the next higher details, assemblies or installations as shown on other drawings; lists the model of the final usage; and shows the number of parts required for such usage. See Fig. 13-21. The application block is generally located at the left of the title block along the lower border of the drawing.

13.17 Standard parts

In the design and manufacture of any product, the practice is always to use as many standard parts as are available. It is not uncommon for a contracting firm to specify

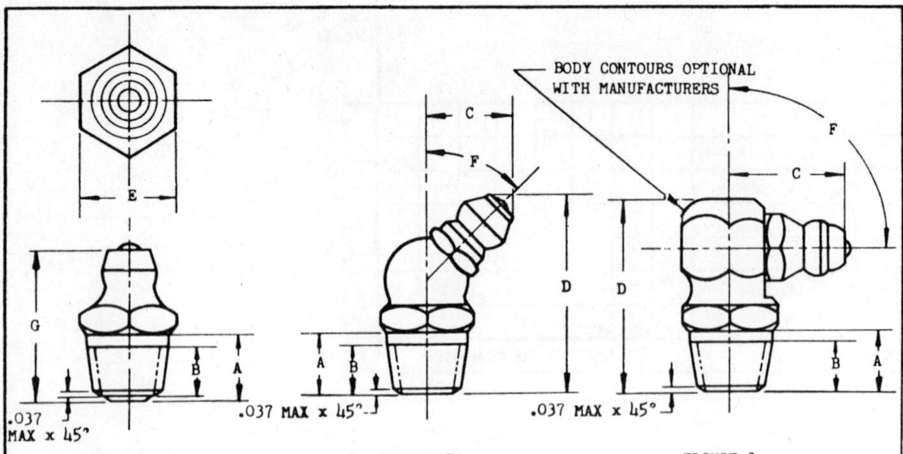

FIGURE 1 FIGURE 2 FIGURE 3

ACCEPTABLE TIP DESIGNS - IN ACCORDANCE WITH MS15000

MS PART NO.	FIG.	(a) THREAD T	A ±1/32	(b) B	C MAX	D MAX	E +.000 -.003	F	G ±1/16	FEDERAL ITEM IDENTIFICATION NO.
MS15003-1	1	1/8	9/32	3/16	- -	- -	.438	- -	11/16	050-4208
MS15003-2		1/8	3/4	3/16	- -	- -	.438	- -	1-1/4	172-0022
MS15003-3	2	1/8	9/32	3/16	3/8	1-5/32	.438	30°	- -	172-0025
MS15003-4		1/8	9/32	3/16	1/2	1-3/32	.438	45°	- -	172-0028
MS15003-5		1/8	9/32	3/16	5/8	31/32	.438	65°	- -	172-0031
MS15003-6	3	1/8	9/32	3/16	5/8	15/16	.438	90°	- -	172-0034
MS15003-7		1/8	9/32	3/16	9/16	1-3/16	.438	105°	- -	172-0037

(a) PIPE THREAD SHALL BE MODIFIED (DRY SEAL) TAPER PIPE THREAD, NPTF, IN ACCORDANCE WITH HANDBOOK H-28 EXCEPT THAT LENGTH OF EFFECTIVE THREAD L2 IS SHORTENED BY ONE THREAD ON SMALL END AND ONE THREAD ON LARGE END. SMALL END OF THREAD SHALL GAGE FROM FLUSH TO MINUS 1-1/2 TURNS FROM SMALL END OF DRYSEAL (NPTF-L1) THIN RING GAGE. WIDTH OF FLAT ON THREAD CREST MAY BE .007 MAXIMUM.

(b) EFFECTIVE THREAD.

MATERIAL: STEEL - SEE PROCUREMENT SPECIFICATION.

FINISH: SEE PROCUREMENT SPECIFICATION.

DIMENSIONS IN INCHES. UNLESS OTHERWISE SPECIFIED, TOLERANCES: ANGLES ±5°.

REVISED

APPROVED

CUSTODIANS Army - O Navy - BuAer Air Force PROCUREMENT SPECIFICATION MIL-F-3541	**MILITARY STANDARD** FITTINGS, LUBRICATION (HYDRAULIC) SURFACE CHECK, 1/8 PIPE THREADS, STEEL, TYPE III	**MS15003** SHEET 1 OF 1

Figure 13-22
Standardized parts are always used in the manufacture of a product when they are available.

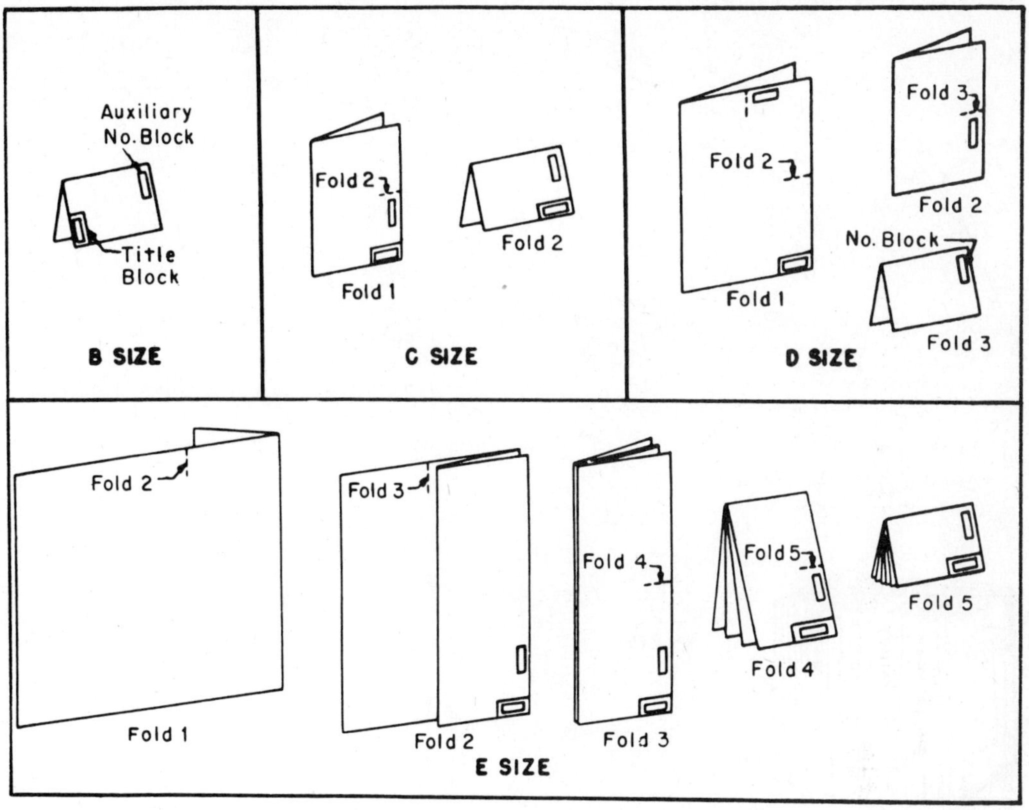

Figure 13-23
For convenience and ease of filing prints, the practice is to fold them in the manner shown here.
ASA Y14.1-1957

to a manufacturer that such parts are to be included in the assembly. The use of standard parts insures a greater degree of interchangeability, faster production, more effective replacement service and the utilization of components that meet acceptable tested specifications. It also eliminates additional costs in preparing countless drawings that, in effect, are not needed.

The largest number of standard parts are those which have been certified by approving agencies. These parts or their controlling manufacturing specifications are identified with symbols designated by the approving agency. See Fig. 13-22. The most common are:

ASA, American Standards Association
JAN, Joint Army and Navy Standards
AN, Army-Navy Specifications
MIL, Military Standards
ORD, Ordnance Engineering Standards

13.18 Folding and filing prints

To facilitate the handling, mailing and storing of prints, drafting departments follow a commonly accepted method of folding prints. The practice is to fold prints to an 8-1/2 x 11 inch letter-size. Regardless of

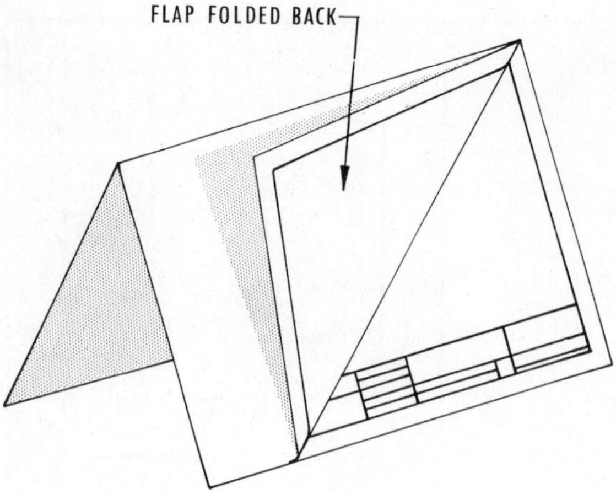

Figure 13-24
When a print is folded with the viewing side unexposed, a corner is turned to show the title block.

Figure 13-25
A variety of files as shown here are used for storing drawings and prints.

the size of the print, the folding is accomplished so that the top edge has a single fold line. This avoids any possibility of filing another print inside the folds of the former when they are filed in a letter-size filing cabinet.

Prints are folded with the viewing side exposed or unexposed. In either case the sequence of the fold lines remains the same. The advantage of folding with the viewing side unexposed is that it protects the viewing side when prints receive rough handling through constant filing. Fig. 13-23 illustrates the direction and number of fold lines for various size prints.

With the exception of B-size, all prints are folded with the title block in the lower right hand corner. Since the title block is not

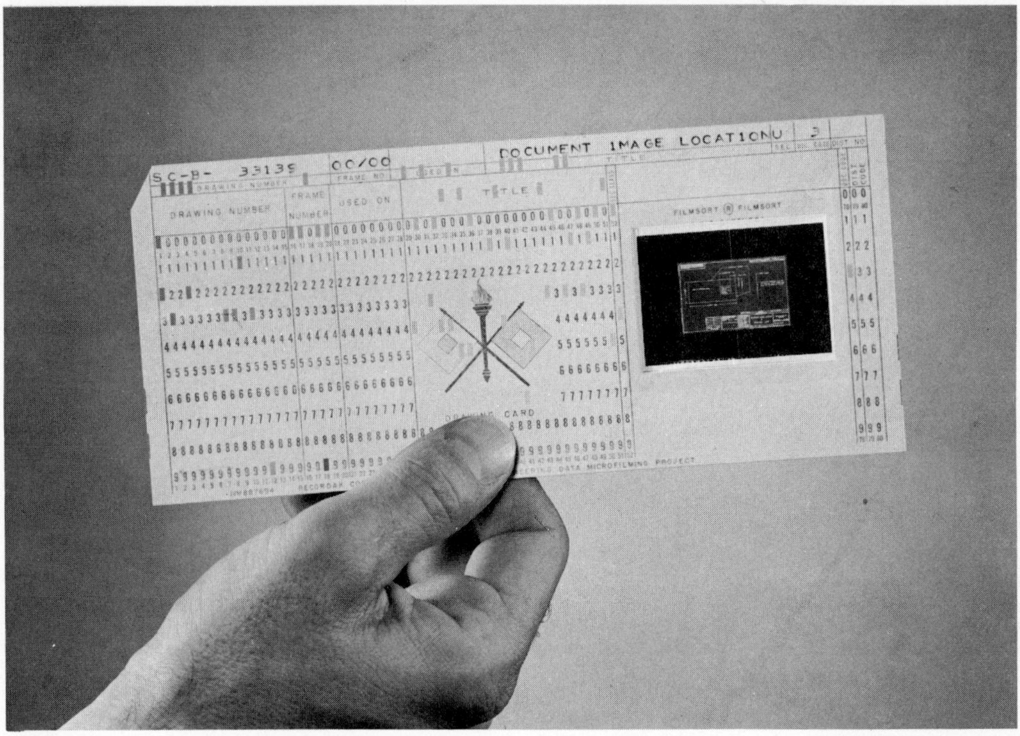

Figure 13-26
Microfilm aperture cards eliminate tedious hand sorting and filing of conventional reproducibles. Recordak Corp.

visible when the prints are folded with the viewing side unexposed, the practice is to fold back one corner of the print in the form of a triangle so as to expose the title block. See Fig. 13-24. An alternate method is to stamp a duplicate title block on the blank side.

To accommodate any type of binding, draftsmen leave a clear margin of 1 to 1-1/2 inches on the left side of all drawings. Fold lines are also indicated on the margin to help guide the folding in the proper location.

Filing prints and drawings. Four types of equipment are used for filing prints and drawings—vertical files, horizontal or flat files, hanging files, and roll files. See Fig. 13-25. The vertical file with three, four or five drawers is probably the most popular. The horizontal or flat file consists of a series of drawers in which prints, drawings and tracings can be laid in a flat position. The hanging file is a closed metal cabinet with hangers on which the prints are suspended. The roll file is a closed metal cabinet equipped with filing bins designed to hold open tubes in a vertical position. The prints are rolled and inserted into these tubes.

13.19 Microfilming drawings

To expedite the handling of engineering drawings and reduce storage space, many industries are resorting to microfilming. Some firms have their drawings microfilmed on frames of 35mm, 70mm, and 105mm. The 35mm frames are usually mounted on cards while the 70mm and 105mm frames are stored in envelopes. The mounting cards are either the conventional 3 x 5 inch file type or punched coded IBM cards. See Fig. 13-26. In either case the microfilm can be used in one of two ways. The frames may be

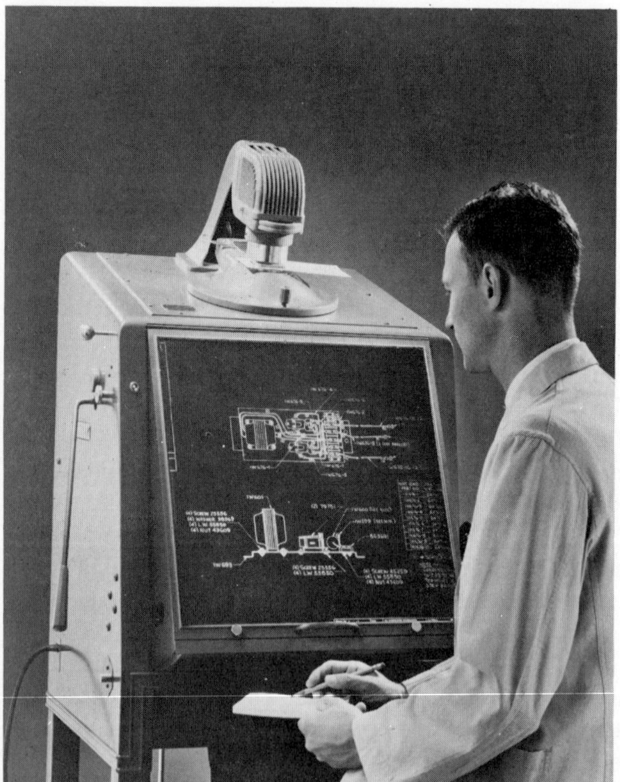

Figure 13-27
By inserting the aperature card in the viewer, the engineer or draftsman has an immediate view of the microfilmed drawing.
Recordak Corp.

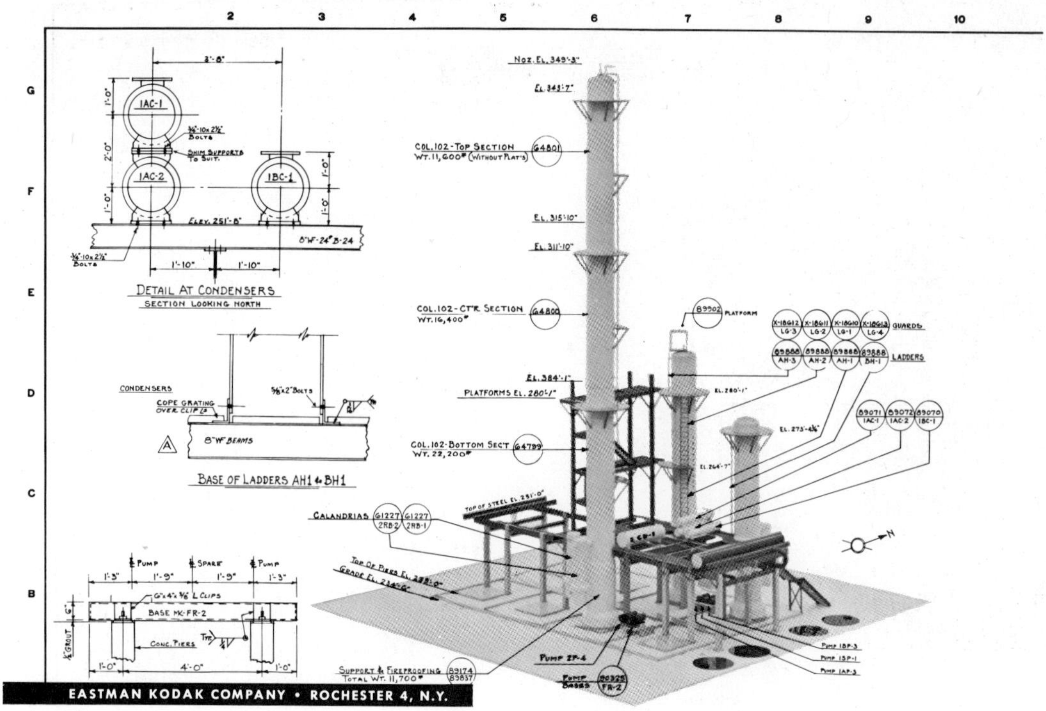

Figure 13-28
A photodrawing combines a photograph and a drawing. Eastman Kodak Co.

enlarged (called *blow-backs*) and the copy used in the same way as the tracing has in the past, or the microfilm is placed in a table viewer. Blow-backs are made on photographic paper with standard photographic darkroom technique. Enlarging machines are now available which expose and develop blow-backs without the need for a darkroom. Table viewers or readers can be secured in various styles. Some produce an enlarged image on a translucent screen and others are simply hand-held magnifiers with the image viewed with ordinary room light. See Fig. 13-27.

Another microfilm system uses 4 x 6 inch negatives. The negatives can be enlarged to any size up to 36 x 54 inches and working prints made on opaque paper or cloth by the Blueprint or Diazo process. The negatives can also be used to make 4 x 6 inch card prints for viewing in a table viewer, or the negatives may be projected onto a large screen.

13.20 Photodrawing

Photodrawing is actually a combination of a photograph and a drawing. A photo of the work involved is taken first to show how the equipment appears to the eye. The view photographed may be a straight-on shot, an overhead plan-view, or an angle perspective.

The photo negative next is copied through a halftone screen to produce a halftone negative. Essential detail information then is inked in on the screened negative and the finished photodrawing produced like a blue or white print.

Photodrawing has several notable fea-

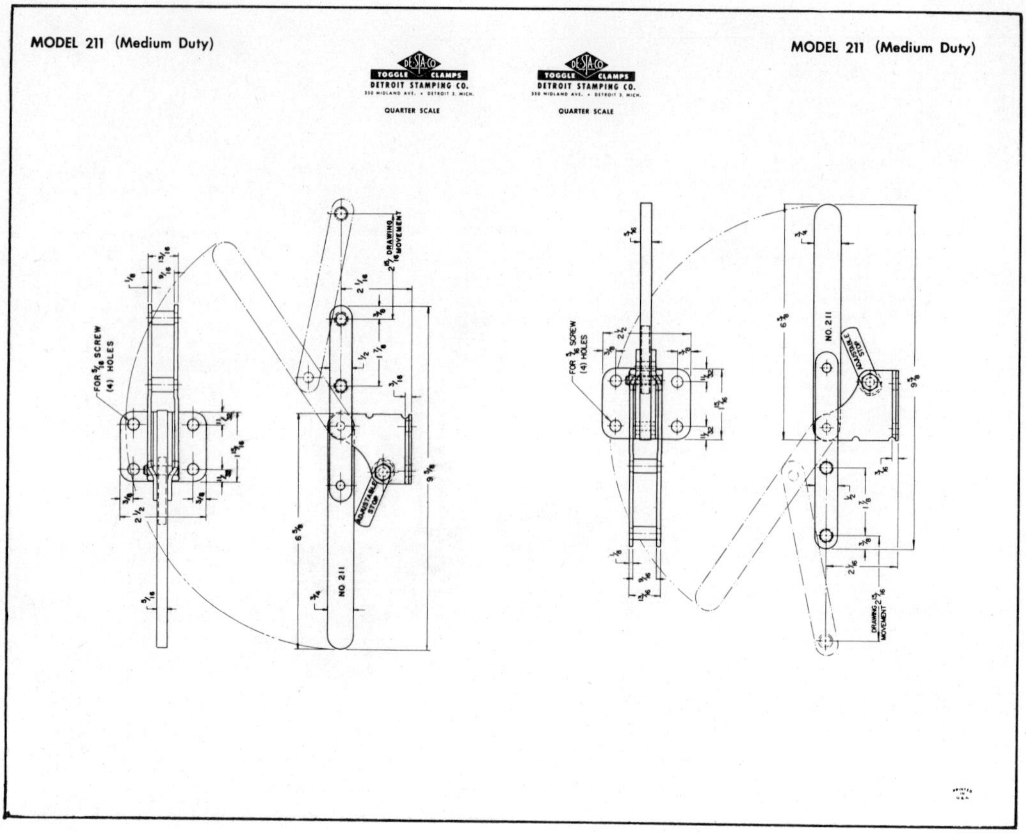

Figure 13-29
Tracing templates of this kind are being used to speed up the preparation of drawings. Detroit Stamping Co.

tures. It can show minor changes on complex drawings without having to redraw the original, it can illustrate existing installations without referring to the original tracing, it simplifies understanding for those who lack a knowledge of print reading, and it bypasses the need for complex and expensive assembly drawings. An example of a photodrawing is shown in Fig. 13-28.

13.21 Drafting aids

The ever increasing need to modify or design new products so as to meet competitive pressures is forcing all industrial departments to find production short cuts. Drafting departments, too, are faced with the problem of speeding up the production of drawings. Expanding production necessitates not only larger quantities of drawings but drawings that are more accurate regardless of their complexity.

Several techniques are employed to produce at minimum cost the ever increasing flow of drawings. Some drafting departments are experimenting with a new simplified method of drawing presentation. (See Section 25 — Simplified Drafting Practices.) Others are introducing a variety of special templates that permit rapid and accurate mechanical reproduction of detail shapes. These templates, for example, eliminate the need to lay out completely such time consuming tasks as bolts, nuts, rivets, hydraulic fittings, electrical fixtures and many others. Not only are there templates for drawing circles, arcs, ellipses and other standard shapes, but in many instances drafting departments are now designing and fabricating their own templates to handle special drafting details.

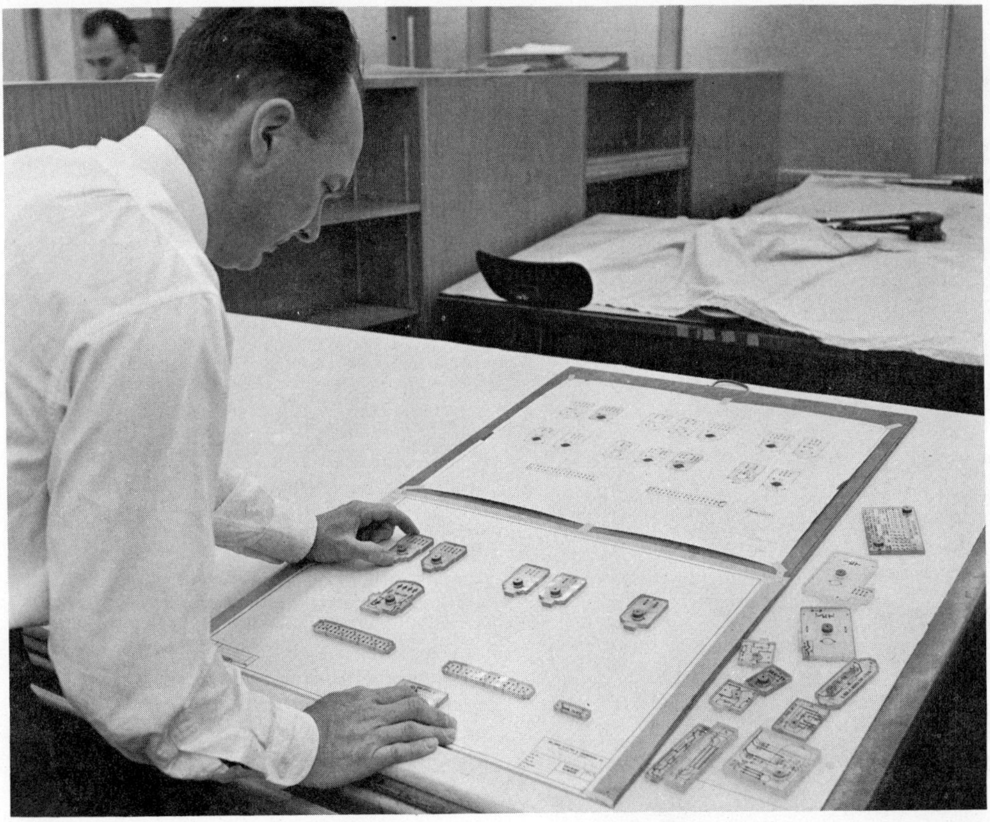

Figure 13-30
Permanent magnets hold these templates on sensitized paper on a metal drafting board. Reliance Electric & Engineering Co.

A wide variety of tracing templates are being used by draftsmen to speed up their work. These tracing templates consist of actual drawings of manufactured components such as bearings, jig and fixture parts, air cylinders, etc., made in 1/4, 1/2, or full size. The draftsman simply positions the template under his tracing and proceeds to trace the item. A typical tracing template is illustrated in Fig. 13-29.

One electric manufacturing company has developed a template form of drawing in which the templates contain a scale drawing on a transparent plastic, representing standard components such as switches, relays, contactors, or terminal blocks. See Fig. 13-30. The units are positioned on sensitized paper over a metal drafting board and held in place by permanent magnets. After the templates are arranged in their correct pattern, the sensitized paper is exposed and developed. The draftsman then completes the drawing by adding the connecting lines necessary to finish the control panel, wiring diagram or switchboard.

Printed acetate sheets known as "Stanpats" are another device used to reduce the time element in drafting. These Stanpats are made of a cellulose acetate sheet with a transparent pressure-sensitive adhesive applied to the front face. Stanpats are available with title blocks, bills of material, nuts, screws, bolts, electronic tubes, standard motors, pumps, wiring diagrams and a variety of other components. The Stanpat is applied to the tracing by first removing its wax-paper protective sheet, then placing it in position on the tracing and rubbing the wax-paper protective sheet on top of the acetate. See Fig. 13-31.

Figure 13-31
Stanpats are cellulose acetate sheets with outlines of drafting components which can be applied to the tracing sheet. Step 1: Peel back free edge and trim off. Step 2: Place exposed adhesive in correct position and remove rest of backing. Step 3: Place backing over the affixed stanpat and rub down.

Problems, section 13

1 Obtain **A, B, C, D,** and **E** size paper and practice folding into letter-size for filing.

2 Obtain a three-ring loose-leaf binder and collect material pertinent to drafting, design, and manufacturing from magazines, manufacturers' literature, etc. Organize the material into suitable sections.

3 Design an A-size sheet format including a title strip, a revision block, application block, etc., so that the sheet may be submitted to a printer for printing.

4 Check the organization of an industrial drafting department and prepare an organizational chart.

5 Using the items listed in Sub-section 13.7, serve as a checker for an assigned period and check drawings completed by students.

6 Design a template for a special drafting detail.

Gears and cams* 14

Gears are used to transfer power and motion from one point to another. They also provide a means of regulating the amount of power or speed to be transmitted, or of altering the direction of motion.

Cams are machine elements in the shape of plates or cylinders which impart predetermined motion to other machine members. By means of cams, rotary motion can be changed to reciprocating motion.

Gear and cam design is a highly technical field. This section is limited to the drawing of some of the more basic types of gears and cams. See Fig. 14-1.

14.1 Types of gears

The following is a general description of the most common types of gears:

Spur. Cylindrical in form with teeth that are formed straight across the face of the gear and parallel to the shaft axis or bore. See Fig. 14-2. They are used on shafts that are parallel to each other and transmit power or motion at the same or different speeds between shafts. Spur gears are manufactured in three different styles: plain, webbed, and spoked. See Fig. 14-3.

Rack. A type of spur gear used to transfer circular motion into straight-line motion. A rack has teeth on the surface of a straight bar instead of a cylindrical gear blank. See Fig. 14-4.

Internal. Gears with teeth parallel to the shaft but on the inside of gear blanks. See Fig. 14-5. Internal gears are often called *ring gears.*

Pinion. A small gear which meshes with the main gear and provides the essential power to run the gear. A pinion is generally referred to as the driver.

Bevel. Shaped like cone sections and transmit power and motion between intersecting shafts at right angles. They are used

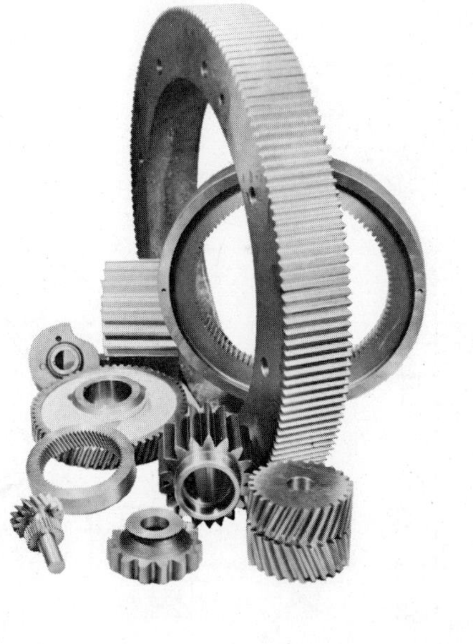

Figure 14-1
The design and manufacture of gears and cams is a specialized field of its own. The Fellows Gear Shaper Co.

* This section was prepared with the assistance of Dale King, Assistant Professor of Drafting, Department of Engineering and Technology, Western Michigan University.

Figure 14-2
Spur gears are the simplest of all gears. Boston Gear Works

Figure 14-4
A rack is used to transfer circular motion into straight-line motion.

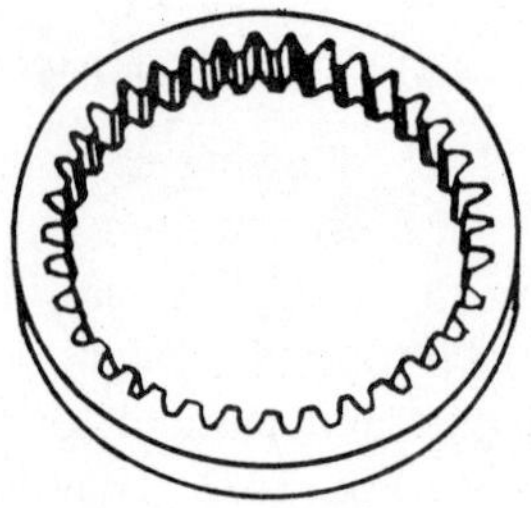

Figure 14-5
Internal gears are cylindrical in form with teeth on the inner surface of the cylinder or ring. SAE

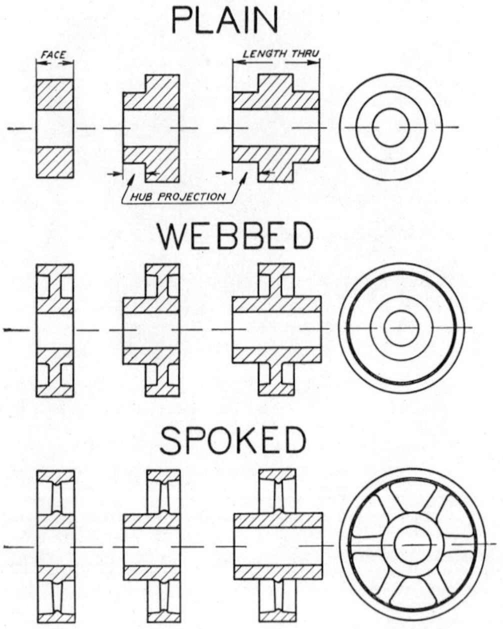

Figure 14-3
These are the main types of spur gear blanks. Foote Brothers Gear and Machine Corp.

to produce a reduction or increase in speed. See Fig. 14-6. Bevel gears having intersecting shafts at other than right angles are often called *angle gears*.

Miter. Bevel gears in which both the driver and driven gear have the same number of teeth. They are made with either curved or oblique teeth and are used in high speed applications. See Fig. 14-7.

Helical. Cylindrical in form with teeth cut at an angle to the shaft axis or bore. Helical gears are designed to connect non-intersecting shafts which may be at any angle with each other. These gears usually run more smoothly and quietly than spur gears. They are often called *spiral gears* or *crossed axis helicals*. See Fig. 14-8.

Worms and worm gears. Used to transmit

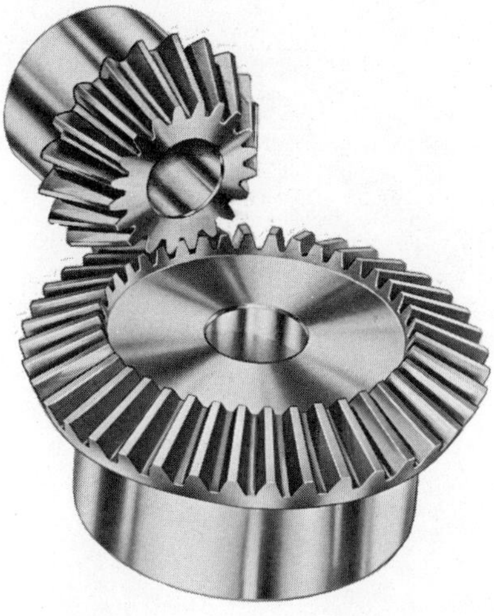

Figure 14-6
Bevel gears on shafts at right angles produce a change in speed.
Boston Gear Works

Figure 14-7
Spiral miter gears transmit more horsepower than straight tooth miter gears.
Boston Gear Works

motion or power between right angle shafts when a high-ratio speed reduction is necessary. The worm is the small gear which drives the larger wormgear. Worm threads resemble screw threads and are made with single, double, triple or quadruple leads. See Fig. 14-9.

Roller chain and sprockets. Used on shafts that are parallel and transmit motion or power at the same or different speeds. Sprocket teeth are cut straight across the face of the sprocket and are parallel to the shaft axis or bore. Sprockets are connected either with a single width or multiple width roller chains. Double chains and sprockets usually transmit twice the horsepower of a single chain and sprocket of the same pitch size. See Fig. 14-10.

Figure 14-8
Helical gears are considered the most practical means of driving non-intersecting shafts. Boston Gear Works

14.2 Standard spur gear terms[1]

The terms defined in the following list are fairly common to all spur gears:

Outside diameter. Diameter of the circle around the extreme outer edges of the teeth. (Fig. 14-11.)

Pitch circle. Theoretical circle on which the teeth of the mating gears mesh. (Fig. 14-11.)

Pitch diameter. Diameter of the pitch circle. (Fig. 14-11.)

Root diameter. Diameter of the root circle. (Fig. 14-11.)

Diametral pitch. Abbreviated DP, refers to tooth size. It is a ratio of the number of teeth in the gear to each inch of its pitch diameter; i.e., a 4-pitch gear has four teeth for each inch of pitch diameter.

1. *Boston Gear Works Manual* (Quincy, Mass.: Boston Gear Works).

Circular pitch. Distance on the circumference of the pitch circle between corresponding points of adjacent teeth. Circular pitch is measured from the center of one tooth to the center of the next tooth on the pitch circle or from the side of one tooth to the corresponding side of the tooth next to it on the pitch circle. (Fig. 14-11.)

Whole depth. Distance from the top of the tooth to the root circle. (Fig. 14-12.)

Addendum. Distance from the pitch circle to the top of the tooth. (Fig. 14-12.)

Dedendum. Distance from the pitch circle to the root circle. It equals the addendum plus the working clearance. (Fig. 14-12.)

Working depth. Depth of engagement of two gears or the sum of their addendums. (Fig. 14-12.)

Working clearance. Distance from the working depth to the root circle. It is the space between the top of one tooth and

Figure 14-9
Worm and wormgears are intended for right angle shafts or non-intersecting shafts where high-ratio speed reduction is required. Boston Gear Works

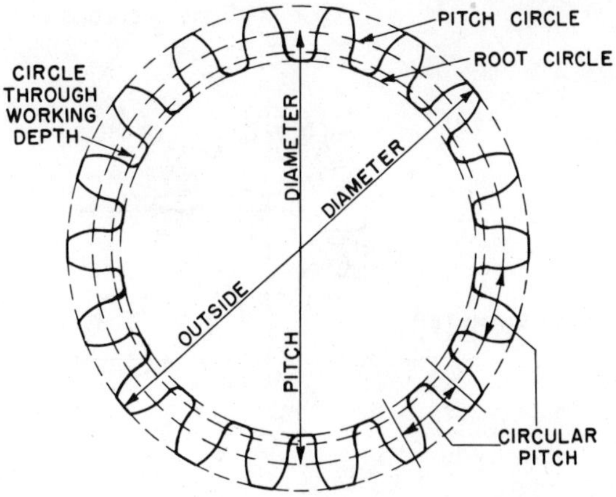

Figure 14-11
Gear terms. Boston Gear Works

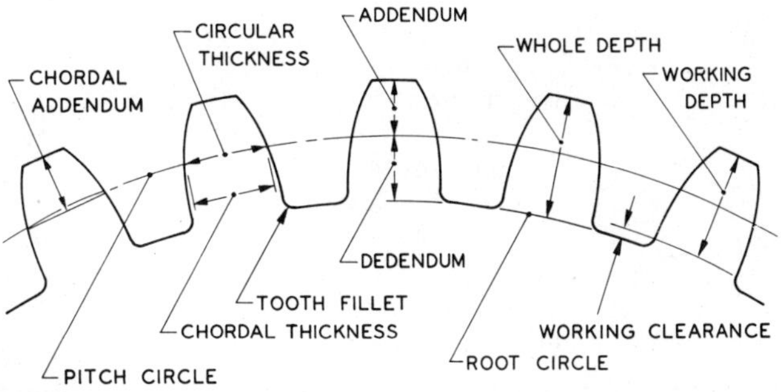

Figure 14-12
Gear terms.

Figure 14-10
A roller chain drive consists of two or more sprockets connected with one or more endless chains. Boston Gear Works

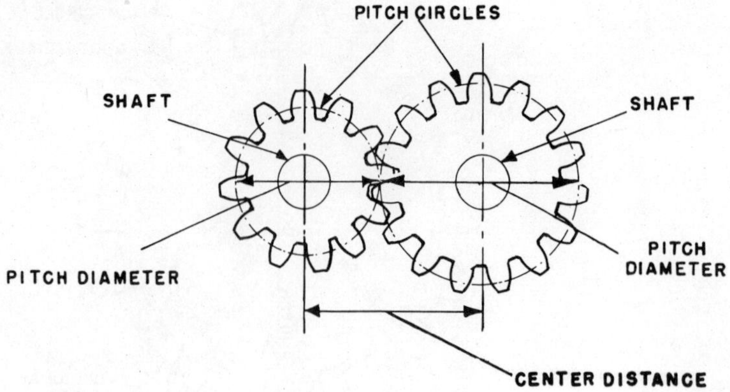

Figure 14-13
Gear terms. Boston Gear Works

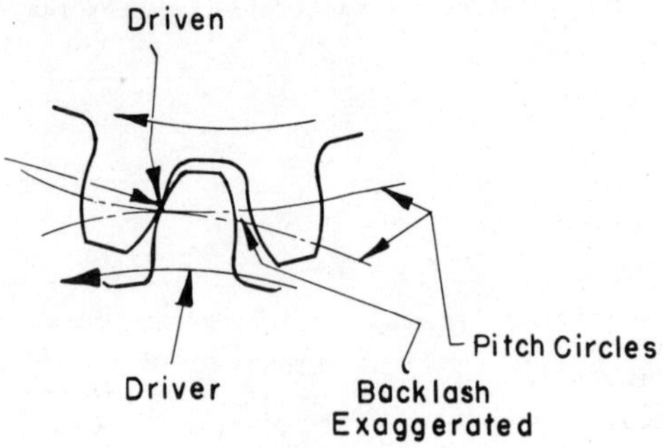

Figure 14-14
Backlash. Boston Gear Works

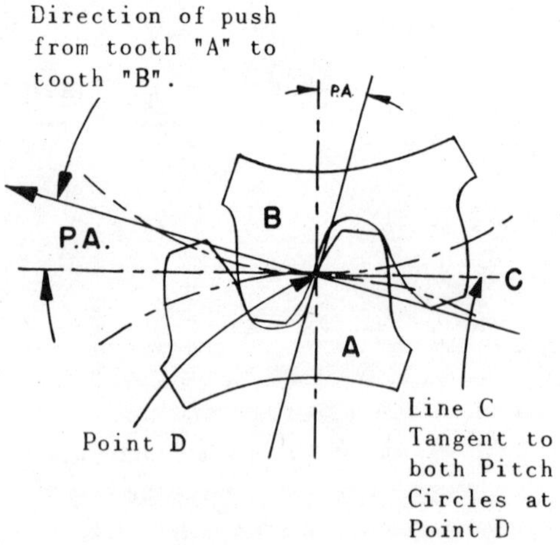

Figure 14-15
Pressure angle.
Boston Gear Works

the bottom of the mating tooth when gears are in mesh. (Fig. 14-12.)

Circular thickness. Length of arc between the two sides of a gear tooth on the pitch circle. (Fig. 14-12.)

Chordal thickness. Thickness of the gear tooth measured along a chord at the pitch circle. (Fig. 14-12.)

Chordal addendum. Radial distance from a line representing the chordal thickness at the pitch circle to the top of the tooth. (Fig. 14-12.)

Center distance. Distance from the center of one shaft to the center of the other shaft. (Fig. 14-13.)

Backlash. Shortest distance or play between mating teeth measured between the non-driving surfaces of adjacent teeth. (Fig. 14-14.)

Pressure angle. Angle that determines the tooth shape, or *tooth form* as well as the base circle. It is the angle at which pressure from the tooth of one gear is passed on to the tooth of another gear. (Fig. 14-15.)

Velocity or *feet per minute.* Distance that any point on the pitch circle will travel in a given period of time.

Base circle. Circle from which the involute tooth profile is formed. (Fig. 14-16.)

Gear ratio. Number of teeth on the gear divided by the number of teeth on the pinion. It is also defined as the relationship of the pitch diameter of the gear to the pitch diameter of the pinion. Ratio is further defined as the revolutions per minute (RPM) of the

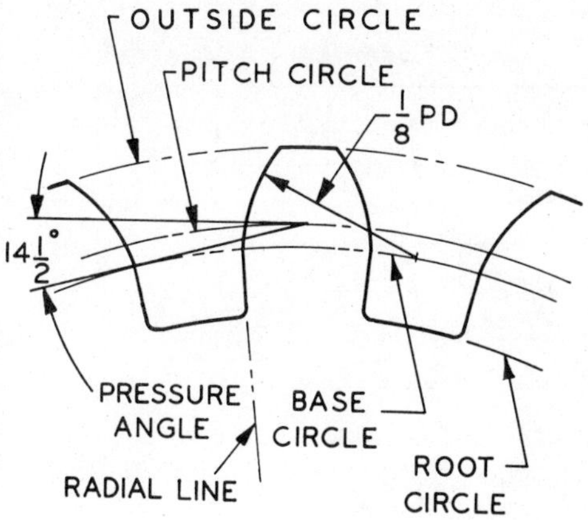

Figure 14-16
This approximate representation of spur gear tooth profile can be produced rapidly and easily.

pinion divided by the revolutions per minute of the gear.

Face of tooth. Surface of the tooth profile that is between the pitch circle and the top of the tooth.

Flank of tooth. Surface of the tooth profile that is between the pitch circle and the bottom land including the fillet.

14.3 Standard spur gear formulas

The proportion and shape of spur gear teeth are based on standardized formulas. Some of the more basic and essential spur gear formulas are included in Figs. 14-17 and 14-18.

14.4 Spur gear tooth profile

A gear tooth profile must be designed so that the gears will transmit power at a constant velocity and with a minimum of vibration and noise. Various curves have been utilized to produce the type of gear tooth profile having the correct geometric form to meet these requirements. From this group, the involute curve has evolved as the most common gear tooth profile in use today. In addition to satisfying the above requirements, involute gears can be easily manufactured by a variety of techniques. Hobbing, shaping, and shaving are the three common methods of manufacturing spur gears. Other methods used to produce spur gears are die casting for light duty gears and stamping for thin section gears.

The shape of the tooth resulting from the involute system is based principally upon the pressure angle, and is generated from the base circle. Therefore, the size of the base circle is governed by the magnitude of the pressure angle.

Spur gears are made with either a 14-1/2° or 20° pressure angle. Gears having the latter angle are gradually replacing the older 14-1/2° angle. The 20° pressure angle tooth shape is considered stronger because of its wider base and less undercut.

Two methods are used to illustrate the shape of a spur gear tooth: *approximate representation* and *true representation.*

Approximate representation is intended for display purposes or when it is necessary to illustrate the relationship between the teeth and some special feature such as a keyway or spline. The construction can be executed rapidly and simply as follows (see Fig. 14-18):

1 Draw the required pitch circle, outside circle, and root circle, determined either by formulas or from gearing tables.

2 Draw radial lines spacing off the teeth on the pitch circle.

3 Draw a line tangent to the pitch circle.

4 Draw a second line at an angle of 14-1/2° or 20° with the tangent. (An approximation of 15° may be used instead of 14-1/2° to facilitate the construction.)

5 Draw the base circle tangent to the 14-1/2° pressure angle line.

6 With centers on the base circle and radii equal to one-eighth the pitch diameter,

	TO FIND	HAVING	RULE	FORMULA
1	Diametral Pitch	Circular Pitch	Divide 3.1416 by Circular Pitch	$DP = \frac{3.1416}{CP}$
2	Diametral Pitch	Pitch Dia. and Number of Teeth	Divide the Number of Teeth by Pitch Diameter	$DP = \frac{N}{PD}$
3	Diametral Pitch	Outside Dia. and Number of Teeth	Divide Number of Teeth plus 2 by Outside Diameter	$DP = \frac{N + 2}{OD}$
4	Pitch Diameter	Number of Teeth and Diam. Pitch	Divide Number of Teeth by Diametral Pitch	$PD = \frac{N}{DP}$
5	Pitch Diameter	Number of Teeth and Outside Dia.	Divide the Product of Number of Teeth and Outside Diameter by Number of Teeth plus 2	$PD = \frac{N \times OD}{N + 2}$
6	Pitch Diameter	Outside Diameter and Diam. Pitch	Subtract from the Outside Dia. the Quotient of 2 divided by the Diametral Pitch	$PD = OD - \frac{2}{DP}$
7	Outside Diameter	Number of Teeth and Diam. Pitch	Divide Number of Teeth plus 2 by the Diametral Pitch	$OD = \frac{N + 2}{DP}$
8	Outside Diameter	Pitch Diameter and Diam. Pitch	Add to the Pitch Diameter the Quotient of 2 divided by the Diametral Pitch	$OD = PD + \frac{2}{DP}$
9	Outside Diameter	Pitch Diameter and No. of Teeth	Divide Product of Number of Teeth plus 2 and Pitch Diameter by Number of Teeth	$OD = \frac{(N + 2) \times PD}{N}$
10	Number of Teeth	Pitch Diameter and Diam. Pitch	Multiply Pitch Diameter by Diametral Pitch	$N = PD \times DP$
11	Number of Teeth	Outside Diameter and Diam. Pitch	Multiply Outside Diameter by Diametral Pitch and Subtract 2	$N = (OD \times DP) - 2$
12	Addendum	Diametral Pitch	Divide 1 by Diametral Pitch	$A = \frac{1}{DP}$
13	Working Clearance	Whole Depth and Addendum	From the Whole Depth Subtract 2 Addendums	$WK = WD - 2 \times A$
14	Chordal Addendum	Number of Teeth, Pitch Diameter, and Addendum	Subtract the cosine of the angle determined by dividing 90° by the number of Teeth from 1; multiply this by 1/2 the Pitch Diameter and add the Addendum	$CA = a + \frac{D}{2}\left(1 - \cos\frac{90°}{N}\right)$
15	Chordal Thickness	Number of Teeth and Pitch Diameter	Multiply the Pitch Diameter by the sine of the angle determined by dividing 90° by the number of teeth	$Th = D \sin\frac{90°}{N}$

Figure 14-17
These formulas apply to all spur gears.
Boston Gear Works

	In Terms of Diametral Pitch[1] (Inches)	In Terms of Circular Pitch[1] (Inches)
1. Addendum	$= \frac{1}{DP}$	$0.3183 \times CP$
2. Minimum Dedendum	$= \frac{1.157}{DP}$	$0.3683 \times CP$
3. Working Depth	$= \frac{2}{DP}$	$0.6366 \times CP$
4. Minimum Total Depth	$= \frac{2.157}{DP}$	$0.6866 \times CP$
5. Pitch Diameter	$= \frac{N}{DP}$	$0.3183 \times N \times CP$
6. Outside Diameter	$= \frac{N + 2}{DP}$	$0.3183 \times (N + 2) \times CP$
7. Basic Tooth Thickness on Pitch Line	$= \frac{1.5708}{DP}$	$0.5 \times CP$
8. Minimum Clearance	$= \frac{0.157}{DP}$	$0.05 \times CP$
9. Radius of Fillet	$= 1\frac{1}{3} \times$ Clearance	

N = Number of Teeth. DP = Diametral Pitch. CP = Circular Pitch.

[1] **Note:** The term Diametral Pitch is used up to 1 DP inclusive and the term Circular Pitch is used for 3 inches CP and over.

Figure 14-18
Basic formulas for full depth tooth proportions for spur gears. ASA B6.1

No. of Teeth	R Face Radius	R' Flank Radius	No. of Teeth	R Face Radius	R' Flank Radius
10	2.28	0.69	28	3.92	2.59
11	2.40	0.83	29	3.99	2.67
12	2.51	0.96	30	4.06	2.76
13	2.62	1.09	31	4.13	2.85
14	2.72	1.22	32	4.20	2.93
15	2.82	1.34	33	4.27	3.01
16	2.92	1.46	34	4.33	3.09
17	3.02	1.58	35	4.39	3.16
18	3.12	1.69	36	4.45	3.23
19	3.22	1.79	37-40	4.20	4.20
20	3.32	1.89	41-45	4.63	4.63
21	3.41	1.98	46-51	5.06	5.06
22	3.49	2.06	52-60	5.74	5.74
23	3.57	2.15	61-70	6.52	6.52
24	3.64	2.24	71-90	7.72	7.72
25	3.71	2.33	91-120	9.78	9.78
26	3.78	2.42	121-180	13.38	13.38
27	3.85	2.50	181-360	21.62	21.62

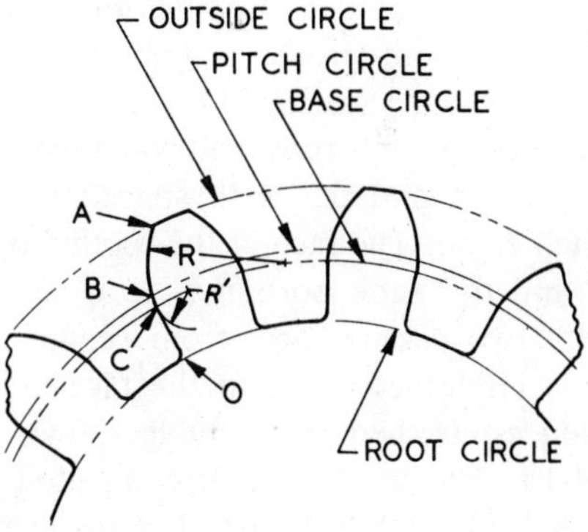

Figure 14-19
The application of Grant's Involute Odontograph system simplifies the drawing of spur tooth profile.

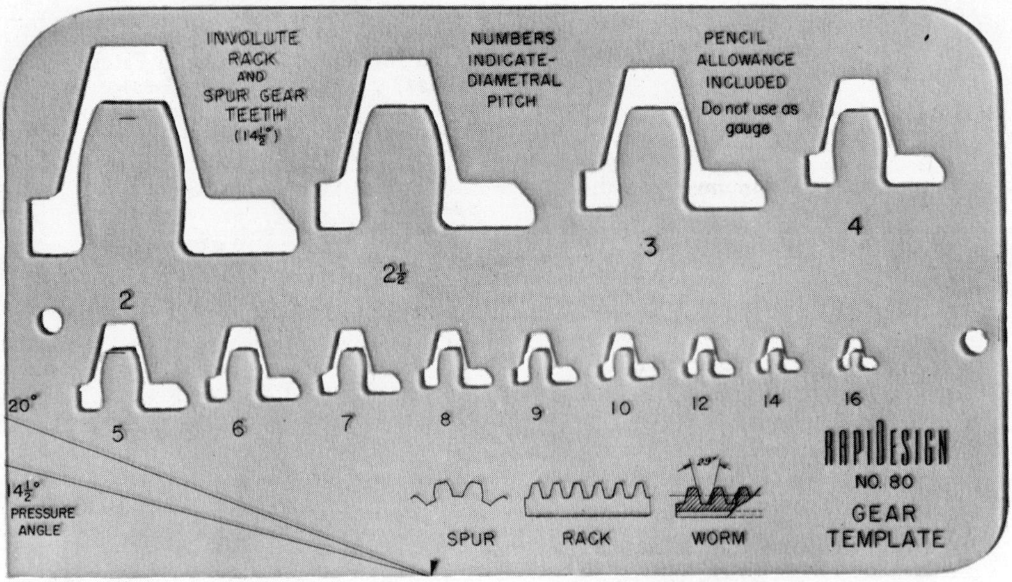

Figure 14-20
The use of a gear template simplifies the drawing of spur gear teeth profiles.

draw circular arcs through spaced tooth points on the pitch circle. Extend the arcs from the outside circle to slightly below the base circle.

7 Draw radial lines from the base circle to the root circle and terminate with fillets to complete the tooth profile.

Another rapid approximation method of drawing tooth profile is known as Grant's Odontograph. See Fig. 14-19. The pitch circle, addendum, root and clearance circles are drawn and the teeth spaced off on the pitch circle. The face of the tooth from *A* to *B* and the flank portion *B* to *C* are drawn with two circular arcs from centers on the base circle according to the face and flank radii established in the table shown in Fig. 14-19. The tooth is then completed with a radial line *CO* and fillet. The table includes the necessary face and flank radii for gears of one diametral pitch. Other size gears can be drawn by dividing the figures in the table by the required diametral pitch.

Drawing an approximate spur gear tooth profile is further simplified with the use of the gear template shown in Fig. 14-20. This template provides profiles of involute rack and spur gear teeth of all common pitches. All that is necessary to use the template is to draw the outer and root circles, space off the required teeth, and position the template to provide the required tooth outline.

True representation. Occasionally it is necessary to lay out the true tooth profile in order to check the backlash or clearance of mating gears. The true representation of a gear tooth profile is drawn from the base circle to the outside circle as an involute of the base circle. See Fig. 14-21. To construct such a curve, proceed as follows:

1 Draw the base circle, outside circle, pitch circle, and root circle.

2 Divide the base circle into any convenient number of equal parts starting with point *O* and numbering them 1, 2, 3, 4, etc.

3 Draw a tangent *AB* to the base circle at point *O*. Divide this line into equal parts having the same lengths as the arcs on the base circle. Number them 1′, 2′, 3′, 4′, etc.

4 Draw tangents to points 1, 2, 3, 4, etc.

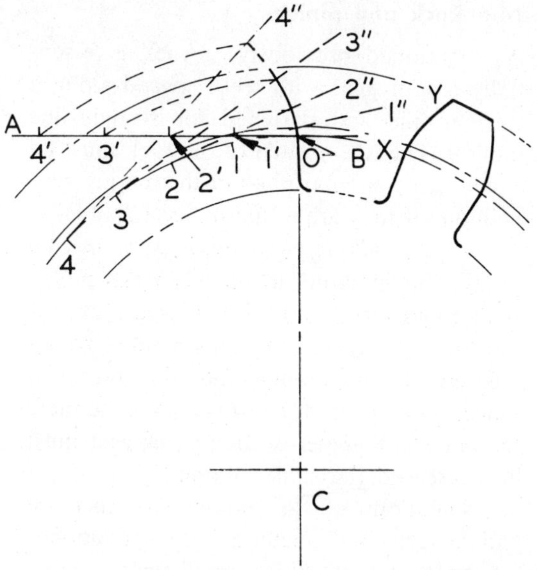

Figure 14-21
Method of laying out a true involute tooth profile.

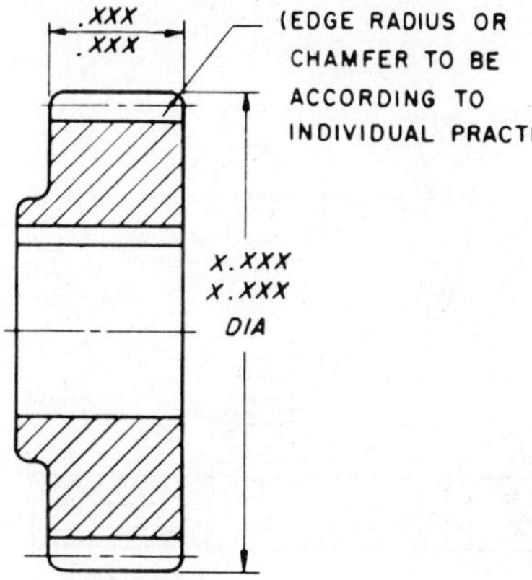

SPUR-GEAR TOOTH DATA

NUMBER OF TEETH	XX
DIAMETRAL PITCH	XX
PRESSURE ANGLE	XX°XX′
PITCH DIAMETER	X.XXXX
CIRCULAR THICKNESS	.XXXX
WHOLE DEPTH (MIN)	.XXX
WORKING DEPTH	.XXX
CHORDAL ADDENDUM (MAX OD)	.XXX
CHORDAL THICKNESS	.XXX–.XXX

Figure 14-22
A single view is often sufficient for a detail drawing of a spur gear.
ASA Y14.7-1958

on the base circle.

5 Using the center of the base circle *C* as the pivot, draw concentric arcs from points 1′, 2′, 3′, 4′, etc., on the base circle tangent AB, to intersect tangents 1″, 2″, 3″, 4″, etc., from the division points on the base circle.

6 The intersection of the arcs with the tangents represents the required points of the involute curve. These points will produce the profile of the tooth extending from *X* to *Y*. The lower portion of the tooth is completed by drawing a radial line and terminating it with the required fillet at the root circle.

14.5 Detail drawing of spur gears

A working drawing of a spur gear is relatively simple. Either a single or two-view drawing is made. See Figs. 14-22 and 14-23. In either case a cross section is used to show the web portion of the gear blank.

Notice in Fig. 14-23 that the outside circle and root circle are drawn as phantom lines and the pitch circle as a centerline circle. As a rule no teeth are included on the drawing of the blank, except one or more teeth may be shown conventionally when it is necessary to illustrate some relationship to a specific feature such as a keyway, locating pin hole or spline.

The gear blank dimensions are shown on the given views and are generally expressed in decimal sizes in thousandths and ten-thousandths of an inch. The essential tooth data is included in chart form.

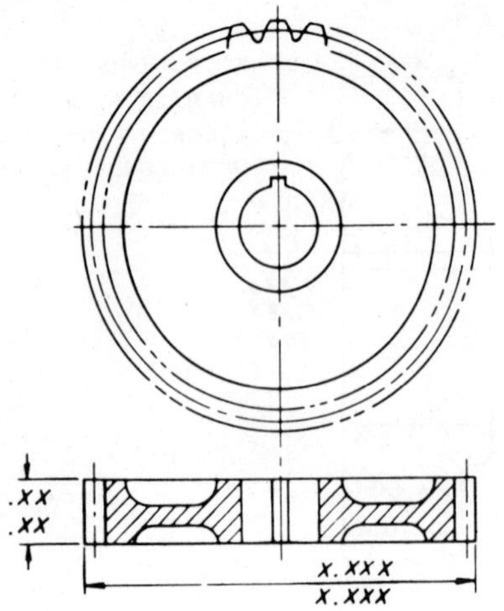

SPUR-GEAR TOOTH DATA

NUMBER OF TEETH	XX
DIAMETRAL PITCH	XX
PRESSURE ANGLE	XX° XX'
PITCH DIAMETER	X.XXXX
CIRCULAR THICKNESS	.XXXX
ADDENDUM	.XXX
WHOLE DEPTH (MIN)	.XXX
CHORDAL ADDENDUM	.XXX
CHORDAL THICKNESS	.XXX –.XXX
PART NUMBER OF MATING GEAR	XXXXX
NUMBER OF TEETH IN MATING GEAR	XX
CENTER DISTANCE	X.XXX

Figure 14-23
Teeth on a gear blank are included when a relationship must be established with a special feature of the gear. ASA Y14.7-1958

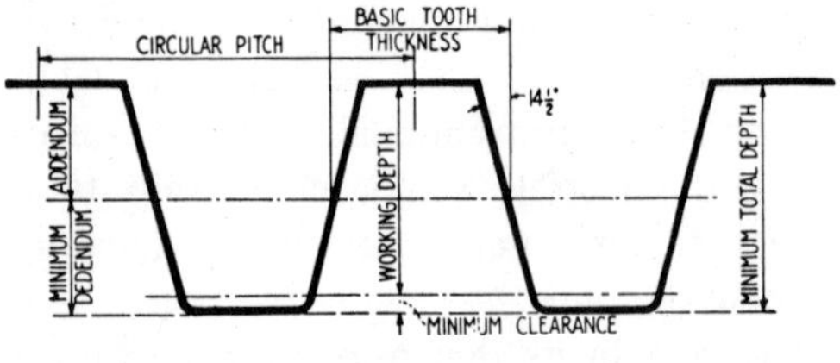

Figure 14-24
Basic rack of the 14-1/2° full depth involute system for spur gearing.

14.6 Rack and pinion

As mentioned previously, a rack is essentially a spur gear with teeth spaced along a straight line and designed for straight-line motion. The linear pitch of the rack must be equal to the circular pitch of the mating gear (pinion) if they are to mesh. See Fig. 14-24.

14-1/2° full depth involute system.[2] To obtain full involute action when the pinion is in contact with a 14-1/2° basic rack, the outside diameter of the pinion must be increased. To maintain standard center distance where a gear is substituted for the rack, the outside diameter of the mating gear must be decreased the same amount.

Tabulations of the amounts of increase and decrease in diameter and the corresponding circular tooth thicknesses on the pitch line of both gear and pinion are included in the table in Fig. 14-25.

Long addendum pinions in mesh with standard addendum gears will run with full involute action, but it is self-evident that in such cases the center distance must be increased to suit the standard size gear.

If the sum of the numbers of teeth in the pinion and the mating gear is less than 64, undercutting will occur in the teeth of the mating gear.

20° full depth involute system. To obtain full involute action when the pinion is in contact with a 20° basic rack (Fig. 14-26), the outside diameter of the pinion must be increased. To maintain standard center distance where a gear is substituted for the rack, the outside diameter of the mating gear must be decreased the same amount.

Tabulations of the amounts of increase and decrease in diameter and the corresponding circular tooth thicknesses on the pitch line of both gear and pinion are included in the table in Fig. 14-27.

Long addendum pinions in mesh with standard addendum gears will run with full involute action, but it is self-evident that in such cases the center distance must be in-

2. Extracted from *Spur Gear Tooth Form, ASA B6.1—1932* (New York: The American Society of Mechanical Engineers, 1932).

Number of Teeth in Pinion	Diameter Increment	Pinion Circular Tooth Thickness	Mating Gear Circular Tooth Thickness	Min Number of Teeth in Mating Gear Avoiding Undercut	Min Number of Teeth in Mating Gear for Full Involute Action
10	1.3731	1.9259	1.2157	54	27
11	1.3104	1.9097	1.2319	53	27
12	1.2477	1.8935	1.2481	52	28
13	1.1850	1.8773	1.2643	51	28
14	1.1223	1.8611	1.2805	50	28
15	1.0597	1.8449	1.2967	49	28
16	0.9970	1.8286	1.3130	48	28
17	0.9343	1.8124	1.3292	47	28
18	0.8716	1.7962	1.3454	46	28
19	0.8089	1.7800	1.3616	45	28
20	0.7462	1.7638	1.3778	44	28
21	0.6835	1.7476	1.3940	43	28
22	0.6208	1.7314	1.4102	42	27
23	0.5581	1.7151	1.4265	41	27
24	0.4954	1.6989	1.4427	40	27
25	0.4328	1.6827	1.4589	39	26
26	0.3701	1.6665	1.4751	38	26
27	0.3074	1.6503	1.4913	37	26
28	0.2447	1.6341	1.5075	36	25
29	0.1820	1.6179	1.5237	35	25
30	0.1193	1.6017	1.5399	34	24
31	0.0566	1.5854	1.5562	33	24

All dimensions in inches.

Figure 14-25
Data for use in obtaining full involute tooth action on pinions of 31 teeth and smaller, when using the 14-1/2° full depth involute system.*

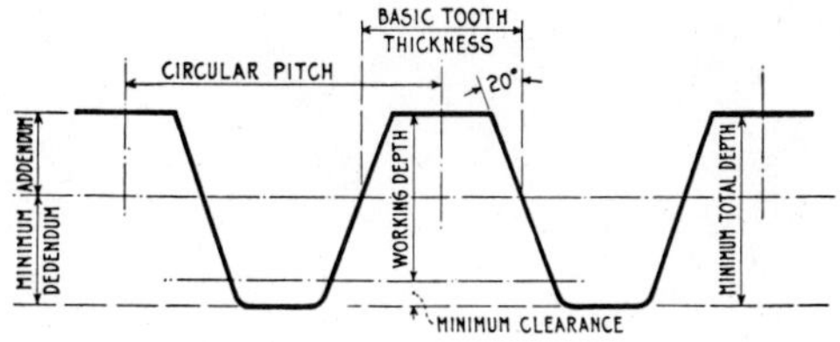

Figure 14-26
Basic rack of the 20° full depth involute system for spur gearing.*

Number of Teeth in Pinion	Diameter Increment	Pinion Circular Tooth Thickness	Mating Gear Circular Tooth Thickness	Min Number of Teeth in Mating Gear Avoiding Undercut	Min Number of Teeth in Mating Gear for Full Involute Action
8	1.0642	1.9581	1.1835	26	16
9	0.9472	1.9156	1.2260	25	16
10	0.8302	1.8730	1.2636	24	16
11	0.7132	1.8304	1.3112	23	16
12	0.5963	1.7878	1.3538	22	15
13	0.4793	1.7453	1.3963	21	14
14	0.3623	1.7027	1.4389	20	14
15	0.2453	1.6601	1.4815	19	14
16	0.1284	1.6175	1.5241	18	13
17	0.0114	1.5749	1.5667	17	13

All dimensions in inches.

Figure 14-27
Data for use in obtaining full involute tooth action on pinions of 17 teeth and smaller when using the 20° full depth involute system.

*NOTE: The dimensions (inches) in the table are based upon one diametral pitch. For other pitches, divide dimensions given by the diametral pitch desired.

		In Terms of Diametral Pitch[1] (Inches)	In Terms of Circular Pitch[1] (Inches)
1.	Addendum	$= \frac{0.8}{DP}$	$0.2546 \times CP$
2.	Minimum Dedendum	$= \frac{1}{DP}$	$0.3183 \times CP$
3.	Working Depth	$= \frac{1.6}{DP}$	$0.5092 \times CP$
4.	Minimum Total Depth	$= \frac{1.8}{DP}$	$0.5729 \times CP$
5.	Pitch Diameter	$= \frac{N}{DP}$	$0.3183 \times N \times CP$
6.	Outside Diameter	$= \frac{N + 1.6}{DP}$	PD + (2 Addendums)
7.	Basic Tooth Thickness on Pitch Line	$= \frac{1.5708}{DP}$	$0.5 \times CP$
8.	Minimum Clearance	$= \frac{0.2}{DP}$	$0.0637 \times CP$

N = Number of Teeth   DP = Diametral Pitch   PD = Pitch Diameter
CP = Circular Pitch

[1] NOTE: The term Diametral Pitch is used up to 1 DP inclusive and the term Circular Pitch is used for 3 inches CP and over.

Figure 14-28
Stub tooth proportions for spur gears.

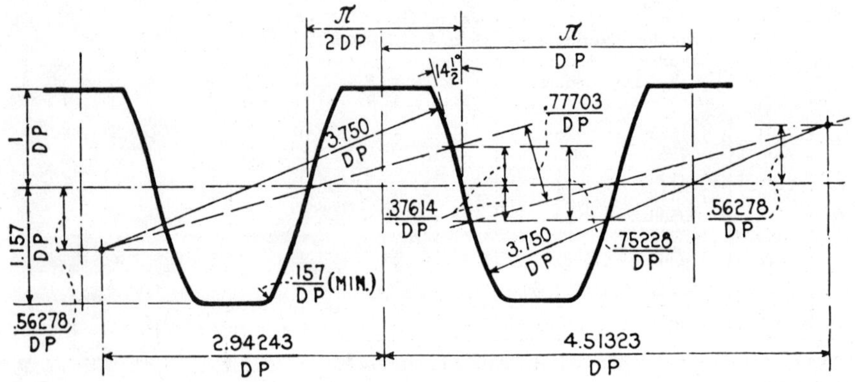

Figure 14–29
Approximation to basic rack for 14-1/2° composite system (full depth tooth). ASA B6.1

creased to suit the standard size gear.

If the sum of the number of teeth in the pinion and the mating gear is less than 34, undercutting will occur in the teeth of the mating gear.

Stub teeth. When the height of the tooth is reduced and the pressure angle increased to 20°, the teeth are known as stub teeth. Teeth of this design are stronger than the standard 14-1/2° involute teeth. Fig. 14-28 includes the basic proportions of stub tooth for spur gears.

14.7 Standard 14-1/2° composite tooth system

The difference between this standard and the 14-1/2° involute full depth system is in the form of the basic rack teeth. The involute straight-sided rack is modified to provide tooth relief by using a cycloidal curve below and above the pitch line to produce a symmetrical tooth for interchangeable gearing. However, the pressure angle remains the same as well as the formulas for obtaining tooth depth, addendum, dedendum, etc. Since it is usually impossible to produce a rack with exact cycloidal curves, the practice is to use the approximate form shown in Fig. 14-29.

14.8 Representing racks

The prescribed method of representing a rack and dimensioning rack teeth is shown in Fig. 14-30. Note that the teeth are dimensioned from the end of the rack blank and from some datum line. The datum line may be the bottom of the blank or any other line which provides accurate features.

14.9 Bevel and miter gears

Bevel and miter gears use the same involute tooth form as spur gears except that the teeth are tapered toward the apex of the cone. Regardless of the similarity in tooth form they are not interchangeable with spur gears. Bevel and miter gears are always designed in pairs.

Most of the gear terms previously discussed for spur gears apply to bevel and miter gears. However, some of the defini-

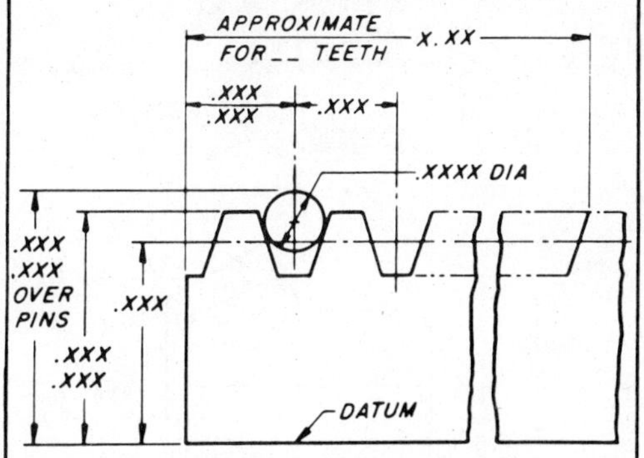

RACK TOOTH DATA

PRESSURE ANGLE	XX°
TOOTH THICKNESS, PITCH LINE	.XXXX
WHOLE DEPTH	.XXX
MAXIMUM ALLOWABLE PITCH VARIATION	.XXX
ACCUMULATED PITCH ERROR, MAXIMUM	.XXX

Figure 14-30
This is the recommended way a rack should be shown on a drawing.
ASA Y14.7-1958

tions must be modified and other terms added so they are more applicable to bevel and miter gears. The following are particularly pertinent (see Fig. 14-31):

Pitch diameter. Diameter of the pitch circle measured at the base of the pitch cone.

Pitch angle. Angle between an element of a pitch cone and its axis.

Cone distance. Slant length of the pitch cone.

Face. Length of the tooth.

Face angle. Angle between an element of the face cone and its axis.

Mounting distance. Distance from the pitch apex to a surface of the gear used for locating in assembly.

Root angle. Angle between an element of the root cone and its axis.

Crown backing. Distance between the rear of the hub and the outer tip of the gear tooth, measured parallel with the axis of the gear.

Crown height. Distance between the cone apex and the outer tip of the gear tooth measured parallel with the axis of the gear.

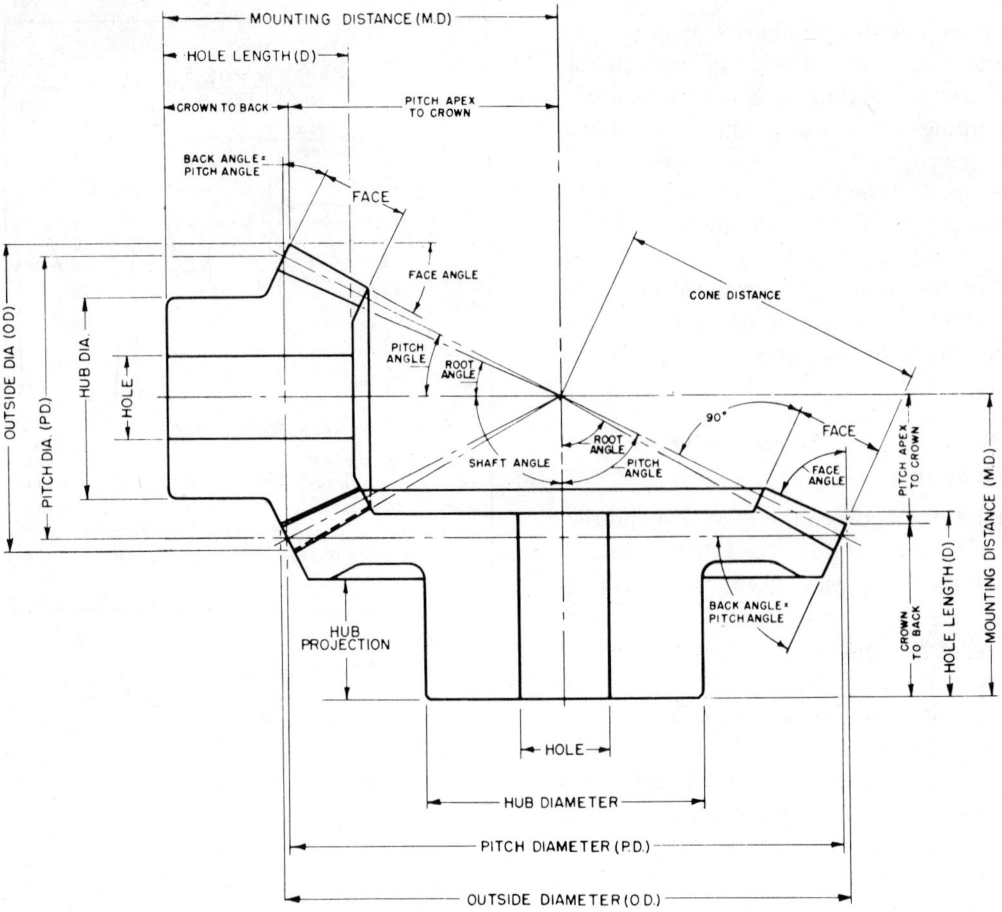

Figure 14-31
Bevel gear terminology.
Boston Gear Works

14.10 Bevel gear formulas

The basic formulas used in computing bevel gear dimensions are included in the table shown in Fig. 14-32.

14.11 Detail drawing of bevel gears

A detail drawing of a bevel gear, like the spur gear, should contain the essential specifications for its manufacture. Two representative detail drawings are illustrated in Fig. 14-33. The gear blank dimensions are shown in a single sectional view and tooth cutting data is presented in tabular form. Note that the gear tooth profile is not generally shown. Essential mounting dimensions such as bore size, keyway, or spline data must also be included.

A drawing of a pair of bevel gears is shown in Fig. 14-34. This type of drawing is not uncommon and has the advantage of illustrating the working relationship of the gears. However detail drawings usually require only the one view and the cutting data.

	TO FIND	RULE
1	Ratio	Divide the Number of Teeth in the Gear by the Number of Teeth in the Pinion
2	Diametral Pitch (DP)	Divide 3.1416 by the Circular Pitch
3	Pitch Diameter of Pinion	Divide Number of Teeth in the Pinion by the D.P.
	Pitch Diameter of Gear	Divide Number of Teeth in the Gear by the D.P.
4	Whole Depth (Of Tooth)	Divide 2.188 by the Diametral Pitch and add .002
5	Addendum	Divide 1 by the Diametral Pitch
6	Dedendum of Pinion or Gear	Divide 2.188 by the D.P. and subtract the Addendum
7	Clearance	Divide .188 by the Diametral Pitch and add .002
8	Circular Thickness Of Pinion or Gear	Divide 1.5708 by the Diametral Pitch
9	Pitch Angle of Pinion	Divide No. of Teeth in Pinion by No. of Teeth in Gear. Quotient is the tangent of the Pitch Angle
	Pitch Angle of Gear	Subtract the Pitch Angle of Pinion from 90°
10	Cone Distance	Divide one half the P.D. of the Gear by the sine of the Pitch Angle of the Gear
11	Addendum Angle of Pinion	Divide the addendum of the Pinion by the Cone Distance. Quotient is the tangent of the addendum angle
	Addendum Angle of Gear	Divide the addendum of the Gear by the Cone Distance. Quotient is the tangent of the addendum angle

	TO FIND	RULE
12	Dedendum Angle of Pinion	Divide the Dedendum of Pinion by Cone Distance. Quotient is the Tangent of the Dedendum Angle
	Dedendum Angle of Gear	Divide the Dedendum of Gear by Cone Distance. Quotient is the tangent of the Dedendum Angle
13	Root Angle of Pinion	Subtract the Dedendum angle of pinion from Pitch Angle of the Pinion
	Root Angle of Gear	Subtract the Dedendum Angle of the Gear from Pitch Angle of the Gear
14	Face Angle of Pinion	Add the Addendum Angle of the Pinion to the Pitch Angle of the Pinion
	Face Angle of Gear	Add the Addendum Angle of the Gear to the Pitch Angle of the Gear
15	Outside Diameter of Pinion	Add twice the Pinion Addendum times cosine of Pinion Pitch Angle to the Pinion P.D.
	Outside Diameter of Gear	Add twice the Gear Addendum times cosine of Gear Pitch Angle to the Gear P.D.
16	Pitch Apex to Crown of Pinion	Subtract the Pinion Addendum times the sine of Pinion Pitch Angle from half the Gear P.D.
	Pitch Apex to Crown of Gear	Subtract the Gear Addendum times the sine of the Gear Pitch Angle from half the Pinion P.D.
17	Chordal Thickness at large end of tooth in Gear or Pinion	Multiply the pitch diameter by the sine of the angle found by dividing 90° by the number of teeth
18	Chordal Addendum at large end of tooth in Gear or Pinion	Multiply the square of the circular thickness by the cosine of the pitch angle; divide product by 4 times the pitch diameter and add the quotient to addendum

Figure 14-32
Formulas to obtain straight bevel and miter gear dimensions for 90° shaft angle. Boston Gear Works

STRAIGHT BEVEL GEAR

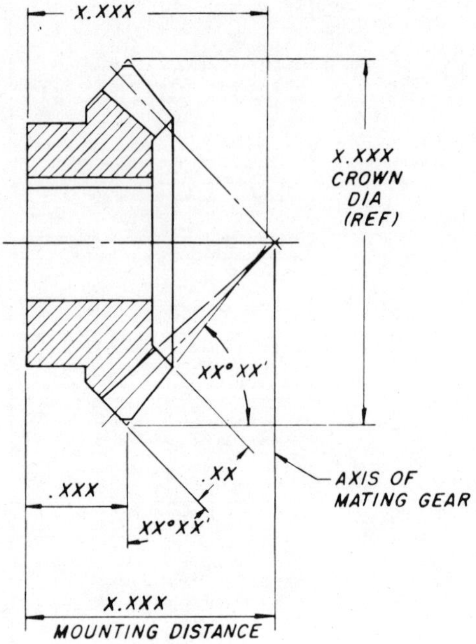

GEAR TOOTH DATA

NUMBER OF TEETH	XX
DIAMETRAL PITCH	XX
PRESSURE ANGLE	XX°XX'
CONE DISTANCE	X.XXX
PITCH DIAMETER	X.XXX
CIRCULAR THICKNESS (REF)	.XXXX
PITCH ANGLE	X°XX'
ROOT ANGLE	XX°XX'
ADDENDUM	.XXX
WHOLE DEPTH (APPROX)	.XXX
CHORDAL ADDENDUM	.XXX
CHORDAL THICKNESS	.XXX
PART NUMBER OF MATING GEAR	XXXXX
TEETH IN MATING GEAR	XX
SHAFT ANGLE	XX°XX'
BACKLASH (ASSEMBLED)	.XXXX
TOOTH ANGLE (APPROX)	X°XX'
LIMIT POINT WIDTH	.XXX
TOOL EDGE RADIUS	XXX

SPIRAL BEVEL GEAR

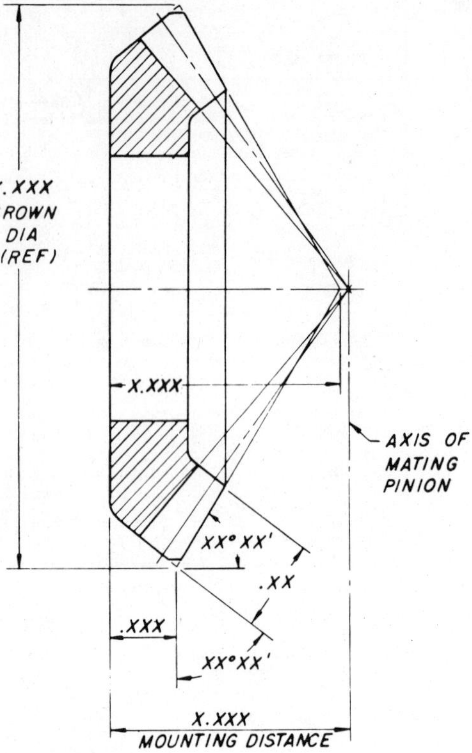

SPIRAL BEVEL GEAR TOOTH DATA

NUMBER OF TEETH	XX
DIAMETRAL PITCH	XX
PRESSURE ANGLE	XX°XX'
CIRCULAR THICKNESS	.XXXX
SPIRAL ANGLE	XX°XX'
HAND OF SPIRAL	(R OR L)
CONE DISTANCE	X.XXX
PITCH DIAMETER	X.XXX
PITCH ANGLE	X°XX'
ROOT ANGLE	X°XX'
ADDENDUM	.XXXX
WHOLE DEPTH (APPROX)	.XXX
NORMAL CHORDAL ADDENDUM	.XXX
NORMAL CHORDAL THICKNESS	.XXX
PART NUMBER OF MATING GEAR	XXXXX
TEETH IN MATING GEAR	XX
SHAFT ANGLE	X°XX'
BACKLASH (ASSEMBLED)	.XXX
SUMMARY NUMBER	XXXXX

Figure 14-33
Typical detail drawings of bevel gears with required tooth cutting data.
ASA Y14.7-1958

CUTTING DATA		
	GEAR	PINION
DIA PITCH	5	
NO. OF TEETH	30	15
TOOTH FORM	20° STD INV	
ROOT ANGLE	59° 23′	22° 31′
CHORDAL ADD.	0.2041	0.2074
CHORDAL THICK.	0.3140	0.3136

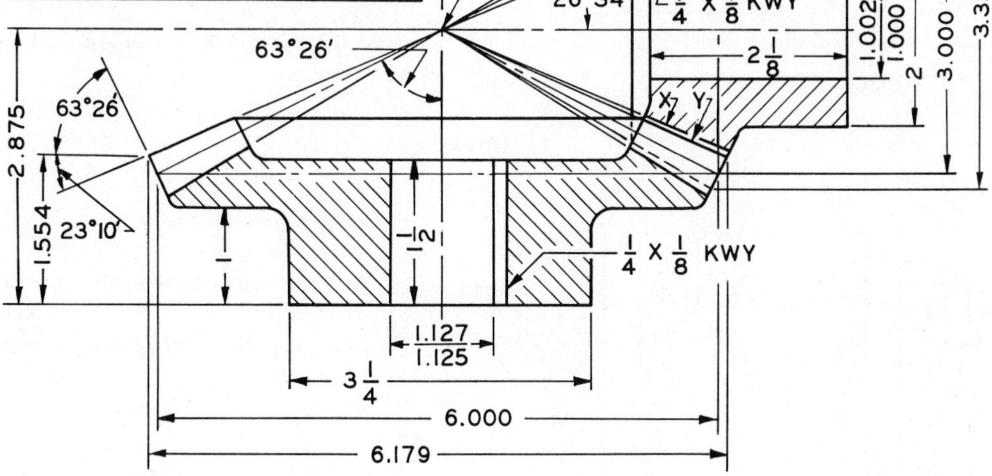

Figure 14-34
A detail drawing of mating bevel gears showing the working relationship of the gears.

14.12 Approximate method of drawing a pair of involute bevel gears

When it is desirable to draw a pair of bevel gears in mesh, the following procedure is suggested, see Fig. 14-34:

Draw the axes of the two bevel gears perpendicular (the shaft angle) to each other. Lay out in sequence the pitch angle, cone distances, pitch diameter, addendum and dedendum. Note that both the addendum and dedendum are measured at the large end of the tooth and are perpendicular to line *OP*. Using construction lines, draw lines from the pitch point *O* to the addendum and dedendum, thus completing the root and face angles. The face of the tooth is measured along the cone distance. The lines *X* and *Y* representing the face of one gear and a root-cone element of its mating gear are often drawn parallel to each other with the computed clearance illustrated. Information concerning the bore, hub diameter, other casting information and mounting distances should be obtained from the gear designer.

14.13 Wormgears

Wormgears, like helical gears, are used to transmit power between non-intersecting shafts. These shafts are nearly always at ninety degrees to each other with the worm generally acting as the driver.

A wormgear is meshed with a unit called a worm. The worm can be described as a cylinder having each tooth wrapped around the cylinder in a helical manner. The resulting configuration resembles a threaded bolt as in Fig. 14-35. Frequently the teeth of the

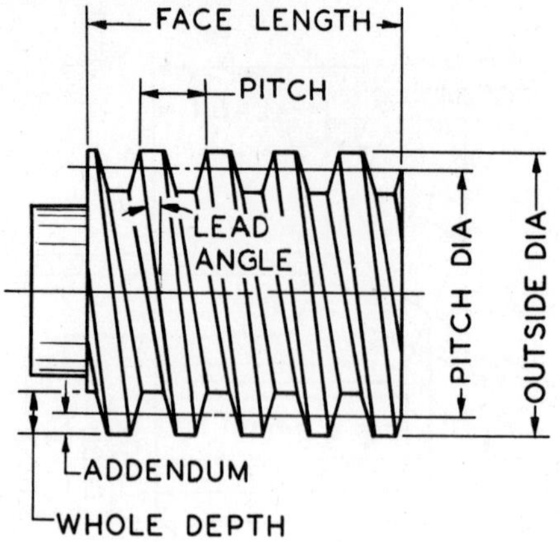

Figure 14-35
A worm has threads which resemble those of a screw thread.

WORM

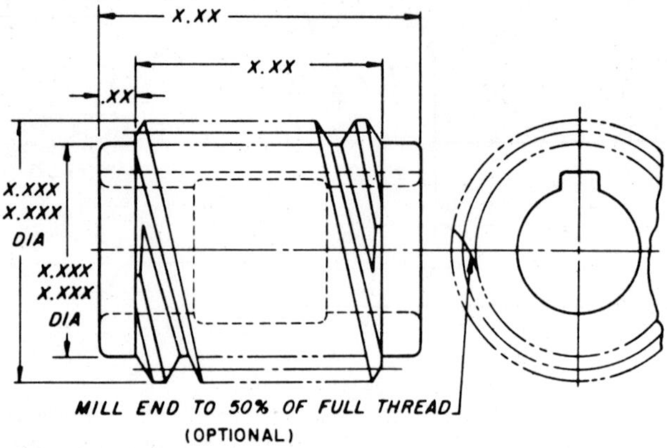

WORM TOOTH DATA	
MANUFACTURING METHOD	--------
NUMBER OF THREADS	XX
PITCH DIAMETER (NOMINAL)	X.XXX
AXIAL PITCH	X.XXXX
LEAD RIGHT (OR LEFT) HAND	X.XXXX
LEAD ANGLE	XX°XX'
NORMAL PRESSURE ANGLE (NORMAL)	XX°
ADDENDUM	.XXX
WHOLE DEPTH (APPROX)	.XXX
NORMAL CHORDAL ADDENDUM	.XXX
NORMAL CHORDAL THICKNESS	.XXX –.XXX
WORMGEAR PART NUMBER	XXXXX

Figure 14-36
Detail drawing of a worm. ASA Y14.7-1958

WORMGEAR

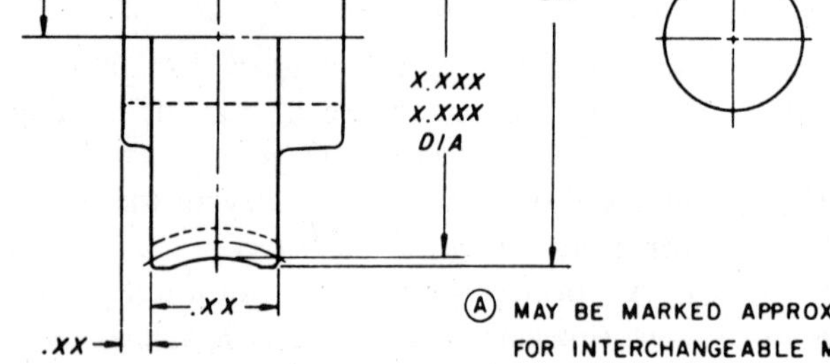

WORMGEAR TOOTH DATA	
NUMBER OF TEETH	XX
PITCH DIAMETER	X.XXX
ADDENDUM	.XXX
WHOLE DEPTH (APPROX)	.XXX
WORM PART NUMBER	XXXXX
BACKLASH ASSEMBLED	.XXX–.XXX
HOB NUMBER	XXXXX
WORM DATA (REFERENCE)	
NUMBER OF THREADS	XX
AXIAL PITCH	.XXXX
LEAD RIGHT (OR LEFT) HAND	X.XXX
PITCH DIAMETER (NOMINAL)	X.XXX
LEAD ANGLE	XX°
NORMAL PRESSURE ANGLE (NOMINAL)	XX°

Ⓐ MAY BE MARKED APPROXIMATE UNLESS OTHERWISE REQUIRED – FOR INTERCHANGEABLE MANUFACTURE, LIMITS SHOULD BE GIVEN.

Figure 14-37
Detail drawing of a wormgear. ASA Y14.7-1958

To Obtain	Having	Rule
Circular Pitch	Diametral Pitch	Divide 3.1416 by the Diametral Pitch.
Diametral Pitch	Circular Pitch	Divide 3.1416 by the Circular Pitch.
Lead (of Worm)	Number of Threads in worm & Circular Pitch	Multiply the Circular pitch by the number of threads.
Circular Pitch or Linear Pitch	Lead and number of threads in worm	Divide the lead by the number of threads.
Addendum	Circular Pitch	Multiply the Circular pitch by .3183.
Addendum	Diametral Pitch	Divide 1 by the Diametral Pitch.
Pitch Diameter of Worm	Outside Diameter and Addendum	Subtract twice the Addendum from the Outside Diameter.
Pitch Diameter of Worm	Select Standard Pitch Diameter when Designing	Worm Gears are made to suit the mating worm.
Pitch Diameter of Worm Gear	Circular Pitch and Number of Teeth	Multiply the number of teeth in the gear by the Circular Pitch and divide the product by 3.1416.
Pitch Diameter of Worm Gear	Diametral Pitch and No. of Teeth	Divide the number of teeth in gear by the Diametral Pitch.
Center Distance between Worm and Worm Gear	Pitch Diameter of Worm and Worm Gear	Add the Pitch Diameters of the worm and worm gear then divide the sum by 2.
Whole Depth of Teeth	Circular Pitch	Multiply the Circular Pitch by .6866.
Whole Depth of Teeth	Diametral Pitch	Divide 2.157 by the Diametral Pitch.
Bottom Diameter of Worm	Whole Depth and Outside Diameter	Subtract twice the whole depth from the Outside Diameter
Throat Diameter of Worm Gear	Pitch Diameter of Worm Gear and Addendum.	Add twice the Addendum to the pitch diameter of the Worm Gear.
Helix Angle of Worm	Pitch Diameter of the Worm and the Lead	Multiply the Pitch Diameter of the Worm by 3.1416 and divide the product by the Lead, the Quotient is the cotangent of the Helix Angle of the Worm. Worm.
Ratio	Number of Starts (or threads) in the Worm and the number of teeth in the Worm Gear	Divide the number of teeth in Worm Gear by number of starts (or threads) in worm.

Figure 14-38
Worm gear formulas.
Boston Gear Works

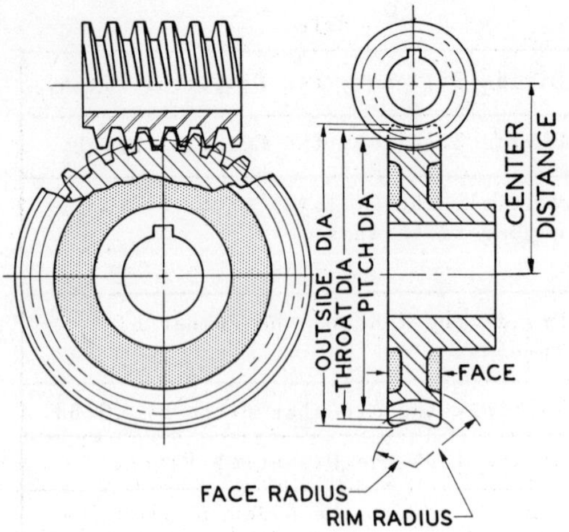

Figure 14-39
Assembly drawing of a worm and wormgear.

worm are referred to as *threads* and as such, the terms pitch and lead apply as they do with regular screws. Thus *pitch* is the distance between corresponding points on adjacent teeth as measured parallel to the axis of the worm. *Lead* is the axial distance that a thread advances in one turn of the worm. As in threads, the lead is a multiple of the pitch. In a single thread worm, the lead equals the pitch; the lead is twice the pitch for a double thread worm, triple the pitch for a triple thread worm.

14.14 Detail drawings of wormgears

Detail drawings of the worm and wormgear are generally shown separately as illustrated in Figs. 14-36 and 14-37. These sample drawings contain the minimum information needed by the gear manufacturer. Formulas for securing wormgear data are included in the table in Fig. 14-38. Three types of data should be included on the detail drawing: (1) gear blank information, (2) tooth cutting data, and (3) reference data pertinent to the mating part. This last item is especially important when the mating parts are being made by different manufacturers.

A similarity exists between the drafting construction of the worm, wormgear combination, and a rack and spur gear. Fig. 14-39 shows a worm and wormgear with their teeth engaged. Note that the worm, shown in section, is identical with a rack and that the wormgear also shown in section, is identical with a spur gear. The difference in drafting construction is illustrated in the right side view where the face radius and rim radius are constructed. These latter items alter the front view accordingly. Consequently, the construction is initiated by first laying out the center distance. The pitch diameters of the worm and wormgear, throat diameter, face radius, outside diameter and the rim radius are drawn in sequence. An approximate representation of involute spur gear teeth is generally used for the wormgear teeth. The teeth of the worm are drawn as teeth on the involute rack and are considered as threads.

14.15 Gearing schematics

A gearing schematic drawing is one which illustrates the arrangement of a gearing system. Its primary function is to help analyze a gearing system such as to trace the direction of motion or to determine the ratio of mating gears.

A gearing schematic should be presented as simply as possible. The gearing and associated mechanisms of the system should be represented pictorially in shapes resembling the actual outline of the components. It is not necessary to draw the schematic to scale. Sizes of parts should be in near proportion to each other even though their exact proportion cannot be represented.

Fig. 14-40 illustrates how gearing units and associated mechanisms are drawn in a gearing schematic. The incorporation of these representations in a complete gearing schematic drawing is shown in Fig. 14-41.

Direction of motion is indicated by directional arrows at points where the direction can be easily followed. If it is necessary to place a directional arrow on a representation of a shaft, the directional arrow should be drawn as illustrated in Fig. 14-42.

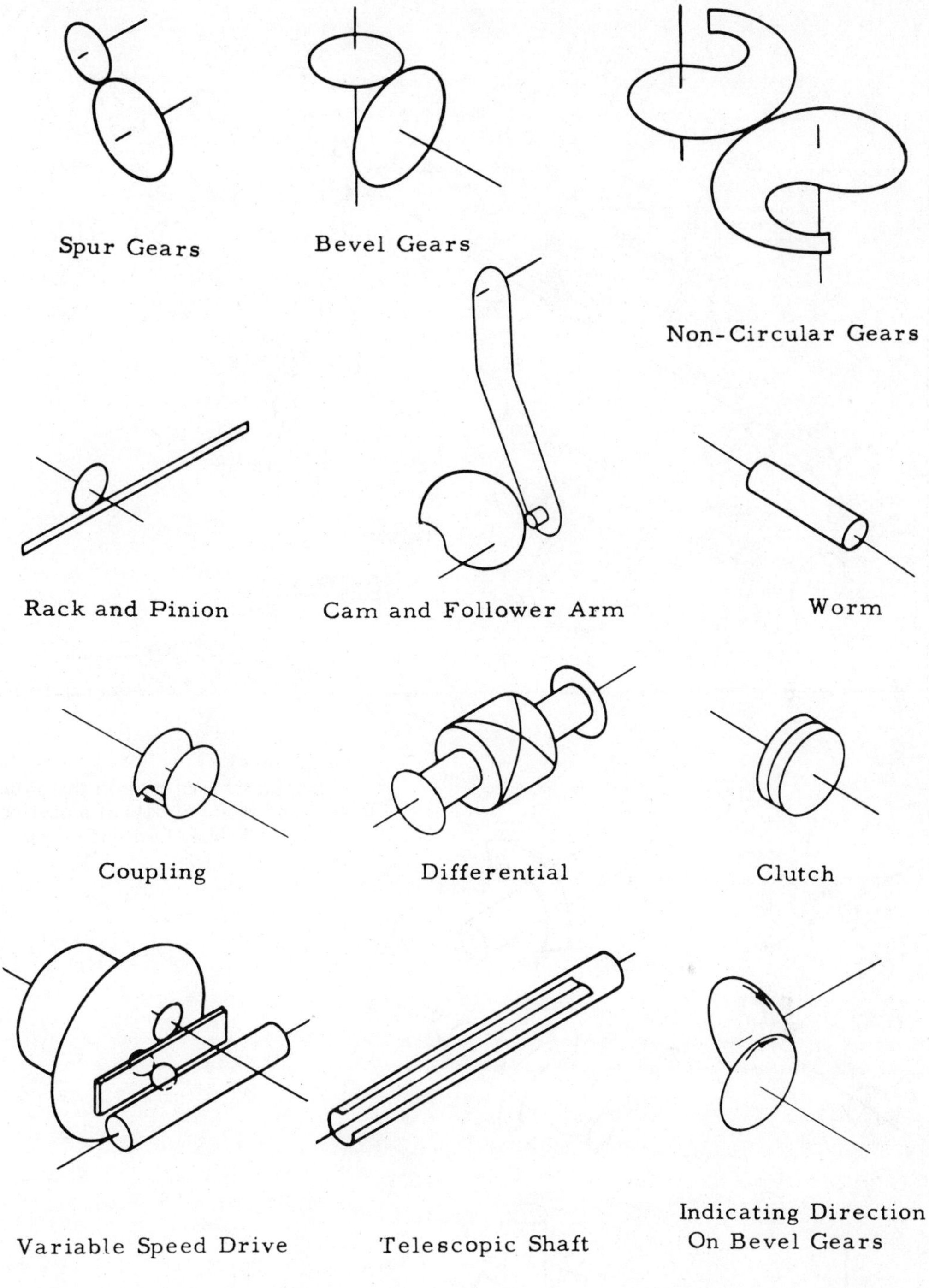

Figure 14-40
These are the representations of gears and associated mechanism used in a gear schematic drawing.
US Army Ordnance Corps

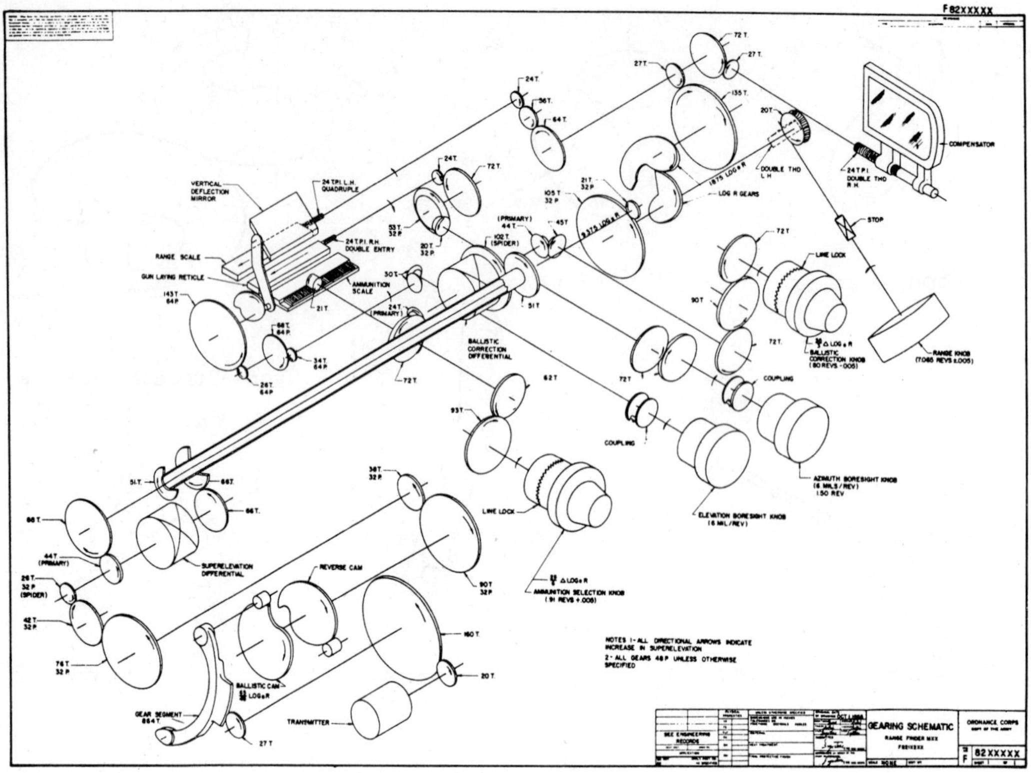

Figure 14-41
A gearing schematic shows the arrangement and essential data of a gearing system. US Army Ordnance Corps

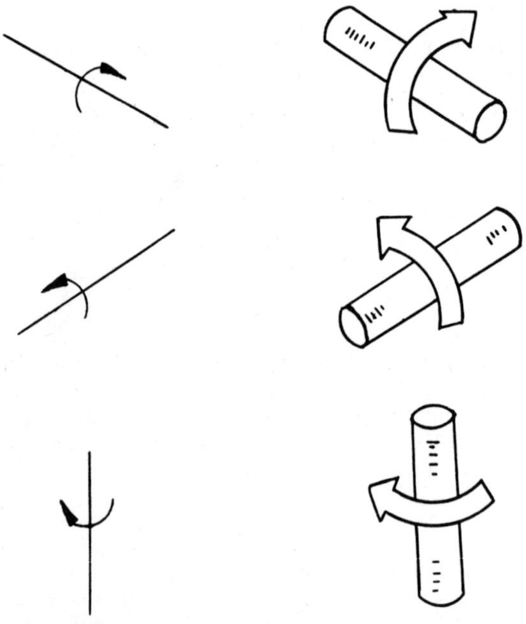

Indication on Drawing

How Interpreted

Figure 14-42
Directional arrows on a shaft representation indicate direction of motion.
US Army Ordnance Corps

FORMULAS FOR W, h, and d, (See base note)							
NO. OF SPLINES	ALL FITS	PERMANENT FIT (A)		TO SLIDE NOT (LOADED (B)		TO SLIDE LOADED (C)	
	W	h	d	h	d	h	d
4	0.241	0.075	0.850	0.125	0.750		
6	0.250	0.050	0.900	0.075	0.850	0.100	0.800
10	0.156	0.045	0.910	0.070	0.860	0.095	0.810
16	0.098	0.045	0.910	0.070	0.860	0.095	0.810
To obtain dimension multiply table figure by D, (major diameter).							

6 SPLINE—B FIT ON MAJOR DIAMETER

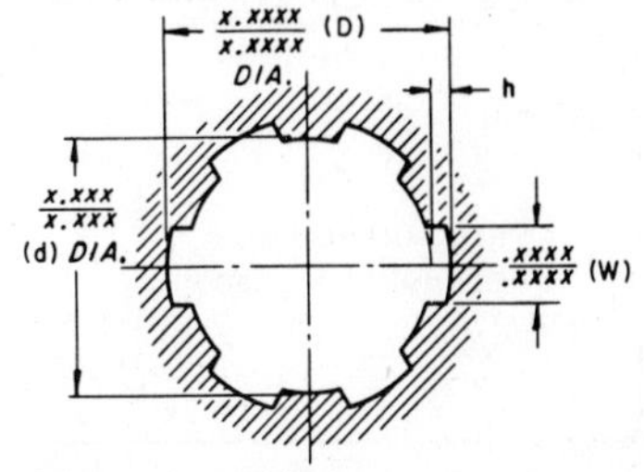

NUMBER OF SPLINES 6
MAXIMUM CUMULATIVE PITCH ERROR .XXX
MAXIMUM LEAD ERROR (PER FOOT) .006
MAXIMUM OUT OF ROUNDNESS .XXX

4 SPLINE—B FIT ON MINOR DIAMETER

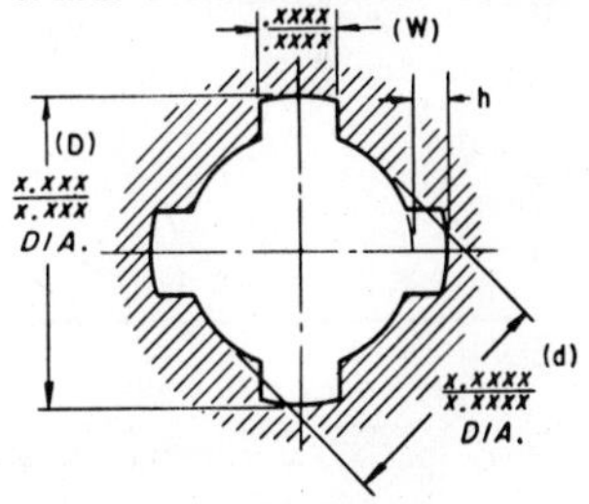

NUMBER OF SPLINES 4
MAXIMUM CUMULATIVE PITCH ERROR .XXX
MAXIMUM LEAD ERROR (PER FOOT) .006
MAXIMUM OUT OF ROUNDNESS .XXX

10 SPLINE—B FIT ON ALL SIDES

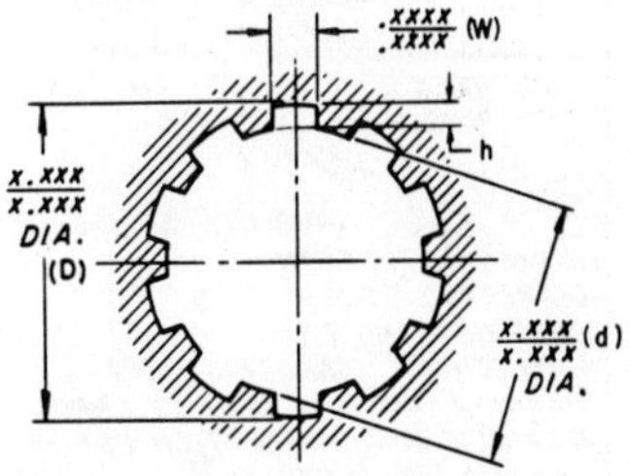

NUMBER OF SPLINES 10
MAXIMUM CUMULATIVE PITCH ERROR .XXX
MAXIMUM LEAD ERROR (PER FOOT) .006
MAXIMUM OUT OF ROUNDNESS .XXX

Figure 14-43
Fits of splines may be controlled on the major diameter, minor diameter, or sides. SAE

The number of teeth on a gear is indicated by placing the number of teeth followed by the letter T at the end of a leader line terminated by an arrow which touches the edge of the representation of the gear. If the diametral pitch must be included, it should be placed below the figure of the number of teeth.

14.16 Splines

Splines are multiple keys which provide a positive connection between shafts and related members to prevent relative rotation. Spline teeth are either straight or helical in direction, straight or curved on their working profile, and straight or tapered along their length.

Since the most common splines are those having straight teeth along their length, the following discussion will be confined to this type. The involute spline has a depth equal to one-half the depth of a standard gear tooth. The standardized diametral pitches of involute splines are:

1/2	4/8	8/16	16/32	32/64
2.5/5	5/10	10/20	20/40	40/80
3/6	6/12	12/24	24/48	48/96

The numerator of these pitches controls the pitch diameter and tooth thickness, and the denominator controls the addendum and dedendum.

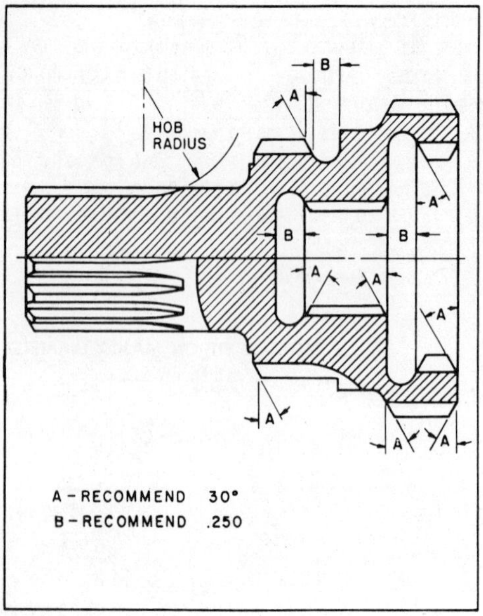

Figure 14-44
Representation of splines. SAE

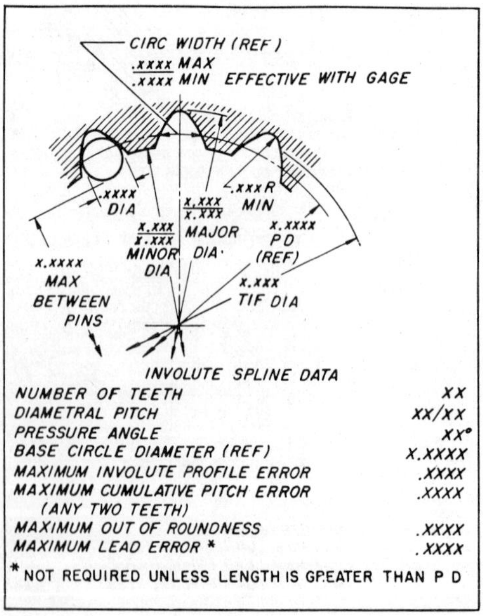

Figure 14-45
Specimen drawing showing internal spline dimensioning. SAE

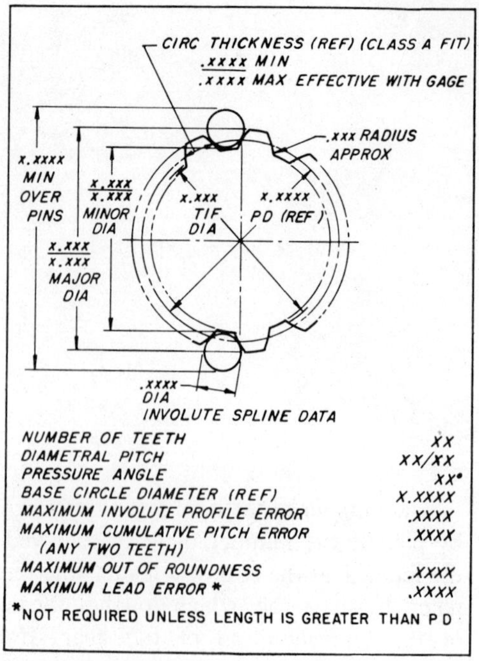

Figure 14-46
Specimen drawing showing external spline dimensioning. SAE

DIAMETRAL PITCH	MAJOR DIAMETER RANGE	DIAMETRAL PITCH	MAJOR DIAMETER RANGE
10/20	0.7000-10.1000	48/96	0.1459-1.2709
16/32	0.4375- 6.3125	64/128	0.1875-0.5000
24/48	0.2917- 4.2083	80/160	0.1500-0.3500
32/64	0.2188- 1.9063	128/256	0.0937-0.1953
40/80	0.1750- 1.5250		

Figure 14-47
Standard serrations are made in several diametral pitches. SAE

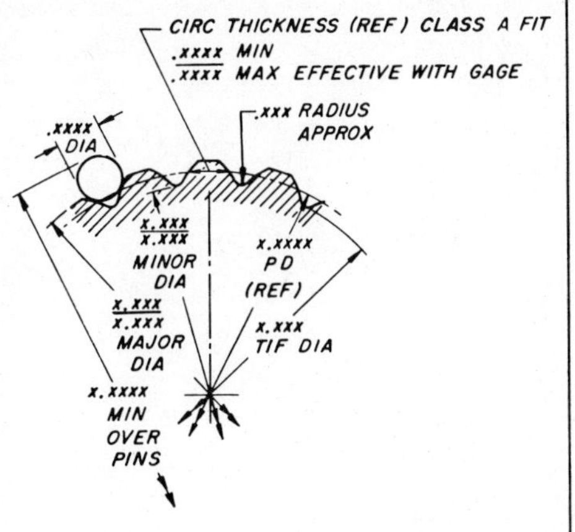

INVOLUTE SERRATION DATA

NUMBER OF TEETH	XX
DIAMETRAL PITCH	XX/XX
PRESSURE ANGLE	XX
BASE CIRCLE DIAMETER (REF)	X.XXXX
MAXIMUM INVOLUTE PROFILE ERROR	.XXXX
MAXIMUM CUMULATIVE PITCH ERROR (ANY TWO TEETH)	.XXXX
MAXIMUM OUT OF ROUNDNESS	.XXXX
MAXIMUM LEAD ERROR *	.XXXX

* TO BE USED ONLY FOR SERRATIONS OF LENGTH EXCEEDING PITCH DIAMETER

Figure 14-48
Specimen drawing of external serration dimensioning. SAE

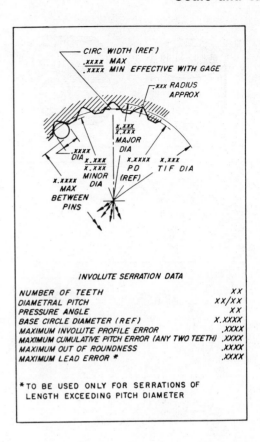

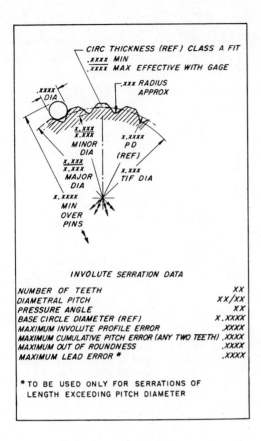

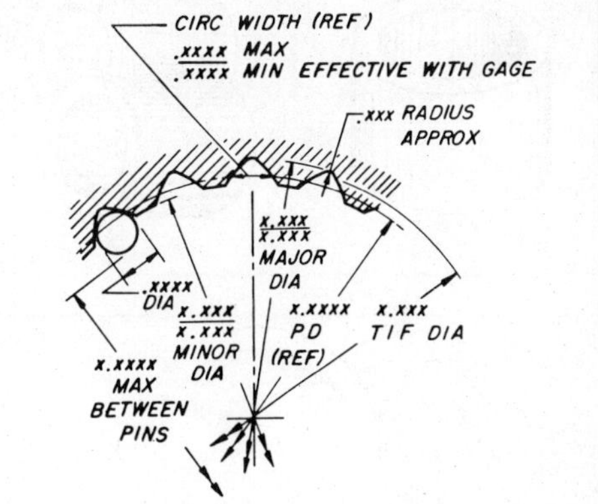

INVOLUTE SERRATION DATA

NUMBER OF TEETH	XX
DIAMETRAL PITCH	XX/XX
PRESSURE ANGLE	XX
BASE CIRCLE DIAMETER (REF)	X.XXXX
MAXIMUM INVOLUTE PROFILE ERROR	.XXXX
MAXIMUM CUMULATIVE PITCH ERROR (ANY TWO TEETH)	.XXXX
MAXIMUM OUT OF ROUNDNESS	.XXXX
MAXIMUM LEAD ERROR *	.XXXX

* TO BE USED ONLY FOR SERRATIONS OF LENGTH EXCEEDING PITCH DIAMETER

Figure 14-49
Specimen drawing of internal serration dimensioning. SAE

The two basic types of splines are the *flat root* and *fillet root*. The flat root is designed for moderate stresses and thin walls and the fillet root for highly stressed parts. A fillet root external spline may be used with a flat root internal spline. A flat root external spline may be used with a fillet root internal spline.

Splines are made with three types of fits: *sliding, close* and *press* which may be applied on the major diameter, minor diameter or sides of the teeth. These fits are usually designated as *A, B* or *C*. See Fig. 14-43. The fitting of parts is controlled by making the internal spline constant and the external spline varied to secure the required fit.

Figs. 14-44, 14-45, and 14-46 are specimen drawings which illustrate enlarged sectional views of both internal and external splines.

14.17 Serrations

Serrations like splines are considered as multiple keys to prevent rotary motion. However, serrations are primarily intended for parts which must be permanently fitted together. They are made for use with uniform or tapered diameters. The standard diametral pitches of serrations are included in Fig. 14-47. Figs. 14-48 and 14-49 show specimen drawings of typical serrations.

14.18 Bearings

A bearing is a device used to reduce friction between moving elements of a mechanism. The following are some of the more basic

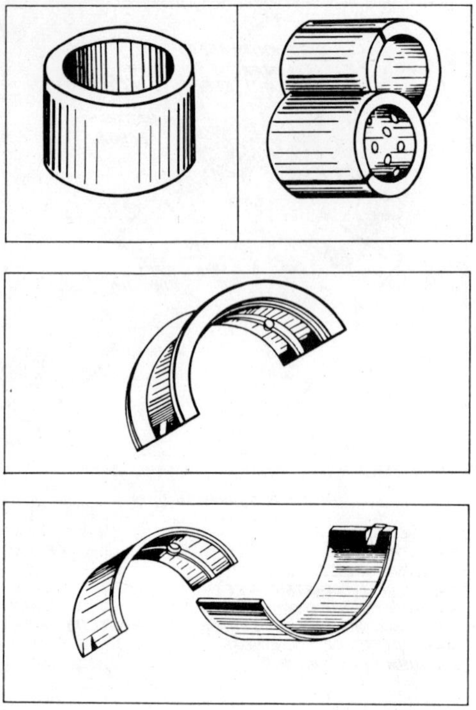

Figure 14-50
Sleeve bearings are used to support rotating or oscillating shafts. General Motors Corp.

types of bearings:

Sleeve bearings. Sleeve bearings are hollow cylinders that support a rotating or oscillating shaft. A clearance between the bearing and shaft permits a lubricant to coat the metal surfaces and prevent scoring and seizure. The two most common sleeve bearings are the plain and flanged. See Fig. 14-50. Plain sleeve bearings are either full or split. Flanged bearings have one or both ends flanged and are designed for applications where both axial thrust and radial loads are encountered.

Ball bearings. Ball bearings are probably the most common anti-friction bearings in use. See Fig. 14-51. These bearings consist of two grooved race rings, a set of balls and a separator. Ball bearings are made in several types such as single row radial, angular contact, thrust, and self-aligning. The *single row radial* bearings are designed primarily for radial loads, although they can carry a considerable amount of thrust load as well. *Angular contact bearings* are either single or double row and are made specifically to support combined loads where the thrust component may be large and the axial deflection must be confined to close limits. Double row bearings are generally preferred where maximum resistance to misalignment is necessary. *Thrust bearings* are made to support pure thrust loads only. The balls are held by two washer type rings one of which is usually stationary and supported by the housing, while the other revolves with the shaft on which it is mounted. *Self-aligning radial* ball bearings are used where the bearing seats cannot be maintained in line. Ball bearings are also available in the shielded and sealed types. The shielded bearing has a metal shield or plate on one or both sides of the bearing. The chief functions of the shields are to retain the lubricant and to keep dirt and chips from getting into the bearing. Sealed bearings have a felt, rubber or plastic seal mounted on the outer ring of the bearing

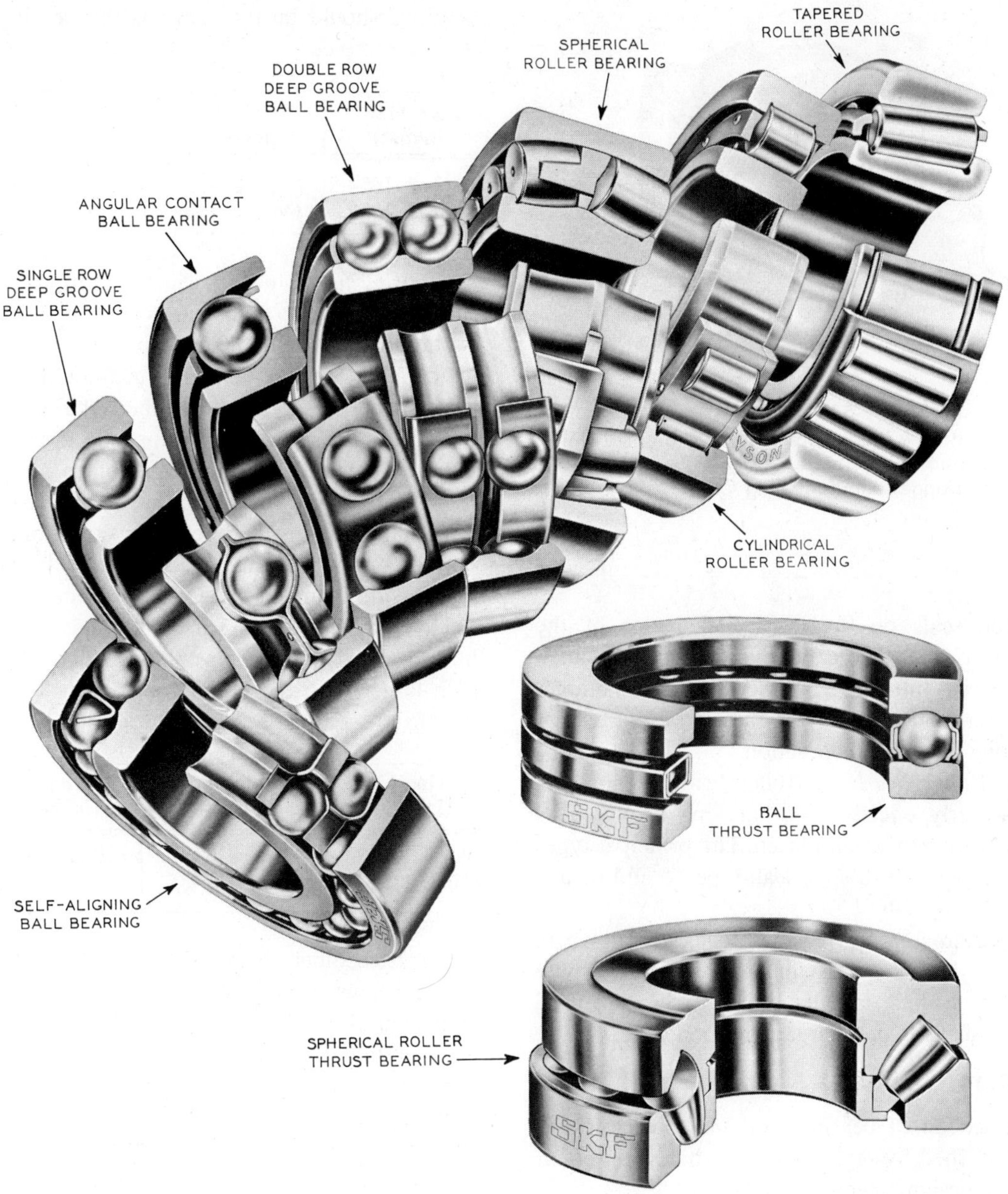

Figure 14-51
Examples of ball and roller bearings.
SKF Industries, Inc.

Figure 14-52
Pillow blocks are designed to carry light and heavy loads.
Dodge Manufacturing Corp.

and seals on the outside diameter of the inner ring. These bearings are filled with a special lubricant by the bearing manufacturer and require no further attention for long periods of operation.

Roller bearings. Roller bearings are particularly effective for handling heavy loads in relatively small places. The principal types are cylindrical, spherical, tapered and thrust. See Fig. 14-51.

Pillow blocks. Pillow blocks, as shown in Fig. 14-52, consist of a housing fitted with either a ball or roller bearing. They are used on shafting or as a part of a machine.

14.19 Selection of bearings

Selection of bearings for any mechanism is governed by such factors as shaft size, housing design, speed and load.

Shaft size. Shaft size is an important consideration since the bearing must be mounted firmly in place and held securely against the shaft shoulder. A loosely fitted inner ring will creep on the shaft, leading to wear. On the other hand, the shaft fit should not result in any undue tightness of the bearing. Any excessive tension in the ring would cause expansion which would disturb the internal fit of the bearing and lead to heating and increase power consumption. In general, shaft size and tolerance for seating precision bearings should be the same as the bearing bore. Example:

Bore Size (inches)	Shaft Dia. (inches)	Average Fit
Max 2.1654 Min 2.1652	Min 2.1652 Max 2.1654	Line-to-line

Housing fits.[3] Under normal conditions of shaft rotation, the outer ring of the bearing is stationary and should be mounted with a hand push to a light tapping fit. Should the housing be the rotating member, the same fundamental considerations apply in mounting the outer race as in the case of an inner ring mounted on a rotating shaft. As a rule, the minimum housing bore dimension should be .0001 inch less than the maximum bearing outside diameter (O.D.). If the bearing O.D. tolerance is .0003 inch, the maximum housing bore should be established as .0003 inch larger than the minimum housing bore dimension. Example:

Bearing O.D. (inches)	Housing Bore (inches)	Average Fit (inches)
Max 3.5433 Min 3.5430	Min 3.5432 Max 3.5435	.0002 loose

On exceedingly high speed and other applications where an adjacent heat input is prevalent along the shaft, it is extremely important that the floating bearing can move longitudinally to compensate for thermal changes. It cannot float laterally if restricted by a tight housing bore or by the radial expansion of the bearing itself due to thermal changes. It is equally important that all shaft and housing shoulders be absolutely square, and that the faces of spacers be square and parallel within .0001 inch.

General housing design. Housings are usually made of cast iron or steel and generally heat treated to lessen possible distortion. For smaller high speed shaft applications, steel housings are preferable.

In many cases of housing design, it is ad-

3. *The Fafnir Bearing Company Manual* (New Britain, Conn.: The Fafnir Bearing Co., 1959).

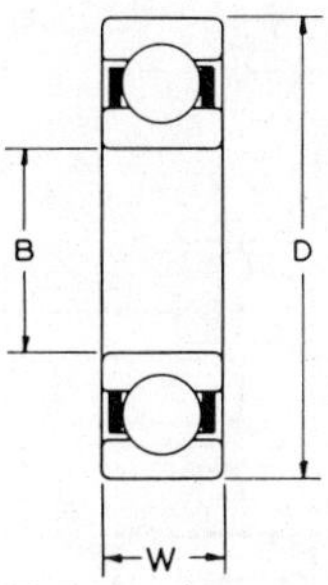

SPECIAL-PRECISION ABEC-3
MEDIUM
M300K SERIES

DIMENSION—TOLERANCES

bearing number	bore, B mm	inches	tolerance +.0000 to minus, in.	inner ring eccen. inches	outside diameter, D mm	inches	tolerance +.0000 to minus, in.	outer ring eccen. inches	width, W +.000, −.005 mm	inches	fillet radius■ inches	balls no.	size, in.
M305K-CR	25	.9843	.0002	.0003	62	2.4409	.0004	.0005	17	.6693	.040	7	15/32
M306K-CR	30	1.1811	.0002	.0003	72	2.8346	.0004	.0005	19	.7480	.040	7	17/32
M307K-CR	35	1.3780	.0003	.0004	80	3.1496	.0004	.0005	21	.8268	.060	7	9/16
M308K-MBR♦	40	1.5748	.0003	.0004	90	3.5433	.0004	.0007	23	.9055	.060	8	5/8
M309K-MBR♦	45	1.7717	.0003	.0004	100	3.9370	.0004	.0007	25	.9843	.060	8	11/16
M310K-MBR♦	50	1.9685	.0003	.0004	110	4.3307	.0004	.0007	27	1.0630	.080	8	3/4
M311K-MBR♦	55	2.1654	.0004	.0004	120	4.7244	.0004	.0007	29	1.1417	.080	8	13/16
M312K-MBR♦	60	2.3622	.0004	.0004	130	5.1181	.0005	.0008	31	1.2205	.080	8	7/8
M313K-MBR♦	65	2.5591	.0004	.0004	140	5.5118	.0005	.0008	33	1.2992	.080	8	15/16
M314K-MBR♦	70	2.7559	.0004	.0004	150	5.9055	.0005	.0008	35	1.3780	.080	8	1

■ Maximum shaft or housing fillet radius which bearing corners will clear.
♦ Also available as CR for high speed machines, such as routers, shapers and moulders.

SPECIAL-PRECISION ABEC-3
MEDIUM
M300K SERIES

LOAD RATINGS

Rated Radial Load Capacity in Pounds at Various rpm
Based on 500 hours minimum life—2500 hours average life

bearing number	Nd^2	specific dynamic radial capacity @ 33.3rpm	revolutions per minute 50	100	200	300	500	900	1200	1500	1800	2400	3600	5000
M305K-CR	1.54	4080	3560	2830	2240	1960	1650	1360	1240	1150	1080	980	855	770
M306K-CR	1.98	5160	4500	3580	2840	2480	2090	1720	1560	1450	1360	1240	1080	970
M307K-CR	2.21	5780	5050	4010	3180	2780	2340	1930	1750	1620	1530	1390	1210	1090
M308K-MBR	3.12	7660	6700	5310	4220	3680	3110	2560	2320	2160	2030	1840	1610	1440
M309K-MBR	3.78	9130	7970	6330	5020	4390	3700	3040	2760	2570	2420	2190	1920	1720
M310K-MBR	4.50	10700	9340	7410	5880	5140	4330	3560	3240	3000	2830	2570	2240	2010
M311K-MBR	5.28	12400	10800	8570	6800	5940	5010	4120	3740	3480	3270	2970	2600	...
M312K-MBR	6.12	14200	12400	9810	7790	6800	5740	4720	4290	3980	3740	3400	2970	...
M313K-MBR	7.03	16000	14000	11100	8820	7700	6500	5340	4850	4500	4240	3850	3360	...
M314K-MBR	8.00	18000	15700	12500	9900	8650	7300	6000	5450	5060	4760	4330	...	...

Figure 14-53
Bearings must be selected to meet specific shaft sizes and loads.
The Fafnir Bearing Co.

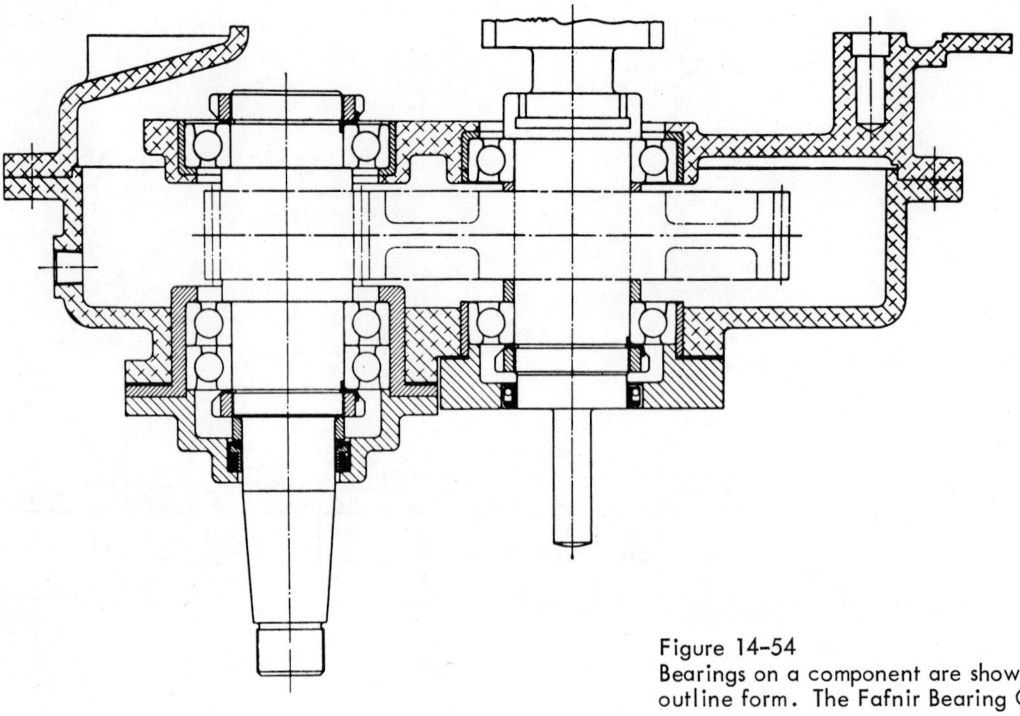

Figure 14-54
Bearings on a component are shown in outline form. The Fafnir Bearing Co.

vantageous to employ a sub-housing or a steel sleeve between the outer ring of the bearing and the machine frame, thus allowing assembly of the bearings on the shaft and insertion of the entire unit into the machine frame. This method also provides a surface of proper hardness where machine frames are made of a material that has a low Brinell value, such as aluminum and other soft metals.

Shaft shoulders and housing shoulders should be square and true. The choice between fillets and undercut relief depends upon the individual shaft design and the conditions surrounding its normal use.

Where screws are used to fasten parts into the main housing, adequate section should be left under the screw hole to prevent distortion of the housing bore when the screws are pulled up and the covers or other parts pulled tightly into place.

Loads. Bearings are designed to meet practically any specified loads. Once the design load of a mechanism is established, all the draftsman needs to do is consult a bearing manufacturer's catalog and select from the given charts the correct type of bearing. A typical bearing chart is shown in Fig. 14-53. This chart specifies the type of bearing that is required in terms of shaft size and load in pounds at various rpm.

14.20 Representing bearings on a drawing

Bearings are included on the assembly drawing of a component. The bearings are shown in outline form as illustrated in Fig. 14-54. Specifications of the bearing are given in the parts list or bill of material. The bearing is often identified by the symbols designated by the bearing manufacturer. As yet, bearing symbols of different manufacturers have not been standardized.

14.21 Cams

A cam is a direct-contact machine element designed primarily to convert constant rotary motion into timed irregular motion. This basic action is illustrated in Fig. 14-55 where an irregularly shaped disk revolves on a constant-speed shaft and imparts irregular motion to a follower. The follower is a plunger that is held in contact with the profile of the cam by means of gravity or a spring. The special movements made possible by the use of cams generally are not easily obtained by any other mechanical means. Evidence of this is the universal use of cams in automatic screw machines, sewing machines, textile machinery and engines.

The cam mechanism consists of a cam and a follower. Each of these components has many possible design variations. However, the two main types of cams are: (1) *plate or radial* and (2) *cylindrical.* Both types rotate with their respective drive shafts but differ in the action of their followers. The follower of the radial cam operates in a plane perpendicular to the axis of the camshaft, whereas the follower of the cylindrical cam oscillates in a plane parallel with the axis of the cam shaft.

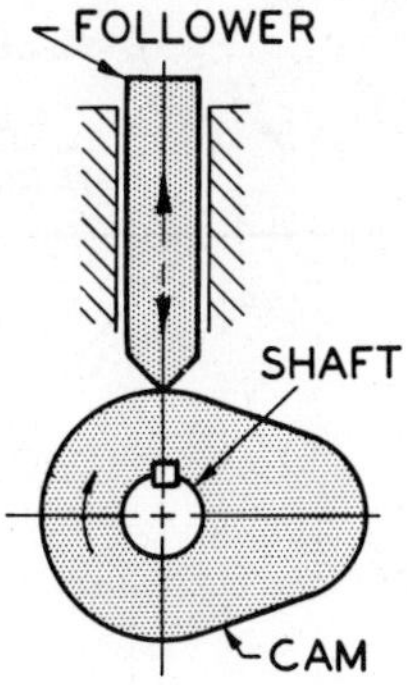

Figure 14-55
A cam is designed to convert constant rotary motion into timed irregular motion.

14.22 Cam followers

Cam followers may have a variety of physical forms. Four common cam follower types are: (1) Knife-edge or pointed, (2) roller, (3) flat-faced and (4) spherical-faced. See Fig. 14-56. The type used depends upon such factors as mechanism speed, cam profile, possible misalignment and stresses involved. Space requirements may also influence the designer to modify one of the basic followers. A pivoted or swinging follower is one example of such a modification. See Fig. 14-57. The design requirements often necessitate that the follower be offset from the center line common with the cam.

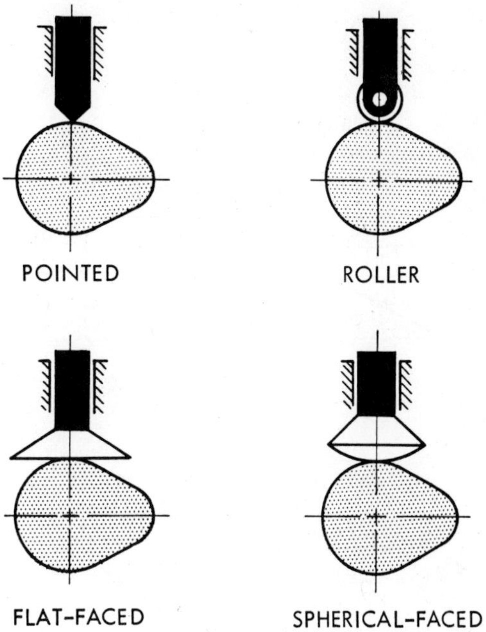

Figure 14-56
Basic types of cam followers.

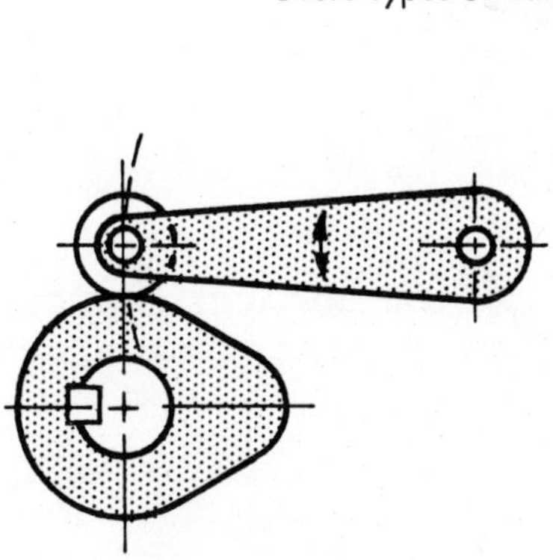

Figure 14-57
A cam follower may have to be modified from the basic types to meet special requirements.

14.23 Cam motion

A cam may be used to produce nearly any motion, even if the resulting motion defies definition. However, three definable motions are frequently used: *uniform* or *constant*

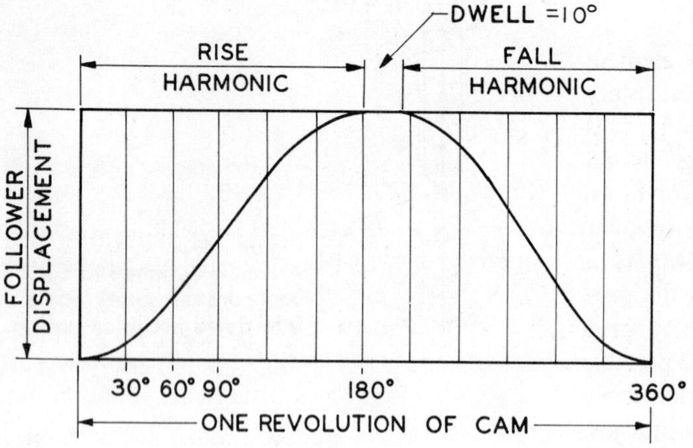

Figure 14-58
An example of a motion diagram showing cam rise and fall.

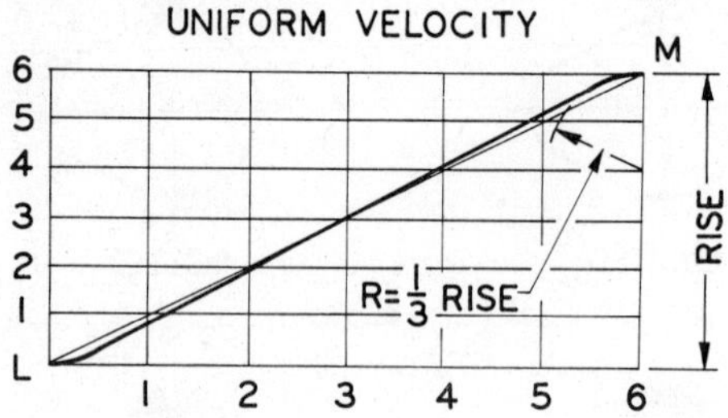

Figure 14-59
Uniform motion diagram.

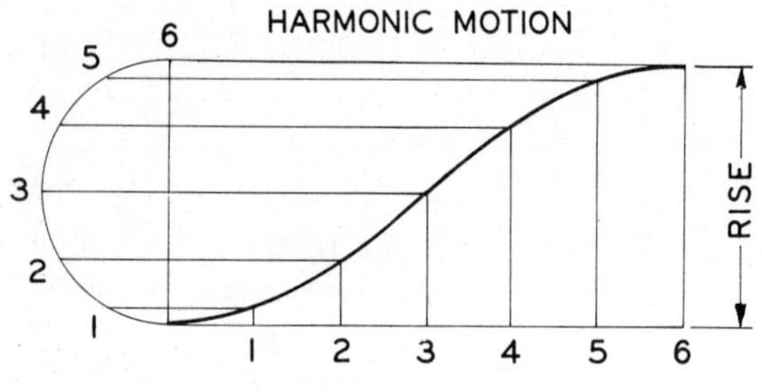

Figure 14-60
Harmonic motion diagram.

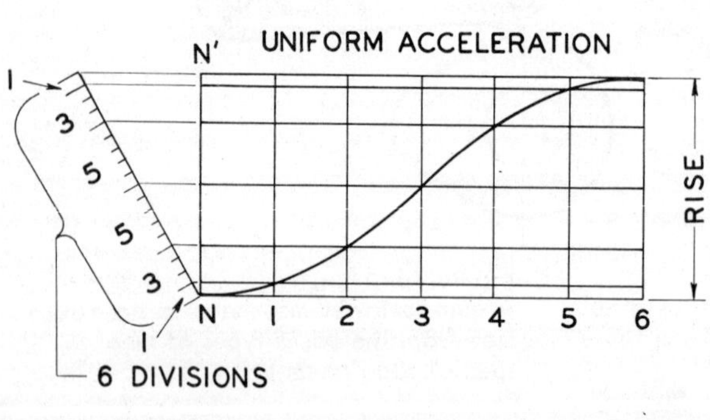

Figure 14-61
Uniform acceleration diagram

velocity, harmonic, and *uniform accelerated and retarded.* These motions may be used separately or in any combination. The draftsman must select the type of cam profile curve that will result in the desired follower motion.

14.24 Motion diagrams

Motion diagrams, often termed displacement diagrams, are used to graphically analyze cam curvature in addition to aiding the draftsman with the layout of the cam disk. The diagram is generally drawn prior to laying-out the cam curve. This permits the draftsman to modify a theoretical curve as needed to insure smooth follower action. Later, the draftsman may transfer points from the diagram to a drawing of the disk cam.

As shown in Fig. 14-58, the displacement diagram is constructed on the abscissa (horizontal base line) which represents one revolution of the cam. The abscissa may be any length. However, this length is sometimes drawn equal to the circumference of a circle, having a radius equal to the distance from the center of the camshaft to the highest point in the cam rise. The ordinate (vertical scale) is drawn to scale equal to the maximum rise of the cam follower. The abscissa or horizontal baseline can be divided to represent time intervals or angle of cam rotation. The motion diagram illustrated in Fig. 14-58 is for a follower which rises with harmonic motion in a 180 degree revolution, dwells for 10 degrees, and returns to its starting point by harmonic motion. Single-motion diagrams illustrating uniform motion, harmonic motion and constant acceleration are drawn with the abscissa at any convenient length and the ordinate equal to the rise. To draw these, proceed as follows:

Uniform motion. This is constant velocity or straight-line motion. As shown in Fig. 14-59, divide the ordinate and the abscissa into any number of equal parts. Connect points *L* and *M* with a straight line. Note that line *LM* is modified by an arc at each end. This is done to eliminate abrupt starting at the beginning and ending of motion interval. Any convenient curve could be used which would be tangent to the rise line, but a radius of 1/3 the rise is recommended. This curve permits the follower to rise equal distances in each equal time interval.

Harmonic motion. See Fig. 14-60. The abscissa and ordinate are drawn as for the previous diagram. The problem is to divide the rise so that the velocity of the follower will increase from zero at the beginning, to a maximum at its midpoint, and then decrease to zero at the end of the motion. To accomplish this, construct a semicircle having a radius equal to 1/2 the rise. Next divide the semicircle as illustrated into the same number of equal parts as the abscissa has been divided. Draw horizontal lines from the points in the semicircle to intersect the vertical lines drawn from the division points on the abscissa. Draw a curved line through the intersections to complete the construction of the displacement curve.

Uniform accelerated and retarded motion. This is constant acceleration or parabolic motion. See Fig. 14-61. Again the abscissa and the ordinate are drawn to represent the position in degrees and the rise respectively. The problem is to divide line *NN′* and *N6* into the same number of parts. However, each unit of line *NN′* must be proportional to the square of the time interval. Thus line *NN′* will be divided into increments of 1, 3, 5, etc. Horizontal lines are drawn through these divisions and intersect the vertical lines drawn from the time intervals on the baseline. A line is drawn through the intersecting points completing the uniform accelerated phase. A change in velocity is now indicated by uniform retarded motion constructed by reversing the increments as 5, 3, 1, from this point to the end of the cycle.

14.25 Constructing the plate-cam profile (roller follower)

The general method of constructing a cam profile is to consider the cam as being stationary, and the follower as moving around the cam in a direction opposite to the true cam rotation. This method is illustrated in Fig. 14-62, where a profile is developed for a plate cam having an offset roller follower.

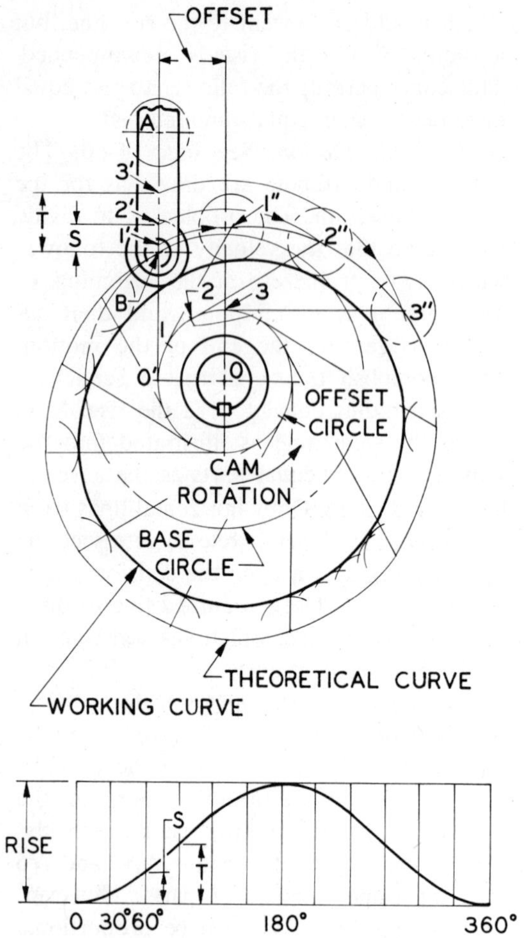

Figure 14-62
Constructing a plate-cam profile having an offset roller type followers.

The procedure for developing this profile is as follows:

The displacement diagram is constructed as a preliminary step to the actual layout of the cam profile, whereas the construction of the cam can be considered to initiate with the drawing of the base circle.

The base circle is constructed with the follower shown in its lowest position. Next, using *O*, the center of the cam as the center, draw the offset circle with a radius *OO′*, equal to the offset distance. The offset circle is then divided into the same number of divisions as was previously used in the displacement diagram. In the example shown, twelve divisions are used. Lines are drawn from each of these divisions tangent to the offset circle. Note that these divisions are numbered in a direction opposite to the cam rotation. The numbering of these points aids the draftsman in the construction only and will not appear on the finished drawing.

The ordinate or vertical distances, *S* and *T* are transferred from the displacement diagram to the centerline of the follower. These distances *A*1′, *A*2′, *A*3′, etc., represent successive positions of the follower. Consequently, in the example shown, the follower will have risen *T* distance from its initial position when the cam has rotated 90°.

Points 1′, 2′, 3′, etc., are next successively revolved in a direction opposite to cam rotation. This is accomplished by using the cam center *O* and a radius equal to *O*1′, *O*2′, etc. These arcs intersect their corresponding tangent lines (tangents to the offset circle) resulting in intersecting points which are the locations of the center of the follower at

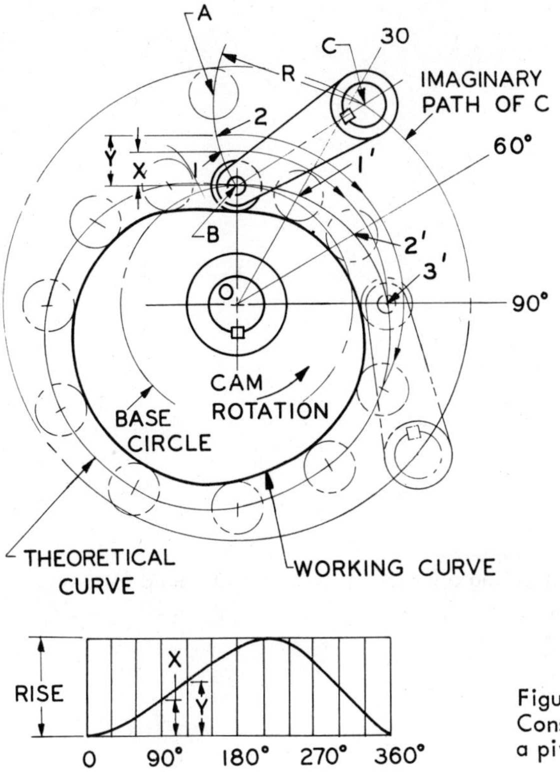

Figure 14-63
Constructing a profile of a plate-cam having a pivoted follower.

these various positions.

Using a radius equal to the radius of the follower, and the centers just found, draw arcs as indicated. The line drawn tangent to these arcs will be the true cam profile.

A smoother cam profile will result if a theoretical or pitch curve is utilized as a center line for closely spaced roller circles as illustrated. The pitch curve is the smooth curve drawn through points 1″, 2″, 3″, etc. Generally, neither the pitch curve or the alternate positions of the cam follower are shown on a detail drawing. When they are shown, however, they are represented by phantom outlines.

14.26 Profile of a plate-cam having a pivoted follower

The profile of a plate-cam having a pivoted follower is constructed similarly to the method previously described. The exact procedure for drawing the profile is shown in Fig. 14-63.

Construction of the displacement diagram precedes the cam layout. Note that the true path of the follower is an arc. Thus the height of the ordinate distance in the displacement diagram will equal the rectified length of arc *AB*.

First draw the base circle with the roller follower in its lowest position. Next locate *C*, the center of the follower pivot. The base circle is then divided into the same number of divisions as were utilized in the displacement diagram. Radius *R* is drawn using *C* as a center.

Now, transfer distances *X, Y,* etc. from the displacement diagram to the cam drawing as illustrated. These distances are then rotated into position; that is, radius *O*1 is rotated to the 90° radial position, radius *O*2 is rotated to the 120° position, etc. Small arcs representing the roller follower are drawn from points 1′, 2′, 3′, etc. The cam profile is then drawn tangent to these small arcs. As was previously suggested, a smoother

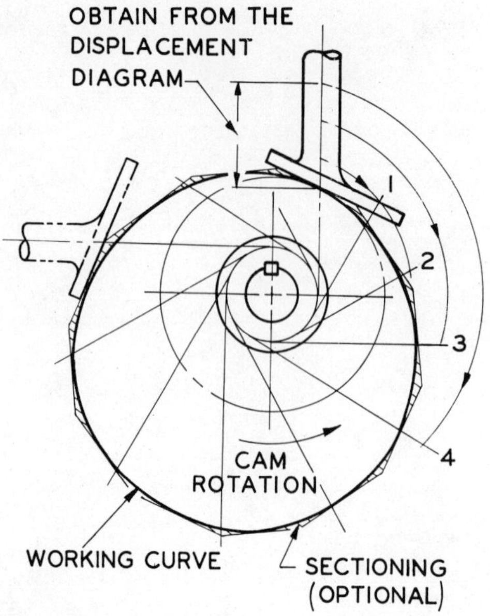

Figure 14-64
Constructing a plate-cam with a flat-faced follower.

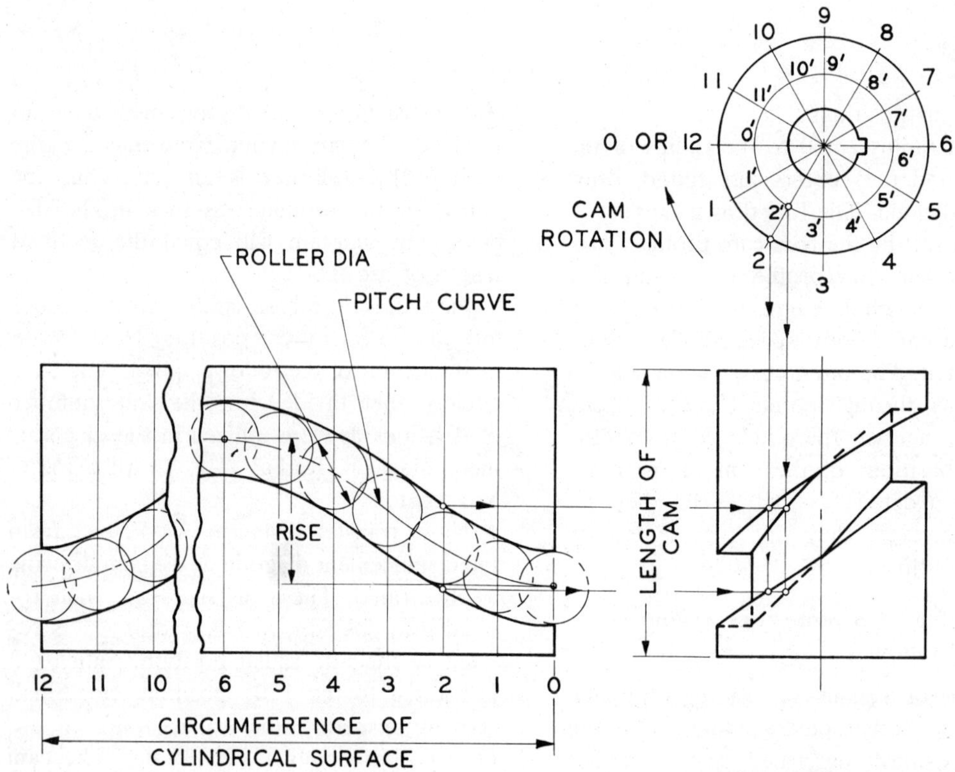

Figure 14-65
Construction of a cylindrical cam development.

and more accurate curve will result if the pitch curve is drawn first, permitting the draftsman to locate centers for the roller-arcs.

14.27 Profile of a plate-cam with a flat-faced follower

The procedure for constructing the profile of a plate cam having a flat-faced follower employs methods previously discussed. The construction of the displacement diagram, base circle, offset circle, and location of points is identical with the steps described in Sub-section 14.25.

Note in Fig. 14-64 that the initial contact point between the cam profile and the follower changes as the follower rises. The cam profile is drawn tangent to the face of the follower in the positions previously established.

14.28 Cylindrical cam development

The procedure for drawing a cylindrical cam follows the general method of a plate-cam layout, much as if the follower were moving in a direction opposite to the cam's rotation with the cam stationary. See Fig. 14-65. The actual construction starts with the displacement diagram which is laid out as a plane development of the cylindrical surface. That is, the length of the diagram representing 360° is accurately laid out equal to πD, and the ordinate distance is drawn equal to the height of the cylinder. Thus the resulting curves will be an accurate development of the outer surface of the cam cylinder.

The displacement diagram is drawn adjacent to the space reserved for the front view. This location permits the direct projection of points from the displacement diagram to the front view.

The theoretical or pitch curve is constructed for the desired motion. Circles, equal to the roller diameter, are then drawn using the pitch curve as a location for the roller centers. Curves are drawn tangent to these roller circles with an irregular curve.

The top view of the cam is drawn next. This permits the projection of points from both the displacement diagram and the top view. For example, in Fig. 14-65, points 2 and 2′ are easily located in the front view by projection. Note that a separate inner cylindrical layout would be needed if a true picture of the inner curve were desired. Since this information is seldom required, and the development of the outer cylinder provides the necessary information for the cam manufacturer, such a curve is usually omitted in the front view.

TABLE I*

Problem	Number of Teeth	Diametral Pitch	Face (in.)	Style	Bore (in.)	Hub O.D. (in.)	Hub Proj. (in.)
A	16	5	1-1/4	Plain	1-1/16	2-3/8	1/2
B	24	3	2	Webbed	1-7/16	3	3/4
C	35	5	2-1/2	Webbed	1-1/4	2-3/4	0
D	20	8	1-1/4	Plain	7/8	1-1/2	1/8
E	32	16	5/16	Spoked	5/16	3/4	1/8
F	18	8	5/8	Plain	15/16	1-1/2	0
G	96	10	1-1/8	Spoked	1-1/8	2-1/4	3/8

*Material: SAE3115

Problems, section 14

1 Draw a detail drawing of a 4-Pitch, 14-1/2° involute full depth tooth spur gear having the following specifications: 12 teeth, 1-1/2″ face, 2″ diameter hub, and 1-3/16″ diameter bore projecting 1/2″ on one side. Material: Cast steel SAE 3120.

2 Make complete detail drawings of the problems given in Table I as assigned. Each gear is an involute full depth tooth spur gear with a pressure angle of either 14-1/2° or 20°.

3 Make a single-view layout drawing of an involute spur gear rack and pinion in mesh. Show a minimum of 6 teeth on each part. Use the approximate method of constructing the involute gear tooth. Given: 14-1/2° pressure angle, 5-pitch, number of gear teeth to be 32. Calculate the addendum, whole depth dimensions, in addition to the linear pitch of the rack. Choose suitable bore and hub sizes with standard keyway for pinion.

4 Make a single-view drawing of a 3-pitch spur gear, pinion and rack in mesh. The large gear is to be placed between the pinion and the rack. Develop the involute tooth profile accurately and show all teeth. A template may be used to transfer tooth outlines. The gear and pinion are to have 24 and 15 full depth teeth respectively, and 14-1/2° involute form. Use plain style gears with 1-7/16″ diameter bores and standard keyways.

5 Prepare a detail drawing of a bevel gear with the following specifications: 8-pitch, 20° pressure angle, 40 teeth, 1-7/16″ bore, 3-7/8″ mounting distance, having a 3″ hub diameter projecting approximately 1-1/4″. Material: SAE 3115. Pinion to have 30 teeth.

6 Make a single-view drawing of a pair of miter gears in mesh. The gears are to be of steel and have the following specifications: 6-1/2″ pitch diameter, 14-1/2° pressure angle, 1-3/16″ bore, 42 teeth, 3-3/4″ mounting distance, 3-1/2″ diameter hub, projecting approximately 1-1/2″. Show all dimensions.

7 Construct a detail drawing of a right hand, 12-pitch, 14-1/2° bronze wormgear having 80 teeth. The face is to be 1-1/2″ wide and the bore 1-3/16″. A 2″ diameter hub is to project 3/4″.

8 Make a detail drawing of a worm for the wormgear in Problem No. 7. The worm is to have a 1-3/4″ pitch diameter and a 1/2″ bore.

9 Make a two-view assembly drawing of the wormgear and worm described in Problems No. 7 and 8.

10 Make a two-view assembly drawing of a worm and wormgear with the following specifications: 32-pitch, double thread, 7/32″ face,

TABLE II

Prob-lem	Rise	Cam Rotation	Follower Motion: Rise	Follower Motion: Dwell	Follower Motion: Fall	Roller Follower (DIA)
A	1"	Counter-clockwise	0° - 180° Modified Uniform	180° - 210°	210° - 360° Harmonic	3/4" DIA
B	1-3/16"	Clockwise	0° - 180° Parabolic	None	180° - 360° Harmonic	3/4" DIA
C	1-1/2"	Counter-clockwise	0° - 150° Uniform	150° - 180°	180° - 360° Harmonic	3/4" DIA
D	1-1/4"	Counter-clockwise	0° - 160° Parabolic	160° - 180°	180° - 360° Modified Uniform	3/4" DIA
E	2"	Clockwise	0° - 265° Harmonic	None	265° 360° Parabolic	3/4" DIA

100 teeth on the wormgear. The wormgear to be of the spoked type having a 1-1/16″ diameter hub that projects 5/16″ on each side. The gear is to be bored to 5/16″ diameter. The worm is to have a 7/16″ pitch diameter and bored to 7/32″ diameter.

11 Using the tables shown in Fig. 14-53, determine the shaft outside diameter and housing inside diameter with tolerances for the following bearings: (1) Bearing No. M307K-CR and (2) Bearing No. M312K-MBR.

12 A bearing is required to have a radial load capacity of 2030 pounds at 1800 rpm. Using the tables shown in Fig. 14-53, select a bearing to meet this condition. Design a partial end section of a shaft for mounting this bearing. Show complete dimensions for the diameter on which the bearing is to be mounted, shoulder radius, and shoulder diameter.

13 For each cam assigned in the problems shown in Table II, a displacement diagram and a complete detail drawing are to be made. In all of these problems the cam dimensions are as follows: base circle = 3-1/2″ diameter, hub = 1-1/2″ diameter with a 15/16″ diameter bore and standard keyway to suit. Material: Steel. Supply all other necessary design information.

14 Construct the pitch curve and working curve for a plate cam to have a flat-face follower, the face of which is to be perpendicular to the centerline of the follower. The base circle diameter is to be 3-1/2″. The follower is to be offset 1/2″ to the left of the center of the camshaft. The diameter of the hub, camshaft and size of the keyway are to be selected. Follower movement outward is to be 1-1/4″ with uniform accelerated and retarded motion to be 120° of cam rotation. Return in 150° with harmonic motion and dwell for 90°.

15 Construct the front and top views of a cylindrical cam having a 3-1/2″ diameter cylinder, 2-3/4″ high, roller 1/2″ diameter, roller depth 3/8″, cam shaft 3/4″ diameter, follower rod 5/8″ wide and 5/16″ thick. Motion: Up 1-1/2″ in 180° with harmonic motion, return to initial position in 180° using the same motion. The cam to rotate clockwise.

16 Same as Problem 15, except: Up motion to be 1-3/4″ using parabolic motion in 120°, dwell 60°, down with harmonic motion in 180°.

17 Design a disk edge cam that will move a roller follower 1-3/8″ by uniform motion and return in one revolution. Diameter of shaft 1.250″, diameter of hub 2-1/2″, roller follower 1-1/4″ diameter, hub length 1-5/8″, cam thickness 3/4″. Use a standard flat key. See Fig. 14-66.

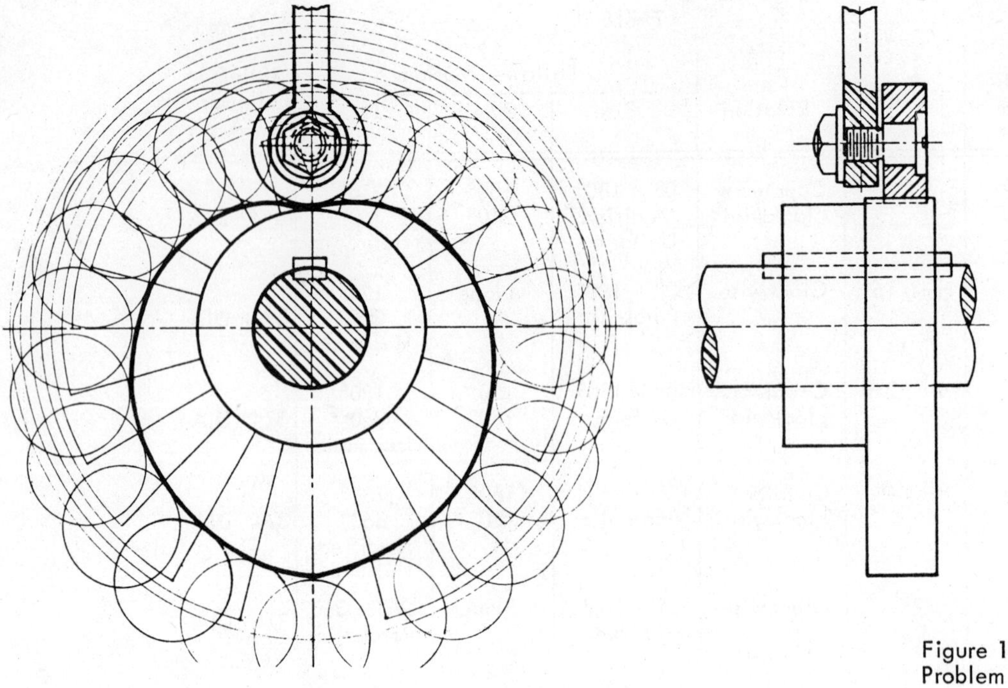

Figure 14-66
Problem 17.

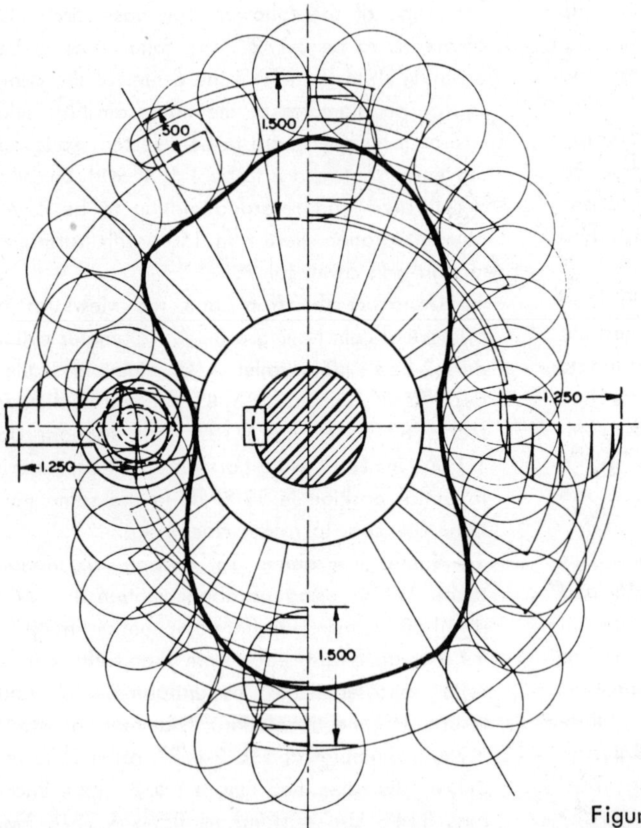

Figure 14-67
Problem 18.

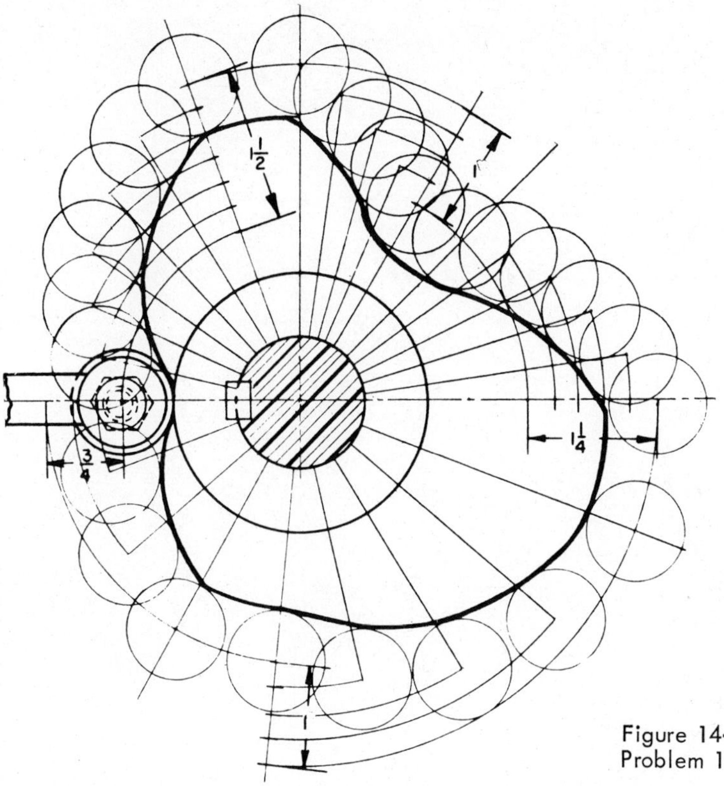

Figure 14-68
Problem 19.

18 Design a disk edge cam that will move a reciprocating roller follower by harmonic motion through a 1.250″ rise in 45°, dwell 15°, .500″ rise in 30°, 1.500″ drop in 90°, 1.250″ rise in 60°, dwell 30°, and return to origin through the remainder of the revolution. Shaft diameter 1.250″, hub diameter 2.500″, hub length 1-3/4″, cam thickness 3/4″. Use a standard flat key. See Fig. 14-67.

19 Design a uniform motion plate cam to be welded to a 2-1/2″ diameter x 1-1/8″ long hub that will actuate a 1″ diameter x 3/8″ thick roller follower to rise 3/4″ in 60°, dwell 25°, rise 1″ in 75°, dwell 20°, fall 1-1/4″ in 45°, dwell 15°, rise 1″ in 30°, dwell 20°, drop through the remaining angle to the starting point. Cam thickness 3/8″, shaft diameter 1-1/4″. See Fig. 14-68.

20 Design a disk path cam that will move a roller follower through 2-1/4″ in 180° by harmonic motion and return to origin. Shaft diameter 1.00″, hub diameter 2.000″, roller diameter 1.00″, plate diameter 9-1/8″. Draw plan view only. See Fig. 14-69.

21 Design a cam to move a 1-1/4″ diameter roller follower through 1.500″ uniform rise in 45°, 1.000″ harmonic rise through 30°, dwell through 15°, .750″ uniform rise in 45°, dwell 30°, harmonic drop through the remaining angle to origin. Draw plan view only. Shaft diameter 1.250″ and hub diameter 2.500″. See Fig. 14-70.

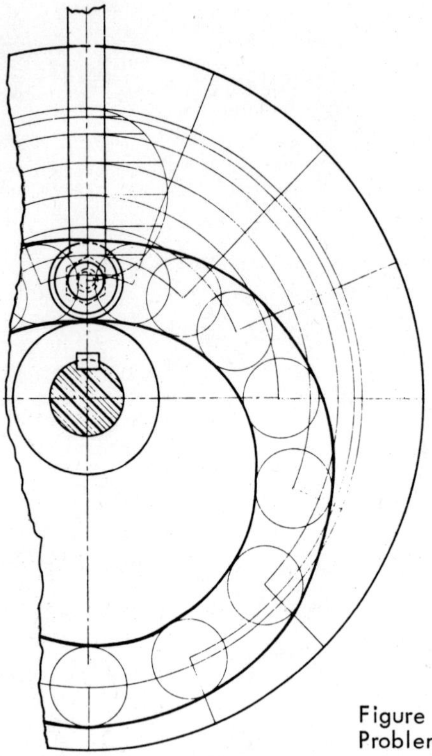

Figure 14-69
Problem 20.

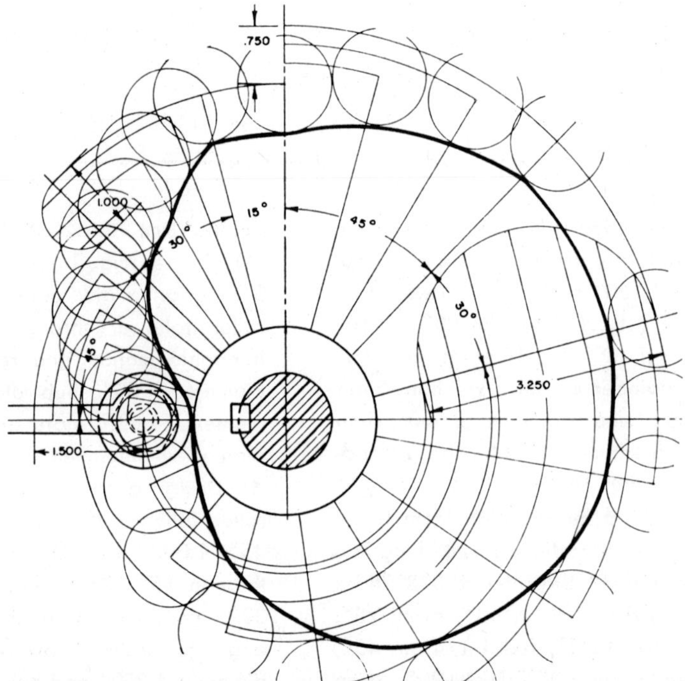

Figure 14-70
Problem 21.

For many years industry relied entirely on conventional multiview drawings to convey ideas and to provide the essential information for manufacturing purposes. Many multiview drawings are often complex and require time and special training to interpret. During recent years manufacturers, in order to reduce costly print-reading errors and to clarify engineering multiview drawings, have begun to use *pictorial drawings,* often called *graphic illustrations,* more extensively. See Fig. 15-1.

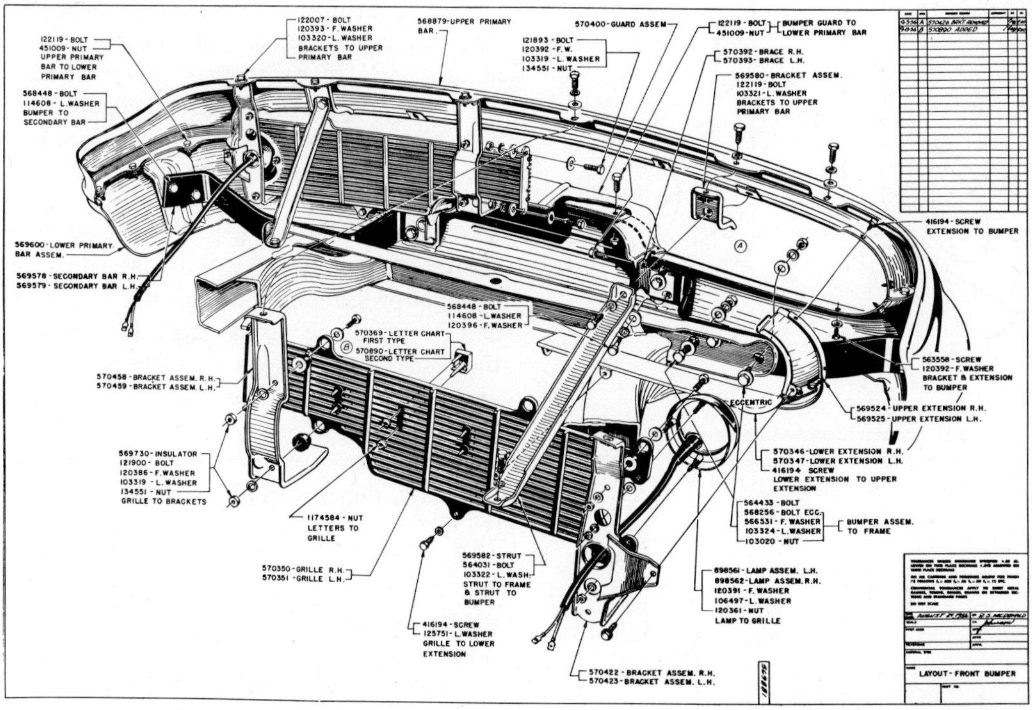

Figure 15-1
With complicated parts such as this, it is easier to visualize their shapes with a pictorial drawing. General Motors Corp.

Pictorial drawings have been found to be of particular value to the product designer when explaining design ideas, and to the process engineer and tool designer in helping to better visualize the requirements for tooling and assembly procedures. Drawings of this kind are also being used by the quality control and inspection departments to facilitate checking and inspection. They have be-

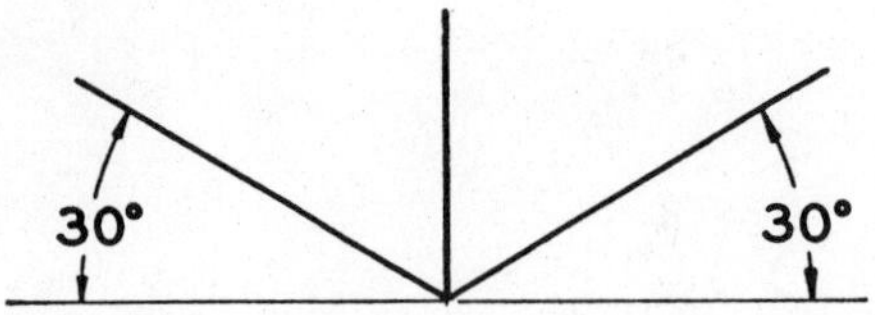

Figure 15-2
An isometric drawing is developed about three axes.

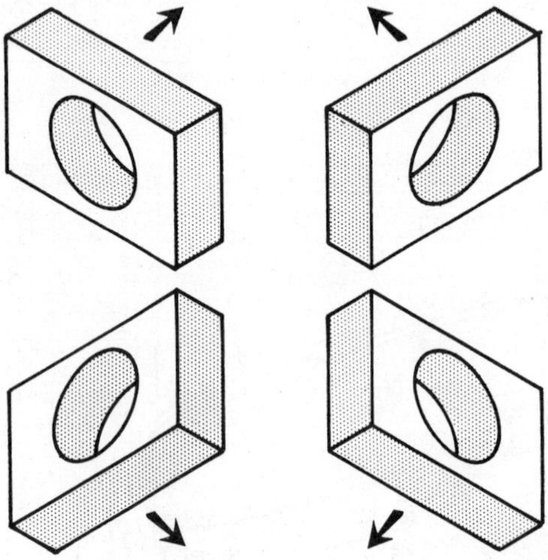

Figure 15-3
An isometric drawing can be produced with the object placed in any one of these positions.

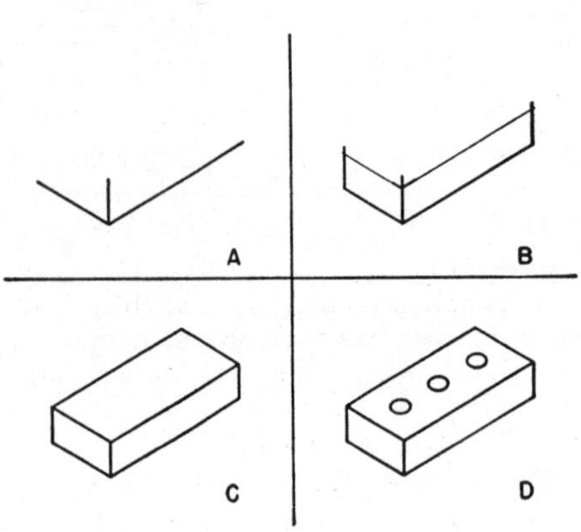

Figure 15-4
These are the basic steps in laying out an isometric drawing.

come invaluable to the shop foreman and new worker in visualizing with greater ease the sequence of assembly and installation of parts. Graphic illustrations are proving especially helpful in purchasing, advertising, dealer training; for parts catalogues, maintenance and installation manuals, and service bulletins.

Pictorial drawings fall into three main groups: *axonometric, oblique,* and *perspective.* The methods of preparing these various drawings are described in this section.

15.1 Types of axonometric drawings

An axonometric drawing is one in which the lines of sight are perpendicular to the plane of projection but the principal faces of the object are inclined to the plane of projection. The principal faces or axes may be shown at any angle to each other except at 90°. Since the principal surfaces and edges of the object are inclined to the plane of projection, the general proportion of the object will vary, depending upon the placement of the object. Variation in proportion is effected by foreshortening the lines that are inclined to the plane of projection. The degree of foreshortening is governed by the angle formed with the plane of projection. Thus the greater the angle the greater will be the degree of foreshortening.

Axonometric projection is classified as isometric, dimetric, and trimetric.

15.2 Constructing an isometric drawing

An isometric drawing is constructed by using three axes, one of which is vertical and the other two drawn to the right and left at an angle of 30° to the horizontal. See Fig. 15-2. The object can be rotated so it is tilted either to the right or left with the top or bottom visible. See Fig. 15-3. The position in which the object is rotated depends entirely upon which is the most advantageous side to show.

The actual width, height, and depth of the object are measured on the three axes and each surface is completed by drawing the necessary lines parallel to the axes. See Fig. 15-4. Hidden lines, as a rule, are omitted on an isometric drawing unless they are absolutely essential for shape description.

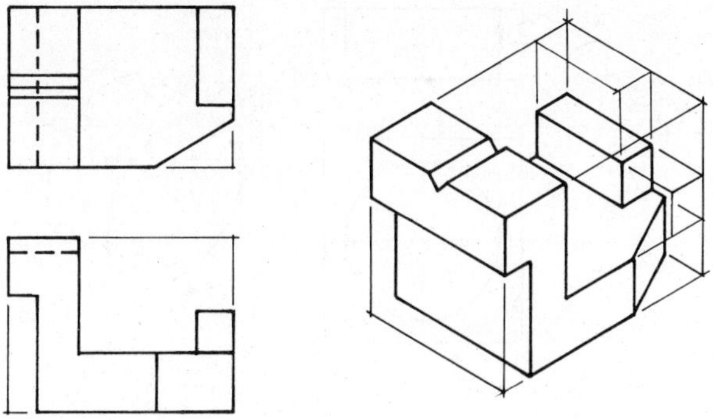

Figure 15-5
The box construction method simplifies drawing isometrics of irregularly shaped objects.

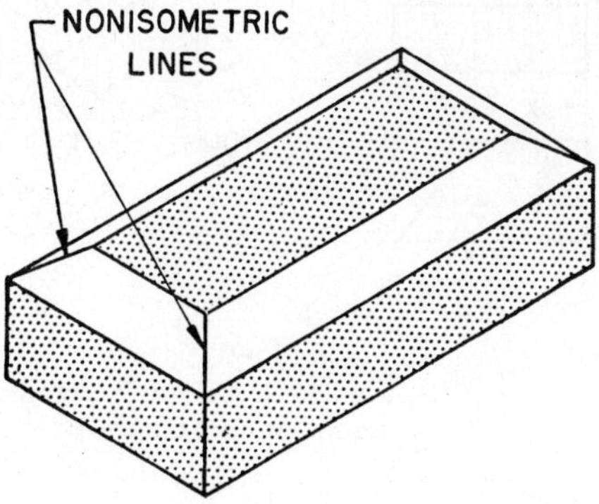

Figure 15-6
Lines that are not parallel to the isometric axes are called nonisometric.

15.3 Isometric by the box construction method

In making isometric drawings of irregularly shaped objects, the process is often simplified if the box construction method is used. One or more rectangular or square boxes are drawn having sides that coincide with the main faces of the object. The box or boxes are made with light construction lines, and the irregular features of the object are then drawn within the framework of the boxes. See Fig. 15-5.

15.4 Nonisometric lines

When an object has sloping lines that do not run parallel to the isometric axes, the lines are called nonisometric lines. See Fig. 15-6. Since lines of this kind will not appear in their true length, they cannot be measured in the same manner as normal isometric lines. To draw nonisometric lines first locate the extreme ends of the lines. These locations may be found by the box construction method; that is, the extreme points are located on the regular isometric lines and the slanted lines drawn connecting the designated points. Thus, in Fig. 15-7, points are located and then lines are drawn connecting these respective points.

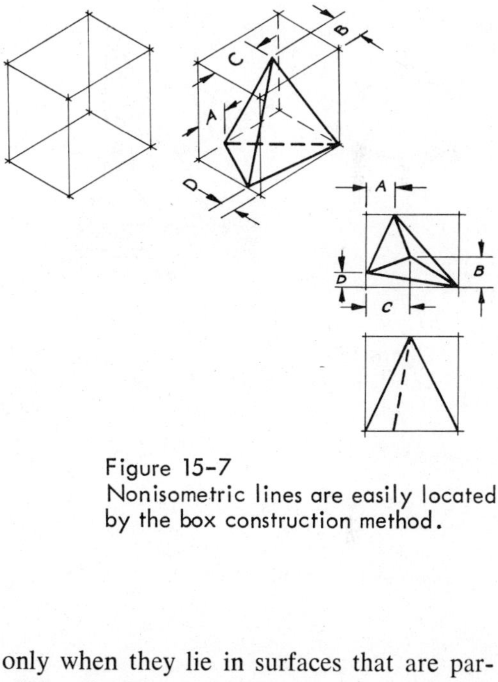

Figure 15-7
Nonisometric lines are easily located by the box construction method.

15.5 Angles in isometric

Angles will normally appear in their true size only when they lie in surfaces that are parallel to the planes of projection; consequently, they cannot be shown in their true size in an isometric drawing. Such angles are laid off by coordinates drawn parallel to the isometric axes. An exact orthographic view drawn to the same scale as the isometric drawing is prepared first. Locating points on the angular lines are then transferred from this view to the isometric lines as shown in Fig. 15-8 and the points connected to show the lines isometrically.

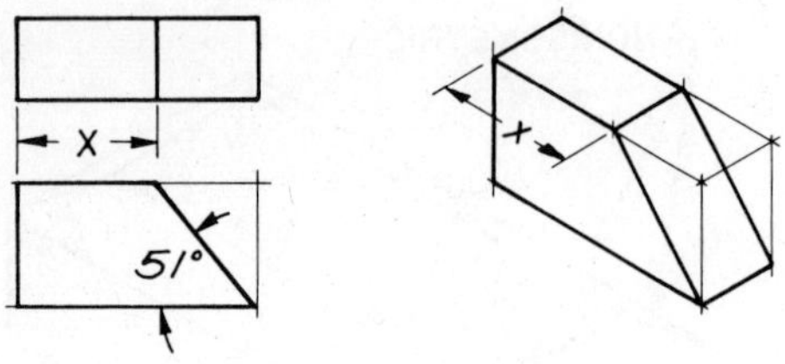

Figure 15-8
Angles in isometric are drawn by means of coordinate points.

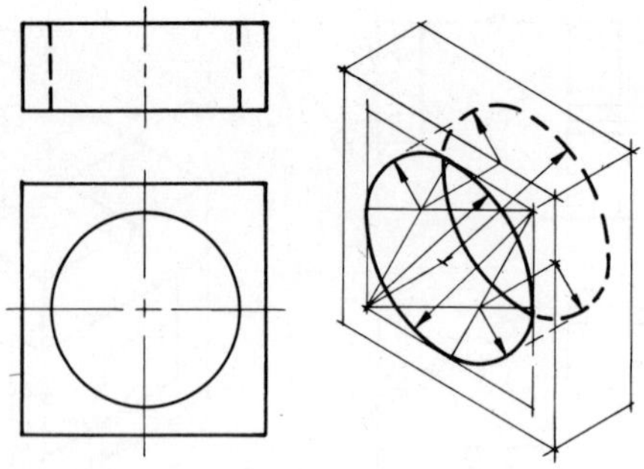

Figure 15-11
On some isometric drawings a portion of the back side of a hole must be shown.

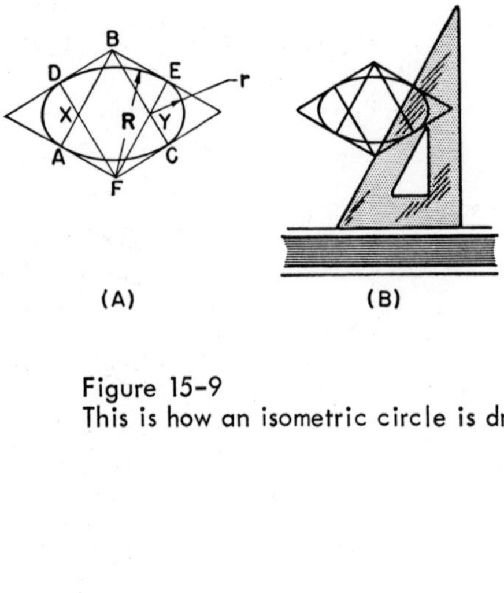

Figure 15-9
This is how an isometric circle is drawn.

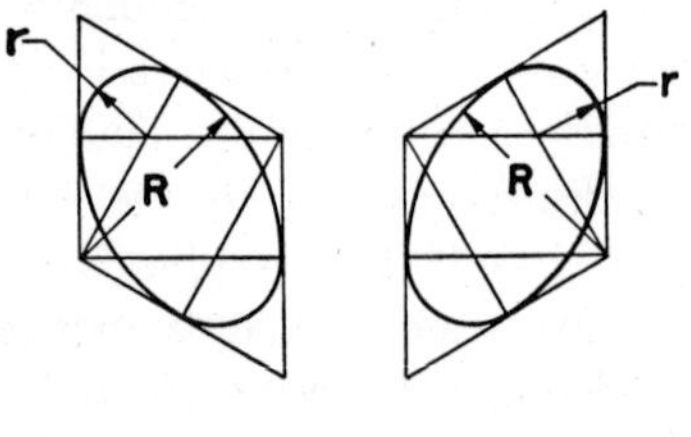

Figure 15-10
Method of drawing isometric circles when located in different positions.

15.6 Isometric circles

An isometric circle is drawn by the four-center system which is sufficiently accurate for most work. First, an isometric square of the required size is laid out and the center of each side of the square is located. From the mid-points of these sides, the lines *AB, BC, DF,* and *EF* are constructed as shown in Fig. 15-9*A* and *B*. The same slanted lines can be made by means of a 60° triangle. Then with *R* as a radius, and *X* and *Y* as centers, arcs *EC* and *AD* are drawn. With *R* as a radius and *B* and *F* as centers, arcs *DE* and *AC* are drawn. Fig. 15-10 illustrates the procedure for drawing circles located in different positions.

Very often a portion of the rear side of a hole must be shown. To do this, lay off the thickness of the piece or depth of the hole and find the center for the required radius as shown in Fig. 15-11.

15.7 Isometric arcs

The same four-center method is used to draw isometric arcs as described for circles. However, it is not necessary to draw the entire construction as for a circle. Only the radius needed for drawing the arc is laid out. Fig. 15-12 illustrates how isometric arcs are made.

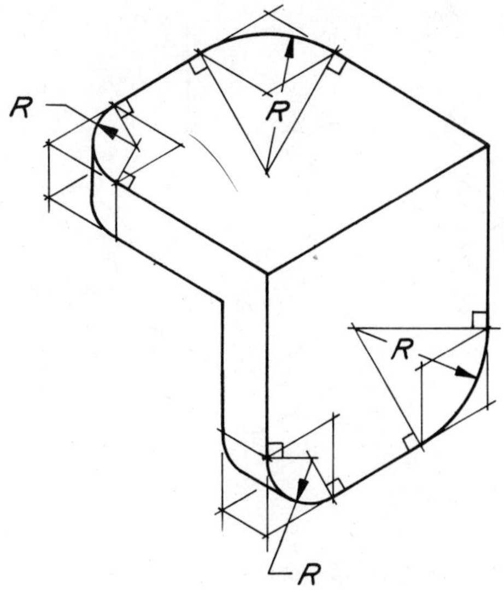

Figure 15–12
This is the procedure for drawing an isometric arc.

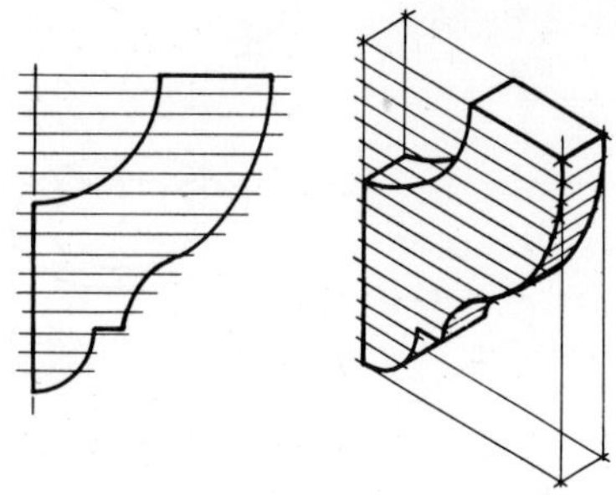

Figure 15–13
Irregular curves in isometric are produced by a series of reference lines as shown here.

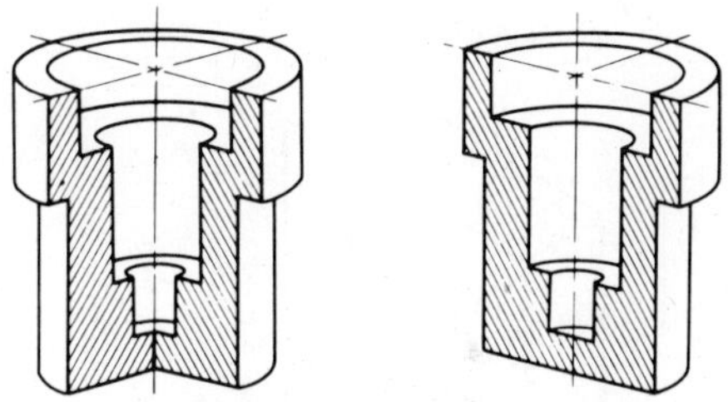

HALF SECTION FULL SECTION

Figure 15–14
Sections in isometric may be necessary to show clearly some internal feature.
ASA Y14.4–1957

15.8 Irregular curves in isometric

If an object to be drawn in isometric contains an irregular curve, the true shape of the curve is drawn first as an orthographic view as shown in Fig. 15-13. This view must have the same scale as the isometric drawing. The exact shape of the curve is determined by a series of reference lines (coordinates). These coordinates are then drawn in isometric and the points of the curve plotted on them by transferring their distances from the orthographic view.

15.9 Isometric sections

Although an isometric drawing is used principally to show the exterior of an object, occasionally it may be advantageous to illustrate the internal construction of the object in isometric. The cutting plane may be passed in any position as discussed in Section 8. Usually it is best to lay out the full shape of the object first and then remove the required portion. Section lining should be carried out as in multiview drawings. The important consideration is to have the section lines run in the direction which produces the best effect. Fig. 15-14 illustrates two sections in isometric.

15.10 Isometric dimensioning

Generally speaking, the same dimensioning rules which are used for multiview drawings apply to isometric drawings. All dimension and extension lines must be parallel to the principal isometric axes. Fig. 15-15 shows how dimension and extension lines should be positioned in the unidirectional and pictorial plane systems of dimensioning pictorial drawings. Although it is desirable to keep dimensions off of the view, this cannot always be done. Note that in the unidirectional system, dimensions read from the bottom of the drawing. With the pictorial plane system dimensions are perpendicular to the dimension lines and in the same plane with the corresponding extension and dimension lines. Fig.

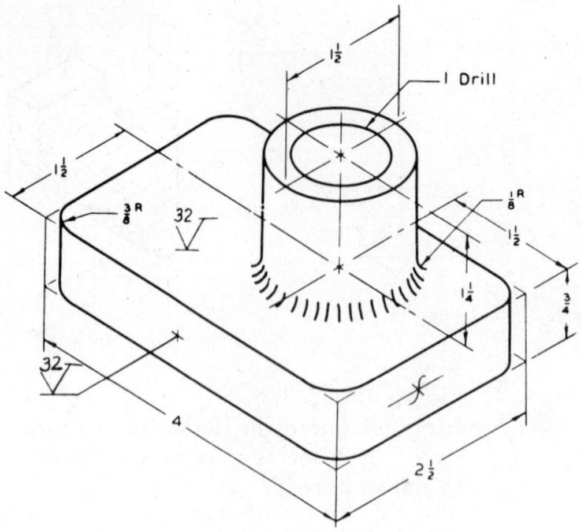

UNIDIRECTIONAL
DIMENSIONING

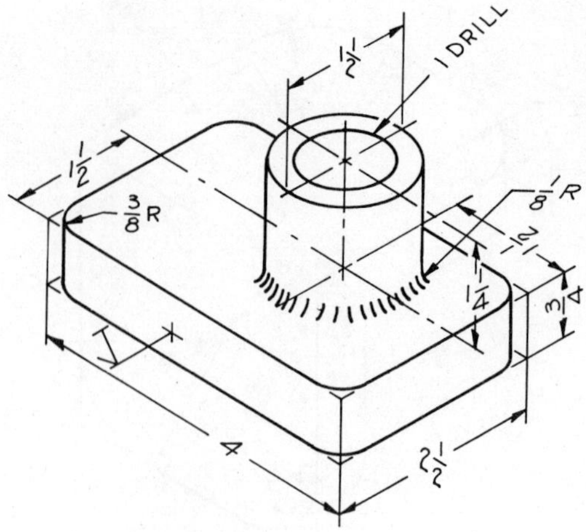

Figure 15-16
Improper way of placing dimensional figures in an isometric drawing.

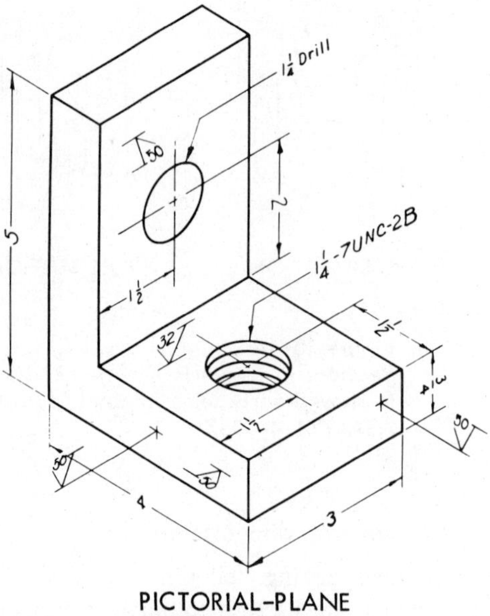

PICTORIAL-PLANE
DIMENSIONING

Figure 15-15
Examples of where dimension and extension lines may be located on an isometric drawing. ASA Y14.4-1957

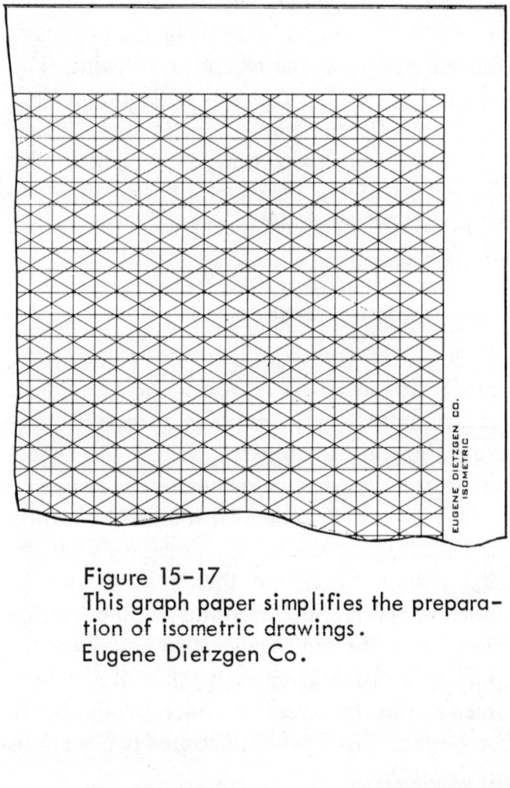

Figure 15-17
This graph paper simplifies the preparation of isometric drawings.
Eugene Dietzgen Co.

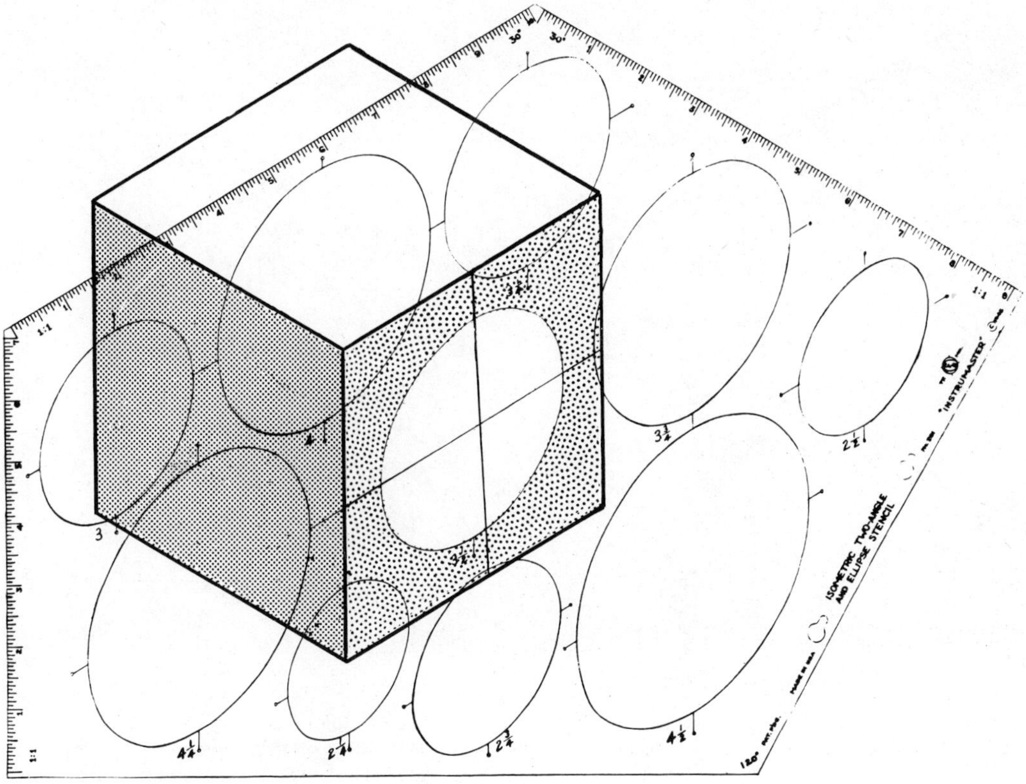

Figure 15–18
Drawing a circle with an isometric template. John R. Cassell Co.

15-16 illustrates an incorrect method of placing dimensional figures.

15.11 Equipment for isometric drawing

To simplify the task of preparing isometric drawings, special isometric graph paper and templates have been developed. Fig. 15-17 illustrates a type of graph paper frequently used. This paper consists of grid lines drawn in isometric. The drawing can be made directly on the graph paper or the graph paper can be placed beneath the tracing paper. Figs. 15-18, 15-19, 15-20 and 15-21 show several types of isometric templates. With these templates isometric drawings can be produced quickly and accurately.

15.12 Oblique projection

An oblique projection is one in which the lines of sight are parallel to each other but the projectors are oblique to the plane of projection. The principal face is placed parallel to the plane of projection and therefore appears in its true shape. The three kinds of oblique projections are: cavalier, cabinet and general oblique.

Cavalier projection. When the projectors make any angle of 0°-90° with the plane of projection, and the same scale is used on all axes, the result is a cavalier projection. See Fig. 15-22.

Cabinet projection. An oblique projection in which the receding lines are foreshortened

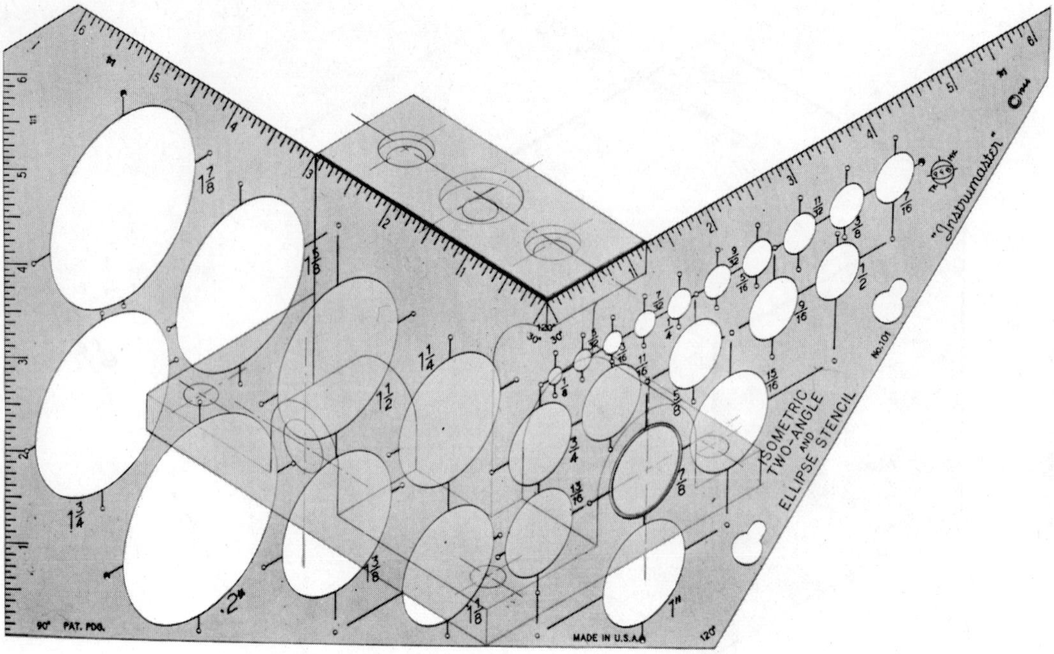

Figure 15–19
Templates of this type speed up the process of preparing isometric drawings. John R. Cassell Co.

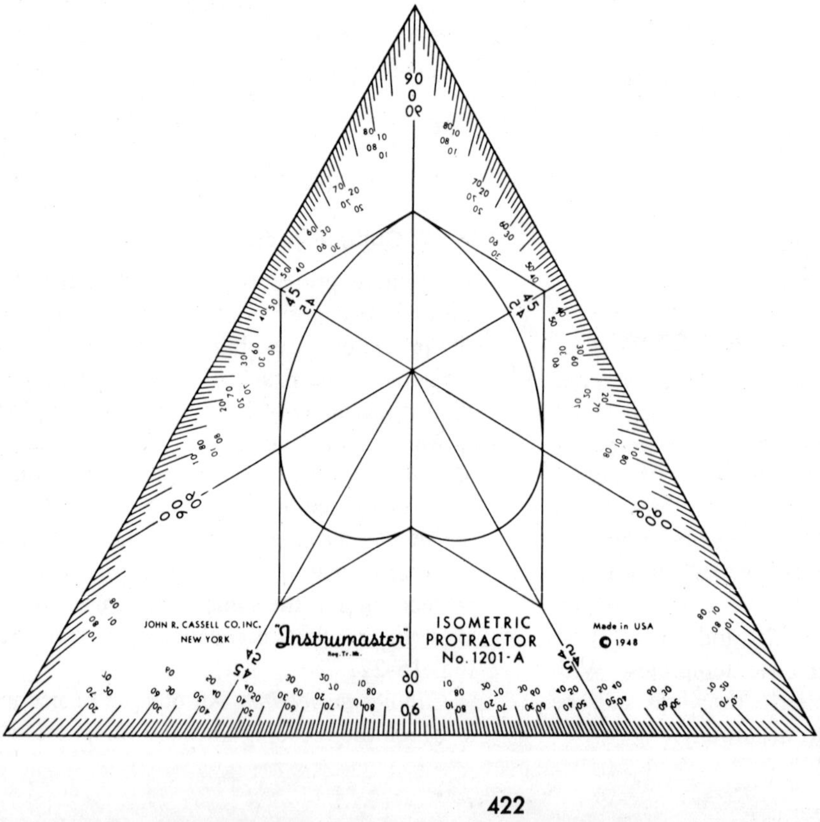

Figure 15–20
Isometric protractor. John R. Cassell Co.

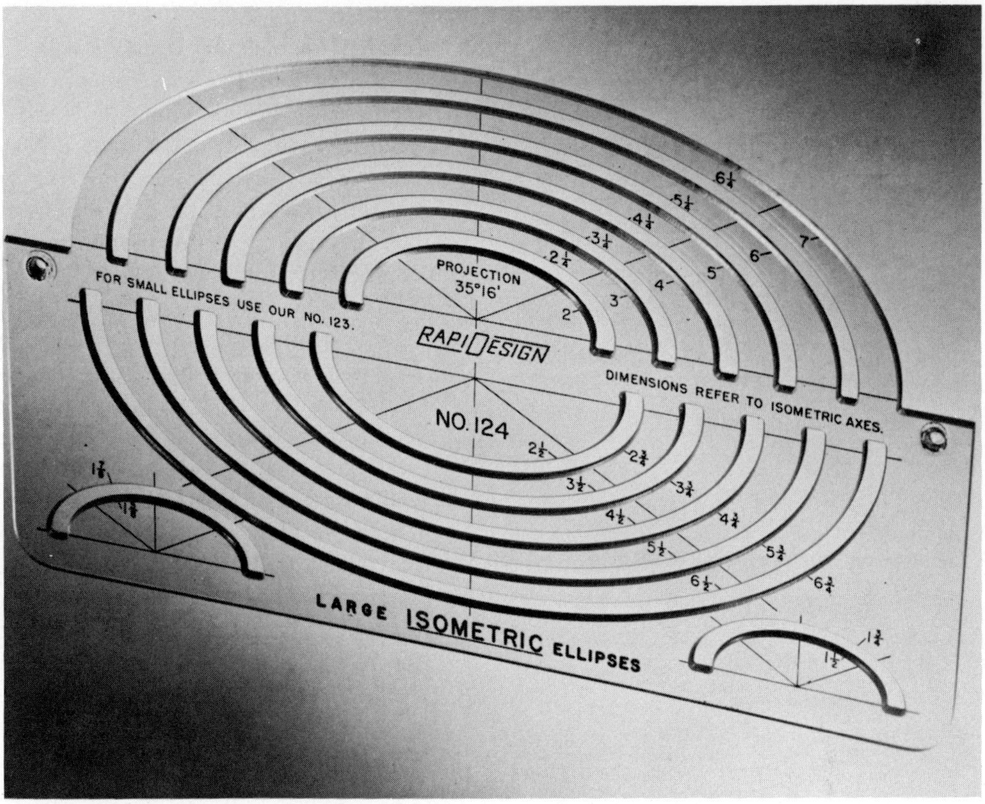

Figure 15-21
This is another type of isometric template for drawing ellipses. RapiDesign

Figure 15-22
Cavalier drawing. ASA Y14.4-1958

Figure 15-23
Cabinet drawing. ASA Y14.4-1958

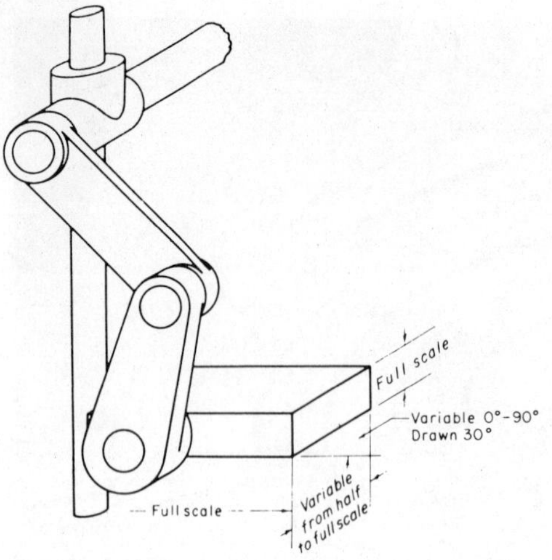

Figure 15-24
General oblique drawing. ASA Y14.4 -1958

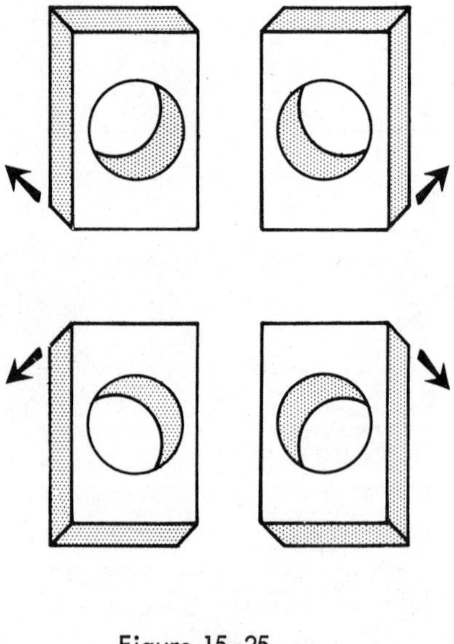

Figure 15-25
Oblique drawings may be made so the inclined axes assume a variety of positions.

one-half their actual length is called a cabinet projection. The shortening of the receding lines tends to eliminate some of the distortion which is often quite noticeable in cavalier projections. See Fig. 15-23. The receding axes may be drawn at any angle, but they are more commonly made at 30° or 45° with the horizontal.

General oblique projection. A general oblique projection is one in which the projectors make any angle with the plane of projection and the receding axes vary in length from full to one-half scale. For practical purposes, the angle of projection normally should be kept between 30° and 60°. The angle used will depend on the shape of the object and the effects desired. Thus a large angle may be selected to obtain a better view of some special surface. The scale on the receding axes will depend on the angle used. The governing principle is to employ a scale that produces the least amount of distortion. See Fig. 15-24.

15.13 Position of object for oblique projection

In making oblique drawings, the object may be placed so that the receding faces assume any number of positions, as shown in Fig. 15-25. In each instance the front face, regardless of the position of the inclined axes, remains parallel to the plane of projection.

The principal or front face of an oblique drawing should consist of the view that shows the most essential features of the object. This is especially important for irregular surfaces or those having circles and curves.

Circles and arcs, if drawn on the front face, may be made with a compass since they will appear in their true size and shape. However, if they appear on receding faces, circles and arcs will have to be drawn with an irregular curve or by means of the four-center ellipse method.

The object should also be drawn so the largest dimensions appear in the front face. Too much distortion results when the long features are placed in receding faces. See Fig. 15-26.

15.14 Circles and arcs in oblique projection

When circles and arcs must be made in receding faces, the four-center ellipse system can be used, providing the receding faces are drawn to the same scale as the principal face. Such a system is applicable in cavalier projections and in some general oblique projections when the receding faces are drawn full scale. If the receding surfaces are foreshortened, then circles and curves may be approximated with an irregular curve, or by the offset method described in Sub-section 15.15 or with ellipse templates.

The four-center ellipse system for oblique projection will necessitate a flatter parallelogram than in isometric. Accordingly, the perpendicular of the side bisectors will not intersect in the corners of the parallelogram, but will intersect either on the outside or at some point within the parallelogram, depending on the angle of the receding axes. Thus, if the receding axes are drawn at a 45° angle with the horizontal, the bisectors will intersect on the outside of the parallelogram. See *A*, Fig. 15-27. If the angle is less than 45° as shown in *B* of Fig. 15-27, the perpendicular bisectors will intersect within the parallelogram.

To make a circle or curve in an oblique drawing, lay out the parallelogram in the required position and find the perpendicular bisector of each side. The intersection of these perpendicular bisectors will provide the necessary centers for the required radii of the circle.

15.15 Offset measurements for oblique projection

The offset measuring system is used to draw circles, arcs and other irregular curves for oblique projections having foreshortened receding axes. A series of parallel reference lines are first located on a regular multiview projection as shown in Fig. 15-28, and the curve or circle located on these lines. The points are then transferred to similar parallel coordinates drawn on the oblique view. The circle or arc is completed with an irregular curve.

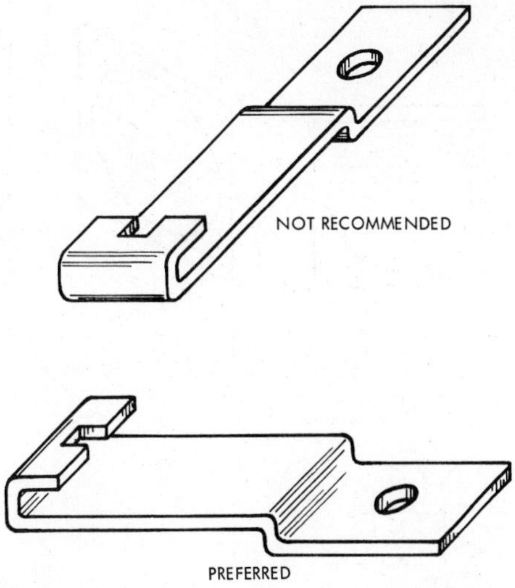

Figure 15-26
For oblique pictorial drawings position the object so the longest features are parallel to the plane of projection.

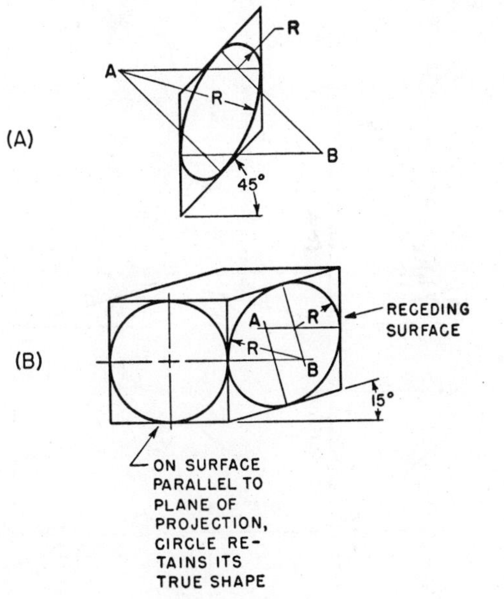

Figure 15-27
Circles and arcs for oblique projection can be constructed by the four-center ellipse system on receding surfaces.

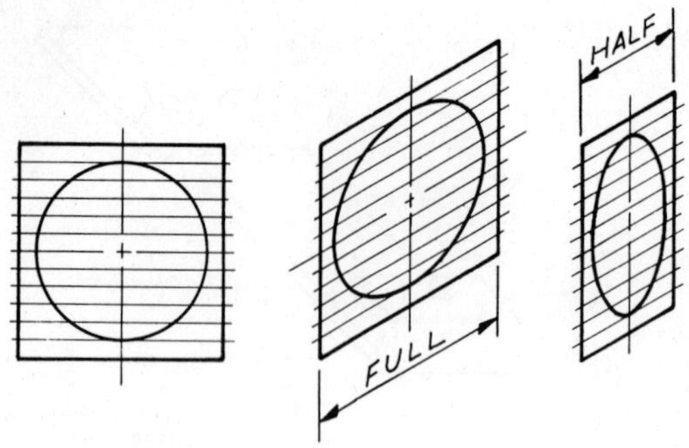

Figure 15-28
How to lay off circles, arcs and irregular curves by the offset measurement system for oblique projection.

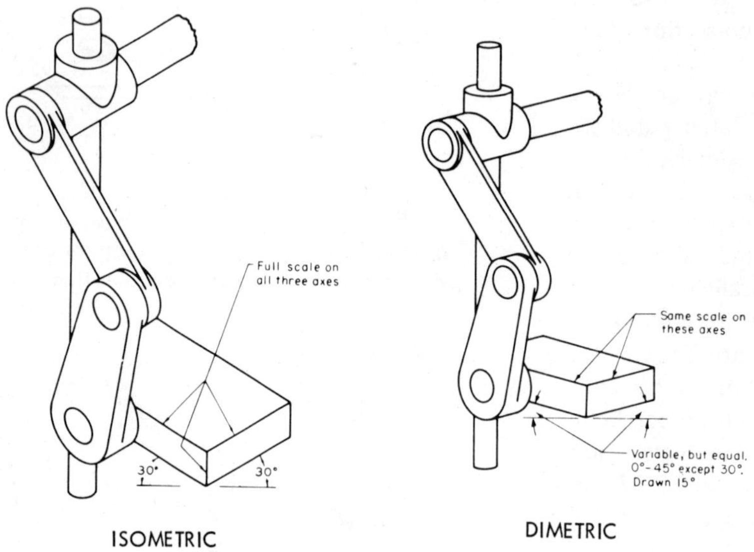

Figure 15-29
A dimetric projection is similar to an isometric but has less distortion.
ASA Y14.4-1958

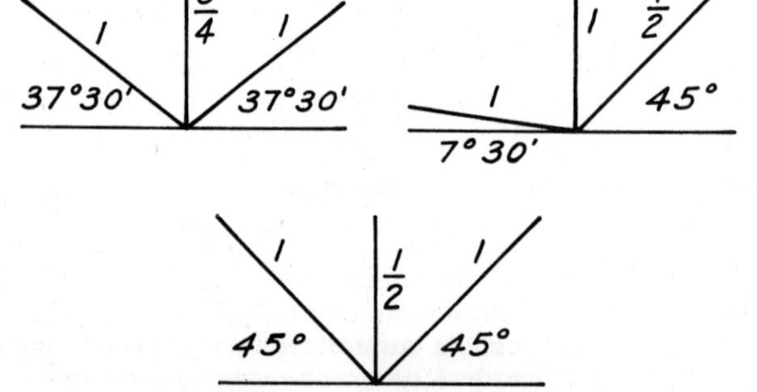

Figure 15-30
The positions and scales illustrated here will be suitable for almost any dimetric drawing.

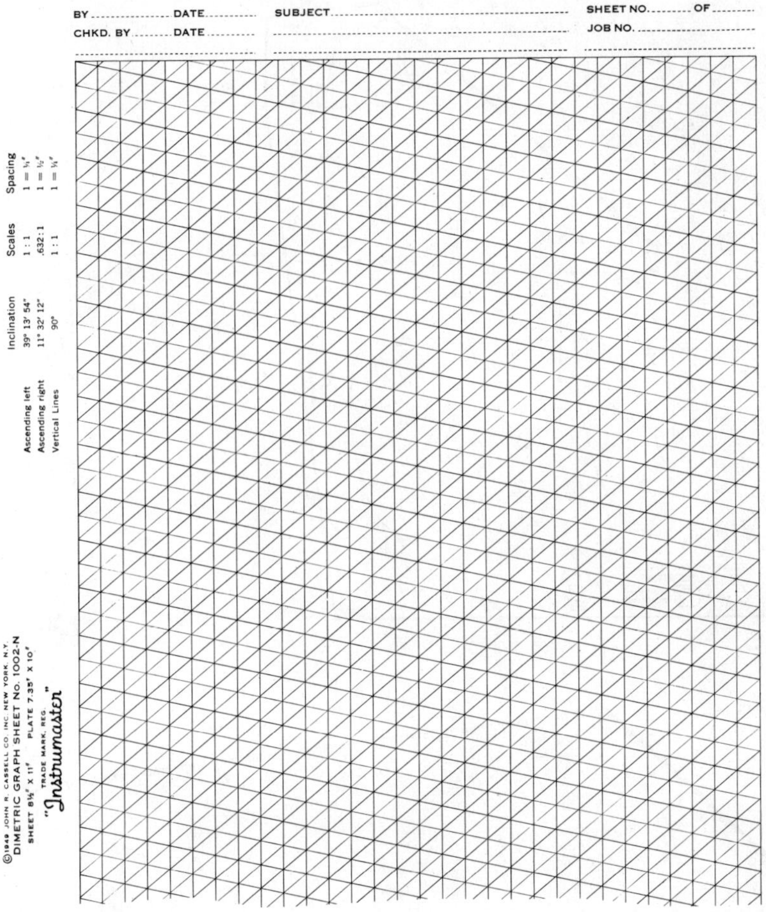

Figure 15-31
Dimetric graph paper.
John R. Cassell Co.

15.16 Oblique dimensioning

An oblique drawing is dimensioned in much the same way as an isometric drawing. The important factor is to place all dimensions in the planes to which they apply. Dimensions should be kept off the object as much as possible, but if greater clarity is achieved they may be placed directly on the object.

15.17 Dimetric projection

An axonometric projection in which two axes make equal angles with a plane of projection while the third axis makes a different angle is called a dimetric projection. The edges that are parallel to the first two axes are foreshortened the same amount but those edges that are parallel to the third axis are foreshortened to a different value. This necessitates the use of two different scales.

A dimetric drawing is prepared much like an isometric. See Fig. 15-29. Its advantage over the isometric is that by using two scale values the resulting shape has less distortion. The principal limitation of dimetrics is having to use two separate scales for measurement, which is more time consuming.

The usual practice in preparing a dimetric drawing is to place the object so that one of its main axes is at a 90° angle to the horizontal. The receding axes can be located at various angles. The scales to be selected may be determined graphically or mathematically but since true dimetrics are not actually necessary, the procedure is to utilize regular scales of assumed ratios. The angles and scales shown in Fig. 15-30 generally will be suitable for most dimetric drawings.

Special grid paper is available for making dimetric drawings. See Fig. 15-31. Dimetric templates with their appropriate scales are also made to simplify the task of preparing dimetric drawings. See Fig. 15-32.

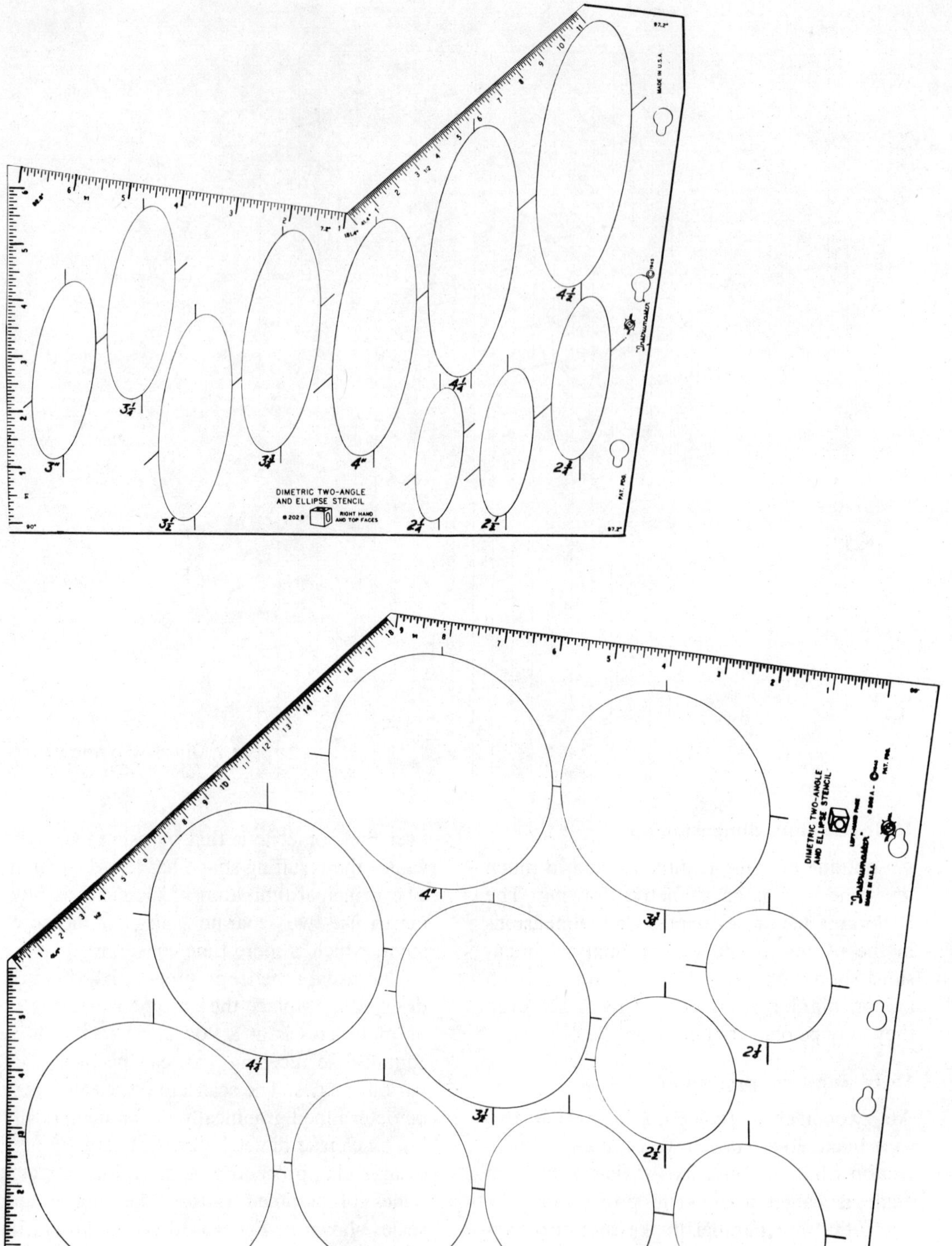

Figure 15-32
Dimetric templates. John R. Cassell Co.

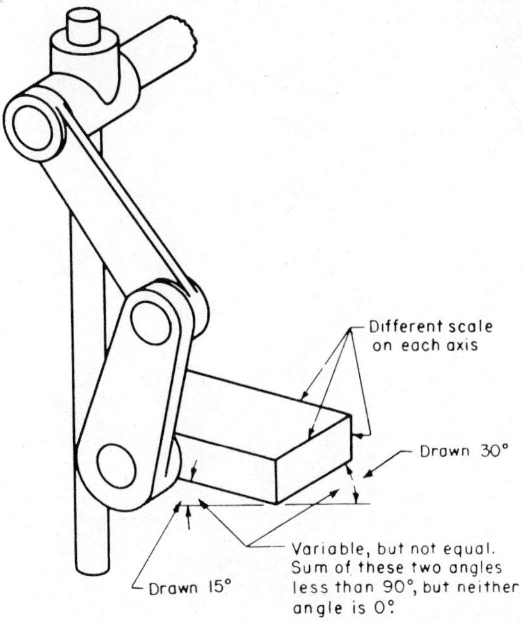

Figure 15-33
A trimetric drawing has all the edges that run parallel to the three axes foreshortened to different ratios. ASA Y14.4-1958

Figure 15-34
A perspective drawing more nearly represents an object as it actually appears to the eye.

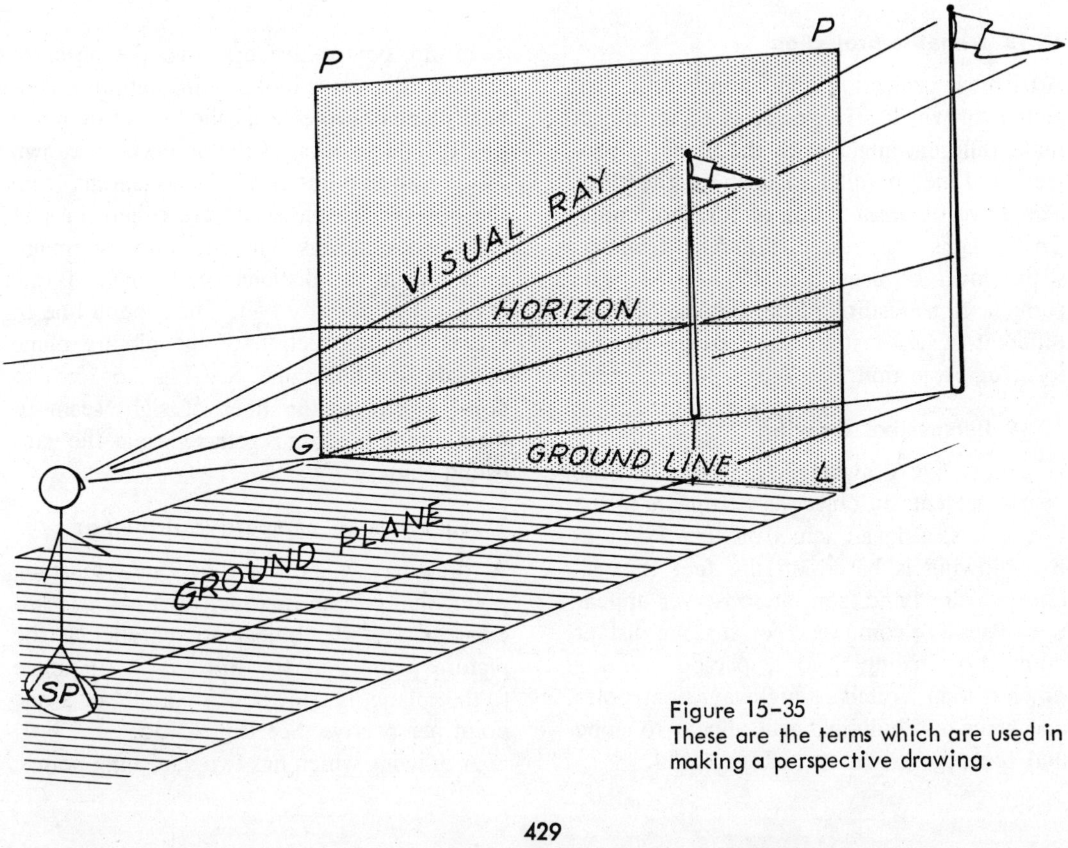

Figure 15-35
These are the terms which are used in making a perspective drawing.

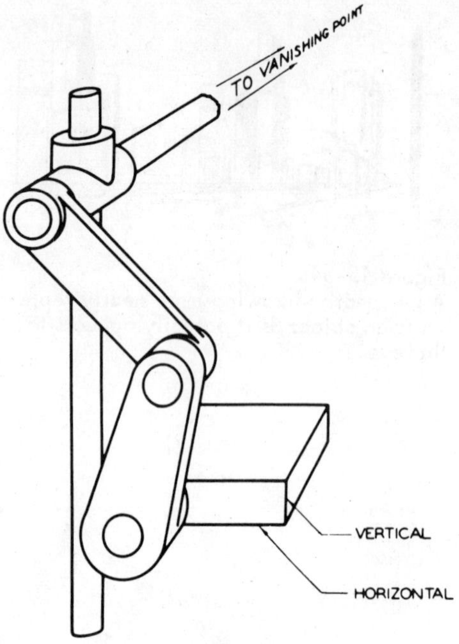

PARALLEL OR
ONE-POINT PERSPECTIVE

Figure 15-36
A one point perspective. ASA Y14.4-1958

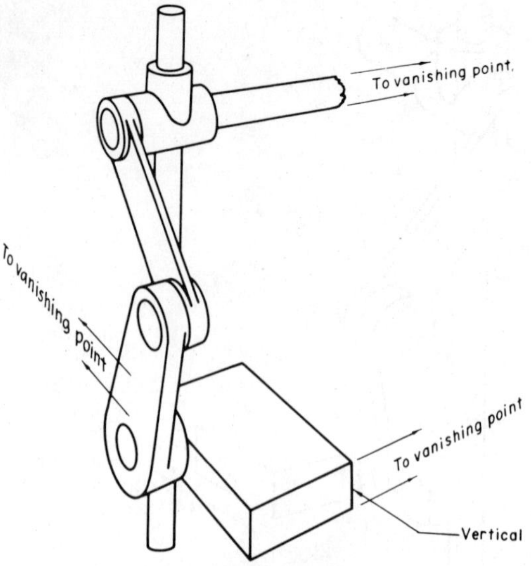

TWO-POINT
PERSPECTIVE

Figure 15-37
A two point perspective. ASA Y14.4-1958

15.18 Trimetric projection

A trimetric projection is an axonometric projection in which all three axes of an object make different angles with the plane of projection. Lines parallel to each of the three axes have different ratios of foreshortening. This means that three different trimetric scales must be used. See Fig. 15-33. The complications resulting from the use of three different scales restrict wide usage of this form of projection.

15.19 Perspective drawing

A perspective drawing is one which more nearly presents an object as it appears to the eye or is seen in an actual picture. Perspective drawing is based on the fact that all lines which extend from the observer appear to converge or come together at some distant point. For example, to a person sighting down a long stretch of highway, light poles and wires and buildings will appear to slope and converge as shown in Fig. 15-34.

In any perspective drawing, the observer assumes that he is looking through an imaginary plane of projection called a picture plane or *PP*. The position of the observer is known as the station point or *SP*. Lines leading from the observer to the scene are called lines of sight or visual rays. The horizon is an imaginary line in the distance and represents the eye level of the observer. The ground line or *GL* is the intersection of the picture plane with the ground plane. See Fig. 15-35. The point where all the lines of sight seem to meet on the horizon is referred to as the vanishing point or *VP*.

15.20 Types of perspective drawings

A drawing which has but one vanishing point, that is, one in which two of the principal axes of the object are parallel to the picture plane and the third is at an angle to that plane, is known as a parallel or a one point perspective. See Fig. 15-36.

A drawing which has two vanishing points,

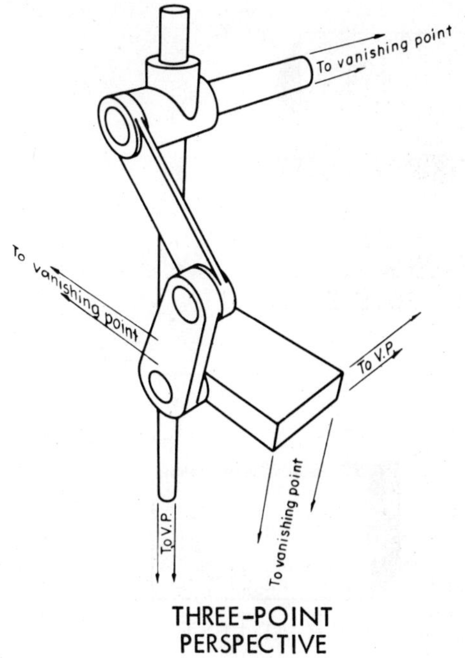

Figure 15-38
A three point perspective. ASA Y14.4-1958

that is, one where the vertical axis is parallel to the picture plane and the other two axes are inclined to it is called an angular or two point perspective. See Fig. 15-37.

A drawing having three vanishing points, that is, one in which all three principal axes of the object are oblique to the picture plane is called an oblique or three point perspective. See Fig. 15-38.

15.21 Location of the picture plane

For most perspective drawings, the picture plane is assumed to be between the object and the point of sight. In this position the perspective drawing is smaller than the actual size of the object. As the picture plane is moved further away from the object, the perspective drawing becomes smaller. See *A*, Fig. 15-39.

If the perspective drawing is to be larger than the true size of the object, the object is placed between the observer and the picture plane. See *B*, Fig. 15-39.

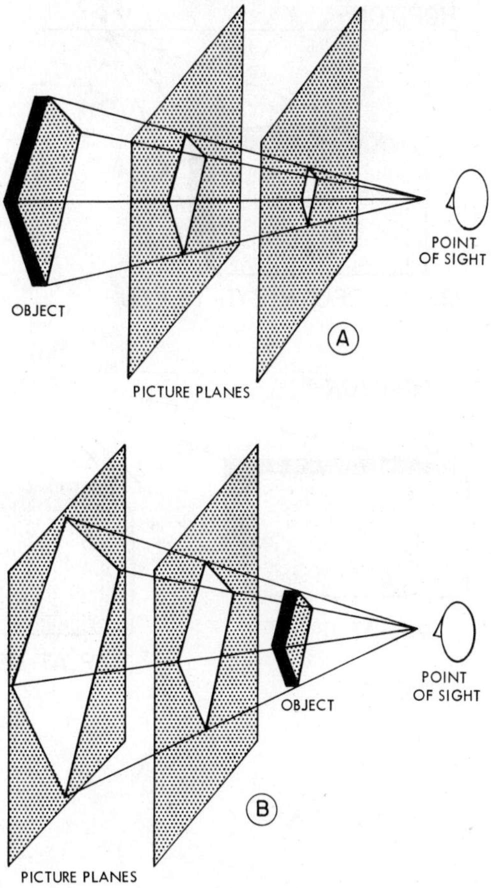

Figure 15-39
The location of the picture plane affects the size of the perspective drawing.

15.22 Location of the station point

A perspective can be altered to a considerable extent by the location of the point of sight. Thus by placing the point of sight above the object, a view of the top will be seen. If the point of sight is below the object, a view of the bottom will be shown. Similarly, the point of sight can be stationed to the right or left of the object to reveal either side. See Fig. 15-40. As a rule, the point of sight for most small and medium size objects is assumed to be slightly above the horizon. For large objects the horizon is located approximately 5′2″ or 5′6″ above the ground.

In preparing a perspective with the least amount of distortion, the station point should be located at a distance so that the cone of

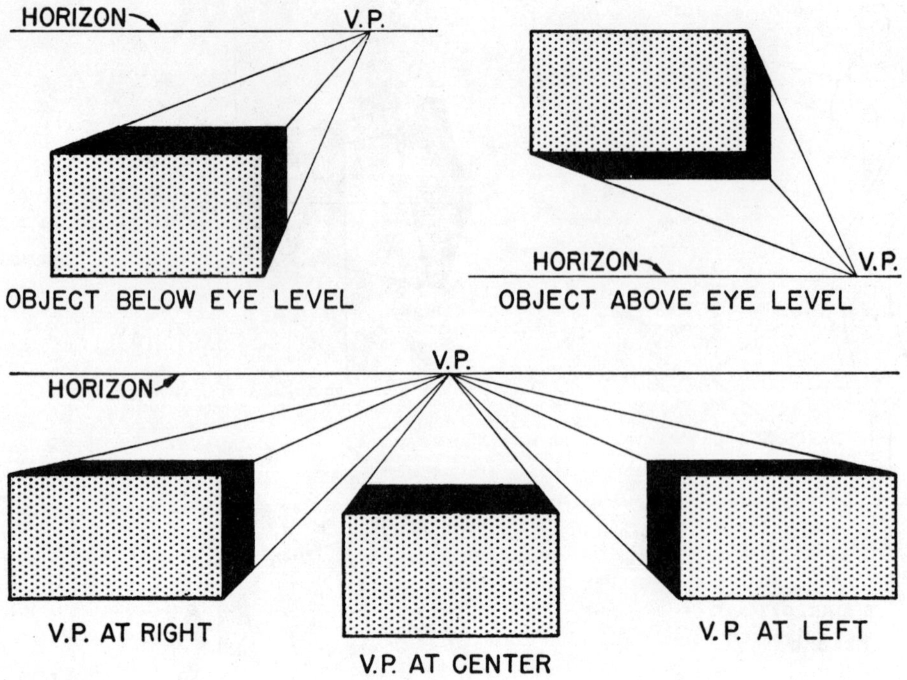

Figure 15-40
The shape of the perspective is determined by the location of the point of sight.

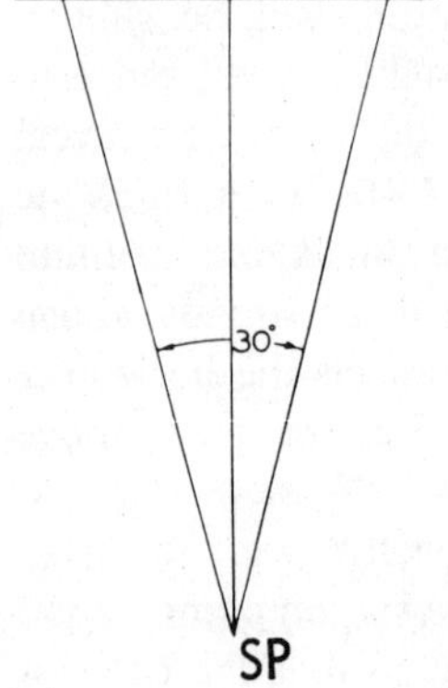

Figure 15-41
The station point should be located so the visual rays will enclose the object in a cone not greater than 30°. ASA Y14.4-1958

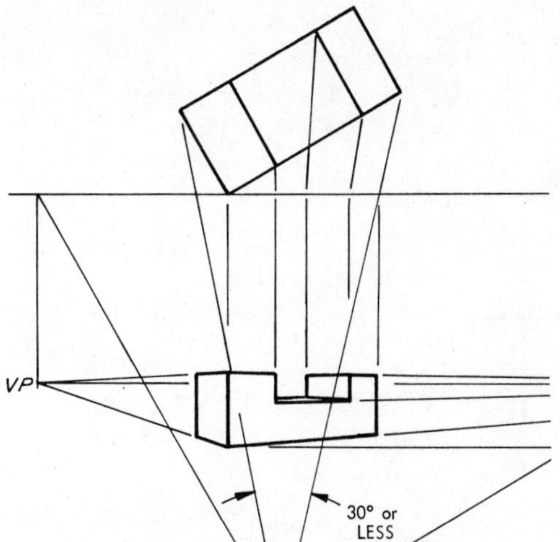

Figure 15-42
If the cone formed by lines of sight are too great, the drawing will be distorted.

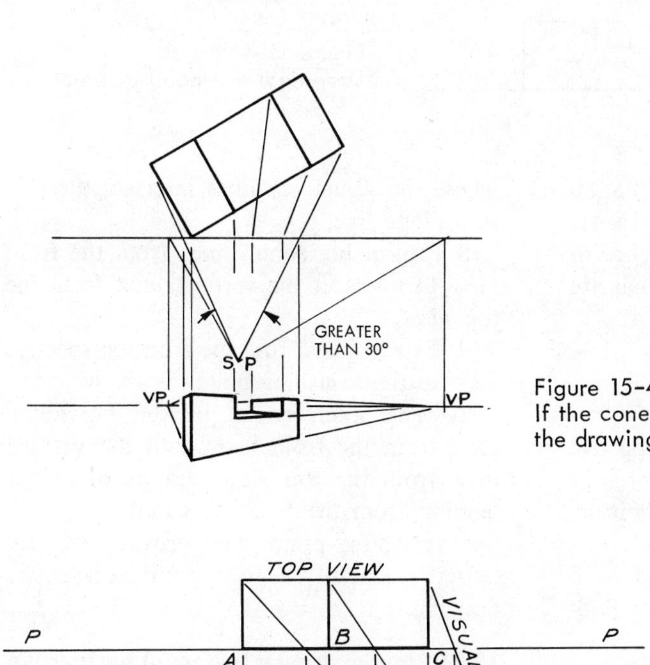

Figure 15-43
Constructing a one-point perspective drawing.

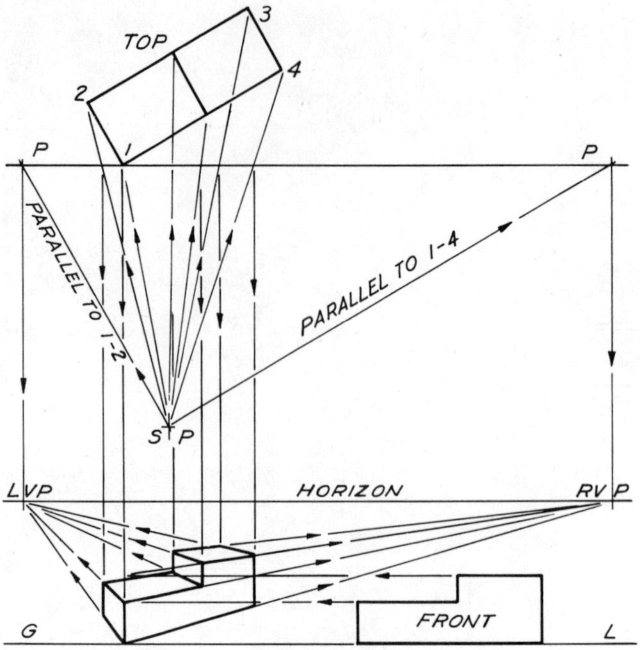

Figure 15-44
Drawing a two-point perspective.

visual rays will enclose the entire object at an angle not greater than 30°. See Fig. 15-41. If larger angles are used, the convergence of horizontal lines will result in shapes that are badly distorted as shown in Fig. 15-42.

15.23 How to draw a parallel or one point perspective

The steps in making a one point perspective are as follows (see Fig. 15-43):

1 Draw the ground line *GL* and on it lay out the front view of the object.

2 Locate the picture plane *PP* and on it draw the top view of the object. See Subsection 15.21.

3 Draw the horizon line at any convenient distance from the ground line.

4 Locate the station point. See Sub-section 15.22. Locate the station point so that the cone of visual rays will enclose the object at an angle not greater than 30°.

5 From the station point, draw a vertical line to the horizon which provides the vanishing point *VP*.

6 Draw visual ray lines from the station point to all of the top points in the top view.

7 Extend vertical lines downward from the bottom points of the top view as well as where the visual ray lines intersect the picture plane line.

8 Project horizontal lines from the front view to intersect the vertical lines from the top view.

9 Extend lines from the front perspective view to the vanishing point.

10 The intersections of the horizontal lines from the front view with the vertical lines from the top view and the lines extending from the front perspective view to the vanishing point will provide the required shape of the one point perspective drawing.

15.24 How to draw a two point perspective

To prepare a two point perspective, proceed as follows (see Fig. 15-44):

1 Draw the ground line *GL,* the horizon, and picture plane *PP*.

2 Draw a front view of the object on the ground line and a top view on the picture plane. Revolve the top view at any convenient angle on the picture plane.

3 Locate the two vanishing points by first drawing lines from *SP* to *PP* so they are parallel to the edge lines of the top view. Then drop perpendiculars from the picture

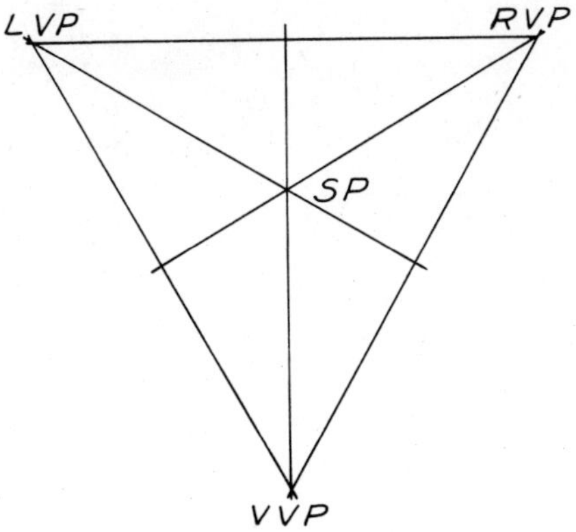

STEP 1

plane line to the horizon.

4 Draw visual ray lines from *SP* to the essential features of the top view.

5 From the points where the visual ray lines intersect the picture plane line, drop vertical projectors to intersect the lines drawn to the vanishing points.

15.25 How to draw a three point perspective

Fig. 15-45 illustrates the steps in preparing a three point perspective. Proceed as follows:

1 Lay out an equilateral triangle and let the corners represent the three vanishing points. Make the triangle as large as can be conveniently drawn on the sheet.

2 From each corner of the triangle construct a perpendicular bisector to the opposite side of the triangle. The point of intersection of the three lines is the required *SP*.

3 Through *SP* draw two measuring lines, one *ML* parallel to *LVP-RVP* and the other M_1L_1 parallel to *RVP-VVP*.

4 On the horizontal measuring line *ML* lay out the actual length of the object from *SP* to the left of *SP* and its true width from *SP* to the right of *SP*. From these points draw visual rays to the right and left vanishing points respectively.

5 Lay out the height of the object on the measuring line M_1L_1 and draw visual ray lines to the corresponding *VP*.

6 Complete the perspective by drawing the remaining visual ray lines to their respective *VPs*. *(Text continued on page 439)*

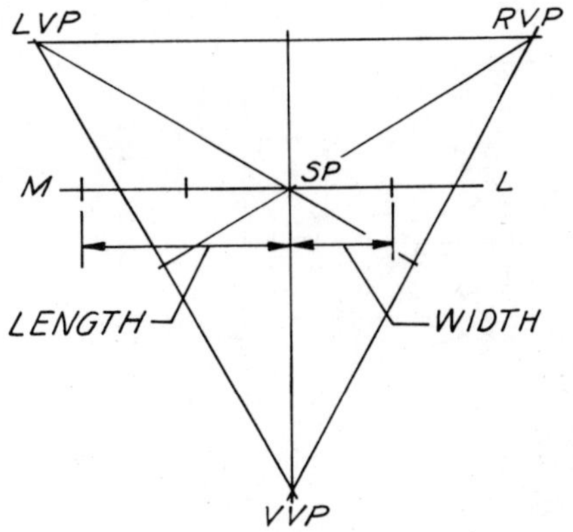

STEP 2

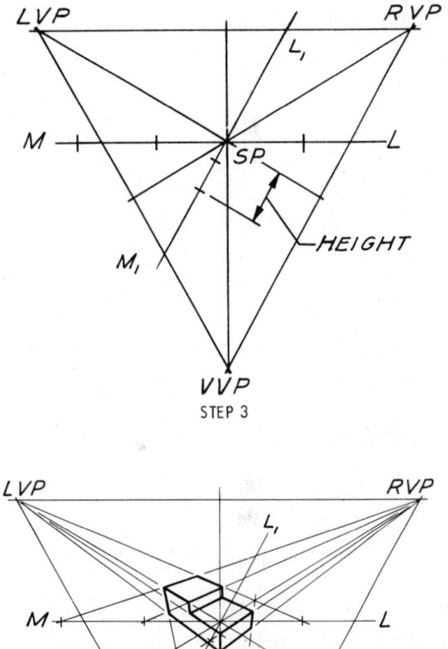

STEP 3

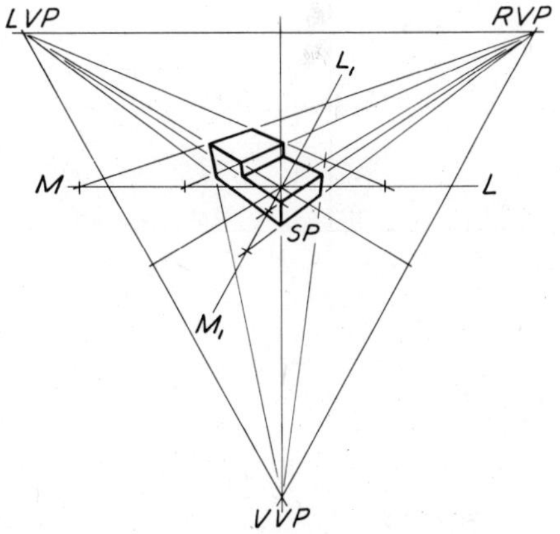

STEP 4

Figure 15-45
Drawing a three-point perspective.

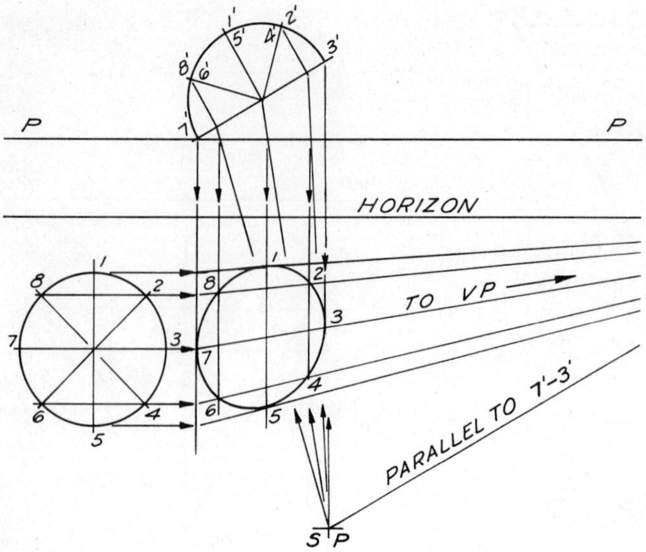

Figure 15-46
Drawing a circle in a one-point perspective.

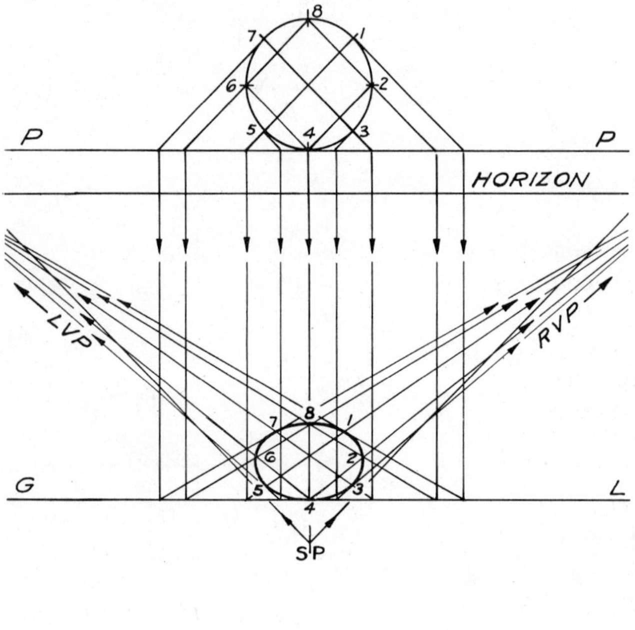

Figure 15-47
Procedure for drawing a circle in a two-point perspective.

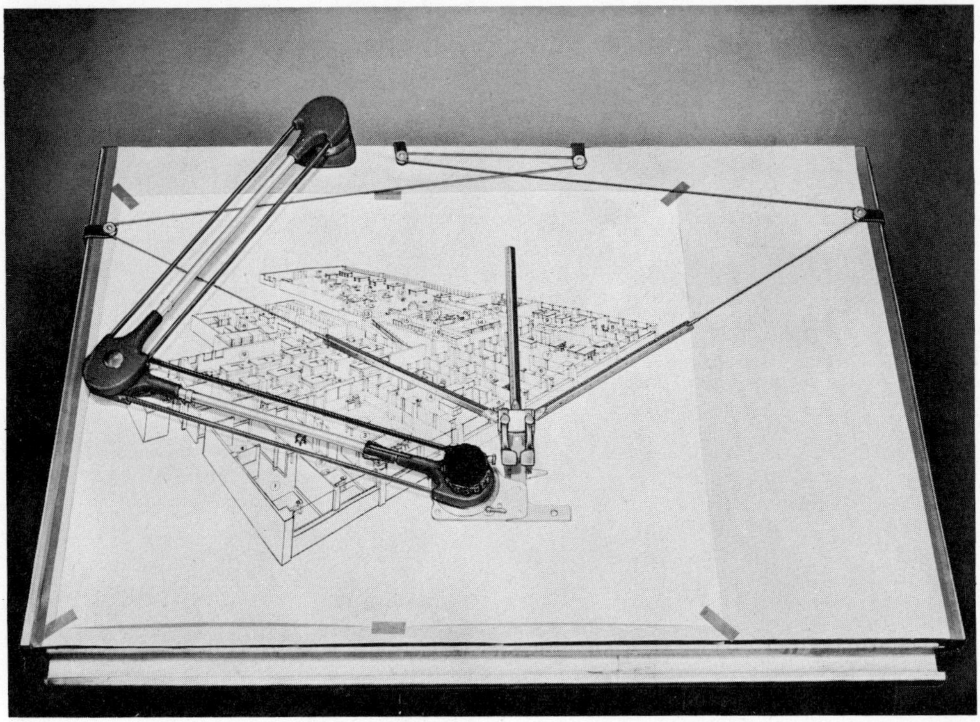

Figure 15-48
This device simplifies the preparation of perspective drawings.
Charles Bruning Co.

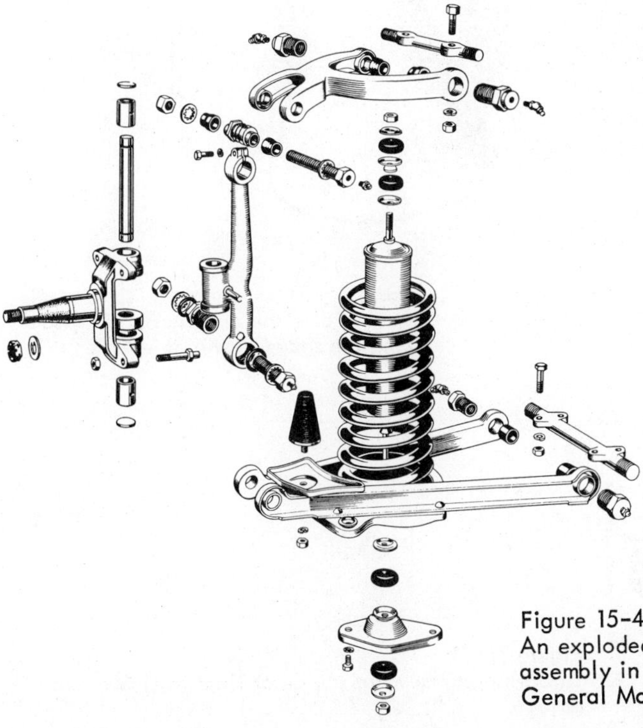

Figure 15-49
An exploded drawing shows the various parts of an assembly in their corresponding pulled-out position.
General Motors Corp.

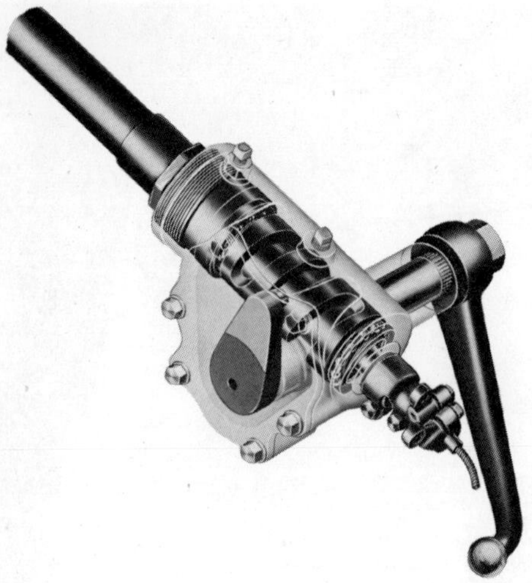

Figure 15-50
A phantom drawing is one that shows in pictorial form the internal shape of an object. ASA Y14.4-1958

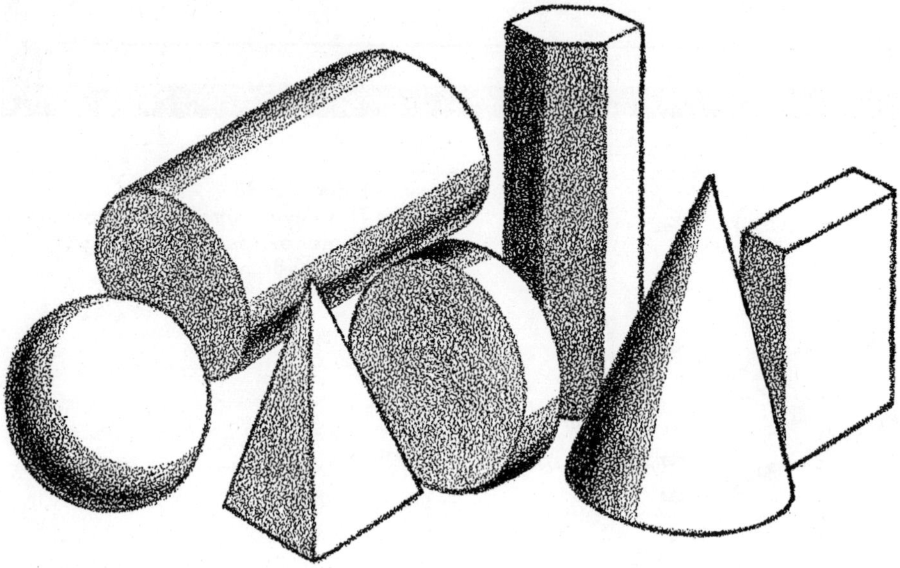

Figure 15-51
Shading aids the imagination in visualizing the shape of the object.

Figure 15-52
Direction of the main source of light falling on an object.

15.26 Perspective of a circle or arc

If a circle or arc is parallel to the picture plane, it assumes its true shape and can be drawn with a compass. When the circle or arc is inclined to the picture plane, its shape (for a one point perspective) may be found as follows:

1 Draw a front view of the circle or arc and divide it into any number of equal parts. See Fig. 15-46.

2 Draw horizontal lines through the points and extend them to the vanishing point.

3 Construct a plan view of the circle on the picture plane and lay out the same numbered divisions. From these numbered points draw lines to *SP*. Drop vertical lines from the intersection of the visual ray lines and picture plane. The corresponding intersection of these lines with the vanishing point lines will provide the necessary points for constructing the perspective circle or arc.

Fig. 15-47 illustrates the procedure for drawing a circle in a two point perspective.

15.27 Preparing perspectives with the Perspect-O-Metric

The Perspect-O-Metric makes it comparatively simple to create complicated perspective drawings. This device guides the pencil at the proper angle and automatically realigns itself for every position on the drawing board. It provides a special scale which instantly reduces distant portions of the subject to their correct proportions. See Fig. 15-48.

The Perspect-O-Metric consists of an attachment which fits any standard drafting machine. By the addition of a special adapter, it also fits any parallel ruling straight edge. It has three scale arms. Of these, the central scale arm is fixed in a position at right angles to the established base line. The left and right scale arms pivot in the plane of the drawing board.

Any movement of the Perspect-O-Metric creates a corresponding angular motion of the floating scale arms. No matter where the Perspect-O-Metric is placed on the drawing board, the scale arms remain oriented to their chosen vanishing points. To prevent the scales from shifting under the pressure of the pencil, a left and a right brake lever are provided. A pressure of the thumb locks the scale arms in position while the line is being drawn.

Although the Perspect-O-Metric provides what is known as the two point perspective which covers about 90 percent of ordinary drawings, the pulleys can easily be relocated to permit any number of vanishing points.

15.28 Exploded illustrations

Exploded illustrations are pictorial drawings showing the various parts of an assembly in a separate or pulled-out position but with all of the parts aligned in the correct order for reassembly. See Fig. 15-49. The principal advantage of this type of drawing is that it readily discloses how the individual parts of a mechanism fit together. It is of particular value to those who are unable to read multiview drawings. Exploded illustrations are widely used in design, manufacturing, sales and service. These drawings may vary from simple sketches to elaborate shaded illustrations.

Drawings of this kind can be prepared either in axonometric, oblique or perspective form. As a rule the perspective technique is preferred because it gives a more pleasing appearance. When parts are strung out along a single axis by the axonometric or oblique method, a certain amount of distortion is inevitable.

To make a perspective exploded drawing, a perspective of the assembly is made first. A piece of tracing paper is next placed over the assembly drawing and one or more parts drawn with the perspective axes clearly shown. The overlay sheet is removed and another sheet is positioned on which some other part is drawn. When all of the parts have been drawn, the individual sheets are arranged so each part is in its normal spread-out position and a final drawing is then made.

An experienced illustrator achieves the same results by tracing the main part of the mechanism and then moving the overlay sheet each time to the correct distance and tracing the remaining parts.

It must be remembered that a perspective made with overlay sheets will not produce a final true perspective of each part removed from the original assembly. Nevertheless this is the result desired since a true perspective would reduce the individual parts to an unusually small proportion.

15.29 Phantom drawing

Any pictorial drawing that shows the shell or covering of the interior parts of a mechanism is called a phantom drawing. The contrast between the interior and exterior shape is achieved by shading. The interior sections are rendered in dark tones and the outer covering in very light tones. See Fig. 15-50.

15.30 Shading

One of the main purposes of a pictorial drawing is to achieve better visualization of an object. It is a means of bridging the gap between an actual photograph and the natural object. To make a pictorial drawing appear more natural, a process of shading is often used. By means of shading depth or distance can be achieved, thereby imparting the desired form or shape to an object. Shading is simply a technique of varying the light intensity on the surfaces by lines or tones. Notice in Fig. 15-51 how shading helps to better visualize the shape of these objects.

Location of shaded areas. Since shading is a result of light intensity on a surface, the first consideration in producing a shaded effect is to determine the source of light falling on the object. Generally speaking, one can proceed on the basis that the principal source of light is shining over the observer's left shoulder or from the upper corner of the drafting board, as shown in Fig. 15-52. This, however, is not necessarily a fixed rule since sources of light from other directions may often produce an even more pleasing appearance. However, if we assume that the standard direction of light is over the left shoulder, then the top and front surfaces of the object receive the most light. The sides that form the smallest angle with the light rays have less light, and the surfaces that are directly opposite the light source are in deep shade. See Fig. 15-53.

By following this rule, shading can be accomplished by sketching contrasting weights of lines over the surfaces affected by the light. It is well to keep in mind, too, that a more pleasing effect can be obtained by having the shaded area of one plane adjacent to the light area of an adjoining surface. See Fig. 15-54.

Before actually proceeding with any shading, it is good practice to outline with a very fine line the areas that are to be shaded. The line should be light enough so it can be erased after the shading is completed. See Fig. 15-55.

Line shading. The simplest method of producing shading effects is by means of contrasting weights and spacing of lines. Fig. 15-56 shows how such lines are sketched on flat surfaces. The spacing of lines should be judged by eye. Notice that the darker the area, the closer will be the lines. Actually no hard and fast rule can be given as to the amount of space to leave between lines. Practice and judgment will serve as the best guide. At any rate, remember to visualize the intensity of light cast on the object and then space the lines so they will best reflect the effects of this light.

The weight of lines can be achieved by varying the pressure on the pencil. Notice in Fig. 15-56 that the heaviest lines are used where the surface is to have the darkest areas. It is also possible to produce shaded effects by keeping all the lines light and varying the spacing. See Fig. 15-57, As a rule, better results will be achieved by varying both the spacing and weight of lines.

The direction of the lines must also be taken into consideration. Usually, it is best to shade vertical faces with vertical lines and the other faces with lines parallel to one of the edges of the object. See Fig. 15-58.

To shade curved surfaces, the lines may be sketched straight or curved. The practice is to shade approximately one-fifth of the surface nearest the source of light, then leave the next two-fifths white and shade the two-fifths that are the farthest from the light. See

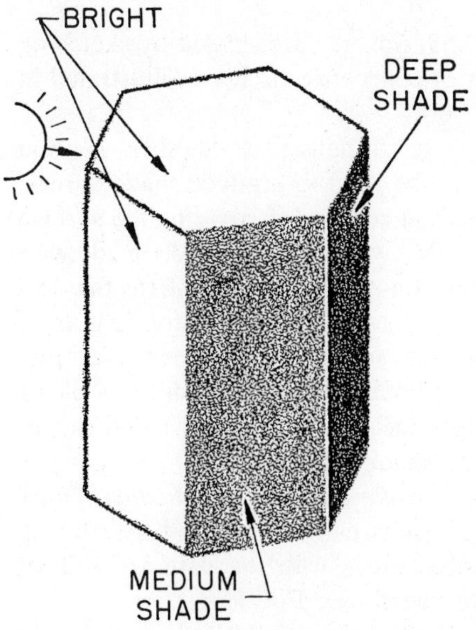

Figure 15-53
How the direction of light affects the surface of an object.

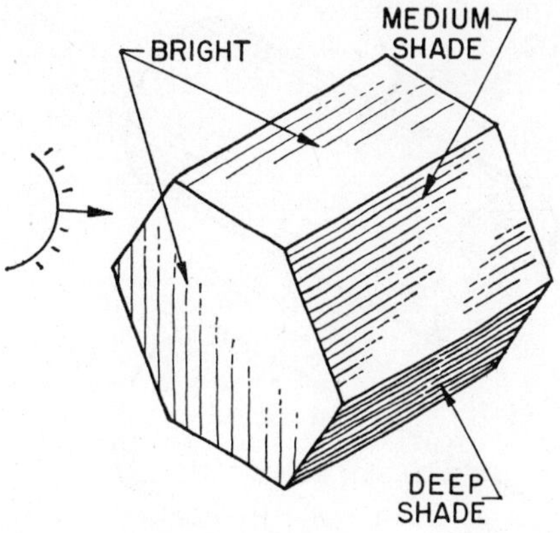

Figure 15-56
This shows line shading on flat surfaces.

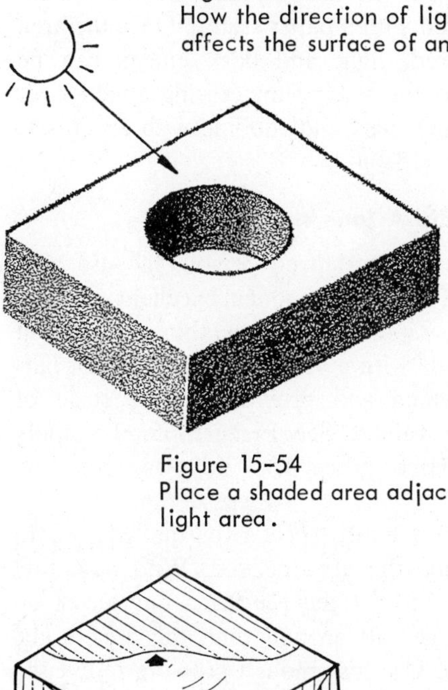

Figure 15-54
Place a shaded area adjacent to a light area.

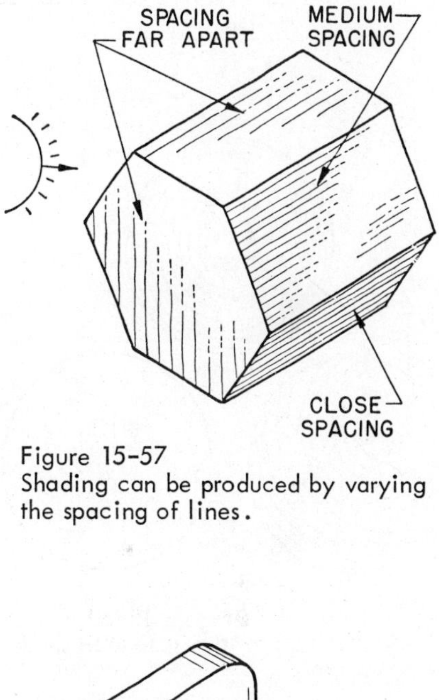

Figure 15-57
Shading can be produced by varying the spacing of lines.

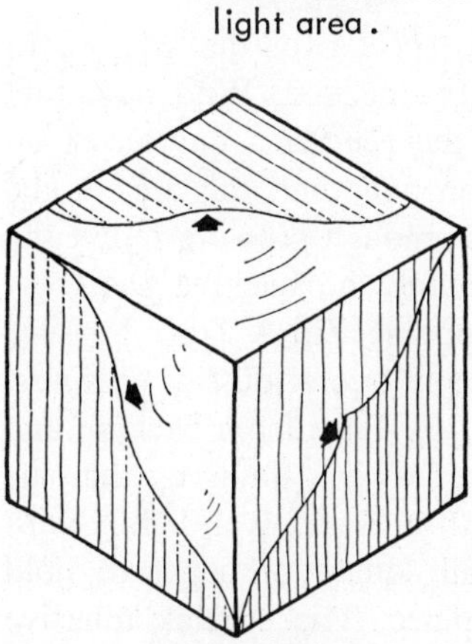

Figure 15-55
Sketch the outline of the shaded areas with a fine line.

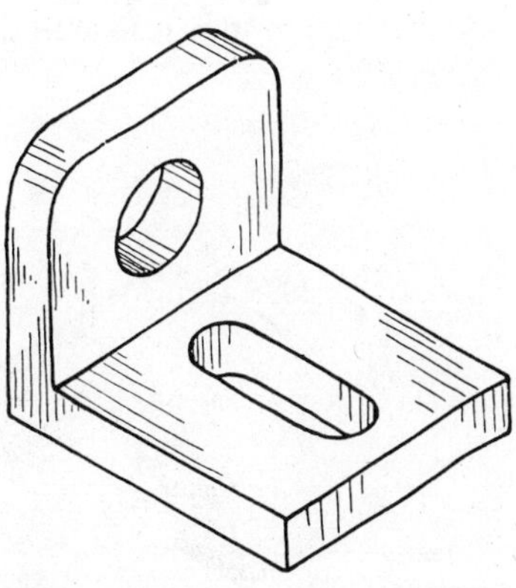

Figure 15-58
This shows the direction of lines for the best shading effects.

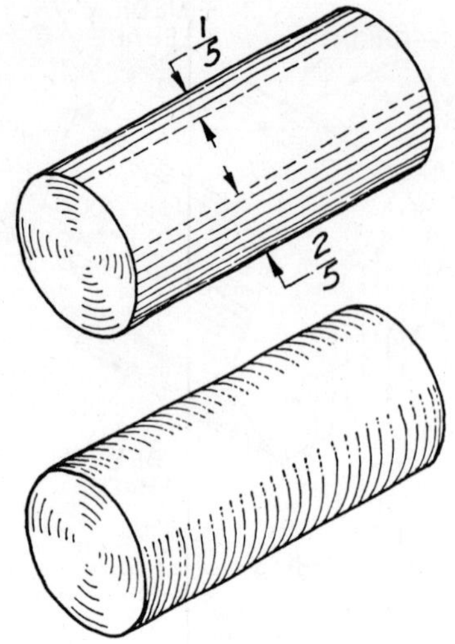

Figure 15-59
This is how a curved surface can be shaded.

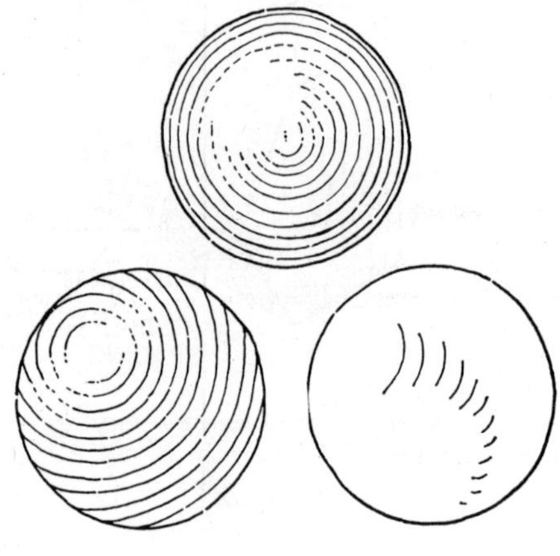

Figure 15-60
This is how to shade a sphere.

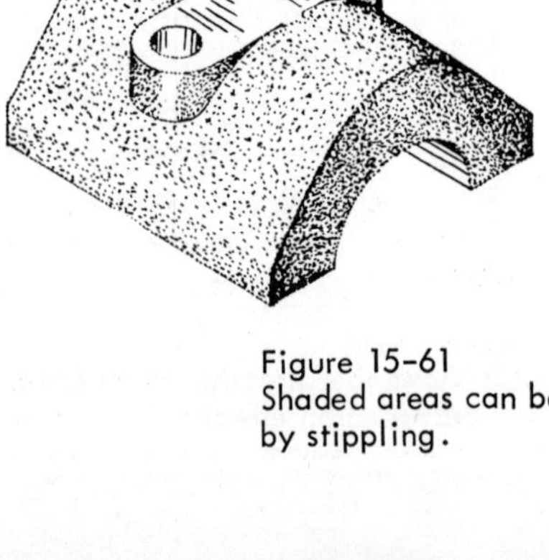

Figure 15-61
Shaded areas can be achieved by stippling.

Fig. 15-59. Spheres are shaded by sketching a series of concentric circles, as illustrated in Fig. 15-60.

Stippling. Stippling is another method which can be used to produce shaded areas. This method consists of covering the surface to be shaded with a series of dots made with the point of a pencil. For dark areas the dots are placed closer together, and for light areas the dots are spaced widely apart. See Fig. 15-61. Although stippling produces a pleasing appearance, the process is much slower than line shading.

Broad stroke and smudge shading. Good shading results can be achieved by rubbing the desired areas with the flattened side of the lead pencil. See Fig. 15-62.

If a smudge effect is desired, as shown in Fig. 15-63, the broad pencil strokes should be rubbed with a paper stump. Once the area is covered, light and dark effects can be achieved by placing an erasing shield over the shaded part and rubbing with an eraser. See Fig. 15-64.

15.31 Zip-A-Tone shading

For the inexperienced person, the use of a Zip-A-Tone will produce excellent shading results. Zip-A-Tone is a thin transparent film made with a variety of line and dot patterns which will provide a wide scale of shading values. See Fig. 15-65. To apply Zip-A-Tone proceed as follows (see Fig. 15-66):

1 Place entire sheet over the artwork to determine the area needed. With a cutting needle, cut out the acetate a quarter of an inch larger all around than the area to be covered. Use just enough pressure to cut the acetate only, leaving the backing sheet intact. Before removing Zip-A-Tone be sure artwork is clean and free of dust or erasures.

2 Remove Zip-A-Tone from backing and place directly on drawing, lining up the pattern squarely with artwork. Rub lightly with fingertip or small square of paper to hold temporarily in place. The special adhesive on Zip-A-Tone does not seize the paper; the pattern can be moved into position quickly and accurately.

3 Use the cutting needle to cut out the pattern exactly where it is wanted. The surplus Zip-A-Tone is easily removed without damaging the drawing or tracing. The pattern may now be bonded permanently with the drawing by placing a sheet of paper over the acetate and rubbing it thoroughly with a bone or hardwood burnisher.

15.32 Inking

The original working drawing is never sent to the shop. Instead reproductions, either blueprints or whiteprints, are made and distributed to the various departments involved in the fabrication of the product. In most instances the original drawings are prepared in pencil. Rarely is ink used. The only exception is when the original must be preserved for a long time and is not subjected to frequent modifications. However inking is often used in making drawings or sketches for illustration purposes.

Preparation of an ink tracing is accomplished by placing a tracing medium, usually a transparent cloth, on the original pencilled drawing and tracing over it in ink. Sometimes the pencilling is done directly on the tracing medium and then inked.

The two main types of ruling pens used for inking are the wide blade and narrow blade. See Fig. 15-67. Both are available with several styles of handles. The wide blade pens, often called detail pens (*B*), are best for drawing long heavy lines, and the narrow blade (*A*) for inking medium and fine lines. The contour pen (*C*) is designed for tracing freehand curves such as contours on maps. The railroad pen (*D*) is used to draw two parallels, particularly to represent railroad tracks or highways on maps.

The blades or nibs of ruling pens are opened and closed by a thumb screw. Adjustment of this screw controls the width of the lines.

15.33 Filling a ruling pen

To fill a ruling pen, remove the stopper from the ink bottle by a turning motion. Close the nibs of the pen and pass the dropper end of the bottle cap or the point of an ink cartridge

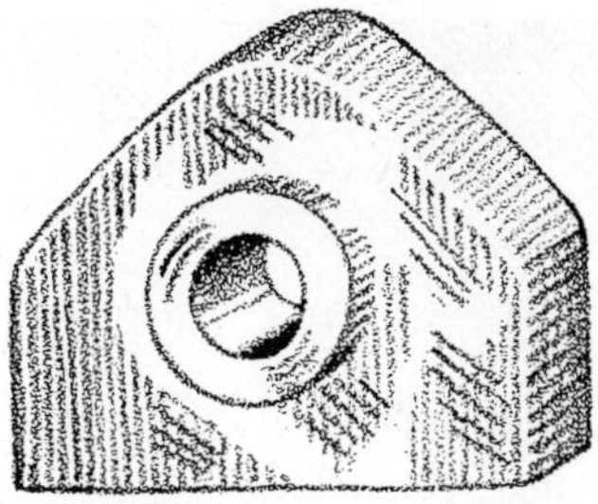

Figure 15-62
This is an example of broad stroke shading.

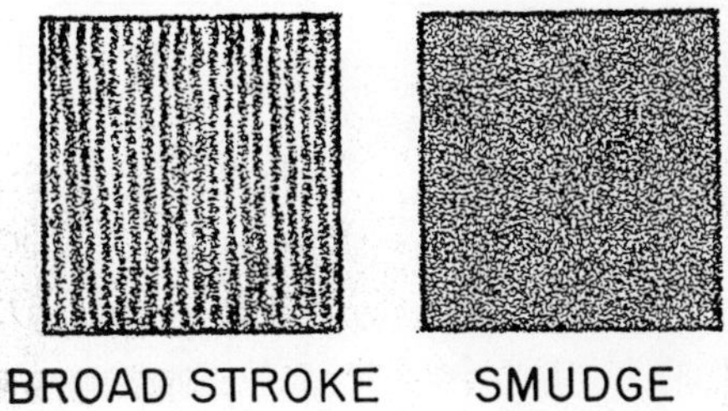

Figure 15-63
Broad strokes are first drawn and then rubbed to produce smudge shading.

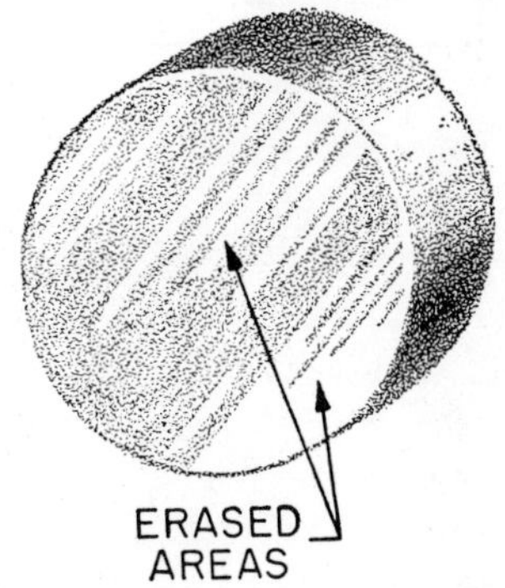

Figure 15-64
Erasing in a shaded area produces light spots.

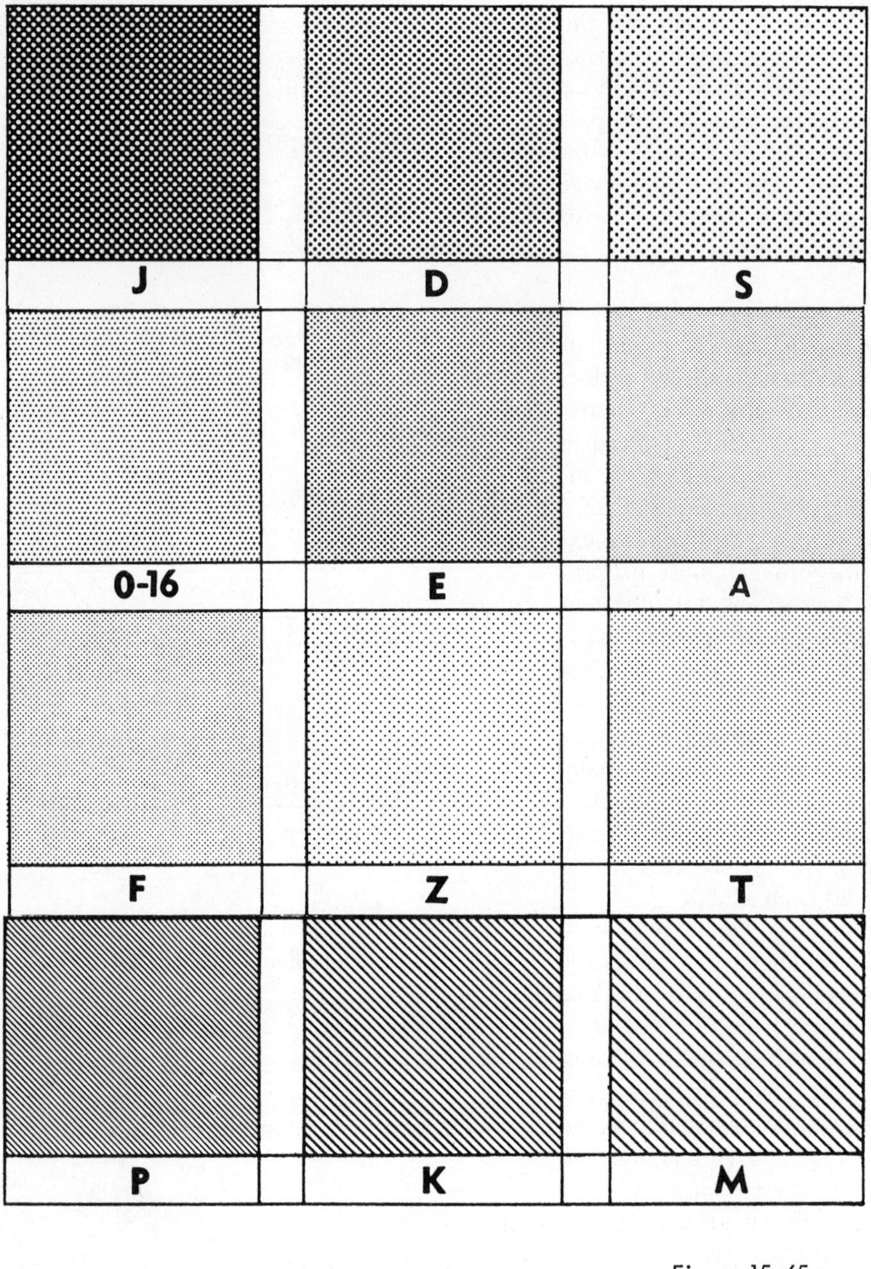

Figure 15-65
A variety of shading effects can be produced with Zip-A-Tone. Letters are for purposes of identity.

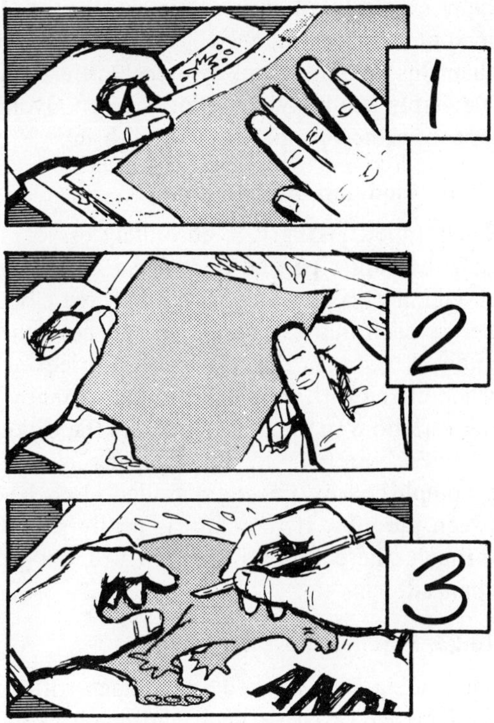

Figure 15-66
Zip-A-Tone should be applied in this manner. Para-Tone Incorporated

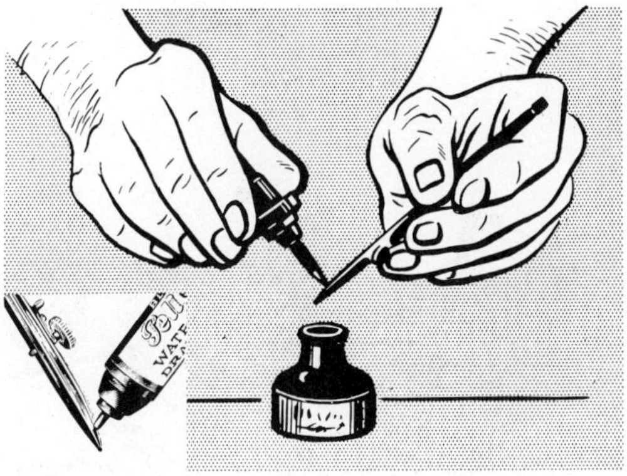

Figure 15-68
Do not drop more than 1/4" of ink in the pen.

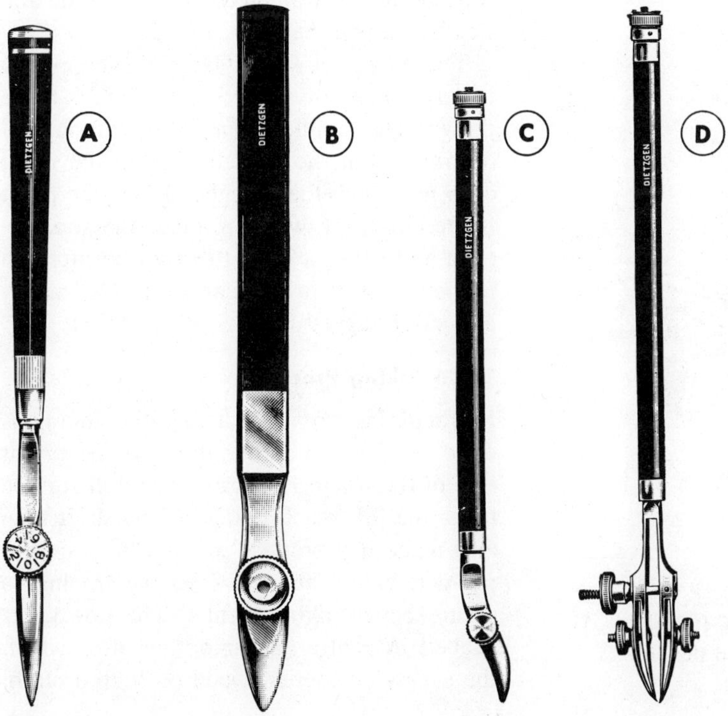

Figure 15-67
Common types of ruling pens.

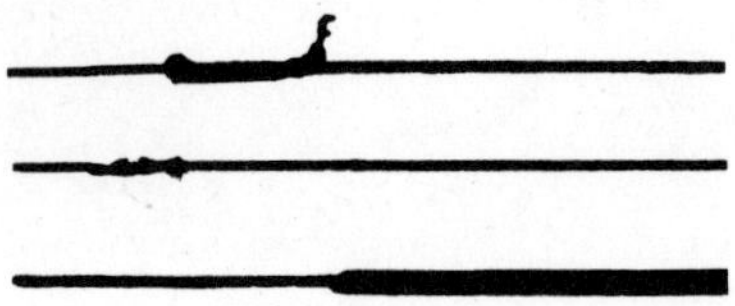

Figure 15-69
If the ink is left to dry between the nibs of the pen, irregular or rough lines will result.

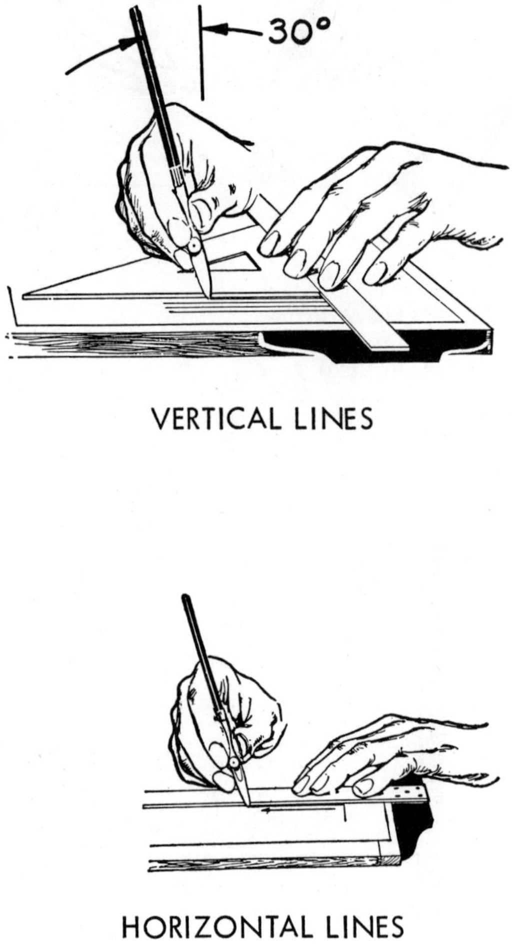

Figure 15-70
Hold the ruling pen much like a pencil. Incline it in the direction the line is drawn.

between the blades so not more than 1/4 inch of ink flows in. See Fig. 15-68. If more than this amount of ink is used blotting will inevitably result. While filling the pen, avoid smearing the outside surfaces with ink.

15.34 Cleaning the ruling pen

To do good inking it is absolutely essential that the ruling pen be kept clean. The pen should always be wiped with a lint free cloth before each filling. The ink should never be allowed to dry in the pen because dried ink when mixed with fresh ink will cause annoying variations in the flow of ink and the width of lines. See Fig. 15-69. Cleaning is best accomplished by passing a folded cloth between the nibs. If the cloth is gently pulled through, the setting of the pen will not be changed.

15.35 Holding the ruling pen

The ruling pen is used in contact with a straightedge or curve. It is held much like a pencil, that is, by the thumb and forefinger with the blade resting against the second finger. The adjusting screw should be pointed outward from the straightedge. The third and fourth fingers are positioned so as to slide along the straightedge to help guide and steady the pen. See Fig. 15-70.

The ruling pen should be inclined approximately 30° in the direction the line is to be drawn. The handle should also lean slightly outward from the straightedge so the point does not touch the straightedge. If the point is too close, ink will run under the straightedge and cause a blot. Forcing the nibs too far inward will prevent an even flow of ink and cause ragged lines. See Fig. 15-71.

15.36 Inking Procedure

In preparing an ink tracing, the inking is done on the dull rather than on the bright side of the tracing medium. The dull surface takes the ink much better. Many draftsmen also make it a practice to sprinkle a special powder, called pounce, over the tracing to secure better inking results. The powder is rubbed in gently and smoothly after which the excess powder is wiped off with a cloth.

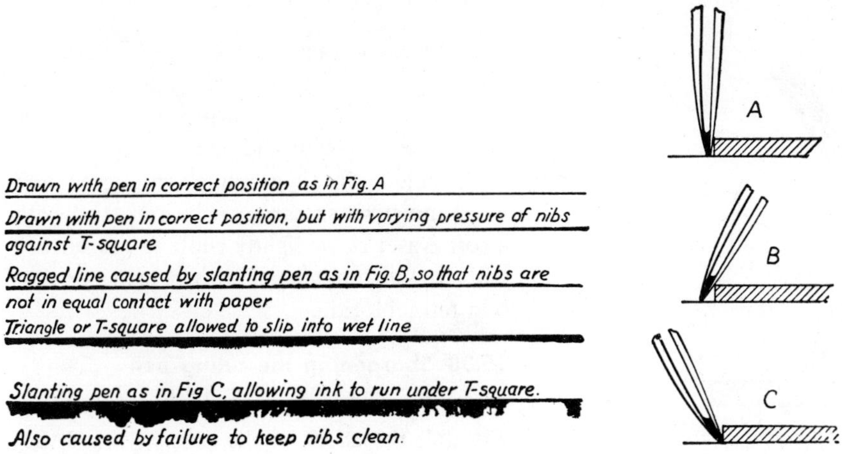

Drawn with pen in correct position as in Fig. A
Drawn with pen in correct position, but with varying pressure of nibs against T-square
Ragged line caused by slanting pen as in Fig. B, so that nibs are not in equal contact with paper
Triangle or T-square allowed to slip into wet line
Slanting pen as in Fig C, allowing ink to run under T-square.
Also caused by failure to keep nibs clean.
A
B
C

Figure 15–71
Do not get the point too near or too far away from the straightedge.
Eugene Dietzgen Co.

To do a satisfactory job of inking, certain precautions and procedures should be observed. The following are particularly significant:

1 In adjusting the pen, always run test lines on the margin of the tracing cloth or on a scrap of the same material.

2 After a few lines are drawn, a particle of dirt or dried ink will often lodge on the outside of the nibs of the pen. This will cause the width of the line to increase or make it impossible to draw fine lines. To remedy this, rub the sides of the tip on a piece of paper or clean the nibs and then refill with ink.

3 Watch the quantity of ink in the pen. Never start a line if the amount of ink is judged to be insufficient to complete the line. Not enough ink will cause the line to split at the end. However, too much ink will cause excessive flow.

4 Use extreme care in removing the straightedge from a heavily drawn line. Even the slightest movement towards the line may cause the ink to smear.

5 Do not try to ink corners and intersections until the previously made lines have dried completely, otherwise blotting may result.

6 Center the ink lines over the pencil lines to ensure proper junctures at tangent points of arcs, circles and irregular curves.

7 Use a definite procedure in inking a drawing. The following order of inking will produce more uniform lines and avoid unnecessary delay in waiting for lines to dry:

(a) Arcs of circles
(b) Small circles
(c) Large circles
(d) Irregular curves
(e) Horizontal straight lines
(f) Vertical straight lines
(g) Slanting straight lines
(h) Section lines
(i) Dimensions and arrows
(j) Notes and title
(k) Border

15.37 Erasing an ink tracing

Removal of lines, dirt or smudges from the tracing medium can be achieved successfully if proper care is used. Erasing should be done with the tracing resting on a hard smooth surface such as a triangle. A soft eraser is used and the erasing action must be gentle to prevent generation of heat. An erasing shield should be used to prevent the washing out of adjacent lines. After the ink is removed, the erased surface should be rubbed with a clean fingertip or bone burnisher. A surface cleaned in this way will take ink as well as the original surface.

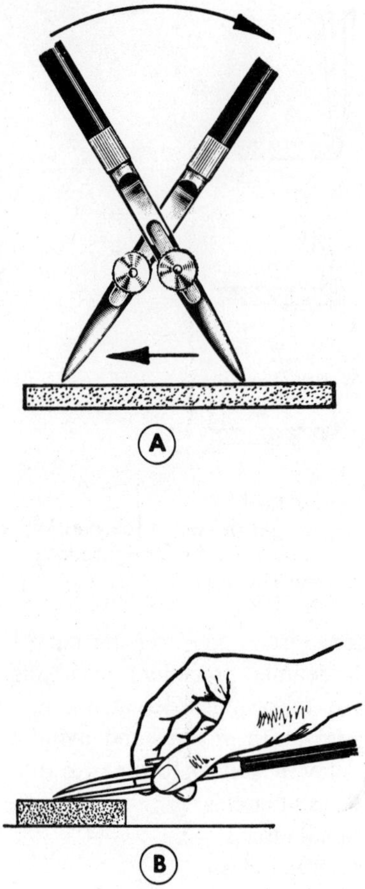

Figure 15-72
These two actions are required to sharpen a ruling pen correctly.

A knife or razor blade should never be used to remove errors. Such implements usually destroy the glazed surface and cause the ink to seep through and run.

Pencilled lines, graphite smudges, and hand moisture smears can be removed with a soft eraser or by lightly rubbing the surface with a cloth moistened with benzine or carbon tetrachloride.

15.38 Sharpening the ruling pen

Continuous use of a ruling pen will eventually dull the edges of the nibs so that it becomes difficult to produce fine lines or lines of uniform width. The pen must then be resharpened.

To re-sharpen a pen, close the nibs so they will just touch. Hold the pen vertically over a fine-grain Arkansas oil stone and swing it back and forth across the stone like a pendulum. This action equalizes the nibs and corrects their shape. See *A,* Fig. 15-72. The pressure against the stone must be kept uniform.

When the nibs are restored to their proper length and correct elliptical shape, hold the pen in a flat position as shown in *B,* Fig. 15-72, and slide it back and forth across the stone with a rolling motion. Test the pen occasionally by filling it with ink and drawing test lines. Avoid rounding the point too much since ink will run too freely from it. Also be careful not to get the point too sharp because a sharp point will cut into the surface of the tracing medium.

15.39 Freehand pens

Several choices of pen points are available for freehand lettering and preparing illustrative drawings or sketches. For ordinary lettering and work requiring fine stroke lines, the fine steel points shown in Fig. 15-73 are used. These points are made in several different sizes to meet the requirements for different weight lines. Lettering is also done with ink lettering instruments described in Section 3.

Generally speaking, a pen point should not be too flexible. An overly flexible point

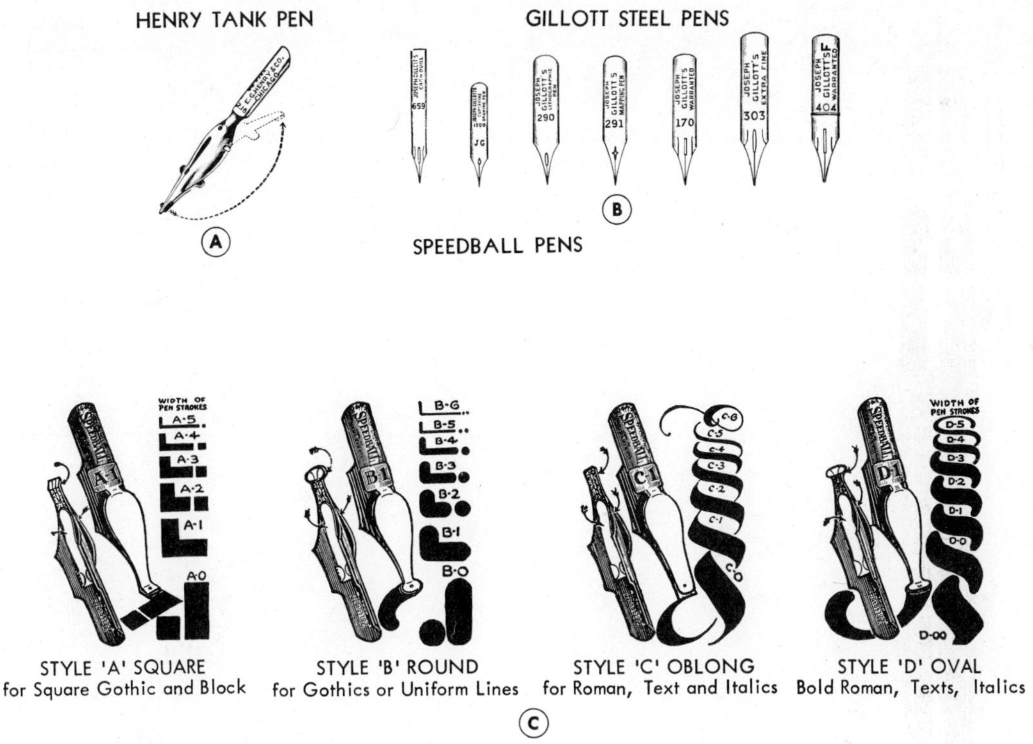

Figure 15-73
A draftsman should keep a wide assortment of pen points for different inking requirements.

makes it too difficult to produce uniform strokes. The ideal point is one that has just enough resistance from spreading out under normal hand pressure.

The Henry tank pen illustrated in *A* of Fig. 15-73 is particularly adapted for lettering purposes. This pen has a reservoir that holds ink above the point and allows it to flow evenly as the pen is used. A projecting device underneath the pen keeps the point from spreading out, thereby maintaining more uniform lines.

In Fig. 15-73, the Gillott, *B,* and Speedball pen points, *C,* are employed for a variety of straight-stroke inking as well as decorative lettering and artwork. Notice the different type of lines that can be produced with these pen points.

Freehand pens should be inked by placing a drop of ink on the underside of the pen with the stopper quill. It is not good practice to dip the pen in the ink bottle because too much ink will accumulate on the point and cause a blot on the first stroke. To keep the strokes uniform and the ink flowing smoothly the pen should be wiped frequently with a cloth.

The Rapidograph is still another type of pen developed for a variety of drafting functions. See Fig. 15-74. It can be used for ruling, lettering, tracing or writing with equal facility. The advantage of this pen is that it has a refillable ink cartridge with interchangeable point sections for different line widths.

Figure 15–74
This Rapidograph pen has a refillable ink cartridge and can be used for ruling and lettering.

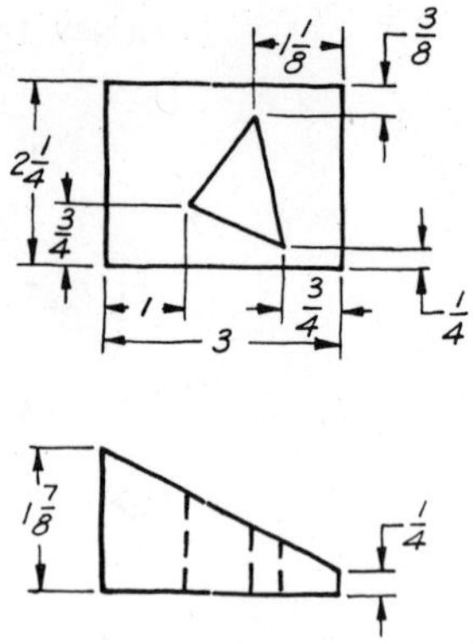

Figure 15–76
Problem 2.

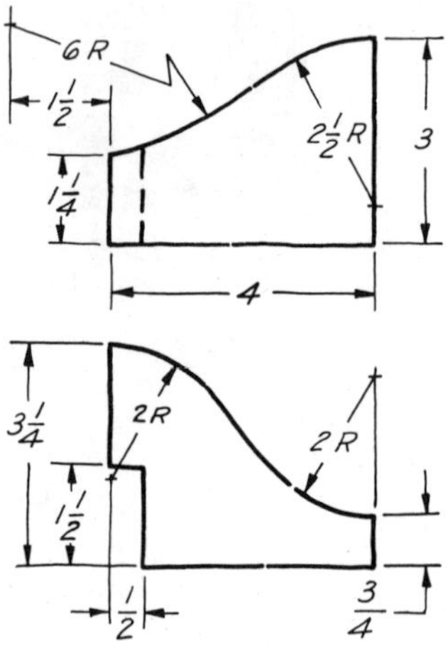

Figure 15–77
Problem 3.

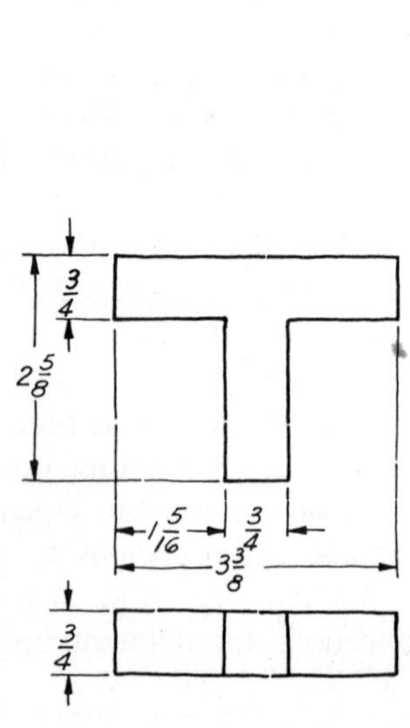

Figure 15–75
Problem 1.

Problems, section 15

1-10 Prepare isometric, dimetric or trimetric drawings of the problems shown in Figs. 15-75—15-84. Use proper shading effects and dimension completely.

11-22 Prepare oblique drawings of the problems shown in Figs. 15-85—15-96. Use proper shading effects and dimension completely.

23-28 Prepare perspective drawings of the problems shown in Figs. 15-97—15-102. Use proper shading effects.

29-30 Prepare an exploded drawing of Problem 14 or 19, Fig. 12-81, 12-86. Use proper shading effects.

31 Make a perspective drawing of the house shown in Fig. 15-103.

32 Make a perspective drawing of the house shown in Fig. 15-104.

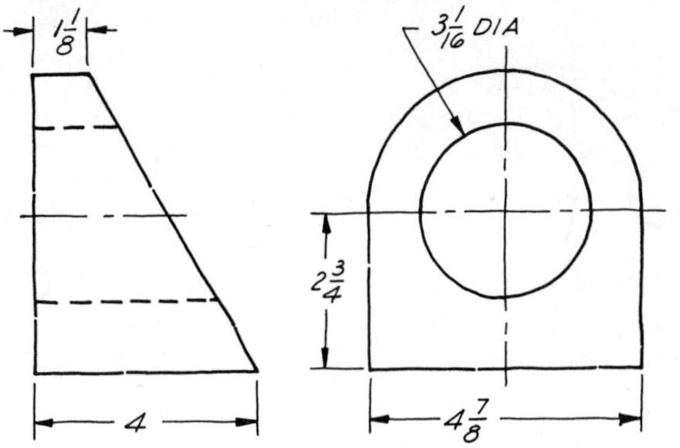

Figure 15-78
Problem 4.

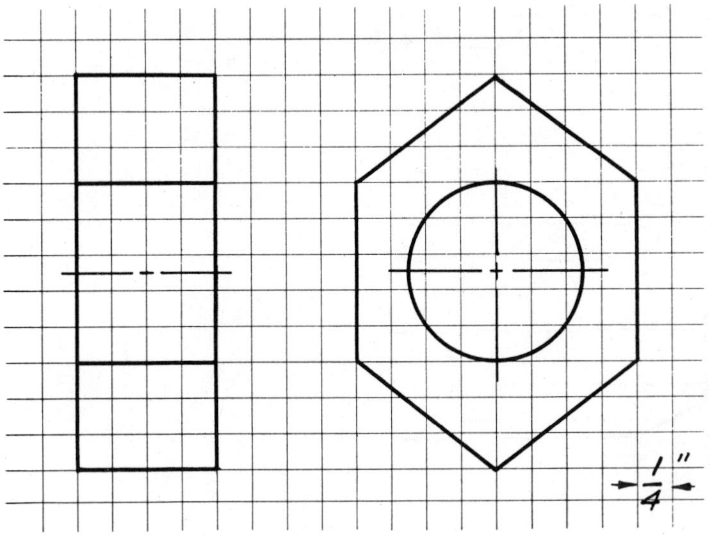

Figure 15-79
Problem 5.

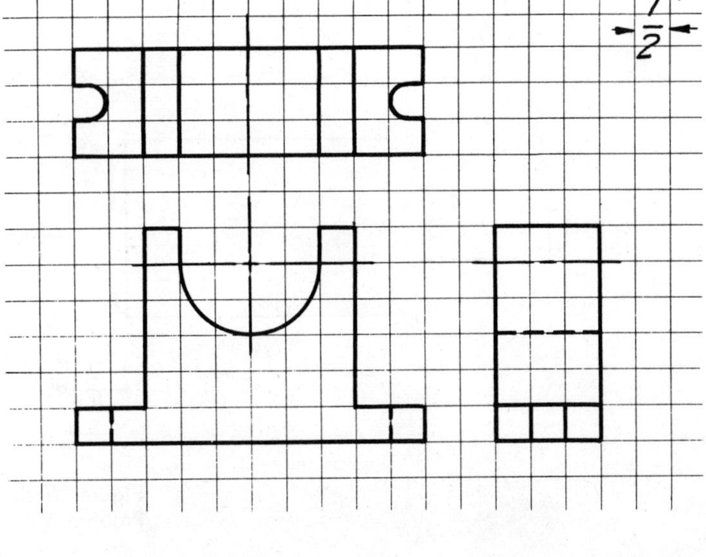

Figure 15-80
Problem 6.

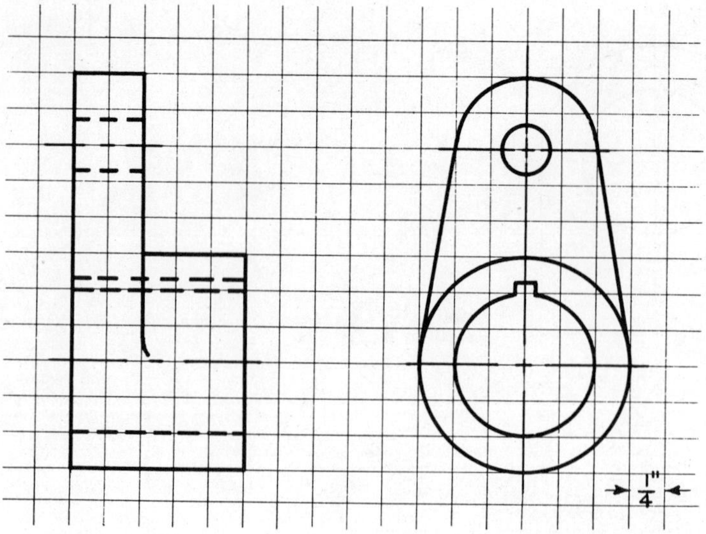

Figure 15-81
Problem 7.

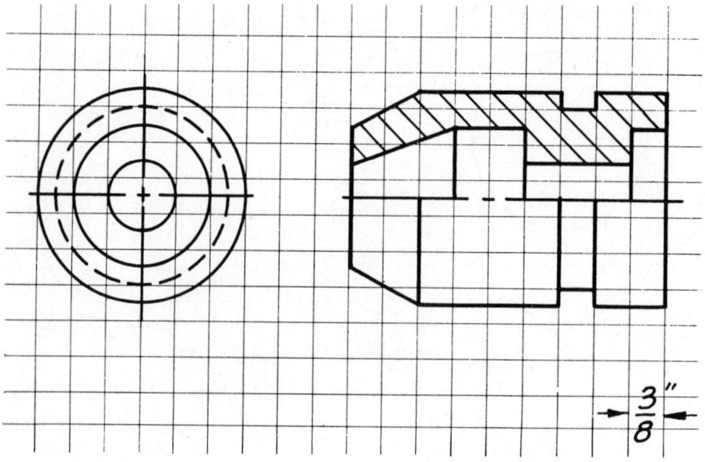

Figure 15-82
Problem 8.

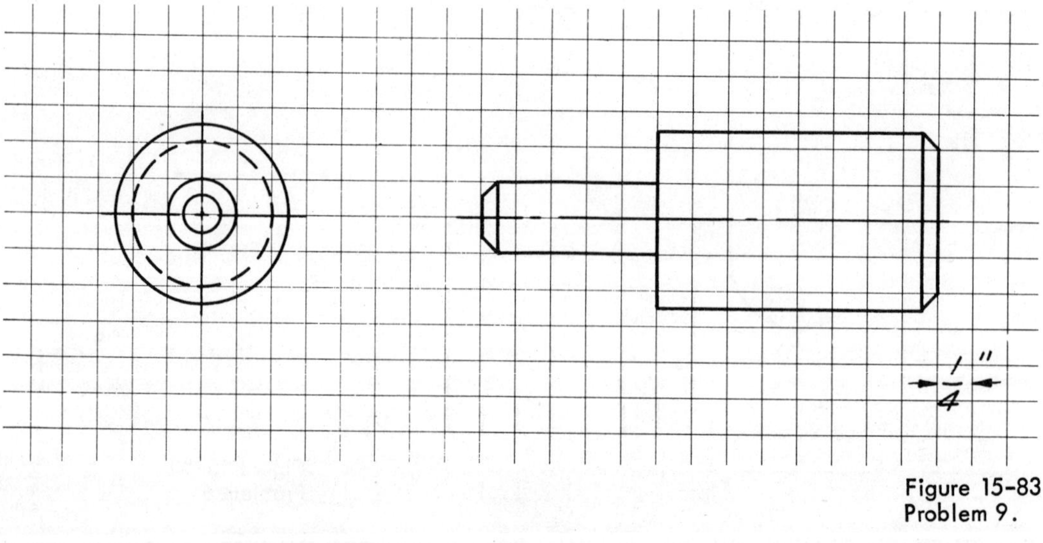

Figure 15-83
Problem 9.

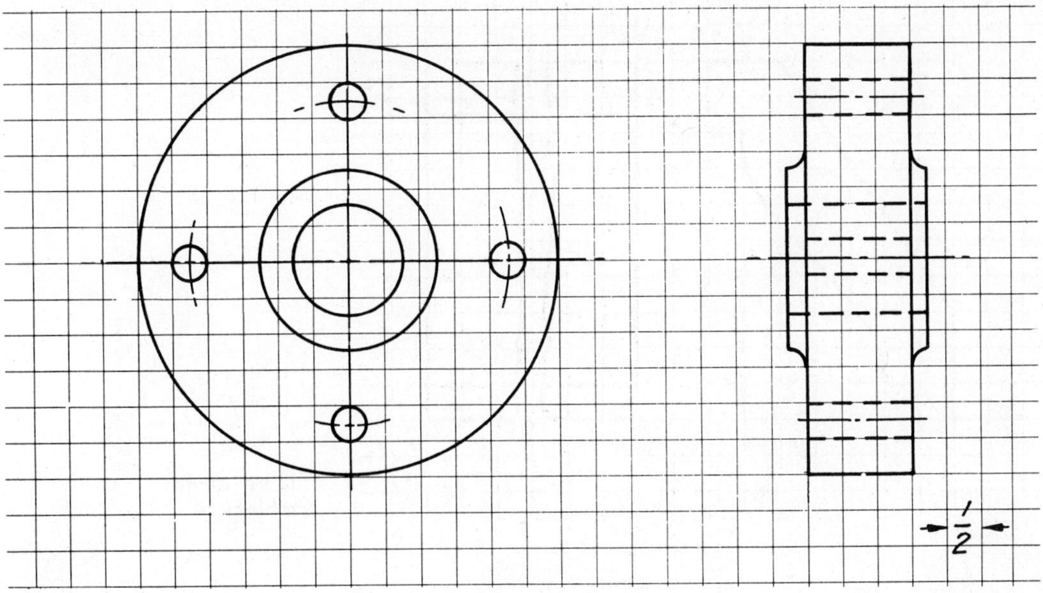

Figure 15-84
Problem 10.

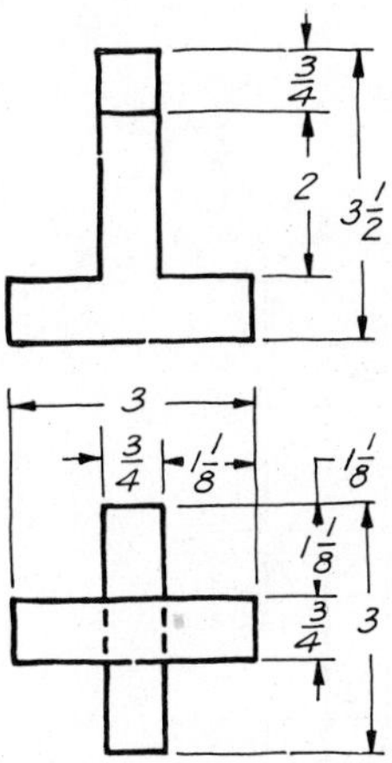

Figure 15-85
Problem 11.

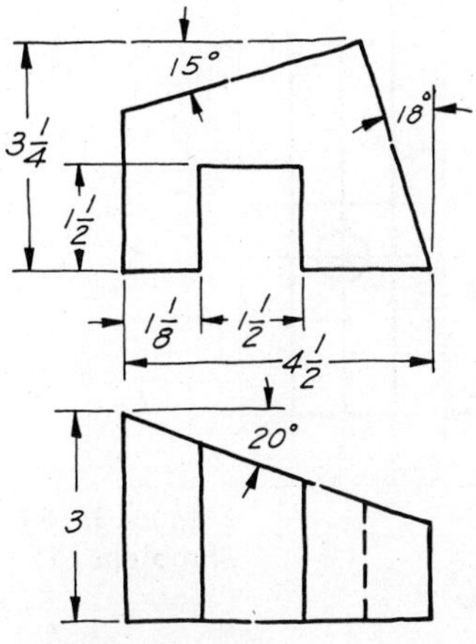

Figure 15-86
Problem 12.

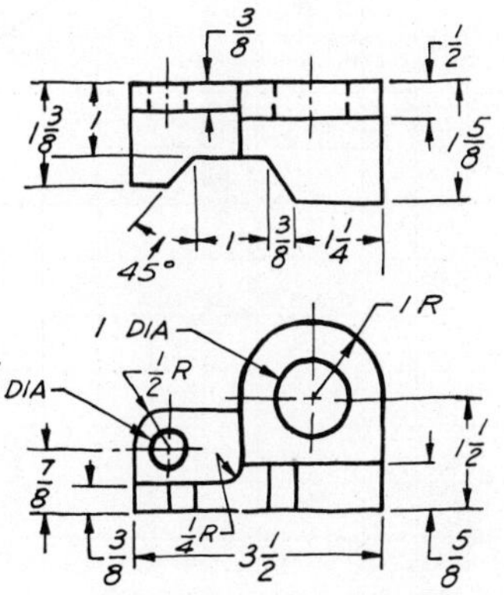

Figure 15-87
Problem 13.

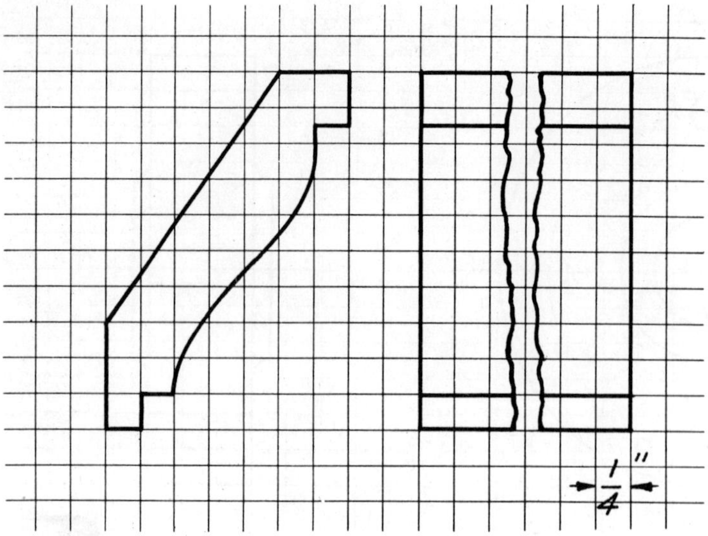

Figure 15-88
Problem 14.

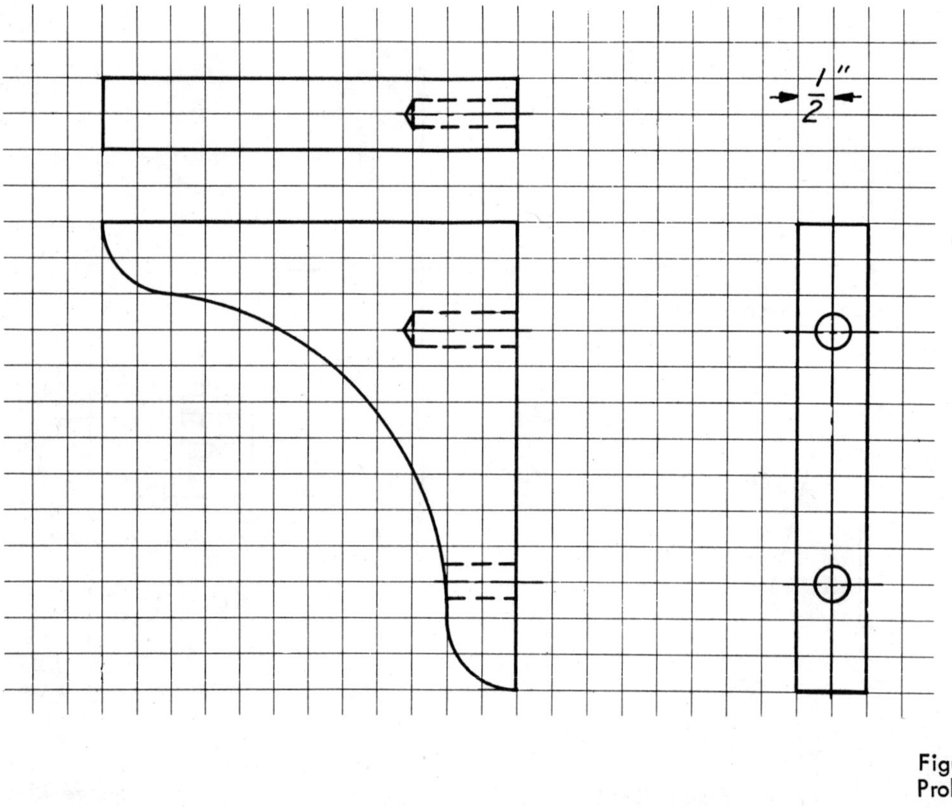

Figure 15-89
Problem 15.

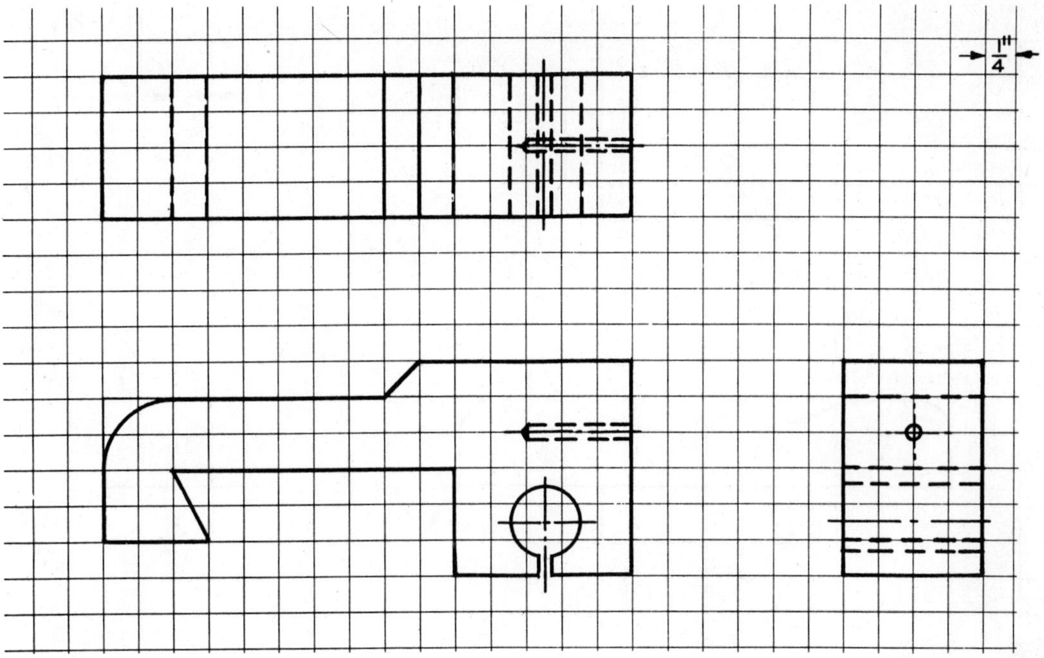

Figure 15-90
Problem 16.

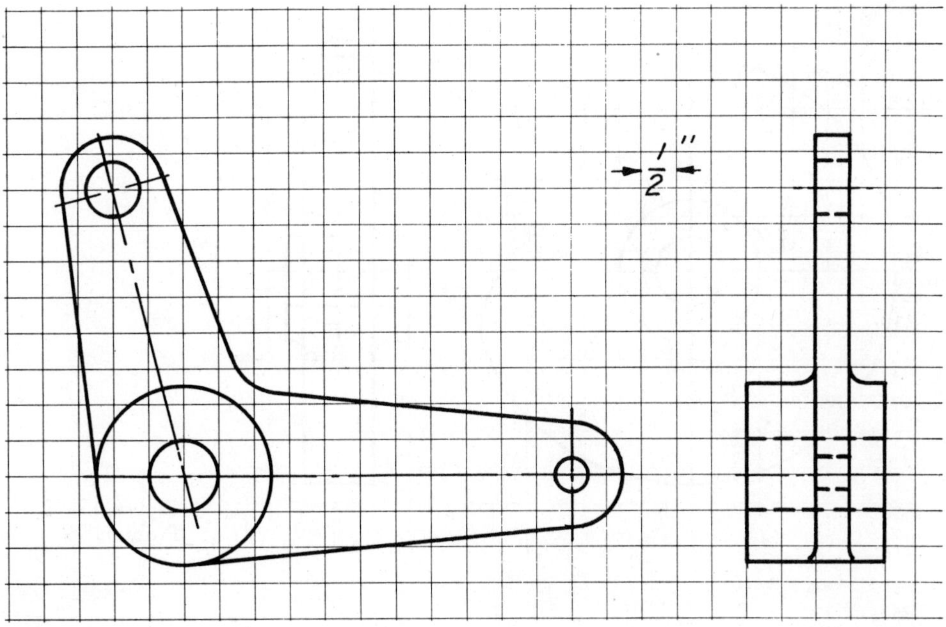

Figure 15-91
Problem 17.

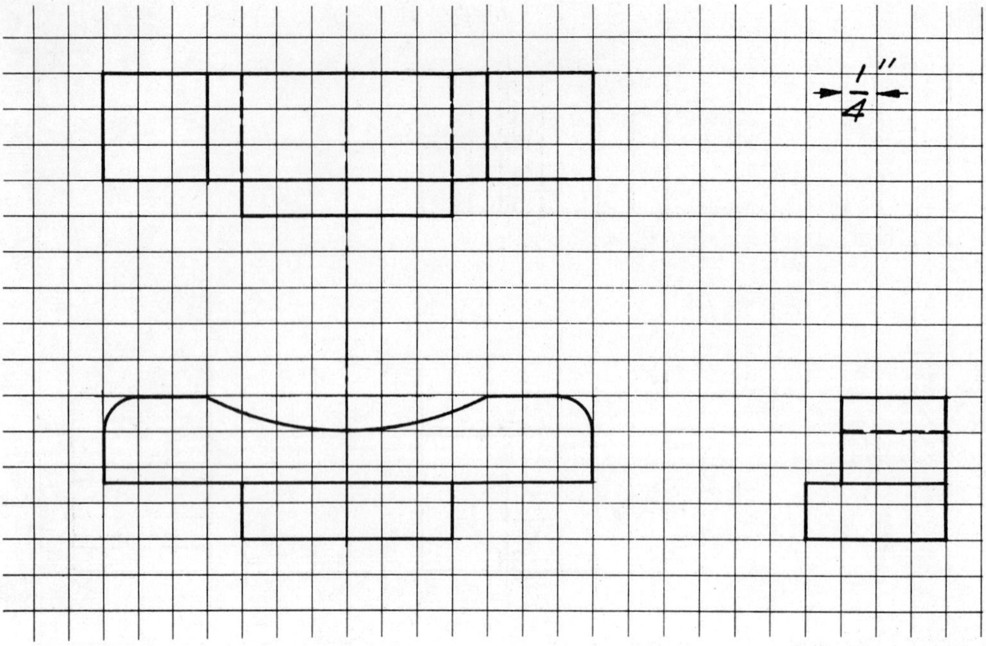

Figure 15-92
Problem 18.

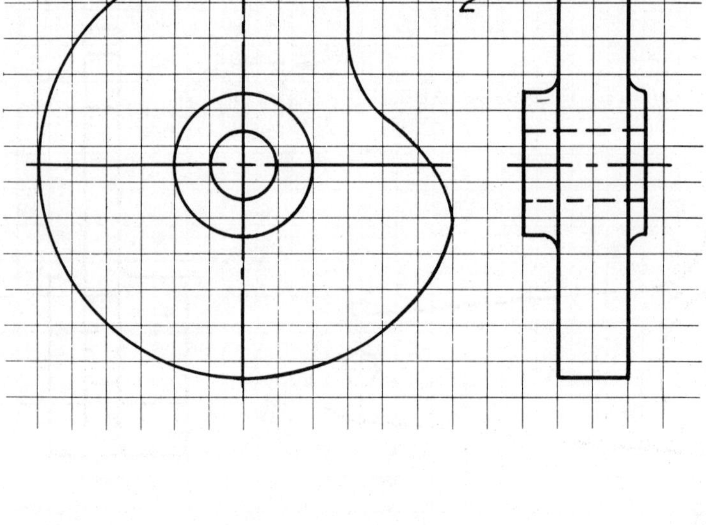

Figure 15-93
Problem 19.

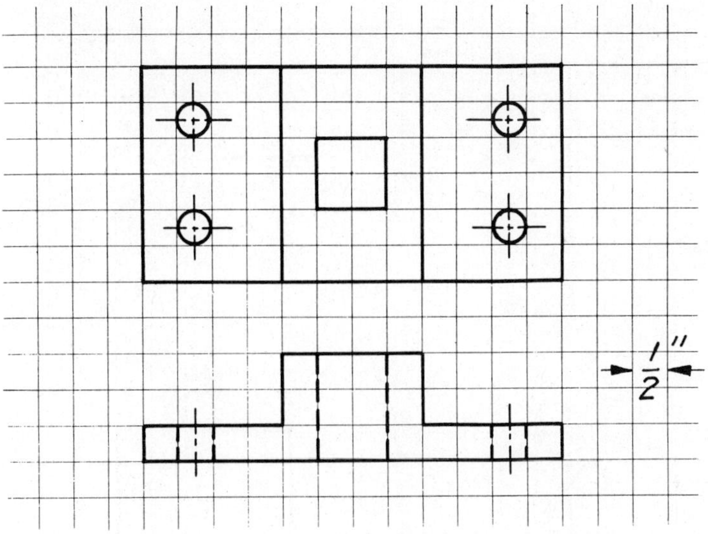

Figure 15-94
Problem 20.

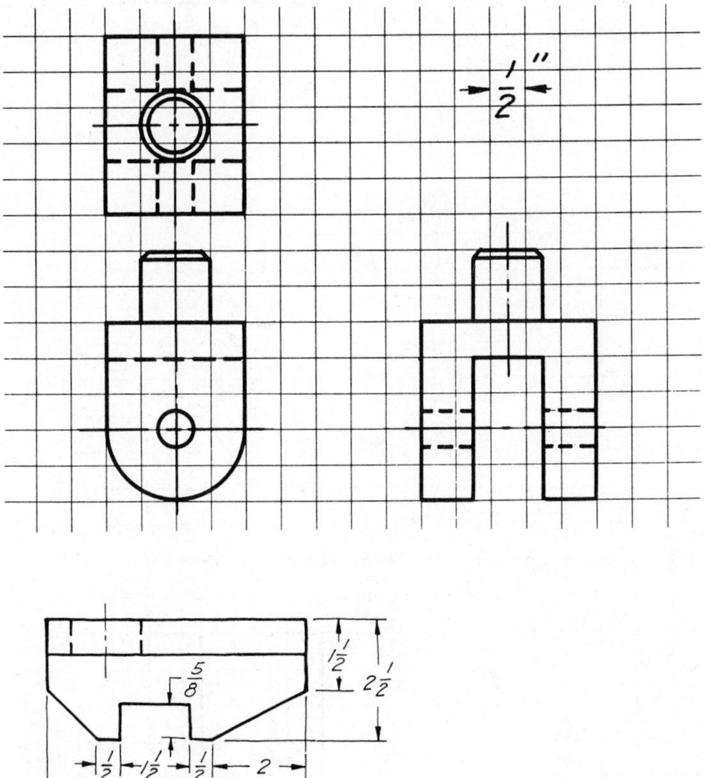

Figure 15-95
Problem 21.

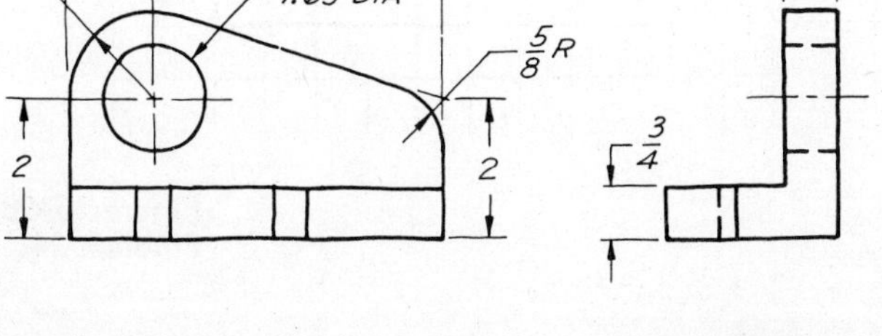

Figure 15-96
Problem 22.

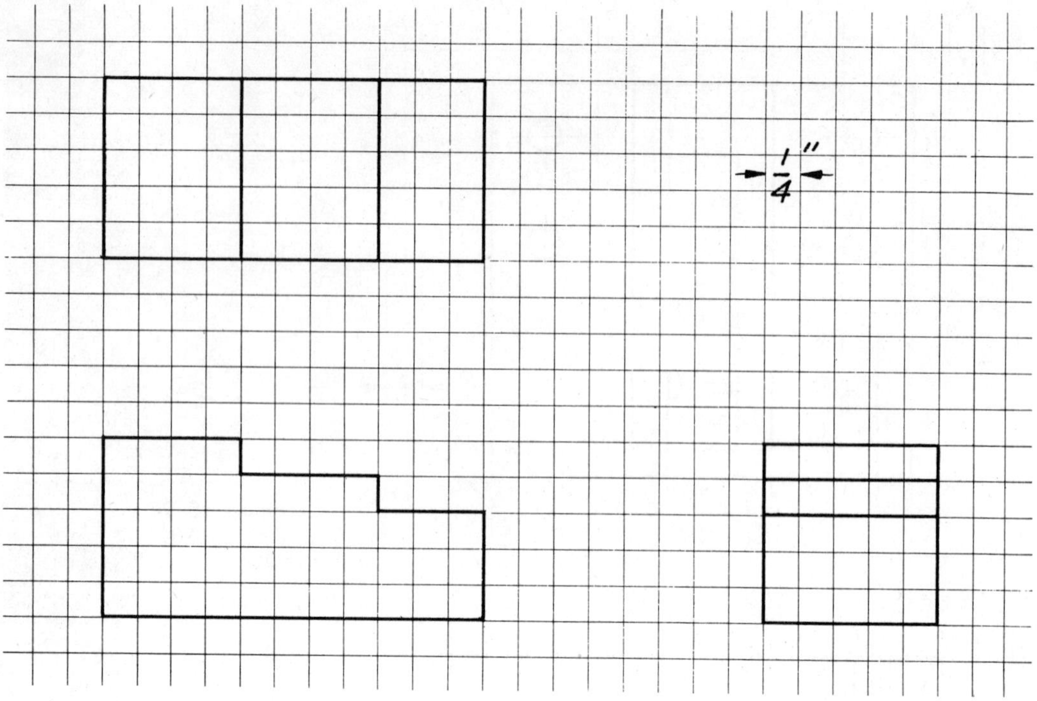

Figure 15-97
Problem 23.

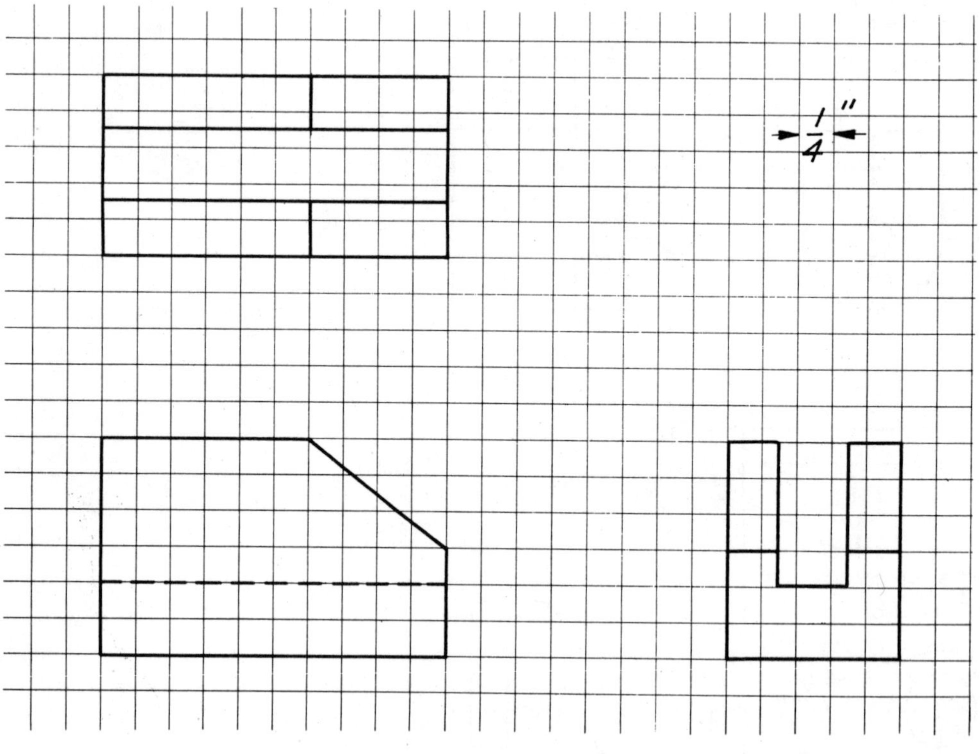

Figure 15-98
Problem 24.

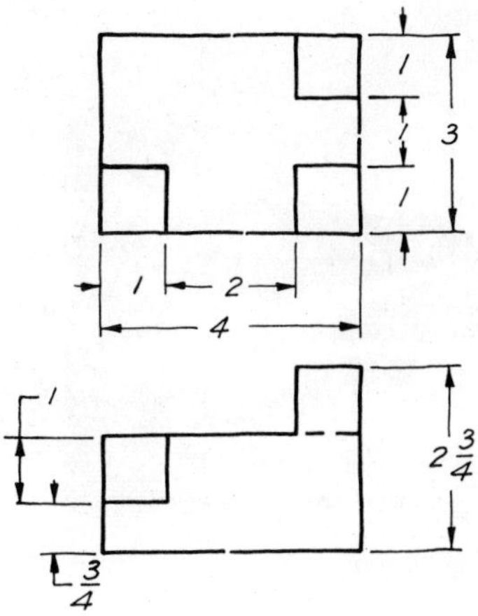

Figure 15-99
Problem 25.

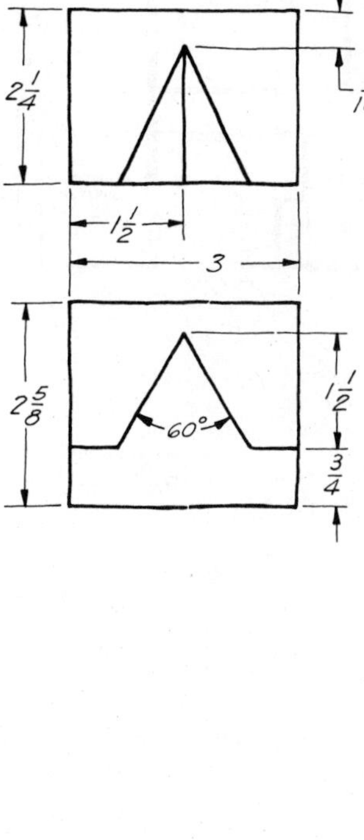

Figure 15-100
Problem 26.

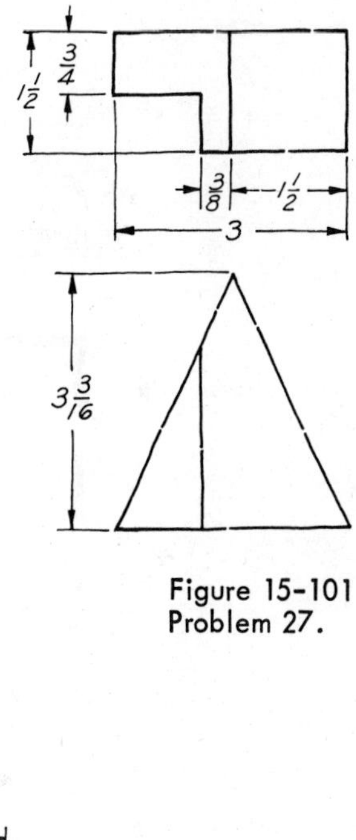

Figure 15-101
Problem 27.

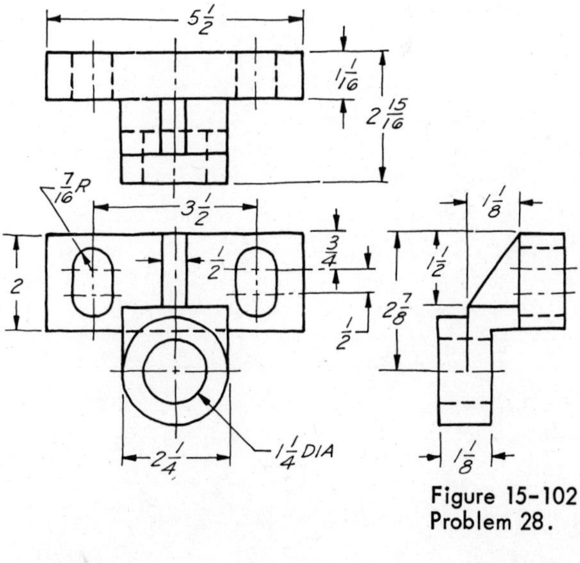

Figure 15-102
Problem 28.

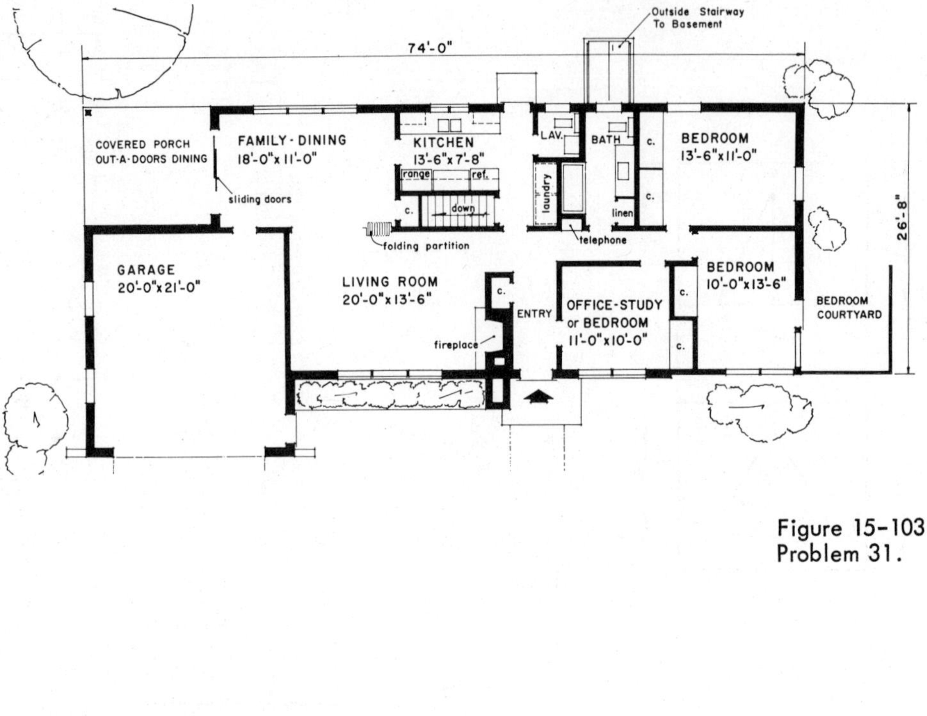

Figure 15-103
Problem 31.

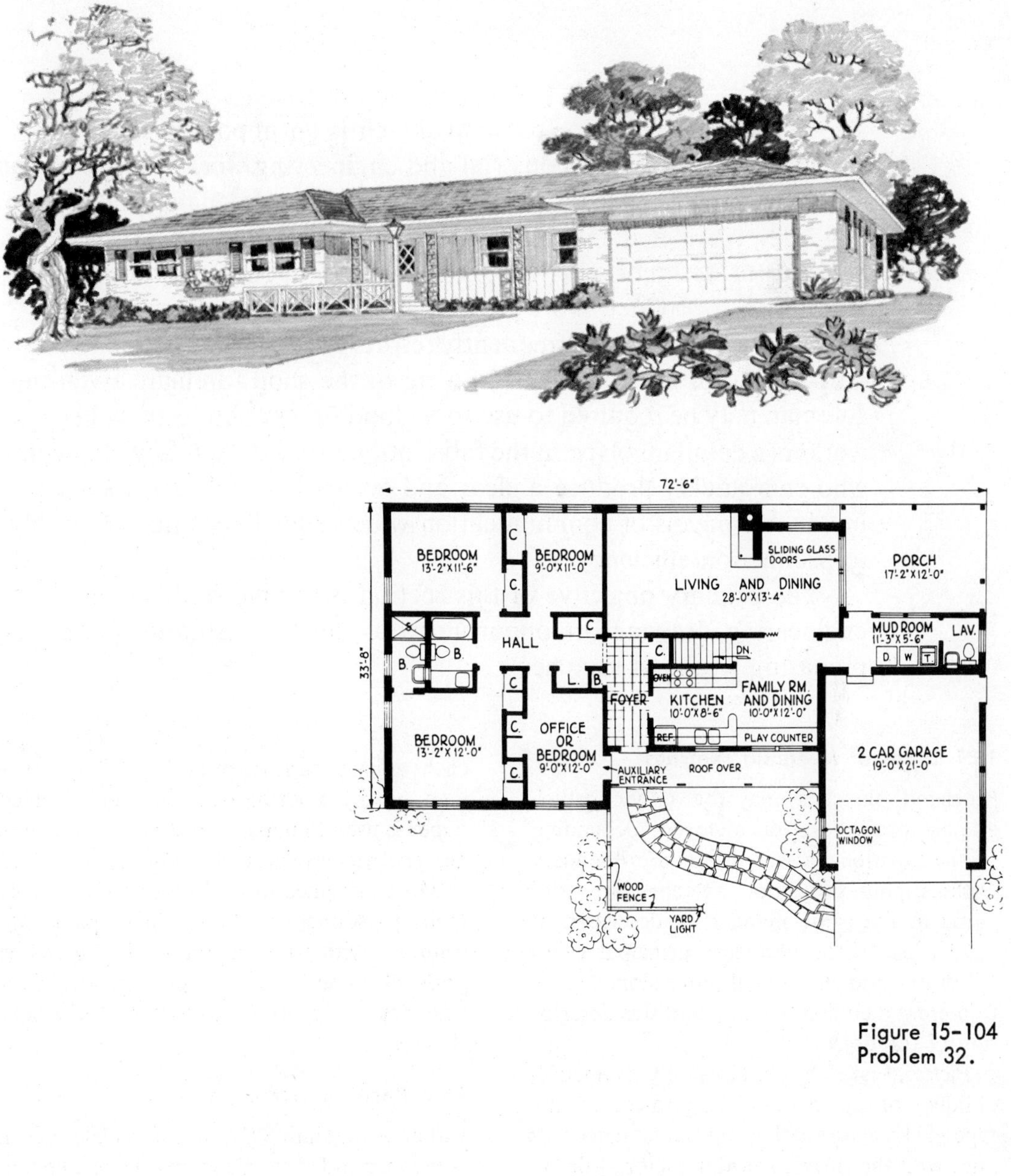

Figure 15-104
Problem 32.

Freehand sketching 16

The ability to produce a freehand sketch is an important asset to anyone associated with industrial and engineering work. Most ideas are usually expressed first through the medium of a freehand sketch and later translated into finished engineering drawings. Thus, the engineer or designer will very likely sketch out the preliminary features of a product and then pass them on to the draftsman for detailing. The draftsman frequently resorts to a freehand sketch to convey information of a mechanical drawing to the shop foreman. Even the foreman may be required to use some kind of a sketch to show his workers a detail involved in the fabrication process. Actually, any person who can quickly produce a clear and accurate sketch possesses an invaluable means of communication which contributes immeasurably to production efficiency.

The primary objective of this section is to give students of engineering drawing an opportunity to develop essential skills in preparing freehand sketches.

16.1 Types of freehand sketches

Freehand sketches may be either orthographic projections or pictorial, depending on the function for which they are intended. Orthographic projection sketches are prepared in the same manner as described in Section 5. All the necessary principal views are drawn and each detail dimensioned so as to present a complete shape and size description of the object.

Pictorial sketches are usually isometric, oblique, or perspective. Regardless of the type of sketch used, they are made in accordance with the rules governing pictorial drawing as discussed in Section 15.

16.2 Paper for sketching

Experienced draftsmen and engineers may use plain, unruled paper for sketching. However, it is usually better to sketch with cross-section paper, since it is easier to draw straight lines and secure good proportions. Cross-section paper also simplifies laying out exact sizes without employing a scale. Thus if the paper has grids of a consistent size, each square can represent 1/4 inch, 1/2 inch, or any other desired size. Special ruled paper is used to make isometric, oblique, and perspective drawings. See Fig. 16-1.

Most engineering departments supply their personnel with sketching pads imprinted with non-reproducible blue-line grids. Sketches can then be reproduced as ordinary white prints without the grid lines showing.

16.3 Position of the pencil

Either a medium (F) or soft (HB) pencil is recommended for sketching. Hold the pencil loosely about 1-1/2 to 2 inches away from the point, as in Fig. 16-2. As the pencil is used, rotate it slightly. This keeps the point sharp longer and makes clearer lines. The general practice is to slant the pencil at an angle of 50 to 60° from the vertical for drawing straight lines and about 30° for circles. See Fig. 16-3. Some draftsmen hold the pencil in a flat position for straight lines. In this position, the hand is guided on the back of the fingernails. See Fig. 16-4.

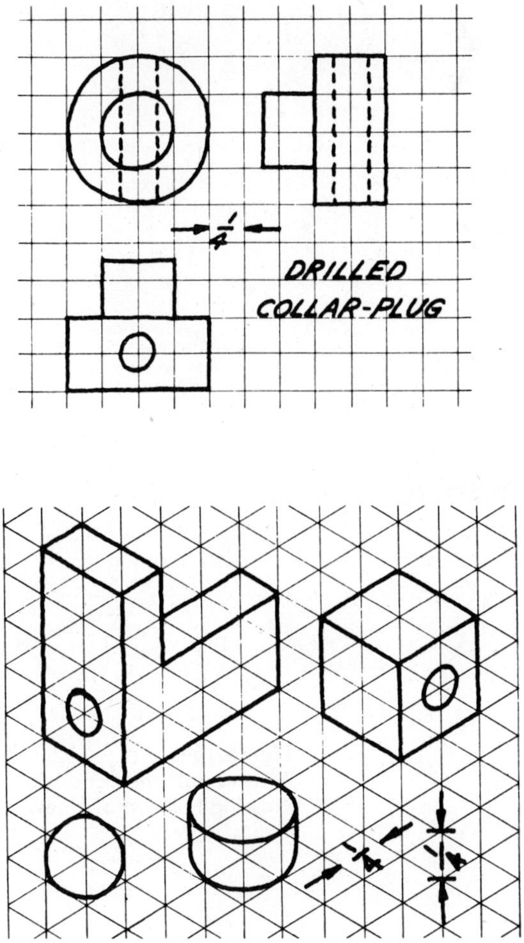

Figure 16-1
Note how squared paper simplifies making a sketch. U.S. Navy

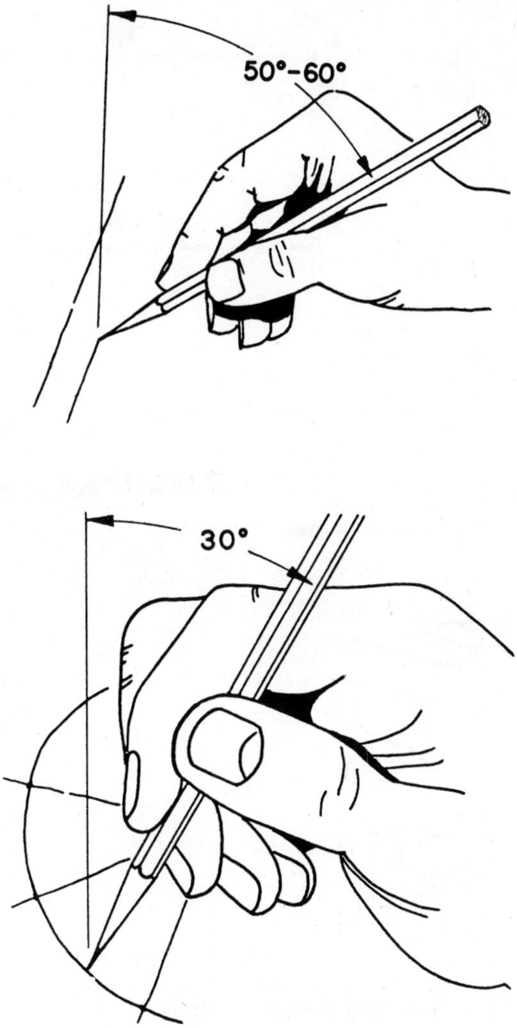

Figure 16-3
Slant the pencil at these angles for lines and circles.

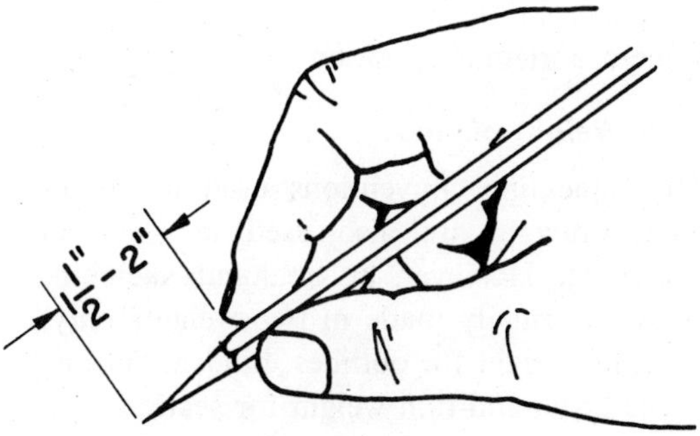

Figure 16-2
Hold the pencil in this position for most sketching purposes.

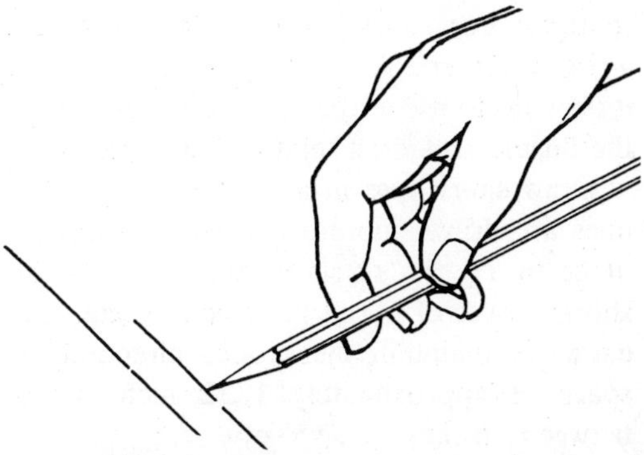

Figure 16-4
Some draftsmen prefer to hold the pencil in a flat position for making straight lines.

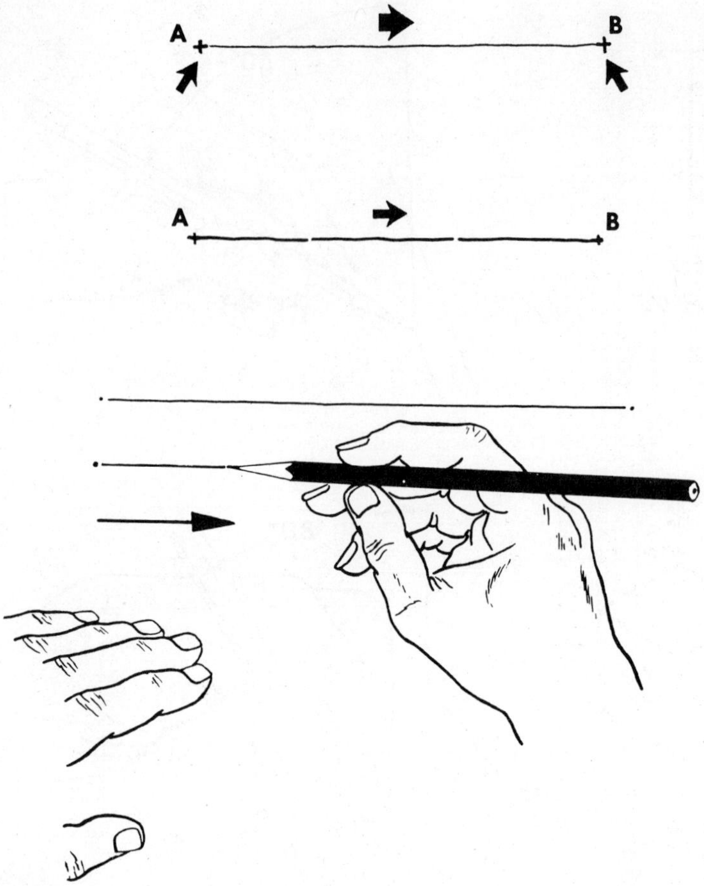

Figure 16-5
Always pull the pencil in drawing horizontal lines. U.S. Navy

16.4 Sketching horizontal lines

To draw horizontal lines, first mark off two points to indicate the position of the lines. See Fig. 16-5. Then sketch the line between the two points, moving the pencil from left to right. For short lines, use a finger and wrist movement. As the line becomes longer, it is better to use a free arm movement, since the fingers and wrist tend to bend the line.

Draw short lines in a single stroke. Long lines are drawn more accurately if they are made in a series of short strokes. By using short strokes of 1-1/2 to 2 inches long, it is easier to maintain the proper direction. A space of approximately 1/32 inch is left between strokes.

Always pull the pencil in sketching straight lines and curves. If the pencil is pushed, it may catch the surface of the paper and puncture or tear it.

16.5 Sketching vertical and slanted lines

Sketch vertical lines by starting at the top end of the line and moving the pencil downward. Slanted lines can be sketched better if the pencil is moved from left to right. See Fig. 16-6. Sometimes it is advisable to turn the paper so the vertical or slanted lines assume a horizontal position as in Fig. 16-7.

16.6 Weight of lines

The same line conventions used in instrument drawing are also used in freehand sketching. However in freehand sketching lines are usually made in two weights only: medium weight for outlines, hidden, cutting-plane lines; and thin weight for section, center, extension and dimension lines. The contrast in weight should not be made by degrees of darkness but by difference in thickness. This can be done by varying the

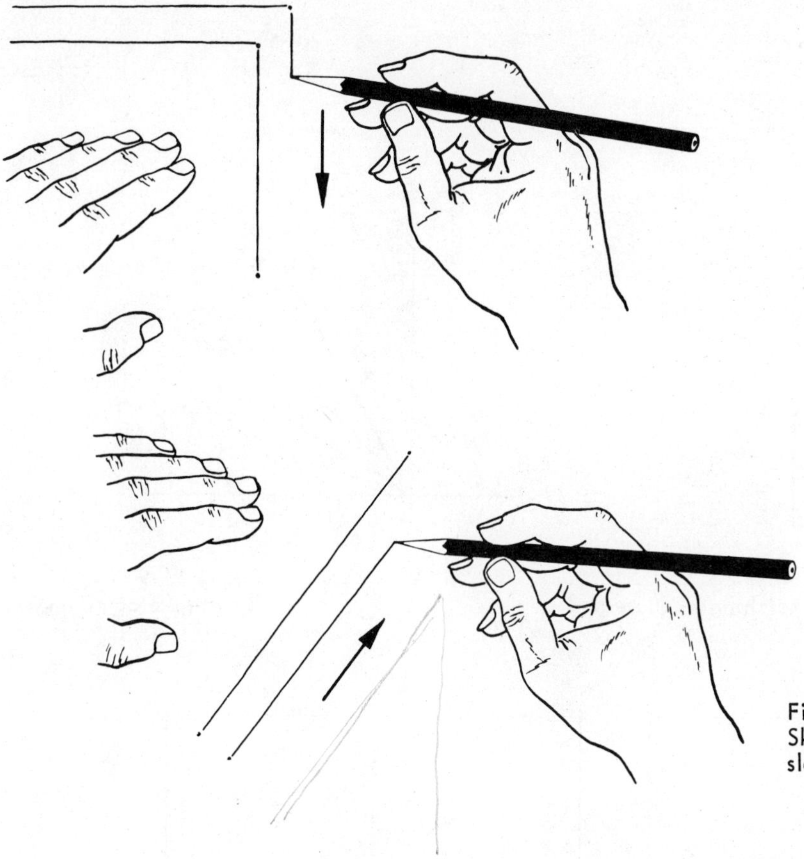

Figure 16-6
Sketching vertical and slanting lines. U.S. Navy

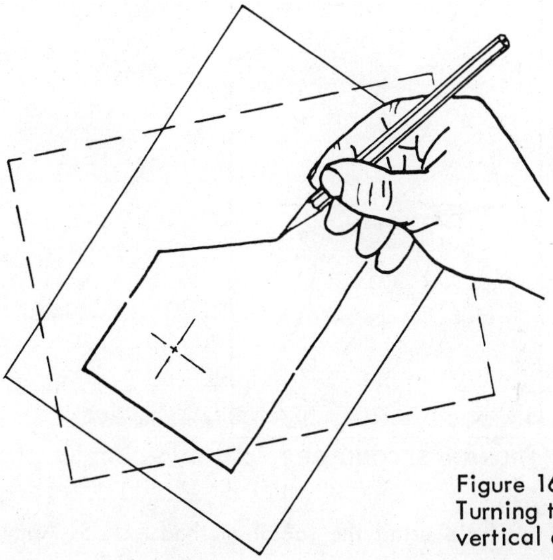

Figure 16-7
Turning the paper will simplify sketching vertical and slanted lines.

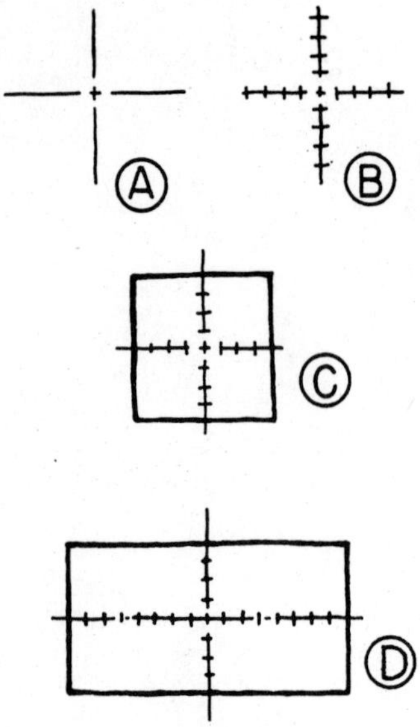

Figure 16-8
Procedure for sketching a square and a rectangle.

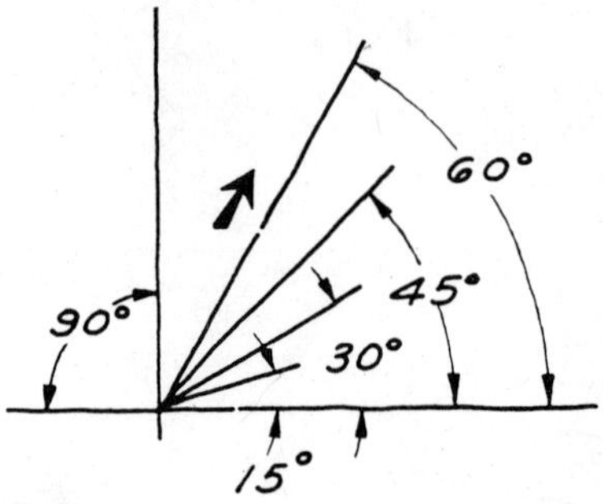

Figure 16-9
How to sketch an angle.

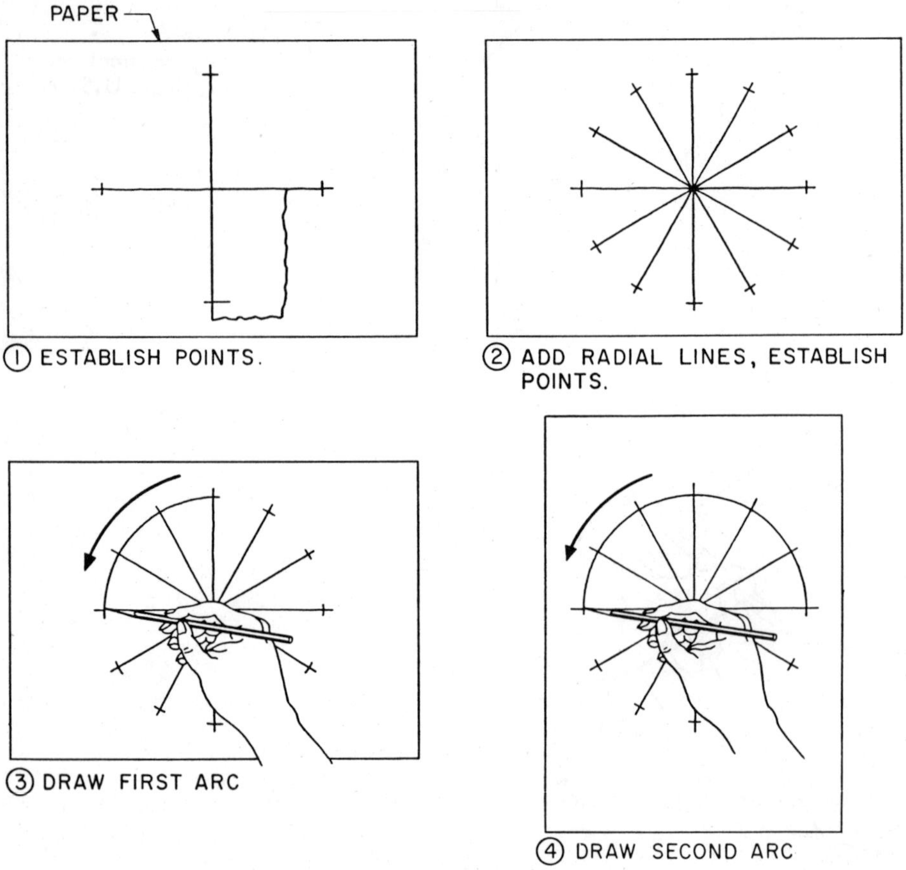

Figure 16-10
Drawing a circle using the radial method. U. S. Army

amount of pressure on the pencil.

In freehand sketching, it is a good practice to make all lines as light as possible to start with. The desired weight of lines can be attended to after the sketch is completed. In this way, lines can easily be corrected without having to erase a great deal.

16.7 Sketching squares and rectangles

To sketch a square, draw a vertical and horizontal line as shown in *A* of Fig. 16-8. Space off equal distances on these lines as in *B* of Fig. 16-8. Sketch light horizontal and vertical lines through the outer points to form the square. Then darken the lines as in *C*.

A similar procedure can be used to sketch rectangular shaped objects. See *D* in Fig. 16-8.

16.8 Sketching angles

To sketch an angle, draw two lines to form a right angle. Divide the angle into equal spaces. Project a line through the point that represents the angle desired. Notice in Fig. 16-9 the direction in which angular lines are drawn.

16.9 Sketching circles and arcs

To sketch a circle, draw a horizontal and vertical line through a point marking the center of the desired circle. On a piece of scrap paper mark off the desired radius and transfer the distance to the main axes. Draw diagonal lines at various intervals and locate the outer radial points using the scrap paper. Complete the circle by drawing short arcs through one quadrant at a time. By rotating the paper, the stroke can be made in the same direction each time. See Fig. 16-10.

Large and small circles can also be sketched by the pivot method. As shown in *A* of Fig. 16-11, the hand is positioned with the second finger resting at the center of the proposed circle. With the pencil lightly touching the paper, rotate the paper with the other hand. Then darken the line by resting the hand on its side and tracing over the light line with the hand pivoting at the wrist as in *B* of Fig. 16-11.

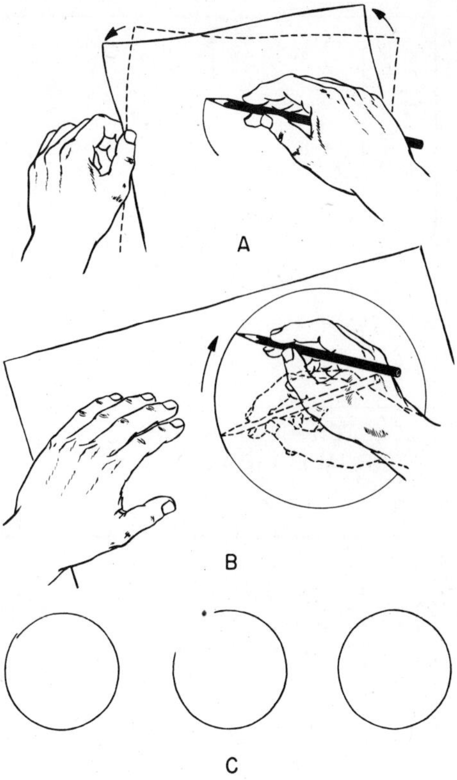

Figure 16-11
Sketching a circle by the pivoting method. U.S. Navy

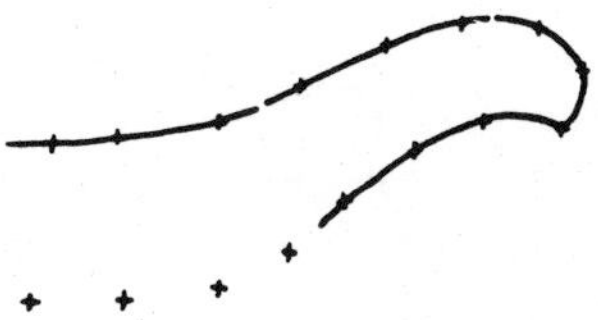

Figure 16-12
How to sketch an irregular curve.

16.10 Sketching irregular curves

For any irregular curve, locate a number of points to represent the shape of the required curvature. Complete the curve by drawing a series of arcs through these points. See Fig. 16-12.

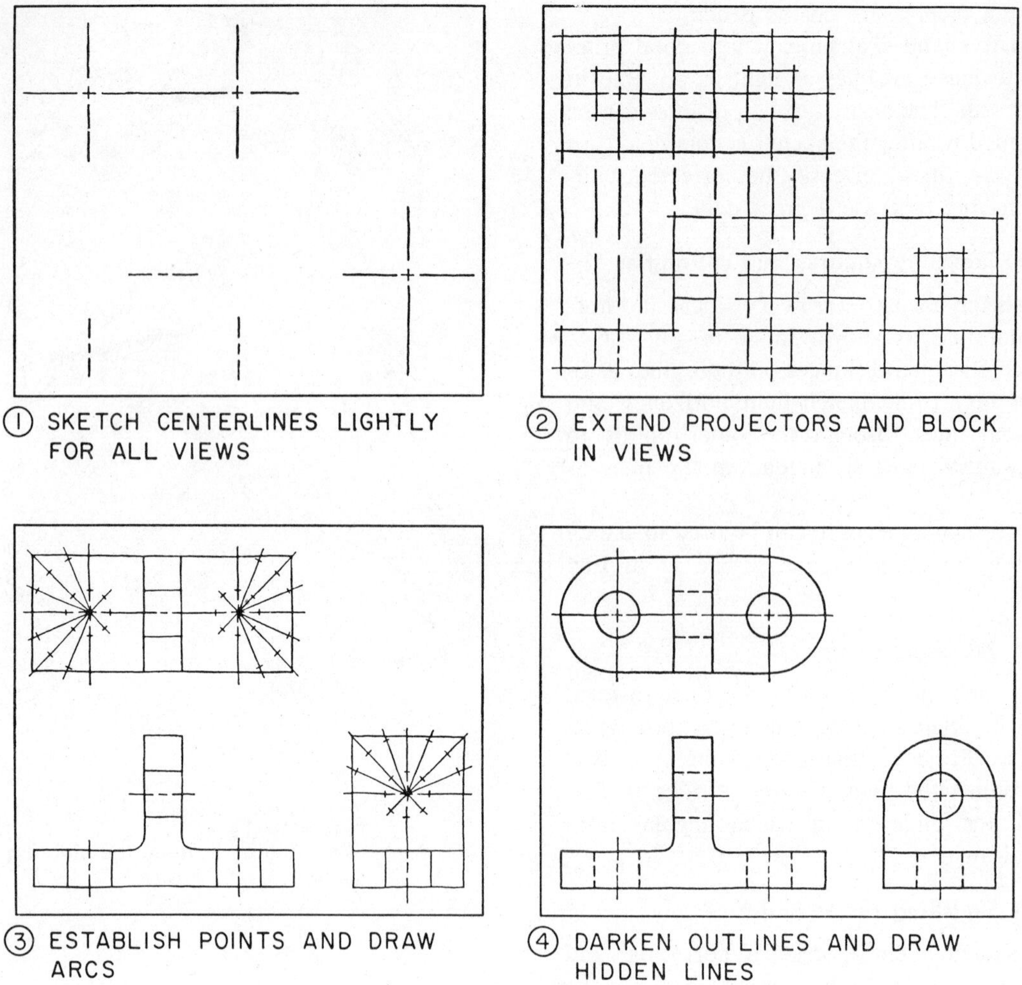
① SKETCH CENTERLINES LIGHTLY FOR ALL VIEWS
② EXTEND PROJECTORS AND BLOCK IN VIEWS
③ ESTABLISH POINTS AND DRAW ARCS
④ DARKEN OUTLINES AND DRAW HIDDEN LINES

Figure 16–13
Follow these steps in preparing a multiview sketch. U.S. Army

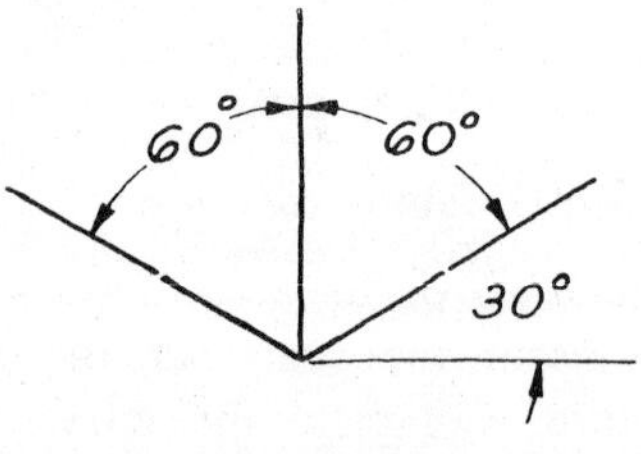
60°
60°
30°

Figure 16–14
The main axes of an isometric sketch.

16.11 Making a multiview sketch

A multiview sketch conforms to all of the practices used in making a mechanical orthographic projection. In proceeding to prepare such a sketch, the first consideration is the number of views which must be shown. As stated in Section 5, some objects may be limited to two views, whereas for more complicated objects three or more views will be required. In either case, it is important that each view be placed in its true plane of projection.

The sketch need not be made to any specific scale; however, reasonable proportions should be maintained. If interior features of the object must be shown, a sectional view should be included as described in Section 8. If necessary, the sketch should be completely dimensioned according to practices discussed in Section 6.

In general, the following steps should be carried out in making a multiview sketch (see Fig. 16-13):

1 Locate the main centerlines or baselines of the views.
2 Block in the views, using light construction lines.
3 Locate all radius points and sketch in circles, arcs and curves.
4 After the views are properly formed, darken all necessary visible and hidden lines.
5 Sketch in extension and dimension lines and include dimensions, notes, and other essential information.

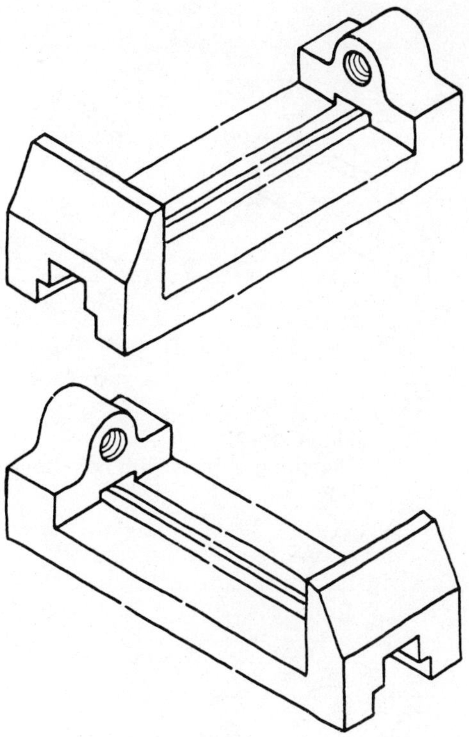

Figure 16-15
An isometric sketch can be made with the object rotated to the right or left.

16.12 Making a pictorial sketch

Whether a sketch should be isometric, oblique, or perspective will depend on the function of the sketch. Since the basic purpose of any pictorial sketch is to convey to the person who has not been trained to read multiview drawings the true shape of the object, the important consideration is to select the kind of drawing that will show the object with the least amount of distortion. For some objects an isometric sketch will prove satisfactory while for others an oblique or perspective sketch will be more effective.

Isometric sketch. An isometric sketch shows three sides of an object. These sides are drawn along one vertical axis and two angular axes. The angular axes extend to the right and left of the vertical axis at an angle of 60° (30° to the horizontal). See Fig. 16-14. The object can be rotated so that either the right or left side is visible. See Fig. 16-15. Whether the object is drawn with its main surfaces extending to the right or left depends entirely upon which side is the most advantageous to show. As a rule, hidden lines are not used on an isometric sketch.

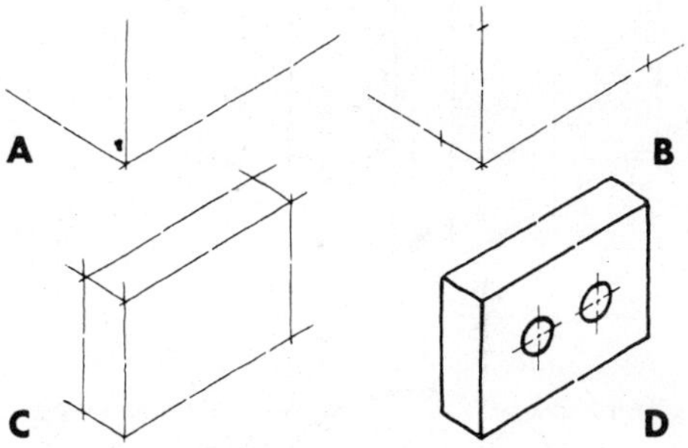

Figure 16-16
Follow these steps in making an isometric sketch.

To make an isometric sketch, proceed as follows (see Steps *A, B, C, D,* in Fig. 16-16):

1 Draw a vertical line. From the top or base of this line, extend two slanted lines at an angle of 30° to the horizontal.
2 Lay out the actual width, length, and height on these three lines.

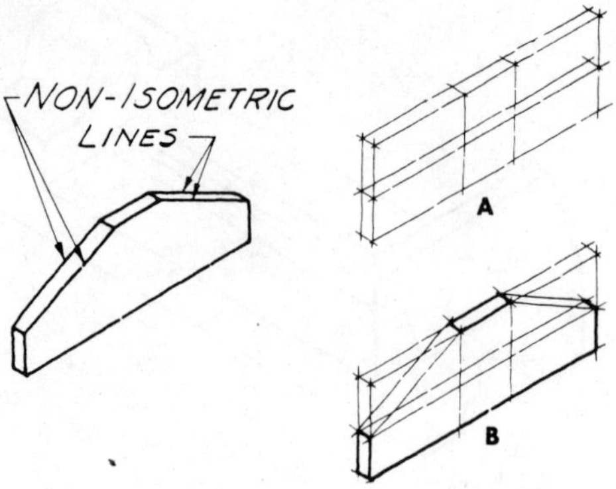

Figure 16-17
Sketching objects with non-isometric lines.

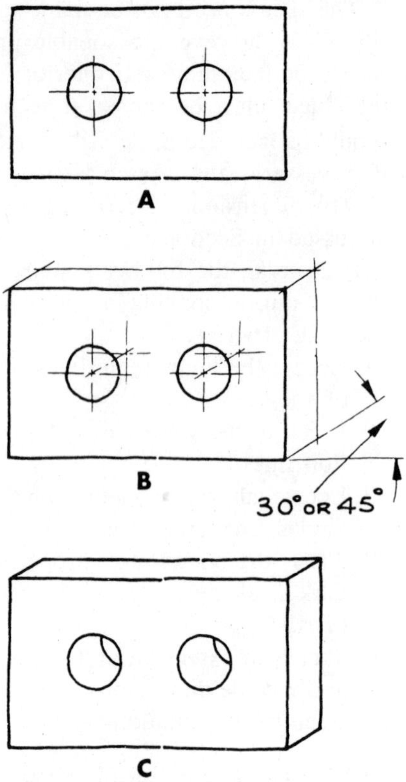

Figure 16-19
This is the procedure for making an oblique sketch.

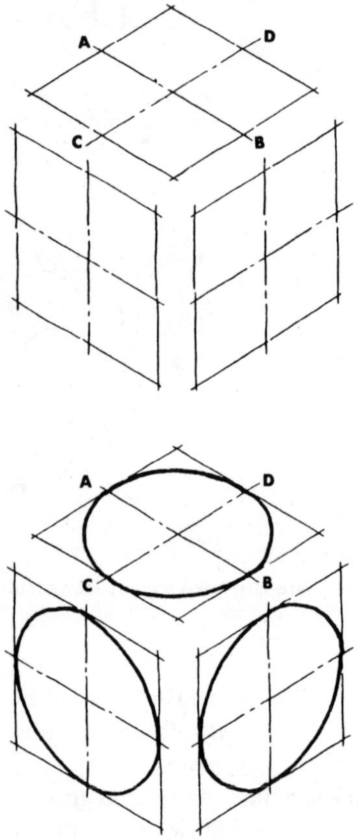

Figure 16-18
Procedure in sketching isometric circles.

3 Complete each surface by drawing the necessary lines parallel to the axis.
4 Draw in the remaining details of the object.
5 When an object has slanted lines that do not run parallel to the main axis, these lines are called non-isometric lines. To draw non-isometric lines first lay out one of the views as for a multiview sketch. Then project the points from this view to the isometric lines. The same procedure can be used to sketch angles and irregular curves. See Fig. 16-17.
6 To sketch an isometric circle or arc, draw an isometric square of the desired size. Draw center lines *AB* and *CD* parallel to the axis of the square. See Fig. 16-18. Sketch short arcs from *A* to *C*,

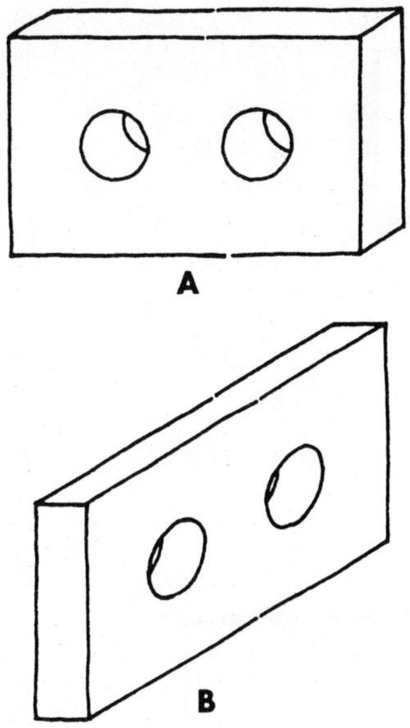

Figure 16-20
Avoid distortion in oblique sketches by placing surfaces with long dimensions in front.

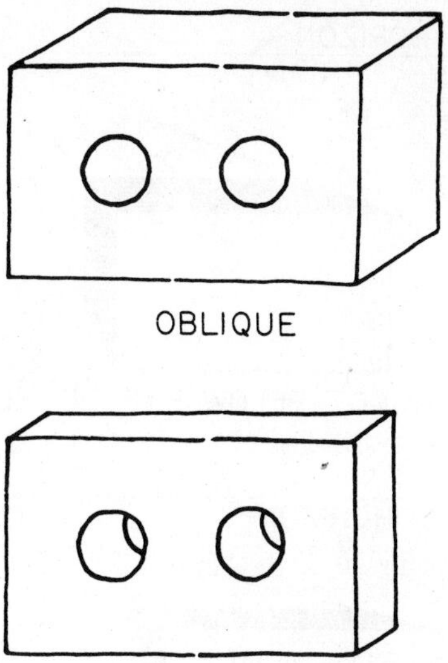

Figure 16-21
An oblique sketch compared with a cabinet sketch.

C to *B, B* to *D,* and *D* to *A*.

Oblique sketch. An oblique sketch is similar to an isometric sketch, except that the front face is seen in its true shape, much as the front view of a multiview sketch. The two sides or ends are made to recede at some convenient angle from the horizontal, such as 30° or 45°. See Fig. 16-19. The common practice is to select the face that is most irregular or complicated in shape to serve as the front. To avoid undue distortion, and produce a more pleasing appearance, it is advisable to place the face with long dimensions in front, as in Fig. 16-20, instead of in a receding position.

Since the receding faces of an oblique sketch are shown in their true size, the result often produces a slightly distorted appearance for some objects. This distortion can be minimized by foreshortening the receding lines, usually one-half. A sketch, when made in such a way, is referred to as a cabinet sketch. See Fig. 16-21.

Perspective sketch. A perspective sketch is based on the fact that all lines which extend from the observer appear to converge or come together at some distant point. The point where all lines seem to meet is known as the vanishing point. The vanishing point is located on the horizon, which is an imaginary line in the distance, and at eye level. All lines below eye level have the appearance of rising upward to the horizon, and all lines above eye level appear to go downward to the horizon. The object can be sketched so the vanishing point is either to the left or to the right, or directly in the center of vision. See Fig. 16-22.

A perspective may be made with one, two, or three vanishing points. The number of vanishing points to be used will depend on the shape of the object as well as the general effects to be achieved. In general most freehand perspective sketches are drawn with one or two vanishing points. To make a perspective sketch, proceed as follows (see

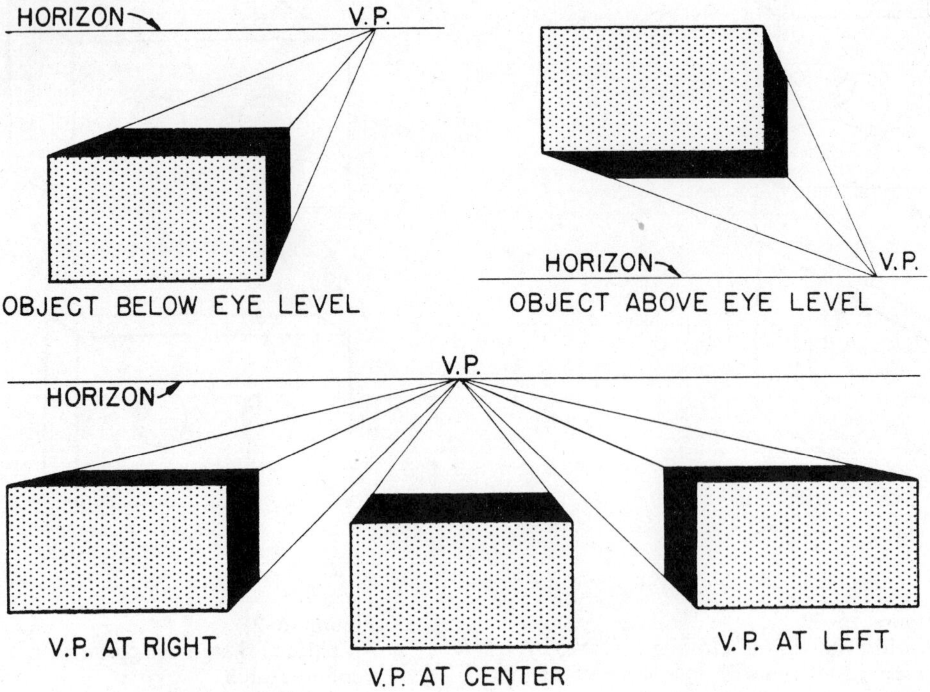

Figure 16-22
These are the positions of the vanishing point in parallel perspective sketches.

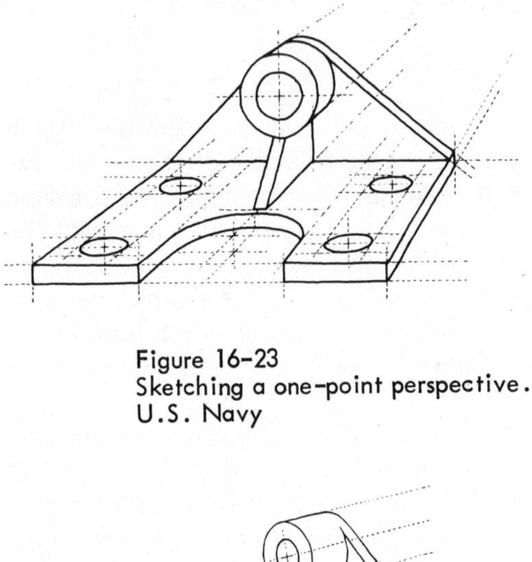

Figure 16-23
Sketching a one-point perspective.
U.S. Navy

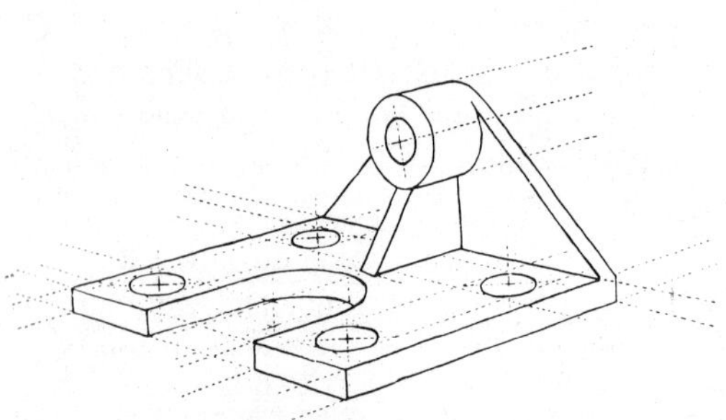

Figure 16-24
Sketching a two-point perspective.
U.S. Navy

Figs. 16-23 and 16-24):

1 Assume the location of the horizon line.
2 Locate the position of the vanishing point.
3 For a one point (parallel) perspective, draw a front view of the object. If a two point (angular) perspective is to be made, draw a vertical line and, on it, lay off the full or scaled height of the object.
4 From the front view or vertical line, draw light construction lines back toward the vanishing points.
5 The points designating the length or depth of the object may be found by the projection method as described in Section 15. However, this procedure is used only for an accurate mechanical perspective. For most purposes, location points for depths are simply assumed, that is, the vertical lines representing the ends of the object are placed in a position that produces the most pleasing effect.
6 Darken in all outlines. Surfaces that lie in a shaded area may be shaded lightly.

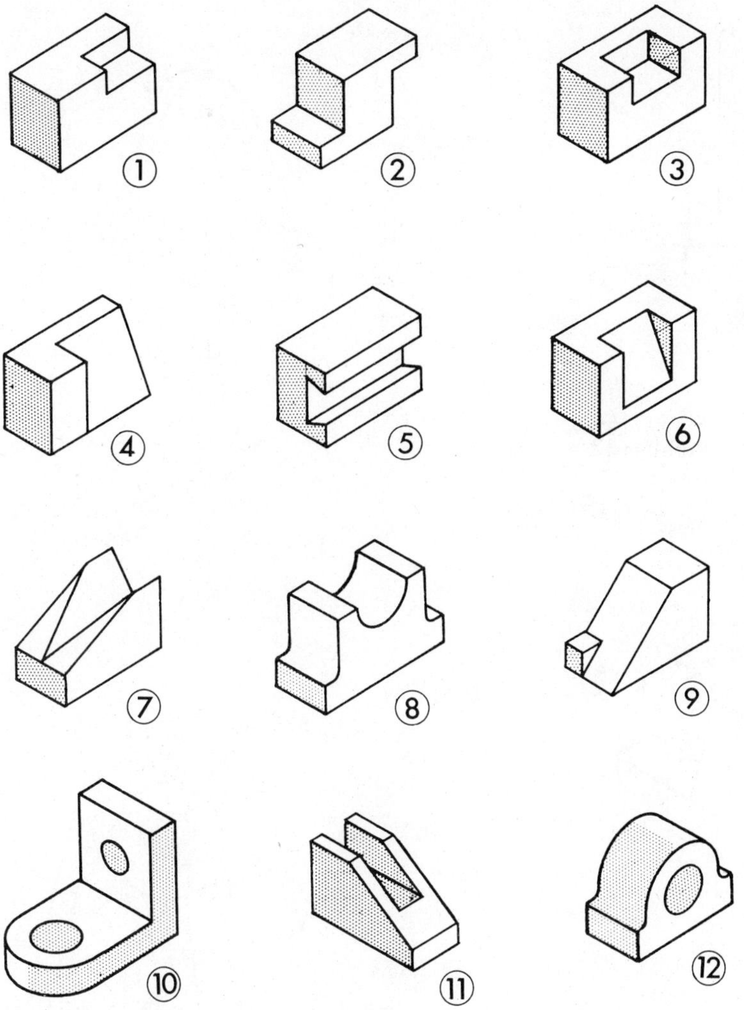

Figure 16-25
Problems 1-12.

Problems, section 16

1-12 Make multiview freehand sketches of the Pictorial Drawings shown in Fig. 16-25. Draw only the necessary views. Select all required dimensions.

13 Make a single-view freehand dimensioned sketch of the Gasket in Fig. 16-26.

14 Sketch and dimension the required views of the machined steel Block in Fig. 16-27.

15 Sketch the Support in Fig. 16-28 showing dimensions.

16 Make a dimensioned sketch showing the necessary views of the Bracket in Fig. 16-29.

17 Make a two-view sectional sketch of the object in Fig. 16-30. Assume all sizes.

18 Sketch the necessary views of the object in Fig. 16-31. Assume all sizes.

19 Make a cabinet sketch of the object in Fig. 16-32.

20 Make an isometric sketch of the object shown in Fig. 16-33.

21 Make a two-point perspective of the object in Fig. 16-34.

22 Make an oblique sketch of the object in Fig. 16-35.

23 Make a dimensioned cabinet sketch of the Adapter in Fig. 8-43.

24 Make isometric sketches, fully dimensioned of Figs. 8-38 and 8-40.

25 Make a cabinet sketch of Fig. 11-59.

26 Make one-point perspective sketches of Fig. 9-23 and Fig. 11-53.

27 Make an isometric dimensioned sketch of the problem sketched in Fig. 11-58.

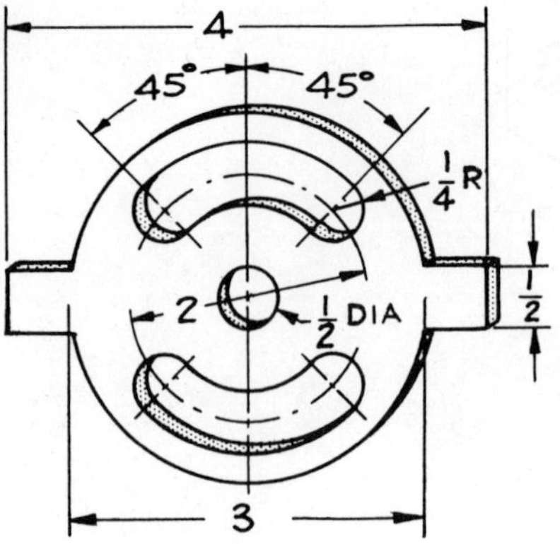

Figure 16-26
Problem 13.

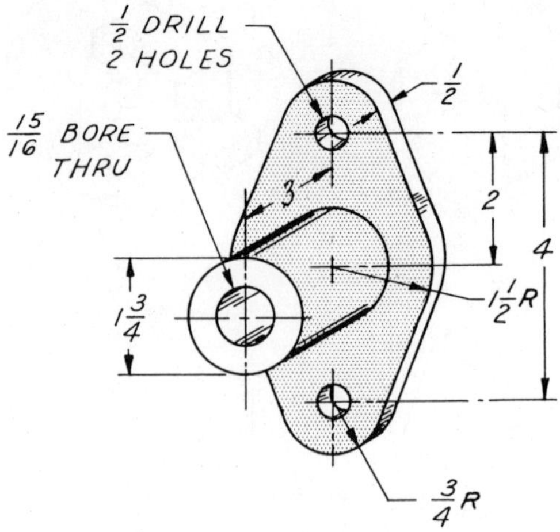

Figure 16-28
Problem 15.

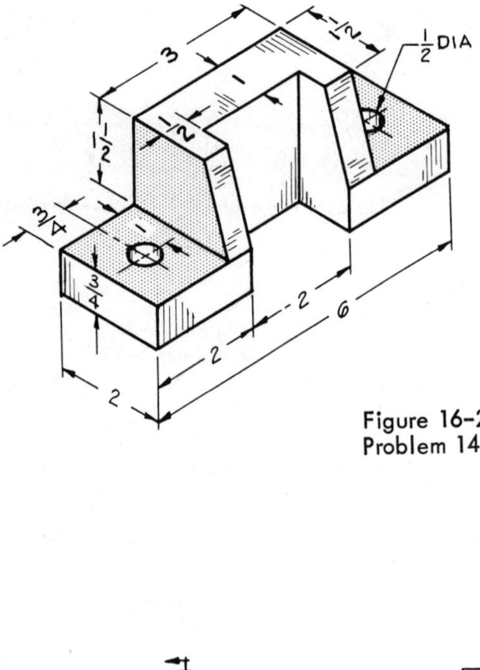

Figure 16-27
Problem 14.

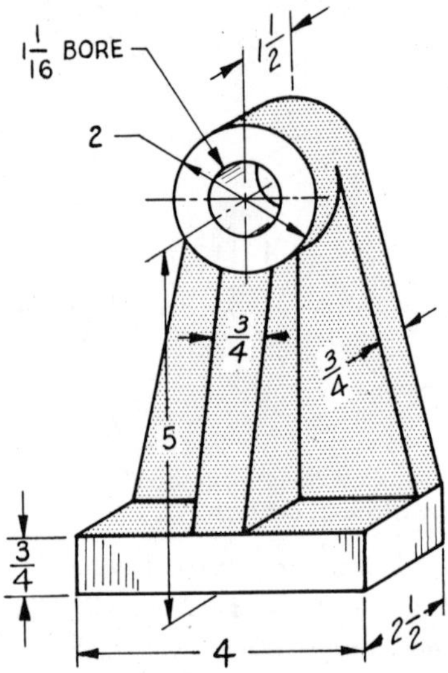

Figure 16-29
Problem 16.

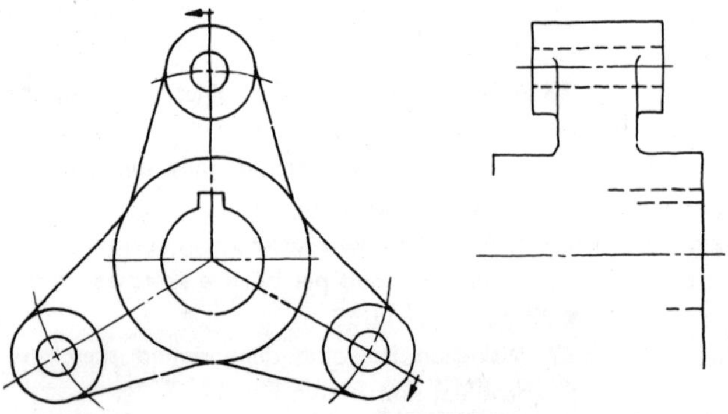

Figure 16-30
Problem 17.

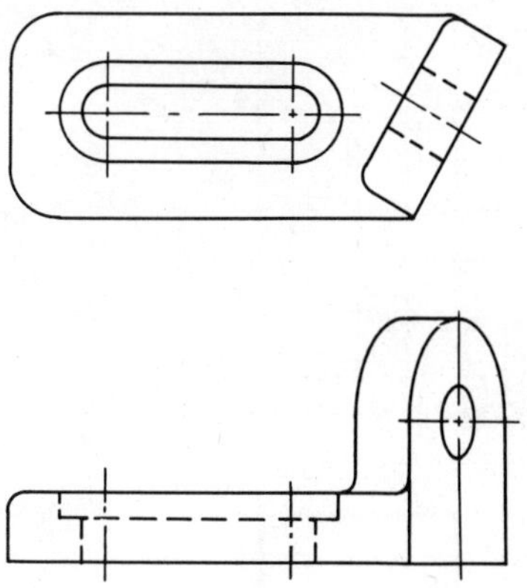

Figure 16-31
Problem 18.

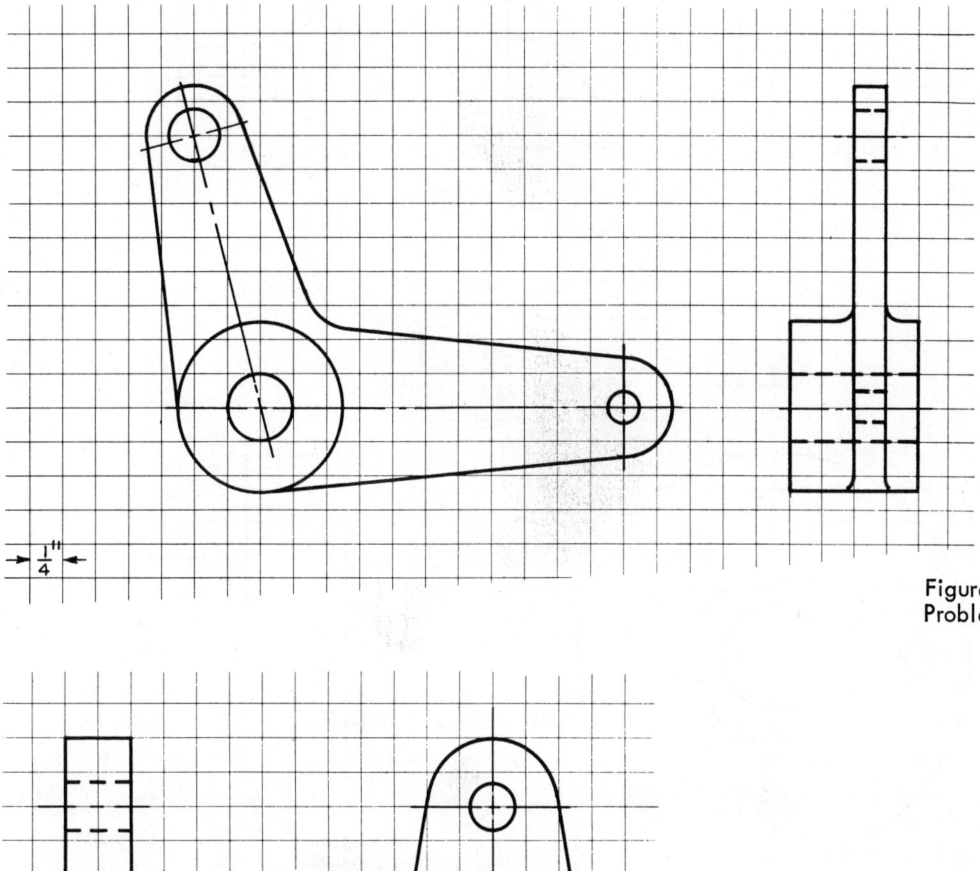

Figure 16-32
Problem 19.

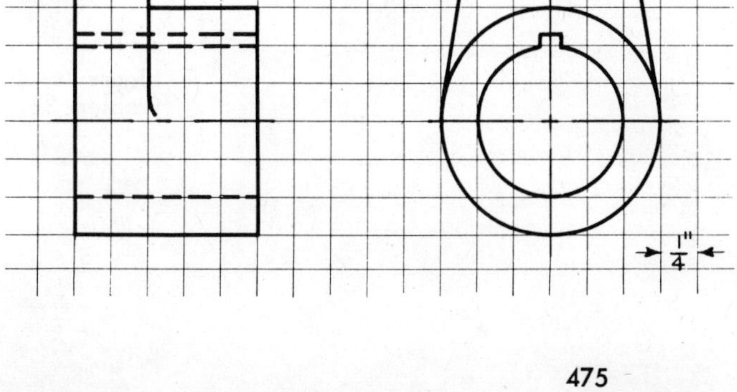

Figure 16-33
Problem 20.

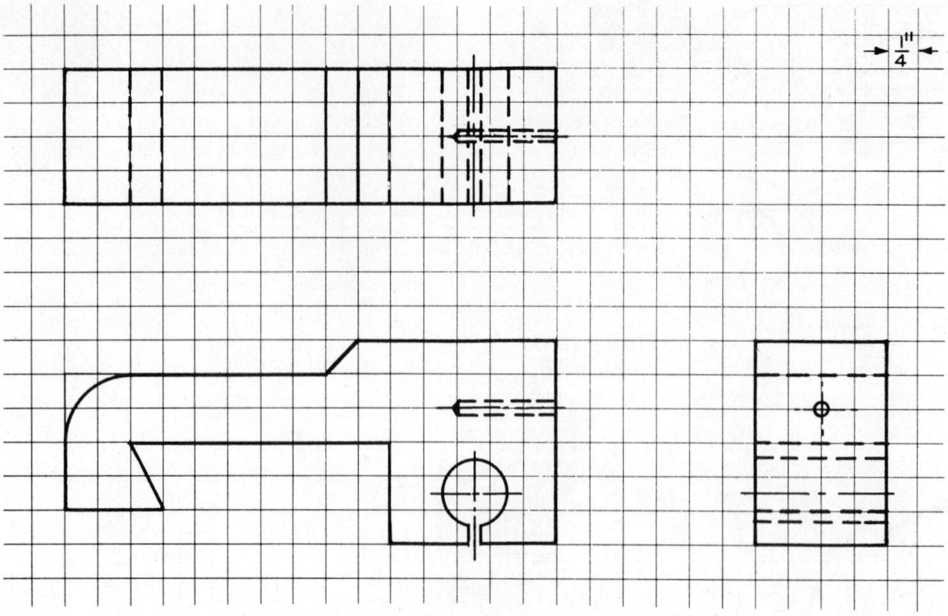

Figure 16-34
Problem 21.

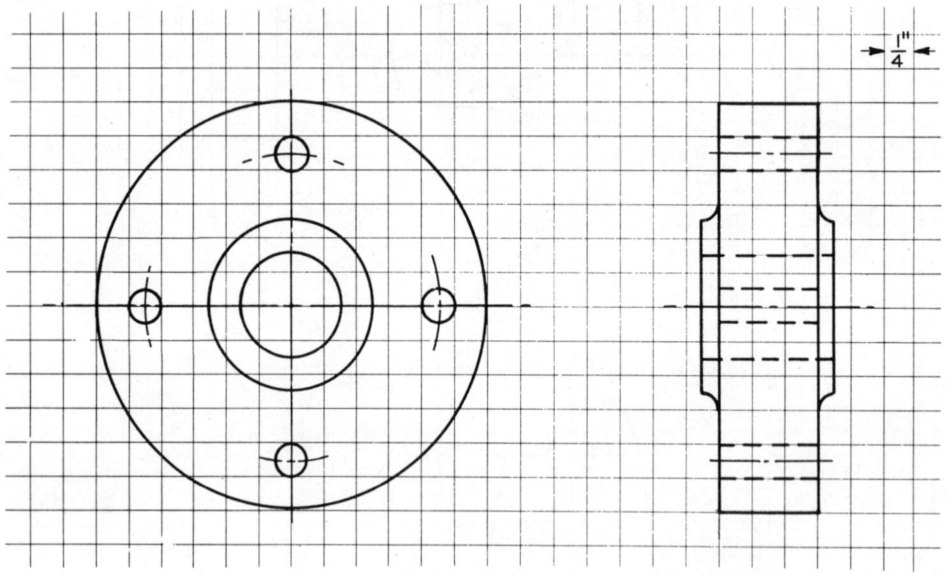

Figure 16-35
Problem 22.

Architectural drafting 17

The basic techniques of architectural drafting are essentially the same as those for other forms of drafting except that special application of conventions, symbols and construction details are involved. The scope of architectural services are centered around the contributions of a team of specialists, which includes the architect, mechanical engineer, electrical engineer and architectural draftsman. In some instances, one person may often function in several capacities, particularly in the design of small buildings. On large building projects, the practice is to utilize the knowledge and skill of all these specialists.

Because of his extensive education and experience with building materials and methods of construction, the architect generally acts as the professional advisor and representative of the owner throughout the planning and construction stages. The mechanical engineer is responsible for planning the building's plumbing, heating, ventilating system and other mechanical features. The electrical engineer plans the necessary circuits and fixtures for power, lighting and, if required, the fire alarm system, the clock system, the intercommunication system and the telephone system.

The draftsman, under the guidance of the architect, prepares detailed plans of the entire construction project. His knowledge and skill are extremely important since plans, if properly executed, will make the entire building program more satisfactory to the owner, architect and contractor.

Most building programs involve four stages: preliminary planning, preparation of working drawings, writing the specifications, and supervision of the actual construction.

It is not the purpose of this section to provide in detail all of the significant aspects of these stages but simply to present to the student of engineering and drafting an overview of the main elements involved.

17.1 Preliminary planning

The first phase of any building program consists of gathering and analyzing data and establishing certain premises upon which the programming will be based. This is the function of the architect who obtains from his client information defining space requirements and then analyzes various factors of the building program, such as type of structure, location and orientation of the building, availability of utilities, topography, traffic pattern of surrounding streets, and costs.

At this stage budget problems are of primary consideration and will remain the controlling factor throughout the entire planning and production period, since the available funds must be correlated with space requirements and the prevailing square footage cost of construction. A cost approximation is arrived at by determining the total area of the building and multiplying it by the cost factor. In general, the owner usually seeks a program that is much more elaborate than the budget can support. It then becomes the responsibility of the architect to reach a balance between needs and the available funds. As a rule, this balance can be achieved by careful study of space requirements and a reduction of area where it can best be spared.

BUDGET ANALYSIS

A. PROJECT:

B. B.A.# ________

DATE ________

JOB NO. ________

C. Materials Approval Committee:

Date ________

Signed: ________

D. Research & Design Committee Approval

Date ________

Signed: ________

E.	LAND PURCHASE		$ ________
F.	BOUNDARY SURVEY		________
G.	TOPOGRAPHICAL SURVEY		________
H.	SOIL TESTS		________
I.	PERCOLATION TESTS		________
J.	CONSTRUCTION COSTS		________
	1. Site Preparation	________	
	2. Architectural Trades	________	
	3. Mechanical Trades	________	
	4. Electrical Trades	________	
	5. Elevators	________	
	6. Fixed Equipment	________	
	7. Site Development	________	
	TOTAL CONSTRUCTION COST		________
K.	MOVABLE EQUIPMENT		________
L.	ARCHITECTS & ENGINEERS FEES		________
M.	CONSULTING FEES		________
N.	ATTORNEY FEES		________
O.	BONDING ATTORNEY FEES		________
P.	FINANCIAL CONSULTANT FEES		________
Q.	PRINTING & PUBLISHING COSTS		________
R.	ADMINISTRATIVE COSTS		________
S.	CONTINGENCIES		________
T.	CLERK-OF-WORKS		________
U.	ACCRUED INTEREST		________
V.			
W.			
X.			
Y.			
	TOTAL BUDGET ESTIMATE		$ ________

Figure 17-1
A budget form is an important factor in the preliminary planning of a building project. Louis C. Kingscott & Associates

Further economies can also be made in later phases of the planning when materials and equipment are selected.

The fact that the owner will have expenses other than those of construction cost alone cannot be overlooked. Important among other expenses are those for equipment not included in the construction contract, for site development over and above grading and paving in the immediate building area, for site acquisition, financing costs, architects' fees and other related expenses. In addition, an architect usually recommends setting aside a contingency fee of approximately five percent of the anticipated construction cost as a cushion to meet such items as increased labor and material costs, and other features which the owner may want added during the later design stages or construction period. To assist the owner in formulating a budget, the architect often uses a budget form as shown in Fig. 17-1. This form includes all possible costs; some, obviously, are not applicable to every job, but this listing gives the owner an idea of the scope of his project and the need for providing funds in excess of the cost of the building alone.

17.2 Preparation of preliminary presentation sketches

Preparation of preliminary presentation sketches involves two steps. First rough schematic sketches are made and second, these sketches are refined into scaled and display drawings.

The schematics are often freehand sketches made on grid sheets, as shown in Fig. 17-2, and serve as a means of analyzing the functions of the building and determining the greatest possible operational efficiency of these functions. The sketches are usually limited to room arrangements. Frequently, several schemes are prepared for the owner's consideration. This is done not only to offer a choice, but also to help develop the ultimate design. By using several approaches to the problem, certain features can be taken from each scheme and combined into a final design. If these schematics are developed through intelligent planning, the final work will be limited largely to refinements, thereby reducing elaborate and costly revisions later.

Once the basic problems of the scheme are resolved, preliminary scaled drawings are made. These include main floor plans, elevations, and a perspective rendering. Only the main general features are dimensioned; all construction details are omitted. The drawings are made on tracing paper so that various relationships of the floor plan arrangement can be shown by placing one sheet over another. Prints can also be produced to assist in the preliminary presentations.

17.3 Display drawings

Display drawings are actually preliminary drawings which are embellished in order to make them more attractive and understanding to the client. They are often rendered in a combination of pencil, ink, or water colors. In addition to the perspective, main floor plans and front elevation, they frequently include imaginary backgrounds such as trees, shrubbery, drive, garden and other features to achieve a more realistic effect. See Fig. 17-3.

17.4 Working drawings

From the preliminary sketches and display drawings, the draftsman makes a complete set of working drawings (usually referred to as *working plans*). These drawings must provide sufficient information so that along with the written specifications no significant decision is left to the discretion of the contractor. The set of plans will therefore include all essential building details such as plot plan, foundation plan, floor plans, elevations, sections, and as many clarification details as are necessary. Finished drawings are also prepared which detail the electrical, heating, plumbing and ventilating systems. For large buildings separate drawings are included to show the structural framing.

In the course of preparing the plans, the draftsman refers to numerous catalogs, architectural handbooks and building literature for exact sizes of structural materials, such as doors, windows, and other essential items. He uses various symbols to designate

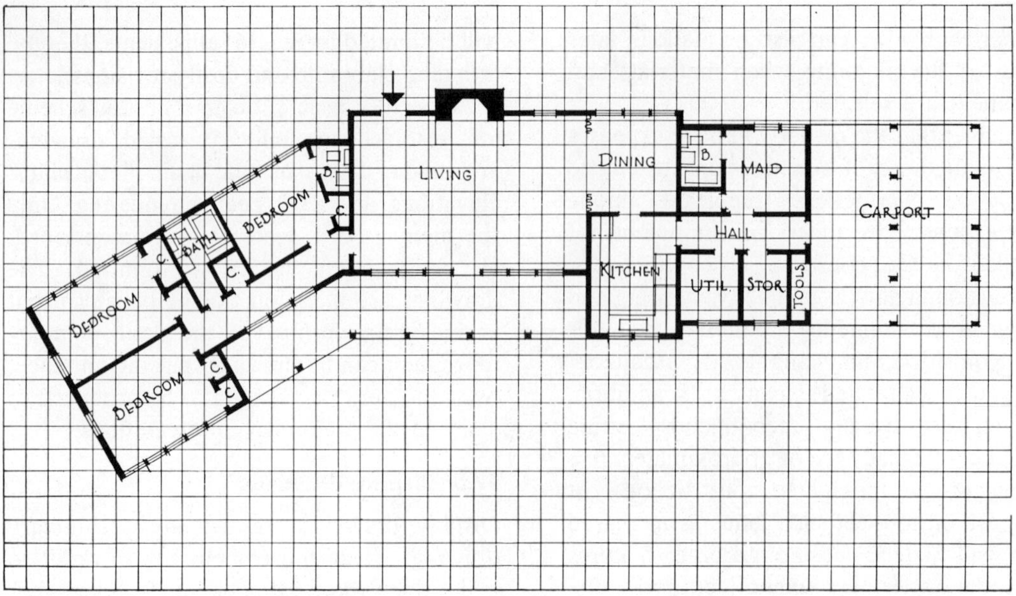

Figure 17-2
Grid sheets are frequently employed in preliminary planning to visualize major design functions and to establish relationship of structural elements.

Figure 17-3
Preliminary planning includes the preparation of a perspective rendering to show the general appearance of the complete building.

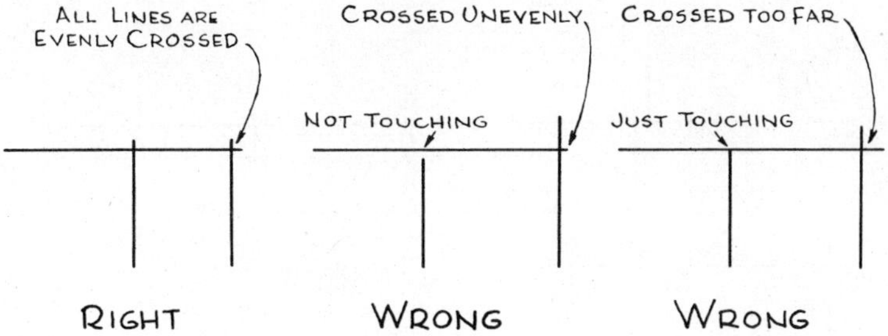

Figure 17-4
Crossing of lines at corners is standard practice in architectural drawing.

Figure 17-5
These architectural alphabets are the most commonly used in architectural drawing.

materials, fixtures, and construction details.

Unlike machine drawing where all object lines are made to meet at corners, overrunning of corners is permissible in architectural drawing. See Fig. 17-4. The architectural draftsman while preparing working drawings also has greater freedom in style of lettering and ways of embellishing certain construction details.

17.5 Scale of working drawings

The scale selected for architectural drawings is governed by the size of the structure. The common scales for most plan, sectional, and elevation drawings are:

1/16″ = 1′-0″
1/8″ = 1′-0″
1/4″ = 1′-0″
3/16″ = 1′-0″

Detail drawings of large features are generally made at scales of:

1/2″ = 1′-0″
3/4″ = 1′-0″
1-1/2″ = 1′-0″

Detail drawings of small features are drawn at:

Full size
3″ = 1′-0″
6″ = 1′-0″

17.6 Lettering

There is considerable variation in the styles of lettering used in architectural drawing. The most common is the single stroke alphabet based on the old Roman form. See Fig. 17-5. Frequently the single stroke Gothic alphabet is employed. There is evidence to

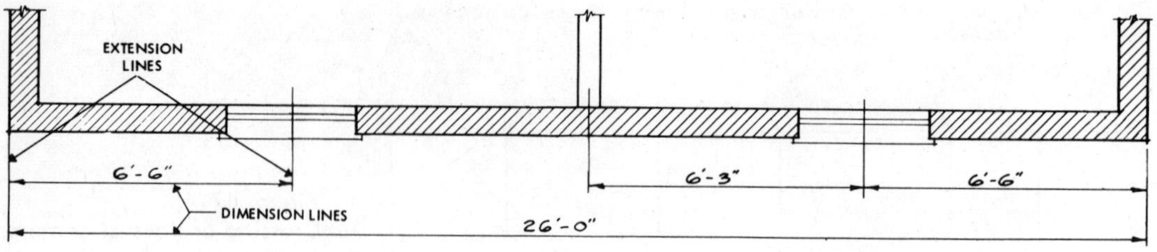

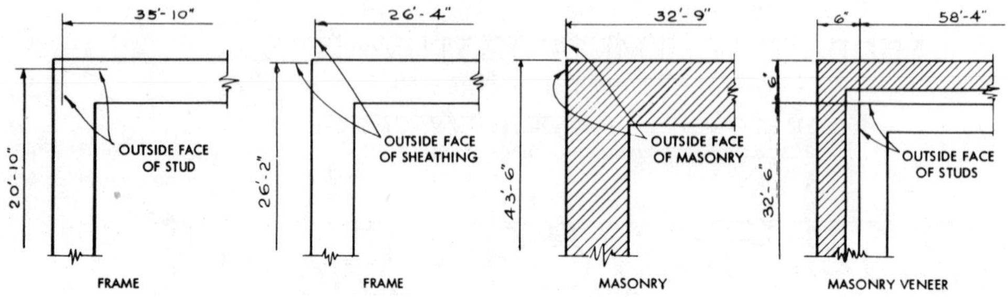

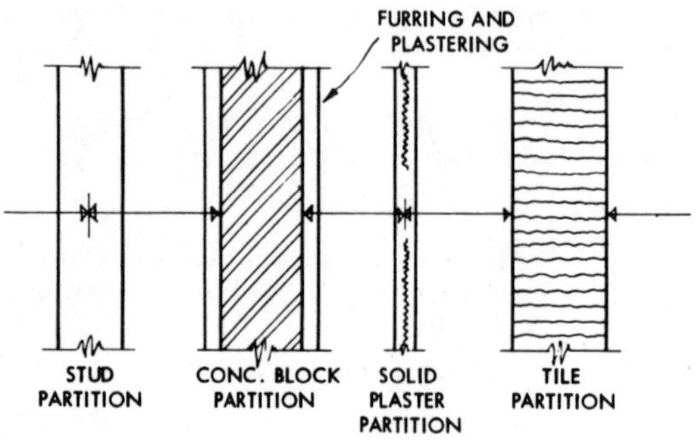

Figure 17-6
Most dimensions are given as center-to-center distances except for some of the dimensions used on plan views.

indicate that upper-case letters are gaining in favor over the lower-case. Many architectural firms use upper-case for titles and subtitles and lower-case for explanatory notes. Insofar as letter size and spacing is concerned, the same basic rules apply as prescribed in Section 3.

17.7 Dimensioning architectural drawings

In general, dimensioning procedures for architectural drawing is more or less similar to the dimensioning techniques used for other forms of drafting. The following are notable exceptions:

1 Dimension lines are not broken but are made continuous with the dimension figures placed above the line.

2 Dimensional units are expressed with their identifying mark and are indicated in this manner:

(a) If fractions or inches are used alone no zero follows, thus: 3/8″ or 6″.

(b) When inches are used in combination with fractions they are shown as: 4½″.

(c) A dimension requiring feet and inches is expressed thus: 6′-7″.

(d) If feet is used without inches a zero follows the foot unit, thus: 8′-0″.

(e) Feet and fractions are designated as: 3′-0¼″.

(f) The unit one foot is always given as 1′-0″, never 12″.

3 Unlike machine drawing, where accuracy must often be specified in thousandths of an inch, thereby requiring the use of decimal tolerances, architectural dimensioning usually cannot be expressed with this degree of accuracy. Lumber and other construction materials often vary slightly in size which makes it impractical to indicate actual values to edges of structural members. Dimensions, therefore, are given as center-to-center distances so that even if structural members vary somewhat in size, the true location is always achieved. A few variations from this practice are shown in Fig. 17-6, and these apply to certain dimensions on plan views only.

17.8 Notes on architectural drawings

A great many more notes are used in architectural drawing than in most other types of drawing. Notes are employed to augment dimensioning information or to explain some detail which otherwise cannot be shown clearly. In practice, the same basic rules apply for notes as are followed in other forms of drafting.

17.9 Building symbols and conventions

Many different symbols and conventions are used in preparing building plans. These symbols and conventions represent types of material, structural elements, or construction details. The symbols and conventions are fairly well standardized and are familiar to all architects, draftsmen, contractors and tradesmen. Thus if the foundation is to be of concrete blocks the foundation outlines will show cross hatching with small triangles. Concrete is represented by a series of dots which surround small triangles. Structural steel is indicated by double line cross hatching. The most commonly used material symbols are included in Fig. 17-7. Whenever new material or equipment is employed for which there are no standard symbols, the items are identified by numbered or lettered circles and described completely by note, detail, or in the specification form.

Along with building material symbols, various conventions are utilized to designate doors and windows. See Fig. 17-8. For example, windows are indicated by openings in the wall and the openings are scaled to represent the widths of the sash. Lines are drawn through the openings to show glass and sill. Doors are shown by angular lines extending from the walls with arcs to specify the direction of door swing.

Special symbols are also used to designate various electrical, plumbing and heating units. These symbols are included in Section 19.

17.10 Window and door schedule

Windows and doors on drawings are coded with letters enclosed in circles. The same letters are used for all windows and all doors when they are of similar construction and alike in size. A door and window schedule similar to the one in Fig. 17-9 is prepared which completely describes each unit. The same coded letters as used on the drawings are included in the schedule to identify the doors and windows.

17.11 Plot plan

The plot plan is the first sheet in a set of working drawings and gives the overall picture of the location and orientation of the building. See Fig. 17-10. If the ground is hilly, contour lines show the extent of grading changes which the contractor must make. The plot plan also includes provisions for water supply, sanitary sewers, storm water drainage, utilities, walks and driveways.

The plot plan is drawn from sketches and notes based on survey information. The individual making the survey must have a knowledge of map drawing and be able to use various types of surveying instruments. It is his job to secure boundary line positions, ground elevations and other physical features of the building site. The responsibility of the draftsman is to interpret the field data obtained and then prepare a finished drawing of the plot plan as shown in Fig. 17-10. See also Section 20.

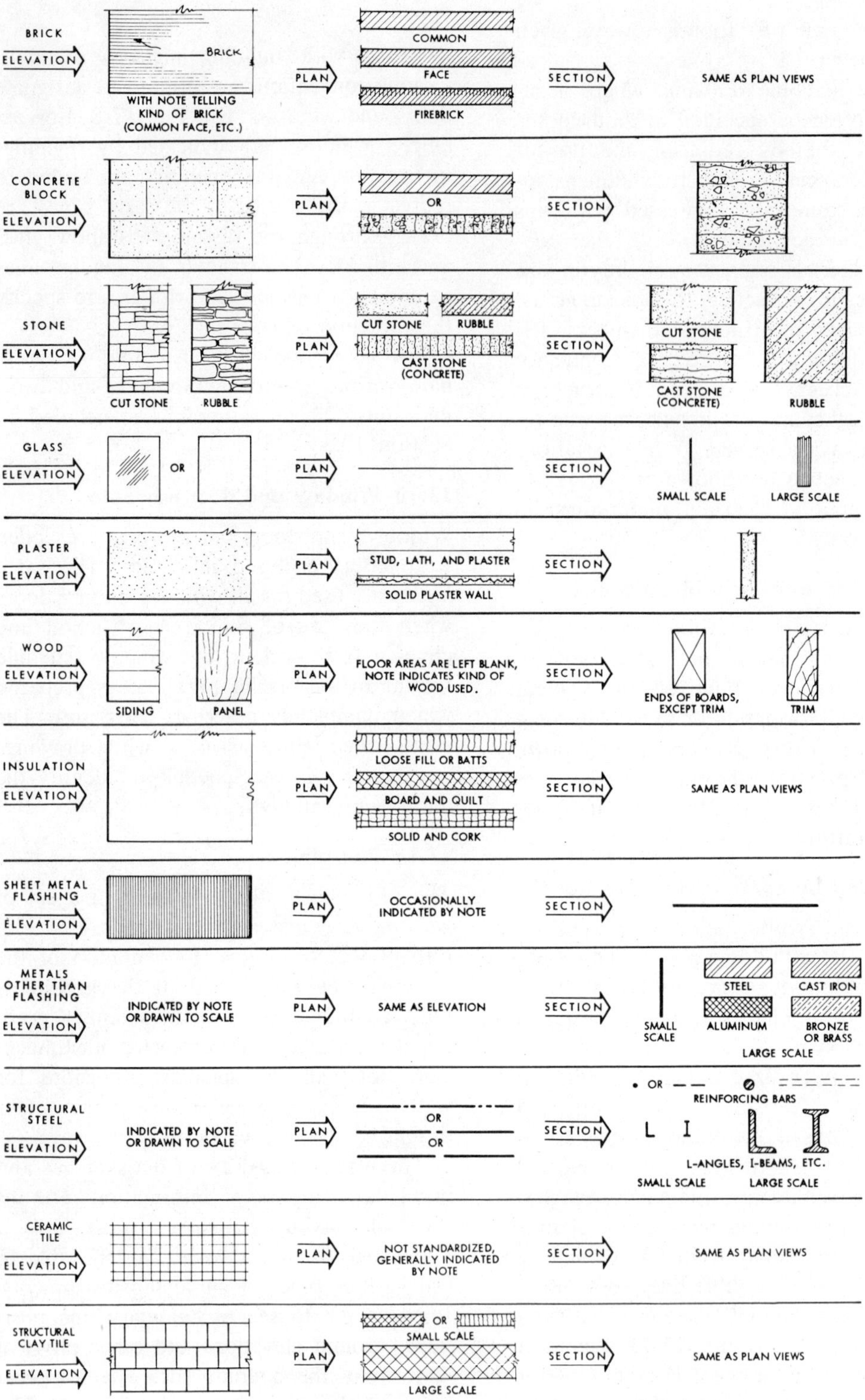

Figure 17-7
These are typical symbols used to represent various building materials in a working drawing.

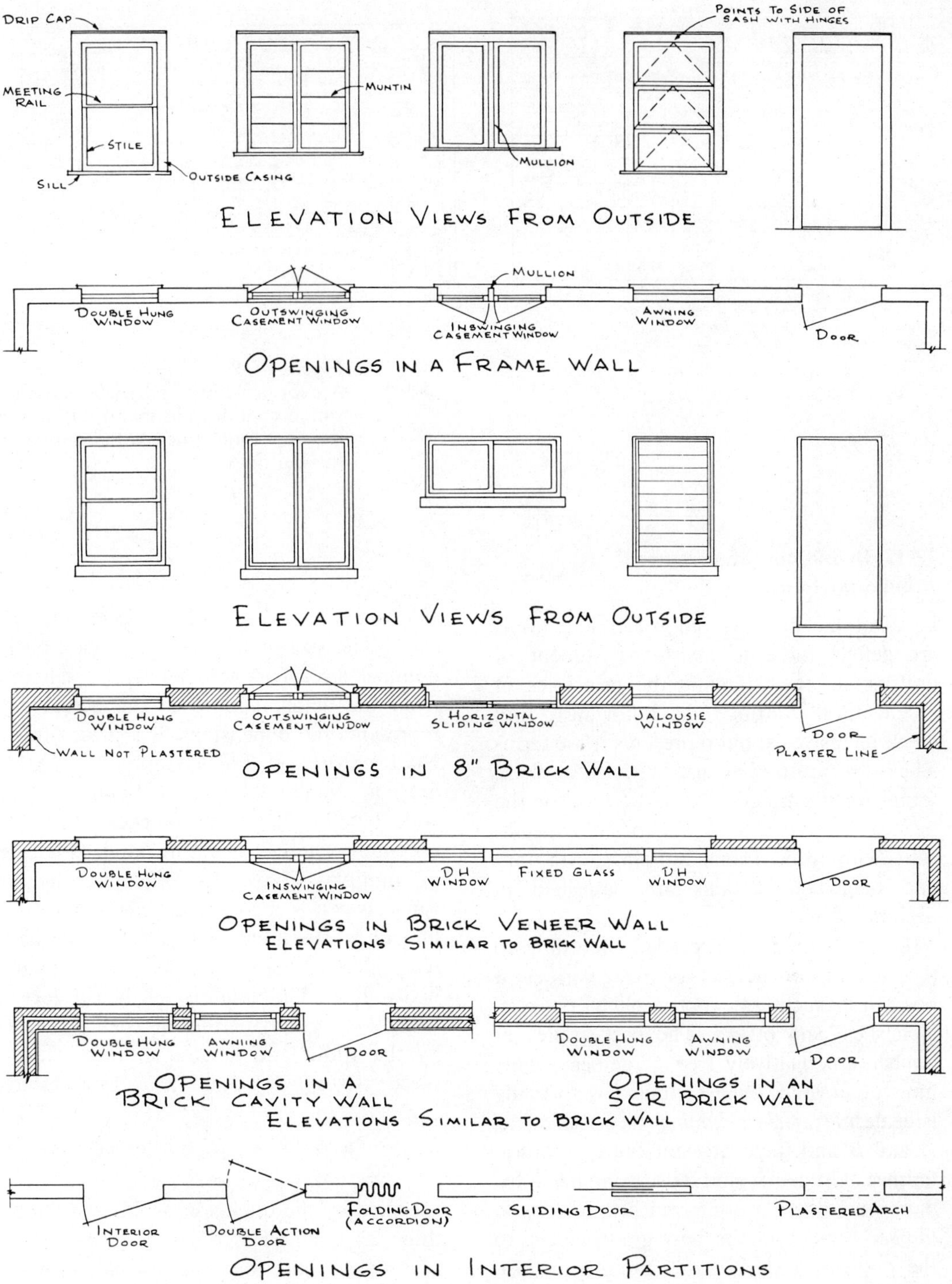

Figure 17-8
These conventions are used to represent doors and windows in working drawings.

·DOOR·SCHEDULE·

CODE	QUAN	TYPE	DOOR SIZE	MFRS NO	REMARKS
(A)	2	WD, 1 PANEL, 1 GL	3'-0"×6'-8"×1 3/8	3070D	SEE ELEVATION VIEWS FOR PANEL DESIGN
(B)	2	GL SLIDING	3'-0"×7'-0"×1"	3070G	1" THERMOGLAZE GL
(C)	1	OVERHEAD	7'-0" × 8'-0"	7080	SEE ELEVATION VIEW FOR PANEL DESIGN
(D)	2	WD, HOLLOW CORE *	2'-10"×6'-8"×1 3/8"	21068	BIRCH
(E)	5	WD, HOLLOW CORE * SLIDING	2'-8"×6'-8"×1 3/8"	2868	"
(F)	3	WD, HOLLOW CORE *	2'-6"×6'-8"×1 3/8"	2668	"
(G)	3	" " " *	2'-4"×6'-8×1 3/8"	2468	"
(H)	4	" " " *	3'-0"×6'-8"×1 3/8"	3068	"
(J)	2	" " " *	2'-0"×6'-8"×1 3/8"	—	"
(I)	1	WD, HOLLOW CORE *	2'-8"×6'-8"×1 3/8"	2868	"

* FLUSH DOOR

·WINDOW·SCHEDULE·

CODE	QUAN	TYPE	SASH SIZE	MFRS NO	REMARKS
(K)	7	AWNING 3 LTS	2'-9 7/8"×4'-6"	66	SEE SPEC FOR GL
(L)	3	" 3 LTS	3'-9"×4'-3 1/4"	1010	" " " "
(M)	1	" 2 LTS	3'-4"×3'-4"	86	" " " "
(N)	3	DH 2 LTS	1'-7"×2'-0 5/8"	2	OBSCURE GL SEE SPEC
(O)	1	DH 2 LTS	1'-1"×2'-0 5/8"	3	SEE SPEC FOR GL
(P)	2	AWNING 1 LT	3'-9"×1'-6"	10	" " " "
(Q)	2	FIXED 1 LT	8'-0"×5'-5"	918	1" THERMOGLAZE GL
(R)	1	AWNING 3 LTS	3'-3"×4'-6"	1003	SEE SPEC FOR GL
(S)	1	" 3 LTS	2'-9"×4'-3"	1007	" " " "

Figure 17–9
A door or window schedule is a chart which contains the specifications of the doors and windows to be used in the building.

17.12 Definitions of common building terms

Some of the more common building terms are defined here to assist the student of drafting in understanding the principles of architectural drafting. The following is not an all-inclusive list but represents those terms which are most often used. Many of these terms are illustrated in Fig. 17-11. For the most part these terms are associated specifically with wood frame buildings. Masonry and steel constructions are described in Section 18.

Lumber. Lumber is graded according to the amount of defects or irregularities it possesses, such as knots, pitch pockets, blemishes, and others. The best grades of lumber are relatively free of defects, while most other grades will contain few to many irregularities. *Select lumber* is classified as *A* and *B* and these are suitable for natural finishes. Grades *C* and *D* are intended for paint or other opaque finishes. *Common lumber* runs from the best grade No. 1 to the poorest grade No. 5. Lumber is also classified as rough or dressed. *Rough lumber* refers to material as it comes from the saw, unplaned. *Dressed lumber* has one or more sides and edges planed. Thus lumber marked *S1S* means *surfaced on one side; S2S, surfaced on two sides; S1S1E, surfaced on one side and one edge; S4S, surfaced on four sides.* The size of lumber is specified by its nominal size. The nominal size is different from the actual size since the actual size represents the dimensions of a piece after it has been dressed. For example, 2 x 4 studs are not actually 2 inches thick and 4 inches wide but 1-5/8 x 3-5/8 inches. With few exceptions, lumber is cut in standard lengths of multiples of two feet. Standard lengths run between 8 and 20 feet. The quantity of lumber is measured in board feet or linear feet. Nominal sizes are used to calculate board feet. The number of board feet is found by multiplying the thickness in inches by the width and lengths in feet. Thus a piece 1-5/8″ x 3-5/8″ x 6′ would have

$$2 \times \frac{4}{12} \times 6 = 4 \quad BF.$$

Lumber sizes are specified by the thickness, width and length, thus: 2″ x 6″ x 8′.

Footings and foundation wall. Footings are constructed of plain or reinforced concrete and rest on portions of the ground called foundation beds. Footings serve as bases for foundation and retaining walls and usually extend around the entire building structure. The thickness of a footing de-

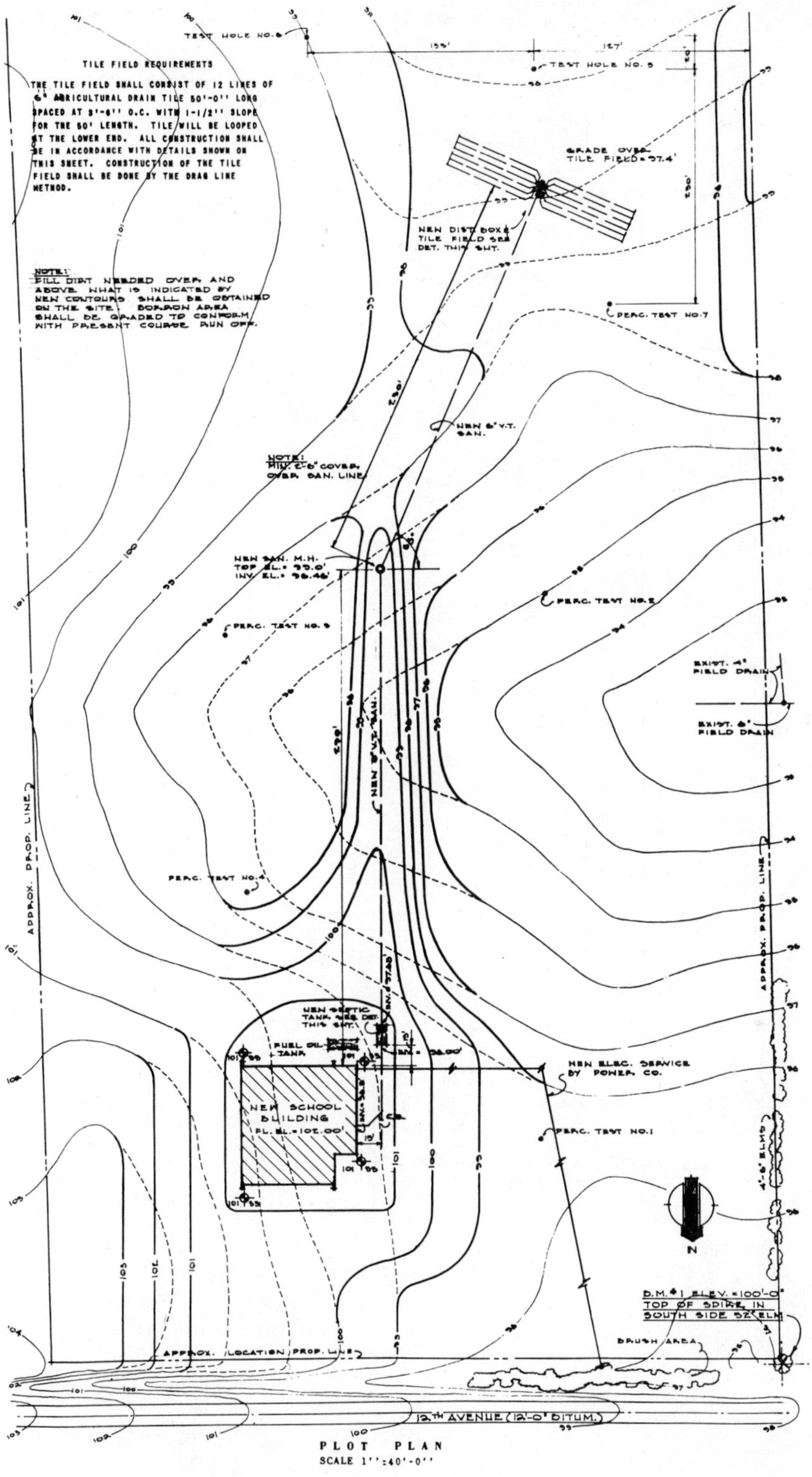

Figure 17-10
The plot plan is the first sheet in a set of plans and among other information gives the general orientation of the building. Louis C. Kingscott & Associates

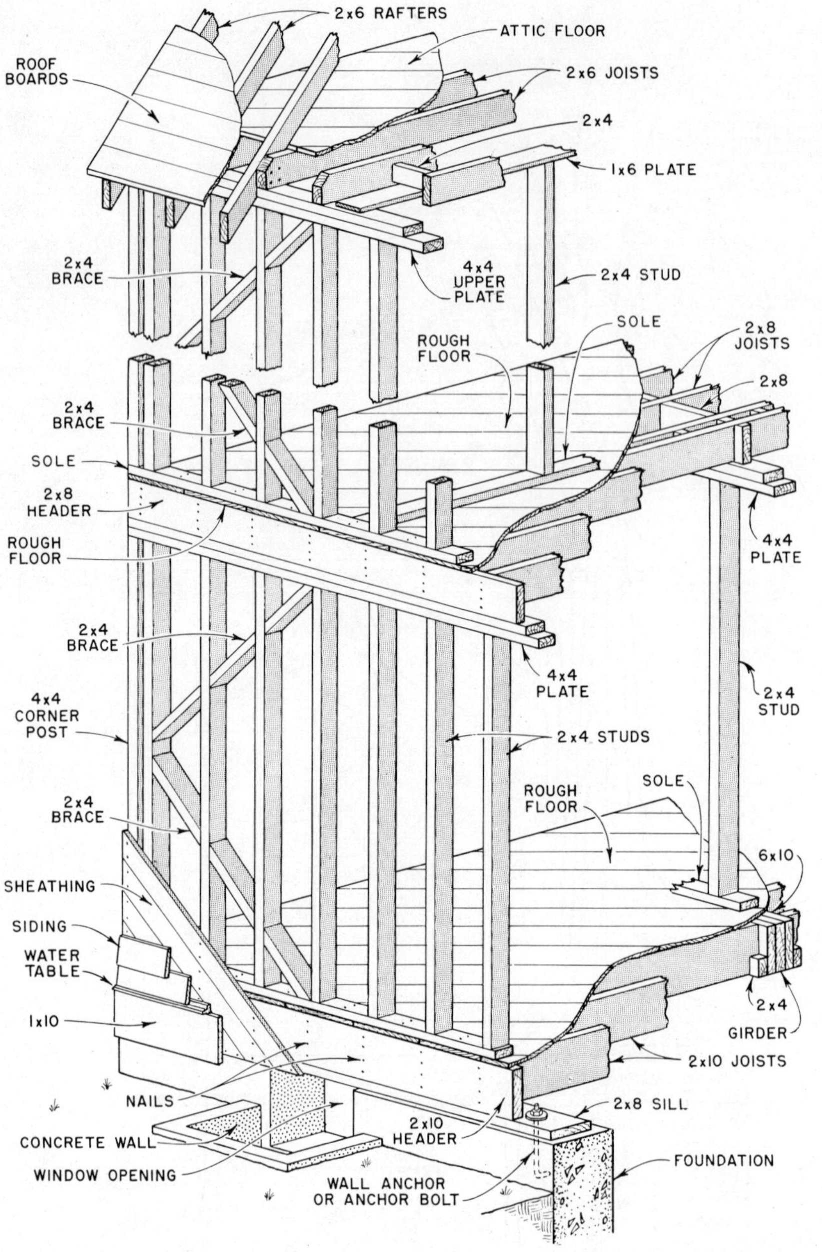

Figure 17-11
Common type of framing used in a wood building.

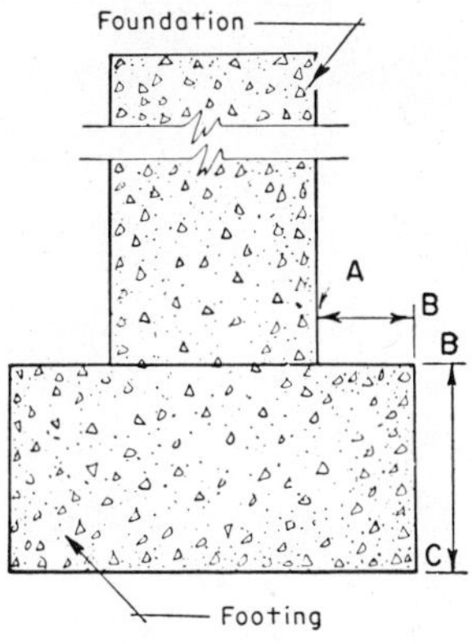

BC = 2 x AB

Figure 17-12
The size of a footing depends on the size of wall it is to carry.

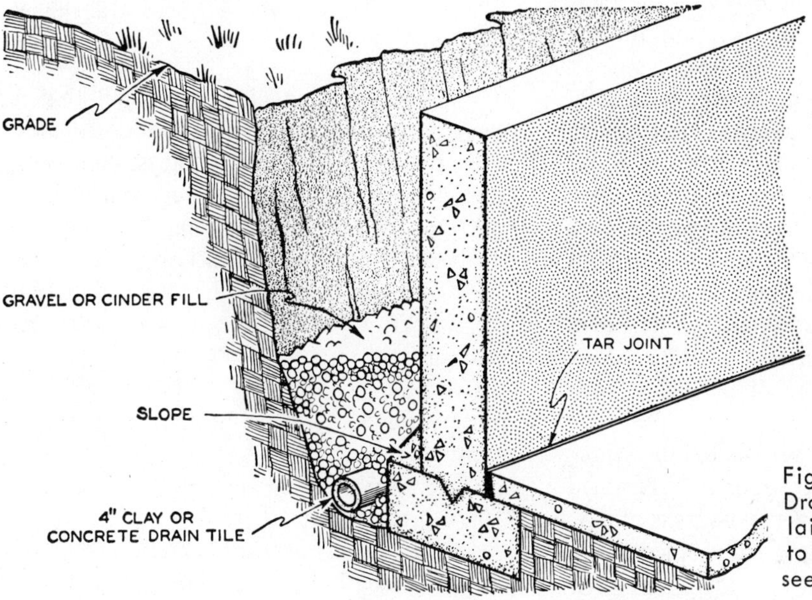

Figure 17-13
Drain tile is often laid around the footing to prevent water from seeping into the basement.

pends on the load it is to carry. As a rule, this thickness is figured at twice the width of its projecting portion. See Fig. 17-12. Foundation walls are designed principally to support the structure, to serve as basement walls to hold back the earth around the sides of the excavation, and to prevent water from flowing in. Several kinds of materials are used for foundation walls; the two most common are poured concrete and concrete blocks. The thickness and height of foundation walls are governed by the size and type of the building. These sizes are usually stipulated in the building code which prevails in the community.

To ensure that water does not seep into the basement, particularly where the soil is predominantly clay, and water does not flow off readily, a line of drain tile may be placed around the outside footing. See Fig. 17-13.

Sill. A sill is the member that rests directly on the foundation wall and extends completely around the building. A thin strip of non-rusting metal such as copper or aluminum is placed between the foundation wall and sill to act as a barrier against termites.

Header. A header is the piece that rests on the sill or plate and forms the outside frame which ties together the floor joists.

Floor joists. Joists form the frame which

support the flooring. Floor joists may be 2 x 8, 2 x 10, depending on the span and floor load. They are usually spaced 16 inches on centers.

Posts. Posts are members consisting of 4 x 4's or two 2 x 4's nailed together and are placed at all corners where bearing partitions meet the outer wall.

Studs. Studs are 2 x 4 vertical members for wall framework. On standard wood-frame construction, studs are spaced 16 inches on center. Double studs are used around doors, windows and other openings.

Plate. A plate is the member which ties the studs at the top. This piece is usually a 4 x 4 or two 2 x 4's nailed together. The plate serves as the lower base for the ends of the roof rafters, or as a support for the header in a multistory structure.

Girders. Girders are heavy horizontal members supported by columns which carry the load of joists. They are either of wood or steel and their size depends on the structural load they must carry. Girders are used in large buildings where the span is great and additional members are needed to support opposite ends of joists. Wood girders may be one solid piece, such as a 4 x 6, 6 x 8 or 8 x 10, or may consist of several 2 inch planks placed together.

Bridging. Bridging refers to the short pieces, usually 1 x 3, which are fastened between joists to stiffen the floor assembly. Occasionally, preformed metal pieces are used for this purpose.

Rafters. Rafters are the members that form the frame for the roof. They are usually spaced 16 inches on center.

Sole. A sole is the piece that rests on the rough flooring and supports a partition wall.

Lintels. Lintels are beams which span door and window openings and support the structure above these openings.

Sheathing. Sheathing is the material that is nailed to studs, rough flooring, and rafters to provide a base for the finish material. Fabricated fiber board, plywood, or boards are used for sheathing.

Girts. Girts or ribbons are horizontal pieces fastened to vertical studdings and corner posts to strengthen the structure.

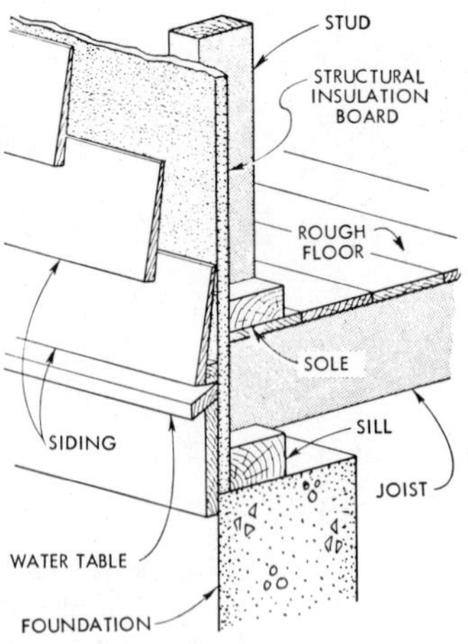

Figure 17-14
Exterior wall covered with siding.

Flashing. Flashing is sheet metal that is carried up under clapboards and shingles, and around such areas as valleys, chimneys, skylights and other units to keep out water.

Gutters. Gutters are troughs fastened to the fascia of a cornice to carry off rain water.

Fascia. A fascia is the flat horizontal member of a cornice that runs in a vertical position.

Cornice. A cornice is the horizontal projection which crowns or finishes the eaves of a building.

Eave. An eave is the part of the roof which projects over the side wall.

Exterior wall covering. Exterior walls on a wood frame building are covered with siding, shingles, stucco, brick veneer, or stone. In many instances a combination of these materials is used. Siding of either wood or aluminum is applied directly over the wallboard sheathing. See Fig. 17-14. Wood or asbestos shingles are often preferred for the exterior covering. See Fig. 17-15. Stucco is a type of rough plaster which is spread over the exterior walls. When this material is employed the wallboards or sheathing is furred with 1 x 2 strips of wood and covered with metal lath. Stucco is then applied to the lath. See Fig. 17-16. If brick veneer or stone is utilized, an air space of approximately 1 inch is left between the brick or stone and the sheathing. See Fig. 17-17.

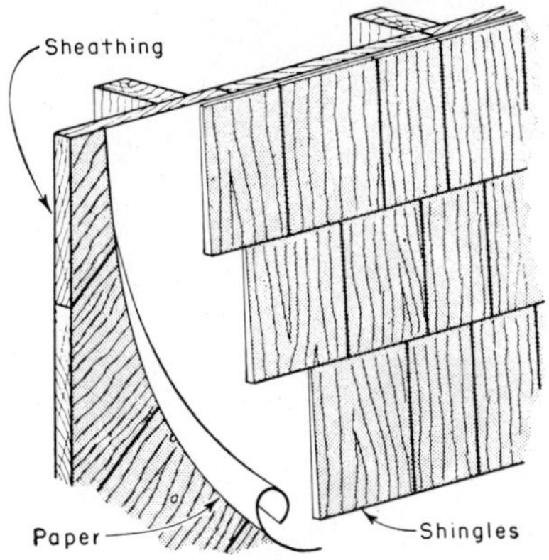

Figure 17-15
Exterior wall covered with shingles.

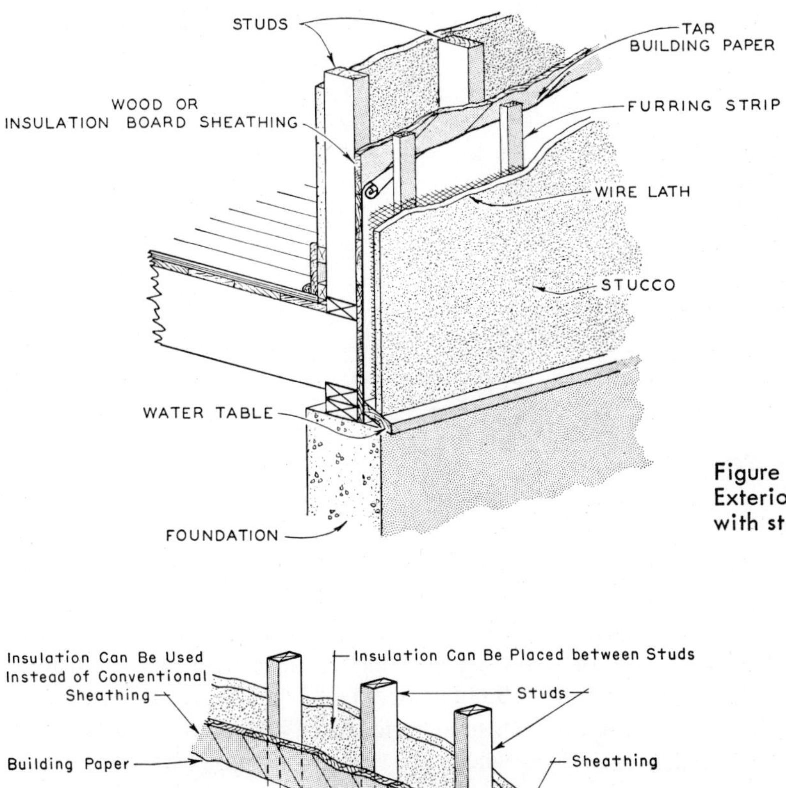

Figure 17-16
Exterior wall covered with stucco.

Figure 17-17
Exterior wall covered with brick veneer.

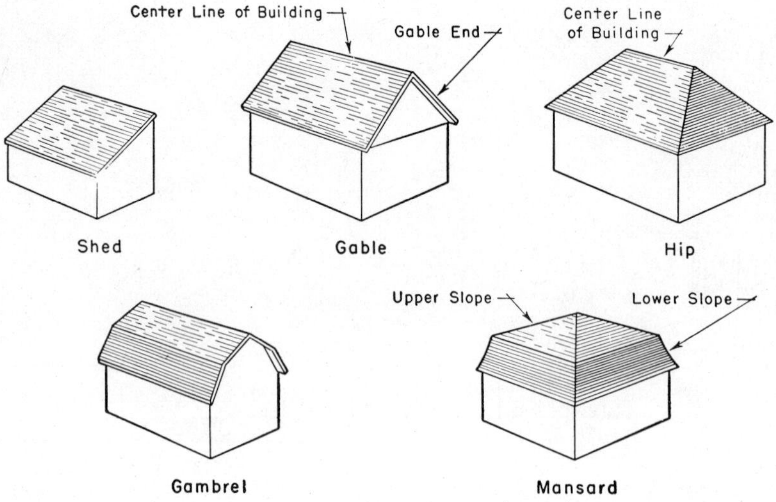

Figure 17-18
Types of roofs.

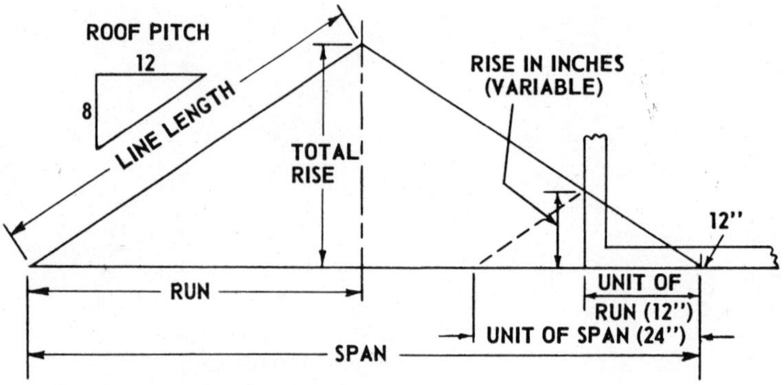

Figure 17-19
Roof terms. U.S. Navy

Interior wall covering. Before interior walls are fastened, insulating material is usually applied in the form of mineral wool or pack wool batts. A plaster backing is then nailed to the studs in the form of gypsum board sheets. Plaster is next spread over the gypsum sheets. In place of the gypsum board and plaster type of interior wall covering, a dry wall construction is often used. This form of covering eliminates the need for plaster. Special material in the form of plywood, tileboard, or gypsum board is secured to the studs and the desired decorative finishes applied directly to the surfaces. When gypsum board is used the joints are covered with tape and cement to produce a smooth finish.

Balloon, braced, western framing. Balloon framing is a type of structure in which the studs run the full length in a multistory building, from sill to rafters. A braced frame is more rigid than a balloon frame and is one where the exterior studs extend between floors only and are topped by girts that form a sill for the joists of the succeeding floor. Western framing is somewhat similar to braced framing except that it utilizes a boxed-sill construction at each floor.

Roofs. The five principal types of roofs are shed or flat, gable, hip, gambrel and mansard. See Fig. 17-18. The terms used in roof construction are span, rise, run and pitch. *Span* is the distance between the outer edges of the side walls that support a roof.

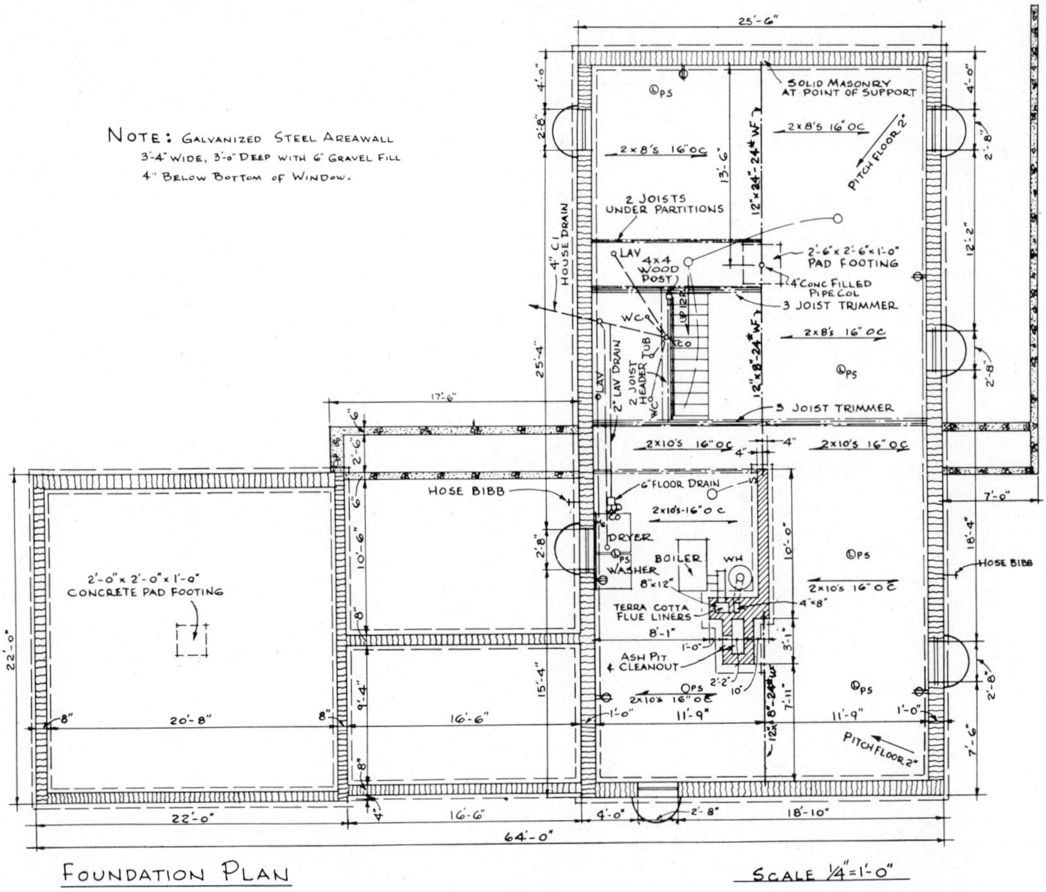

Figure 17–20
Foundation plan.

Rise is the vertical distance between the outer edge of the plate and the ridge. *Pitch* is the slope of the rafters expressed as a ratio of the rise to the run, thus pitch = rise/run. See Fig. 17-19.

17.13 Foundation plan

A foundation plan is a top view of the foundation showing the size of footings, various distances from reference and boundary points to footing centerlines, location of supporting beams and columns, wall material, wall openings and other pertinent details. See Fig. 17-20. Foundation walls are dimensioned to their corners and not from center-to-center. Regular symbols are used to designate the construction material.

The foundation plan as well as all floor plans are orientated on the sheet so that the front of the building is facing the bottom of the sheet.

If the building has a basement, the foundation plan will usually show the necessary units to be installed there. Thus partition walls will be indicated, basement equipment located, heating and cooling units included.

17.14 Floor plan

A floor plan shows a horizontal view of a building area as seen from above. See Fig. 17-21. A complete set of building plans will contain a separate drawing for each floor.

Included in a floor plan will be the outside shape of the building, the required room ar-

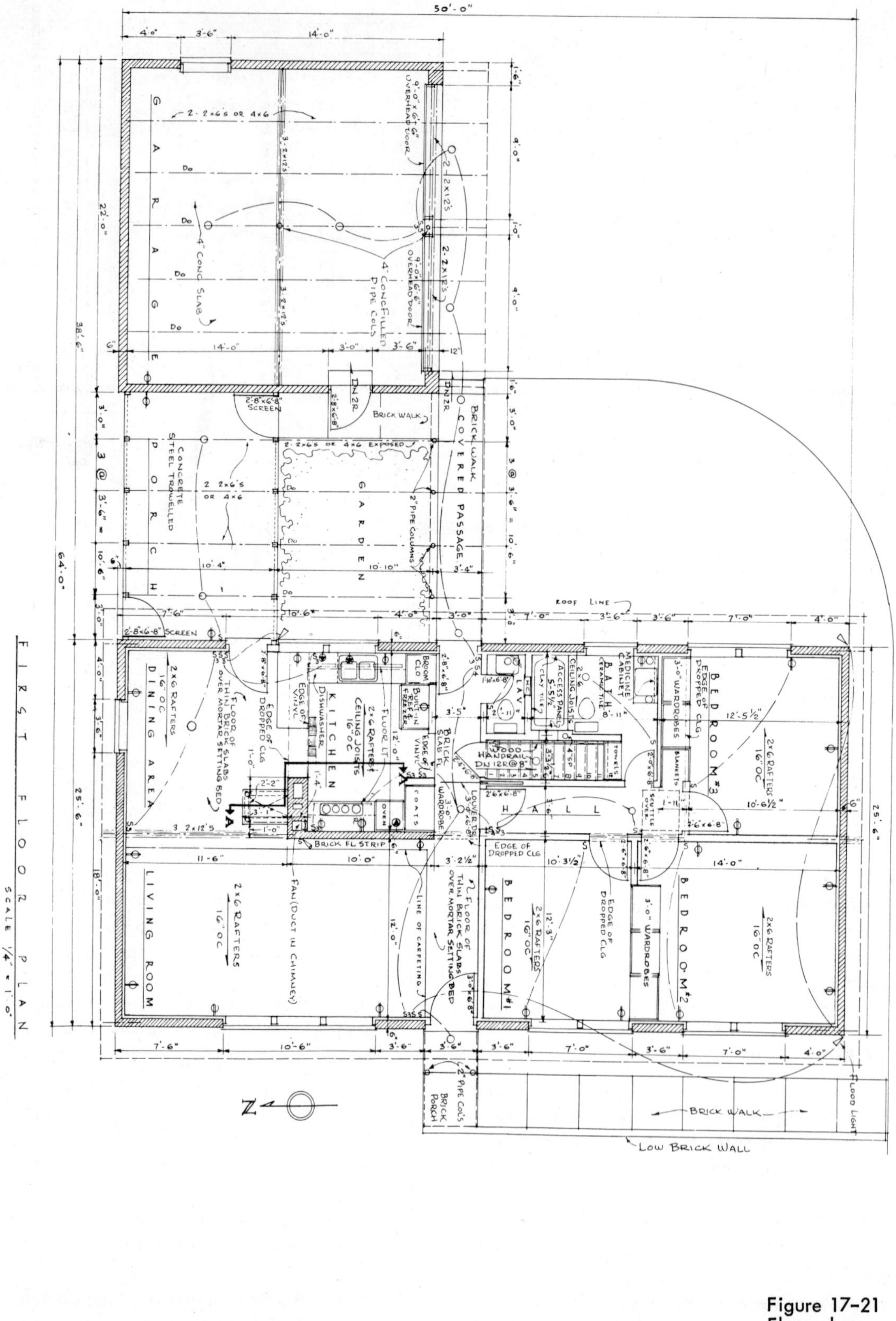

Figure 17–21
Floor plan.

rangement, size and shape of each room, as well as closets, halls and other auxiliary areas. Cabinets, special ornamental work, utility units and various features which are to be built in the rooms are shown. Stairways, if needed, are designated by showing approximately one-half of the full flight to the floor below or above with the exact number of risers stipulated. All openings for doors, windows, heating and ventilating outlets are shown in their correct location.

For small buildings, the practice is to include all of the necessary electrical, heating and plumbing details on the floor plans. On large buildings, this information is generally shown on separate drawings.

Dimensions are included both on the outside and inside the building lines of plan views. Outside dimensions are limited to overall sizes and sizes of openings in exterior walls. Inside dimensions locate sizes between the inside faces of building walls.

17.15 Elevations

Elevations are external views of the upright walls of a building; that is, flat representations of the sides of the structure projected on a vertical plane. Normally four views are shown, front, right side, left side, and rear. These views are sometimes labeled north elevation, east elevation, west elevation, and south elevation. See Figs. 17-22 to 17-25. The number of views drawn depends on the complexity of the shape. Views are not duplicated if the walls are similar in description. A building that is symmetrical about a centerline in the plan view may include an elevation showing adjacent half elevations of the rear and front. In this case a vertical centerline separates the two halves and each half is then identified by its proper title.

Elevation drawings show the exact shape and size of the height and width of each wall, window and door. They also present the external finish such as wood, brick, stone or glass by means of standard symbols. If a special arrangement of building material is necessary the construction pattern is so designated. Invisible lines are rarely used on elevations except to indicate the outline of the building below the grade line or possibly a roof line which may be concealed.

Very few dimensions are given on elevations. Height location of windows, ceiling, etc., are specified. Usually no horizontal dimensions are included. All other essential sizes are placed either on the floor plan or sectional views.

Elevation drawings will generally include the slope diagram of the roof. This is shown by a triangle that indicates the ratio of vertical rise in inches per foot of horizontal span. The roof diagram slope is placed just above the roof line.

Lines in elevation drawings are sometimes accentuated by rule line rendering to give meaning and tone to surface texture.

The basic steps in preparing elevations are:

1 First complete a plan and sectional view at the same scale. These correspond to the top and side views in regular orthographic projection.

2 Tape the plan and sectional view in their correct position on the sheet on which the elevation is to be drawn. Lines now can be projected from both the plan and side views in proceeding to lay out the elevation.

3 Show foundation below the grade level with hidden lines. All other lines should be visible. Use exterior material symbols for surface finish.

4 Designate finished floor and grade elevations by a note accompanied with a dimension on the line used for this purpose. Note in the illustrations showing elevations that this information is placed on the portion of the line that extends beyond the building.

5 Draw all doors, windows, roof drains, and other features that are to be located on the walls. Identify all views with their appropriate title.

17.16 Sectional views

Sectional views are vertical projections which show how a structure looks when cut by a vertical cutting plane. The cutting plane is

(Text continued on page 499)

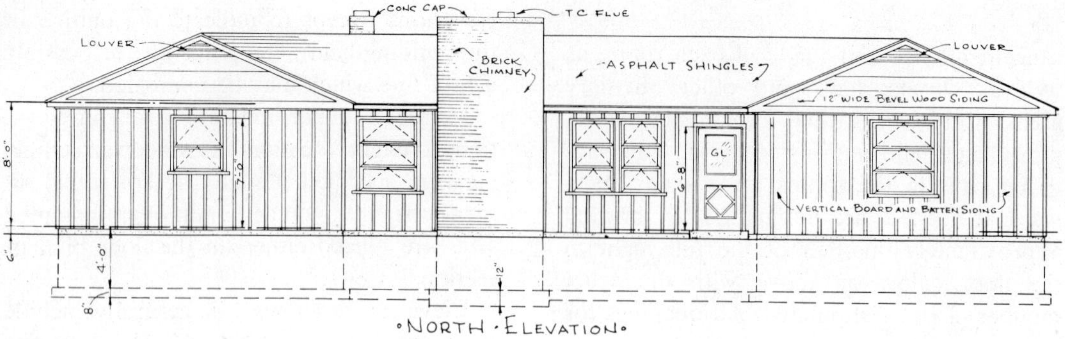

Figure 17–22
North elevation.

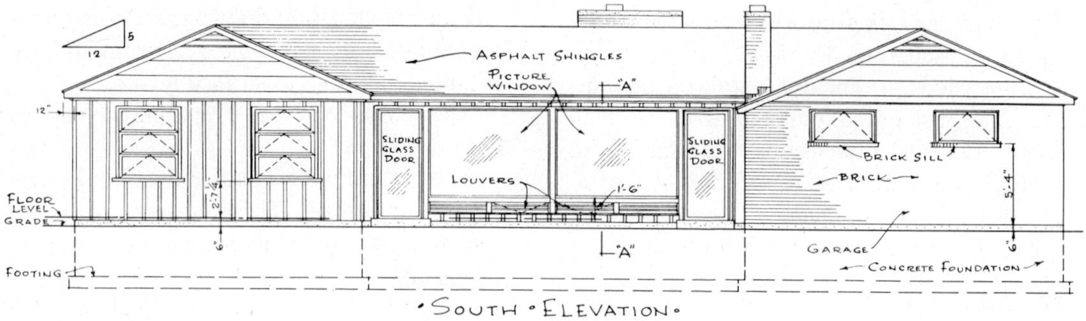

Figure 17–23
South elevation.

Figure 17–24
East elevation.

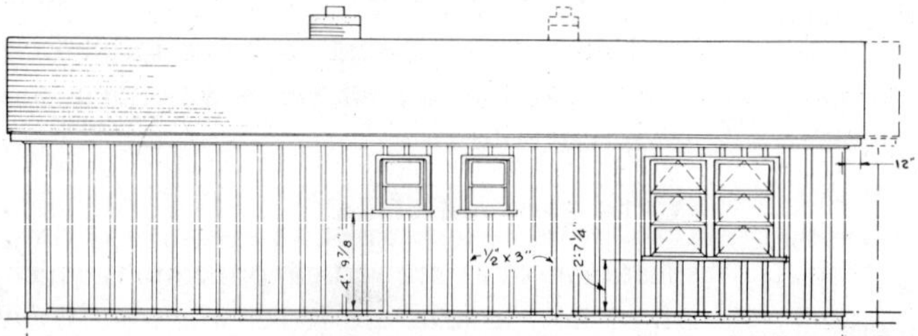

Figure 17–25
West elevation.

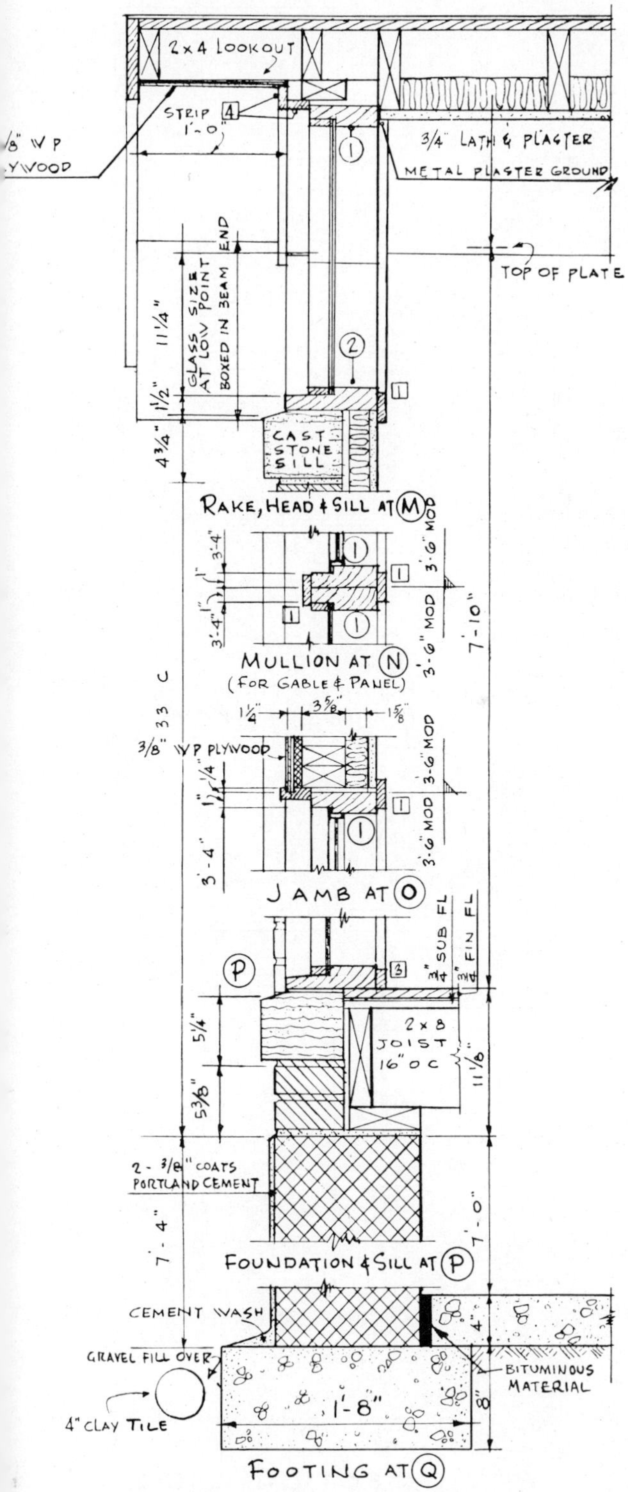

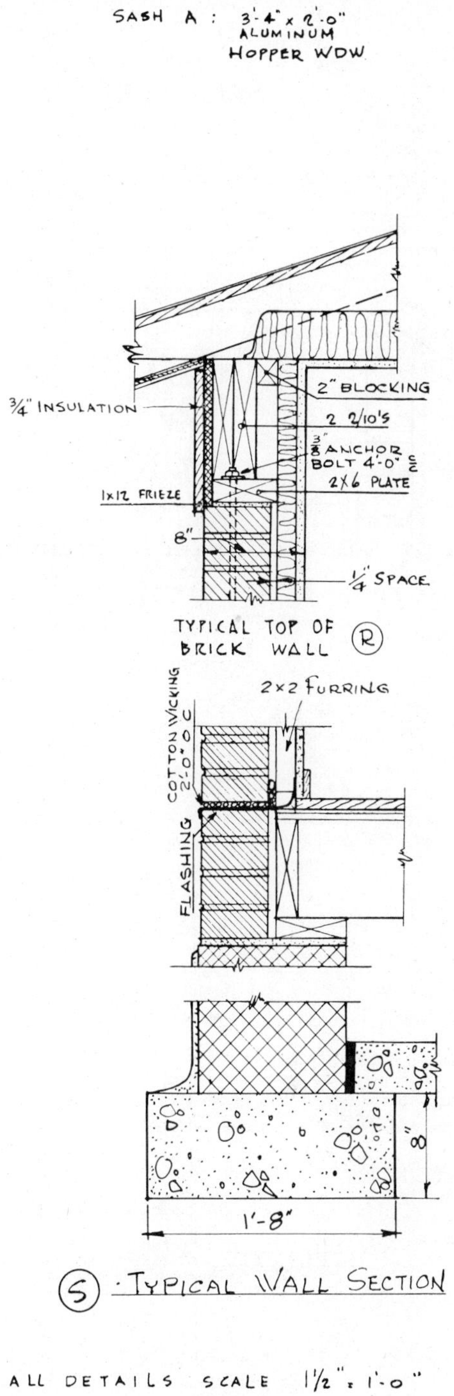

Figure 17–26
An architectural set of plans will contain one or more typical sections showing complete construction details of common building features.

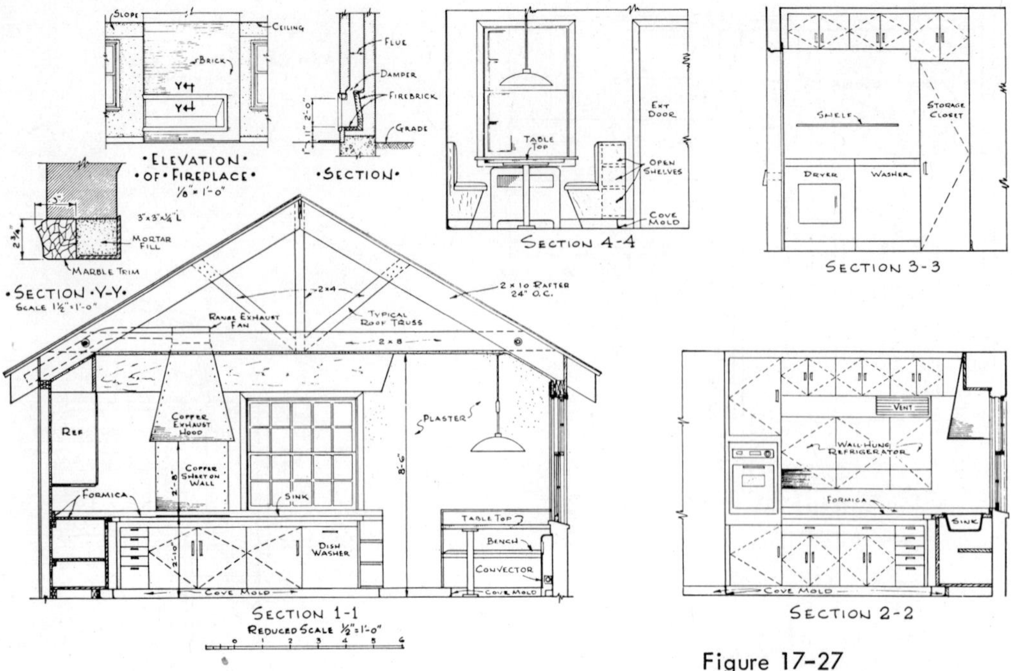

Figure 17-27
Transverse section through kitchen wing and fireplace details.

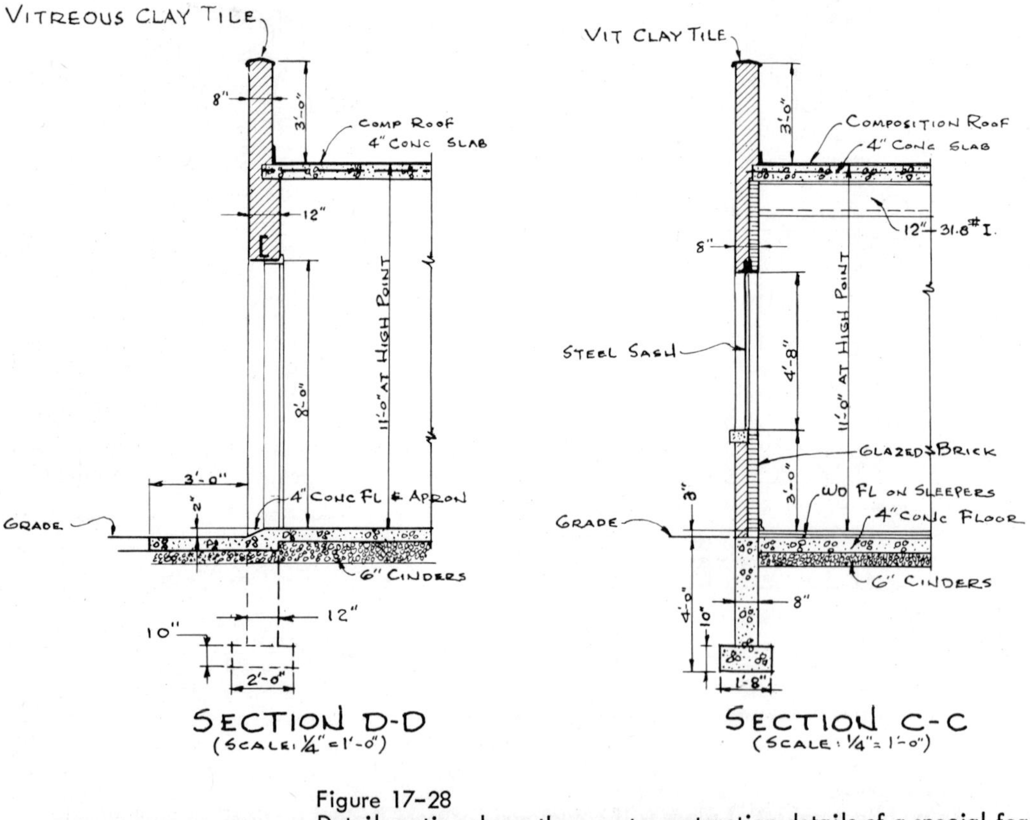

Figure 17-28
Detail section shows the exact construction details of a special feature which cannot be conveniently included on other drawings.

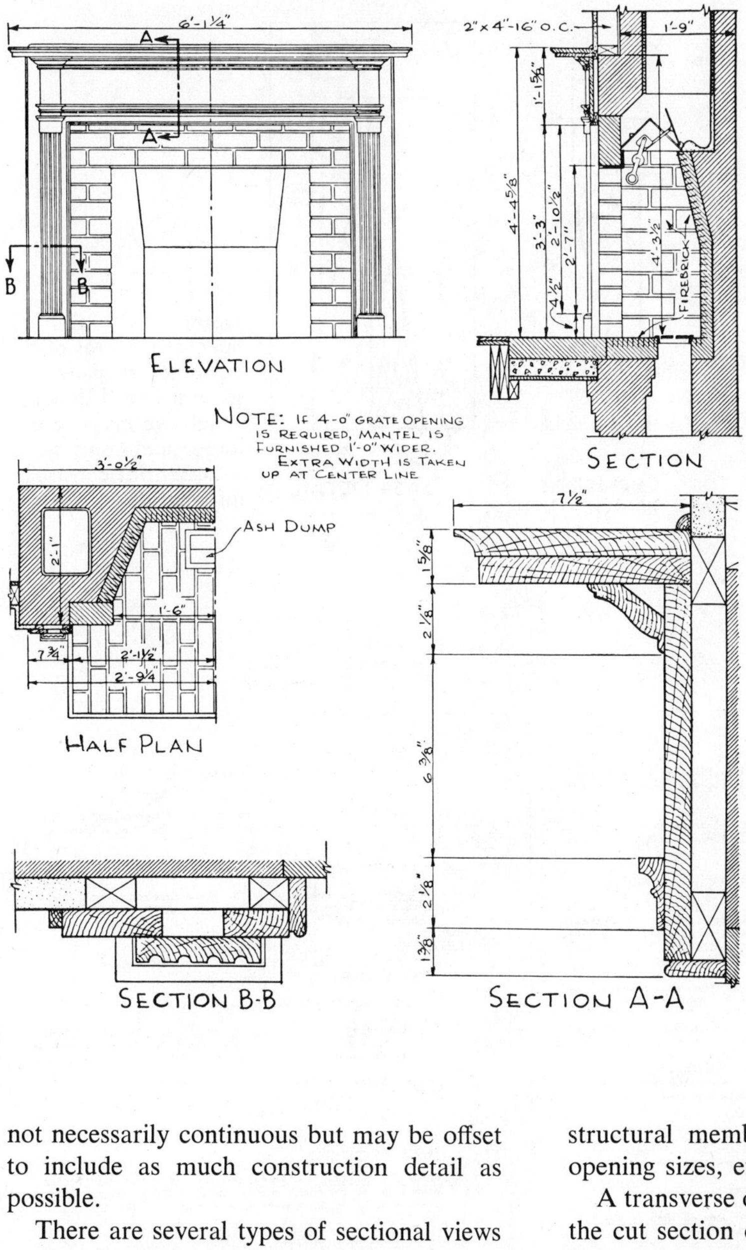

Figure 17-29
Detail section of a fireplace.

not necessarily continuous but may be offset to include as much construction detail as possible.

There are several types of sectional views used in architectural plans; the number or type depends on the complexity of the structure. Section views are classified as typical, transverse or horizontal, and detail. A typical section represents a portion of the structure that is common throughout the building and contains representative construction features which are used repeatedly. For example, Fig. 17-26 illustrates a typical wall section which extends from the foundation bed to the roof. Notice that all important construction details are given, such as size of structural members, type of material, wall opening sizes, etc.

A transverse or horizontal section includes the cut section of the entire building except in a symmetrical building, in which case the structure is shown only to the centerline. When the cutting plane passes across the narrow portion of the building the view is known as a transverse section; when it cuts across lengthwise it is referred to as a longitudinal section. See Fig. 17-27.

A detail section represents special features which need amplification of certain construction details such as a section of the foundation, fireplace, doorway, or stairway. See Figs. 17-28 and 17-29.

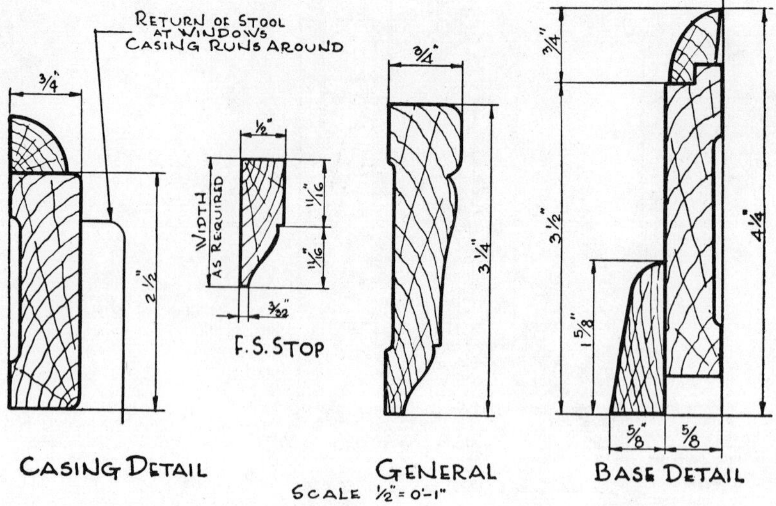

Figure 17-30
Special features of a building are shown by special detail drawings which are made to a larger scale and include all essential construction information.

Sec. 4. GRADING

a. Grading. Do all cutting, backfilling, filling, and grading necessary to bring all areas within property lines to the following subgrade levels:

(1) For paving, walks, and other paved areas to the underside of the respective installation as fixed by the finished grades therefor.

(2) For lawns and planted areas to four (4) inches below finished grades.

b. Material for Backfill and Fill. All material used for backfill and fill shall be free from deleterious materials subject to termite attack, rot, decay or corrosion, and frozen lumps or objects which would prevent solid compaction.

Materials for backfill and fill in various locations shall be as follows:

(1) For Interior of Building. Sand or an approved properly graded mixture of sand and gravel. Foundry sand shall not be used.

(2) For Exterior Under Paving. Use excavated materials free from top soil, or other materials approved by the Architect.

(3) For Use Under Lawns and Planted Areas. Use, after Architect's approval, excavated materials with admixture of top soil or earth. Heavy clay shall not be used.

c. Backfill Against Foundation Walls shall:

(1) Be done only after work to be concealed thereby has been inspected and approved by the Architect.

(2) Be deposited in six (6) inch layers, each to be solidly compacted by tamping and puddling.

d. Subgrades for Lawn and Planted Areas. Slope the subgrade evenly to provide drainage away from building in all directions at a grade of at least 1/4 in. per ft.

e. Settlement of Fills. Fill to required subgrade levels any areas where settlement occurs.

3

DIVISION 2: CONCRETE

Sec. 1. SCOPE. This division includes all concrete and related items required to complete the work indicated on the drawings and/or specified.

Sec. 2. MATERIALS

a. Portland cement shall conform to the requirements as stated in FS SS-C-192 or ASTM Designation C150-49 for standard portland cement Type I.

b. Aggregates. All aggregates for concrete work shall conform to the requirements of FS SS-A-281a or ASTM Designation C33-46 and the following:

(1) Fine aggregates shall be natural sand.

(2) Coarse aggregates shall be crushed stone or gravel free from adherent coatings. Size range for footings shall be as designated "No. 4 to 3/4".

c. Water. Water used for concrete work shall be clean and free from injurious amounts of oils, acids, alkalies, organic, or other deleterious substances.

d. Vapor Barrier Paper shall conform to FS UU-P-264a or ASTM Designation D697-42J.

e. Ready-Mix Concrete shall be used. Certificates shall be furnished by the ready-mix concrete mixing plant that the concrete has a minimum 28-day compressive strength of 3000 lbs per square in.

Sec. 3. DEPOSITING CONCRETE

a. Soil bottoms for footings and slabs shall be approved by the Architect before placing concrete.

b. Deposit concrete as nearly as practicable in its final position to avoid segregation which might occur during rehandling or flowing.

c. Retempering. No concrete that has partially hardened or become

4

Figure 17-31
A specification list, which describes in detail all essential features of the construction project, is included with building plans.

17.17 Detail drawings

Detail drawings are large-scale drawings which show how certain specific items are to be constructed or placed. Thus a detail may present the construction method required at doors, windows, eaves, or cabinets. These drawings are used whenever the information provided in elevation, plan, or sectional views is not sufficiently clear for the workers to follow. Detail drawings are grouped and properly referenced to facilitate ease of location on the other drawings. See Fig. 17-30.

17.18 Building specifications

Once major construction details are crystallized, an architectural specification outline is prepared. This specification form spells out all construction details such as kinds of materials to be used, quality of workmanship, type of heating, ventilating, electrical and plumbing fixtures, interior and exterior wall finishes, grading and other essential building features which the architect deems necessary. The specifications also stipulate legal aspects of responsibility and obligations of contractors, sub-contractors, architectural supervision and financial obligations.

The purpose of the specification list is to supplement the information shown in the working drawings so there is no possibility for misinterpretation. The descriptive specifications give the owner definite assurance that the building project is implemented in accordance with defined agreements. It also gives the contractor and sub-contractor a clear picture of what they are bidding on and what will be required of them during the construction stages. A short section of a specification form is illustrated in Fig. 17-31.

Problems, section 17

1 Make a complete set of plans for the room layout shown in Fig. 17-32.

2 Design a single story house with basement based on the floor plan shown in Fig. 17-33. Each square represents two feet. Prepare all floor plans, elevations, and sections needed. Include window and door schedule.

3 Prepare a complete set of plans for the house shown in Fig. 17-34.

4 Make the necessary drawings for the ranch-style house based on the layout shown in Fig. 17-35.

5 Design a house based on the layout shown in Fig. 17-36. Prepare complete set of building plans.

6 Prepare a complete set of plans for a house based on the layout shown in Fig. 17-37.

7 Prepare a front elevation rendering of a house of your choice.

8 Prepare a complete set of plans of a house of your choice.

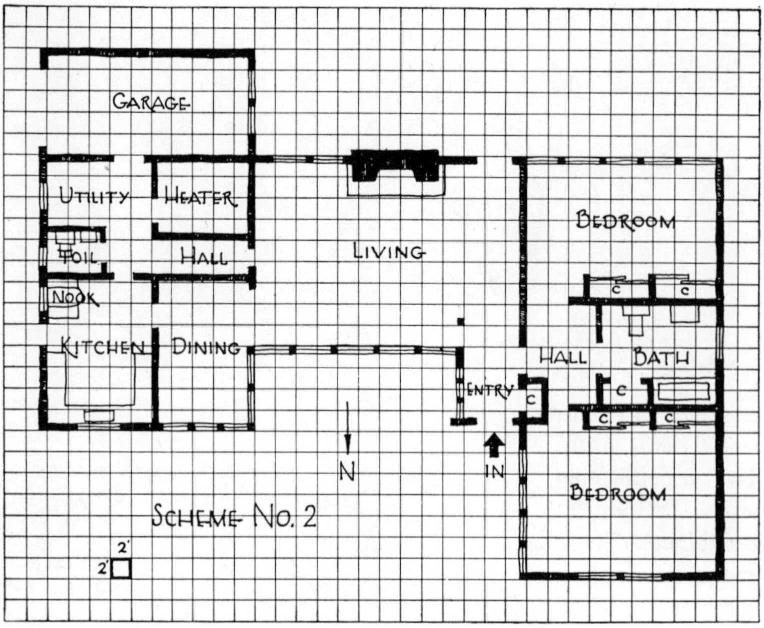

Figure 17-32
Problem 1.

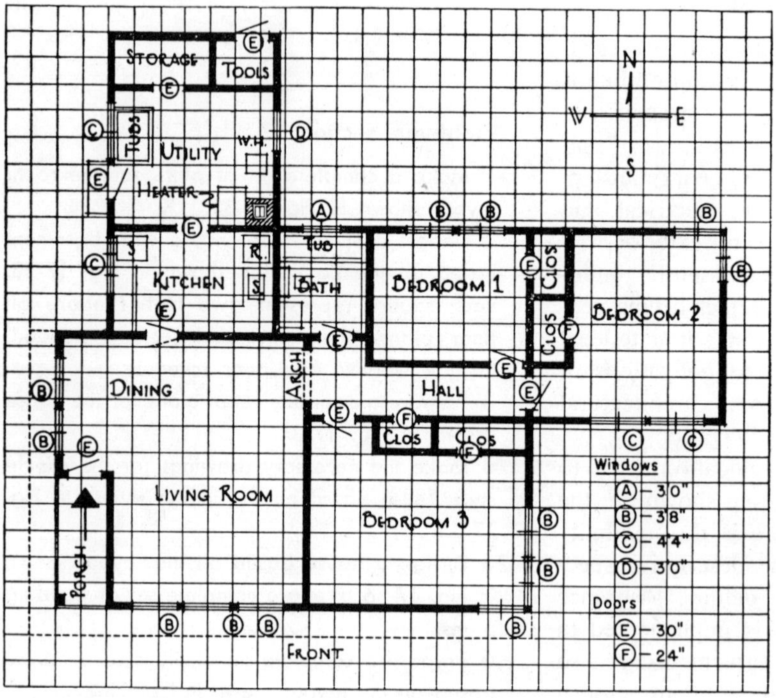

Figure 17-33
Problem 2.

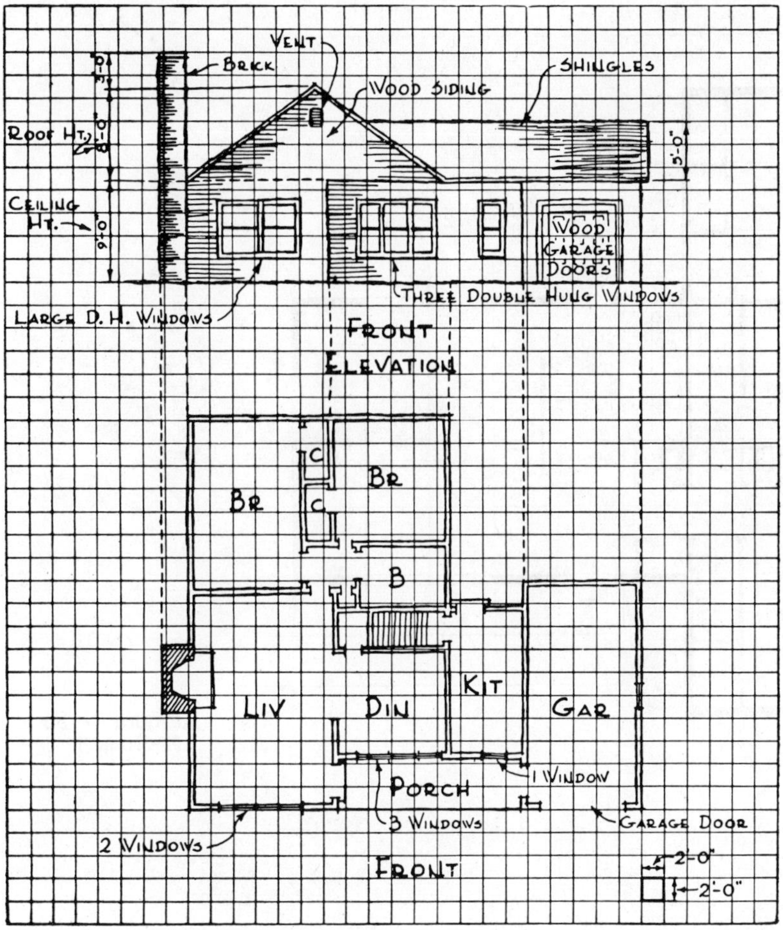

Figure 17-34
Problem 3.

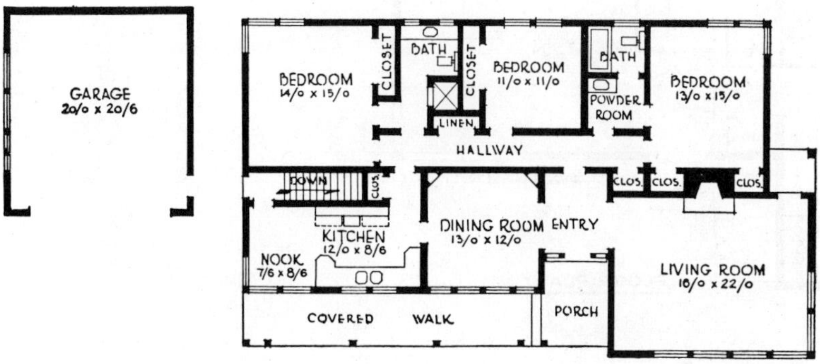

Figure 17-35
Problem 4.

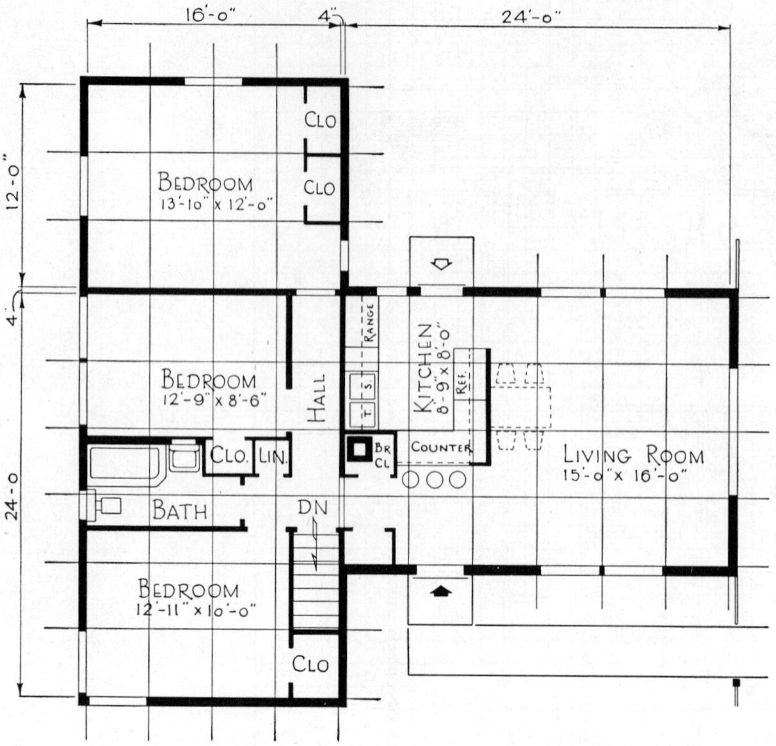

Figure 17-36
Problem 5.

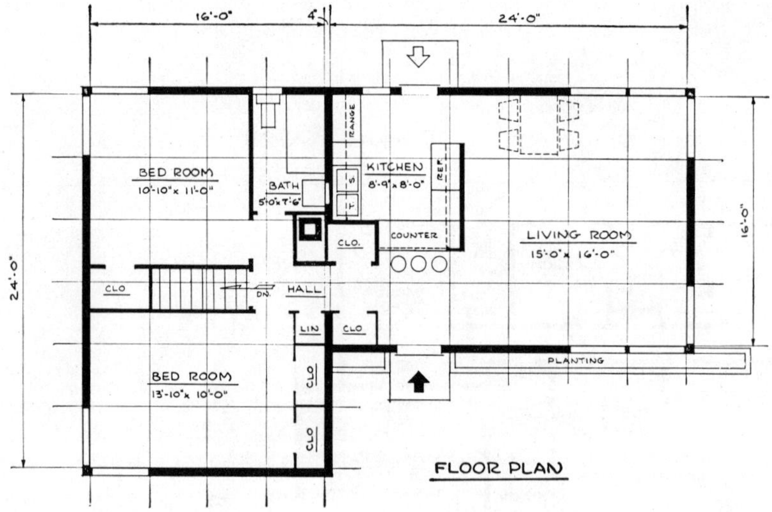

Figure 17-37
Problem 6.

'tructural drawing 18

Structural drawing deals specifically with the preparation of plans for the construction of commercial buildings, industrial plants, schools, hospitals, bridges and other large structures. This type of drawing differs in some respects from the usual orthographic representation commonly associated with machine drawing. Special techniques are used to present form and shape, and frequently certain symbols are employed to describe structural elements.

The civil engineer or structural designer determines the design of the structure. He makes all of the necessary calculations, prepares the preliminary design sketches and provides the technical data concerning structural members in the form of diagrams, notes and computations. While preparing the preliminary sketches, the design engineer takes into consideration such factors as code requirements, availability of materials, conditions in the building trades, ease of erection, aesthetic qualities, site conditions and strength of materials. From the design engineer's data, draftsmen then proceed to make finished design drawings. In addition to the design drawings, draftsmen prepare detailed working drawings, sometimes referred to as shop drawings. These drawings are used by steel fabricators who supply the structural steel or other construction materials. The drawings are made to show exactly how members are to be fabricated and erected in the structural framing.

It is not the intent of this section to discuss all of the design factors involved in structural drawing or to cover completely the entire scope of structural drawing but simply to present a brief orientation of the field to the beginning student of engineering drawing.

18.1 Types of structural building frames

The two most common types of structural building frames are reinforced concrete and steel. In reinforced concrete, columns, beams, floors, stairways, etc., are made of reinforced concrete with an exterior facing of brick or other masonry materials backed up with lightweight concrete blocks. See Fig. 18-1.

Steel frame buildings utilize steel members as the principal framing elements. The structural members are joined in several ways. Usually shop connections are welded or riveted and field connections bolted or welded. The exterior facing is also of brick or some other masonry material backed up with concrete blocks. See Fig. 18-2.

18.2 Steel framing systems

There are three basic steel framing systems: wall-bearing, beam-and-column, and long-span. One or more of these types are often used in the construction of a building.

In the *wall-bearing framing,* the exterior and interior walls are used to support one or both ends of steel framing members. The walls in this case are constructed of masonry and are thick enough to carry the transmitted loads. See Fig. 18-3. Generally, wall-bearing framing is limited to relatively low structures.

Beam-and-column framing consists of steel columns which provide support for the beams spanning between them. This type of framing is used to construct multistory buildings. By spacing columns to support horizontal beams, any number of floor and roof areas can be built by simply duplicating the details of a bay. See Fig. 18-4.

Figure 18-1
A typical reinforced concrete building in which the framing members are made of reinforced concrete. Miller-Davis Co.

Figure 18-2
In a steel frame building, the structural members are of steel and the exterior facing usually of brick and backed with concrete blocks. Miller-Davis Co.

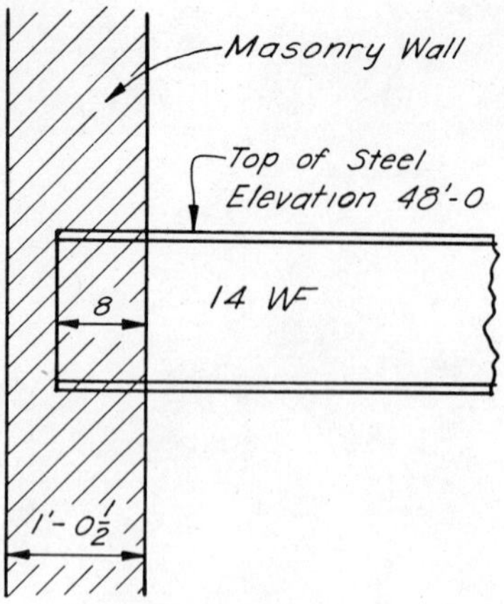

Figure 18-3
The wall-bearing steel framing system utilizes the masonry walls as supporting columns.

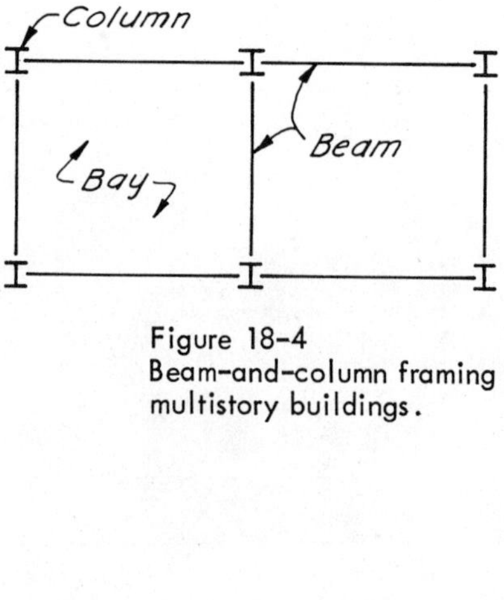

Figure 18-4
Beam-and-column framing is used in multistory buildings.

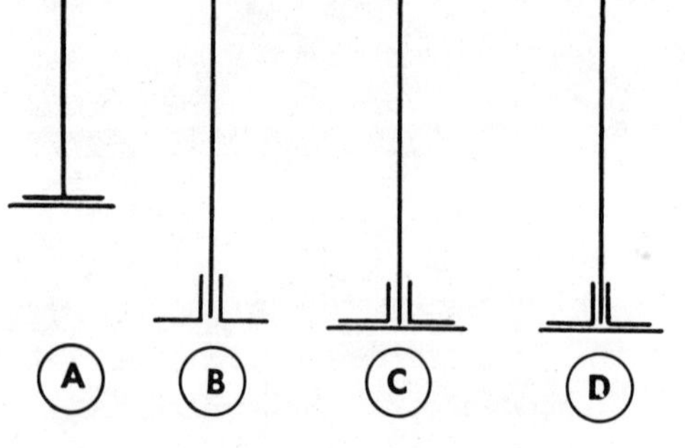

Figure 18-5
Typical profile shapes of girders.

Long-span framing is required when large clear areas are necessary and distances are greater than can be spanned by regular rolled shape members. To achieve long-span framing, built-up girders or trusses are used. Girders are members made up of several sections of steel shapes which are joined together by steel plates. The plates are either riveted or welded in place. Typical profile shapes of girders are shown in Fig. 18-5. Type A consists of cover plates added to the flanges of the beams. Types B and C have plates and angles, and type D uses a channel on the top flange to provide greater bending strength. The plates, as a rule, do not run the entire length of the girder. Their length is governed by the required span of the girder and the amount of bending stress the built-up members must withstand at the various sections along its length. *Trusses* consist of two principal members known as a *top chord* and *bottom chord* which are held together by members called *webs.* The web members are designated as verticals or diagonals depending on their placement in the truss. The trusses are joined by horizontal sections referred to as *purlins.* Trusses are often used instead of girders, especially in places requiring unusually long spans. Since trusses have greater depth, they possess greater stiffness against deflection than girders. The five types of trusses most frequently employed are Pratt, Warren, Fink, Scissors, and Bowstring. See Fig. 18-6.

18.3 Steel structural shapes

Several of the cross sectional shapes of steel components used in building construction are shown in Fig. 18-7. These members serve a variety of functions such as columns, girders, beams, bracings and connections. They are available in a wide range of sizes and weights. Specific dimensions of structural members will be found in the American Institute of Steel Construction Manual.[1] Specification of steel members include nominal depth in inches, group symbol, weight per foot in pounds, and length in feet and

1. *Steel Construction* (New York: American Institute of Steel Construction, 1959).

inches. The following are typical examples of how specifications are listed:

Wide Flange Beam: 27 WF 114 x 28'-10
- Depth — 27
- Group Symbol — WF
- Weight — 114
- Length — 28'-10

American Standard I-Beam: 15 I 42.9 x 16'-3 1/4
- Depth — 15
- Group Symbol — I
- Weight — 42.9
- Length — 16'-3 1/4

Angles: ∠ 4 x 4 x 1/4 x 5'-6
- Group Symbol — ∠
- Leg Widths — 4 x 4
- Thickness — 1/4
- Length — 5'-6

American Standard Channels: 10 [15.3 x 18'-8
- Depth — 10
- Group Symbol — [
- Weight — 15.3
- Length — 18'-8

Structural Tees: ST 16 WF 65 x 6'-0
- Group Symbol — ST
- Depth — 16
- Basic Shape — WF
- Weight — 65
- Length — 6'-0

Zees: Z 5 x 3 1/2 x 17.9 x 4'-10
- Group Symbol — Z
- Depth — 5
- Flange Width — 3 1/2
- Weight — 17.9
- Length — 4'-10

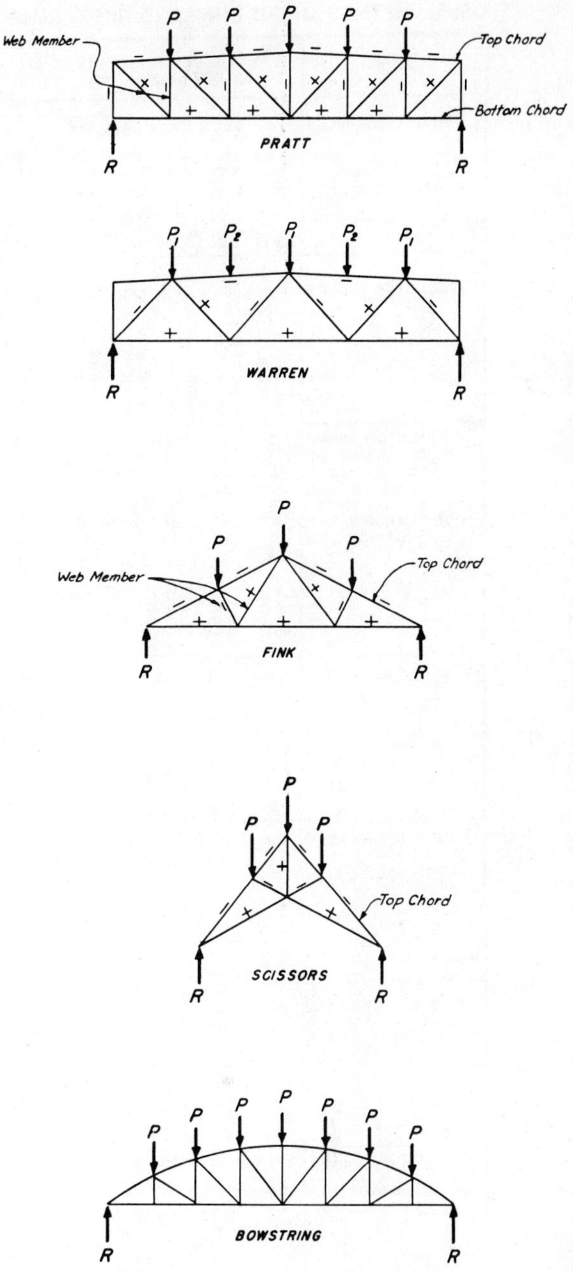

Figure 18-6
Trusses are steel frameworks designed to absorb compression and tension stresses. AISC

USUAL METHOD OF BILLING AND SKETCHING STRUCTURAL STEEL SHAPES ON SHOP DRAWINGS.

<table>
<tr><th>GROUP</th><th>EXAMPLE OF BILLING ON DETAIL BILLING</th><th>CONVENTIONAL WAY OF SHOWING ON DETAIL DRAWINGS AND IDENTIFICATION OF MAJOR COMPONENT PARTS</th><th>REMARKS</th></tr>
<tr><td>EQUAL LEG ANGLES</td><td>∠ 3 1/2 x 3 1/2 x 1/4 x 5'-6
GROUP SYMBOL / LEG WIDTH IN INCHES / LEG WIDTH IN INCHES / THICKNESS IN INCHES / LENGTH IN FT. AND IN.</td><td>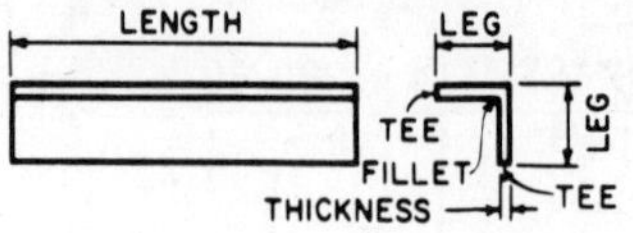</td><td rowspan="2">ON DETAILS MADE TO SCALE OF 1"=1'-0 OR SMALLER, DO NOT SHOW ROUNDED OFF TOES OF ANGLES OR INTERIOR FILLET BETWEEN LEGS. BILL LONG LEG OF UNEQUAL LEG ANGLES FIRST. EXAGGERATE LEG THICKNESS TO SUIT.</td></tr>
<tr><td>UNEQUAL LEG ANGLES</td><td>∠ 6 x 4 x 3/8 x 10'-3
GROUP SYMBOL / LONG LEG IN INCHES / SHORT LEG IN INCHES / THICKNESS IN INCHES / LENGHT IN FT. AND IN.</td><td>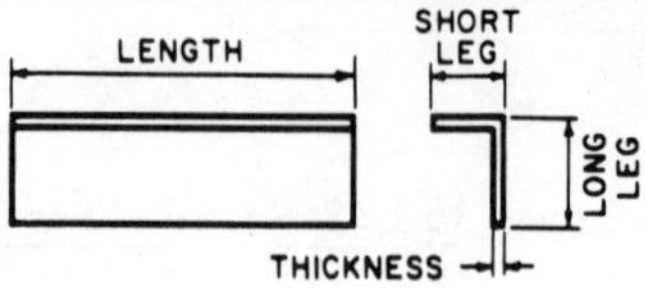</td></tr>
<tr><td>AM. STD. I-BEAMS
MISC. LIGHT BEAMS
STD. MILL BEAMS
JUNIOR BEAMS
JOISTS
WIDE FLANGE BEAMS
BEARING PILES</td><td>15 I 42.9 x 16'-3 1/2
12 B 19 x 8'-2 1/4
8 M 17 x 7'-10
12 JR 11.8 x 9'-3
8 J 10 x 7'-0
27 WF 94 x 26'-10
12 BP 74 x 20'-3
NOMINAL DEPTH / GROUP SYMBOL / WGT. PER FT. IN POUNDS / LENGTH IN FT. & INCHES</td><td>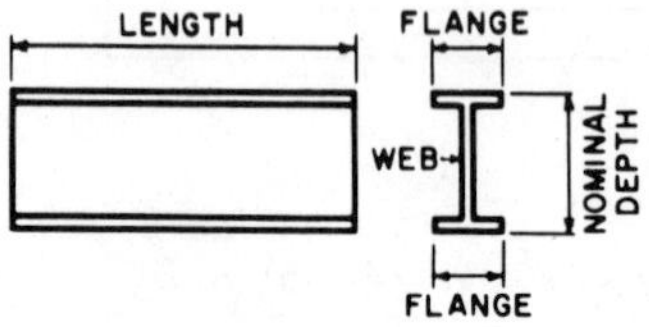</td><td rowspan="2">ON DETAILS MADE TO SCALE OF 1"=1'-0 OR SMALLER, DO NOT SHOW ROUNDED OFF TOES OF FLANGES OR INTERIOR FILLETS BETWEEN WEB AND FLANGES. DO NOT SHOW FLANGE SLOPE FOR THOSE BEAMS WHICH HAVE SLOPING FLANGES. EXAGGERATE WEB AND FLANGE THICKNESS TO SUIT.</td></tr>
<tr><td>MISC. LIGHT COLS.</td><td>8 x 8 M 34.3 x 10'-11
NOMINAL DEPTH IN INCHES / NOMINAL FLANGE IN INCHES / GROUP SYMBOL / WGT. PER FT. IN POUNDS / LENGTH IN FT. AND IN.</td><td>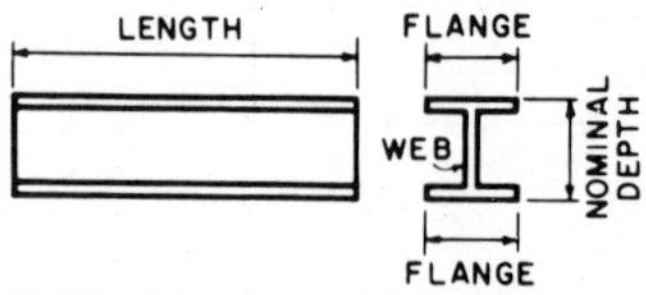</td></tr>
<tr><td>AM. STD. CHANNELS</td><td>10 [15.3 x 18'-8
DEPTH IN IN INCHES / GROUP SYMBOL / WGT. PER FT. IN POUNDS / LENGTH IN FT. AND IN.</td><td>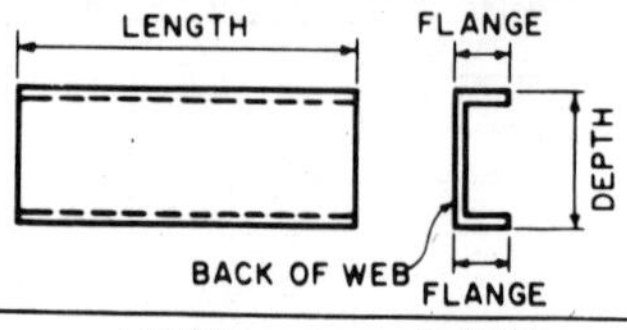</td><td rowspan="3">ON DETAILS MADE TO SCALE OF 1"=1'-0 OR SMALLER, DO NOT SHOW ROUNDED OFF TOES OF FLANGES NOR INTERIOR FILLETS BETWEEN WEB, OR STEM, AND FLANGES. DO NOT SHOW FLANGE SLOPE. EXAGGERATE WEB, STEM AND FLANGE THICKNESS TO SUIT.</td></tr>
<tr><td>CAR & SHIP CHANNELS</td><td>13 x 4 [31.8 x 9'-0
DEPTH IN INCHES / NOMINAL FLANGE IN INCHES / GROUP SYMBOL / WGT. PER FT. IN POUNDS / LENGTH IN FT. AND IN.</td><td>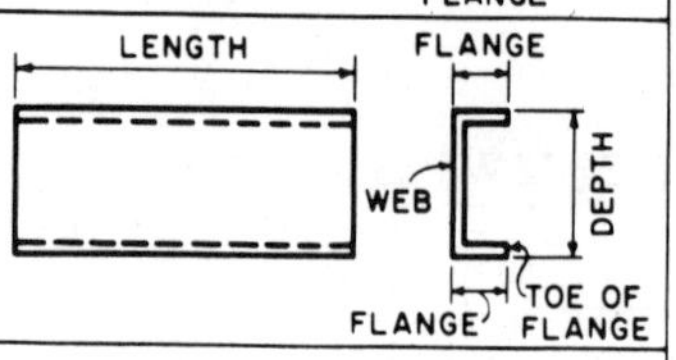</td></tr>
<tr><td>STRUCTURAL TEES</td><td>ST 16 WF 65 x 6'-0
ST 5 I 12.7 x 9'-6
ST 4 B 7.5 x 3'-3
ST 5 JR 4.5 x 9'-3
GROUP SYMBOL / NOMINAL DEPTH IN INCHES / BASIC SHAPE USED / WGT. PER FT. IN POUNDS / LENGTH IN FT. AND IN.</td><td>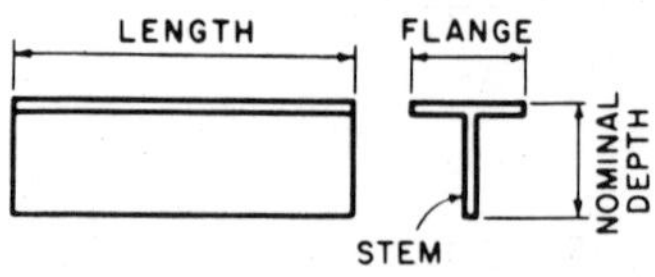</td></tr>
</table>

Figure 18-7
Basic shapes of steel structural members.
ASA Y14.14-1957

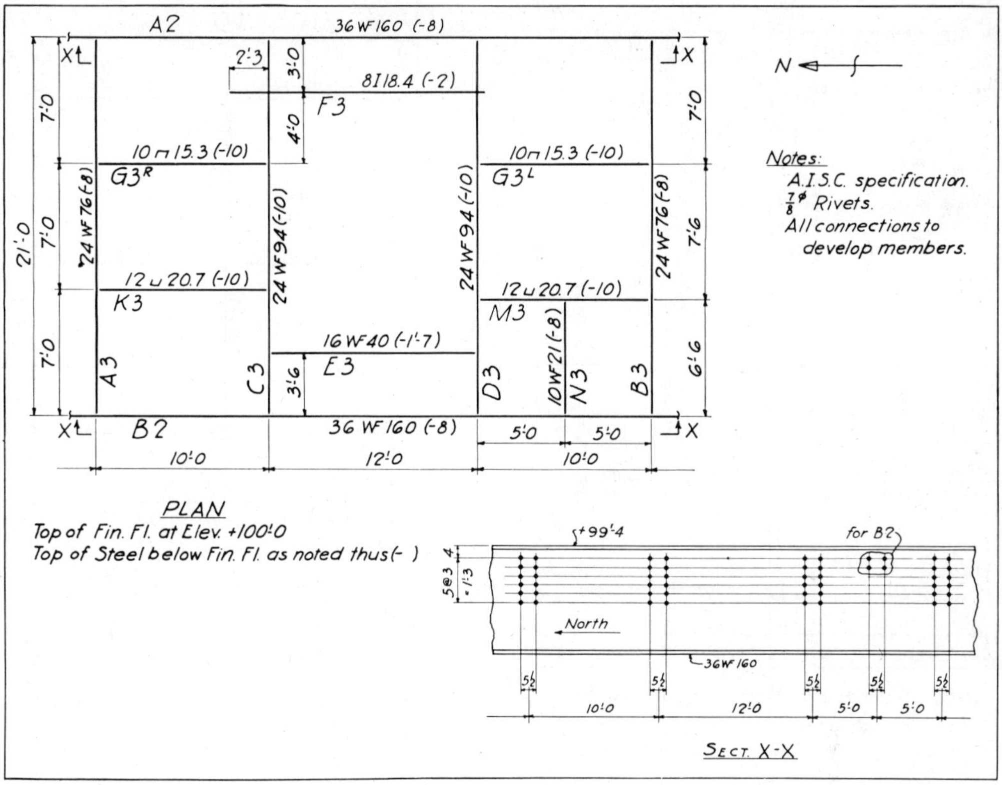

Figure 18-8
A steel framing plan shows the general arrangement of the members as well as their required shape, size and weight. AISC

18.4 Design drawings

Design drawings include all of the essential views required for the erection of a building. A complete set of plans will contain foundation details, room arrangement, elevations, and construction details.

An important function of design drawings is to show the steel framing plan of the building. A typical floor framing plan is illustrated in Fig. 18-8. A framing plan not only presents the layout of the steel members but also indicates the shape, size and weight of each member.

Members in a design drawing are assumed to be parallel or at right angles to one another and with the webs in a vertical plane. Vertical elevations are expressed in feet and inches as 92′-6 or by a note: ALL STEEL FLUSH TOP AT EL. 92′-6.

All like members in a design framing plan are marked with the conventional *do* and never with the symbol (″). See Fig. 18-9. However, some designers refrain from using the conventional *do* to avoid any possibility of confusion. For example, in Fig. 18-9 the members on column line D would be clearly identified as 16WF40 or 18WF50. Since the steel fabricator is not usually responsible for the foundation work, the designer will as a rule include column base details on his drawings.

Beside the properly dimensioned plans of the required framing at various levels, design drawings also include *column schedules* as shown in Fig. 18-9. Columns are identified on the plan by some numbering system.

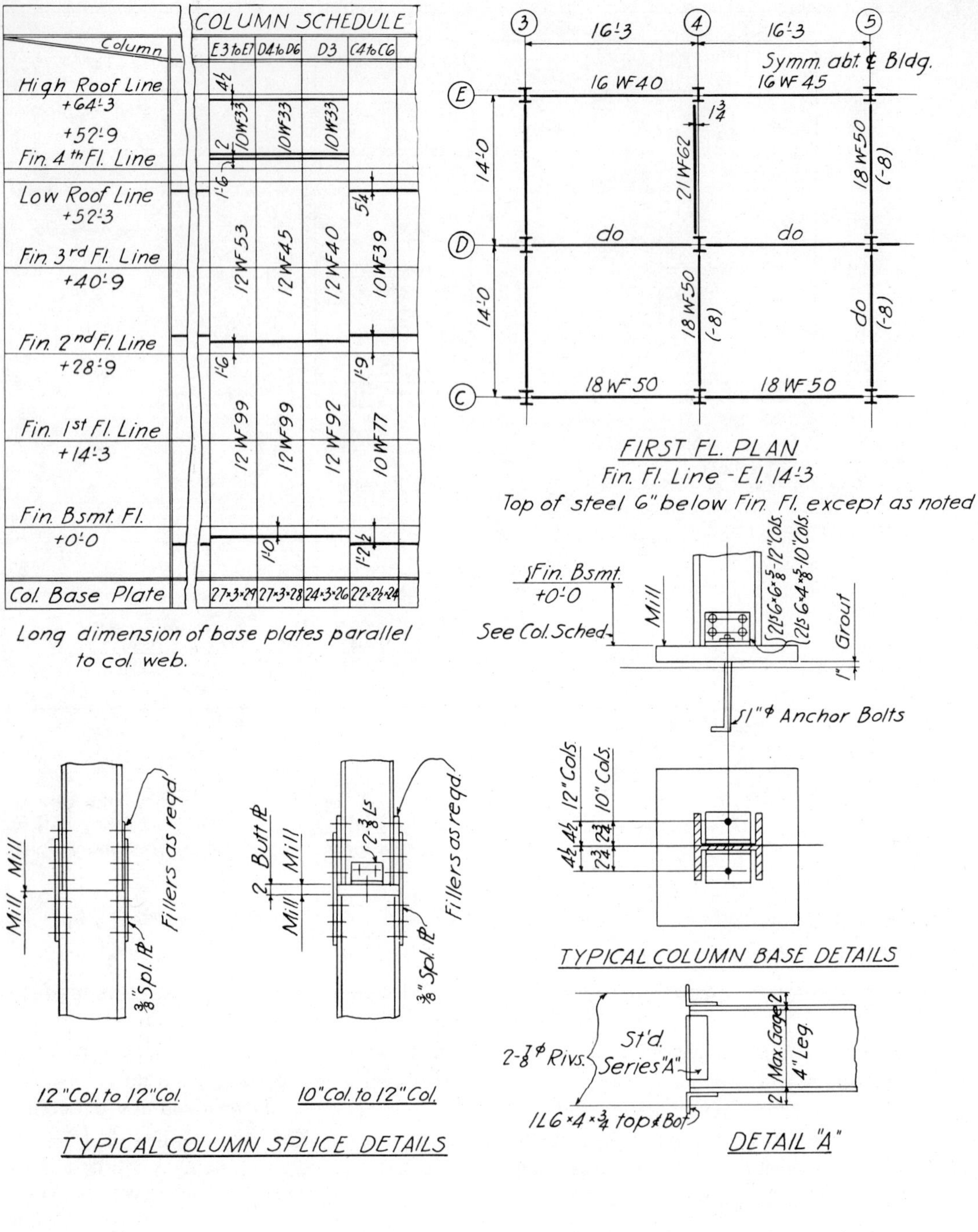

Figure 18-9
A typical column schedule and column details. AISC

DESIGN DRAWING

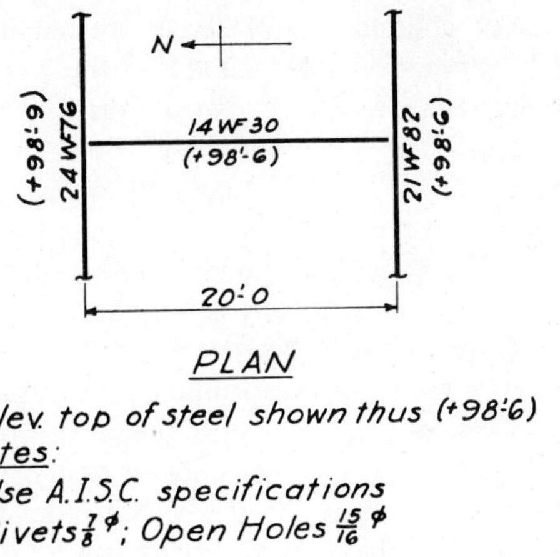

SHOP DRAWING

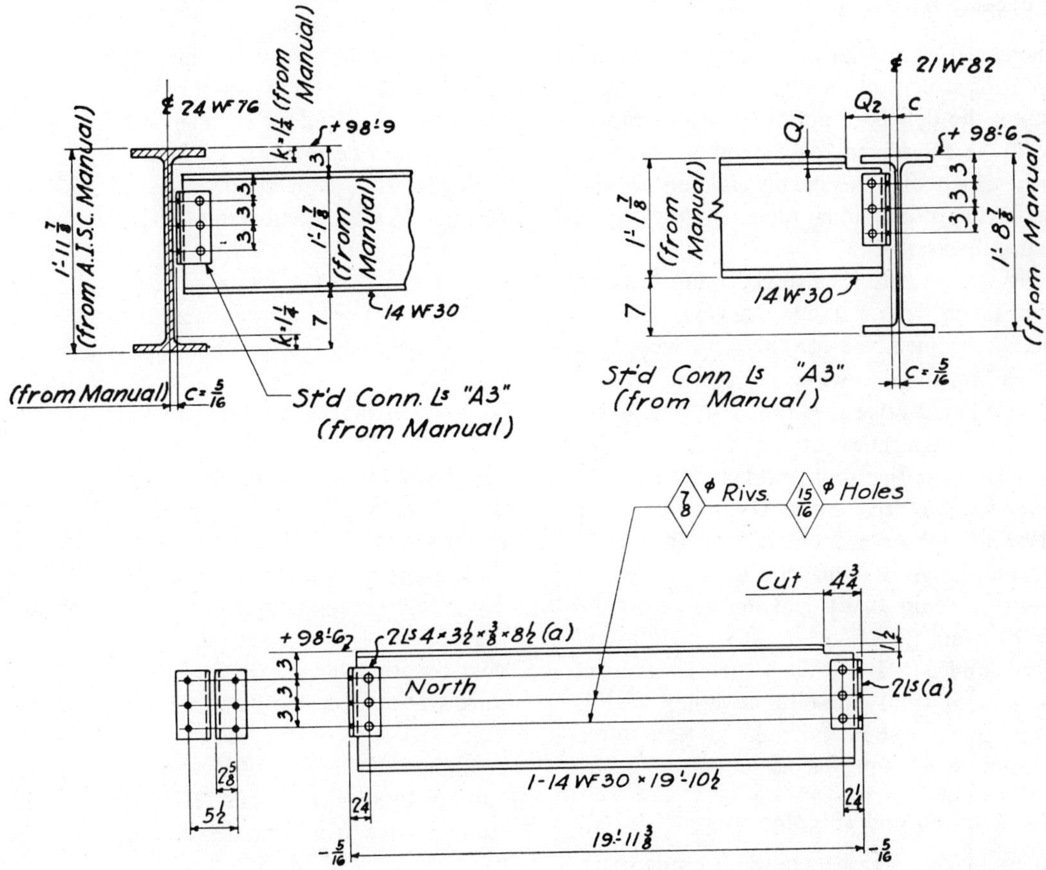

Figure 18–10
A design and shop drawing of a simple square-framed beam unit. AISC

The common practice is to label column reference lines that run in one direction with letters and those that run at right angles by numbers. By this system, the identity of a column at its intersection is D5.

The size and make-up of columns between various levels of framing are given in column schedules. In addition to size, the designer specifies the elevation at which columns must be spliced, as well as the elevation of the top of the column base plate. Column splices are placed high enough above the floor level to clear all necessary beam connections. Base plates are used to distribute the load of the columns to the concrete foundation. Column base plates usually bear on concrete piers or directly on the concrete footings. They are fastened to the foundation with anchor bolts. See Fig. 18-9.

18.5 Shop drawings

Whereas design drawings show the general layout of structural members, shop drawings present the details of how the various pieces are to be fabricated for assembly. All features which are specifically related to the connection of individual members have to be clearly illustrated.

Fig. 18-10 includes a single square-framed beam taken from a design drawing. The details of the members for this unit would be shown in a shop drawing as given below this design plan. Notice that the shop details include the connection at the north end, the connection at the south end and the complete detail of the entire connecting beam 14WF30. Observe too, that at the north end the design drawing of Fig. 18-10 stipulates that beam 14WF is 3 inches below the top of beam 24WF, while at the south end 14WF and 21WF are flush top. To prevent the flanges from bumping together at this point, they must be notched, a term often referred to as cope, block or cut.

18.6 Erection and shipping marks

To ensure that members in the framing structure are properly fabricated and erected in the correct position, each steel piece is given an identification symbol. This marking is placed on the detail shop drawing and is also painted on the member.

No uniform system of marking is in general use. For small, single tier structures when only a few members are required, a common practice is to assign all similar components with a prefix capital letter followed by a number. The number designates the drawing sheet containing the details of the member. Thus *D*4 would identify a member whose details are on sheet 4.

Another system uses as a prefix a capital letter which indicates the shape of the steel member, such as *B*-beam, *C*-column, *G*-girder, *L*-lintel. The number following the prefix refers to the location of the piece in the framing plan.

Erection or shipping marks for multistory tier buildings often identify the members with a beam digit followed by an encircled number. The encircled number identifies the level of framing where the member is to be installed. For example, a number 14 beam which is to be used for both second and third floors would be marked 14② and 14③.

Angles for beam connections are usually designated with small letters. All fittings on a single drawing will carry the same letter. Letters *e, g, i, j, l, o, q, r, u, x, y* and *z* are omitted for marking purposes. If more than 14 different marks are needed on one drawing, the letters are extended to *aa, bb,* etc.

Erection marks are also assigned to columns. In addition to whatever marking legend is followed, the marking also specifies the tier to which a particular section of the column belongs. This is done by adding after the column symbol the note "1st Tier," "2nd Tier," etc. For example, a column for the first tier may be marked "*D*5-1st Tier," the next section above "*D*5-2nd Tier" and the third section "*D*5-3rd Tier." Another convention used is *D*5(0-2), *D*5(2-4), *D*5(4-*R*), meaning that the first piece extends from the base plate to the second floor, the second column runs from the second floor to the fourth floor and the final column from the fourth floor to the roof. Unlike beams, all columns are given a different identification mark even though they may be identical.

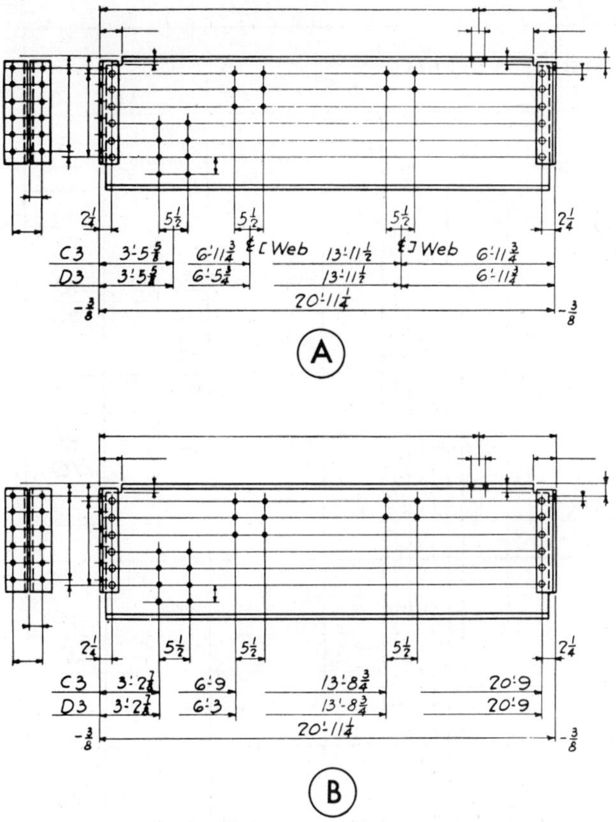

Figure 18-11
Typical dimensioning procedures used in structural shop drawing. AISC

18.7 General dimensioning practices

Dimensioning practices followed in structural shop drawing vary in some instances from dimensioning procedures used in machine drawing. Of particular significance are the following:

1 Dimension lines on structural drawings are unbroken for their full length.
2 Dimensions are placed above the dimension line.
3 Dimension figures carry the feet mark but not the inch mark; thus 6′-3.
4 When dimensions are less than one foot in length, they are indicated, for example, as 4 and not as 0′-4; the inch is always understood.
5 If a dimension is in even feet it is shown as 7′-0 and not 7′.

The American Institute of Steel Construction recommends that the following dimensioning practices be observed:[2]

2. *Structural Shop Drafting, Vol. I* (New York: American Institute of Steel Construction, 1958).

Dimensions should be arranged in a manner most convenient to all who must use the drawing. They should not crowd the sketch, and should cross the fewest possible number of other lines. The longest and overall dimensions should be farthest away from the views. to which they apply. Dimensioning and descriptions of components in general should be placed outside of the picture. Dimensions should not be given to edges of flanges or toes of structural shapes. They should be given to the center lines of beams, to the backs of angles, and to the backs of channels. They should be given to the top or bottom of beams and channels (whichever level is to be held) never to both top and bottom.

Two basic systems of dimensioning holes are shown in Fig. 18-11. Note that in *A* the extension dimensions start from the center line of groups of open holes. In *B* the extension dimensions are taken to the first line of holes in each group, moving from left to right.

SHOP BILL OF MATERIAL

	SHOP BILL									MILL ORDER				
LINE	ASS'BLG MARK	No.	SHAPE	SECTION	LENGTH FT.	LENGTH IN.	REMARKS	WT. PER FT.	WEIGHT	No.	SHAPE AND SECTION	LENGTH FT.	LENGTH IN.	ITEM
1		ONE-BEAM-A3 ONE-BEAM-B3												
2		1	WF	24@76	20	$10\frac{1}{2}$			1586					73
3	a	4	L	$4\times3\frac{1}{2}\times\frac{7}{16}$	1	$5\frac{1}{2}$		10.6	62	1		24	0	110
4		12	Riv.	$\frac{7}{8}$"φ					12					
5									1660					
6		ONE-BEAM-C3 ONE-BEAM-D3												
7		1	WF	24@94	20	$10\frac{1}{2}$			1962					62
8	b^{R}_{L}	4	L	$4\times3\frac{1}{2}\times\frac{7}{16}$	1	$6\frac{1}{2}$			65					110
9		12	Riv.	$\frac{7}{8}$"φ					12					
10									2039					
11		ONE-BEAM-E3												
12		1	WF	16@40	11	$10\frac{1}{2}$			475					86
13	c	4	L	$4\times3\frac{1}{2}\times\frac{3}{8}$		$11\frac{1}{2}$		9.1	35					S
14		8	Riv.	$\frac{7}{8}$"φ					8					
15									518					
16		ONE-BEAM-F3												
17		1	I	8@18.4	14	$7\frac{1}{4}$			269					101
18														
19		ONE-CHANNEL-G3R ONE CHANNEL-G3L												
20		1	[	10@15.3	9	$10\frac{1}{2}$			151			10	$4\frac{1}{2}$	118
21	f^{R}_{L}	2	L	$6\times4\times\frac{3}{8}$		$5\frac{1}{2}$		12.3	11					S
22	h	2	L	$6\times4\times\frac{3}{8}$		$5\frac{1}{2}$			11					S
23		8	Riv.	$\frac{7}{8}$"φ					8					
24									181					
25														
26														
27														
28														

IN CHARGE OF

MADE BY ______ DATE ______

CHECKED BY ______ DATE ______

REV. BY ______ DATE ______

SHOP NO. ______

CONTRACT ______

PAGE NO. 1

DWG. No. 3

CUSTOMER ______ STRUCTURE ______

Figure 18-12
A shop bill accompanies a shop drawing to assist in assembling all of the material required for shipment. AISC

18.8 Bill of materials

One of the important features of a shop drawing is the Bill of Material, often referred to as just shop bill, which lists all of the pieces required for shipment. Shop bills are placed either alongside the detail of the member or are included on a separate sheet. As shown in Fig. 18-12, a shop bill contains such information as number of pieces required, identification of members, their length and weight. Also shown is whether the sections are to be ordered from the mill or taken directly from the fabricator's stock. In cases where the items are available in stock, the letter *S* is placed opposite their description.

18.9 Beam connections

Beams are connected to columns by short angle pieces which are riveted, bolted or welded in position. These connections are either of the frame or seated type. See Fig. 18-13. In the frame connection, the beam is attached to its connecting member by short angles fastened to the web. With the seated connection, the ends of the beam rest on a ledge or seat much as they would if placed on a wall. Seated connections are often preferred, especially if the connections are shop riveted (as opposed to field riveted) to the supporting column: the erection process is simplified because the angles provide support for the beams while they are being aligned in place. Furthermore, seated connections make possible better erection clearance and reduce the number of field rivets or bolts to be driven, which results in greater economy.

Beam connections have been standardized into six series: *A, B, H, HH, K* and *KK*. The type used depends on the loading of the beams and rivets or bolt size. Thus if a 14*WF*38 beam with a 24 foot span has a maximum allowable load of 30 kips (30,000 pounds) the recommended angle connections according to the *AISC* Steel Construction Manual is the *A*3 type. See Fig. 18-14. Similarly if the design drawing specifies the rivet diameter, the draftsman can by checking the Manual find the type of connection to use.

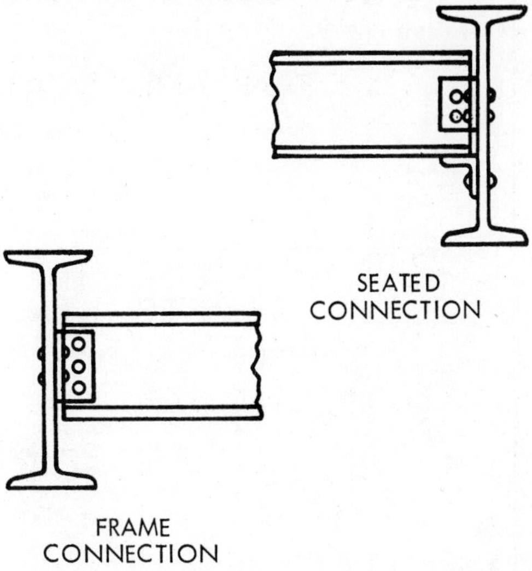

Figure 18-13
Type of beam connections used in steel structural framing.

Framing plans frequently require connection angles and other fittings which are exactly opposite to each other. The practice in preparing shop drawings is to detail the right hand piece only and then call out on the same sheet the requirements of the left hand piece. In labeling these opposite parts for shipment, the letter *R* is added to the erection mark of the right hand piece and the letter *L* for the left hand piece. By this system the markings would be B^R or B^L.

18.10 Beam detail drawing

Two procedures are followed in drawing the details of a beam. With one method a top, front, and bottom view are shown as in Fig. 18-15. The alternate method includes only a front view and a note stating what work, if any, is required on each flange of the beam. See Fig. 18-16.

Beam details are generally drawn to a scale of 1″ = 1′-0 except for the lengths. The lengths, of necessity, are foreshortened but, unlike machine drawing, no break line or any other indication is used in structural drawing. Furthermore, whenever it is required, small distances are exaggerated in order to present details clearly.

HOLES $\frac{15}{16}''$ RIVETS $\frac{7}{8}''$

STANDARD BEAM CONNECTIONS

"A" SERIES

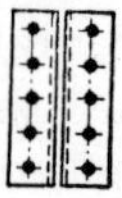

ALLOWABLE LOADS IN KIPS

A

	Rivets in Outstanding Legs		Rivets in Web Legs		Maximum Value			
	No.	Shear	Bearing	Shear	Section	R	Section	R
A 5 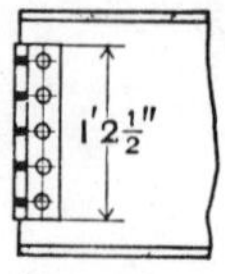 2Ls $4 \times 3\frac{1}{2} \times \frac{7}{16}$	10	90.2	175 t t = thickness of web	90.2	21WF 142 to 96	90.2	20 I 95 to 75	90.2
					82	87.3†	65.4	87.5
					73	79.6†		
					68	75.3†		
					62	70.0†		
A 4 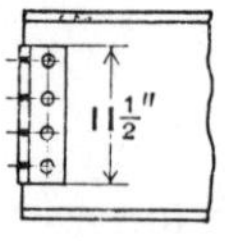 2Ls $4 \times 3\frac{1}{2} \times \frac{3}{8}$	8	72.2	140 t	72.2	18WF 114 to 105	72.2	16 WF 71	68.0
					96	71.7†	64	62.0
					85	72.2	58	57.0
					77	66.5†	50	53.2
					70	61.3†	45	48.4
					64	56.4†	40	43.0
					60	58.3†	36	41.9
					55	54.6†		
					50	50.1†	18 I 70	72.2
							54.7	64.4
					16WF 96	72.2	15 I 50	72.2
					88	70.6†		
					78	72.2		
							42.9	57.4
A 3 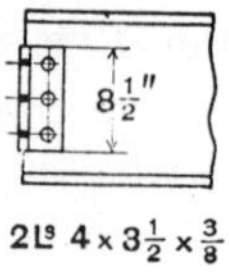 2Ls $4 \times 3\frac{1}{2} \times \frac{3}{8}$	6	54.1	105 t	54.1	14WF 38	32.9†	12 I 50	54.1
					34	30.2†	40.8	48.3
					30	28.4†	35	44.9
							31.8	36.8
					12WF 36	32.0†		
					31	27.8†		
					27	25.2†		
A 2 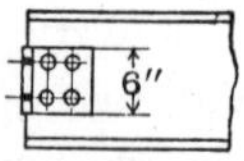 2Ls $6 \times 4 \times \frac{3}{8}$	4	36.1	140 t	72.2	10WF 29	36.1	10 I (35 and 25.4)	36.1
					25	33.0†	8 I 23.0	36.1
					21	30.9†	18.4	28.1
					8WF 20	26.2†		
					17	23.9†		
A 1 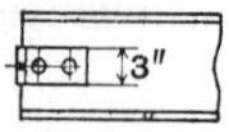 2Ls $6 \times 4 \times \frac{3}{8}$	2	18.0	70 t	36.1	7 I 20	18.0	5 I 14.75	18.0
					15.3	17.5†	10	13.7
					6 I 17.25	18.0		
					12.5	16.1†		

Figure 18-14
Examples of standard A-series beam connections. AISC

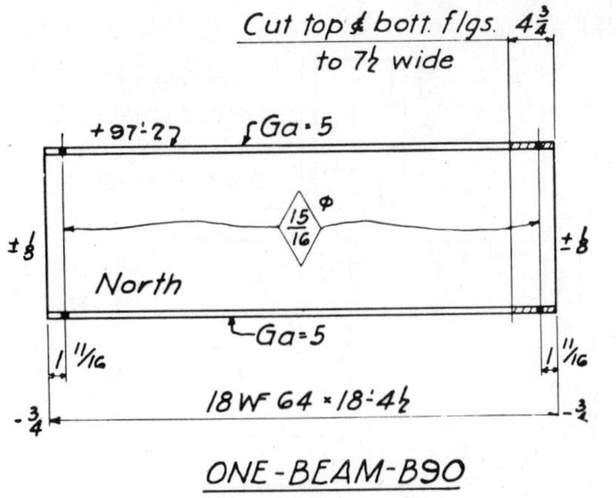

Figure 18–16
A beam detail drawing is simplified if only one view is included. AISC

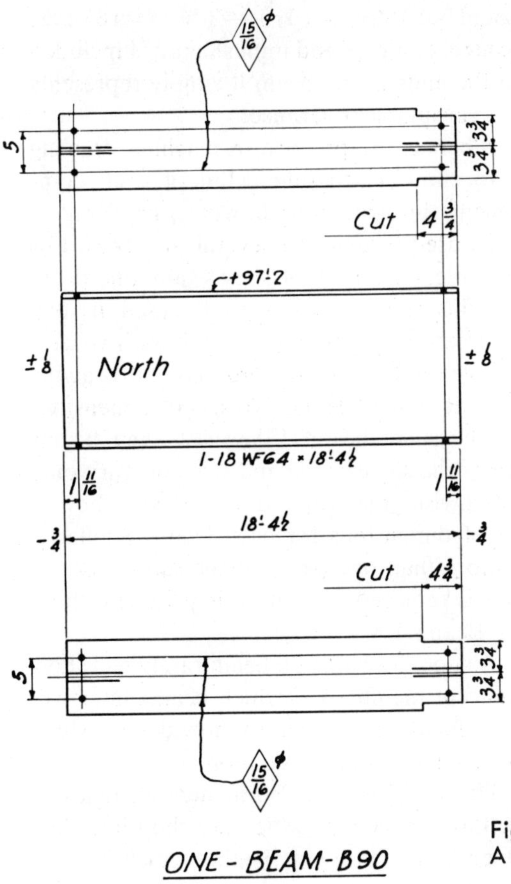

Figure 18–15
A beam detail showing several views. AISC

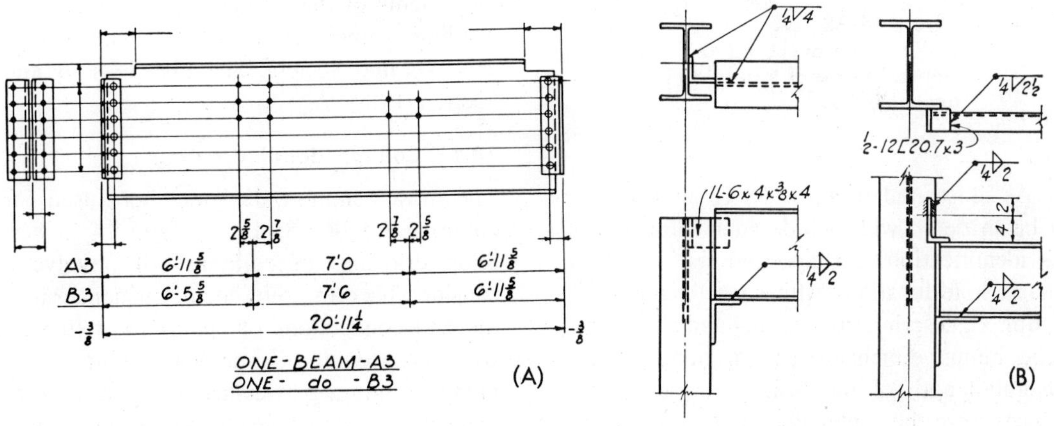

Figure 18–17
The details of several similar beams are often included on one drawing as in A. The illustration in B shows how welded joints are detailed. AISC

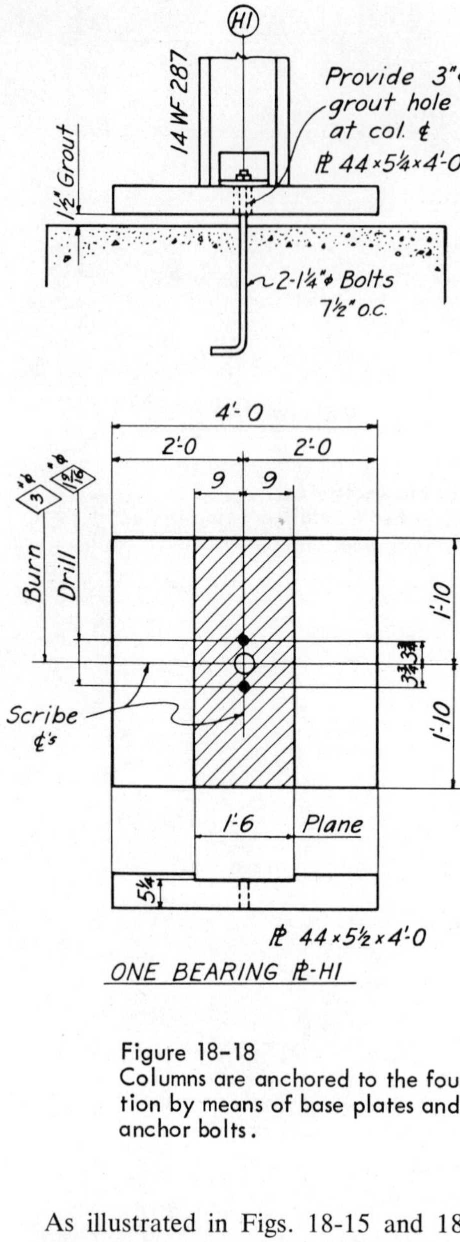

Figure 18-18
Columns are anchored to the foundation by means of base plates and anchor bolts.

As illustrated in Figs. 18-15 and 18-16, a beam detail will include such information as identification of shape and size, erection mark, hole locations with gage lines and, if required, description of coping and clearance. The minus dimension shown opposite the overall length of the beam represents distances from the center line of the supporting columns to the end of the beams. Thus in Fig. 18-15, the true length of the beam is obtained by subtracting the two minus dimensions from the center-to-center distance of the supporting column which in this instance would be: 18′-6 — (¾) — (¾) = 18′-4½. Whenever a plus and minus figure is included on the ends of the beam it simply represents the acceptable tolerance.

Whereas the practice in machine drawing is to show a separate detail of each component, in structural drawing one detail is often used to describe several members. For example, Fig. 18-17*A* shows only one beam but this same beam is to be used in two different locations and must have two sets of hole dimensions. Accordingly, the drawing is made to include the two sets of dimensions on the same beam. Likewise, when beams are of the same shape and size and vary only lengthwise, the same drawing will show a set of dimensions for each beam. Similarly, if more than one beam of the same description is required a notation is included, thus: 5 - Beams B3.

A shop drawing of a beam rarely will show adjacent members to which beams later will be joined, but will merely show details which are related to the installation.

Details of beams also include all holes as well as connections which are shop installed. Open holes represent riveting which is completed in the shop and darkened holes for rivets or bolts which are to be inserted in the field. When steel members are to be welded, the shop drawings include the requirements of the welded joint by means of welding symbols as approved by the American Welding Society. See Fig. 18-17*B* and Section 11.

18.11 Column detail drawing

The most common steel members used for columns are *WF* 8, 10, 12, and 14 inches. Shop drawings of columns will involve a considerable cross-referencing sequence since the end connections of beams must line up with those on the supporting columns. Details of columns particularly must show complete information for splicing and base plate anchorage.

Although the steel fabricator is not directly involved with the foundation work of a building, he is required to supply the necessary base plates and anchor bolts. Bolt holes in

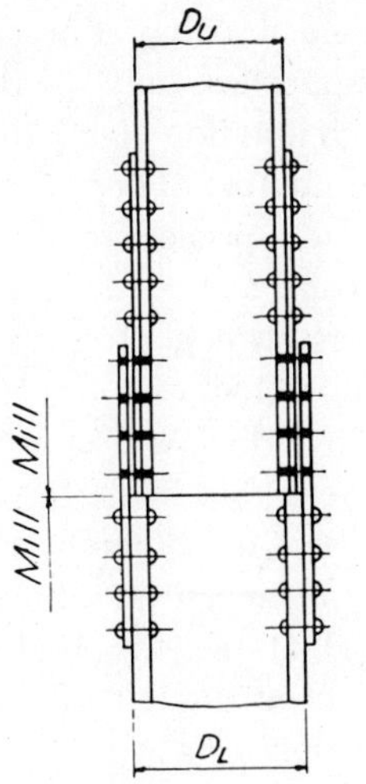

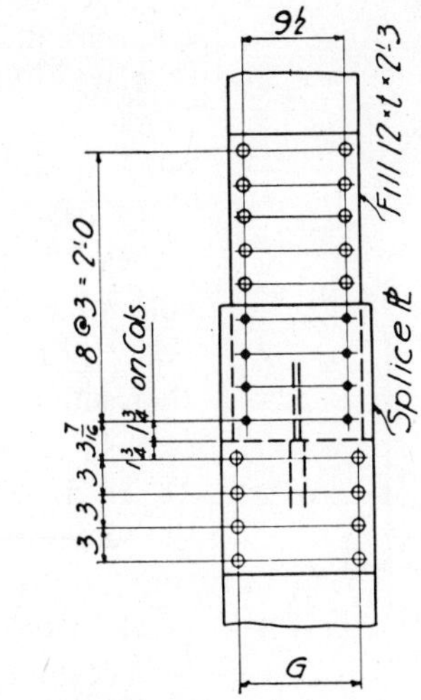

For **12 WF 65** or heavier **12 WF**, over **14 WF 78** or heavier.

When lower shaft is **14 WF 78** or **14 WF 84**:
G = 9½"
Use 12 x 3/8 x 2'-0 splice plates.
When lower shaft is **14 WF 87** or heavier:
G = 11½"
Use 14 x 1/2 x 2'-0 splice plates.

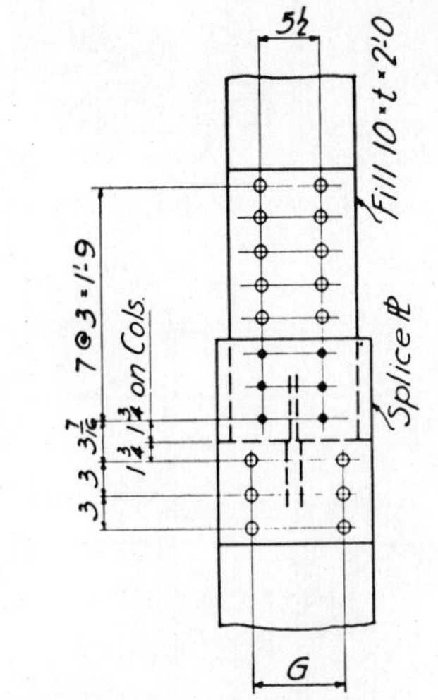

For **10 WF 49** or heavier **10 WF**, over **12 WF 65** or heavier **12 WF**. Also for **12 WF 53** and **12 WF 58**, over **14 WF 78** and heavier **14 WF**.

When lower shaft is **12 WF** or **14 WF 78** or **14 WF 84**:
G = 9½"
Use 12 x 3/8 x 1'-6 splice plates.
When lower shaft is **14 WF 87** or heavier:
G = 11½"
Use 14 x 1/2 x 1'-6 splice plates.

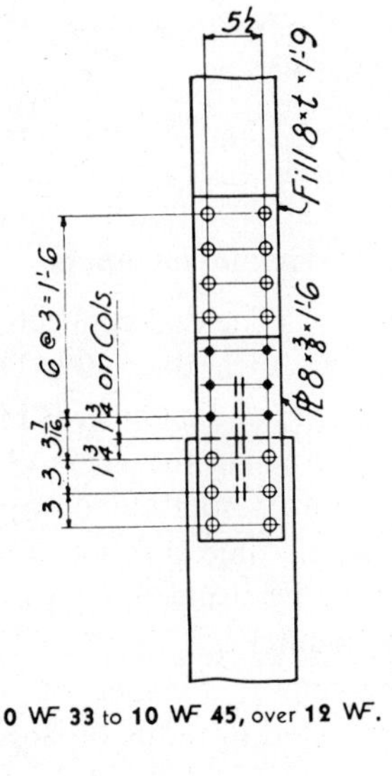

For **10 WF 33** to **10 WF 45**, over **12 WF**.

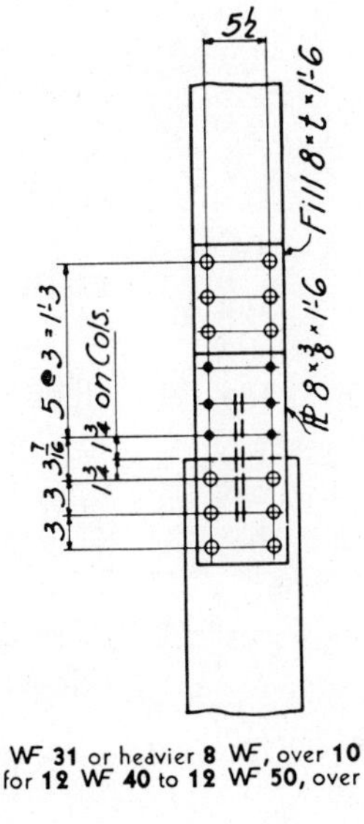

For **8 WF 31** or heavier **8 WF**, over **10 WF**. Also for **12 WF 40** to **12 WF 50**, over 14 WF.

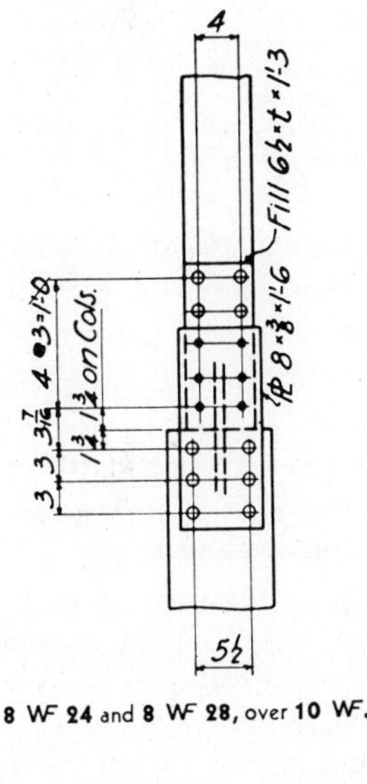

For **8 WF 24** and **8 WF 28**, over **10 WF**.

Figure 18–19
These typical column splices are used in joining columns for multistory structures. AISC

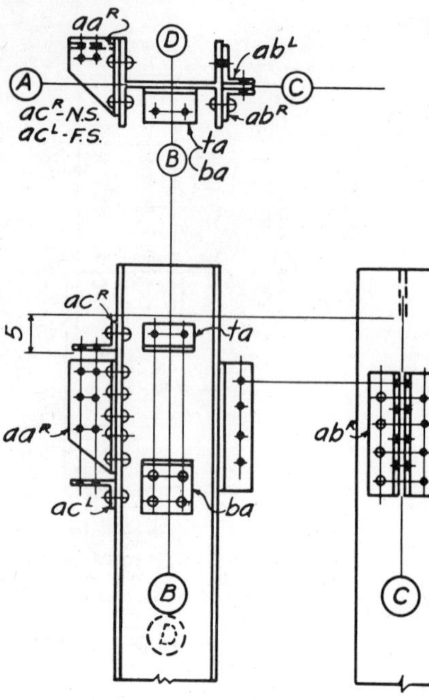

Figure 18-20
Detail of a column showing the column in an upright position.
AISC

base plates are usually made 5/16″ to 9/16″ larger than the bolt diameters. This is done to compensate for any inaccuracies that may result in setting the bolts. As shown in Fig. 18-18, tops of concrete foundations where plates are located are kept 1-1/2 in. below the base of the plate. The plates are then positioned by means of shims, and grout is poured under the plate to provide the necessary bearing area underneath the plate.

Column splicing is necessary when several tiers are involved. Splicing details are more or less standardized. Typical column splices are illustrated in Fig. 18-19.

A column shop drawing will show the columns either in an upright or horizontal position. If drawn upright, the bottom of the shaft is at the bottom of the sheet. When drawn horizontally, the bottom of the column is to the left of the sheet.

The practice is to include two or more columns in a single drawing. For columns that are alike or opposites, only the detail of one is shown with a notation giving the number required or the number of opposite pieces. It is also a common procedure in a shop drawing to label each of the four faces of a column with letters, which progress alphabetically in a counterclockwise direction for right hand pieces and clockwise direction for opposite hand pieces. See Figs. 18-20 and 18-21. In either case, the different views of the columns are arranged in alphabetical order with face *A* at the top for vertical position drawings or at the left of the sheet for horizontal position drawings.

Identical right and left hand beams are appropriately designated on the drawing and by erection markings. The shop detail will show one beam and carry the following notation:

One Beam *B* 150^R as shown
One Beam *B* 150^L opposite hand

If two opposite pieces are included on the same drawing but are not exactly alike, the notation would read:

One Beam *B* 150 as shown and noted
One Beam *B* 150 opposite hand and noted

18.12 Detailing skewed members

A skewed member is one that connects to another at some other angle than 90°. The first step in detailing a skewed member is to figure from the design drawing the angle of skew. This process involves solution of right triangles. Considerable time is saved in making these calculations by using Smoley's or Inskip's tables of squares.

In shop drawing the values of a right triangle are expressed in terms of slope (hypotenuse), rise (altitude), and base. The value of an angle is never given in degrees, minutes and seconds but is shown as a bevel, meaning the amount of rise in inches as produced by the angle for a certain amount of base distance per feet. For most work this base distance is determined as 12 inches, and is indicated by a small triangle attached to the skewed connection. See Fig. 18-22.

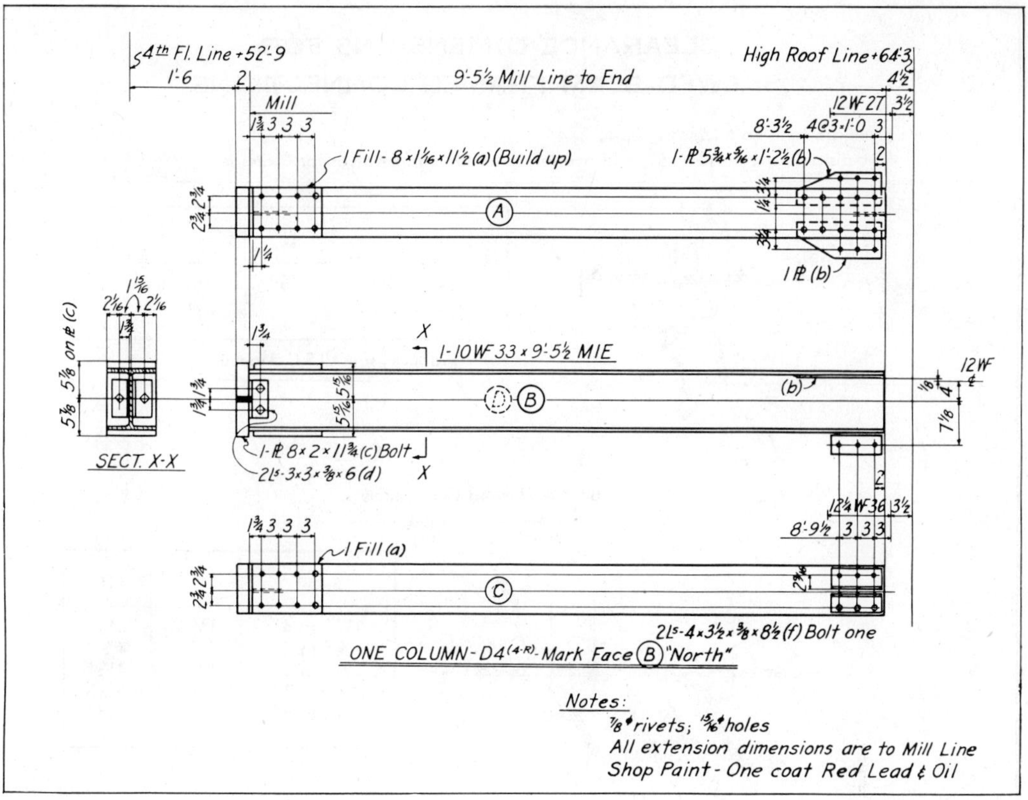

Figure 18–21
Shop drawing of a column drawn in a horizontal position. AISC

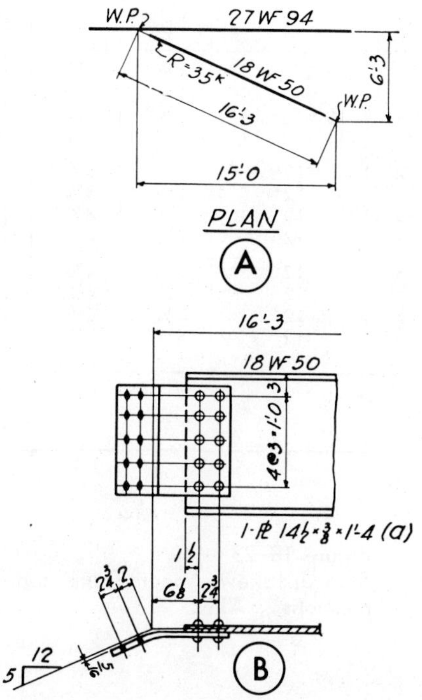

Figure 18–22
A typical detailed skewed connection as required by the design drawing. AISC

CLEARANCE DIMENSIONS FOR SKEWED-BEAM FRAMED CONNECTIONS

Values given are for web thicknesses up to 3/4″.
When the c-distance exceeds 7/16″, add overrun to be tabulated values for D and H.

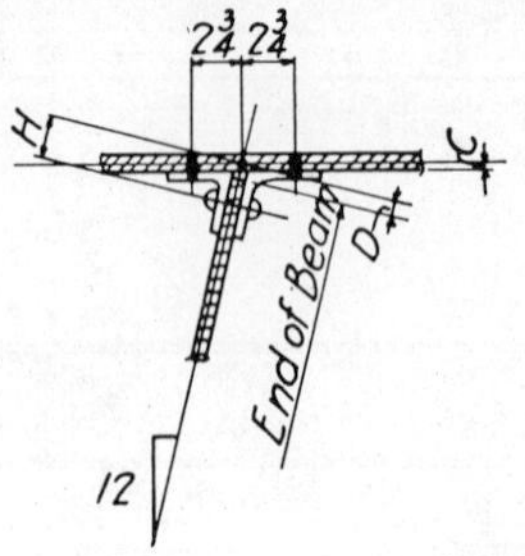

Bevel	D	H
⅛″ to 2″	⅞″	2¼″ plus "c"
2⅛″ to 3″	1″	2¼″ plus "c"

For c-distances see A.I.S.C. Manual.

Type B A Skewed Connections

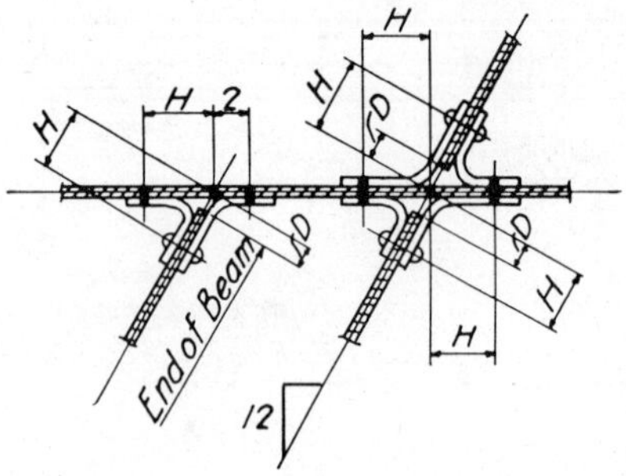

Bevel	D	H
3⅛″ to 4″	1⅛″	3½″
4⅛″ to 5″	1¼″	4″
5⅛″ to 6″	1⅜″	4½″
6⅛″ to 7″	1⅜″	5″
7⅛″ to 8″	1½″	5½″

Type B P Skewed Connections

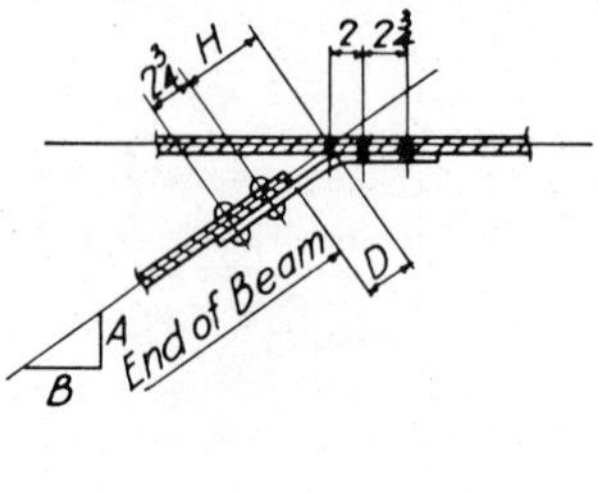

A	B	D	H
12″	8⅛″ to 9″	1⅝″	3⅛″
12″	9⅛″ to 10″	1¾″	3¼″
12″	10⅛″ to 11″	1¾″	3¼″
12″	11⅛″ to 12″	1⅞″	3⅜″
11⅛″ to 12″	12″	2″	3½″
10⅛″ to 11″	12″	2⅛″	3⅝″
9⅛″ to 10″	12″	2⅜″	3⅞″
8⅛″ to 9″	12″	2½″	4″
7⅛″ to 8″	12″	2⅞″	4⅜″
6⅛″ to 7″	12″	3¼″	4¾″
5⅛″ to 6″	12″	3¾″	5¼″
4″ to 5″	12″	4⅝″	6⅛″

Type S B P Skewed Connections

Figure 18-23
Standard skewed beam frame connections. AISC

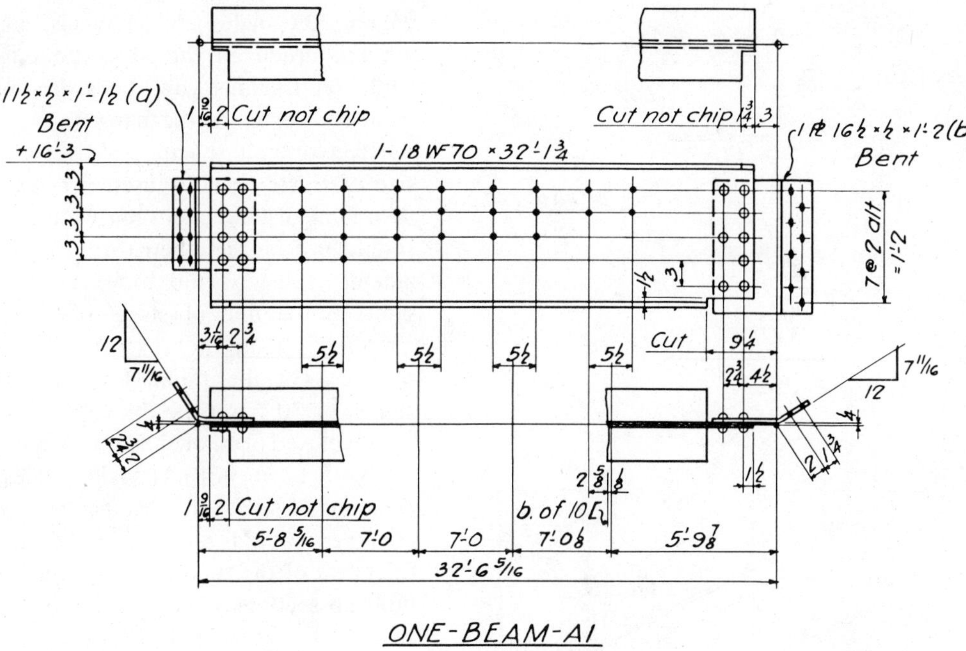

Figure 18-24
A complete detail shop drawing of a beam with skewed connections. AISC

Once the draftsman has computed the bevel of skew, the standardized tables of skewed connections (see Fig. 18-23) will tell him the type of connection that is required. The detailing then involves laying out the correct hole spacing. Note in Fig. 18-22 that distances are measured from working points. A working point is the intersection of two center lines.

For example, assume that the beams shown in Fig. 18-22 are to be detailed. The bevel that beam 18*WF*50 makes with beam 27*WF*94 is calculated to be 5 inches in 12 inches. Turning to the standardized table of skewed connections, a type *SBP* connection is required. This connection gives the distance *H* from the working point to the first line of rivets as 6-1/8 inches and the distance between rows of rivets as 2-3/4 inches. The draftsman now can proceed to lay out the detail of the skewed connection. A complete beam detail with skewed connection is shown in Fig. 18-24.

18.13 Detailing sloping beams

As shown in Fig. 18-25, sloping beams for roof framing are detailed either in their true position as in *B* or in a horizontal position as in *C*. Dimensions in each case are referred to the working points as established in the design drawing. Detailing of the sloping beam involves finding the exact length of the member and locating the essential holes. Note that the first hole is positioned according to the working point shown in the design drawing.

18.14 Riveting and bolting

The most common practice of joining steel structural members in the field is by bolting with machine and high strength bolts or by welding. However, in certain instances riveting is used. Bolts of the same nominal diameter may be substituted in any joint for rivets.

The placement of rivets or bolts is controlled by gage lines. The location of gage

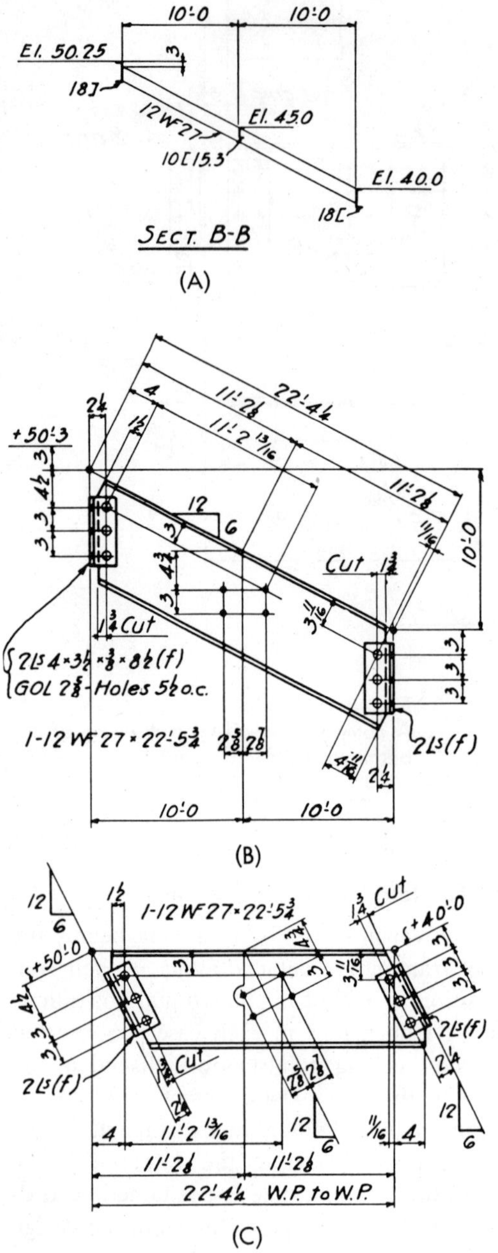

Figure 18-25
Method of detailing sloping numbers. AISC

lines has been standardized to a considerable degree. On angles and channels, gage lines are measured from the backs of the members while on I-beams gage lines are measured from the center of the flanges.

Rivet or bolt spacing is governed by the size of rivets or bolts used. In general, the minimum distance between centers of holes should not be less than three times the diameter of the rivet or bolt. The maximum pitch in the line of stress of compression members should not exceed 16 times the thickness of the thinnest outside plate or shape, or 20 times the thickness of the thinnest enclosed plate or shape, with a maximum pitch of 12 inches. At right angles to the direction of stress, the distance between lines of holes should not exceed 32 times the thickness of the thinnest plate. For angles in built-up sections having two gage lines with staggered rivets or bolts, the maximum pitch in each gage line should not exceed 24 times the thickness of the thinnest plate, with a maximum pitch of 18 inches.

The pitch of rivets or bolts at the ends of compression members should not exceed four diameters of the rivets or bolts for a length equal to 1-1/2 times the maximum width of the member.

The minimum edge distance from the center of holes is shown in Fig. 18-26. The maximum edge distance should be 12 times the thickness of the plate but should not exceed 6 inches.

Holes for rivets or bolts are made 1/16 inch larger than the rivet or bolt diameter. Rivets driven in the shop are called shop rivets and those driven in the field, field rivets. On a drawing, shop rivets are shown as open circles and field rivets or bolts as blackened circles.

18.15 Riveted truss members

Members of riveted trusses are in most instances made up of angles. Generally a pair of angles are used with one angle placed on either side of the connecting gusset plate. The number of rivets employed at the joint as well as the size of the gusset plate depends on the calculated reaction loads. Fig. 18-27 illustrates a design drawing of a truss unit

Rivet Diameter, Inches	Minimum Edge Distance (Inches) for Punched Holes		
	In Sheared Edge	In Rolled Edge of Plates	In Rolled Edge of Structural Shapes
1/2	1	7/8	3/4*
5/8	1 1/8	1	7/8*
3/4	1 1/4	1 1/8	1 *
7/8	1 1/2	1 1/4	1 1/8*
1	1 3/4	1 1/2	1 1/4*
1 1/8	2	1 3/4	1 1/2*
1 1/4	2 1/4	2	1 3/4*

*May be decreased 1/8 inch when holes are near end of beam.

Figure 18-26
Minimum rivet edge distance. AISC

along with the detail shop drawing. Notice that in the design drawing the loads are given for each member.

For angles of the size specified in the design drawing shown, either a 1/4 or 3/8 inch plate will be suitable for the gusset plate. Since the design calls for 3/4 inch rivets, a check of the *AISC* Manual will disclose that a 3/4 inch rivet has an allowable load of 11.3 kips for 3/8 inch plate and 7.50 kips for 1/4 inch plate. By dividing the given load of each member by the load factor of the rivet, the required number of rivets to be utilized in the joint can be found. Thus for the left diagonal member having a load of 36.5^k the computation would be:

$$\frac{36.5^k}{11.3^k} = 3.2, \text{ or 4 rivets for 3/8 inch plate,}$$

or

$$\frac{36.5^k}{7.5^k} = 4.9, \text{ or 5 rivets for 1/4 inch plate.}$$

Once the number of rivets is determined, the size of the gusset can be laid out by taking into consideration the common minimum rivet spacings. As a rule, a clearance of 1/4 to 3/8 inch is allowed between the members meeting at a joint, and 1/2 inch for heavier work.

With the exception of long span trusses, gusset plates are often omitted if the pieces are to be welded. In such cases the web members are welded to the stems of the chords.

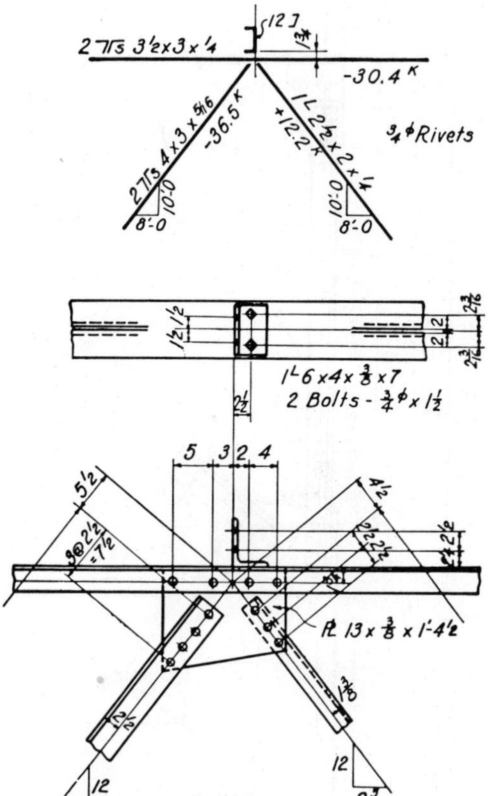

Figure 18-27
Method of detailing connecting members in a bracing unit. AISC

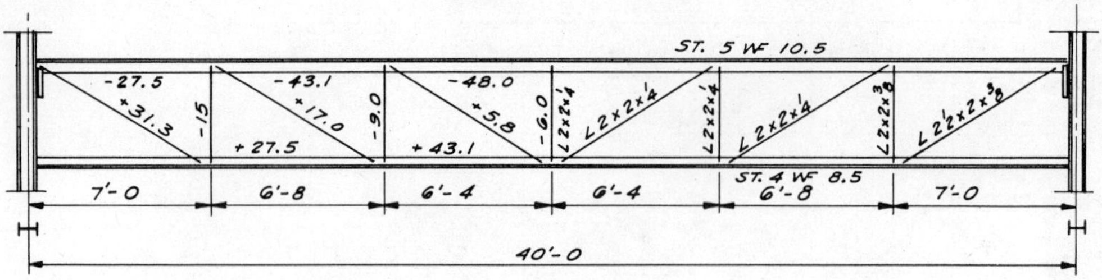

Figure 18-28
A design drawing of a truss.
Miller-Davis Co.

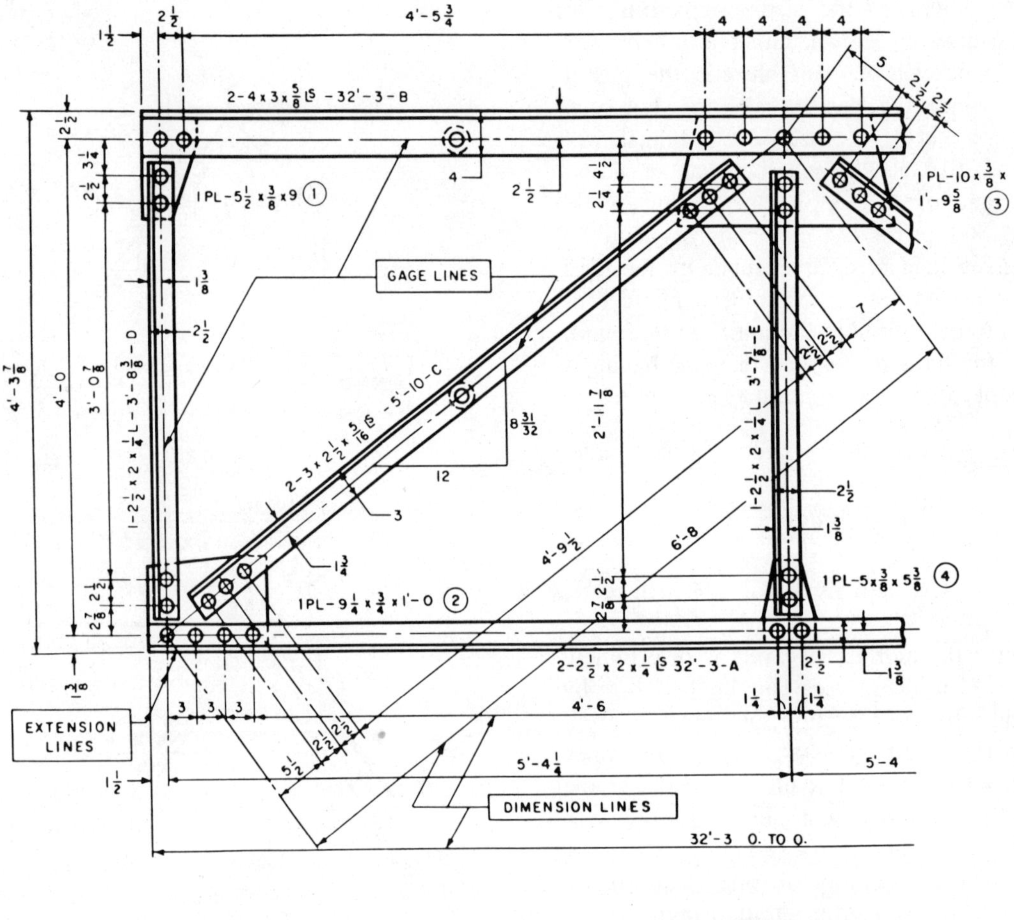

Figure 18-29
A detail shop drawing will contain all of the essential dimensions to fabricate the truss. ASA Y14.14-1957

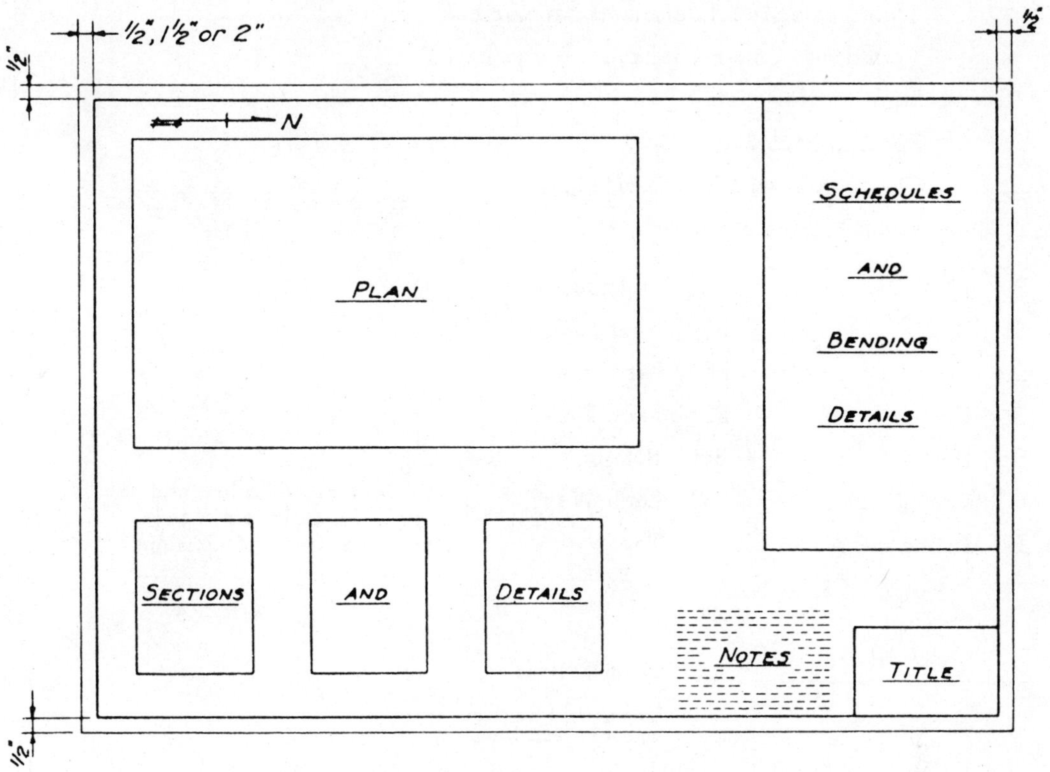

Figure 18-30
A commonly used layout for reinforced concrete drawings. ACI

18.16 Detailing truss members

A truss is made up of angles and is shipped either completely assembled or the parts are assembled at the building site. As a rule, the individual pieces of a truss do not carry erection marks. Instead each fully assembled truss is marked as *T*1, *T*2, *T*3, etc.

In laying out the details of a truss, the length of each piece must be determined. To do this the working lines must be located from the design plan. See Fig. 18-28. These lines will correspond to the gage lines which will appear on the shop detail drawing. Only the left half of a symmetrical truss needs to be shown.

To ensure that the details do not become distorted, a single scale is used for plotting the intersection points of horizontal and vertical members such as 1″ = 1′-0, 1/2″ = 1′-0, 3/8″ = 1′-0, or 3/4″ = 1′-0. However, the same scale need not be used in laying out the details along the working lines, especially if a larger scale will reduce crowded or confusing shape descriptions.

Once the diagonal members are positioned the gusset plates, if they are to be used, must be designed. The rivet holes are first located on the connecting members, and the gussets then planned to fit. Care is taken to follow the recommended practices for rivet spacing and edge distances.

It is customary in dimensioning a truss to place the working dimensions (those dimensions appearing on the design plan) on the outside of all other lines or dimensions. The next prominent dimensions are lines locating intermediate panel points or other points near the intersection of working lines. Figs. 18-28 and 18-29 illustrate a design and shop drawing of a simple truss.

#	To indicate size of deformed bar number.
∅	Round, used mainly for plain round bars.
□	Square. (Not ⌀)
@	Spacing center to center.
←→	Direction in which bars extend.
|←→|	Limits of area covered by bars.

Pl	Plain Bar	OF	Outside Face
Bt	Bent	NF	Near Face
St	Straight	FF	Far Face
Stir	Stirrup	EF	Each Face
Sp	Spiral	Bot.	Bottom
CT	Column Tie	EW	Each Way
IF	Inside Face	T	Top

Figure 18-31
Common abbreviations and symbols used in reinforced concrete structural drawings.

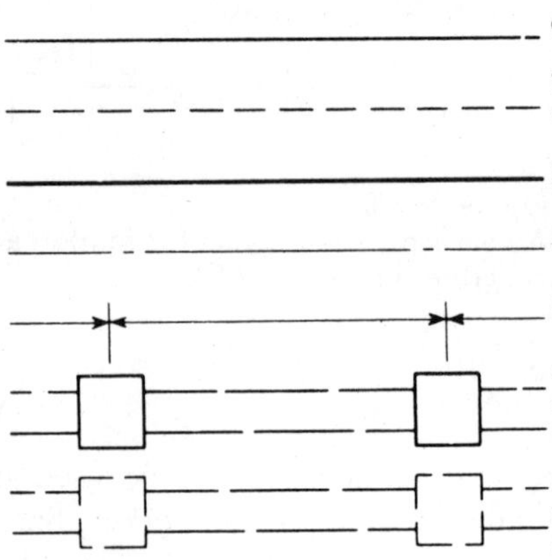

Figure 18-32
Drawing time is reduced if standardization of line is used.

18.17 Reinforced concrete drawing standards

The two principal sets of drawings used in reinforced concrete framing are designated as *engineering drawings* and *placing drawings*.

Engineering drawings are those prepared by the designer and show the general arrangement of the structure, size and reinforcement of the members, and other essential information necessary to interpret the design of the structure.

Placing drawings are detail drawings and show the size, shape and location of all bars in the structure, how bars are to be placed in the forms and schedules of beams, joints, columns and girders.

Usually drawings for reinforced concrete buildings are made on 24″ x 36″ sheets, which are large enough to accommodate most structures and yet small enough to handle conveniently.

Drawings generally include plan, elevation, and section and detail views along with schedules of footings, columns, beams and slabs. As a rule, the plan of the building is drawn in the upper left corner of the sheet with elevations and details below and to the

Beam Mark	Size W	Size D	Longitudinal No. Size	Longitudinal Remarks	Stirrups No. Size	Stirrups Spacing From Face Of Support
2B1	12	20	2-#6	Bot. Str.	12-#3	3@7, 3@12
			2-#7	Bent		
2B2	12	20	1-#7	Bot. Str.	10-#3	3@8, 2@12
			2-#7	Bent		
2B3	12	24	2-#6	Bot. Str.	18-#3	3@7, 6@12
			1-#7	Bent		
2B4	8	14	2-#5	Bot. Str.	12-#3	3@7, 3@12
			1-#5	Bent		
2B5	12	20	2-#7	Bot. Str.	18-#3	3@7, 6@12
			2-#8	Bent		
2B6	14	30	3-#8	Bot. Str.	20-#3	3@6, 2@8, 5@12
			2-#10	Bent		
2B7	14	24	2-#8	Bot. Str.	20-#3	3@6, 7@12
			3-#8	Bent		
2B8	12	20	1-#7	Bot. Str.	10-#3	3@8, 2@12
			2-#7	Bent		
2B9	12	20	2-#6	Bot. Str.	12-#3	3@7, 3@12
			2-#7	Bent		

Figure 18-33
A typical beam schedule.
ACI

right of the plan. Schedules usually are placed in the upper right corner of the sheet. See Fig. 18-30. An arrow indicating either a northerly or westerly direction is placed at the top of the sheet so the builder may easily orient the drawing.

The following scales are preferred for reinforced concrete drawings:

Plan: 1/8″ = 1′-0, 1/4″ = 1′-0.

Elevation: 1/4″ = 1′-0, 3/8″ = 1′-0, 1/2″ = 1′-0.

Section: 1/4″ = 1′-0, 3/8″ = 1′-0, 1/2″ = 1′-0, 3/4″ = 1′-0, 1″ = 1′-0.

18.18 Concrete building symbols[3]

The use of standard designations, symbols, and abbreviations will reduce drafting time and make drawings simple and clear. Time is saved by omitting unnecessary designations. Sometimes the foot and inch marks in dimensions can be omitted without causing confusion. An example of unnecessary abbreviations or symbols is the use of O.C. or C.C. in connection with the spacing of bars. The use of the symbol @ is sufficient, such as # 5 @ 8, meaning #5 bars spaced at 8 inches center-to-center. The center-to-center distance of parallel bars is always measured perpendicular to the longitudinal axes of the bars. Some of the abbreviations and symbols most commonly used are shown in Fig. 18-31.

In using symbols, abbreviations, and notes, care should be exercised to make the meaning clear and subject to only one interpretation. As an example, the notation *12-#5 both directions* may be interpreted as 12 in each direction, or 6 in each direction making a total of 12. To avoid this, it is better to use the word *each* rather than *both,* as *12-#5 each direction.* The same would be true in referring to each face of a concrete structure.

Clarity and ease of reading drawings are improved if the same type of line is used throughout for the same purpose. The weight of lines may be varied to accentuate the important features. A standardization of the types of lines for all drawings will also speed up the preparation and use of the plans. See Fig. 18-32.

3. Extracted from *Manual of Standard Practice for Detailing Reinforced Concrete Structures* (Detroit: American Concrete Institute, 1957).

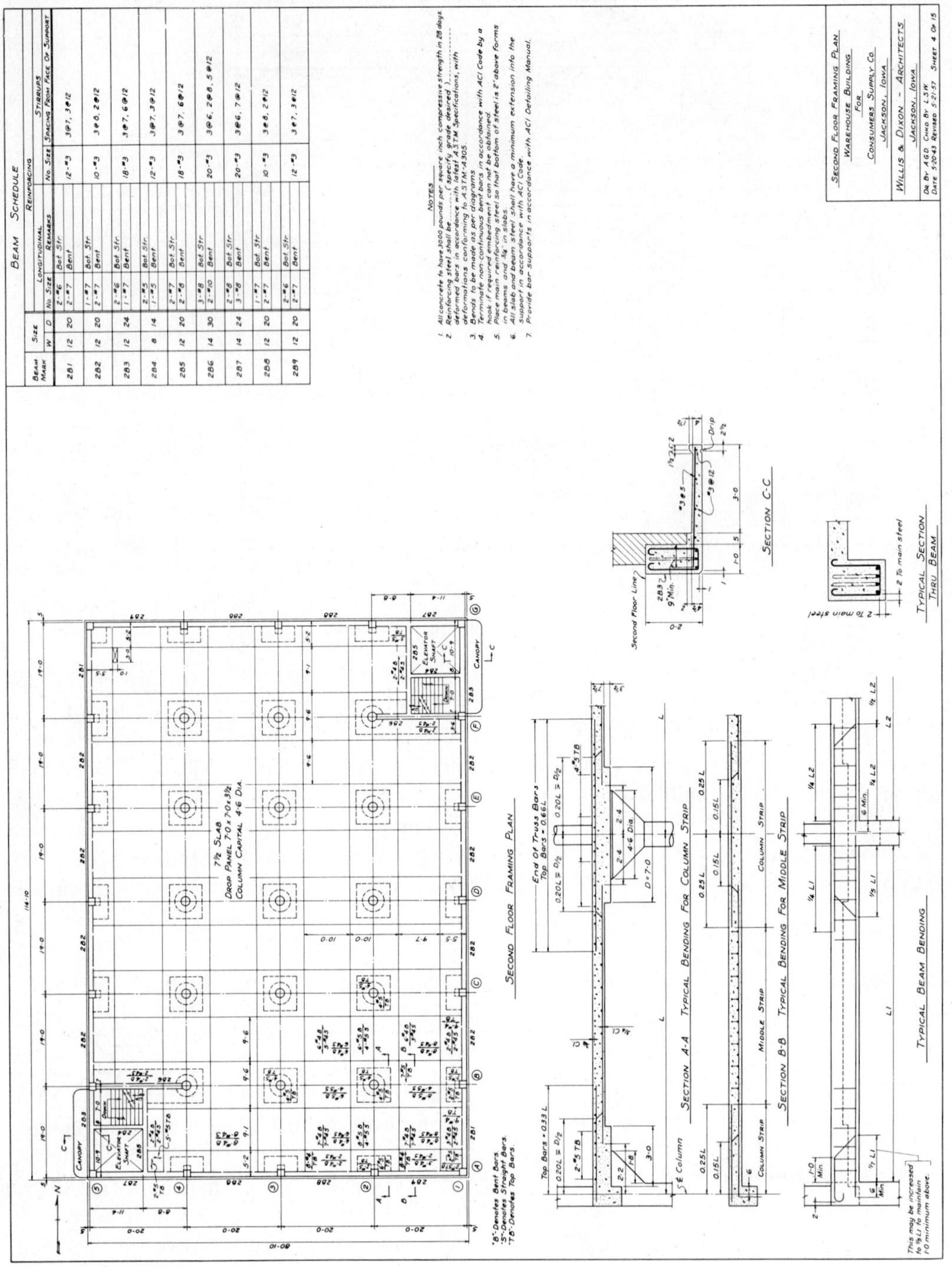

Figure 18–34
An example of an engineering drawing showing a front wall elevation.

18.19 Building marks

The various parts of a building are indicated by marks which designate the floor, type of members, and identification of a specific member. Thus 2*B*3 would mean second floor beam number three. The letters used to show the types of members are:

B—Beams	*L*—Lintels
C—Columns	*S*—Slabs
D—Dowels	*T*—Ties
F—Footings	*U*—Stirrups
G—Girders	*W*—Walls
J—Joists	

Columns and footings are numbered consecutively. Vertical lines representing columns are usually lettered *A, B, C,* etc., and horizontal lines numbered 1, 2, 3, etc. Bent bars in a member are assigned the marks of the designated member with suffix *A, B,* etc., when more than one type of bent bar is used. An alternate method is to label bars with a mark that show the floor, type of member, size, and serial number of the bar. Thus 2*B*605 would mean second floor beam, with the digit 6 referring to the bar size and the last two digits the specific bar in its sequence of marking.

18.20 Schedules

A schedule is a summary of all the bars in the structure in the order of their use, complete with the number of pieces, sizes, lengths, marks, and bending details. See Fig. 18-33. Schedules are of two types: horizontal and vertical. In the horizontal type bars and stirrups are listed in a horizontal line, whereas in the vertical type schedule bars and stirrups are listed under each other.

18.21 Design drawings

The following are a few points recommended by the American Concrete Institute governing the preparation of design drawings for reinforced concrete buildings:

Design drawings must be complete to the extent that every bit of information regarding the size and arrangement of concrete members, and the size, positioning, and detailing of reinforcing bars is completely covered, either by a drawing, description, diagram, note, rule, or reference to a standard manual. See Fig. 18-34.

It is not necessary for the designer to make complete drawings of each member nor to schedule completely the bending of bars in each member, but schedules should be so prepared that this information is determined unequivocally by diagrams, notes, and references.

The designer should include in every set of plans a typical slab, joist, beam, and column detail, showing the exact arrangement of reinforcing steel desired.

It is not necessary for the designer to work out all the dimensions but it is definitely his function to show where he wishes bars bent and to what points they are to be extended.

Schedules should be prepared carefully and no abbreviations or symbols should be used without explanation. A schedule needs to be supplemented with diagrams establishing the minimum fireproofing, termination and bending of bars, and similar data.

There should always be a notation as to the quality of concrete and the grade of reinforcing bars upon which the design is based, also the live loads which the structure is capable of carrying, as well as the assumed capacity of foundation soil, or other miscellaneous items not readily apparent. The designer will often do well to indicate at least some of the more obvious construction joints so that all of the trades are working along the same line.

In all but the simplest structures, separate framing plans are desirable. It is practically impossible to superimpose the structural elements upon the architectural plans without confusing both. Time will be saved for the designer, better jobs will result, cost will be reduced, and time will be saved in checking shop drawings, if the structural elements are shown separately.

Notice in Fig. 18-34 that the necessary engineering information is shown on the completely dimensioned plan and typical sections supplemented by a beam schedule. In-

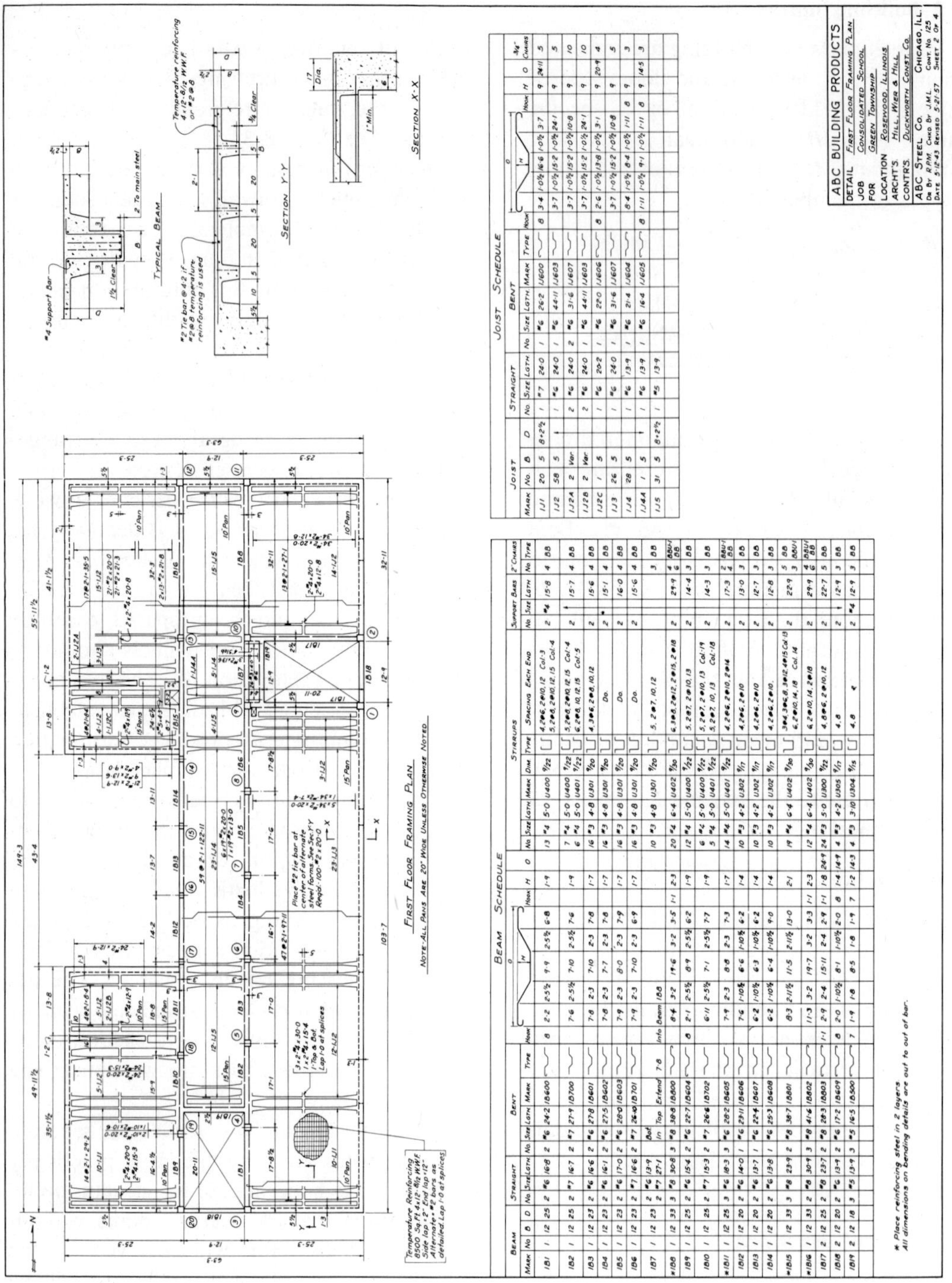

Figure 18-35
Concrete joist floor placing drawing. ACI

formation on the reinforcement required in the slab is given on the plan and that for the beams is given in the schedule. The lengths of bars and points of bends can be determined from information given on the typical sections.

On this drawing all similar beams are given the same designation. The coordinate system is used for designating the columns; i.e., the column in the upper left hand corner is designated *A*5 while the one diagonally opposite in the same panel is designated *B*4.

18.22 Placing drawings

Placing drawings, which are prepared by the fabricator, are sometimes called *detail drawings* since they show details for fabrication and for placing. They are not for use in building form work and consequently the only required dimensions are those necessary for the proper location of the steel.

Placing drawings show the size, shape, and location of the bars in the structure, serve as the basis for ordering the reinforcing steel from the warehouse, and show how the bars are to be placed in the forms.

The responsibility of the detailer in preparing placing drawings is limited to carrying out all instructions on the engineering drawings and, where nothing specific is stated, to conforming to the requirements of current building codes.

Some of the basic elements in the preparation of placing drawings as specified in the Manual of Standard Practice for Detailing Reinforced Concrete structures, are reproduced here.[4] See Figs. 18-35, 18-36, and 18-37.

Beams and joists. For beams, joists and girders, the reinforcement is usually shown in schedules. For placing drawings, those schedules should show: number, mark, and size of member; number, size, and length of straight bars; number, size, total length, mark, and bending details of bent bars and stirrups; spacing of stirrups; bar supports; and any other special information necessary for the proper fabrication and placement of reinforcement. Among the special items which should be noted are: overall length of bar and height of truss bar or hook where such dimensions are controlling; and location of bar with respect to supporting members where the bar is not placed symmetrically.

Slabs. The reinforcement for slabs is generally indicated on the plan, with details for the various types of bent bars shown in a schedule. This schedule is the same as for bent bars in beams, except that the number of bars is not given but must be obtained from the plan. Panels exactly alike are given an identifying letter; reinforcement is shown for only one panel of each kind. In skewed panels, bars are fanned to maintain given spacing at midspan. Openings are often reinforced with additional bars.

Columns. The reinforcement for columns is shown in a column schedule. The main schedule is supplemented with a smaller schedule for ties and bent bars, diagrams showing the arrangement and bending of the ties, and any special feature of the construction pertinent to the fabrication and placing of the column reinforcement.

Dowels. Dowels should be detailed with the reinforcement in the first section placed so that they will be delivered with it and be available for placement at the proper time.

Bar supports. Bar supports specified on the engineering drawings should be specifically listed on the placing drawings. Where a bar schedule is used, it is usually best to show the bar supports in the same schedule.

18.23 Typical bar bends and slants

To simplify the listing of bent bars in a schedule, diagrams of the bars are designated by letters. Fabricators usually have a standard chart of typical bar bends with numbers assigned to each type. See Fig. 18-38.

Fig. 18-39 illustrates the method of determining the necessary slant distance for various heights of bends. These slants are for bars bent at a 45° angle only, which is considered to be the standard slope.

4. *Ibid.*

(Text continued on page 541)

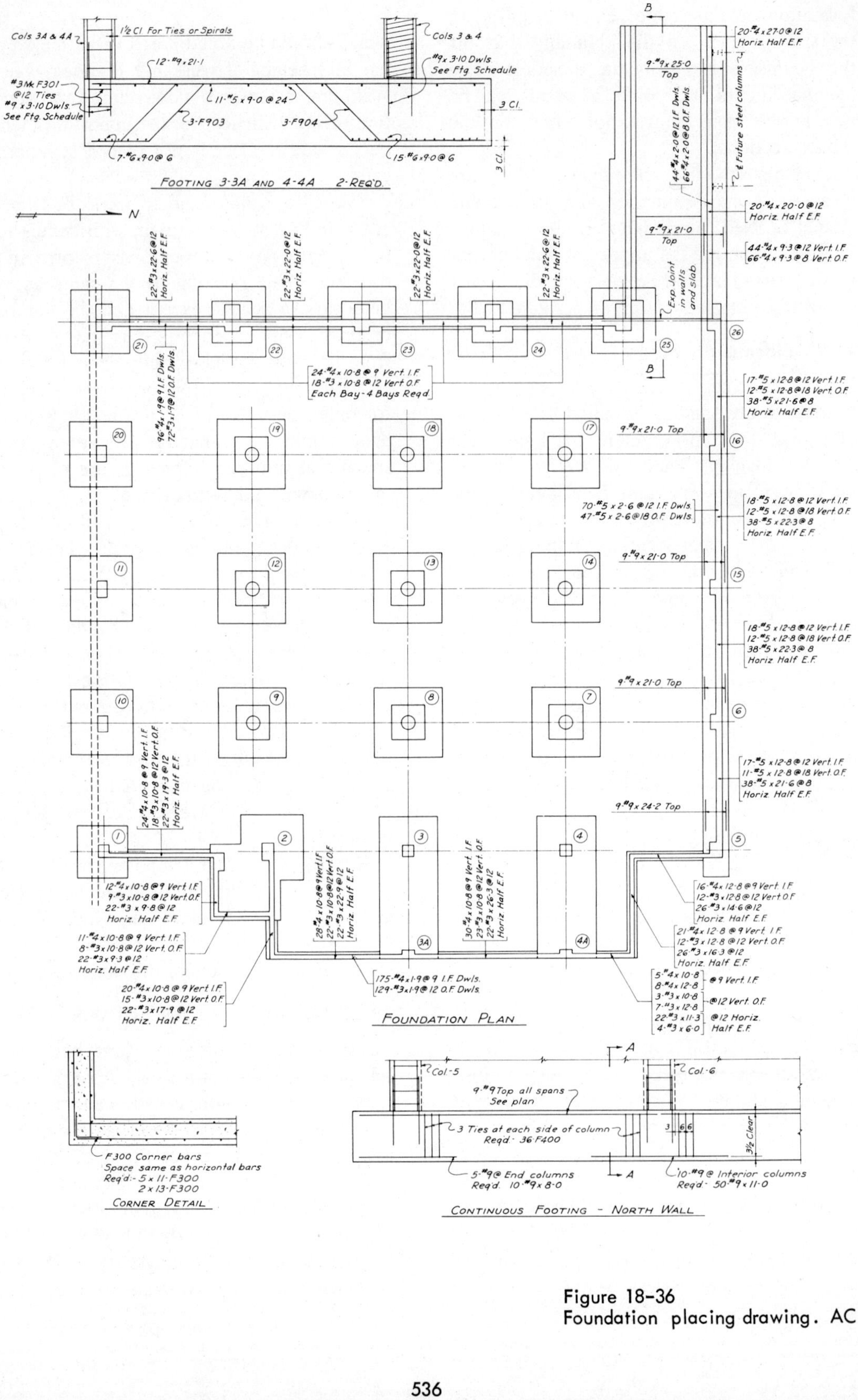

Figure 18-36
Foundation placing drawing. ACI

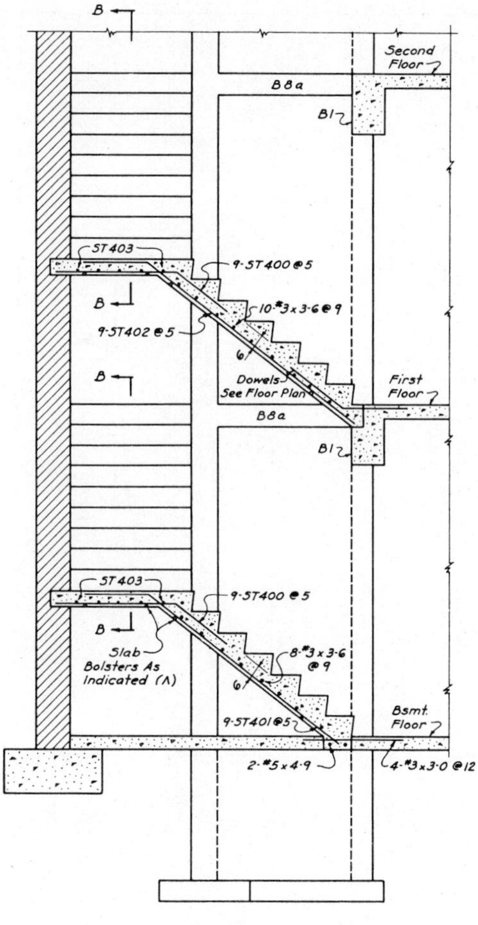

Section A-A   Stair No. 1

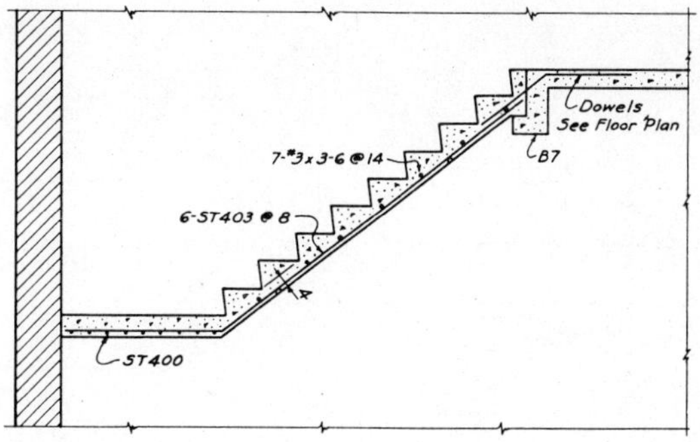

Section B-B   2-Req'd.

Figure 18–37
Stair details placing drawing. ACI

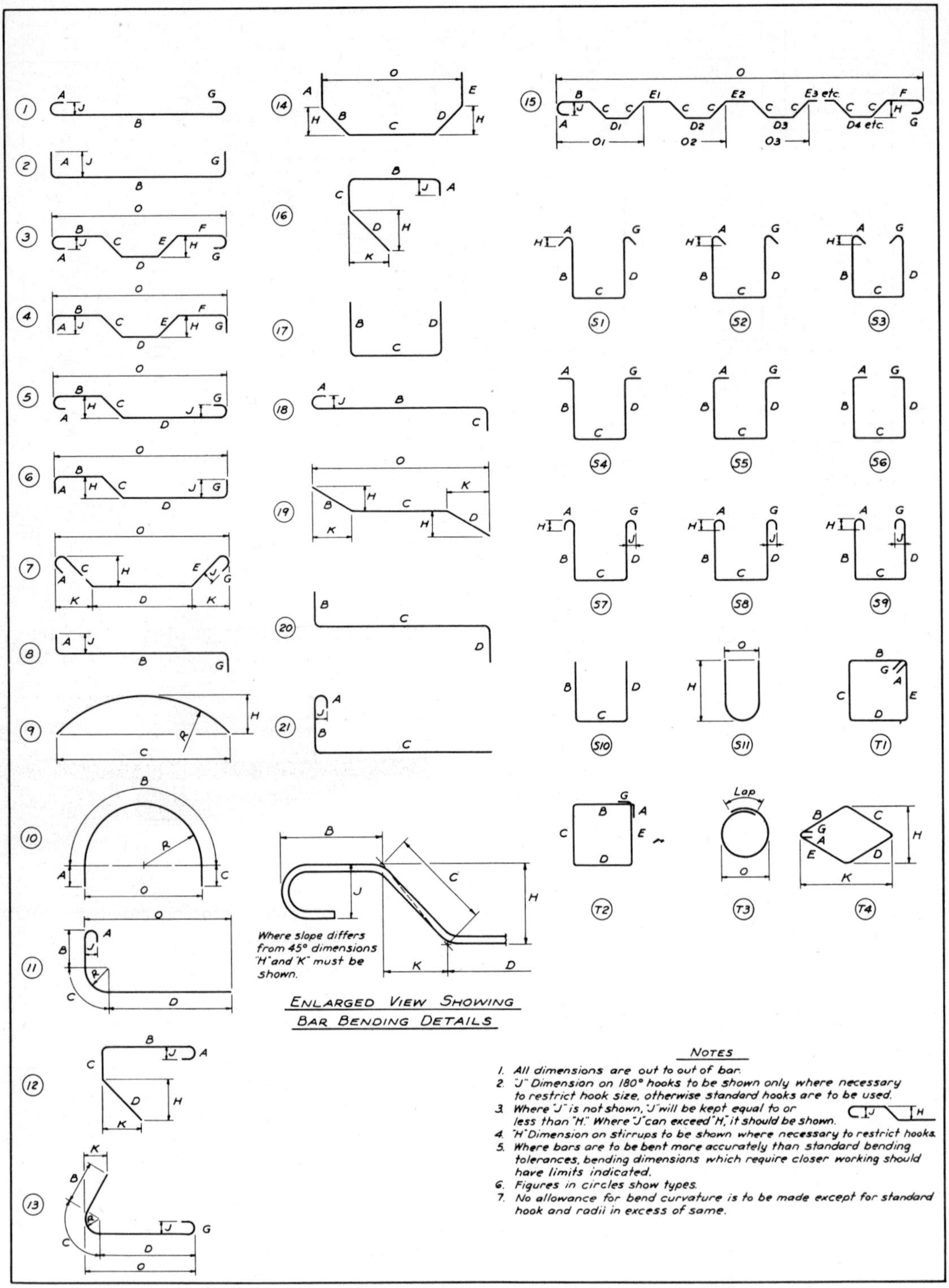

NOTES

1. All dimensions are out to out of bar.
2. "J" Dimension on 180° hooks to be shown only where necessary to restrict hook size, otherwise standard hooks are to be used.
3. Where "J" is not shown, "J" will be kept equal to or less than "H." Where "J" can exceed "H," it should be shown.
4. "H" Dimension on stirrups to be shown where necessary to restrict hooks.
5. Where bars are to be bent more accurately than standard bending tolerances, bending dimensions which require closer working should have limits indicated.
6. Figures in circles show types.
7. No allowance for bend curvature is to be made except for standard hook and radii in excess of same.

Figure 18-38
Typical bar bends used in reinforced concrete. ACI

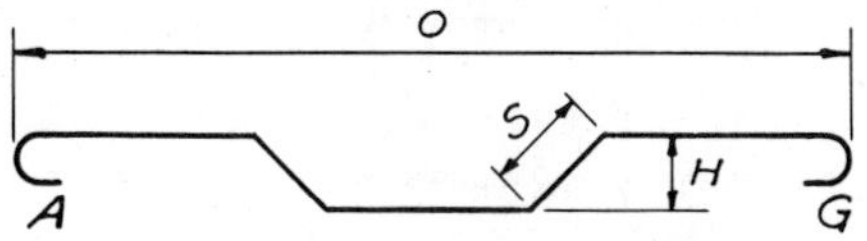

O = Overall Bar Dimension.
H = Height Of Bend
S = Slant = 1.414 H To Nearest ½ Inch
I = Increment = S − H

HEIGHT H	SLANT S	INCREMENT 2 SLANTS 2I	HEIGHT H	SLANT S	INCREMENT 2 SLANTS 2I	HEIGHT H	SLANT S	INCREMENT 2 SLANTS 2I
			1-1	1-6½	11	3-1	4-4½	2-7
			1-2	1-8	1-0	3-2	4-5½	2-7
			1-3	1-9	1-0	3-3	4-7	2-8
2	3	2	1-4	1-10½	1-1	3-4	4-8½	2-9
2½	3½	2	1-5	2-0	1-2	3-5	4-10	2-10
3	4	2	1-6	2-1½	1-3	3-6	4-11½	2-11
3½	5	3	1-7	2-3	1-4	3-7	5-1	3-0
4	5½	3	1-8	2-4	1-4	3-8	5-2	3-0
4½	6½	4	1-9	2-5½	1-5	3-9	5-3½	3-1
5	7	4	1-10	2-7	1-6	3-10	5-5	3-2
5½	7½	4	1-11	2-8½	1-7	3-11	5-6½	3-3
6	8½	5	2-0	2-10	1-8	4-0	5-8	3-4
6½	9	5	2-1	2-11½	1-9	4-1	5-9½	3-5
7	10	6	2-2	3-1	1-10	4-2	5-10½	3-5
7½	10½	6	2-3	3-2	1-10	4-3	6-0	3-6
8	11½	7	2-4	3-3½	1-11	4-4	6-1½	3-7
8½	1-0	7	2-5	3-5	2-0	4-5	6-3	3-8
9	1-0½	7	2-6	3-6½	2-1	4-6	6-4½	3-9
9½	1-1½	8	2-7	3-8	2-2	4-7	6-6	3-10
10	1-2	8	2-8	3-9	2-2	4-8	6-7	3-10
10½	1-3	9	2-9	3-10½	2-3	4-9	6-8½	3-11
11	1-3½	9	2-10	4-0	2-4	4-10	6-10	4-0
11½	1-4	9	2-11	4-1½	2-5	4-11	6-11½	4-1
1-0	1-5	10	3-0	4-3	2-6	5-0	7-1	4-2

Increment For 2 Slants = 2 x (S − H)
All Dimensions Are Out To Out Of Bar.
Scheduled Length Of Bar Is Sum Of The Detail Dimensions. (Length = O + 2I + A + G).

Figure 18-39
Slants and increments for 45° bar bends. ACI

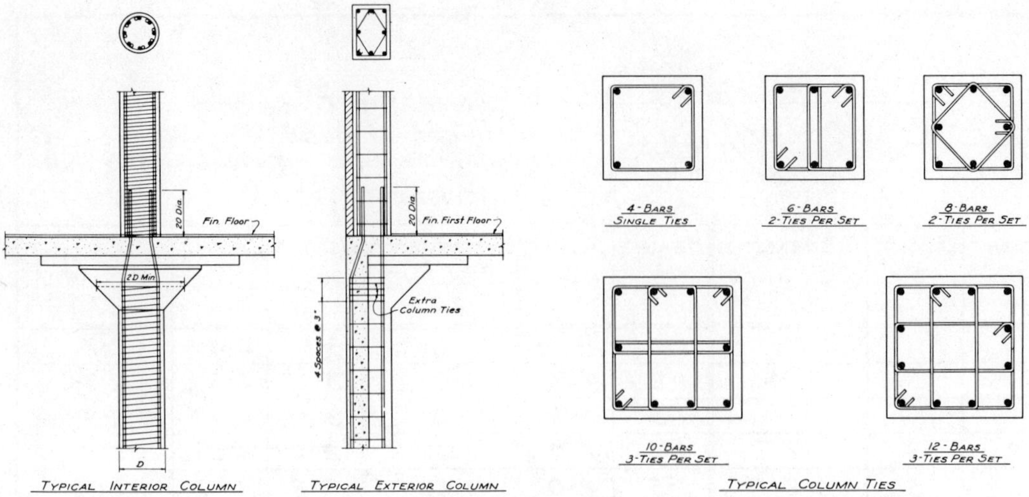

Figure 18-40
Typical column detail and standard column ties. ACI

MAXIMUM SPACING OF COLUMN TIES

Vertical bar size	Size and spacing of ties, in Maximum spacing not to exceed least column dimension		
	#2	#3	#4
#5	10	10	10
#6	12	12	12
#7	12	14	14
#8	12*	16	16
#9	12*	18	18
#10	12*	18	20
#11	12*	18	22

*#2 ties are not recommended for #8 or larger verticals.

Figure 18-41
Maximum spacing of column ties. ACI

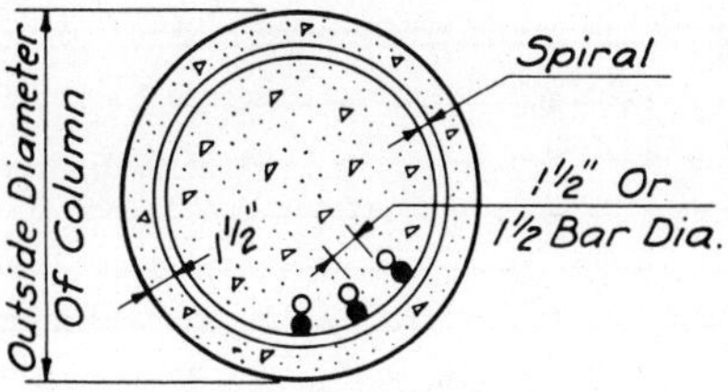

Diameter of column	Spiral size	Bar size						
		#5	#6	#7	#8	#9	#10	#11
14	3/8	12	11	10	9	7	6	—
15	3/8	13	12	11	10	8	7	6
16	3/8	15	13	12	11	9	8	6
17	3/8	16	15	14	12	11	9	7
18	3/8	18	16	15	14	12	10	8
19	3/8	19	18	16	15	13	11	9
20	3/8	21	19	18	16	14	12	10
21	1/2	22	20	19	17	15	13	11
22	1/2	23	22	20	18	16	14	11
23	1/2	25	23	21	20	17	15	12
24	1/2	26	24	22	21	18	16	13
25	1/2	28	26	24	22	19	17	14
26	1/2	29	27	25	23	20	18	15
27	1/2	31	28	26	25	21	19	16
28	5/8	32	30	28	26	22	20	17
29	5/8	33	31	29	27	23	21	17
30	5/8	35	32	30	28	25	22	18
31	5/8	36	34	31	29	26	23	19
32	5/8	38	35	33	31	27	24	20
33	5/8	39	37	34	32	28	25	21
34	5/8	41	38	35	33	29	26	22

Figure 18-42
Maximumn number of column bars for round columns. ACI

18.24 Column ties

To reduce the possibility of buckling, vertical bars in columns must be tied. The standard tie arrangements are shown in Fig. 18-40. The spacing of ties is governed by the size of the column and of the vertical bars. The maximum spacing permitted by the *ACI* code is given in Fig. 18-41.

The number of bars in a column is also controlled by code regulations. Fig. 18-42 illustrates the maximum number of bars according to *ACI* code requirements.

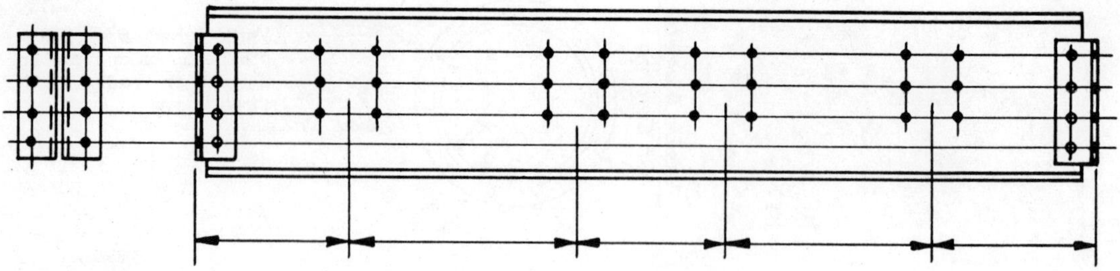

Figure 18–43
Problem 1.

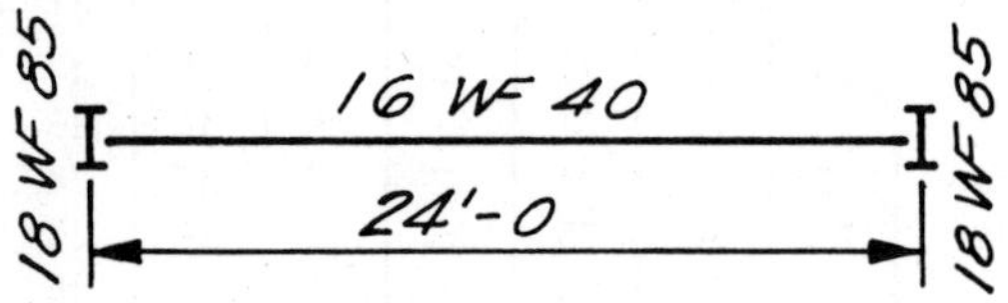

Figure 18–44
Problem 2.

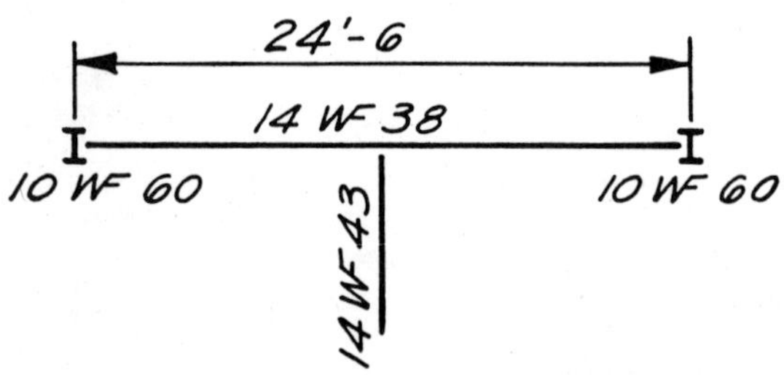

Figure 18–45
Problem 3.

Problems, section 18

1 Dimension the 16 **WF** 96 Beam shown in Fig. 18-43. Use **A**4 type connecting angles with 7/8 inch rivets. Space rivet gage lines on beam as follows: 6'-1-3/4, 3'-1-1/2, 10'-2-1/4, 3'-1-1/2, 6'-1-3/4, 3'-1-1/2, 10'-2-1/4, 3'-1-1/2, 6'-1-3/4.

2 Make a complete shop drawing of the framing shown in Fig. 18-44, using 3/4 inch rivets and **B**4 standard connections.

3 Make a complete shop drawing of Beam 14 **WF** 38 with **A**3 connections and 7/8 inch rivets shown in Fig. 18-45.

4 Prepare a shop detail drawing of Columns **C**4 and **C**5 in Fig. 18-46.

5 Detail the necessary connections for Beams **A** and **B** in Fig. 18-47 to meet the loads specified.

6 Design the necessary gusset plate for the members in Fig. 18-48. Observe proper rivet spacing. Gusset plate to be 1/4 inch thick.

7 Detail the connecting members in Fig. 18-49 showing complete gusset details. Use 3/8 inch plate for gusset, and 11.3 kips for rivets. Minimum rivet spacing to be 2–1/4 inches with edge distance of 1 inch and end pitch not to exceed four times the rivet diameter.

8 Make a shop drawing of the Beam 18 **WF** 60 in Fig. 18-50, with required skewed connection. Refer to Fig. 18-22.

9 Make a detailed shop drawing of the truss shown in Fig. 18-51. All connections to be welded.

10 Using the Engineering Drawing in Fig. 18-52, prepare a Placing Drawing with a complete Beam Schedule.

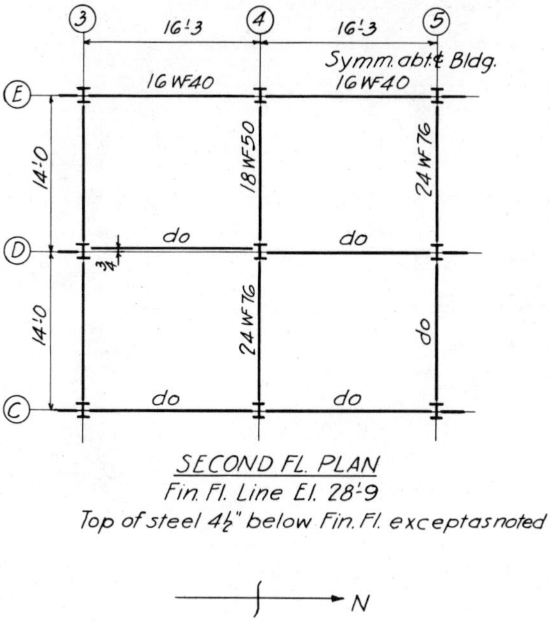

Figure 18-46
Problem 4.

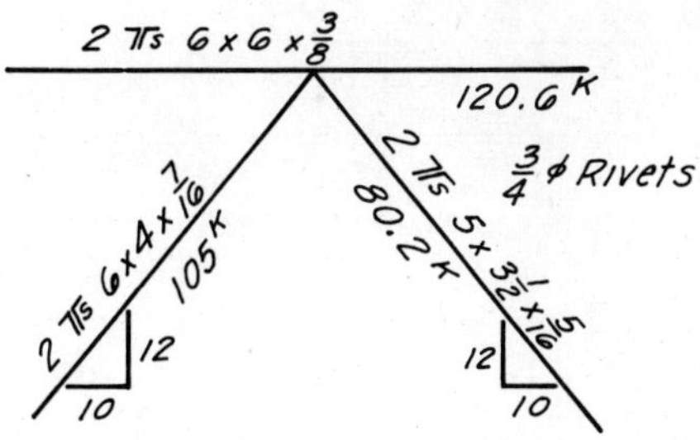

Figure 18-49
Problem 7.

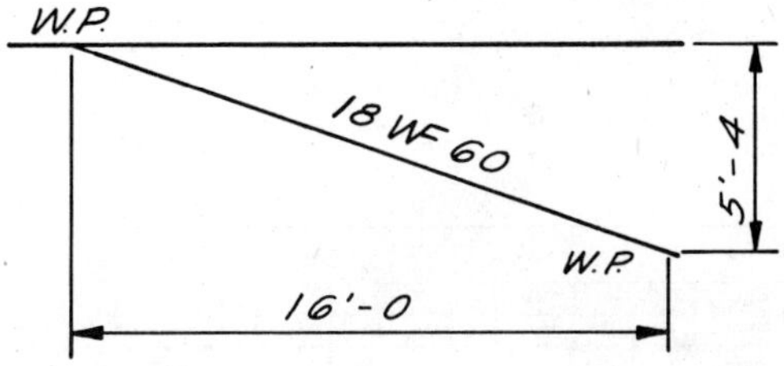

Figure 18-50
Problem 8.

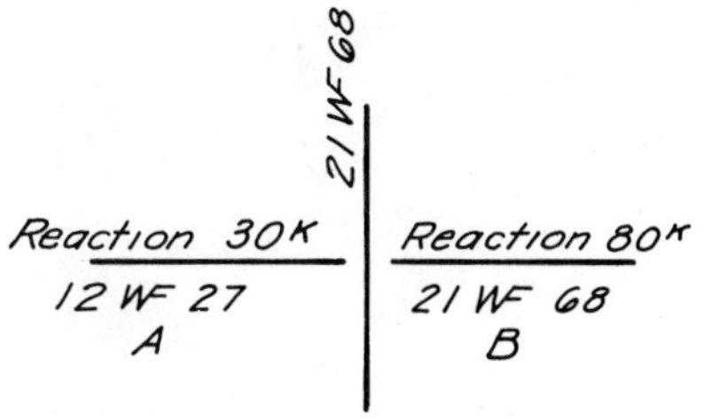

Figure 18-47
Problem 5.

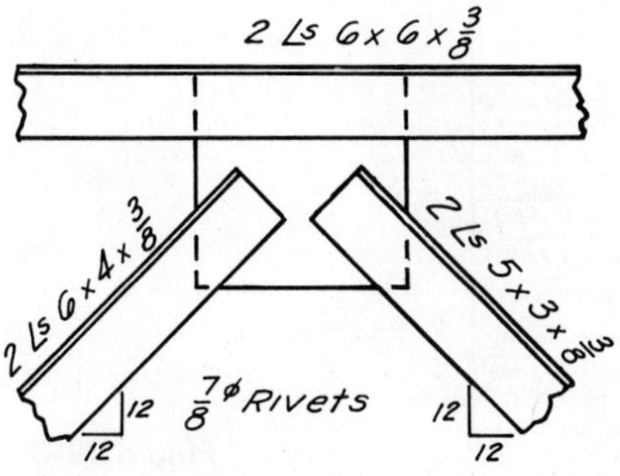

Figure 18-48
Problem 6.

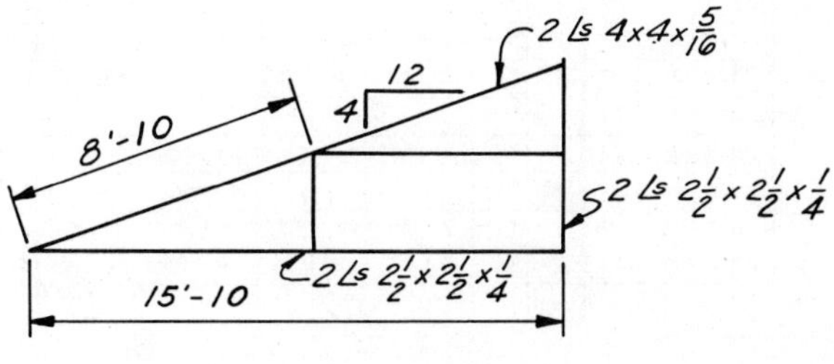

Figure 18-51
Problem 9.

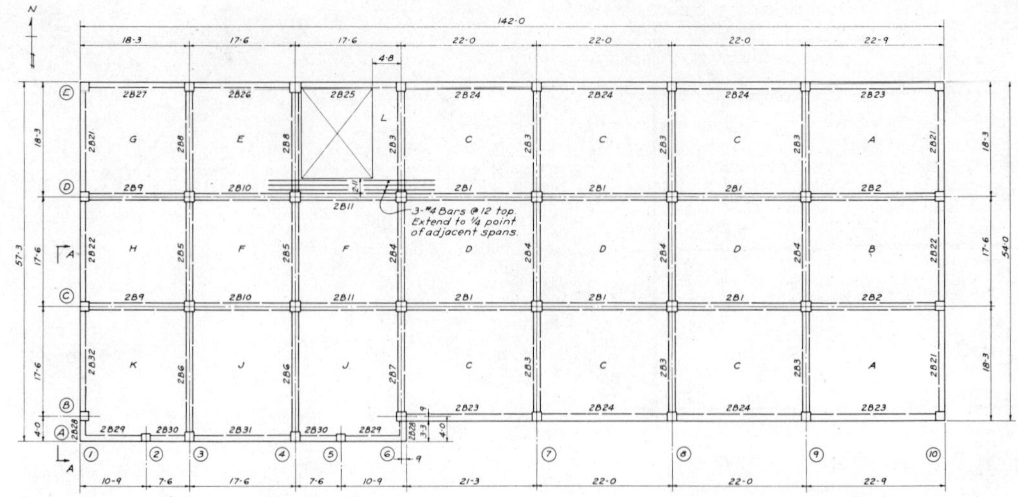

Second Floor Framing Plan
All Slabs 6" Thick

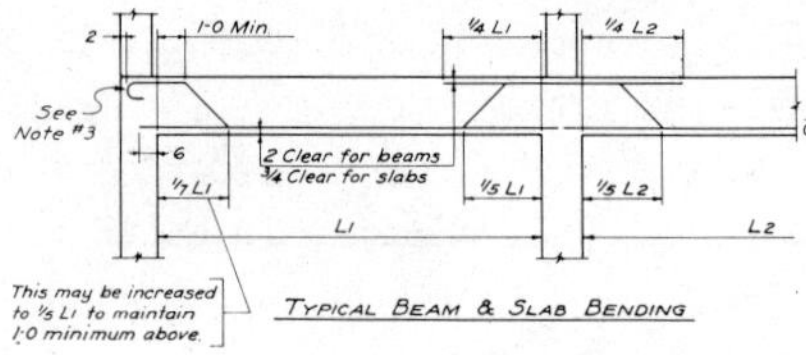

Typical Beam & Slab Bending

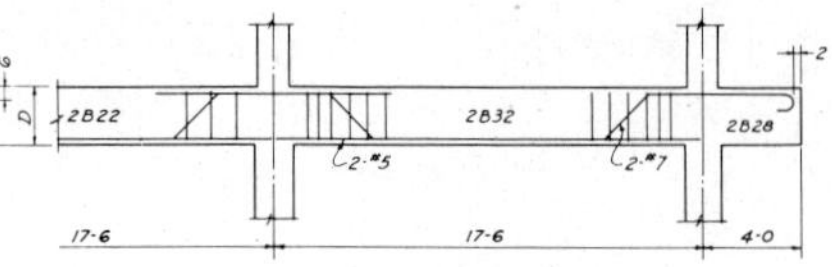

Elevation A-A
Beam 2B7 Similar

Beam Schedule										
Beam Mark	Size W	Size D	Straight No.	Straight Size	Truss No.	Truss Size	Stirrups No.	Stirrups Size	Stirrups Spacing Each End	Remarks
2B1	14	27	2	#7	2	#9	28	#3	6@3, 4@6, 2@9, 2@12	
2B2	14	27	2	#7	2	#10	28	#3	6@3, 4@6, 2@9, 2@12	1-#6 Top @ interior column
2B3	14	20	2	#7	2	#9	20	#3	2@3, 4@6, 2@9, 2@10	
2B4	14	20	2	#6	2	#8	20	#3	2@3, 4@6, 2@9, 2@10	
2B5	14	20	2	#6	2	#8	20	#3	2@3, 4@6, 2@9, 2@10	
2B6	14	27	2	#6	2	#9	16	#3	3@6, 2@9, 3@10	
2B7	14	20	2	#7	2	#9	20	#3	2@3, 4@6, 2@9, 2@10	Extend truss bars across 2B28.
2B8	14	20	2	#6	2	#9	18	#3	2@3, 3@6, 4@9	
2B9	14	20	2	#7	2	#9	18	#3	2@3, 3@6, 4@9	1-#6 Top @ interior column.
2B10	14	20	2	#6	2	#8	18	#3	2@3, 3@6, 4@9	
2B11	14	20	2	#6	2	#7	16	#3	4@6, 4@9	
2B21	11	27	2	#5	2	#7	6	#2	1@9, 2@12	
2B22	11	27	2	#5	2	#6	6	#2	1@9, 2@12	
2B23	14	27	2	#7	2	#9	28	#3	4@3, 4@6, 3@9, 3@12	
2B24	14	27	2	#6	2	#9	28	#3	4@3, 4@6, 3@9, 3@12	
2B25	11	27	2	#6			14	#2	2@3, 2@6, 2@9, 1@12	2-#5 Top bars extend into 2B24 & 2B26
2B26	11	27	2	#5	2	#7	16	#2	2@3, 3@6, 2@9, 1@12	
2B27	11	27	2	#6	2	#7	16	#2	2@3, 3@6, 2@9, 1@12	
2B28	11	27								Extend truss bars from 2B7 & 2B32
2B29	11	27	2	#5	2	#5				Extend truss bars across 2B30
2B30	11	27	2	#5						Extend truss bars from 2B29 & 2B31
2B31	11	27	2	#6	2	#8	16	#2	2@3, 3@6, 2@9, 1@12	Extend truss bars across 2B30
2B32	11	27	2	#5	2	#7	12	#2	3@6, 3@9	Extend truss bars across 2B28

Figure 18-52
Problem 10.

Plumbing, heating, and electrical drawings 19

The primary purpose of this section is to present those aspects of drawing as they apply to three specific areas: plumbing, heating, and electrical installations. No attempt is made to discuss engineering design in any of these highly specialized phases. Only such material is included that may be needed by a draftsman in preparing finished drawings involving these installations.

19.1 Pipe

Pipe is made of various materials, the most common being cast iron, steel, wrought iron, copper, brass and lead. The type of pipe used depends on its intended function.

Cast iron pipe is particularly suitable for underground installations to convey gas, water or steam. It has high corrosion-resistance qualities and can withstand considerable stresses of expansion, contraction and vibration.

Steel pipe is utilized for a great many purposes, not only in carrying fluids of different kinds, but in structural work as well. Very often pipe is substituted for steel structural shapes to function as columns or in constructing rail guards, scaffolds, frames, etc. Steel pipe is resistant to high temperatures and pressures and has an outstanding advantage in that connections can be made easily by welding. When steel pipe is dipped in molten zinc to prevent rust, it is called *galvanized pipe*. Galvanized pipe is intended primarily for lines carrying drinking water.

Wrought iron pipe originally was considered best in situations where high corrosive conditions prevailed. However, installation records and tests show that steel pipe is equal to wrought iron pipe for general purpose work. Consequently today, steel pipe is used more extensively especially since it is less expensive. Where extreme corrosive conditions exist, wrought iron, stainless steel, or other non-corrosive pipes are necessary.

Brass and copper pipe are utilized for general plumbing and heating purposes, gas, steam and oil lines. Brass pipe is extremely resistant to corrosion except under severe acid conditions. Copper pipe is not suitable where continuous high temperatures or repeated severe stresses occur, because under such conditions it deteriorates rapidly. Copper pipe also has wide applications for radiant heating and air conditioning installations. The use of copper or brass pipe in these applications minimizes installation time since they can be shaped readily without the need for special fittings; connections are easily and quickly made by soldering operations.

Lead pipe and lead-lined pipe are widely used for conveying chemicals or in piping systems subjected to acid conditions. Lead-lined steel pipe is designed for situations where more severe corrosion conditions and higher pressures are encountered.

19.2 Sizes of pipe

The three standard weights of steel and wrought iron pipe are classified as *standard, extra-strong* and *double extra-strong*. For any given diameter, each of the three types have different wall thicknesses but for any given nominal size, all have the same outside diameter. When reference is made to a specified inside diameter it does not imply that this size is actually as stated. Thus the inside diameter of a 1″ nominal standard pipe is 1.049″, extra-strong is .957″ and double extra-strong is .599″.

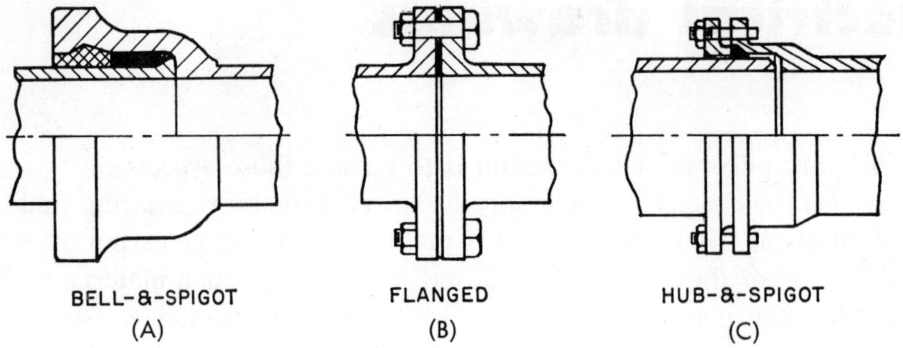

Figure 19-1
Common types of joints used on cast iron pipe.

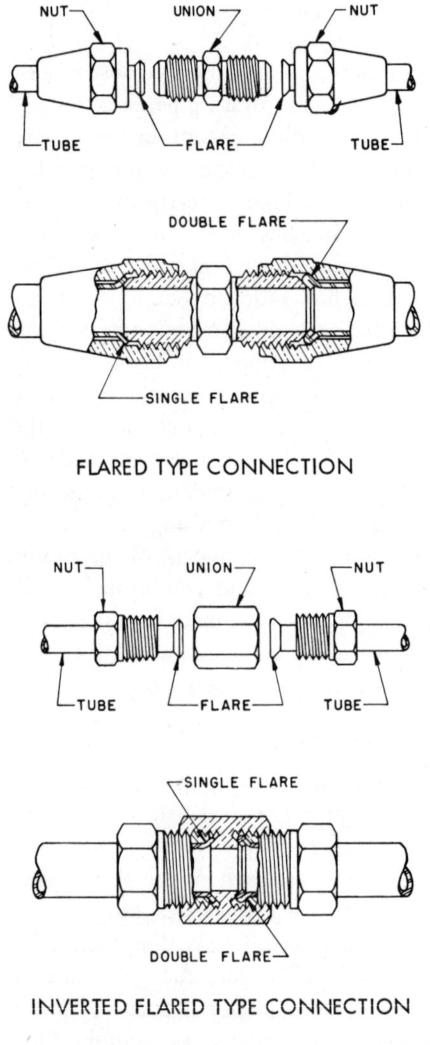

Figure 19-2
Flared tube fittings are used on high pressure lines. General Motors Corp.

Commercial sizes of wrought-iron and steel pipe ranging from 1/8″ to 12″ are designated by their nominal inside diameter (ID). Pipe 14″ diameter and larger is indicated by its outside diameter (OD). The general practice in specifying the size of steel and wrought iron pipe for 12″ and smaller is to indicate the desired weight by the terms standard, extra-strong and double extra-strong. For pipe 14″ or larger the desired wall thickness is given instead of the weight terminology.

The required volume of flow usually governs the inside diameter of pipe to be used. Wall thickness depends on such factors as internal pressure, external pressure and the amount of expansion stresses encountered.

The size of cast iron pipe is designated by the nominal inside diameter, wall thickness and quite often, the strength or working pressure class. (See the Appendix.) The wall thickness of the pipe varies according to its strength and diameter.

Cast iron pipe is available either with flanged ends or with bell-and-spigot ends. The greatest use of the bell-and-spigot is for underground waterlines. This joint when properly calked and leaded makes a very tight joint. See *A* of Fig. 19-1.

Flanged pipe has higher strength values

and is used to convey fluids under greater pressure. See *B* of Fig. 19-1.

Another type of cast iron pipe, known as Universal pipe, is available for gas and water lines of all pressures. The pipe is made with a hub-and-spigot end and the joint held together by two or more bolts. The pipe ends are tapered, providing a tight iron-to-iron contact joint. See *C* of Fig. 19-1.

Brass and copper pipe is manufactured in two standard weights—regular and extra-strong—and in sizes ranging from 1/8 to 12 inches in diameter. Their size is specified by both the inside and outside diameter. The outside diameters are always the same as the corresponding nominal sizes of steel pipe.

Lead pipe is supplied in straight lengths, reels, or coils. The size of both lead and lead-lined pipe is indicated by the inside and outside diameters.

19.3 Tubing

Generally speaking, when piping does not correspond to standard steel pipe wall thicknesses and diameters, it is referred to as tubing. Tubing is manufactured in round, square, rectangular, hex and octagonal shapes. Steel, copper, brass, aluminum and stainless steel are the common materials used for tubing. Copper and brass tubing is especially adaptable for gas, air or fluid lines in heating, refrigeration, air conditioning and plumbing installations. Stainless steel and aluminum tubing have wide applications in high pressure hydraulic lines.

Copper and brass tubing are furnished in three basic weights designated as types *K* and *L* in hard and soft tempers and type *M* in hard temper. Aluminum tubing is specified according to the standard aluminum classification symbols which designate the type of alloy and tempers, such as 3003-*O*, 6061-*F*, etc. Stainless steel tubing is available in a variety of types in the 300 or 400 classification series.

In all cases, the size of round tubing is indicated by the outside diameter and wall thickness. For square, hex and octagonal tubing the distance across flats and the wall thickness are given.

19.4 Pipe and tube fittings

Fittings are designed to make connections in piping systems and to change the direction of flow. They are made of cast iron, malleable iron, steel, brass, copper, aluminum and other special alloys. Pipe fittings fall into four general categories: *screwed, flanged, welded,* and *soldered.*

Screwed fittings are used primarily in small piping systems such as house plumbing, oil and hydraulic lines. Soldered fittings are found where connections must be permanently and tightly sealed, especially in refrigeration units, radiant heating systems, and other small, low pressure fluid lines. Flanged and welded fittings are employed in large piping systems where connections must be strong enough to carry the weight of pipes and withstand high pressures.

Tube fittings are either of the *soldered, welded, flared* or *threaded sleeve* type. Flared tube fittings are widely used for connecting lines which carry liquids or gases at relatively high pressures, such as in hydraulic and air braking systems. See Fig. 19-2. Soldered, welded and threaded sleeve tube fittings are intended mostly for connecting lines which carry either gases or liquids at medium pressures.

In most instances fittings should have the same qualities as those of the pipe or tubing they join. Hence fittings are usually specified according to the nominal piping size, material and strength factor, or pressure rating. Standard pressure rating for cast iron fittings for low and medium pressure lines are 25, 125 and 250 lbs. Steel fittings with high pressure ratings of 150 to 2500 lbs. are available for high pressure lines. Thus a fitting may be specified as follows:

2″ - 125 lb. 90° ELBOW, CAST IRON

Some of the more common fittings are illustrated in Fig. 19-3. Included are the following:

Coupling. For connecting straight sections.

Cap. Fits on the end of pipe to close it.

Plug. Used to close an opening in a fitting.

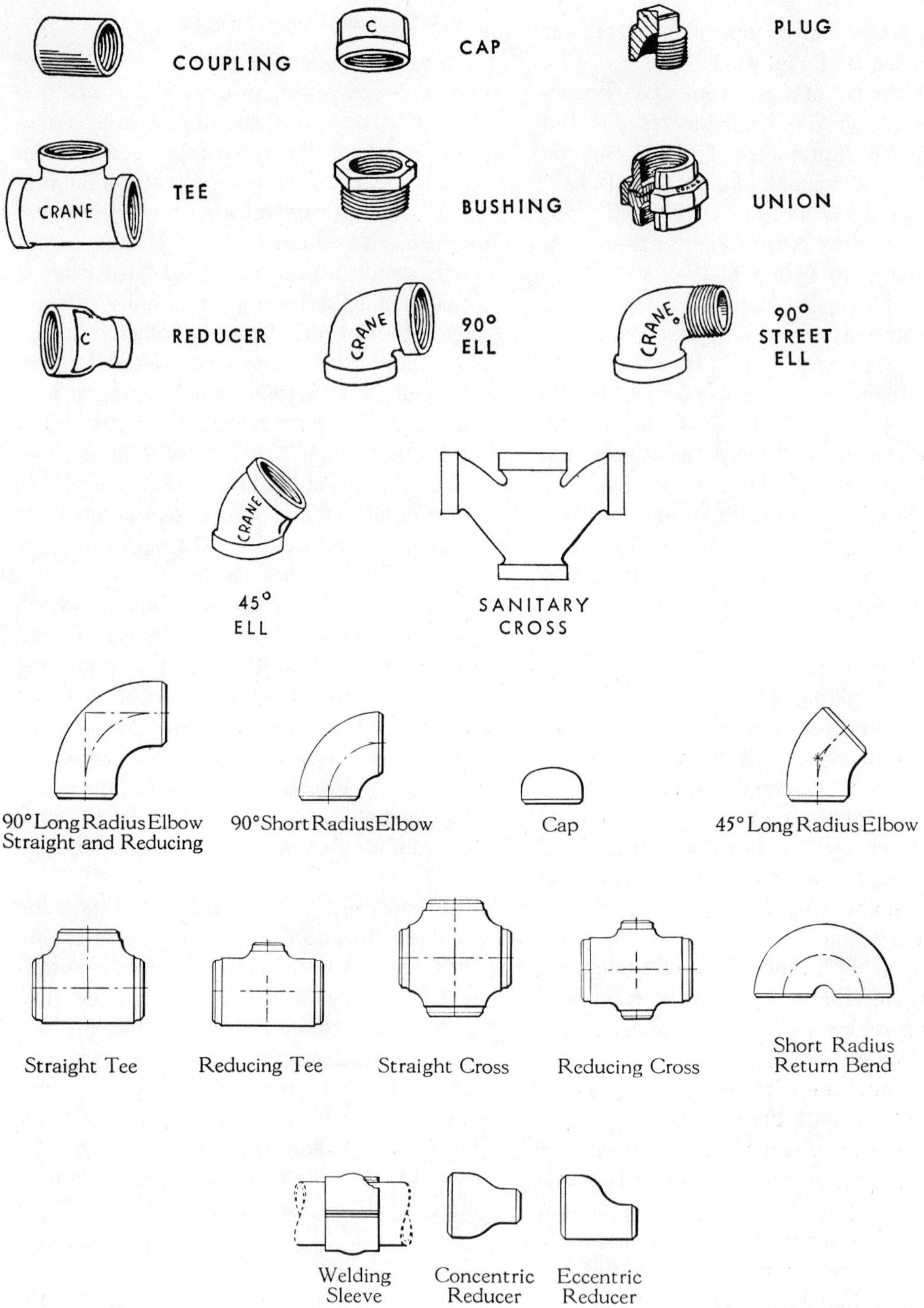

Figure 19-3
These fittings are used to connect various units in a piping system and to change the direction of flow.

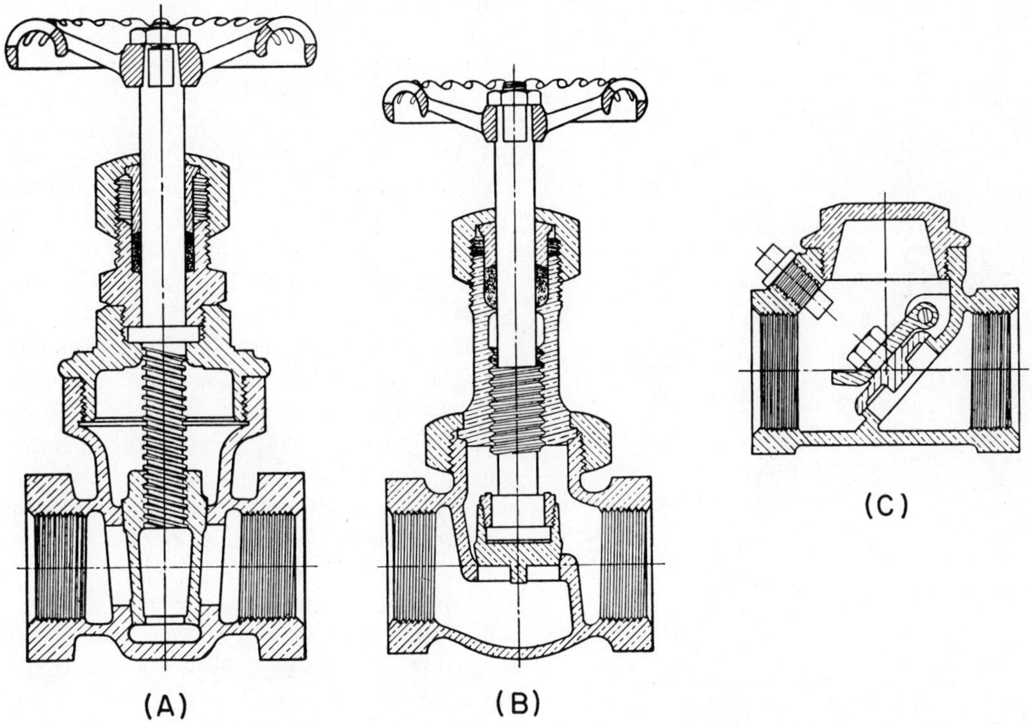

Figure 19-4
These different valves are used in a piping system to control the quantity or the direction of flow. At (A) is shown a gate valve; at (B) a globe valve; at (C) a check valve.

Nipple. Short piece of pipe for making connection to fittings.

Bushing. Reduces the size of an opening in a fitting.

Union. Used to close a piping system and to connect pipes that must be disconnected occasionally for repairs.

Tees, crosses, laterals. Form the connections for lines branching off the piping system.

Ells. Used to change the direction of pipe lines.

Reducer. Permits the use of different pipe sizes in a piping system.

19.5 Valves

The function of a valve is to control the quantity or the direction of flow in a piping system. See Fig. 19.4. There are many different types of valves and they are made of several kinds of metal. Usually valves on small size pipe lines are of brass or bronze. Large piping systems with low and intermediate pressures are equipped with cast iron valves. Pipe lines with high pressure flows have either cast steel or cast alloy valves.

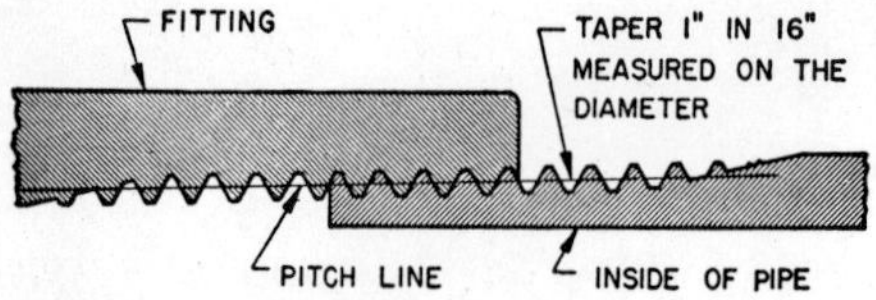

Figure 19-5
Threaded pipe connections are threaded with the American Standard taper pipe thread to insure a tight fitting joint.

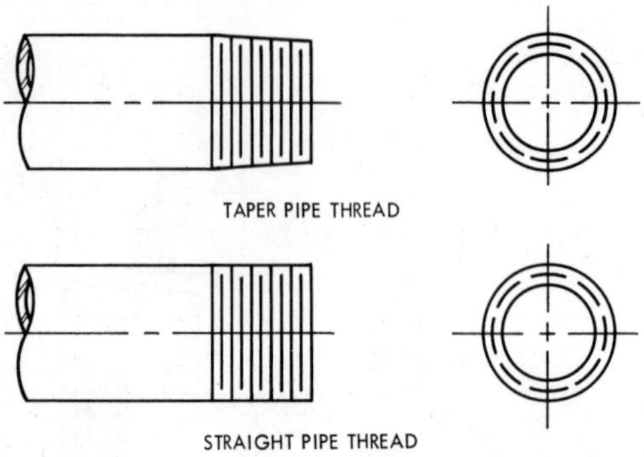

Figure 19-6
Conventional thread symbols.

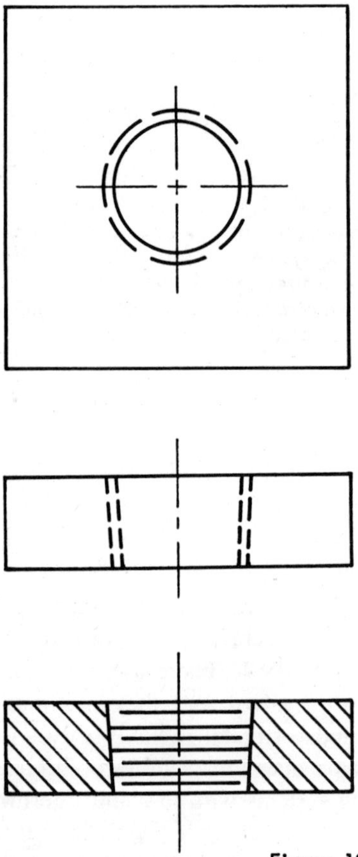

Figure 19-7
Internal pipe threads.

The *gate* valve is probably the most frequently used valve for water and oil lines. This valve is operated by turning a handwheel which raises or lowers a disk or wedge into the flow stream. The quick-opening gate valve is designed so it can be used on lines which must be opened or closed instantly.

The *globe* valve is especially adaptable for throttling steam in low and high pressure lines. Control is effected by raising or lowering a plug or disk into a seat.

The *needle* valve is found in small piping systems where close control of flow is necessary.

The *check* valve is constructed to permit flow of a fluid in one direction only. This valve closes automatically if the flow should reverse its direction.

The *diaphragm* valve is designed for piping systems conveying acids, alkalies and volatile substances. The valve has no metal-to-metal seat; closure is actuated by a rubber diaphragm.

19.6 American Standard Pipe thread

The American Standard Pipe thread is the standard thread used for both internal and external pipe connections. This thread is similar to the regular American Standard thread except that it is tapered 1/16″ per inch. See Fig. 19-5. The slight taper is incorporated to ensure a tight fitting joint.

The American Standard straight pipe thread has the same number of threads per inch as the taper thread and is intended chiefly for couplings and nipples.

A pipe thread is represented on a drawing by the same conventional symbols used for the regular thread series. See Fig. 19-6 and Fig. 19-7. The taper may or may not be shown. When it is indicated the taper should be exaggerated to be seen readily.

If it is necessary to specify pipe threads by means of a note, the designated symbols should be shown as follows:

For a 1-1/4″ American Standard Pipe taper thread

1-1/4—NPT

For a 1″ American Standard Pipe straight thread

1 — NPS

For a 3/8″ American Standard taper pipe thread (dryseal)

3/8 — NPTF

Other American Standard pipe threads include:

NPSC. Straight pipe thread in couplings.

NPSI. Intermediate internal straight pipe thread (dryseal).

NPSF. Internal straight pipe thread (dryseal).

NPSM. Straight pipe thread for mechanical joints.

NPSL. Straight pipe thread for locknuts.

NPSH. Straight pipe thread for hose couplings and nipples.

NPTR. Taper pipe thread for rail fittings.

19.7 Identification of piping

A scheme of identifying a piping system for industrial plants has been approved by *ASA*. This scheme consists of a series of colors which classifies the piping system according to the nature of materials carried. The approved colors are painted over the entire lengths of pipe or several bands are painted at various intervals throughout the piping system. In some instances the contents of the pipe are actually stenciled in abbreviated form over the color bands. The approved color scheme is shown in Table I.

19.8 Pipe bends

Pipe bends are formed lengths of pipe obtainable in practically any size and shape to meet existing situations arising in a piping system. Specifically they are used to: (1) eliminate the need for a number of joints in a pipe line, (2) compensate for expansion and contraction, (3) permit installation of a pipe line around obstructions, and (4) reduce friction in the piping. Some of the more common pipe bends are shown in Fig. 19-8, as well as the method of dimensioning them. Table II contains the recommended radii and tangents of pipe bends for pipe of various sizes.

19.9 Pipe symbols

In preparing a piping drawing or sketch, all fittings, fixtures, valves and other units are shown by means of graphic symbols. Fig. 19-9 illustrates the basic piping symbols that have been approved by the American Standards Association. The use of these symbols simplifies considerably the preparation of piping drawings and conserves a great deal of time and effort.

19.10 Piping drawing

The function of a piping drawing is to show the location, the type and position of various units in a pipe line, and the sizes and description of all parts used in the piping system. The drawing may be a freehand sketch or a finished mechanical drawing. Quite often the preliminary layout is in the form of a freehand sketch and later is made into a finished drawing.

The actual views of a piping system may consist of a single orthographic view, or an isometric or oblique pictorial representation. Occasionally, a two or three view orthographic projection is prepared especially for systems which are basic in design and are installed frequently, or when special valve design or other units in the piping system must be clearly shown. See Fig. 19-10.

The presentation of a piping layout in either orthographic or pictorial form is accomplished by what is known as a single or double line representation. The single line drawing is more commonly used when installation of small-size pipe is involved as well as for laying out small piping systems and making preliminary layouts and calculations. In a single line drawing single lines are employed to designate pipe regardless of the pipe size. Conventional symbols are

(Text continued on page 557)

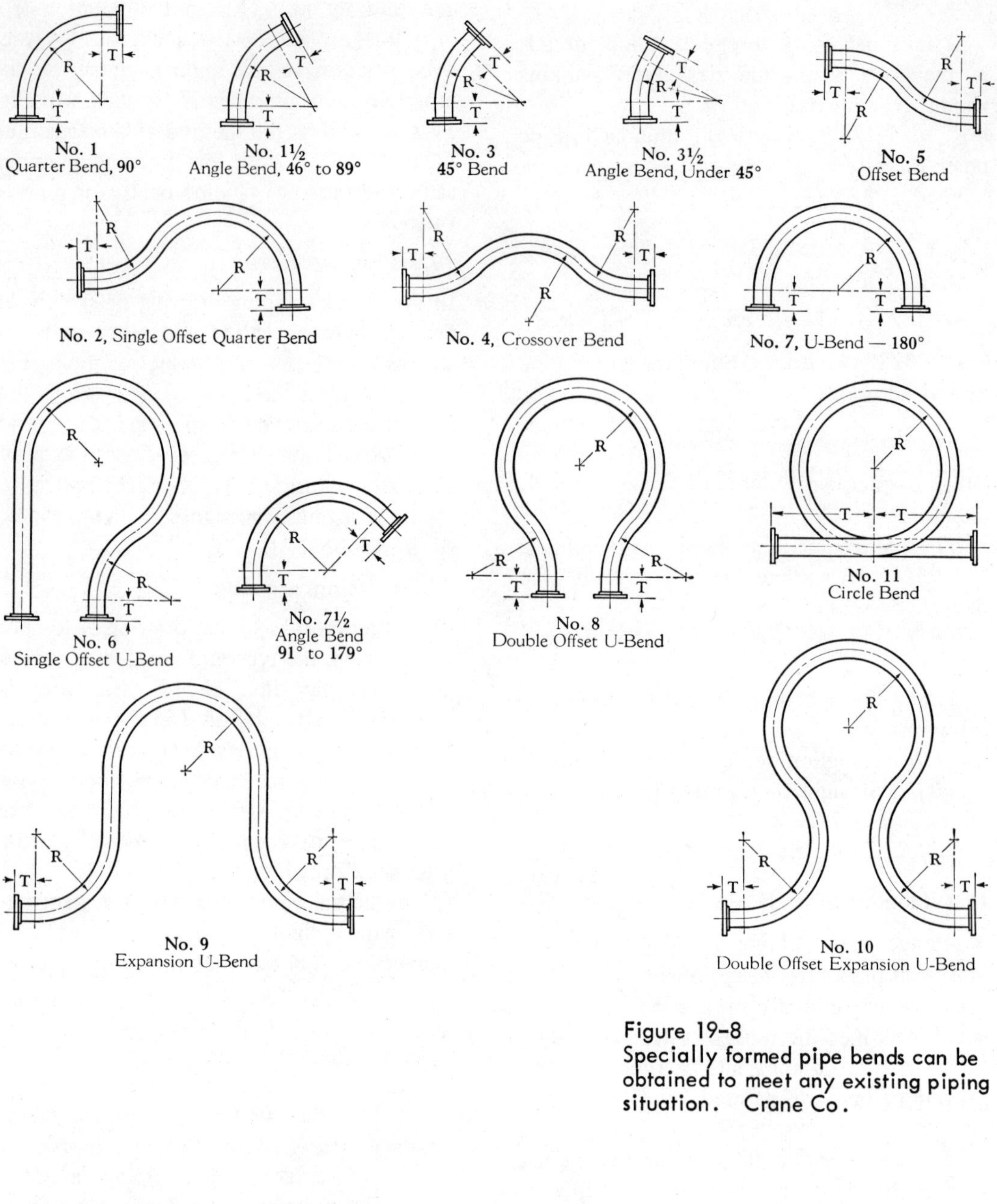

Figure 19–8
Specially formed pipe bends can be obtained to meet any existing piping situation. Crane Co.

TABLE I

Class	Color
Fire Protection Equipment	Red
Dangerous Materials	Yellow or Orange
Safe Materials	Green, White, Black, Gray, or Aluminum
Protective Materials	Bright Blue
Extra Valuable Materials	Deep Purple

TABLE II. RADII AND TANGENTS OF PIPE BENDS, IN INCHES

Size of Pipe	Column "A"	Column "B"				Column "C"
	R Minimum Recommended Radius Steel or Wrought Iron Pipe	R Shortest Radii To Which Pipe Can Be Bent				T Minimum Length of Tangent Steel or Wrought Iron Pipe Standard or Extra Strong
		Steel Pipe Only		Wrought Iron Pipe		
		Threaded Ends, Screwed, or Welded Flanges		Threaded Ends, Screwed, or Welded Flanges		
	Standard or Extra Strong Weight	Standard Weight Pipe	Extra Strong Weight Pipe	Standard Weight Pipe	Extra Strong Weight Pipe	Threaded Ends or Screwed Flanges
1/4	1 1/4	1	5/8	1 1/4	1	1
3/8	1 7/8	1 1/4	3/4	1 7/8	1 1/2	1 1/4
1/2	2 1/2	1 1/2	1	2 1/2	2	1 1/2
3/4	3 3/4	1 3/4	1 1/4	3	2 1/2	1 3/4
1	5	2	1 1/2	4	3	2
1 1/4	6 1/4	2 1/4	1 3/4	5	4	2
1 1/2	7 1/2	2 1/2	2	6	5	2 1/2
2	10	3	2 1/2	8	5	3
2 1/2	12 1/2	5	4 1/4	10	8	4
3	15	8	6	12	10	4
3 1/2	17 1/2	10	8	14	12	5
4	20	12	10	16	12	5
5	25	18	14	20	15	6
6	30	22	15	26	18	7
8	40	30	23	30	28	9
10	50	36	30	36	32	12
12	60	46	36	46	42	14
*14 OD	70	60	48	60	54	16
*16 OD	96	80	60	80	70	18
*18 OD	108	90	66	90	80	18
*20 OD	120	100	72	100	90	18
*24 OD	144	144	108	144	122	18

*For sizes 14-inch O.D. and larger, the radii shown are based upon pipe with a wall thickness of 7/16-inch or lighter under the "Standard Weight Pipe" column, and a wall thickness of 1/2-inch or heavier under the "Extra Strong Weight Pipe" column.

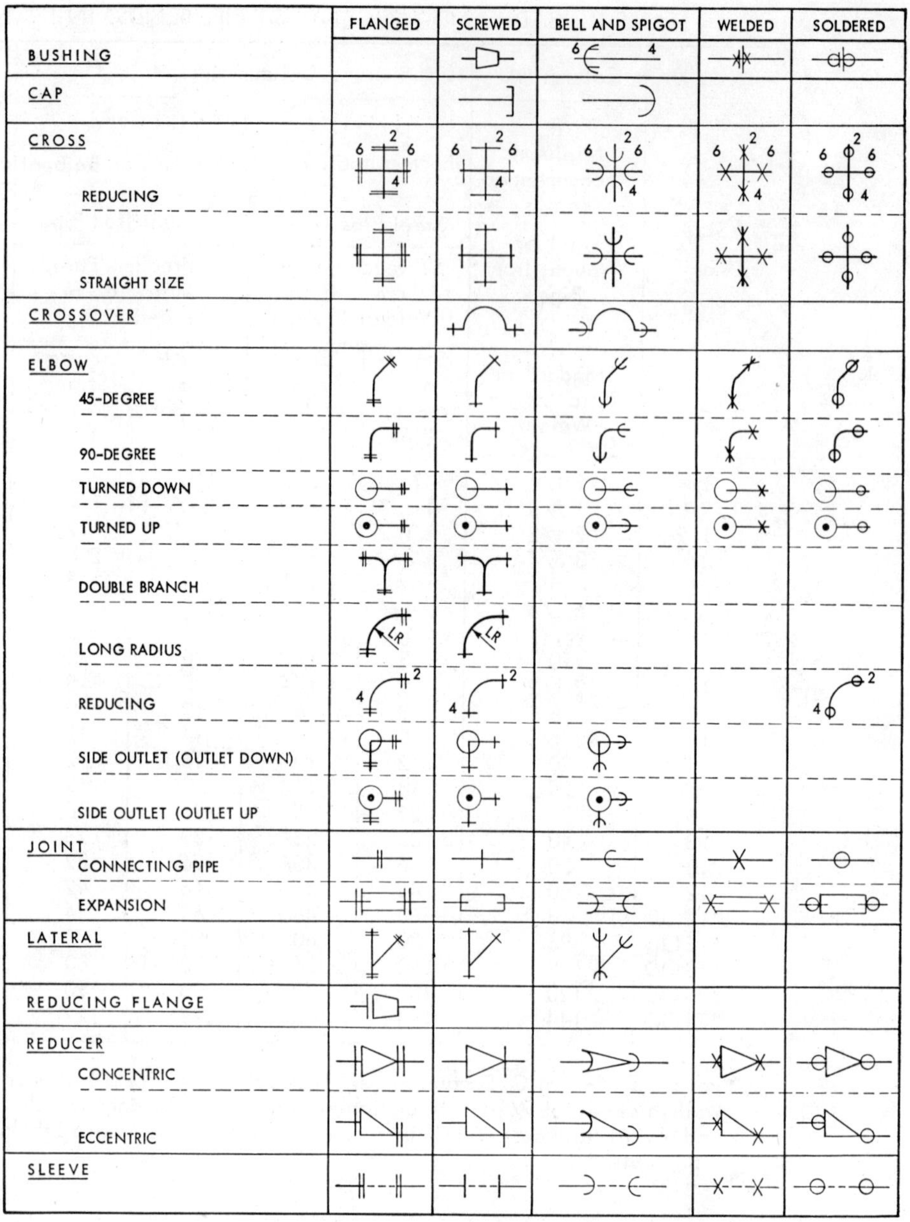
FLANGED
SCREWED
BELL AND SPIGOT
WELDED
SOLDERED
BUSHING
CAP
CROSS
REDUCING
STRAIGHT SIZE
CROSSOVER
ELBOW
45-DEGREE
90-DEGREE
TURNED DOWN
TURNED UP
DOUBLE BRANCH
LONG RADIUS
REDUCING
SIDE OUTLET (OUTLET DOWN)
SIDE OUTLET (OUTLET UP
JOINT
CONNECTING PIPE
EXPANSION
LATERAL
REDUCING FLANGE
REDUCER
CONCENTRIC
ECCENTRIC
SLEEVE

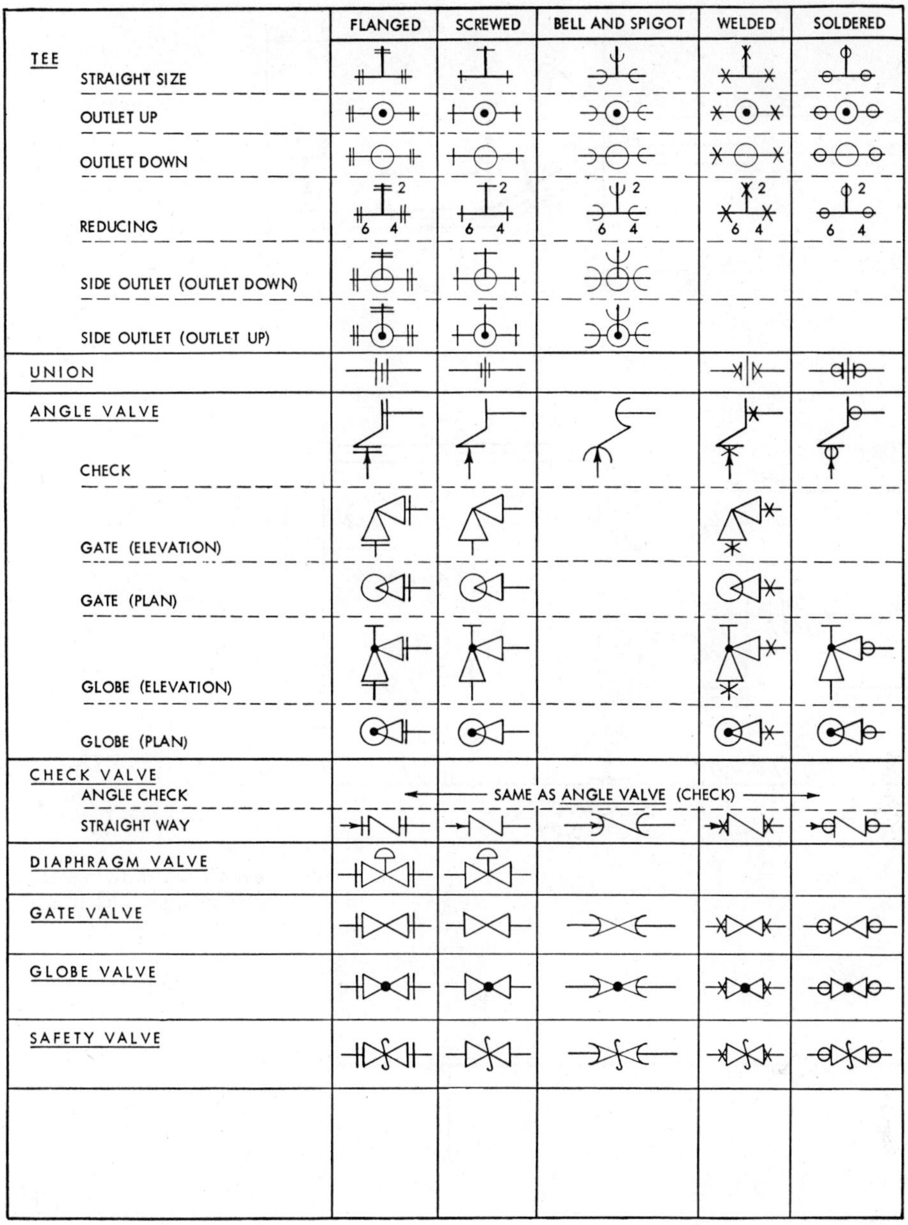
FLANGED
SCREWED
BELL AND SPIGOT
WELDED
SOLDERED
TEE
STRAIGHT SIZE
OUTLET UP
OUTLET DOWN
REDUCING
SIDE OUTLET (OUTLET DOWN)
SIDE OUTLET (OUTLET UP)
UNION
ANGLE VALVE
CHECK
GATE (ELEVATION)
GATE (PLAN)
GLOBE (ELEVATION)
GLOBE (PLAN)
CHECK VALVE
ANGLE CHECK
STRAIGHT WAY
SAME AS ANGLE VALVE (CHECK)
DIAPHRAGM VALVE
GATE VALVE
GLOBE VALVE
SAFETY VALVE

Figure 19-9
These are the graphic symbols used for pipe fittings, valves, etc.
ASA Z32.2.3-1949

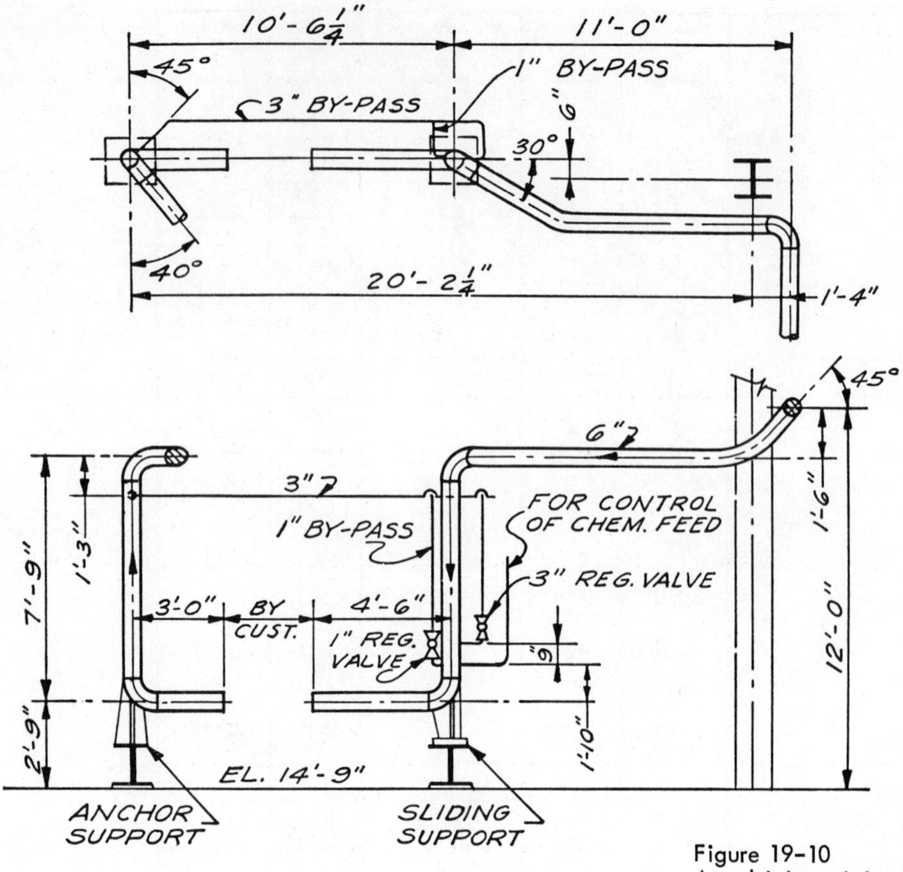

Figure 19-10
A multiview piping drawing is used to show basic designs which are frequently installed.

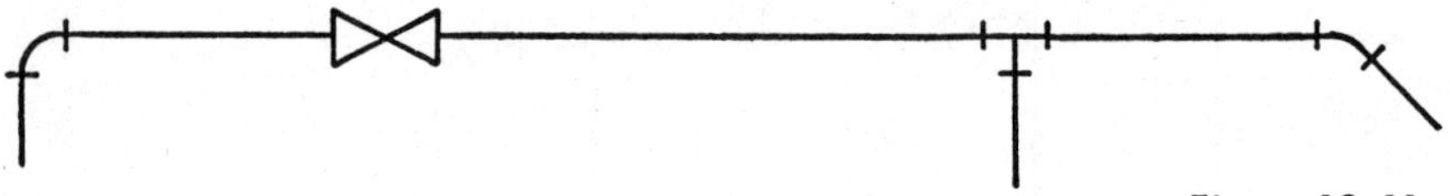

Figure 19-11
A conventional single line piping drawing.

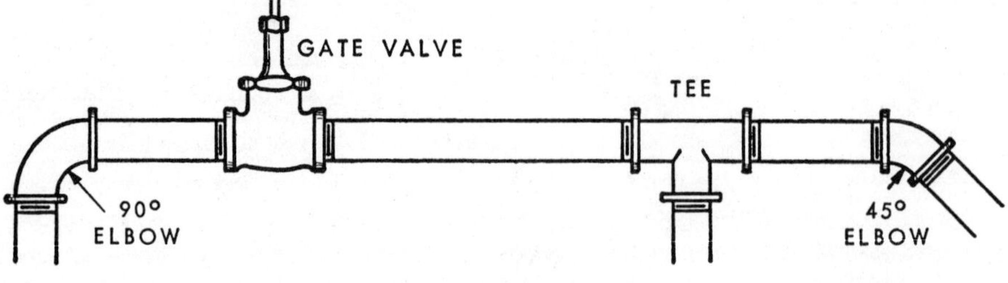

Figure 19-12
A double line drawing is prepared by manufacturers of piping equipment for standard installations.

included for all fittings, valves and fixtures. See Fig. 19-11.

The double line drawing is more often prepared by manufacturers of piping equipment when a drawing is to be used repeatedly on similar installations on numerous projects. A double line drawing is also quite common for large piping systems. See Fig. 19-12.

The pictorial drawing of a piping system has a very decided advantage over orthographic presentations in that it can reveal changes in direction and differences in installation levels. See Fig. 19-13.

19.11 Dimensioning a piping drawing

Generally speaking, the same rules of dimensioning that govern orthographic and pictorial drawings also apply to pipe drawings. In every instance it is important to supply sufficient information so the pipe fitter can proceed with the installation without any guess work.

The following rules are particularly significant in dimensioning a piping drawing:

1 All straight lengths of pipe should be dimensioned.

2 Location dimensions must be clearly indicated.

3 Pipe fittings, valves and other units are located by center-to-center distances.

4 Wherever possible dimensions should be placed on a solid dimension line instead of in between breaks of lines.

5 Size and kind of pipe fittings and valves are identified at their location position or in a bill of material.

6 For some drawings it will be necessary to supply a bill of material, specifying quantity and kinds of material needed for the piping system.

19.12 Heating systems

A heating system is intended to transmit heat from a point of generation to the place of use. A draftsman's job is not to design the heating system but to prepare the plan of the heating system from notes and sketches supplied by the heating engineer. To effectively execute a heating drawing, a draftsman should have some knowledge of heating fundamentals and be familiar with graphic representations of heating systems.

Heating systems are classified according to the medium used to convey the heat. The most common heating mediums are hot water, warm air, and steam. In the hot water and steam systems, the heat is transmitted through a series of pipes to panels or radiators. The horizontal pipes leaving the boiler are called mains. The vertical pipes are referred to as risers. Radiators are located directly beneath the windows in a building. If they are placed along the inside wall, uncomfortable drafts result from the cooling effects caused by the windows. Radiant heating systems also utilize hot water as the heating medium. The heated water circulates in copper pipes which are laid in the floor or ceiling.

In a warm air system, the heat is distributed through sheetmetal ducts and is discharged into a room through registers or grills. Warm air is conveyed to the room either by gravity or is forced in by a fan. The most common system is the forced circulation since it eliminates numerous large ducts radiating from the furnace. Horizontal ducts are called leaders and vertical ducts stacks or risers. Ducts leading away from the leaders are known as branches. See Fig. 19-14. The furnace for a gravity system is usually located in a central position to eliminate long leaders. Long leaders restrict the flow of air and cause considerable heat loss. With forced air, the location of the furnace is not as critical since the fan speeds up the flow of air and thereby reduces the heat loss. Cold air registers are placed in each room so that after the air has lost its heat, the cool air is returned to the heating plant.

19.13 Heating drawings

The main purpose of a heating drawing is to show the location of the units involved in the heating system. The specifications of the various units along with a rough layout sketch are prepared by the heating engineer or contractor. The finished drawing may be either a single view orthographic or it may be drawn pictorially, depending on the function of the drawing. As in plumbing draw-

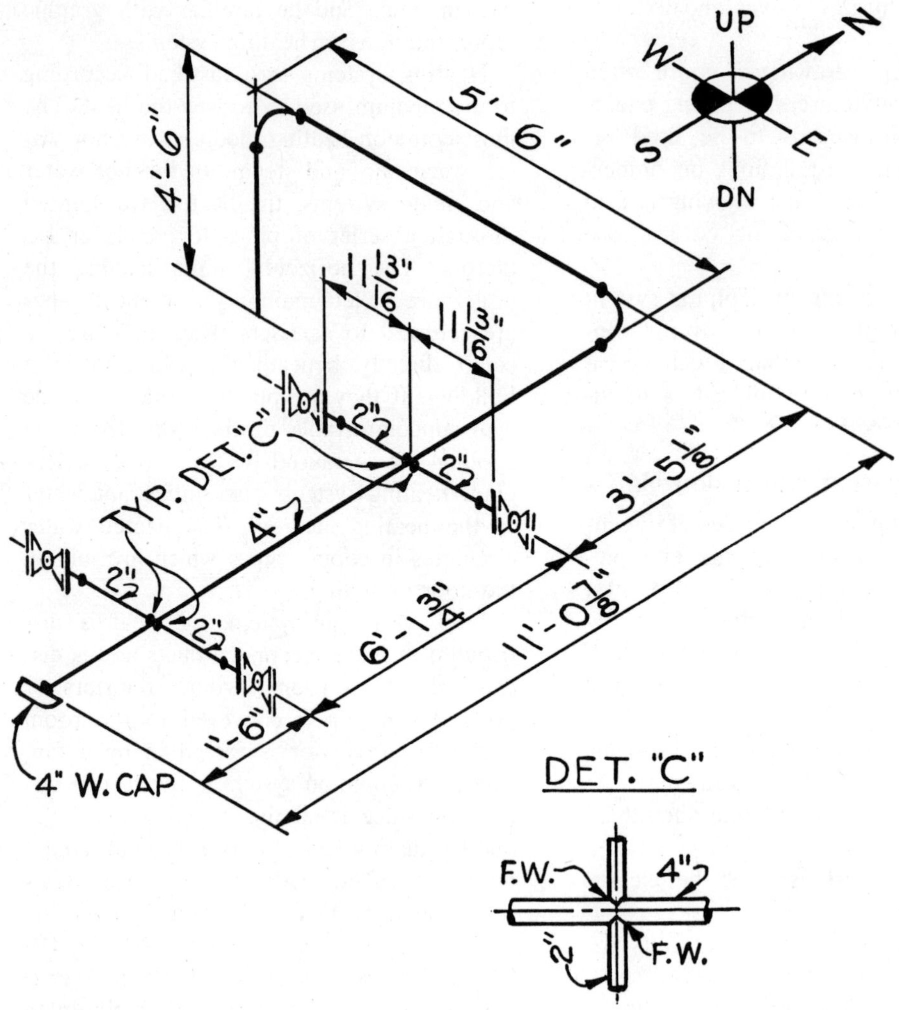

Figure 19–13
A pictorial piping drawing clearly shows complicated piping installations.

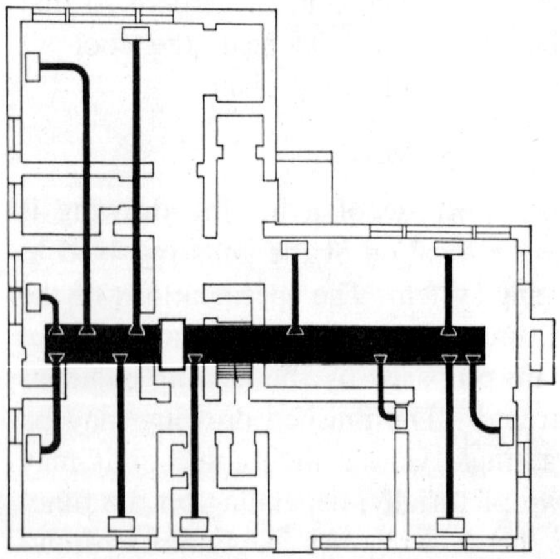

Figure 19–14
A simple warm air duct system.
Reynolds Metals Co.

ings, the work to be installed is shown by single or double lines with heating symbols to identify the units. See Fig. 19-15. Pictorial drawings are used largely to show some special units of a heating system or some particular method of installation.

Steam and hot water pipes are drawn in the same manner as described for plumbing. From Fig. 19-15 it can be seen that warm-air supply ducts are represented by solid lines. Duct sizes are given by showing first the horizontal dimension and then the depth dimension. However, the actual depth of the duct is not shown. Cold air ducts are drawn with dashed lines. Registers are located and scaled in the drawing to the given size. Notice in Fig. 19-16 what a forced air heating drawing looks like when it is completed, while in Fig. 19-17, a representative radiant heating floor arrangement for a small residence is shown.

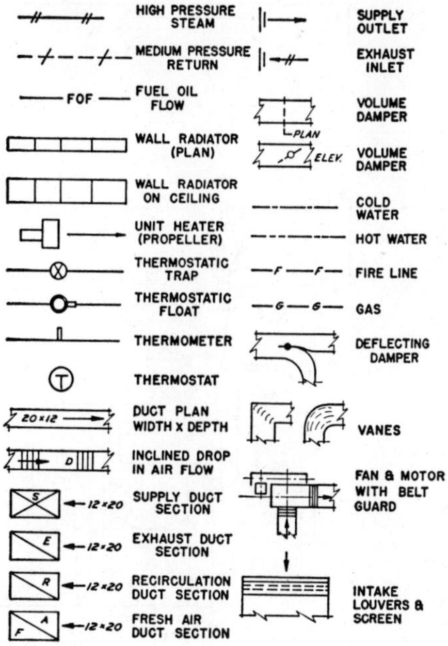

Figure 19-15
These symbols are used in preparing a heating drawing.

19.14 Architectural electrical drawings

A set of building plans usually will include some kind of an electrical diagram. For small and simple structures, the wiring arrangement may be included on the floor plan. On large and more complicated buildings the practice is to prepare separate electrical drawings.

In any electrical drawing or diagram, standard graphical symbols are used to represent lights, outlets, switches, wire runs and other electrical components. See Fig. 19-18. A typical building electrical layout is shown in Fig. 19-19. Notice that the plan presents the location of all lights, outlets and switching arrangements.

According to approved standards, wires that are to be concealed in the walls or ceiling are drawn with a medium-weight solid line. A dash-line symbol designates outlet runs which are to be concealed in the floor or basement ceiling. A two wire conductor is indicated either with or without two parallel dashes across the wire run. If the conductor is to have more than two wires, dashes must be used to show the number of required wires.

Accompanying the electrical plan is usually a fixture schedule and legend. The schedule specifies the quantity and description of the electrical fixtures. Each unit is coded with a letter for identification purposes. The legend consists of the symbols which are used, with their designated meaning, in the electrical drawing. See Fig. 19-20.

19.15 Common electrical terms

A few basic electrical terms are included here for the benefit of the beginning draftsman.

Building services. Conductors that supply electricity to a building from an outside distribution system are known as building services. The point at which the wires enter the building is called the service entrance.

Main switches. The service entrance inside a building is connected to the service switch or main breaker switch which connects and disconnects the electrical power supply to the interior wiring system. From the main switch the power is carried to a panel box. *(Text continued on page 564)*

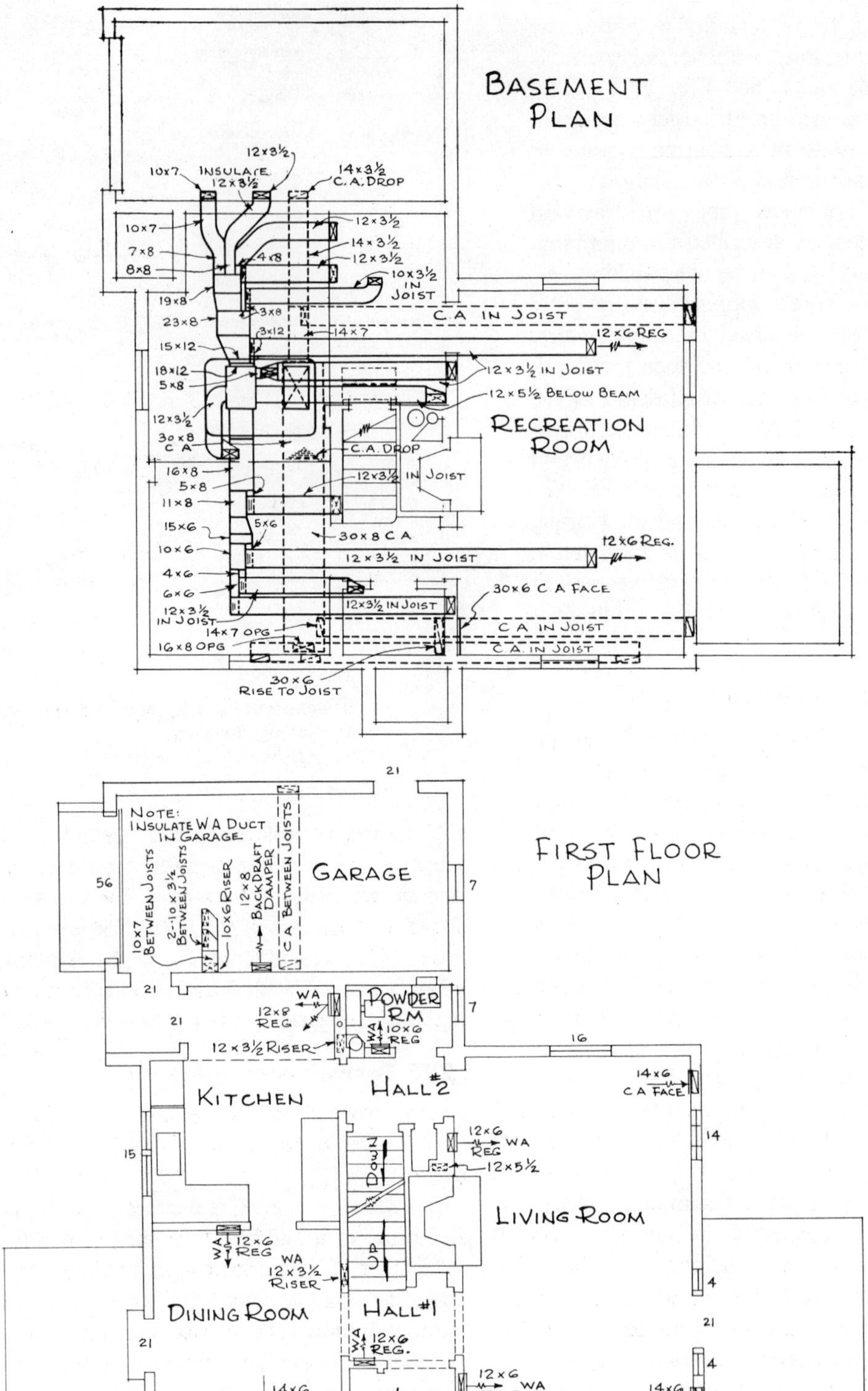

Figure 19-16
A complete heating drawing should look like this.

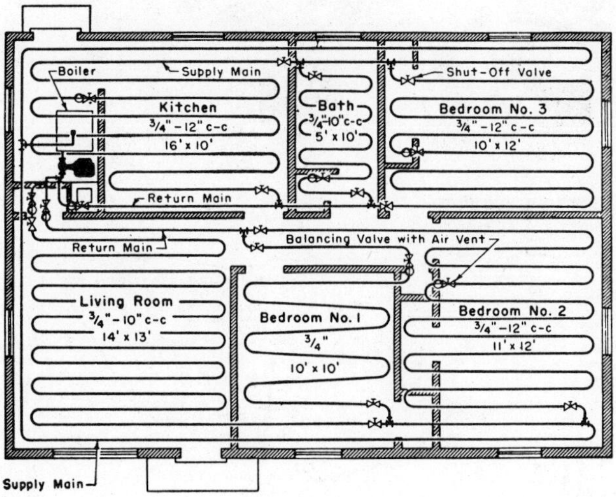

Figure 19-17
This is a typical arrangement for a radiant heating floor panel for a five-room residence.

Ceiling Wall GENERAL OUTLETS

- Outlet.
- Blanked Outlet.
- Drop Cord.
- Electrical Outlet; for use only when circle used alone might be confused with columns, plumbing symbols, etc
- Fan Outlet.
- Junction Box.
- Lamp Holder.
- Lamp Holder with Pull Switch.
- Pull Switch.
- Outlet for Vapor Discharge Lamp.
- Exit Light Outlet.
- Clock Outlet. (Specify Voltage.)

CONVENIENCE OUTLETS

- Duplex Convenience Outlet.
- Convenience Outlet other than Duplex. 1=Single, 3=Triplex, etc.
- Weatherproof Convenience Outlet.
- Range Outlet.
- Switch and Convenience Outlet.
- Radio and Convenience Outlet.
- Special Purpose Outlet. (Des. in Spec.)
- Floor Outlet.

SWITCH OUTLETS

- S Single Pole Switch.
- S_2 Double Pole Switch.
- S_3 Three-Way Switch.

PANELS, CIRCUITS, AND MISCELLANEOUS

- Lighting Panel.
- Power Panel.
- Branch Circuit; Concealed in Ceiling or Wall.
- Branch Circuit; Concealed in Floor.
- Branch Circuit; Exposed.
- Home Run to Panel Board. Indicate number of Cir cuits by number of arrows.
  Note: Any circuit without further designation indicates a two-wire circuit. For a greater number of wires indicate as follows (3 wires) (4 wires), etc.
- Feeders. Note: Use heavy lines and designate by number corresponding to listing in Feeder Schedule.
- Underfloor Duct and Junction Box. Triple System. For double or single systems, eliminate 1 or 2 lines. This symbol equally adaptable to auxiliary system layouts.
- Generator.
- Motor.
- Instrument.
- Power Transformer. (Or draw to scale.)
- Controller.
- Isolating Switch.

AUXILIARY SYSTEMS

- Push Button.
- Buzzer.
- Bell.
- Annunciator.
- Outside Telephone.
- Interconnecting Telephone.

Figure 19-18
Basic symbols used in an electrical drawing.

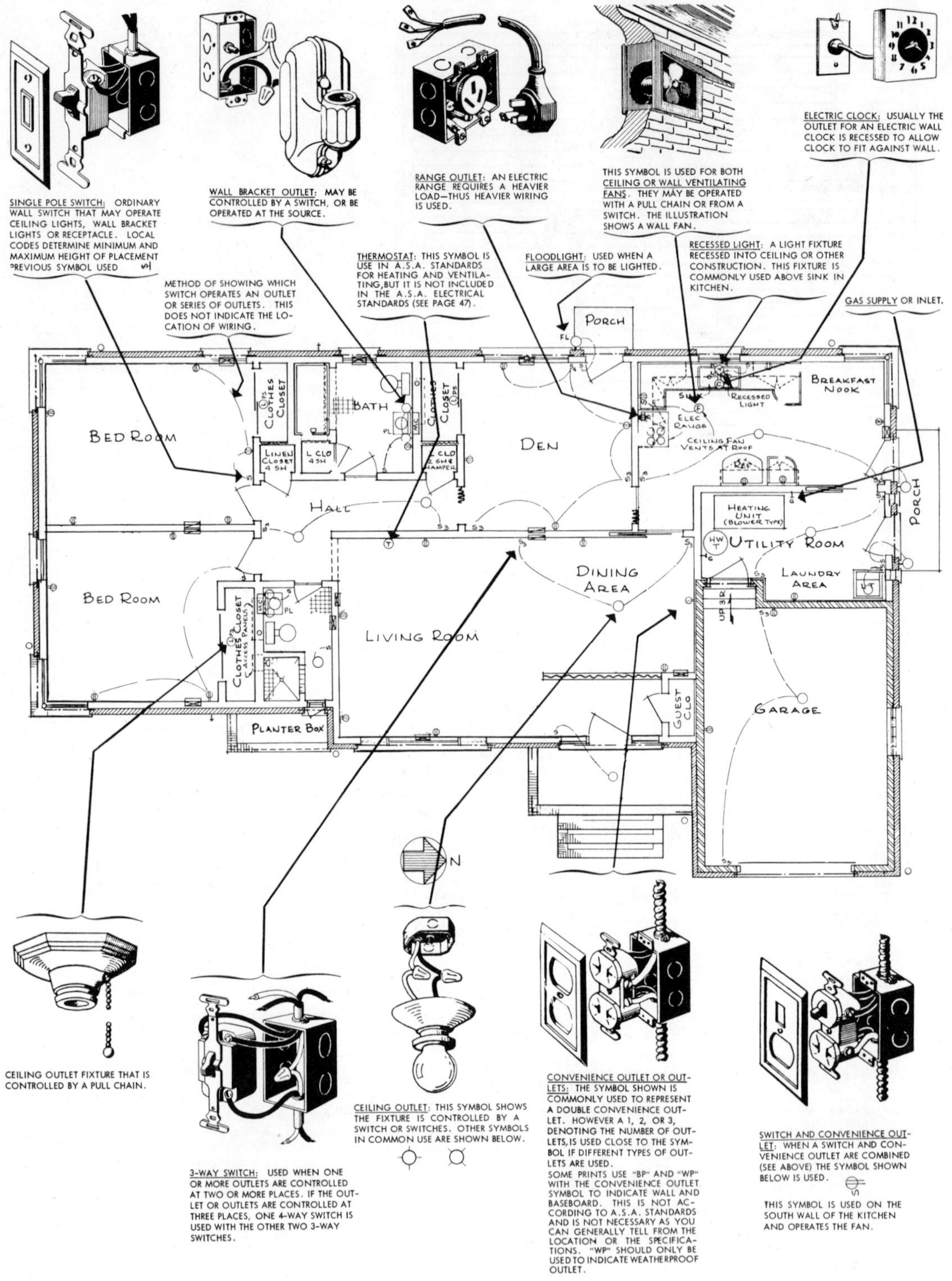

Figure 19-19
A typical electrical drawing showing the wiring layout of a house and the electrical components used.

ELECTRICAL FIXTURE SCHEDULE						
ITEM	MFR.	CAT #	MOUNTING	WATTS	LAMP	FINISH
A	KURTZON	7862 LBA	Recess	40	T-17	ALUM
B	PRESCOLITE	488-6600	Recess	100	I. F.	STD
C	PRESCOLITE	1313-6630	Recess	300	I.F	STD

Figure 19-20
Fixture schedule and legend.

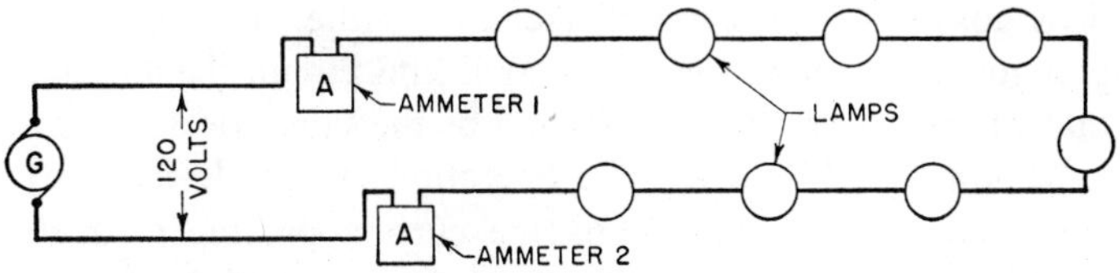

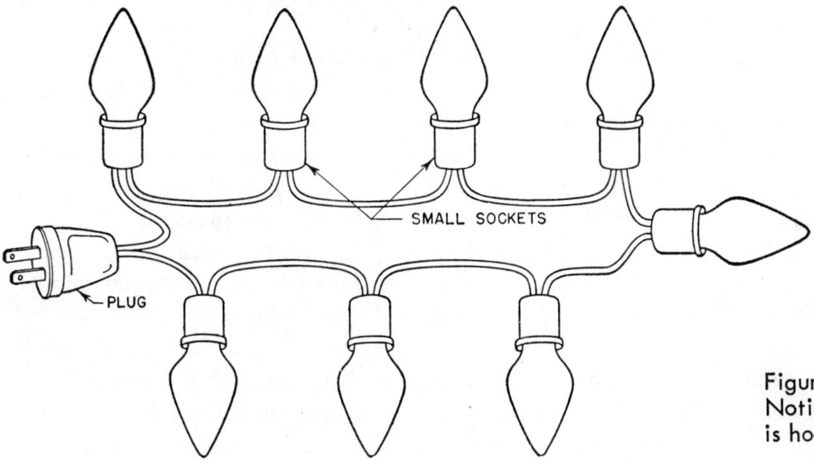

Figure 19-21
Notice how this series circuit is hooked up.

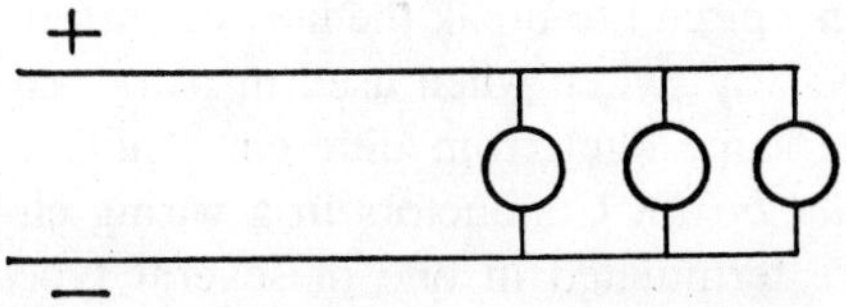

Figure 19-22
The parallel circuit is the most commonly used for house wiring.

Panel box. Houses the safety components of a wiring system in the form of circuit breakers or fuses. A circuit breaker is a protective switch designed to open a circuit when there is an overload or a short circuit in the system. A circuit breaker eliminates the need of fuses and operates automatically.

Fuses. Often used in place of circuit breakers. A fuse consists of a case or tube enclosing a small piece of soft metal that melts and breaks the circuit in event of an overload. Circuit breakers and fuses are intended to protect the wiring, lights and appliances in the building when trouble occurs in the circuit. Panel boxes are wired to include several circuits.

Conductor. Any material through which electricity will flow. In electrical circuits it is usually a copper wire, bar, or ribbon. The size of a conductor used in a circuit is governed by the amount of electricity it must carry. The more common types of conductors for ordinary house wiring are known as non-metallic sheathed cable, flexible armored cable, and conduit. Non-metallic sheathed cable has two or more insulated copper wires covered with a tough braided outer jacket. It is the type most often used for indoor house wiring. Flexible armored cable has two or more insulated wires encased in a heavy galvanized steel protective cover. It is employed for exposed runs on walls or ceiling surfaces or concealed runs in hollow spaces of walls, floors and ceiling. This cable cannot be used for out-of-doors purposes or in damp locations. Special cable must be utilized for out-of-door wiring such as a plastic sheathed cable. Conduit, either of the thin-wall or rigid type, may be used for indoor and outdoor wiring. The conduit is a steel tubing through which two or more insulated wires are drawn.

Circuits. In its simplest form, a circuit consists of the source of power, the devices which consume the electrical power, and the conductor carrying the current from the source to the load and from the load back to the original source. Buildings today are wired to have several circuits to ensure sufficient power to operate all of the customary devices found in a building. Thus there may be one or more circuits for the lights, a special circuit for the electric stove, another for the clothes washer, one for the furnace and several more for various other purposes.

The three basic electrical circuits are series circuits, parallel circuits, and series-parallel circuits. In a series circuit, the conductor runs from the source through two or more devices or loads and back to the source with only one path for the current. All the devices in this circuit must carry the same current. If one device fails to operate, the current ceases to flow and all the other loads stop functioning. A good example of a series circuit is the wiring of the early type Christmas tree lights. See Fig. 19-21. When one light burns out, all the others go out. This circuit is not used for house wiring.

The parallel circuit is the one employed in house wiring. With this circuit the amount of current need not be the same for all loads. Moreover, the operation of one device does not depend on the current passing through another since the circuit provides for the current to flow through more than one path. See Fig. 19-22.

The combination series and parallel circuit provides arrangement for both series and parallel connections.

Volt. The unit used in measuring electrical pressure; comparable to pounds per square inch in measuring water pressure.

Ampere. The unit that measures the electrical rate of flow just as gallons per minute is used in a water system.

Watt. Measures the rate at which electrical energy is being used. Thus when one volt causes one ampere of current to flow, one watt of power is being used. One watt consumed for one hour equals one watt hour and 1000 watt hours equals one kilowatt hour, which is the unit by which electricity is metered.

Switch. A switch is the device incorporated in a circuit to break the flow of current. A three-way switch when used in pairs control the same light from different points.

Outlet boxes. Conductors in a wiring circuit are terminated in one of several types

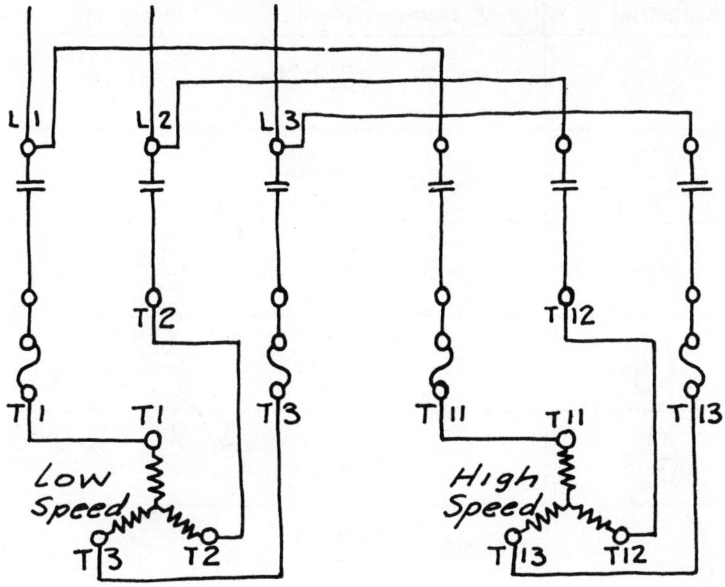

Figure 19-23
An engineer's wiring diagram sketch of a two-speed starter. Allen-Bradley Co.

of metal outlet boxes which then serve as receptacles for light fixtures or appliances.

Hot wires. The black or red wires which carry the power as distinguished from the neutral wires which are usually white.

Grounding. Grounding is the connection of the electrical system to the ground so as to prevent damage from lightning and to reduce the danger of shocks.

19.16 Electrical and electronic drawing

Electrical and electronic circuits are generally designed by the electrical engineer. As a rule, these designs are in the form of freehand sketches which show the essential components and circuit paths by means of standard symbols. The responsibility of the draftsman is to take the engineer's sketch and transform it into a balanced, finished diagram. Fig. 19-23 is a typical example of such a sketch. Some of the more basic electrical and electronic symbols are included in Fig. 19-24.

Most electrical and electronic diagrams can be classified into three main groups: wiring, block, and schematic.

19.17 Wiring or connection diagrams

A wiring diagram is often called a connection diagram and includes all of the devices in an electrical system arranged to show their physical relations to each other. Thus poles, terminals, coils, etc., are drawn in their correct place on each device. Diagrams of this type give the necessary information for actually wiring-up a group of control devices and are particularly useful for tracing wires when trouble-shooting. Connection or wiring diagrams are sometimes further classified as pictorial, highway or baseline.

Pictorial. A pictorial or point-to-point diagram shows how each wire runs from one component to another and from terminal to terminal of respective assemblies. See Fig. 19-25. Wires are represented by uniformly spaced vertical and horizontal lines. Units may be portrayed by means of standard symbols or pictorially. For complicated circuits, diagrams often include a color code so that all wires can be easily identified.

Occasionally a pictorial diagram takes the form of an isometric, oblique or perspective. When drawn in this manner it is possible to

(Text continued on page 569)

Communication		Industrial	Communication		Industrial
	DIODE (KENOTRON)			RECTIFIER OR DIODE	
	FULL-WAVE RECTIFIER			THERMISTOR	
	TRIODE (PLIOTRON)		NONE	THERMOCOUPLE	
	THYRATRON		NONE	THERMAL OVERLOAD	
	PENTODE			AIR-CORE COIL	
	PHOTOCELL			IRON-CORE COIL	
NONE	IGNITRON			SLUG-TUNED COIL	
	P-N-P TRANSISTOR			TRANSFORMER	
	N-P-N TRANSISTOR		NONE	SATURABLE CORE	
	P-N-P TETRODE TRANSISTOR		NONE	3-PHASE TRANSFORMER WINDINGS	
	UNIJUNCTION TRANSISTOR			RELAY COIL	
	P-N-P FIELD EFFECT TRANSISTOR			SLOW-CLOSING RELAY	
	CONTROLLED RECTIFIER			SLOW-RELEASE RELAY	
	SOLAR BATTERY			SLOW-ACTING RELAY	

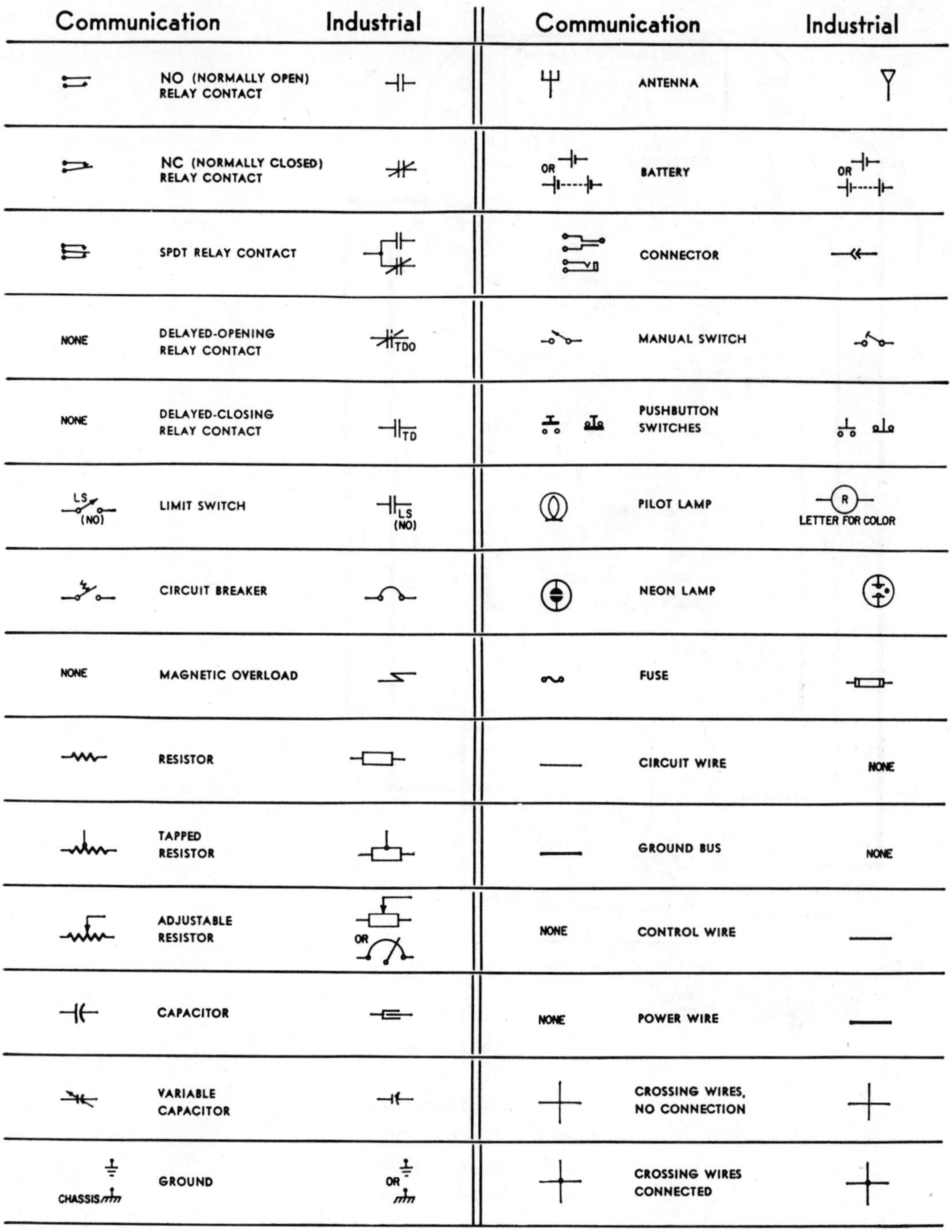
Communication
Industrial
Communication
Industrial
NO (NORMALLY OPEN) RELAY CONTACT
NC (NORMALLY CLOSED) RELAY CONTACT
SPDT RELAY CONTACT
NONE
DELAYED-OPENING RELAY CONTACT
TDO
NONE
DELAYED-CLOSING RELAY CONTACT
TD
LS (NO)
LIMIT SWITCH
LS (NO)
CIRCUIT BREAKER
NONE
MAGNETIC OVERLOAD
RESISTOR
TAPPED RESISTOR
ADJUSTABLE RESISTOR
OR
CAPACITOR
VARIABLE CAPACITOR
CHASSIS
GROUND
OR
ANTENNA
OR
BATTERY
OR
CONNECTOR
MANUAL SWITCH
PUSHBUTTON SWITCHES
PILOT LAMP
R
LETTER FOR COLOR
NEON LAMP
FUSE
CIRCUIT WIRE
NONE
GROUND BUS
NONE
NONE
CONTROL WIRE
NONE
POWER WIRE
CROSSING WIRES, NO CONNECTION
CROSSING WIRES CONNECTED

Figure 19-24
Basic electrical and electronic symbols.

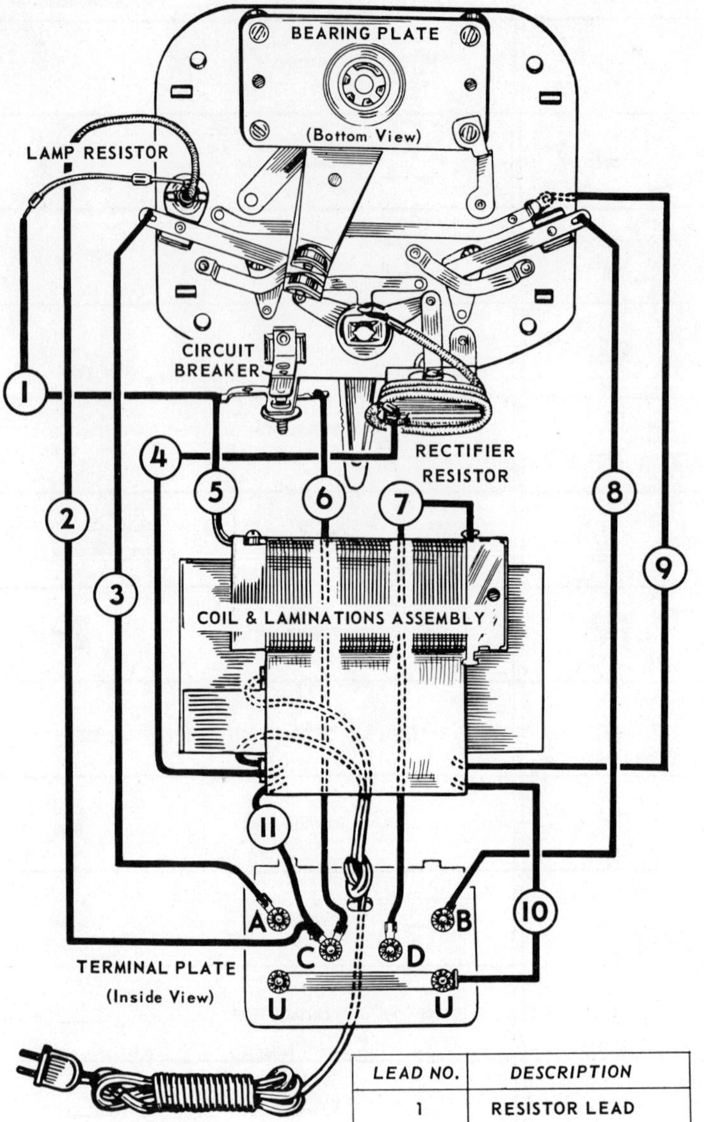

LEAD NO.	DESCRIPTION
1	RESISTOR LEAD
2	LAMP LEAD
4	YELLOW TUBING
5	RECTANGULAR WIRE
9	YELLOW TUBING
10	BLACK TUBING
11	BLACK TUBING

Figure 19–25
A pictorial diagram of a transformer.
Lionel Corp.

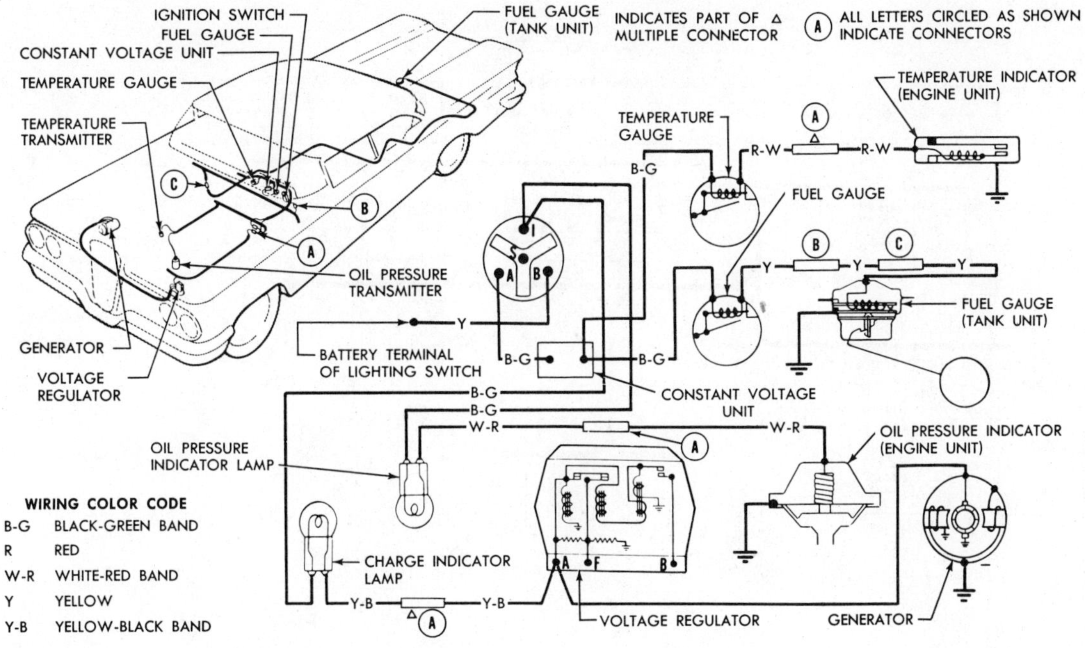

Figure 19-26
Two types of pictorial drawings are combined in this gage circuit diagram. Ford Motor Co.

show the actual location and wiring arrangement of the required device. Pictorial drawings are often combined in a single illustration to make identification of the electrical components easier. See Fig. 19-26.

Highway diagram. A highway diagram is particularly useful in illustrating the wiring of switchboards and panels. In this type of diagram the wires are merged into long lines called highways rather than as separate lines from terminal to terminal in the point-to-point diagram. One or more highways may be shown, depending on the wire routing necessary for the components, with short feed lines running to terminals. The direction a feed line takes when it joins the highway is indicated by a small arc or slanted line. See Fig. 19-27.

In highway diagrams it is recommended that each wire be coded to identify: (1) component, (2) terminal destination, (3) type and size of wire, (4) wire color. Thus a wire tagged E 12-3-B6 would mean

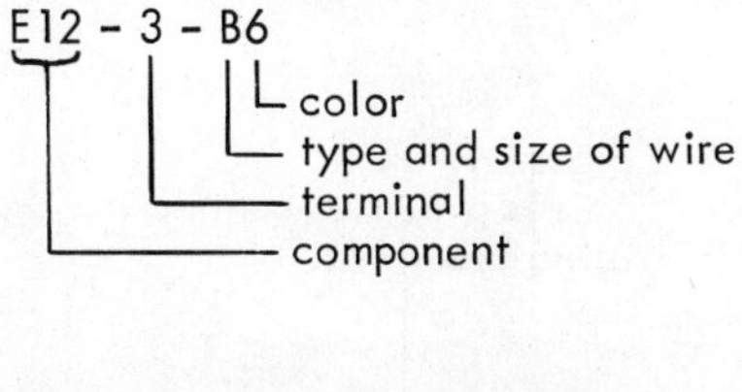

Baseline diagram. The baseline or airline diagram as it is sometimes called is used to show the location of the components in relationship to each other. A horizontal or vertical line serves as the base from which short feed lines are run to the components or terminals. See Fig. 19-28. Each component is properly identified and each wire correctly coded to simplify the task of tracing circuit paths.

19.18 Block diagrams

The main function of a block diagram is to explain the relative function of the parts of an electrical or electronic system. Each unit is laid out beginning from a point where the signal is introduced then progresses through the various stages, each of which performs a specific function, and finally terminating at the output. See Fig. 19-29.

Whenever possible, the circuit path of a block diagram is drawn to run from left to right or from the upper left corner to the

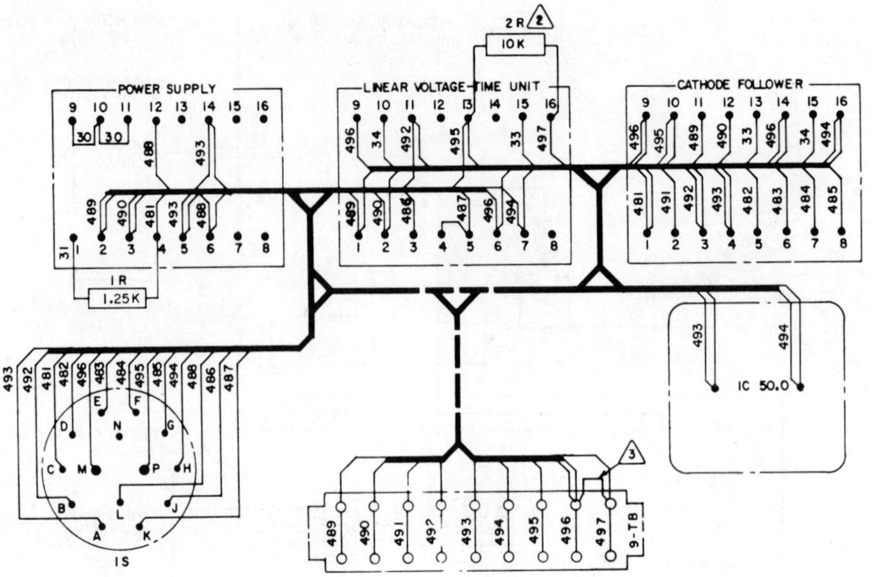

Figure 19-27
A highway diagram of a timed reference voltage supply. Reliance Electric and Engineering Co.

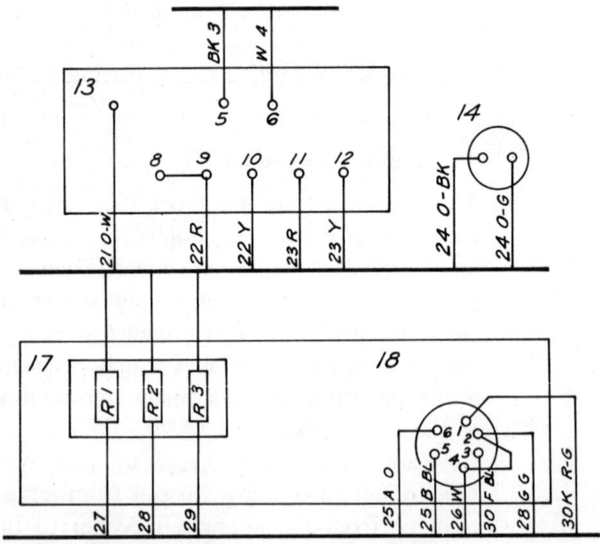

Figure 19-28
This is a partial connection diagram using baselines.

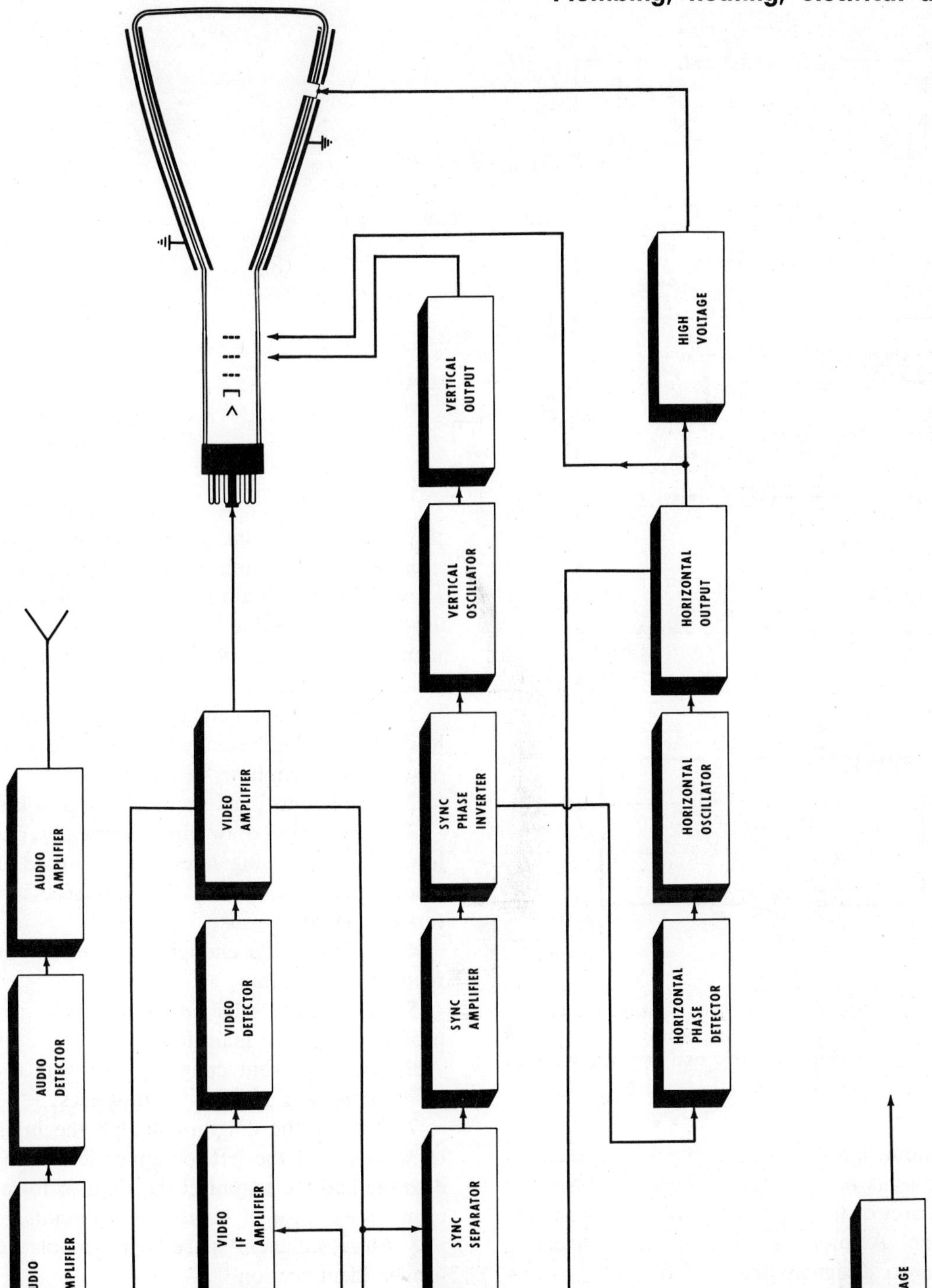

Figure 19-29
A block diagram of a TV receiver.
Howard W. Sams & Co. Inc.

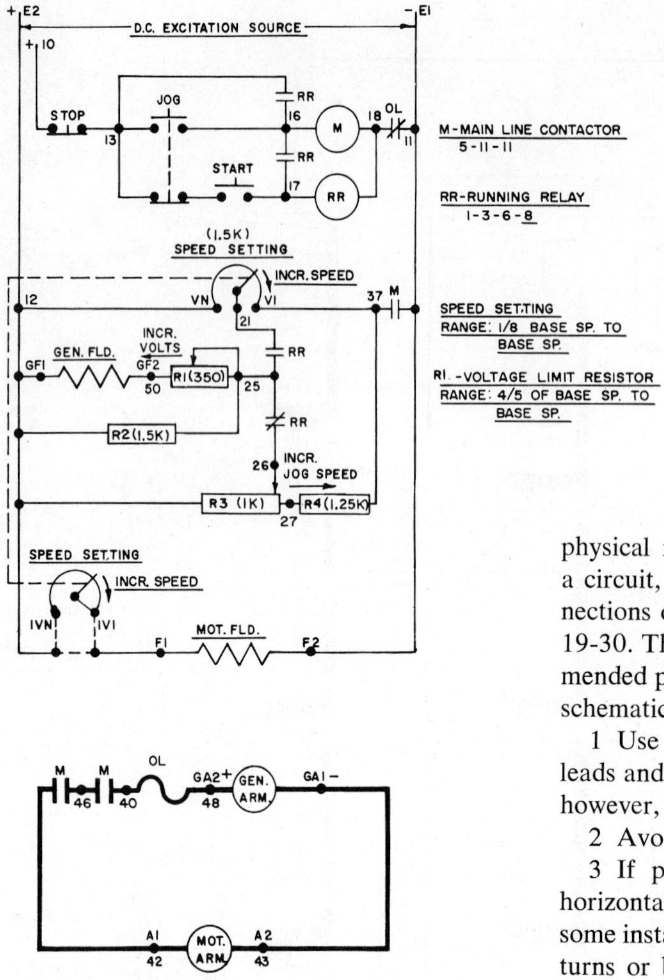

Figure 19-30
This is a typical elementary drawing of 3-speed motor control.
Reliance Electric and Engineering Co.

bottom right corner. The blocks representing the units or stages are shown as rectangles, squares or triangles, with one line connecting them. Arrows are used on the connecting line to designate the direction of flow. A description of each unit is included in the respective block.

19.19 Schematic electrical diagrams

The schematic diagram, which is also known as an elementary diagram, is especially adaptable for electronic circuits. By means of graphical symbols this diagram shows the physical relationships of the components in a circuit, the function of each, and the connections of the circuit arrangement. See Fig. 19-30. The following are some of the recommended practices to be followed in preparing schematic drawings:

1 Use medium-weight lines for wires, leads and symbols. Heavy lines may be used, however, for emphasis of components.

2 Avoid long lines as much as possible.

3 If possible, draw lines vertically and horizontally. Sloping lines may be used in some instances for clarity. Avoid unnecessary turns or bends.

4 Space lines far enough apart for ease in reading the diagram.

5 Arrange the schematic diagram to give prominence to the main features.

6 Try to prevent congested areas in the diagram as well as large white spaces.

7 Arrange the diagram so that the input or source is at the left, or upper left of the drawing and the output at the right or lower right in the case of complicated circuits.

8 Allow sufficient space near symbols for proper identification.

9 If available, use templates for drawing symbols, for both speed and uniformity.

10 If drawings are for publication, exercise care to make the size and spacing of lettering, line-work and symbols suitable for reduction.

11 Have diagram present an overall appearance of symmetry and clarity.

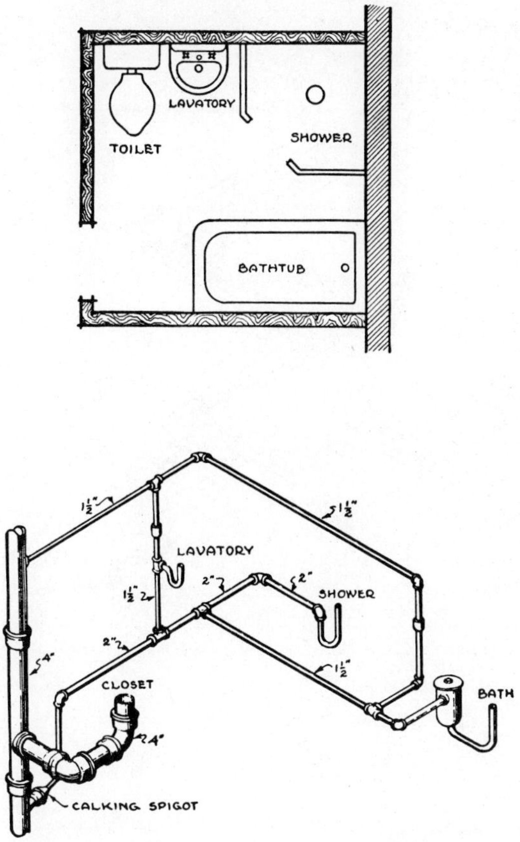

Figure 19-31
Problem 1.

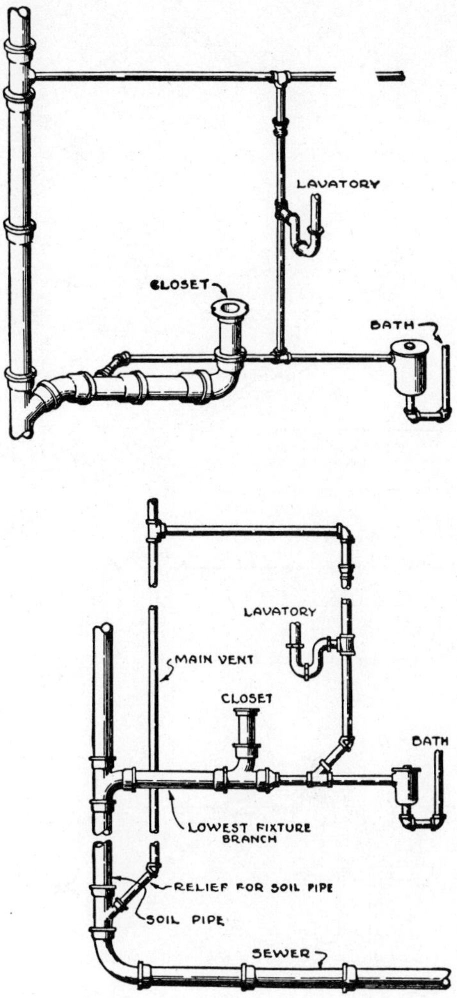

Figure 19-32
Problem 2.

Problems, section 19

1 Prepare a single-line plumbing layout in isometric for the bathroom shown in Fig. 19-31. Use standard symbols.

2 Make single-line developed layouts for the partial plumbing circuits shown in Fig. 19-32. Pipe sizes: 1–1/2 and 4″ std.

3 Prepare a double-line piping layout of the sewer and drainage system shown in Fig. 19-33.

4 Make a single-line schematic drawing of the assembly shown in Fig. 19-34. Use standard symbols where applicable.

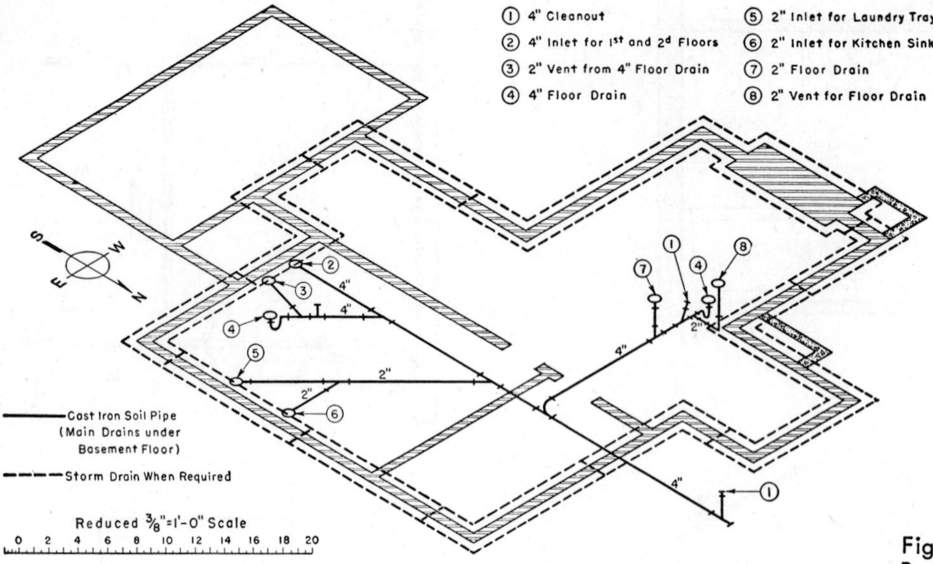

Figure 19-33
Problem 3.

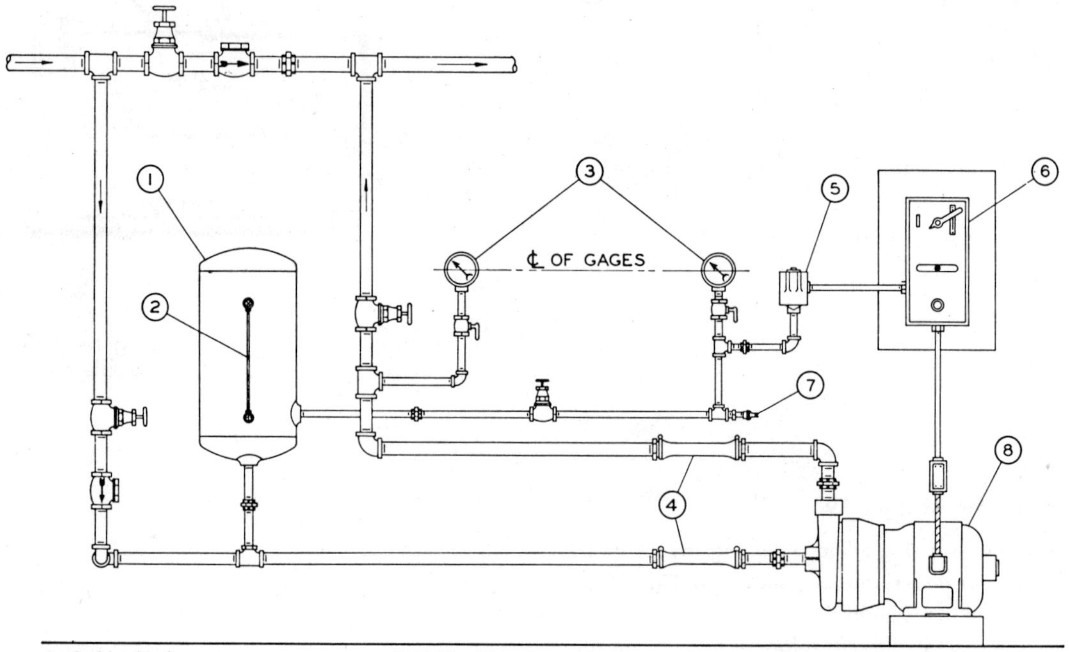

1—Cushion Tank
2—Water Gauge
3—Pressure Gauge
4—Rubber Hose Connection
5—Pressure Switch
6—Combination Starter
7—Tank Valve
8—Centrifugal Pump

Figure 19-34
Problem 4. Peerles Pump Div., Food Machinery & Chemical Corp.

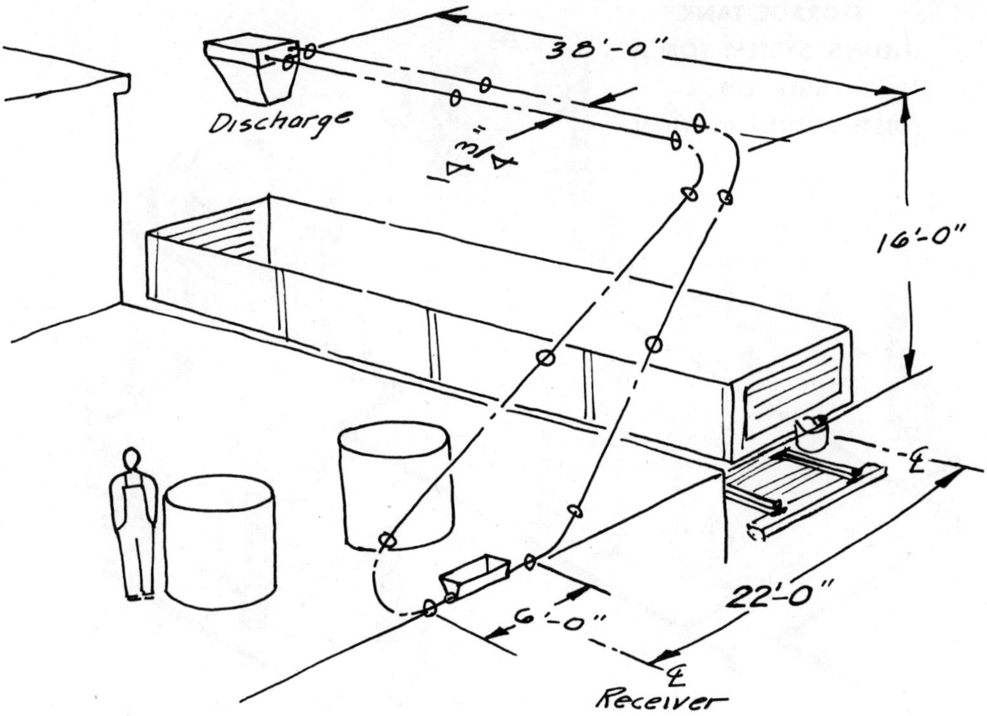

Figure 19-35
Problem 5.
Hapman Conveyors, Inc.

5 From the engineer's proposal sketch, Fig. 19-35, prepare an assembly drawing of the piping for the tubular conveyor system. Omit receiving and discharge units. Make a detail drawing of the pipe bends, which have a typical radius of 24 inches with 6 inch tangent lengths. Determine pipe lengths and prepare a list of pipe sections, bends, flanges, bolts and nuts. All pipe to be 4" std., and all flanges 4" std., 125 lbs., slip-on type.

6 From the pictorial drawing of the Storage Tank Filling system shown in Fig. 19-36, prepare a single-line schematic diagram, developed or in isometric as assigned. Show proper symbols for fittings.

7 Prepare a double-line developed drawing for the low-pressure steam heating system shown in Fig. 19-37. All pipe 1-1/2".

8 Lay out the plumbing, floor radiant heating and electrical wiring systems for the residence shown in Fig. 19-38.

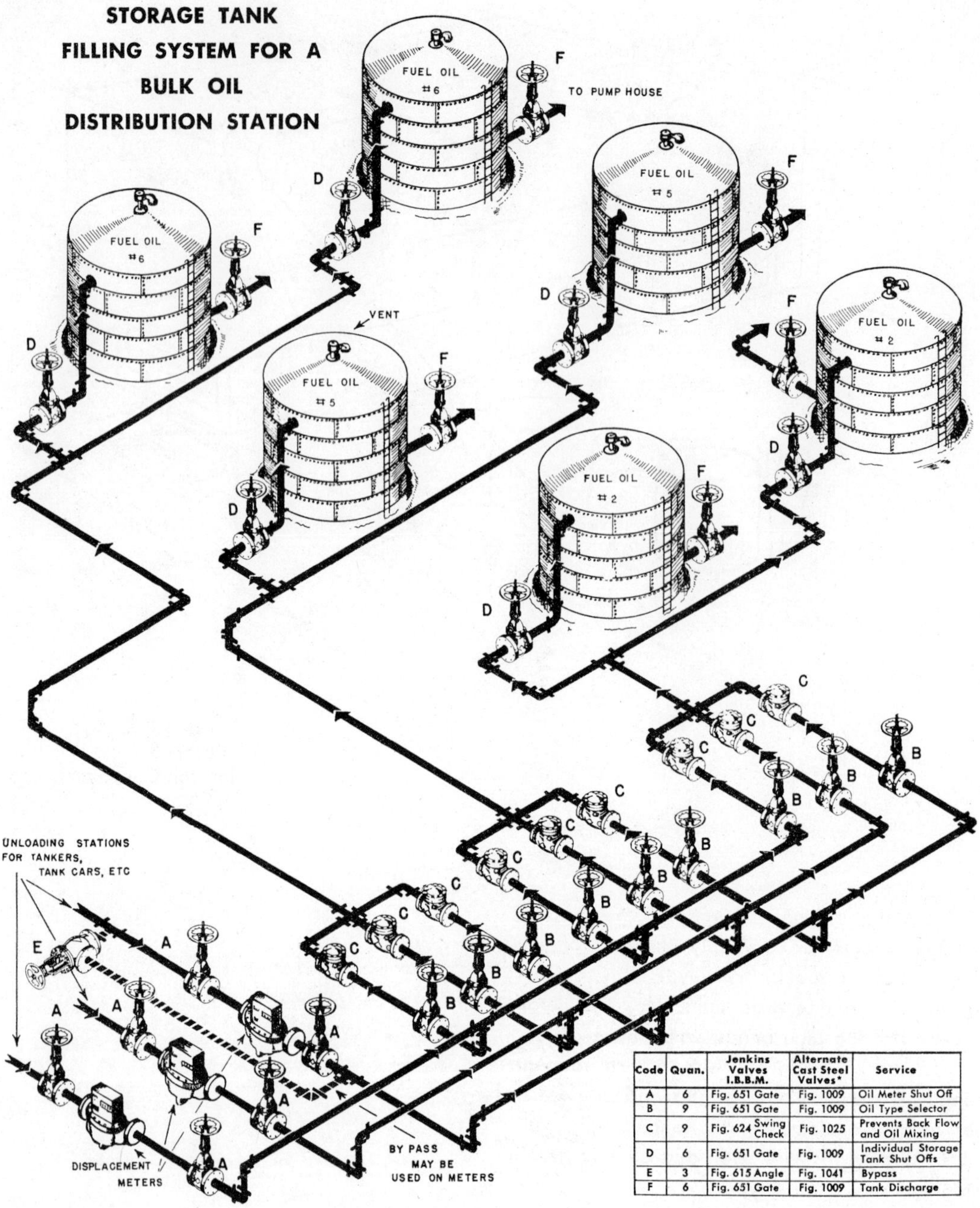

Code	Quan.	Jenkins Valves I.B.B.M.	Alternate Cast Steel Valves*	Service
A	6	Fig. 651 Gate	Fig. 1009	Oil Meter Shut Off
B	9	Fig. 651 Gate	Fig. 1009	Oil Type Selector
C	9	Fig. 624 Swing Check	Fig. 1025	Prevents Back Flow and Oil Mixing
D	6	Fig. 651 Gate	Fig. 1009	Individual Storage Tank Shut Offs
E	3	Fig. 615 Angle	Fig. 1041	Bypass
F	6	Fig. 651 Gate	Fig. 1009	Tank Discharge

Figure 19–36
Problem 6.
Jenkins Bros.

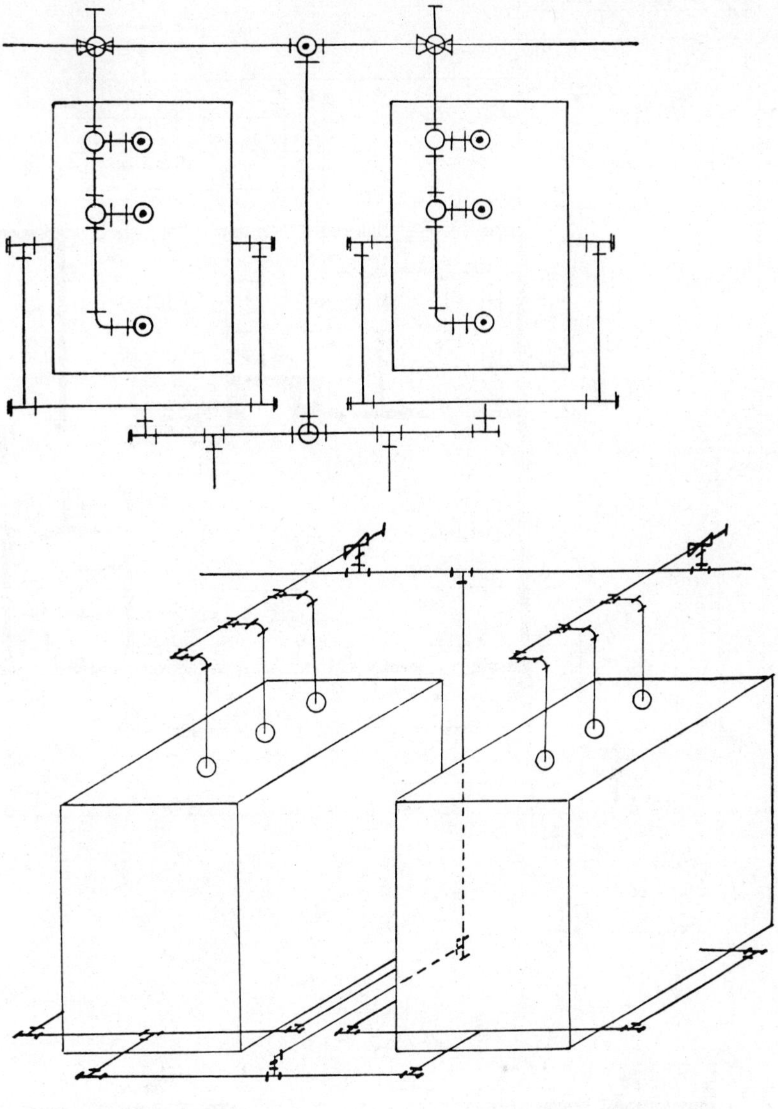

Figure 19-37
Problem 7.

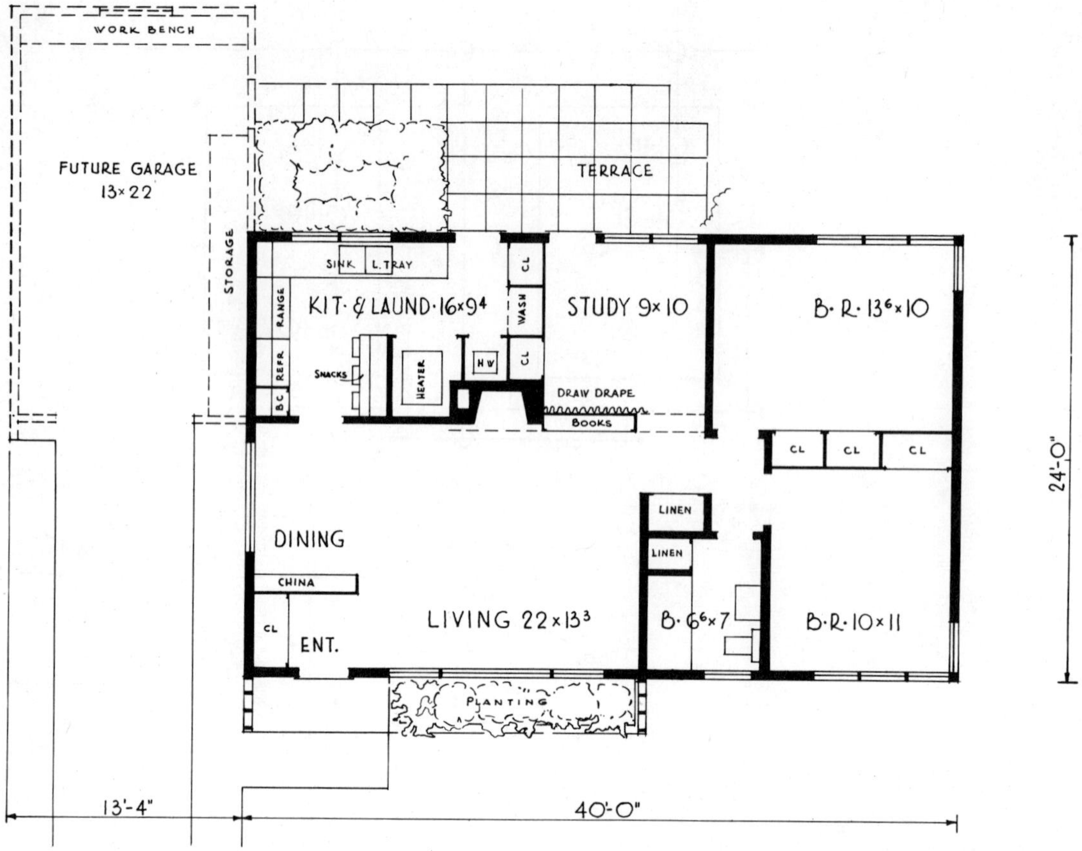

Figure 19–38
Problem 8.
Homograph Corp.

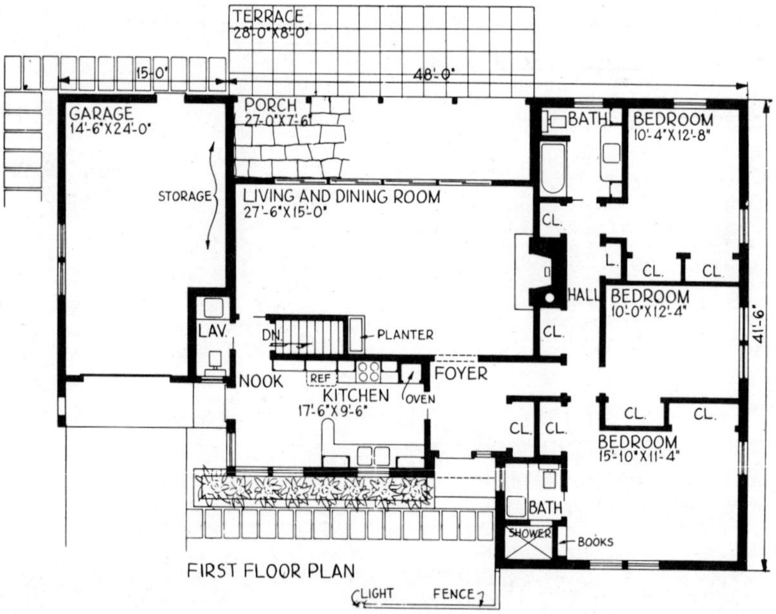

Figure 19–39
Problem 9. Ordan
Publishing Co.

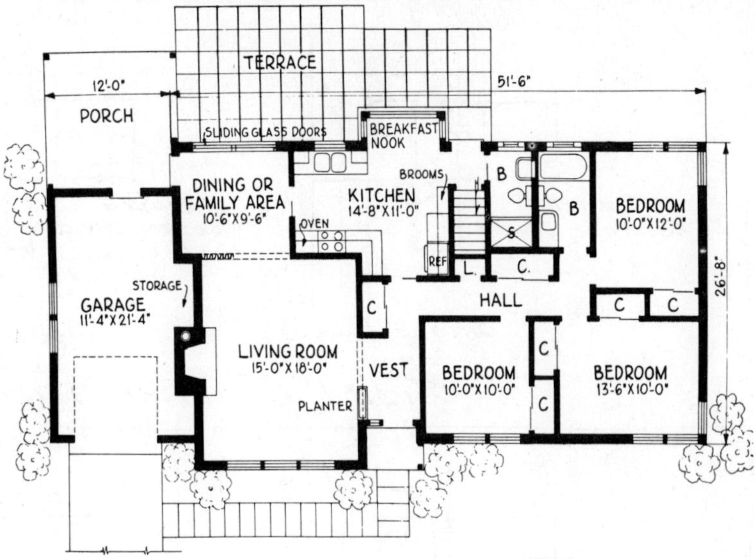

Figure 19-40
Problem 10. Ordan Publishing Co.

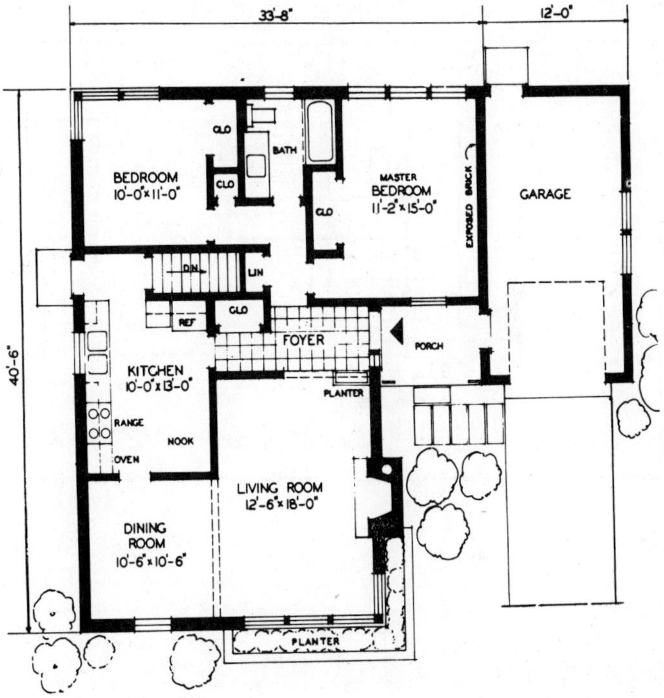

Figure 19-41
Problem 11. Ordan Publishing Co.

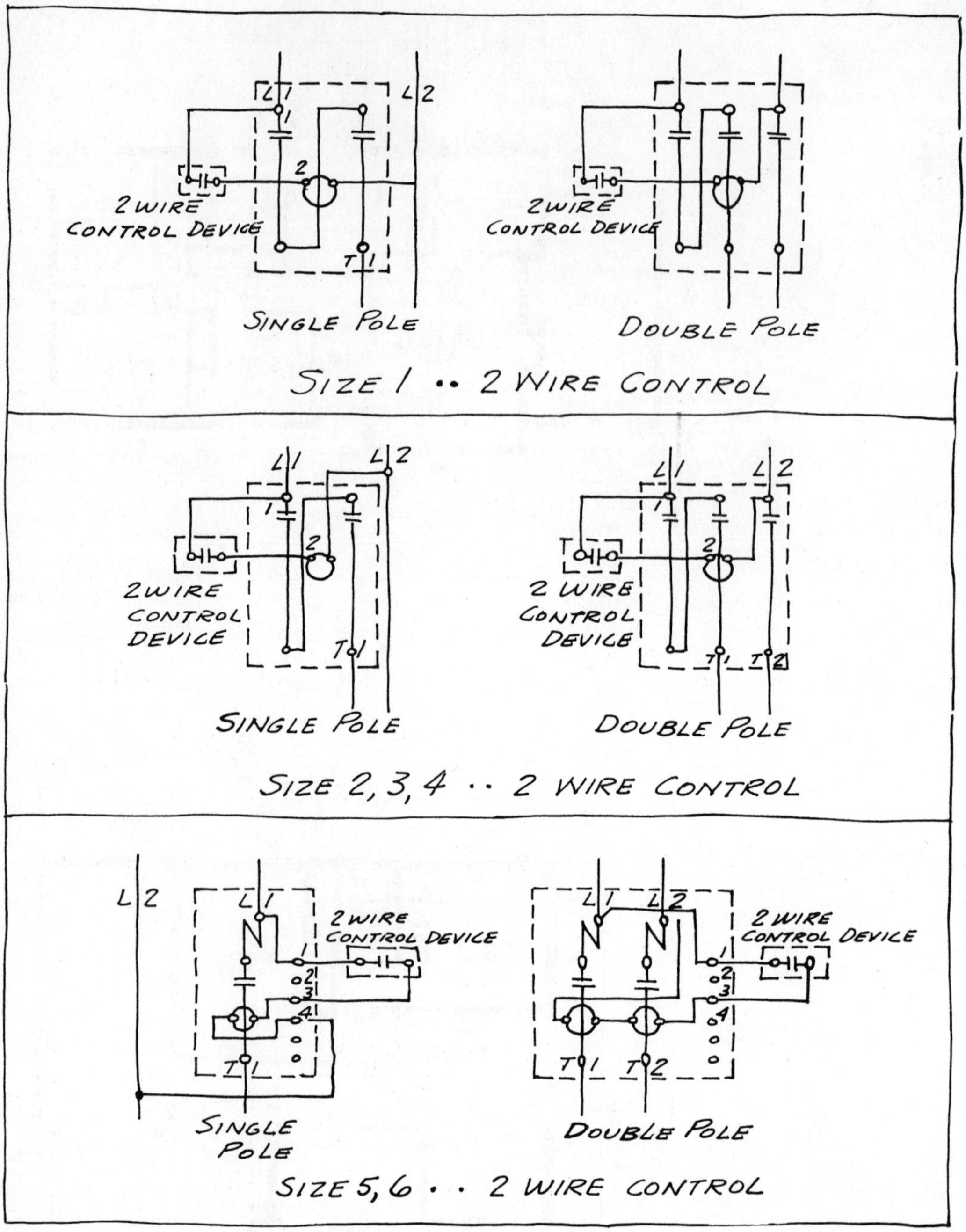

Figure 19–42
Problem 13. Allen Bradley Co.

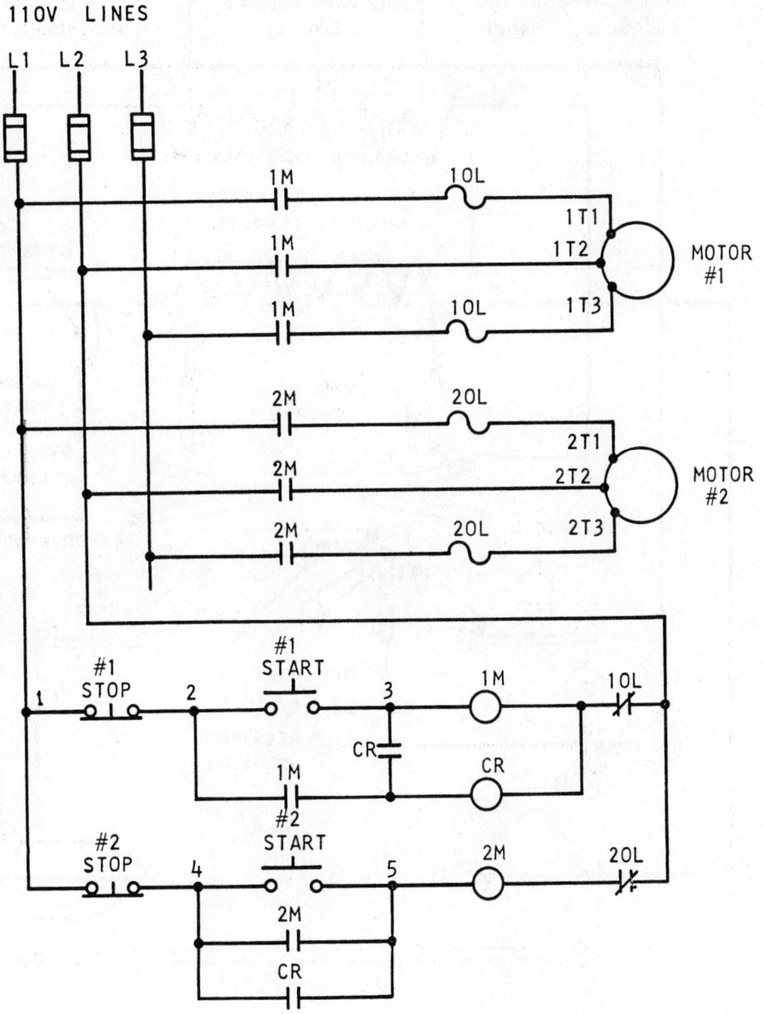

Figure 19-43
Problem 14. Cutler-Hammer, Inc.

9 Make a layout drawing of a forced air heating system for the residence shown in the floor plan of Fig. 19-39.

10-11 Prepare wiring layouts for the residences shown in Figs. 19-40 and 19-41.

12 Make an electrical layout for a drafting room 32′ x 48′. Prepare a fixture schedule from manufacturers' catalogs.

13 The control circuits shown in Fig. 19-42 are to be published in a service manual by a manufacturer of electrical components. Make an ink drawing that will appear 6-3/4″ x 8-3/8″ after it is reduced one-third.

14 Make a drawing of the motor control diagram shown in Fig. 19-43.

15 Prepare a drawing of the wiring for a **KW** transformer, Fig. 19-44, suitable for publication in an instruction manual. Finished size of the illustration is to be 4-1/2″ x 4-3/4″.

16-20 Reproduce any of the electrical schematics shown in Figs. 19-25 to 19-30 as assigned by your instructor.

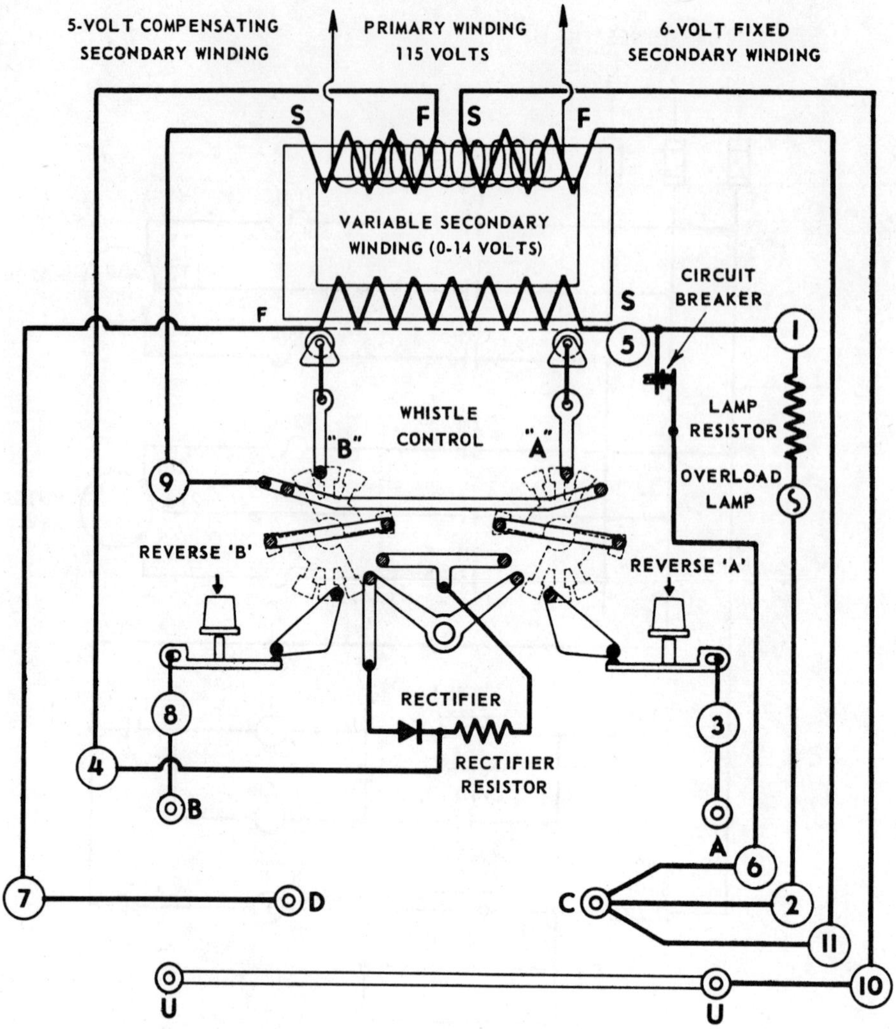

Figure 19-44
Problem 15. Lionel Corp.

Map drawing 20

Topographic or map drawing is a special field of drafting in which features of various portions of the earth's surface are drawn to scale and depicted by conventional symbols. It is a form of drawing combining principles of freehand sketching and mechanical drafting.

In general, maps contain the following information:

1 Elevations and depressions of ground areas.
2 Location and types of objects constructed by man (culture).
3 Hydrographic or water features.
4 Vegetation such as forests, fields, swamps.

There are many different kinds of maps, each serving a particular function. Some of the more commonly used maps and the basic elements of map drawing are described in this section.

20.1 Cadastral maps

Cadastral maps show layouts of cities, towns or county districts. They are often classified as development maps since they may be used to control future planning and growth of municipalities. Such maps serve as records of land property ownership, especially for assessment and taxation purposes. City maps frequently include location of all gas mains, water lines, sewage systems, steam pipes and fire hydrants. To keep maps small enough for convenient filing, large cities are usually divided into several sections and each map then produced to represent one section.

Cadastral maps are drawn to a scale ranging usually from 1 inch = 1 foot to 1 inch = 200 feet in order to clearly establish property lines. Only essential topographic features are included such as roads, streams and railroads. The size and shape of each lot are clearly shown and marked with an identification number to establish its exact location. A typical city map is illustrated in Fig. 20-1.

20.2 Plat of a survey

A plat map is a land map which is part of a legal document and contains an accurate description of a tract of land. This type of map shows the true lengths and bearings of all boundary lines and establishes in note form the exact location in reference to section and township divisions.

A plat map also includes such features as acreage involved, location and description of monuments on the land, highways, streams and ownership of abutting property. Since the plat survey becomes an official document of ownership, state laws usually require that it be properly certified. A sample map of a plat is shown in Fig. 20-2.

Plat of subdivision. This type of plat map usually involves an area which is being developed for building purposes. It contains a complete layout of the lots and land parcels comprising the subdivision. The shape, size and location of each lot is accurately shown and quite often certain features of the subdivisions are embellished to enhance its attractiveness. The map serves two functions: (1) as a record in the county's records office, and (2) as a display drawing for prospective buyers. See Fig. 20-3.

20.3 Building site (engineering) maps

In the construction of a building, whether residential or industrial, the practice is to prepare a plot plan to show the orientation of the building and its surrounding area. Included in a layout of this type will be such features as ground elevation contours, property boundaries, utilities, walks and drives

(Text continued on page 589)

CITY LIMITS
HARBOR
ISLAND
CITY OF GRAND HAVEN
SHELL OIL CO.
SOUTH
CHANNEL
RYCENGA'S
ASSESSOR'S
PEOPLES STATE BANK
SEWAGE DISPOSAL
GRAND TRUNK
PERE MARQUETTE
FREIGHT HO.
G.T. DEPOT
ADAMS ST.
MONROE ST.
JACKSON ST.
BOLTWOOD'S ADDITION
MADISON
ELLIOTT
FULTON
COLUMBUS
WASHINGTON
FRANKLIN
CLINTON
LAFAYETTE
HOWARD
FIRST
SECOND
THIRD
FOURTH
FIFTH
SIXTH
SEVENTH
EIGHTH
HARRIS ST.
CENTRAL PARK
COURT HOUSE
CITY HALL
PLAT NO.
CHAS SCHROEDER
GERBER
PLAT NO. 2
LEGGAT'S
WILLIAM
ADDITION
LIBERTY
LEGGAT
ELIZABETH
LAKE
BUTLER
HILLOCK CT.
MONTAGUE ST.
SLAYTON & VAN DER VEENS
CUTLER
SLAYTON
GRANT
SHELDON'S
COLFAX
HIGH SCHOOL
SHORE'S
DAVIS
14.

WILKINS & WHEATON ENGINEERING CO.
171 Portage Street
Kalamazoo, Michigan
Phone FI 5-0622

Date January 8, 1960

C E R T I F I C A T E O F S U R V E Y

The undersigned, a Registered Land Surveyor, under the laws of the State of Michigan, certifies that he has made a survey of:

Lot One hundred twenty-three (123) except the South One (1) rod also Lots One hundred sixteen (116), one hundred seventeen (117), one hundred eighteen (118), and one hundred nineteen (119), except the North one hundred thirty-two (132) feet of the recorded plat of "Assessor's "B" Plat, Section 16, City of Kalamazoo, Michigan.

Measurements were made and corners perpetuated in accordance with the true and established lines of the property described, and in conformity with the records in the office of the Register of Deeds for Kalamazoo County, Michigan, except if otherwise noted hereon. No encroachments or overhang existed, except if otherwise noted hereon, and the dimensions and lines of the property are indicated on the following plat.

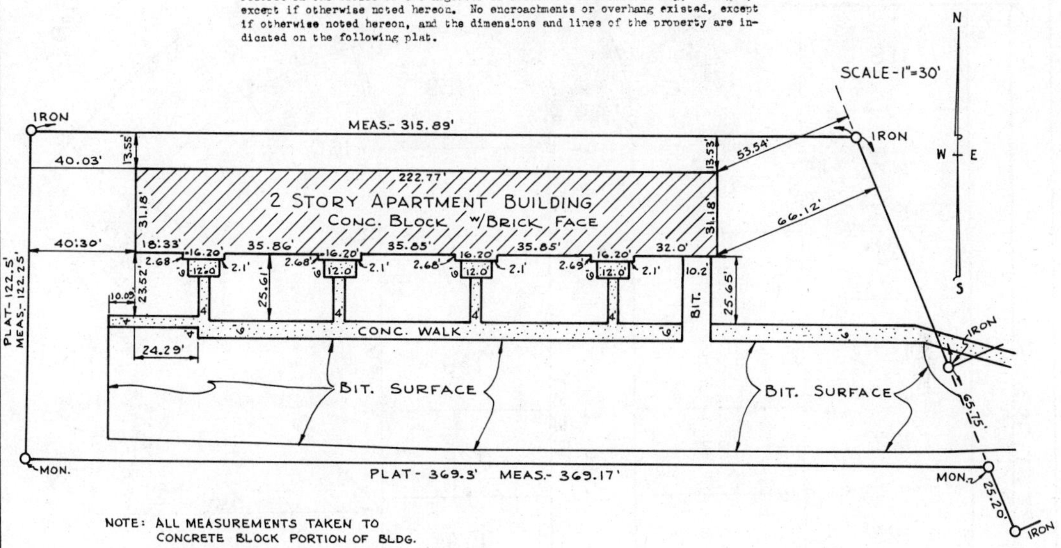

NOTE: ALL MEASUREMENTS TAKEN TO CONCRETE BLOCK PORTION OF BLDG.

SEE ATTACHED CERTIFICATE OF SURVEY FOR PORTION OF LOTS COVERED BY BLDG. & APPURTENANCES.

The above Survey, Plat and Certificate are hereby certified correct.

Surveyed December 31, 1959
for
HARTGER & WILLARD, INC., GRAND RAPIDS, MICHIGAN

Survey No. 139-22

Garth N. Baden
Registered Land Surveyor No. 10679

Figure 20-2
A plat map represents a specific tract of land and serves as an official document of land ownership.
Wilkins and Wheaton Engineering Co.

igure 20-1
cadastral map shows a layout of a own or city. This is a portion of a adastral map.

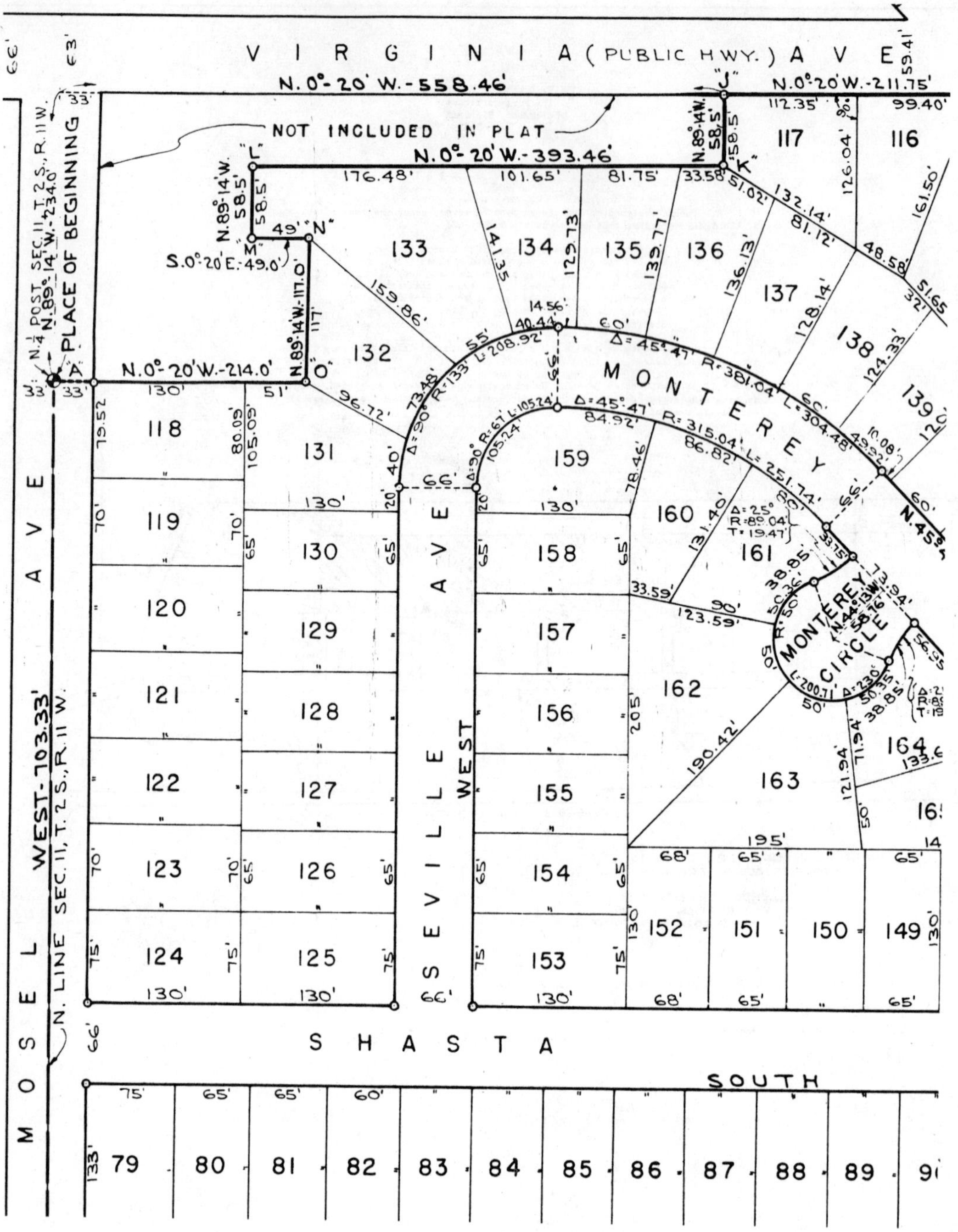

Figure 20-3
A map of a subdivision plat shows the size, shape and location of lots for building purposes in a new development. Wilkins and Wheaton Engineering Co.

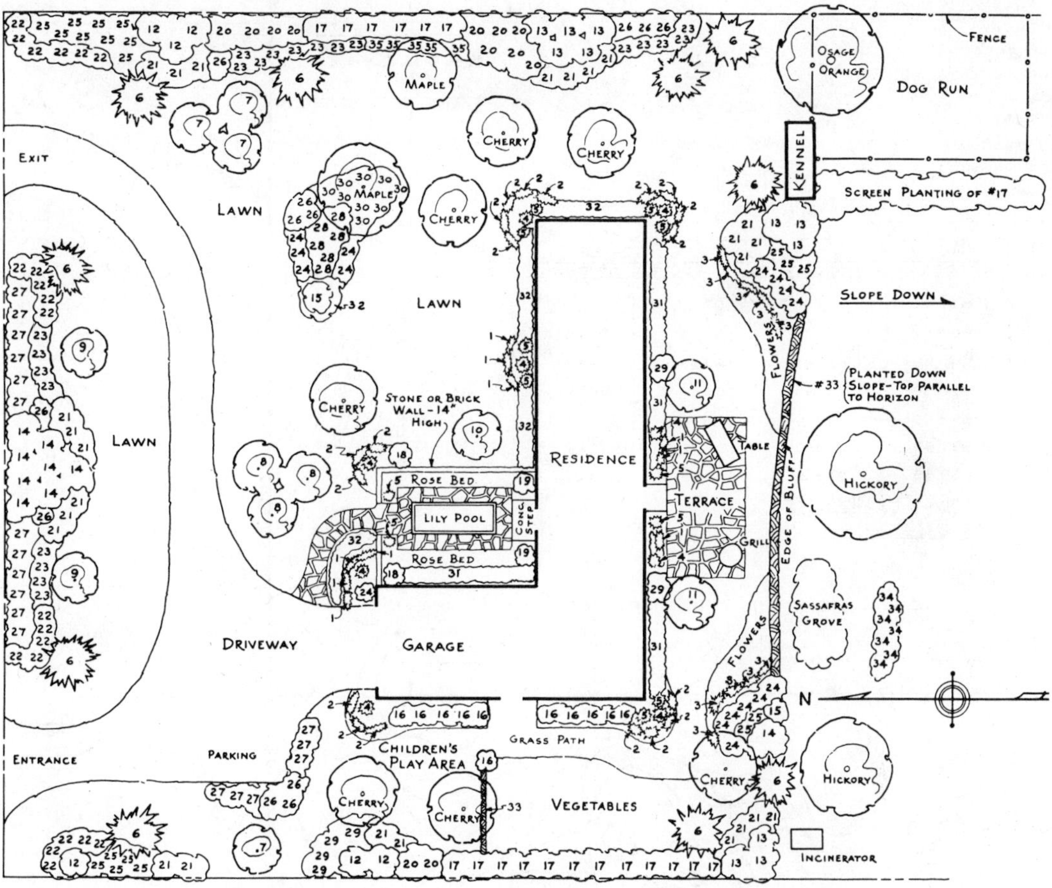

Figure 20-4
A landscape map designed to show the landscaping details of a park or home is keyed to a list of plantings.

PLANT LIST			
KEY	QTY.	NAME	SIZE
1	13	SPREADING YEW	18-24 INCHES
2	19	ANDORRA JUNIPER	18-24 INCHES
3	12	ANDORRA JUNIPER	15-18 INCHES
4	9	UPRIGHT YEW	24-30 INCHES
5	12	HICKS YEW	18-24 INCHES
6	10	COLORADO SPRUCE	3-4 FEET
7	4	HOPA FLOWERING CRAB APPLE	4-5 FEET
8	[illegible]	[illegible] FLOWERING CRA[illegible]	3-4 FE[illegible]

Figure 20-5
A list of plantings for map of Fig. 20-4.

LEGEND

APPLE TREE	A
MAPLE TREE	M
OAK TREE	O
PINE TREE	P
WILLOW TREE	W
WALNUT TREE	WA
POWER POLE	![pole]
TELEPHONE POLE	TP
INLET BASIN	I.B
SEWER MANHOLE	—O—
CONC. MONUMENTS	∘

MANHOLE NO	STORM SEWER		SANITARY SEWER	
	ELV. TOP COVER	INV. ELV.	ELV. TOP COVER	INV. ELV.
21	867.68	852.81	867.57	853.22
20	860.84	852.06	861.03	852.50
19	860.18	851.29	860.39	851.80
18	860.39	850.48	860.67	851.10
17	858.90	849.76	858.76	850.40
16	857.89	848.72	857.96	849.49
15	859.35	848.35	859.35	849.16
14	858.63	N.-849.58 E&W-847.91		

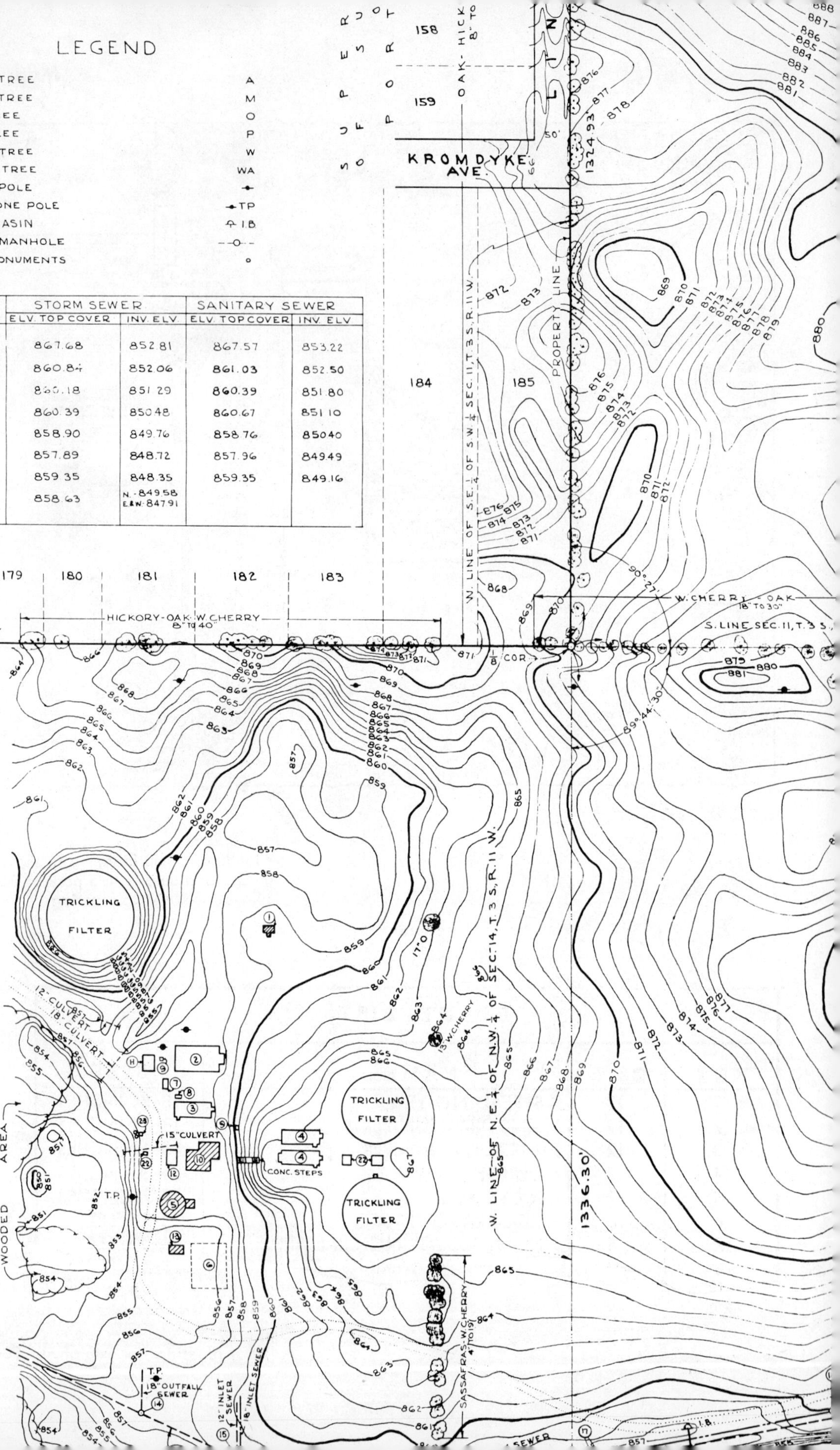

Figure 20-6
A topographic map depicts the essential features of large ground areas.
Wilkins and Wheaton Engineering Co.

to be built and other distinguishing features which are identified with the ground. A building site map or plot drawing is intended primarily to assist the architect and contractor to carry out construction services. An example of a plot layout is shown in Fig. 17-10.

Landscape map. Along with a building site map, a landscape map is often prepared to show how the ground area is to be landscaped. This map is used by the architect and landscape gardener to ascertain the most pleasing arrangement of shrubbery, trees, flower beds, etc. Thus the map will contain exact outlines of vegetation to be planted and each type of shrub, tree and other features is properly identified. Existing ground relief may be shown in full contour with proposed changes designated in dotted lines. The map is made to a large scale usually ranging from 1″ = 10′ to 1″ = 50′. See Fig. 20-4 and Fig. 20-5.

Topographic maps. Show large areas and include only topographic features necessary to fulfill the required function of the map.

Essential features of topographic maps are shown by symbols which include such details as lakes, streams, rivers, hills, valleys and other land shapes. Also indicated by symbols are man made objects like roads, railroads, cities, towns, villages, bridges, significant buildings and electric power lines. Fig. 20-6 is an example of a topographic map.

Hydrographic maps. Contain information concerning bodies of water, shorelines, sounding depths, reefs, shoals, etc. Included in this group of maps are plan charts which show harbor and anchorage details; coasting charts which plot outside courses along a coast; approach charts which present features to enable a ship to make a particular approach to a harbor; and ocean charts for ocean navigation.

Aeronautical maps. Contain cultural and ground shape features for air navigation purposes. They include necessary details and traffic routes to permit navigation by visual ground references and information to utilize radio and electronic navigation aids.

Road maps. Common maps used by motorists. They show the vast network of roads and highways that crisscross a given section of land.

Military maps. Those showing topographic details, distances and direction of objects and areas having military significance.

20.4 National Topographic Map Series[1]

The National Topographic Map Series is a term used to designate collectively the several quadrangle map series of the United States and its possessions. It is a general plan adopted in 1882 for the production of a standard series of topographic maps. Each map in the series covers a quadrangle of area bounded by lines of latitude and longitude. Using this plan, the location of any point on the surface of the earth is readily determined. Maps with these standard boundaries are usually referred to as *quadrangle maps.*

The information shown on topographic maps is divided into three main classes that are distinguished by the colors in which they are printed. Water features, such as oceans, lakes, rivers, streams, glaciers, canals, and swamps are shown in blue. The works of man, such as roads, trails, dams, transmission lines, buildings, airports, railroads, and boundary lines are shown in black. The features printed in brown depict the shape or configuration of the land surface.

Besides the three main classes of map features, most maps contain additional information printed in other colors. Large bodies of water usually are shown with a light blue tint. A light red tint is over-printed on the closely built-up areas of cities, indicating that within the tinted areas only the landmark or other important buildings are shown.

1. *Topographic Maps,* U.S. Department of the Interior (Geological Survey), 1959.

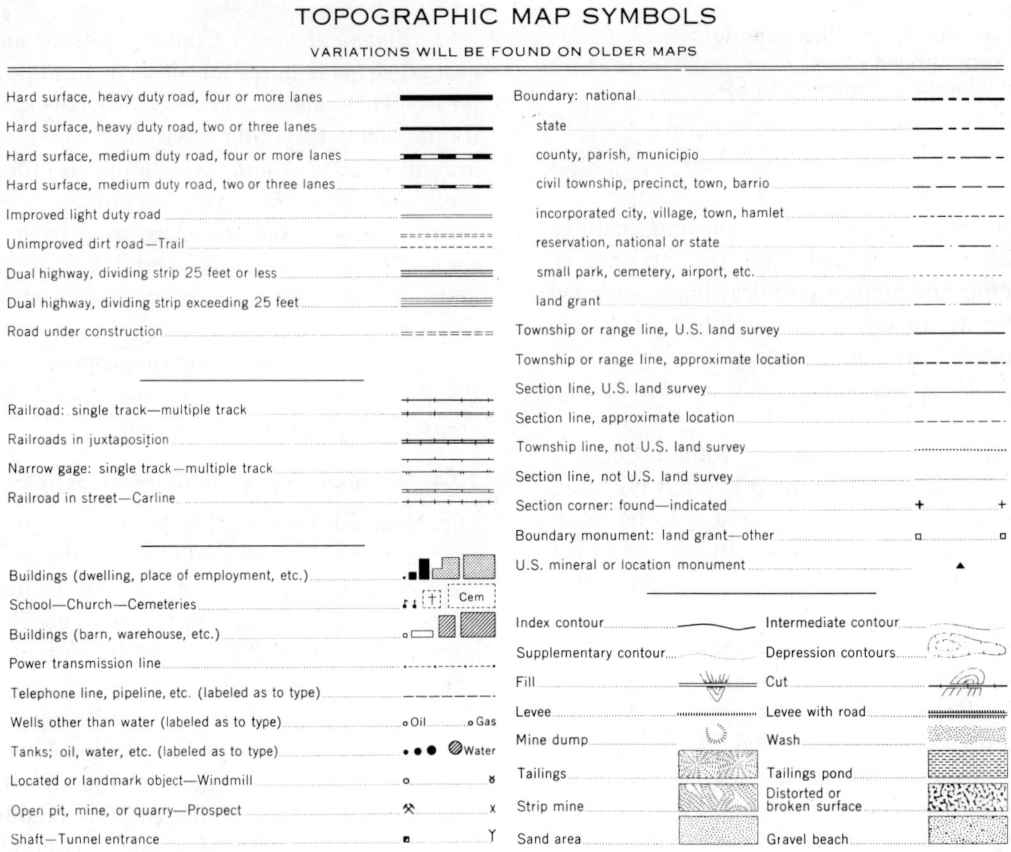
TOPOGRAPHIC MAP SYMBOLS
VARIATIONS WILL BE FOUND ON OLDER MAPS
Hard surface, heavy duty road, four or more lanes
Hard surface, heavy duty road, two or three lanes
Hard surface, medium duty road, four or more lanes
Hard surface, medium duty road, two or three lanes
Improved light duty road
Unimproved dirt road—Trail
Dual highway, dividing strip 25 feet or less
Dual highway, dividing strip exceeding 25 feet
Road under construction
Railroad: single track—multiple track
Railroads in juxtaposition
Narrow gage: single track—multiple track
Railroad in street—Carline
Buildings (dwelling, place of employment, etc.)
School—Church—Cemeteries
Cem
Buildings (barn, warehouse, etc.)
Power transmission line
Telephone line, pipeline, etc. (labeled as to type)
Wells other than water (labeled as to type)
Oil
Gas
Tanks; oil, water, etc. (labeled as to type)
Water
Located or landmark object—Windmill
Open pit, mine, or quarry—Prospect
Shaft—Tunnel entrance
Boundary: national
state
county, parish, municipio
civil township, precinct, town, barrio
incorporated city, village, town, hamlet
reservation, national or state
small park, cemetery, airport, etc.
land grant
Township or range line, U.S. land survey
Township or range line, approximate location
Section line, U.S. land survey
Section line, approximate location
Township line, not U.S. land survey
Section line, not U.S. land survey
Section corner: found—indicated
Boundary monument: land grant—other
U.S. mineral or location monument
Index contour
Intermediate contour
Supplementary contour
Depression contours
Fill
Cut
Levee
Levee with road
Mine dump
Wash
Tailings
Tailings pond
Strip mine
Distorted or broken surface
Sand area
Gravel beach

Figure 20-7
Map symbols.

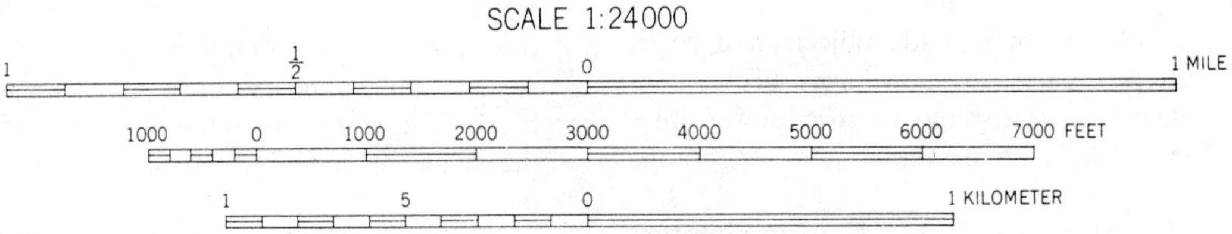

Figure 20-8
A map scale is given as a numerical ratio, and by bars marked in feet, meters, and miles. U.S. Geological Survey

TABLE I

Scale	1 inch equals
1:20,000	Approximately 1,667 feet
1:24,000	Exactly 2,000 feet
1:30,000	Exactly 2,500 feet
1:31,680	Exactly 1/2 mile
1:62,500	Approximately 1 mile
1:63,360	Exactly 1 mile
1:125,000	Approximately 2 miles
1:250,000	Approximately 4 miles
1:1,000,000	Approximately 16 miles

A solid red color is used to emphasize certain cultural features, including the classification of the more important roads and the boundary lines of townships, ranges, sections, and land grants in the states subdivided by public-land surveys. On the more recent maps a green over-print shows wooded areas, scrub, orchards, and vineyards.

20.5 Map symbols

The essential features of a topographic map are shown by means of standard symbols, which in reality constitute a language of maps. Symbols are made to represent objects as they are seen from the air; they should assume as much as possible the form of the actual objects. The size of the symbols as they are portrayed on a map will vary, depending on the scale of the map. However, each symbol is designated to convey the appropriate information. Anyone familiar with map symbols can readily recognize whether they represent manmade objects, ground features, hydrographic details, or common vegetation.

The number of symbols that can be included is limited by the scale of the map. This in turn is often governed by the specific function which the map is intended to serve. To make a map readable, small features must often be represented by symbols that are made larger than their true scale size, otherwise they would not be legible. A few of the more common map symbols are reproduced in Fig. 20-7.

20.6 Map scales

Map scales are ratios expressed to represent a fixed relationship between linear map measurements and corresponding ground distances. Thus the scale 1:62,500 means that one unit, such as 1 inch, 1 foot, or 1 meter on the map represents 62,500 of similar units on the earth's surface.

The graphic scale for measuring map distances as well as the scale ratio is printed on the lower margin of the map. See Fig. 20-8.

Quadrangle maps are published at the scales shown in Table I.

Maps are classified as large-scale maps, medium-scale maps, and small-scale maps. Large-scale maps (1:20,000, 1:24,000, 1:30,000, and 1:31,680) are intended for densely settled areas and areas requiring detail information for engineering planning and other similar purposes. Medium-scale maps (1:62,500 and 1:63,360) are those where detailed planning is not particularly significant. Small-scale maps (1:225,000, 1:250,000 and 1:1,000,000) include large areas on one sheet and are designed for planning statewide and nationwide projects.

20.7 Elevation and relief

The earth's crust is mostly irregular, varying between valleys, plains, and mountain ranges. This variability in the earth's surface is referred to as *relief*. The term used to describe the relief of a given area is *elevation*. The elevations on a map are expressed in units of measurement which are based on a plane

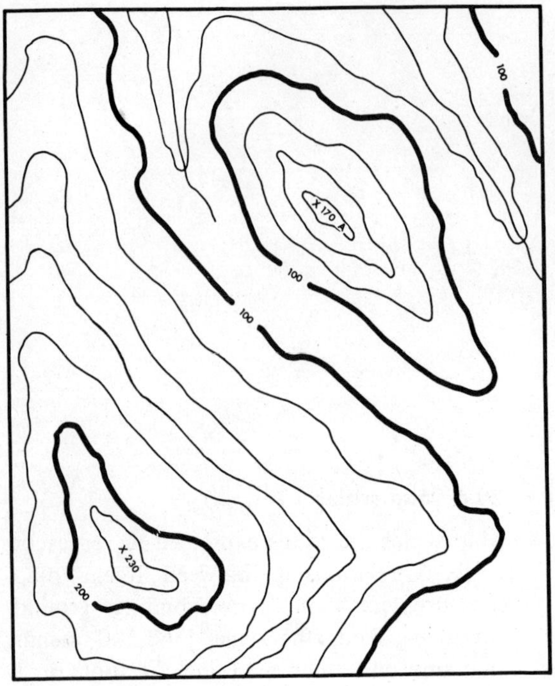

Figure 20-9
A contour is an imaginary line used as a means of expressing relief on a map. U.S.Army FM21-26

having a value of zero. The zero value represents mean sea level which is often designated as a datum plane. Mean sea level is the average level between low and high tides. Every object on the face of the earth is thus figured as a distance above or below the mean sea level.

Relief on a map is portrayed by contours. A contour is defined as an imaginary line on the ground connecting points of equal elevation. Contour lines therefore show the shape at each ground elevation. By counting the number of contour lines it is possible to ascertain the height of each hill, the depth of each valley, and the approximate elevation and slope of the ground. The vertical distance between successive contour lines is known as a contour interval. The interval value is usually given at the bottom of a map. The interval used is one that shows the most important topographic features without producing closely spaced contour lines that are difficult to read. Quadrangle maps of the continental United States are made with intervals of 5, 10, 20, 40, 50, 80 or 100 feet.

When a number is included on the contour line, it represents the elevation above mean sea level. See Fig. 20-9. Wherever X's, triangles, and squares with numbers printed alongside are shown, the values indicate spot elevations, meaning the height of the ground at that exact spot.

The pattern of the contour lines determines the shape of the ground; that is, where the object is evenly round, where it bulges out, where it pinches in. Thus the contours depicting a smooth, rolling hill, without abrupt breaks or sharp ridges are drawn as a series of gently curved lines with no acute angles. The contour lines for rugged, knife-ridged hills with many cliffs, are shown as jagged and bent sharply to indicate these characteristics.

The spacing between contour lines also discloses the slope of the ground. Thus when a hill is steep, the lines appear close together. A hill having a gentle slope would be shown with contour lines spaced fairly far apart. If two hills are close together with a dip between them the contour lines will form a series of V's pointing uphill. See Fig. 20-10*A*. A hill having a concave slope will show

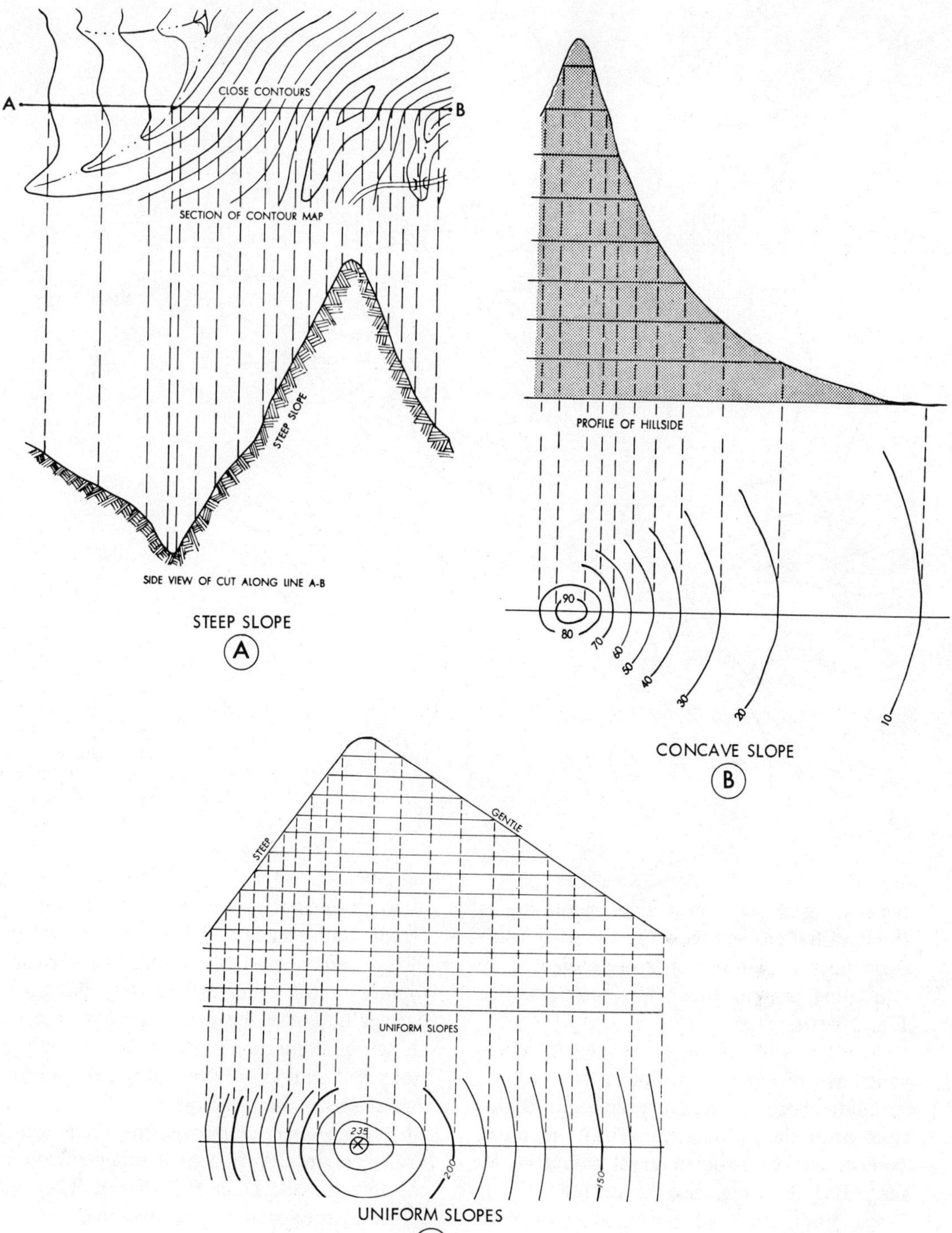

Figure 20-10
Contour lines identify the high ground, low ground, and the changes of shape of the ground in between. U.S. Army FM21-26

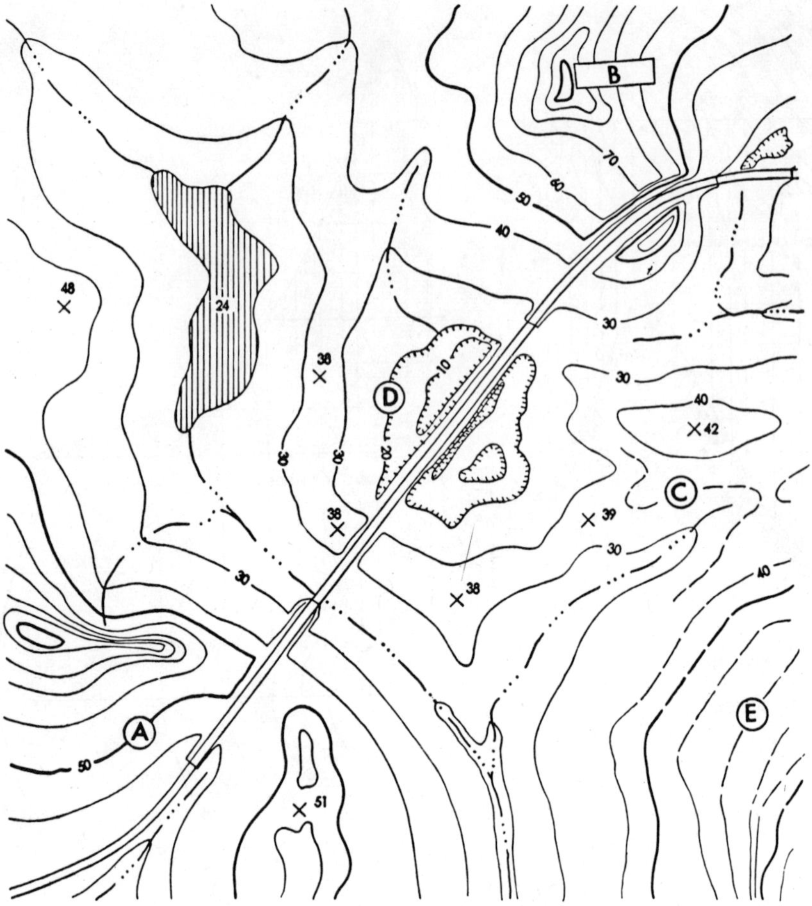

Figure 20-11
Contours express relief on a map. U.S.Army FM21-26

the spacing of the contour lines increasing as the land flattens out. See Fig. 20-10*B*. Uniform steep or gentle slopes are indicated by equal spacings of the slope contours. See Fig. 20-10*C*.

Five types of contours are used to represent lines of equal elevation.

Index contours are every fifth line beginning from the zero plane. Thus the index contour for a 10-foot interval would be 50 feet, 100 feet, etc. See *A* in Fig. 20-11. These lines are distinguishable as heavier lines and are intended to make it easier to read the contours since they can be counted by fives rather than one at a time.

Intermediate contours are the lighter contour lines drawn between indexes. See *B* in Fig. 20-11. These lines are normally labeled only at the edges of the map.

Supplemental contours represent half intervals and are dashed lines. See *C* in Fig. 20-11. They are used to present a clearer picture of the relief in relatively flat areas, especially where the usual contours are not shown as continuous but are drawn in portions and extend only to a distance to properly describe the slope.

Depression contours outline areas which are lower in elevation than other surrounding terrain. See *D* in Fig. 20-11. They are labeled with appropriate elevations.

Approximate contours are approximations of relief shown by broken lines of the same weight as the contour they replace. See *E* in Fig. 20-11. They are used when it is impossible to draw exact contours of inaccessible areas or for relief compiled from other unreliable map sources.

20.8 Map profile

A map profile is a drawing of a section which runs through one or more slopes. Profiles help map readers to visualize changes in the ground surface. Fig. 20-12*A* illustrates how a profile is drawn. In this illustration the line AB in the upper portion of the figure is the area for which a profile is desired. Horizontal lines are constructed below the contour map and vertical lines are dropped from points where each contour has been cut by line AB to corresponding lines in the elevation. By connecting these points, a profile of the area slopes is formed. The horizontal scale of the profile is the same as that used in the plan view. However the vertical scale is made larger in order to show the small variations in the elevation of the ground. Fig. 20-12*B* illustrates a typical profile map for a storm sewer installation.

20.9 Hachures

Relief formation and terrain shapes are shown occasionally by short lines called *hachures,* drawn in the direction of the ground shape. The hachure method is used when elevation data for contour drawing are lacking, or to depict relief in areas having a predominance of distinctive ground features that are too intricate or too small to be accurately shown. Generally hachures are limited to small-scale maps. See Fig. 20-13.

20.10 Compiling map data[2]

To ensure accurate positions and elevations for the features shown on a map, the latitude, longitude, and elevation of many points within the area to be mapped must be determined by control surveys. These surveys are of two kinds: (1) geodetic (or basic control) surveys of third or higher order accuracy, which determine positions or elevations for points that are marked on the ground with metal tablets, and (2) less accurate (fourth order) supplemental control surveys, which determine elevations or positions for points that are identified on aerial photographs but not marked with tablets.

The latitude and longitude of basic horizontal control points may be determined by triangulation, transit traverse, or a combination of these two methods. The elevations of basic vertical control points are established by spirit leveling. However, in mountainous areas, where vertical accuracy requirements are less stringent and extensive spirit leveling would be too expensive, elevations for triangulation stations and other marked points may be established by precise vertical-angle measurements.

From this basic network additional elevations needed for photogrammetric compilation are determined by supplemental control surveys. The most common types are stadia traverse with planetable and alidade, vertical-angle measurements with alidade or theodolite, barometric altimetry, and fly-leveling with spirit level or transit.

Most of the modern topographic maps are plotted from aerial photographs with instruments that operate on the principle of the stereoscope. Photographs usually taken from 6,000 to 25,000 feet above the ground are employed with photogrammetric plotters to compile the map detail, including the contours. The method is suited to mass production and makes it practical to prepare maps of uniform quality. Before 1940, most maps were prepared in the field by planetable methods, and their quality depended on the skill of the individual surveyor.

Nevertheless, field surveys are still needed for photogrammetric mapping. As already explained, the horizontal positions and elevations of many ground points in the quadrangle must then be determined by control surveys. After the map is compiled from photographs, it must be checked and completed in the field. Features, such as names and boundary lines, are added, contours are tested for accuracy, and any small details that may have been misinterpreted from the photographs are corrected. Civil boundaries and public-land lines are mapped according to the best documentary records and evidence recovered on the ground; however, the lines as shown on the map are not intended to be used as conclusive evidence of property ownership or civil jurisdiction. The

2. *Ibid.*

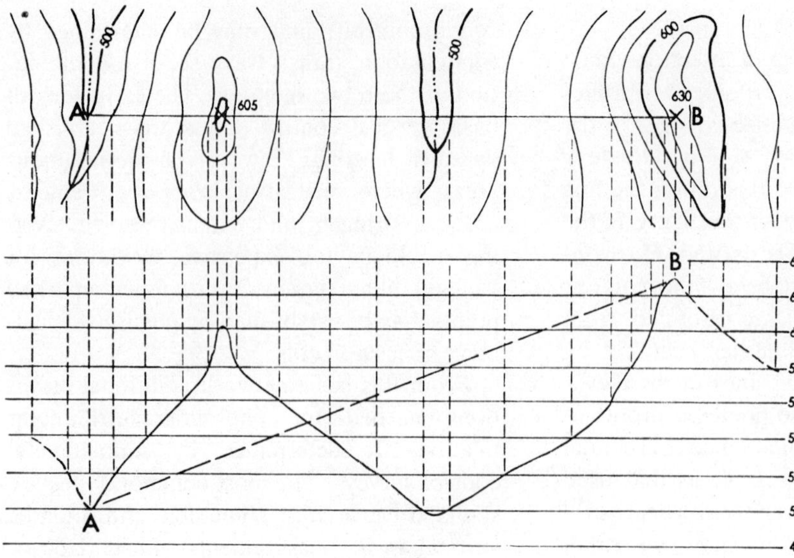

Figure 20-12A
A profile depicts the vertical changes in the ground surface.
U.S. Army FM21-26

Figure 20-12B
The elevations for the installation of a storm sewer drainage system are determined from a map profile. Wilkins and Wheaton Engineering Co.

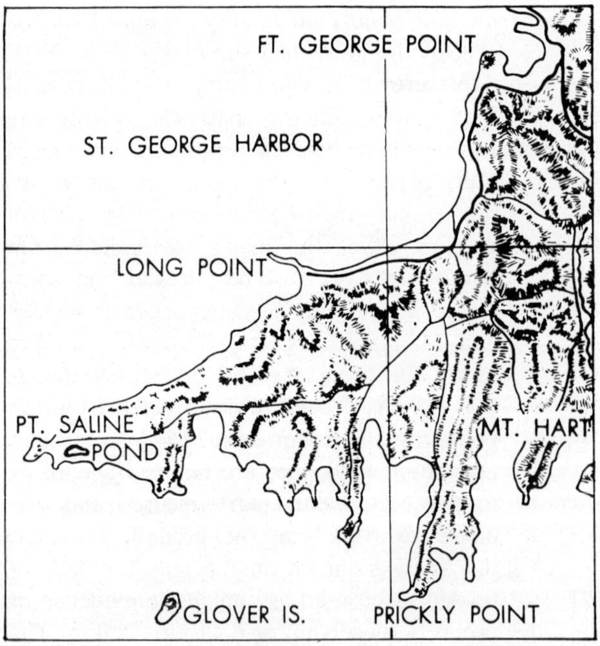

Figure 20-13
Hachures are used to portray relief when accurate contour data is not available.
U.S. Army FM21-26

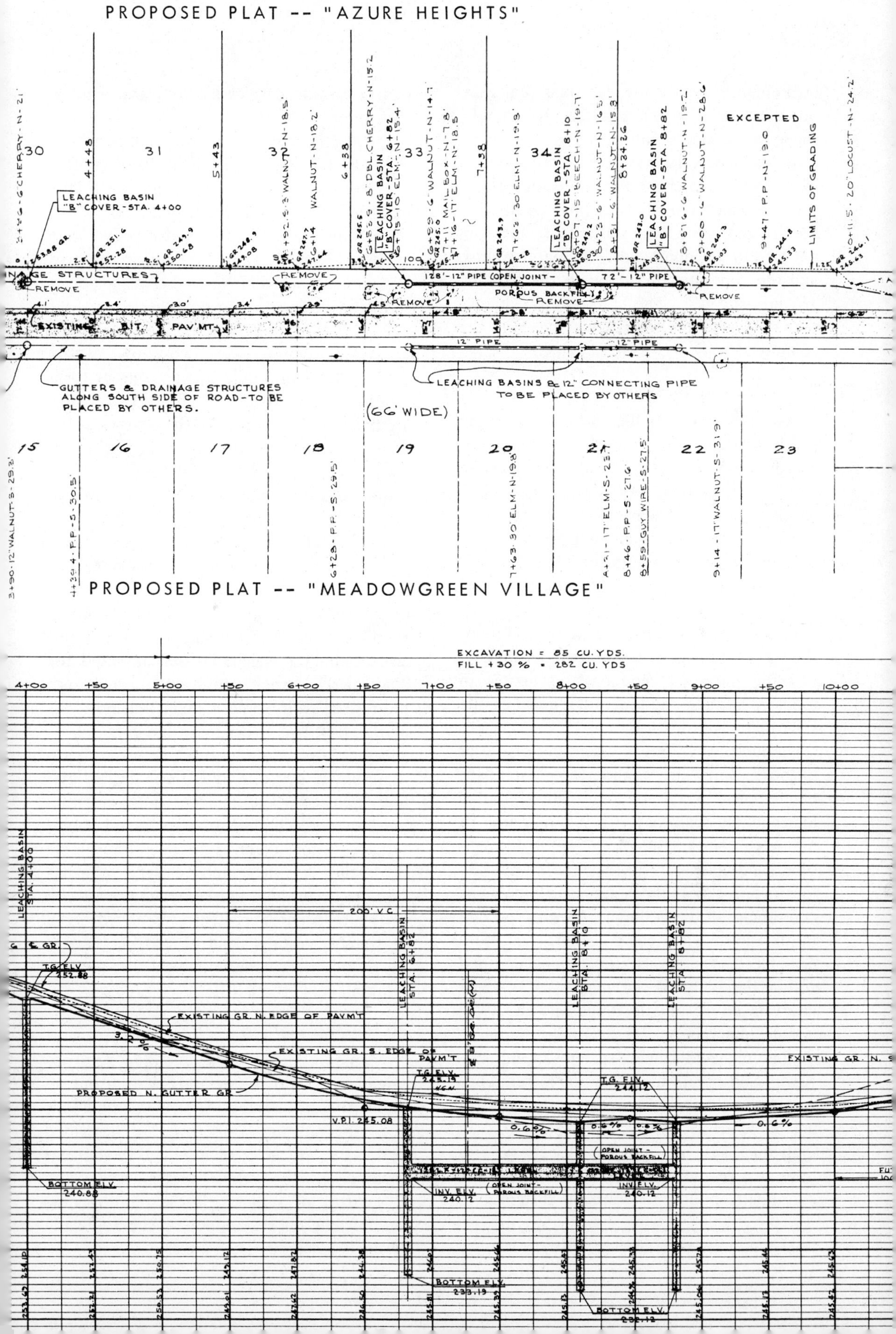

PROPOSED PLAT -- "AZURE HEIGHTS"
EXCEPTED
LIMITS OF GRADING
LEACHING BASIN "B" COVER - STA. 4+00
LEACHING BASIN "B" COVER - STA. 6+82
LEACHING BASIN "B" COVER - STA. 8+10
LEACHING BASIN "B" COVER - STA. 8+82
DRAINAGE STRUCTURES
REMOVE
128'-12" PIPE (OPEN JOINT -
72'-12" PIPE
POROUS BACKFILL
EXISTING BIT PAV'MT
12" PIPE
GUTTERS & DRAINAGE STRUCTURES ALONG SOUTH SIDE OF ROAD - TO BE PLACED BY OTHERS.
LEACHING BASINS & 12" CONNECTING PIPE TO BE PLACED BY OTHERS
(66' WIDE)
PROPOSED PLAT -- "MEADOWGREEN VILLAGE"
EXCAVATION = 85 CU. YDS.
FILL + 30 % = 282 CU. YDS
4+00
5+00
6+00
7+00
8+00
9+00
10+00
LEACHING BASIN STA. 4+00
200' V C
LEACHING BASIN STA. 6+82
LEACHING BASIN STA. 8+10
LEACHING BASIN STA. 8+82
T.G. ELV. 252.88
EXISTING GR. N. EDGE OF PAVM'T
EXISTING GR. S. EDGE OF PAVM'T
PROPOSED N. GUTTER GR.
T.G. ELV. 245.19
V.P.I. 245.08
T.G. ELV. 244.12
0.6 %
(OPEN JOINT - POROUS BACKFILL)
INV. ELV. 240.2
INV. ELV. 240.12
BOTTOM ELV. 240.88
BOTTOM ELV. 233.19
BOTTOM ELV. 232.12

field engineer also maps any areas that were obscured on the photographs by clouds, shadows, or dense forest cover.

In areas of very low relief, contours can be plotted more economically by planetable surveys than from photographs. Ordinarily, the hydrographic and cultural features in flat terrain are compiled from photographs, and the contours are added in the field by ground surveys. The plotted planimetry serves as position control for mapping the contours.

20.11 Coordinate systems[3]

Except for lettering, the lines representing political boundaries, land subdivisions, and coordinate systems are the only items of map information that are not physically evident on the ground. Boundary lines may be based on surveyed ground monuments, or they may be only described by statute. The lines of coordinate systems are mathematical abstractions.

Coordinate systems. Quadrangle maps show two systems of reference coordinates: (1) the universal geodetic coordinates in terms of latitude and longitude, and (2) the state plane coordinates.

Parallels of latitude and meridians of longitude form the boundaries of standard quadrangles. Maps of continental United States at the scale of 1:62,500 measure 15 minutes in latitude and 15 minutes in longitude, and maps at the scale of 1:24,000 measure 7-1/2 minutes on each side. The coordinates of the boundary lines are printed in the margins at each corner, and ticks are placed at intervals along each edge and within the body of the map—at 5-minute intervals on 15-minute maps and at 2-1/2 minute intervals on 7-1/2-minute maps.

State plane-coordinate systems permit surveyors and others to use a simple reference grid and still base their work on the national net of geodetic control. Each state has an individual system, and most state systems have two or more zones. Within zones the coordinates of any point are the distances in feet north and east of an arbitrarily chosen zero point.

Quadrangle maps show the state plane coordinates by labeled grid ticks along the border lines at 10,000-foot intervals. If the mapped area lies in more than one zone, each zone is shown with a distinctive style of tick. The grid can be laid out on the map by drawing straight lines between corresponding ticks on opposite edges.

Public-land subdivisions. The surveyed lines that divide over two-thirds of the United States into mile-square sections form a cadastral grid system. The subdivision lines are property boundaries or the references for boundaries. Frequently they form in part the boundaries of political subdivisions, and in many areas the routes of public roads follow the subdivision lines.

The subdivision lines and corners are shown on quadrangle maps to the extent that their positions can be determined from evidence recovered on the ground. "Found" subdivision corners are shown by heavy red crosses; lighter weight crosses are used for "indicated" corners. Indicated corners are those marked in some manner, but not with markers set by the original surveyors.

Subdivision lines accurately located are represented by solid red lines; dashed red lines are used where the location is uncertain.

Map representation of public-land subdivisions is not intended to be authoritative or official; it is presented as useful information, as accurately and completely as it can be at reasonable cost. In areas where a reasonable amount of field evidence cannot be found, the section lines are sometimes omitted.

20.12 Map plotting

Map plotting consists of taking data obtained by a field survey and laying it out on paper to form a map. Several methods are used for plotting. Only two are described here—the protractor method and the tangent method.

To execute either of these plotting procedures an understanding of the following terms is essential:

3. *Geological Survey Circular 368*, U.S. Department of the Interior (Geological Survey), 1955.

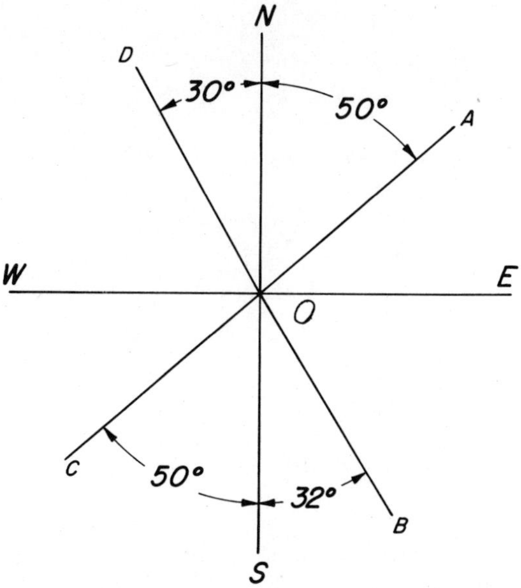

Figure 20-14
The bearing of a line is indicated by the quadrant where the line falls and the acute angle it forms with the meridian in the quadrant.

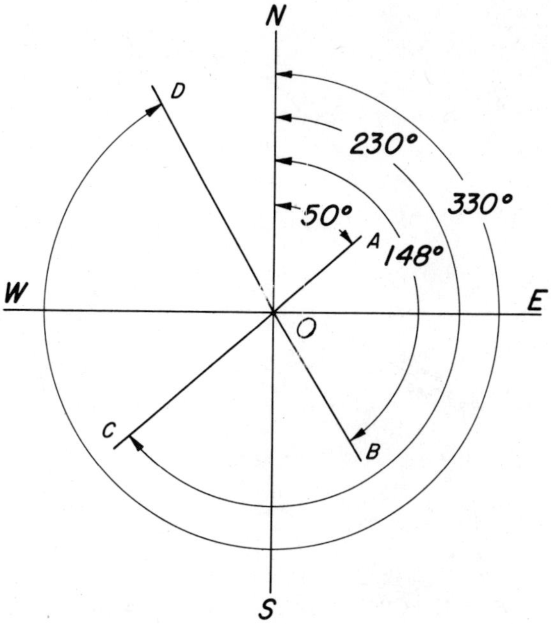

Figure 20-15
Azimuths are directions formed by angles which are measured in a clockwise direction from the north or south point of the meridian.

Bearing. A bearing of any line is its direction with respect to a given meridian. Thus in Fig. 20-14 the bearing of line *OA* is North 50° East which is written as *N*50°*E*. Line *OB* is *S*32°*E, OC* is *S*50°*W* and *OD* is *N*30°*W*.

Azimuths. The azimuth of a line is its direction as shown by the angle formed between the meridian and the line when measured in a clockwise direction, and may have values between 0° and 360°. Zero azimuth is always either south or north. Fig. 20-15 shows azimuths given from the north point of the meridian with *OA*=50°, *OB*=148°, *OC*=230°, and *OD*=330°.

Deflection angle. An angle which is formed by a line and the extension of a preceding line. It is indicated as right (clockwise) or left (counter-clockwise) according to the direction the measurement is taken from the prolongation of the preceding line. Note in Fig. 20-16 the deflection angle at *B* is 45° *R* and the angle at *C* is 40° *L*.

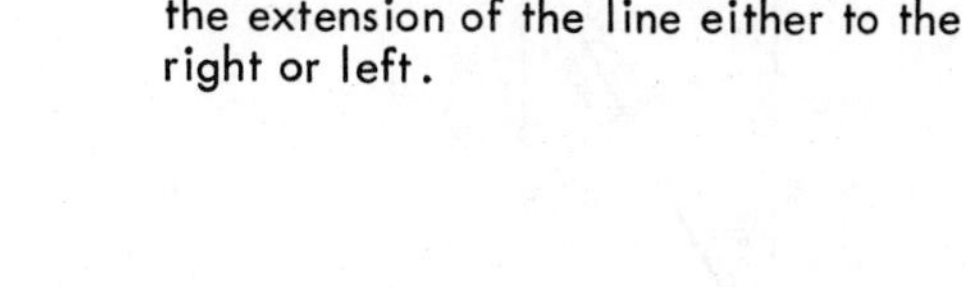

Figure 20-16
The deflection angle is measured from the extension of the line either to the right or left.

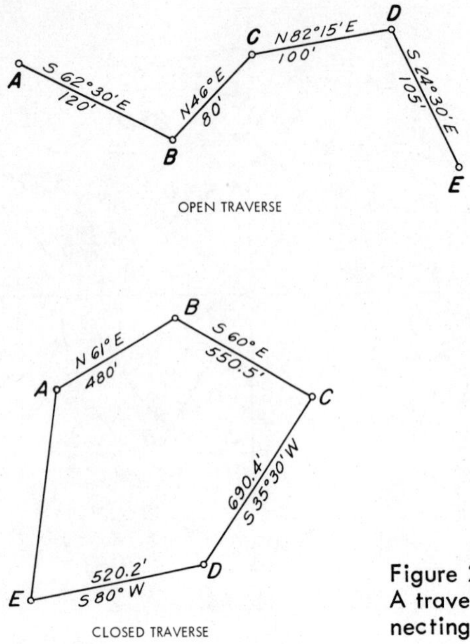

Figure 20-17
A traverse is a succession of straight lines connecting a series of points established by a survey.

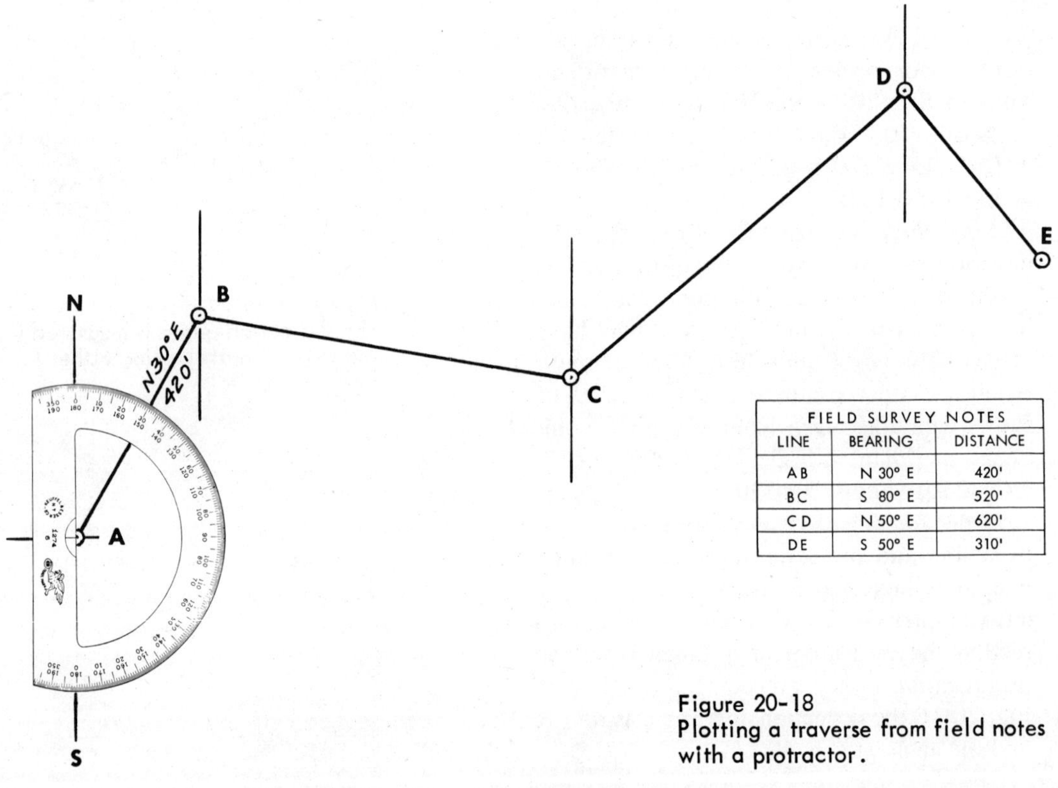

FIELD SURVEY NOTES		
LINE	BEARING	DISTANCE
AB	N 30° E	420'
BC	S 80° E	520'
CD	N 50° E	620'
DE	S 50° E	310'

Figure 20-18
Plotting a traverse from field notes with a protractor.

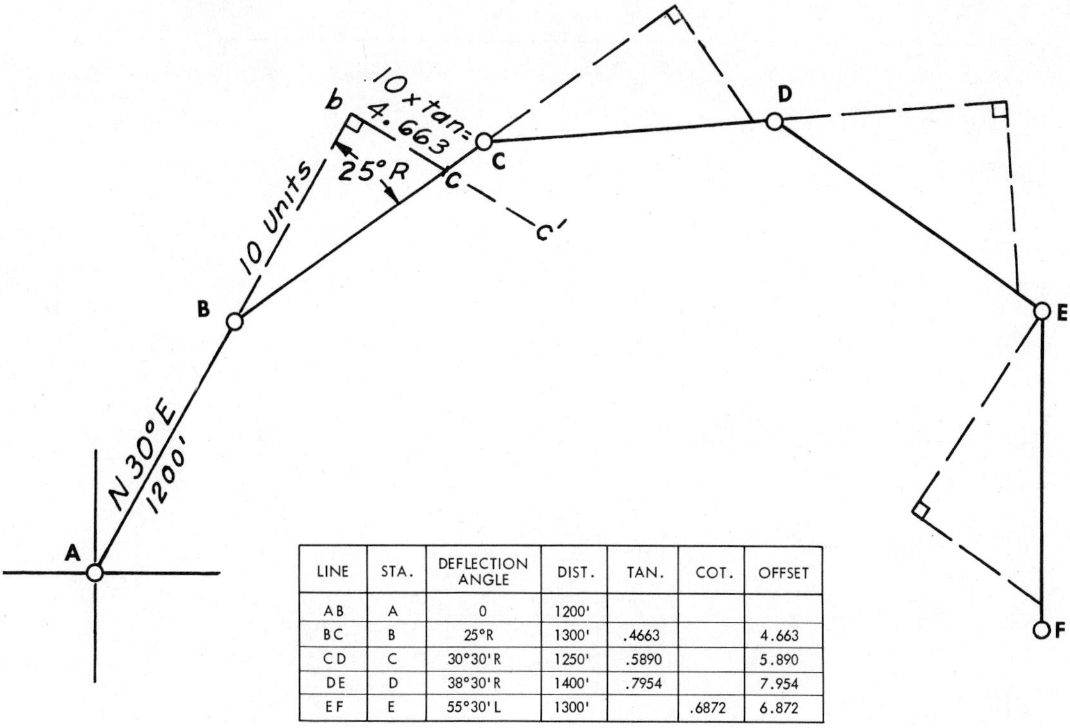

LINE	STA.	DEFLECTION ANGLE	DIST.	TAN.	COT.	OFFSET
AB	A	0	1200'			
BC	B	25°R	1300'	.4663		4.663
CD	C	30°30'R	1250'	.5890		5.890
DE	D	38°30'R	1400'	.7954		7.954
EF	E	55°30'L	1300'		.6872	6.872

Figure 20-19
Plotting a traverse by the tangent method.

Traverse. A series of connected lines having known lengths and directions. If a traverse forms a closed figure it is known as a *closed traverse;* if it is open on both ends it is called an *open traverse.* See Fig. 20-17.

20.13 Protractor map plotting

To plot a traverse by the protractor method from bearings given in the field survey notes as shown in Fig. 20-18, draw a meridian through the known point *A*. Place a protractor along this meridian and lay off the bearing of the first line *N*30°*E*. With an engineer's scale lay off the distance of 420′, which then locates point *B*. Draw a meridian through point *B* and proceed in the same manner to locate points *C*, *D* and *E*.

20.14 Tangent map plotting

To plot a traverse by the tangent method, proceed as follows, see Fig. 20-19:

1 Let *AB* represent the plotted position of the initial line.
2 Extend line *AB* to some convenient distance *b*, usually 10 units.
3 Erect perpendicular *bcc′* from the end of line *Bb*.
4 Find the tangent of the deflection angle at *B*.
5 Multiply the length of the base line *Bb* by the tangent of angle *B*. This provides the offset *bc* and establishes the direction of line *BC*.
6 Draw a line from *B* to *C* of the required distance.
7 Proceed in a similar manner to locate the remaining points.
8 If the deflection angle is greater than 45°, the base line is established as a perpendicular to the preceding line at the last point plotted and not as a perpendicular to the extension of the preceding line. See point *E*. In such cases, the cotangent of the deflection angle is used instead of the tangent.

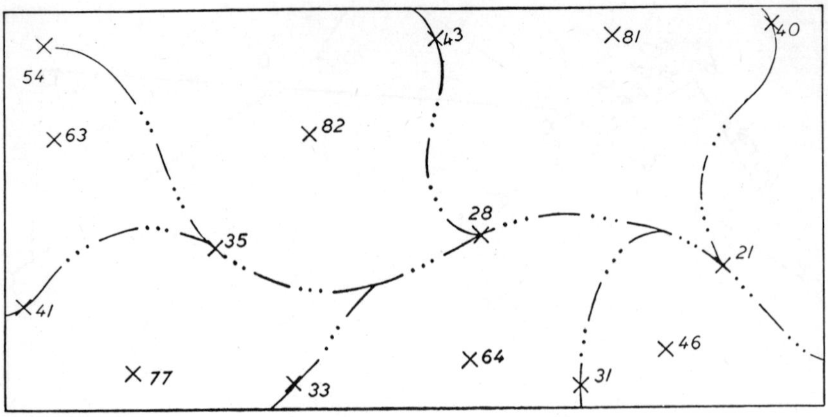

Figure 20–20
Problem 3.

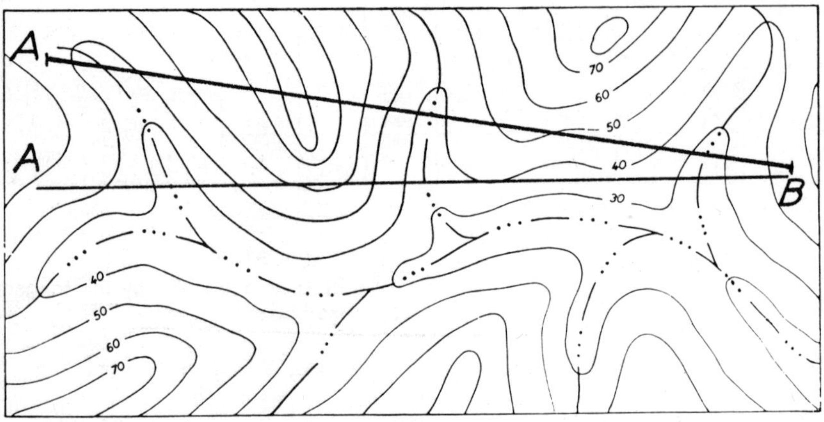

Figure 20–21
Problem 4.

Problems, section 20 (Tables II-V on page 604)

1 Plot the closed traverse and determine the bearing and length of course **FA** using the data shown in Table II. Choose a convenient map scale.

2 Plot the closed traverse by the tangent method from the field survey data given in Table III. Determine the bearing and distance of course **FA**. Choose a convenient map scale.

3 Using the spot elevations and stream network in Fig. 20-20, sketch the contours for a complete topographical map. Use a suitable map scale.

4 Make a profile of the line **AB**, shown in Fig. 20-21, using horizontal and vertical scales as assigned by instructor.

5 Given the data of Table IV, plot the open traverse using the tangent method. Assume initial line to have a bearing of N36° E. Scale: 1″ = 400′.

6 Plot the triangular land parcel shown in Fig. 20-22 using a scale of 1″ = 100′. Determine its area.

7 Given the data of Table V, plot an open traverse using the protractor method. Assume the initial point to be **A**. Scale: 1″ = 400′.

8 Draw a topographic map showing the main highways and streets leading to your school area. Show school buildings, plantings, etc., with an appropriate legend identifying the structures. Choose a suitable scale.

9 Prepare a drawing showing the contour lines for the elevations shown in Fig. 20-23 beginning at elevation 600′ and continuing at 5-foot intervals. Also plot the profile of the survey line using the elevations of stations and half stations as shown. Horizontal scale: 1″ = 100 ft. Vertical scale: 1″ = 20 ft.

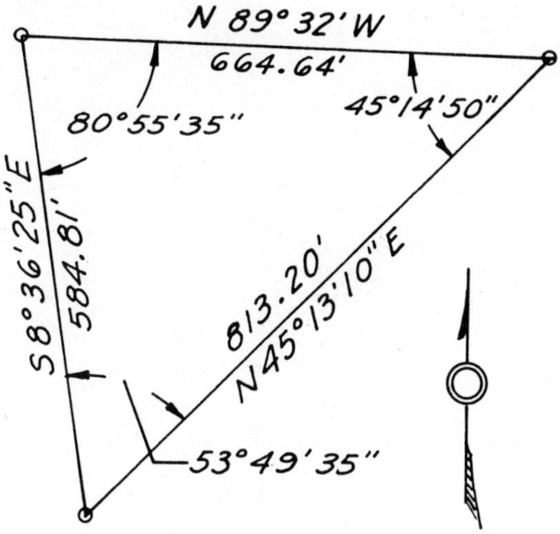

Figure 20-22
Problem 6.

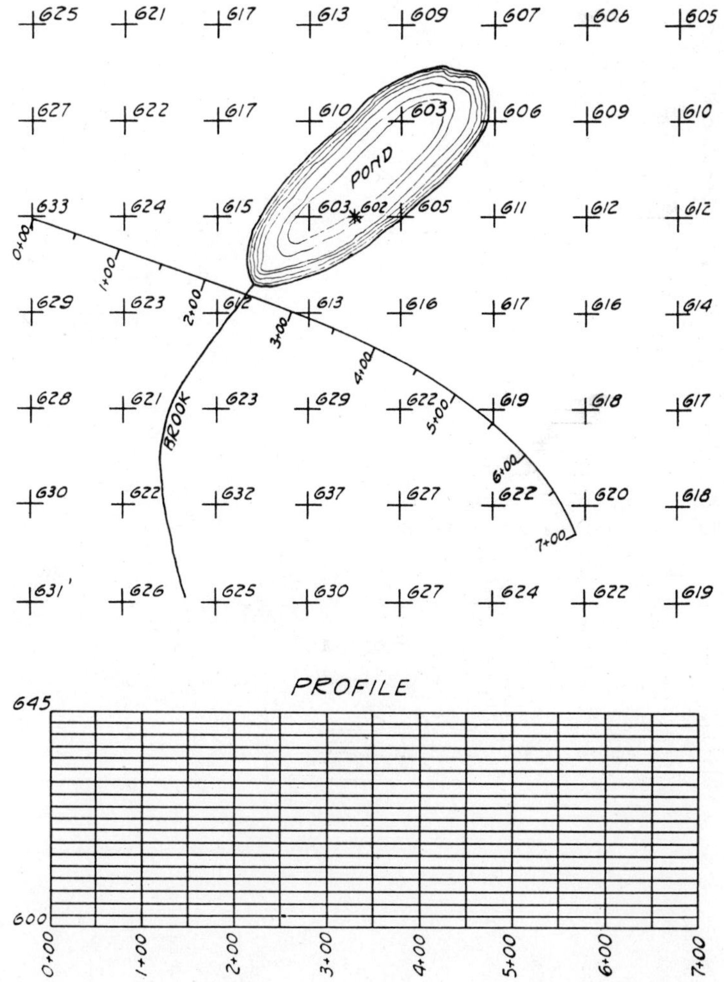

Figure 20-23
Problem 9.

TABLE II. PROBLEM 1.

Course	Bearing	Distance
AB	N60°E	500'
BC	S75°E	680'
CD	S20°W	700'
DE	S16°E	200'
EF	N70°W	720'
FA	?	?

TABLE III. PROBLEM 2.

Course	Bearing	Distance
AB	S15°20'W	322'
BC	S10°30'E	180'
CD	N82°E	648'
DE	S40°E	740.2'
EF	N10°E	1238.5'
FA	?	?

TABLE IV. PROBLEM 5.

Station	Deflection Angle	Distance
A	0	182'
B	16°40'L	250'
C	34°00 L	260'
D	10°30'R	310'
E	48°18'L	465'
F	12°00'L	430'
G	18°20'L	245'
H	4°30'R	165'

TABLE V. PROBLEM 7.

Course	So. AZ.	Distance
AB	120°15'	640'
BC	144°30'	960'
CD	256°10'	382'
DE	284°36'	840'
EF	212°00'	540'
FG	156°00'	940'
HJ	145°30'	1450'

Descriptive geometry and revolutions 21

In engineering drawing the draftsman is continually confronted with problems involving the relationships existing between geometric elements, such as points, lines and planes. Although many of these problems may be solved mathematically, their actual solution by graphic means frequently provides the engineer an added check on his computations. Furthermore, much of the original layout and development of surfaces can be done only by using geometric procedures as described in this section.

While it is not the purpose here to present a complete coverage of descriptive geometry, nevertheless, sufficient material is included to assist the draftsman and engineer to solve the more common geometric problems encountered in engineering drawing. These problems can, for the most part, be solved by one or more of the following basic operations involving the use of auxiliary views:

1 Finding the true length of a line.
2 Determining a point-view of a line.
3 Constructing an edge-view of a plane.
4 Finding the true size of a plane figure.

21.1 Notation

In order to understand the graphic solution of the basic problems included in this section, it is essential that a system of notation be first established. Therefore, points in space are called out as upper case letters *A, B, C,* etc., while projections or views of such points are noted by lower case letters, *a, b, c,* with subscripts to indicate the view. Thus, a_T will designate a top view of point *A*, a_F the front view, a_R the right side view. Auxiliary views of points will be identified with the subscript letter assigned to the respective views—a_A, a_B, a_C, etc.

A line connecting two points is indicated *AB, BC,* etc., and the resulting views are shown as $a_T\, b_T$, $a_F\, b_F$, and $a_R\, b_R$.

Reference lines, or fold lines as they are often called, are placed conveniently between views. These lines are made of long dashes with two short dashes between as shown in Fig. 21-1. The adjacent views are indicated by *T* for Top, *F* for Front and *R* for Right side. These view notations are placed in position on opposite sides of the reference line. Reference lines should be placed "tight," that is, close to the views, to prevent drawings from becoming unnecessarily large.

21.2 The views of a point and a line

A discussion of the proper method for projecting the various views of an object is described in Section 5. Since this section deals only with surfaces of primary objects, it is necessary now to use these same principles as they apply to a point and a line.

In Fig. 21-1, line *AB* is shown in its three principal views—top, front and right side. Observe the notation of points *A* and *B* as well as the reference lines. From this drawing it is quite obvious that the top and front views of a point, as well as a line, are aligned vertically and the front and side views are aligned horizontally. Notice that point *C*, on line *AB* appears on all three views of the line and that the requirements of alignment are true of this point as well as the line. It follows then that any point on a line must appear on that line in all views of the point and line.

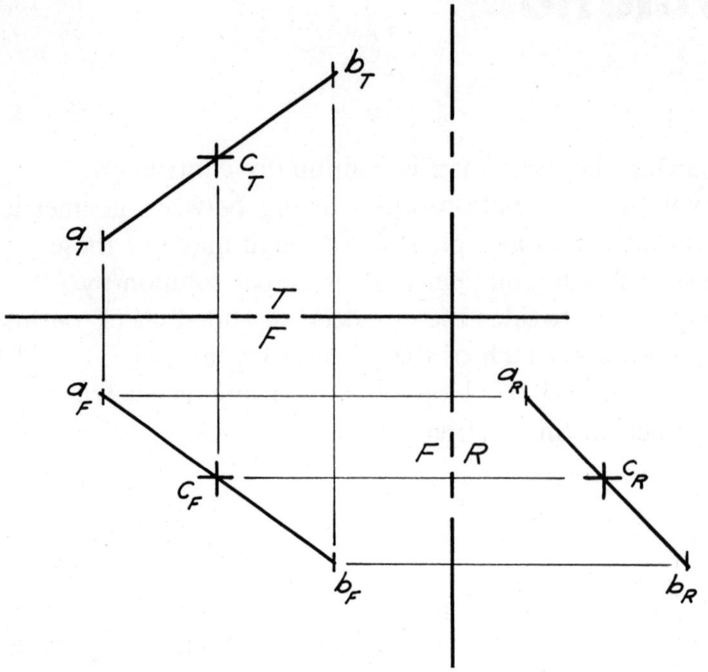

Figure 21-1
Point C on line AB is shown on the three principal views of the line. Notice the notation of the reference lines, points A, B and C, and line AB.

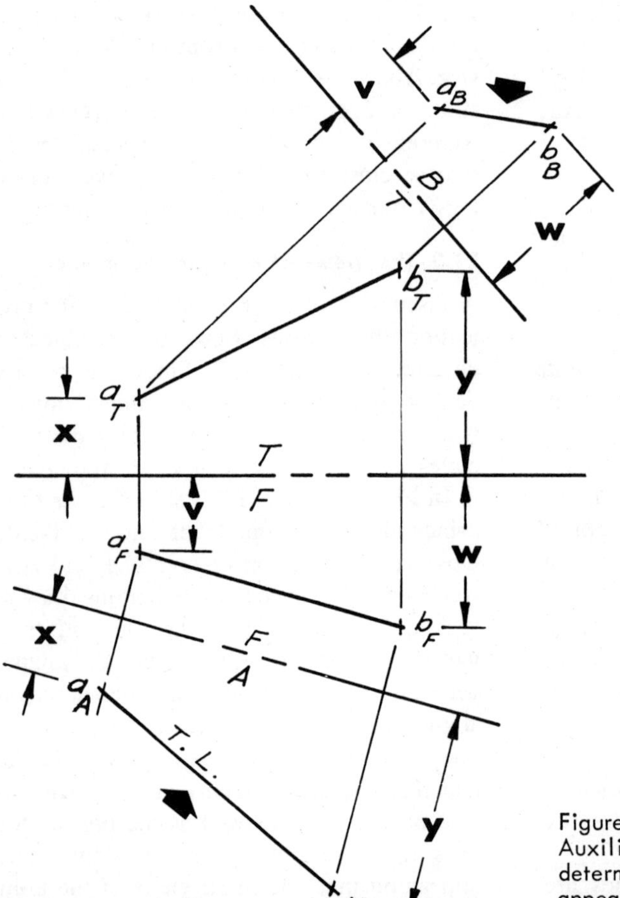

Figure 21-2
Auxiliary views are frequently used to determine true lengths as well as the appearance of a line from some predetermined position.

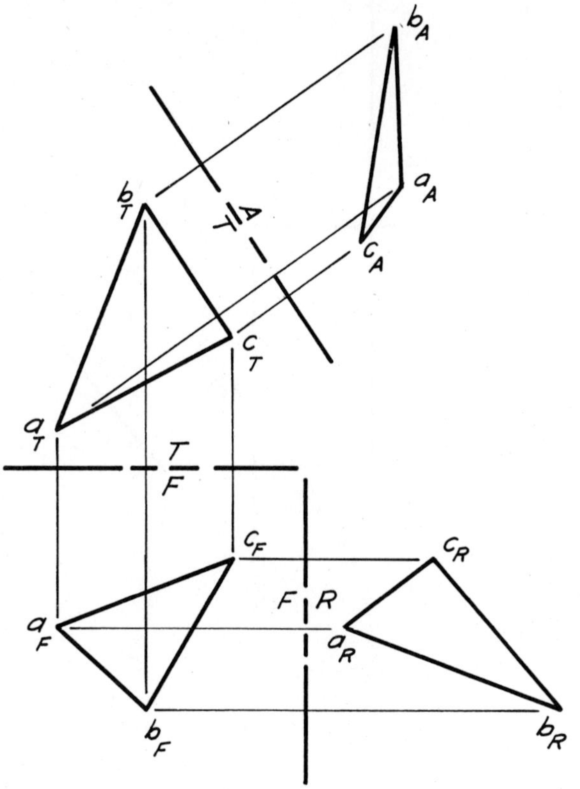

Figure 21-3
Planes and plane surfaces are usually indicated by two or more intersecting lines.

21.3 Auxiliary views

The three principal views of a geometric element do not always give the complete information necessary for an engineering drawing. As it was discussed in Section 9, other views, called *auxiliary views,* are often needed to provide the true size and shape description of a part, especially for inclined surfaces or oblique lines which do not appear in their true shape in the top, front or side views. Moreover, it is frequently necessary to determine how an object appears from a position other than one taken directly from above, in front or side.

In Fig. 21-2, the oblique line *AB* is shown in the top and front views together with two auxiliary views. Auxiliary view *A* is taken by establishing reference line *F-A* parallel to the front view of line *AB*. Distances *X* and *Y* measured from reference line *T-F* to a_T and b_T are laid out from reference line *F-A* on perpendicular projectors drawn from a_F and b_F. This locates the auxiliary view a_A and b_A. Another auxiliary view *B* is shown by drawing reference line *T-B*. By transferring distances *w* and *v* taken from reference line *T-F* to a_F and b_F to projectors from a_T and b_T, view a_B b_B is established. It should be noted that view a_A b_A shows line *AB* in its true length, whereas view a_B b_B does not show the line in its true size.

21.4 A plane surface

A plane surface may be formed by: (1) three points, (2) a point and a line, (3) two intersecting lines, or (4) two parallel lines. However, a plane is usually indicated on a drawing by two or more intersecting lines. Although an actual plane surface is limited in size, it is frequently necessary to consider the plane to extend without limits in order to obtain the solutions required. A typical example of a plane surface with its principal views, including an auxiliary view, is shown in Fig. 21-3.

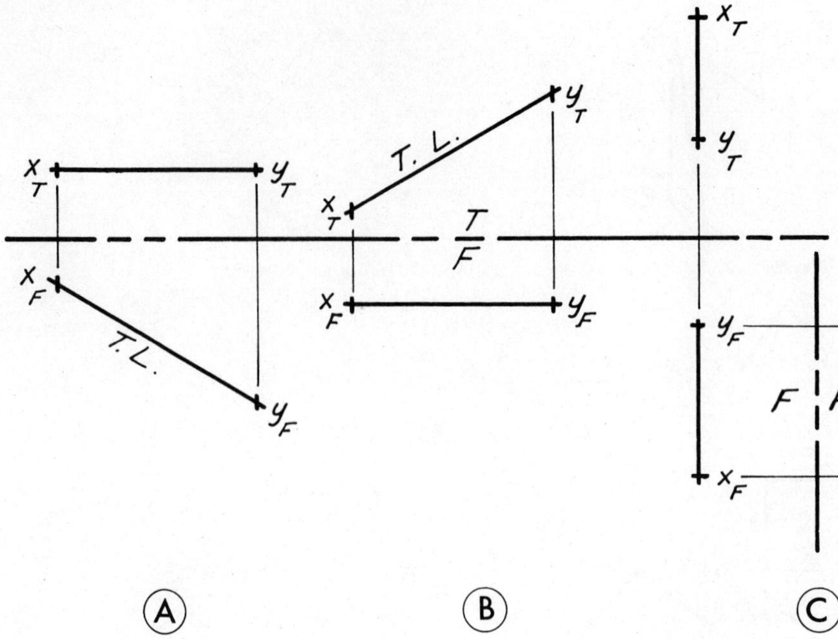

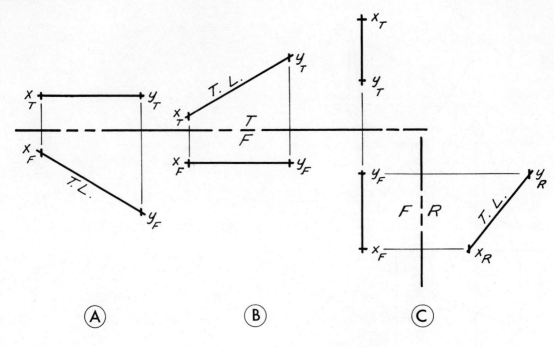

Figure 21-4
Principal lines are those that show their true length in a principal view.

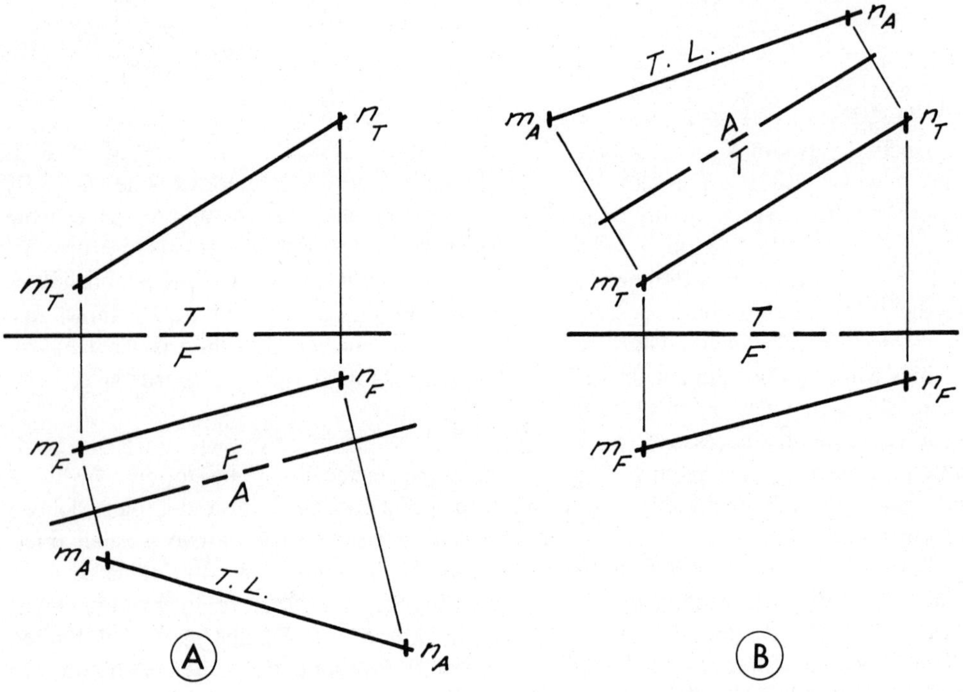

Figure 21-5
The true length of a line may be found in a front-adjacent or top-adjacent view.

21.5 To find the true length of a line

Any line that is parallel to a reference line, or a plane of projection, must necessarily show its true length in the adjacent view. In Fig. 21-4, line *XY* is shown in three positions, each parallel to a reference line. This line appears in its true length in the front view at *A*, in the top view at *B* and in the side view at *C*. Lines in these positions are called *principal lines*. However, most lines to be measured are not principal lines but oblique lines that are slanted to the three principal planes of projection.

To obtain the true length of an oblique line, a reference line that is parallel to one of the principal views must first be established. In *A* of Fig. 21-5, reference line *F-A* is placed parallel to the front view of line *MN*. By taking the distances from reference line *T-F* to $m_T\ n_T$ and laying these distances out from reference line *F-A* on the projectors drawn from $m_F\ n_F$, the true length of *MN* is obtained as $m_A\ n_A$. A similar construction is shown in *B* of Fig. 21-5 in which the true length of the line is located at $m_A\ n_A$ in the top adjacent auxiliary view.

21.6 To find the point view of a line

Once a true length of a line is found, the next step in the solution of many problems is to show the same line as a point view. To find this view, a reference line must be drawn perpendicular to the true length view of the line. By transferring distance *x* as described previously, the line can be shown as a point at $m_B\ n_B$. See Fig. 21.6.

21.7 To find the shortest distance from a point to a line

Another very common measurement that must be determined in engineering drawing is the shortest distance from a given point to a given line. In Fig. 21-7 the shortest distance from point *O* to line *RS* is required. To ascertain this length, proceed as follows:

1 Obtain a true length view of line *RS*. Show point *O* in this view.
2 Show line *RS* as a point view. See Fig. 21-6.

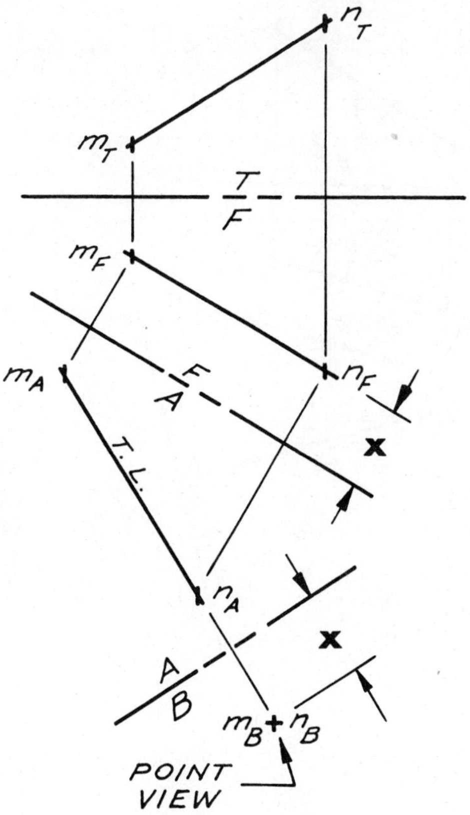

Figure 21-6
A second auxiliary view taken from the true length view shows the line as a point view.

3 By projecting *O* into this view, the actual distance between *O* and *RS* can now be measured.

To find the shortest distance between two parallel lines, the same procedure as above is followed. First, auxiliary views are constructed to determine the true lengths, and then the lines as point views are drawn. This latter view will provide the true distance between the parallel lines.

21.8 The shortest distance between two skew lines

Lines that are neither parallel to each other nor intersecting are called skew lines. The shortest distance between these lines is a measurement often needed to construct bracing of a supporting member, or even to pro-

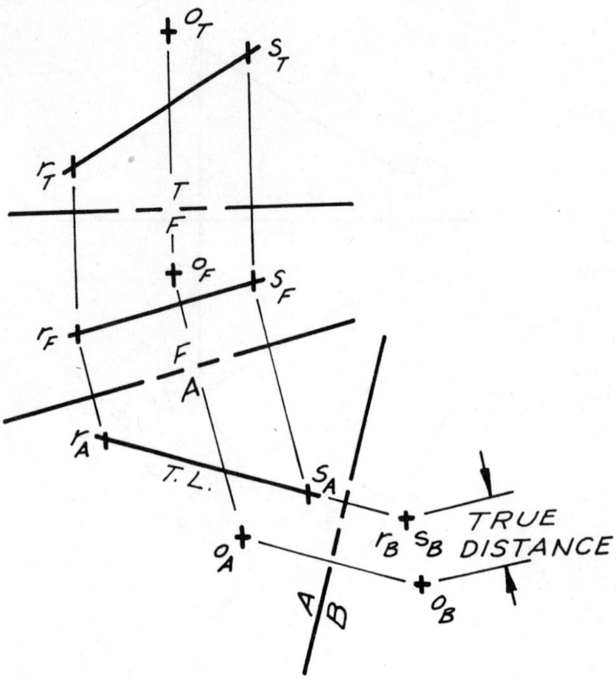

Figure 21-7
The shortest distance from a point to a line is found in the view which shows the line as a point.

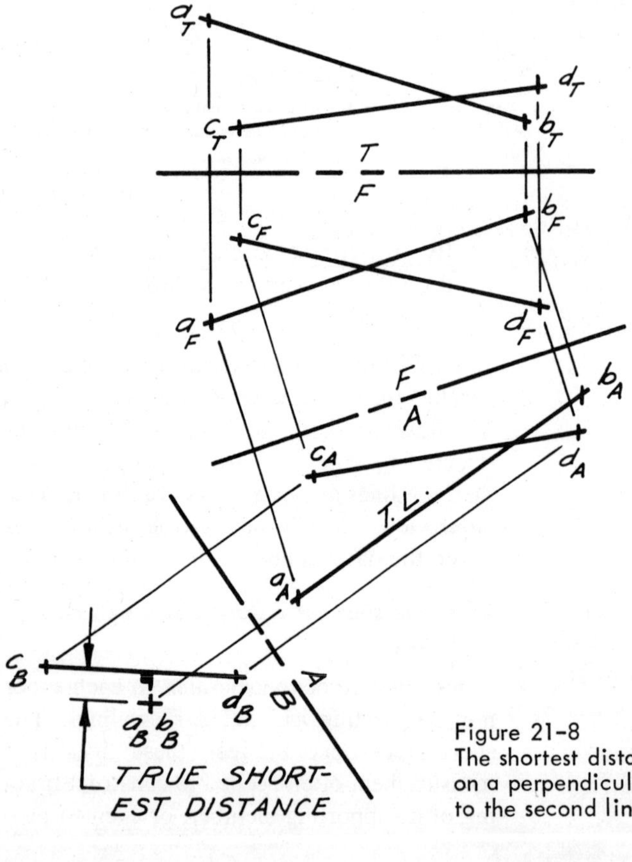

Figure 21-8
The shortest distance between two skew lines is measured on a perpendicular from the line shown as a point view to the second line.

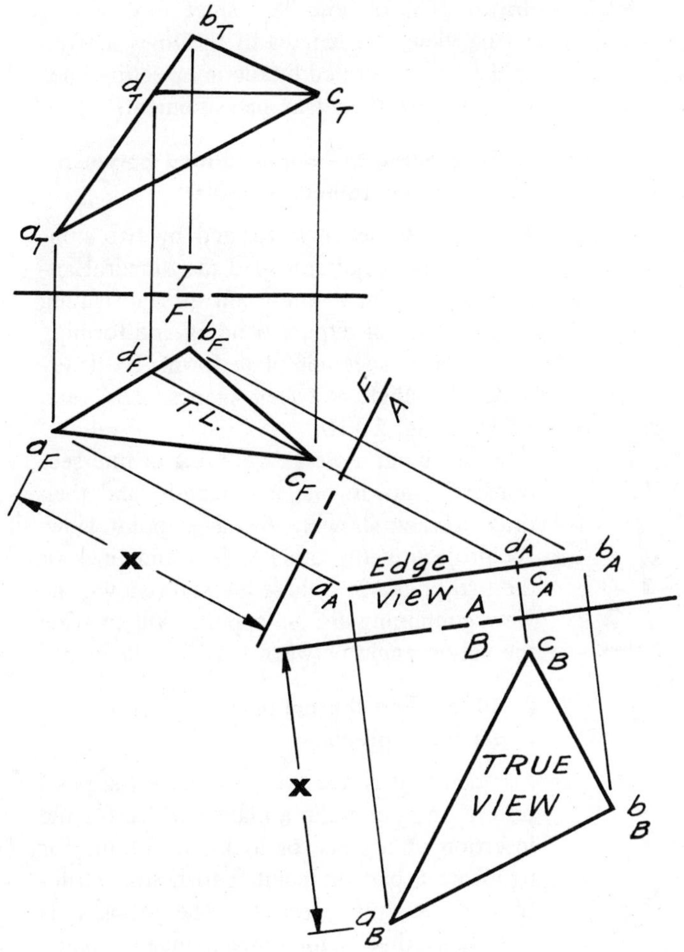

Figure 21-9
The true shape of a plane can be found in the view adjacent to the edge view in which the direction of sight is perpendicular to the plane.

vide a bypass piping unit to transfer flow of liquids from one pipe to another. The procedure for determining this distance is as follows (see Fig. 21-8):

1 Construct an auxiliary view of the skew lines showing one of them in its true length.
2 Draw a second auxiliary view to show the true length line in step 1 as a point. Show the other skew line by normal projection.
3 The perpendicular distance from the point view line to the other skew line can now be measured. This is the shortest distance.

21.9 Plane measurements

The true-size measurements of plane surfaces, the angles formed by intersecting lines, and the true shape description of planes are all magnitudes that are frequently required for layouts as well as for finished production drawings. The problem of true plane measurement involves two basic steps. First the plane, formed by intersecting or parallel lines or by a point and a line, must be drawn as an edge view. From this edge view the true view showing the actual shape can be projected and the required dimensions determined.

Edge view of a plane. A plane will appear as an edge, that is, as a straight line, in a view showing a true length line in the plane as a point view. In order to establish this view, a line first must be drawn in the plane that will appear in its true length in an adjacent view. This can be done by drawing a line in any one of the positions similar to those shown in Fig. 21-4. Thus in Fig. 21-9, the line *DC* is drawn in the top view of plane *ABC* parallel to reference line *T-F*. The line

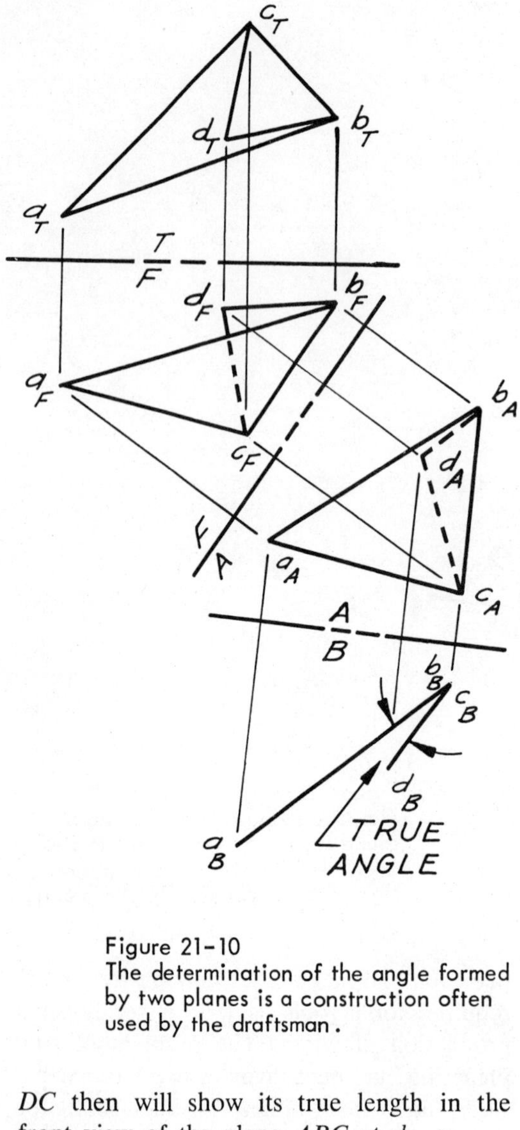

Figure 21-10
The determination of the angle formed by two planes is a construction often used by the draftsman.

DC then will show its true length in the front view of the plane *ABC* at d_F c_F.

A point view must now be constructed of line *DC* by drawing reference line *F-A* perpendicular to the true length of *DC* in the front view and projecting the distances as shown in Fig. 21.6. Likewise by projecting points *A* and *B*, the plane *ABC* now appears as an edge.

True size and shape of a plane. The edge view of the plane *ABC* as previously determined, now may be used as the basis for a second auxiliary view by drawing the reference line *A-B* parallel to the edge view of *ABC*. By projecting the proper distances of points *A*, *B* and *C*, as shown in Fig. 21-9, the true size and shape of the plane may be drawn. It is obvious that since this view is a true view, the lengths of the lines as well as the angles formed by the intersecting lines will all show their true measurements.

21.10 Finding the angle formed between two planes (dihedral angle)

The size of the angle formed by two non-parallel planes, often called the dihedral angle, is especially important in fabricating products which require bending and forming materials in sheet or plate form. To determine the angle between planes *ABC* and *BCD* in Fig. 21-10:

First obtain a view of the line of intersection *BC*, showing its true length, and then draw a view showing *BC* as a point view. By projecting the other points and lines of the two planes into these auxiliary views, the view containing *BC* as a point will provide the actual angle between the two planes.

21.11 Finding the point where a line pierces a plane

Frequently it is necessary to locate the position of an opening in a plane surface for the insertion of a piece of hydraulic tubing, or to locate a pad or member to hold a structural beam, guy wire, etc. The problem is essentially that of finding a point in a plane in which a line pierces it. The solution of such a problem may be found by the edge-view plane method or by the cutting-plane method.

The edge-view plane method. By observing a plane as an edge, the point at which a line pierces the plane can be found at the intersection of the line and the edge-view plane. Thus the edge-view of the plane *ABC* first must be shown as in Fig. 21-11 and the line *MN* drawn in this view. The point of intersection of the line and the plane is found at o_A. The piercing point is then projected back into its front and top views at o_T and o_F.

The cutting plane method. In Fig. 21-12, if a plane is passed through line *MN*, it will intersect plane *ABC* at *EF*. Line *MN* will pierce plane *ABC* at *O*, the intersection of *MN*, with the line of intersection *EF*.

This method of locating a piercing point

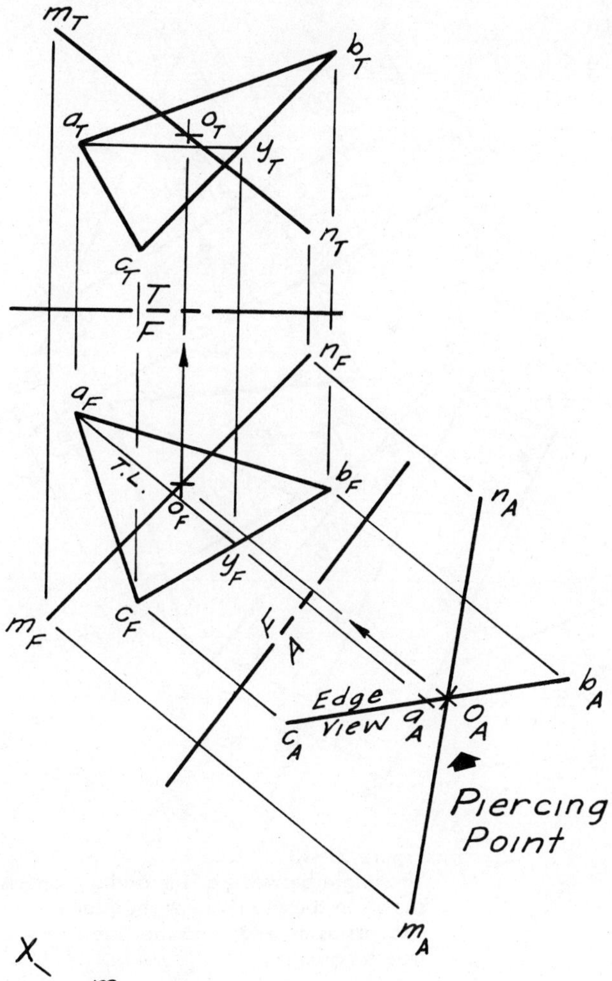

Figure 21-11
The point at which a line pierces a plane can be found in the view showing the plane as an edge view.

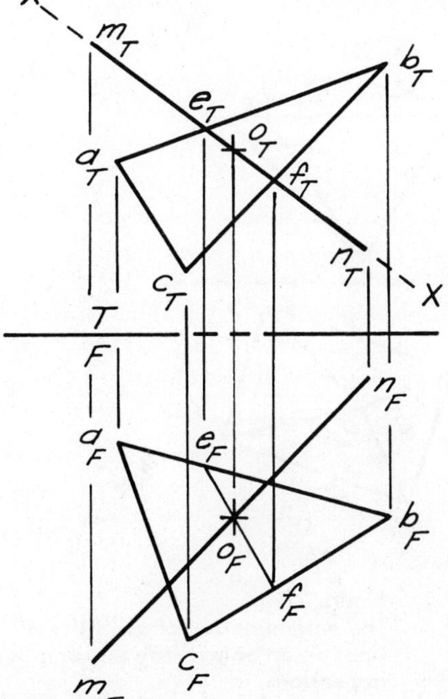

Figure 21-12
The cutting plane method for locating the point where a line pierces a plane is sometimes more convenient than the edge-view plane method.

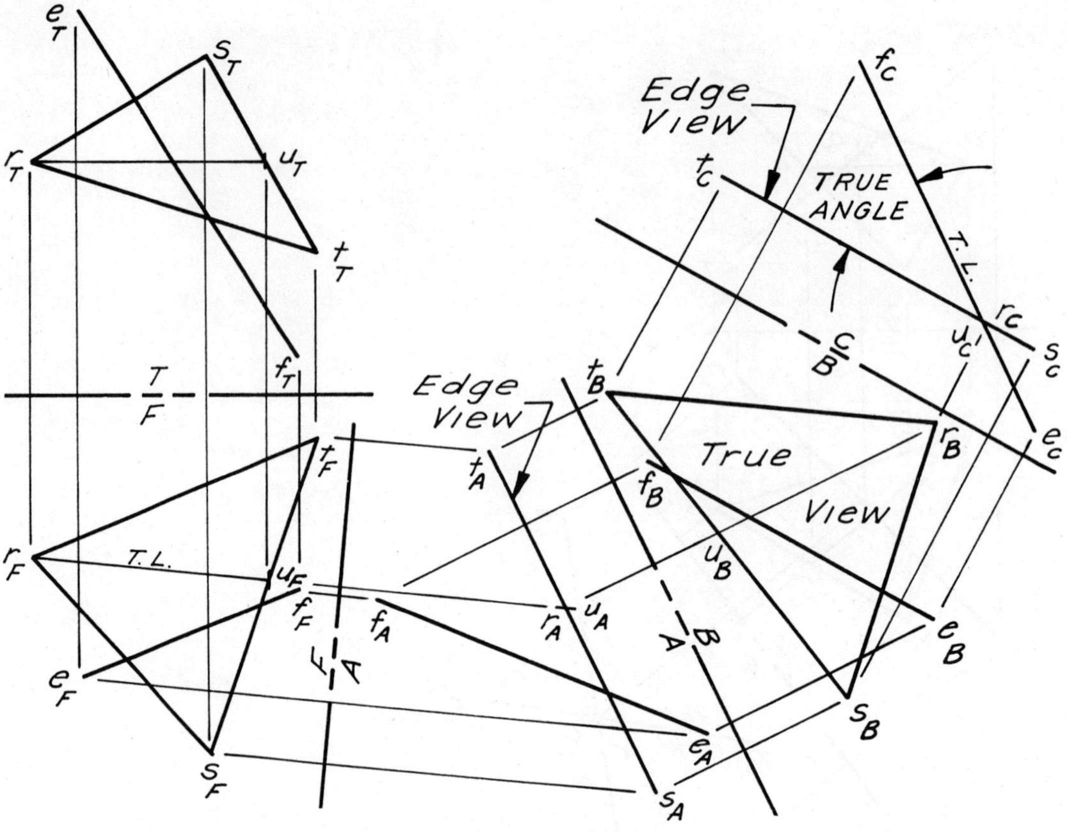

Figure 21-13
The angle between a line and a plane is shown in the view where the plane appears as an edge and the line in its true length.

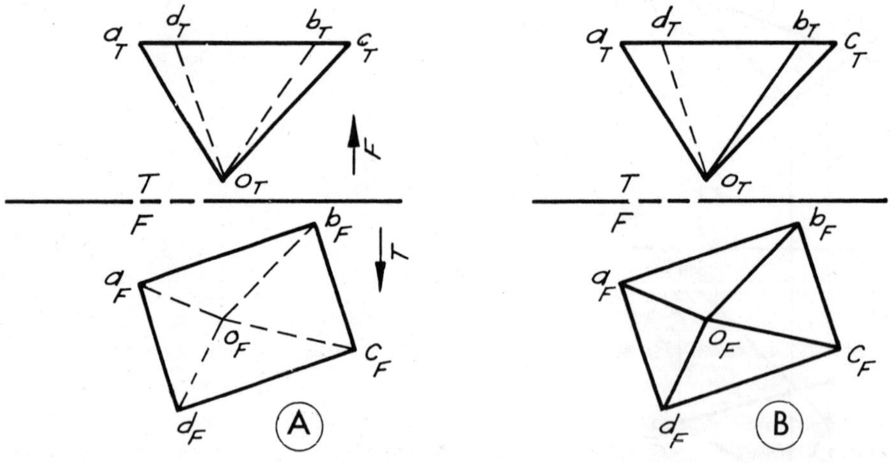

Figure 21-14
The determination of visibility of lines on an object may be done by inspection.

of a line and a plane often saves time since the existing views may be used without the addition of auxiliary views. Accuracy is also increased because transfer of distances into auxiliary views is not needed.

21.12 The angle a line makes with a plane

The true angle between a line and a plane will be shown in the view in which the plane appears as an edge and the line in its true length. Thus if the angle formed by line *EF* and plane *RST* in Fig. 21-13 is required, the procedure is:

1 Find an edge view of plane *RST* and then its true view. Carry the projections of line *EF* into these views.
2 From the true view of *RST*, project a view showing line *EF* in its true length. This view will show plane *RST* again as an edge-view. The angle formed by the true length of *EF* and the edge-view of *RST* is the required angle.

It might be noted that had *RST* been shown as an edge-view in one of the given views, only two supplementary views would have been required for the solution.

21.13 Visibility of lines and surfaces

As it has previously been discussed in Section 5, the determination of visibility of lines and surfaces is a matter of extreme importance in the delineation of engineering drawings. While the outline of a view will always be visible, lines within this outline may be visible or hidden, depending upon their relative positions with respect to the observer's line of sight.

Whether or not a line is visible in a view often may be ascertained by inspection. In *A* of Fig. 21-14, it is obvious that the outline in each view is visible. However, the visibility of the dash lines on the object is determined by the position of point *O*.

In the top view, the point *O* is shown nearest the reference line *T-F*. Since the direction of sight for the front view is in the direction of arrow *F*, it becomes evident that all lines emanating from *O* are visible for this view. See *B* of Fig. 21-14. Similarly, in the top view, by viewing the object in the direction of arrow T, it can be seen that lines *OA* and *OB*, being closest to the observer, must be visible. By the same token, since point *D* is farthest from the observer, line *OD* becomes invisible or hidden.

Thus it might be stated that: (1) the corner or edge of an object nearest the observer will be visible, and (2) the corner or edge farthest from the observer will usually be hidden if it lies inside the outline of the view.

In many views, crossing edges are often located at approximately the same distance from the viewer. The visibility of lines formed by these edges must be determined independently for each view by testing the visibility of the point where the lines cross. See Fig. 21-15.

For example, to determine the visibility of lines *AC* and *BD*, in *A* of Fig. 21-15, the apparent crossing point of $a_T c_T$ and $b_T d_T$ is labeled 1 and 2. These points are then located on the lines in the front view; that is, 1 on $a_F c_F$ and 2 on $b_F d_F$. Since point 1 on $a_F c_F$ is higher and, therefore, nearer the observer, line *AC* in the top view must be visible. See *B* of Fig. 21-15. Likewise, in the front view of *A* of Fig. 21-15, the apparent intersection of *AC* and *BD* is labeled points 3 and 4. By projecting 3 to line $b_T d_T$ and 4 to line $a_T c_T$, point 4 on $a_T c_T$ is nearer the observer and is visible in the front view $a_F c_F$.

The above described procedure must be used in finding the visibility of nonintersecting linear objects such as rods, pipes, wires, etc. In Fig. 21-16, two nonintersecting pipes are shown. Since they do not intersect, it is obvious that one of the pipes must be above the other at the apparent point of crossing in the top view. Likewise, in the front view, one of the pipes must be in front of the other at a similar point of crossing.

If, at the apparent point of crossing in the top view, points 1 and 2 are given, then by projecting these two points to the separate pipes in the front view it is found that the pipe *AB* is above *CD* at that location. This is shown in *B* of Fig. 21-16. By the same method the apparent point of crossing

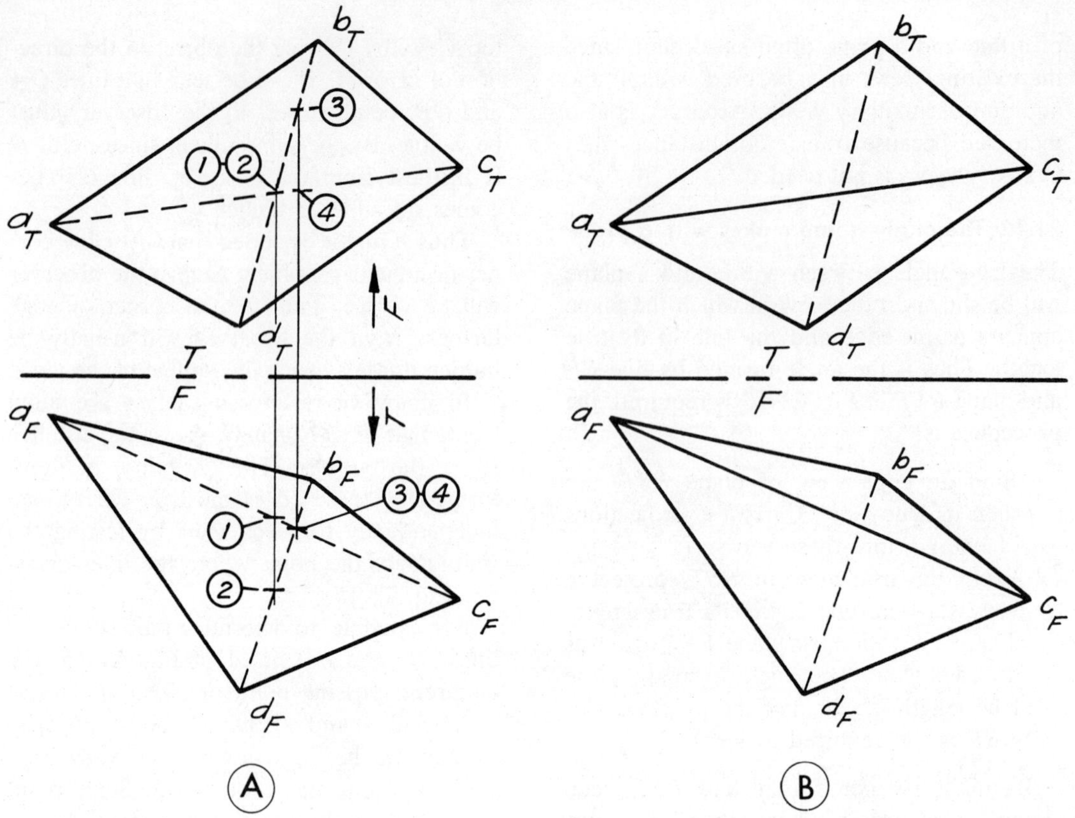

Figure 21-15
The visibility of crossing lines must be determined by testing the visibility of the crossing point.

in the front view is labeled 3 and 4 in *A* of Fig. 21-16 and these points projected to the pipes in the top view. Point 4 on $a_T b_T$ lies in front of point 3 on $c_T d_T$ and therefore the pipe *AB* is visible in the front view.

While this discussion dealt with front and top views only, the same procedure may be used for any other two adjacent views, since by rotating the drawing, the views can be oriented to the position of front and top views. It must be remembered that in such cases, visibility must be determined independently for each view.

21.14 Revolution

While the principal views of an object ordinarily represent the object satisfactorily in a fixed position, it is often necessary to revolve an object or its elements for purposes of measurement and true shape description.

If an object is drawn in an oblique position, that is, revolved about an axis which is perpendicular to a principal plane of projection, it is referred to as *simple revolution.* Three types are involved:

1 Revolution about a horizontal axis perpendicular to a frontal plane.

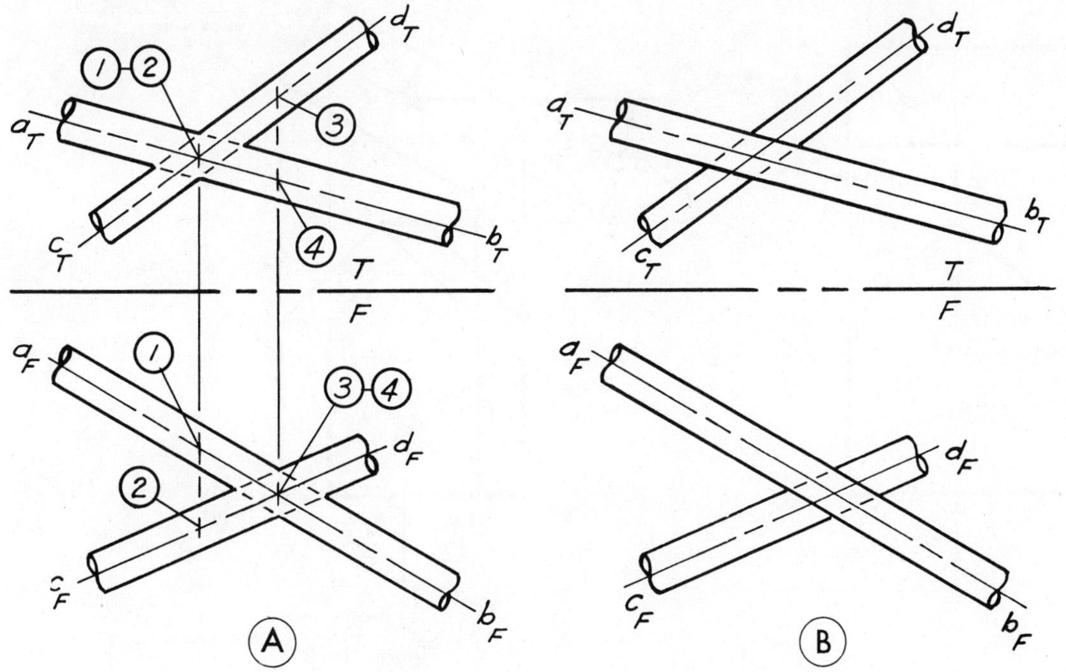

Figure 21–16
The visibility of nonintersecting linear objects must be determined by the use of the apparent point of crossing.

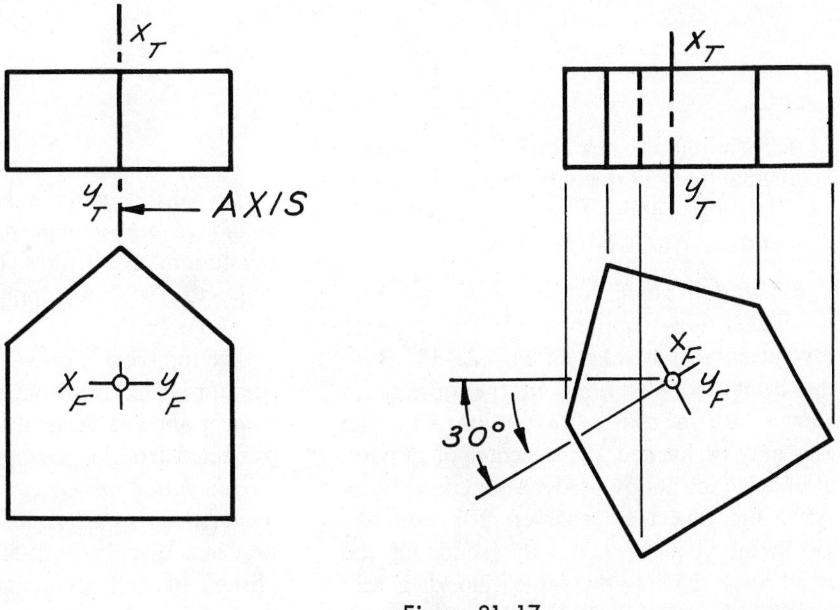

Figure 21–17
By revolving an object about a horizontal axis perpendicular to a frontal plane, the front view changes position while the top view is changed in both size and shape.

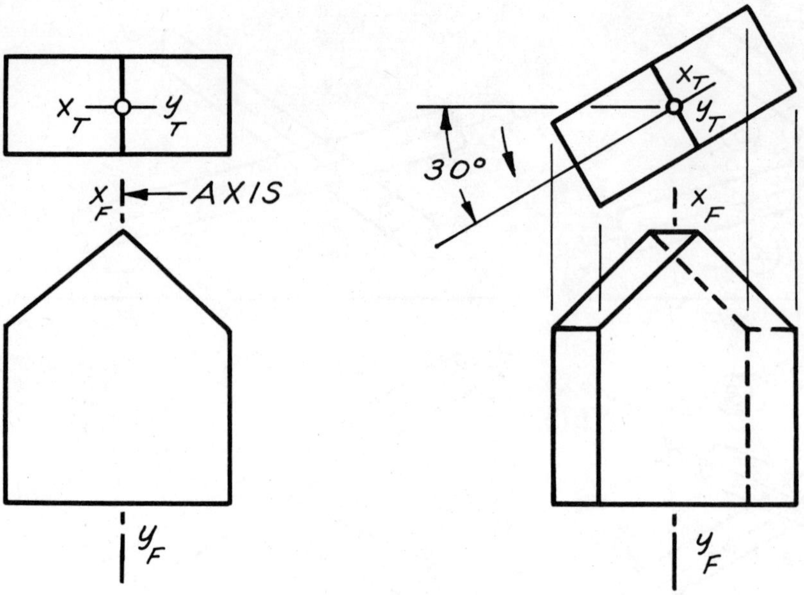

Figure 21-18
When an object is revolved about a vertical axis perpendicular to a horizontal plane, both the size and shape of the front view are changed while only the position of the top view is altered.

2 Revolution about a vertical axis perpendicular to a horizontal plane.
3 Revolution about a horizontal axis perpendicular to a profile plane.

Revolution about a horizontal axis perpendicular to a frontal plane. This type of revolution is illustrated in Fig. 21-17. Both the front and top views of the object are shown with the axis of revolution XY. The axis may be located at the center of gravity, at an edge, or at any predetermined position. After the object is revolved 30° counterclockwise about its axis, the shape of the front view remains the same since it is still parallel to the frontal plane. The top view, however, is elongated but maintains the same thickness. The top view in this position is merely projected from the front view by regular projection methods.

Revolution about a vertical axis perpendicular to a horizontal plane. In this type of revolution the front view changes shape while the top view only changes position. See Fig. 21-18.

The top view is drawn first in the revolved position. The front view is then projected from it and the vertical heights measured or projected from a principal front view.

Revolution about a horizontal axis perpendicular to the profile plane. This revolution is shown in Fig. 21-19, and is accomplished by first revolving the side view into its new position and projecting the top and front views from it. Notice that both the front and top views change in size as well as shape, whereas in the side view only the position changes.

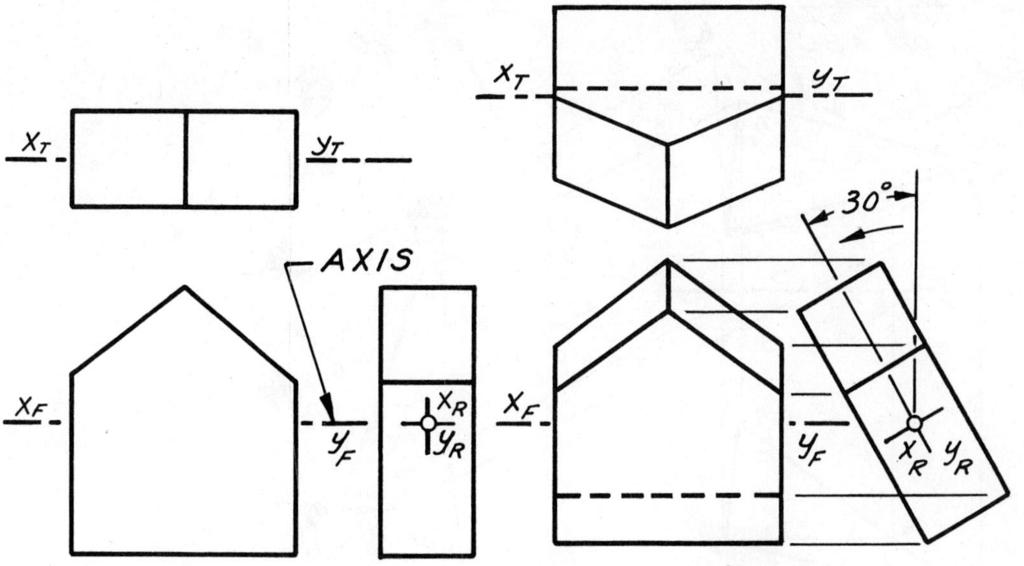

Figure 21-19
When an object is revolved about an axis perpendicular to a profile plane, the side view changes position while the top and front views are altered both in size and shape.

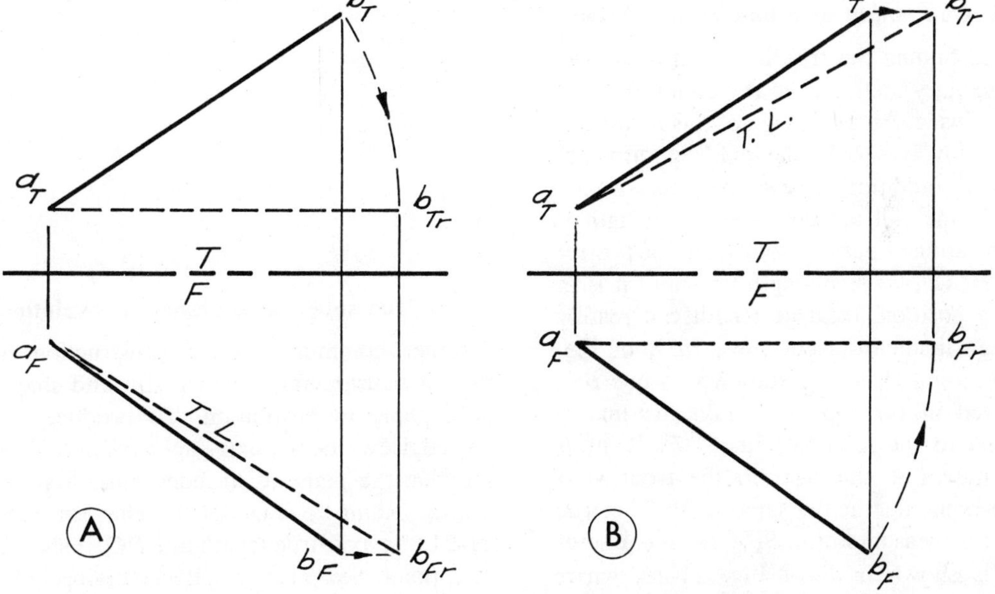

Figure 21-20
The true length of a line may be found by revolving either a top view or a front view.

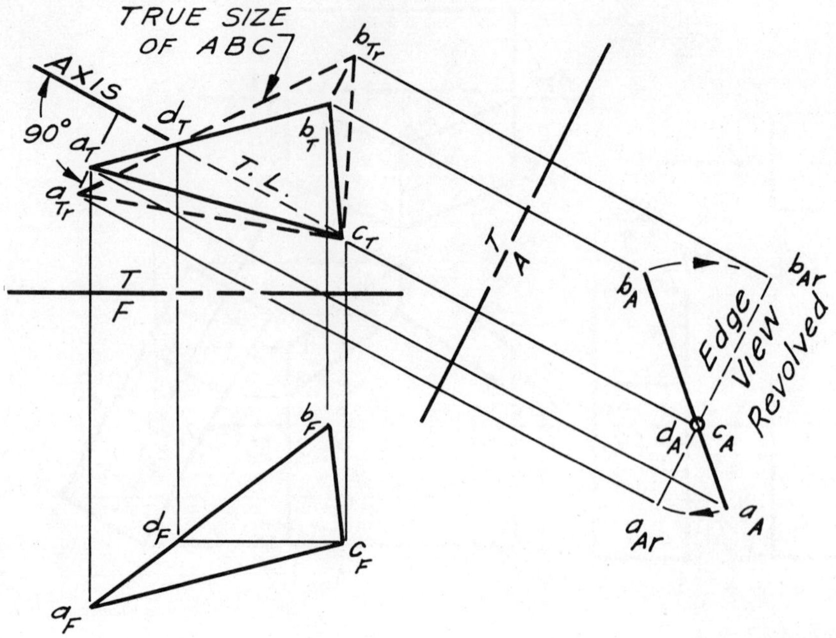

Figure 21-21
The true shape of a plane may be found by revolving the edge view of the plane until it is parallel to the reference line, and projecting the revolved points into the adjacent view.

21.15 True length of a line by revolution

Besides finding the true length of a line by the auxiliary method, the revolution method is often used. An advantage of this method is that it involves only the existing principal views; no additional views are necessary.

Any line will appear in its true length if it is positioned parallel to a plane of projection. Hence, by revolving a line until it is in such a position, the true length can readily be seen in the adjacent view. In *A* of Fig. 21-20, point *A* is kept stationary while *B* is revolved in the top view until the line is parallel to the reference line *T-F*. Point *B* thus moves to the right in the front view while remaining at the same level. The true length is measured at $a_F b_{Fr}$. A similar solution is shown in *B* of Fig. 21-20, where the line is revolved in the front view, using a_F as the axis, until it is parallel to reference line *T-F*. The true length of *AB* is now shown in the revolved position $a_T b_{Tr}$.

21.16 True shape of a plane by revolution

Another common drafting construction is that of determining the true size and shape of a plane by revolution. To produce revolved views of a plane, an auxiliary view showing the plane as an edge must first be drawn. Refer to Fig. 21-9. Thus in Fig. 21-21, the axis, true length line *DC*, is shown as a point view at $d_A c_A$. By revolving both ends of $a_A b_A$ so that it is parallel to reference line *T-A*, the true shape can be drawn by simply projecting the revolved points to the top view.

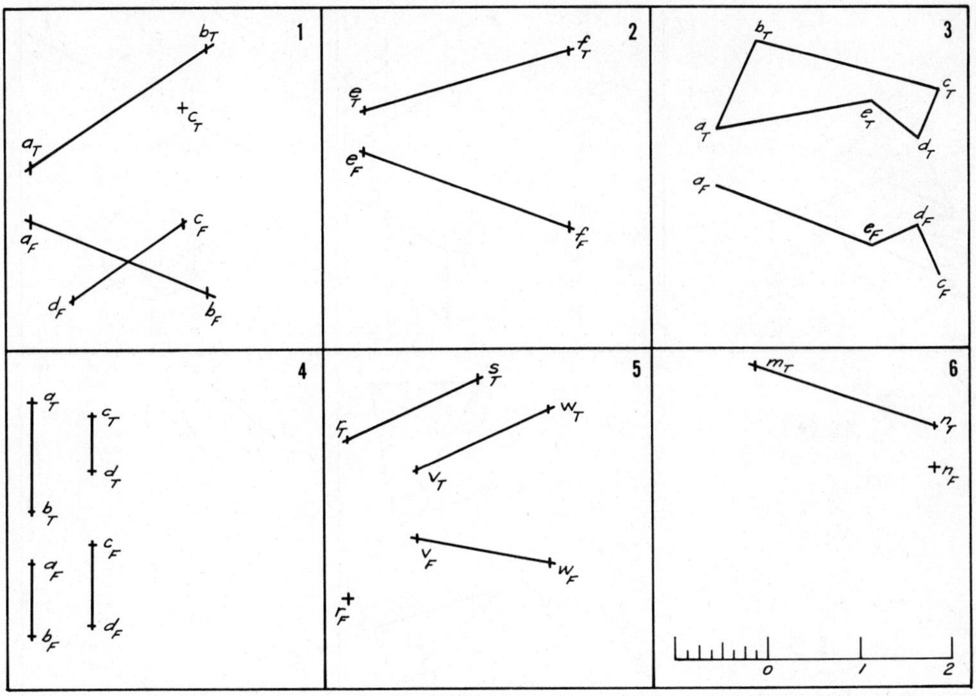

Figure 21-22
Group I.

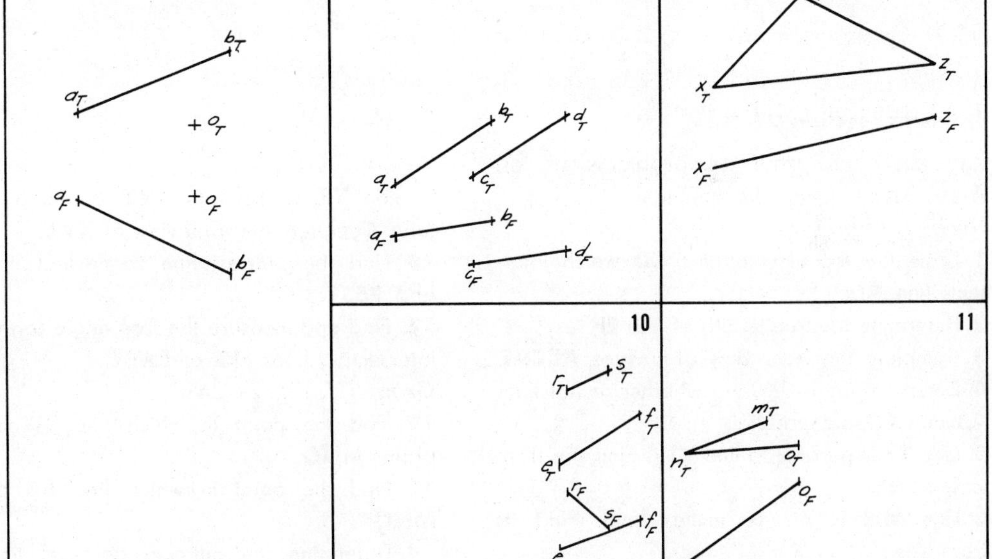

Figure 21-23
Group II.

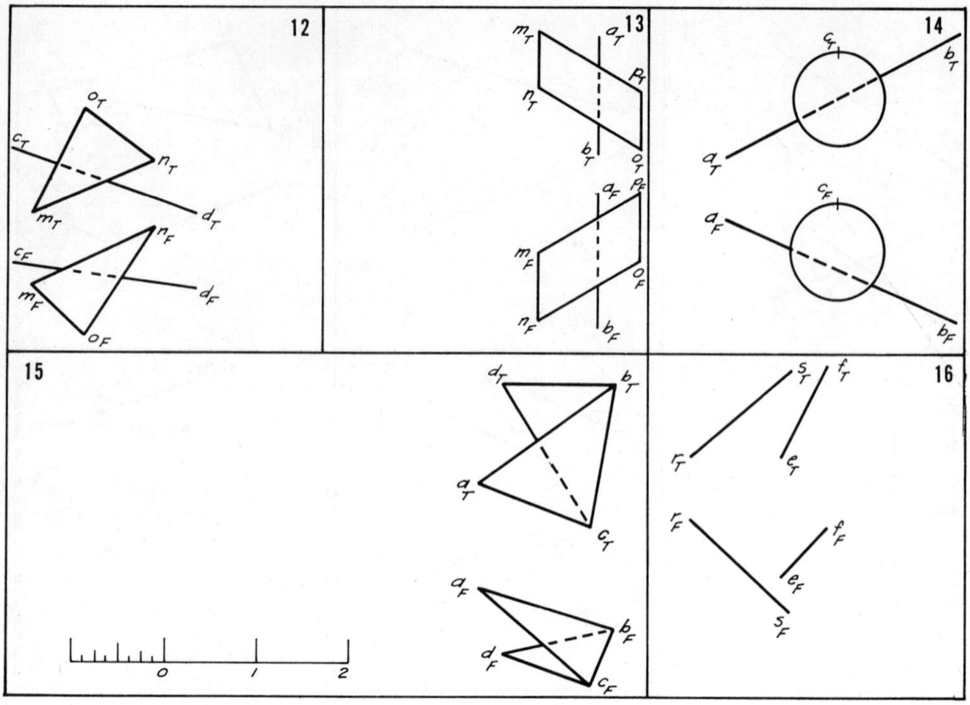

Figure 21-24
Group III.

Problems, section 21

Lay out each group of problems on an A-size sheet, using the scales shown.

Group I, Fig. 21-22.

1 Draw the top view of line **CD** which intersects line **AB.**

2 Determine the true length of line **EF.**

3 Complete the front view of surface **ABCDE.**

4 Determine by a drawing whether or not lines **AB** and **CD** are parallel.

5 Line **RS** is parallel to line **VW.** Find the front view of **RS.**

6 Line **MN** is 2-7/16 inches long. Find its front view.

Group II, Fig. 21-23.

7 Determine the shortest distance from point **O** to line **AB.**

8 Determine the shortest distance between lines **AB** and **CD.**

9 Side **YZ** of triangle **XYZ** is 2-3/8 inches long. Complete the front view of **XYZ.**

10 Find the shortest line connecting lines **EF** and **RS.**

11 Find and measure the true angle formed by intersecting lines **NO** and **MN.**

Group III, Fig. 21-24.

12 Find the point in which line **CD** pierces plane **MNO.**

13 Find the point in which line **AB** pierces **MNOP.**

14 Determine the piercing point of line **AB** and the elliptical surface.

15 Find and measure the true angle formed by the intersecting planes **ABC** and **BCD.**

16 What is the shortest distance between lines **EF** and **RS?**

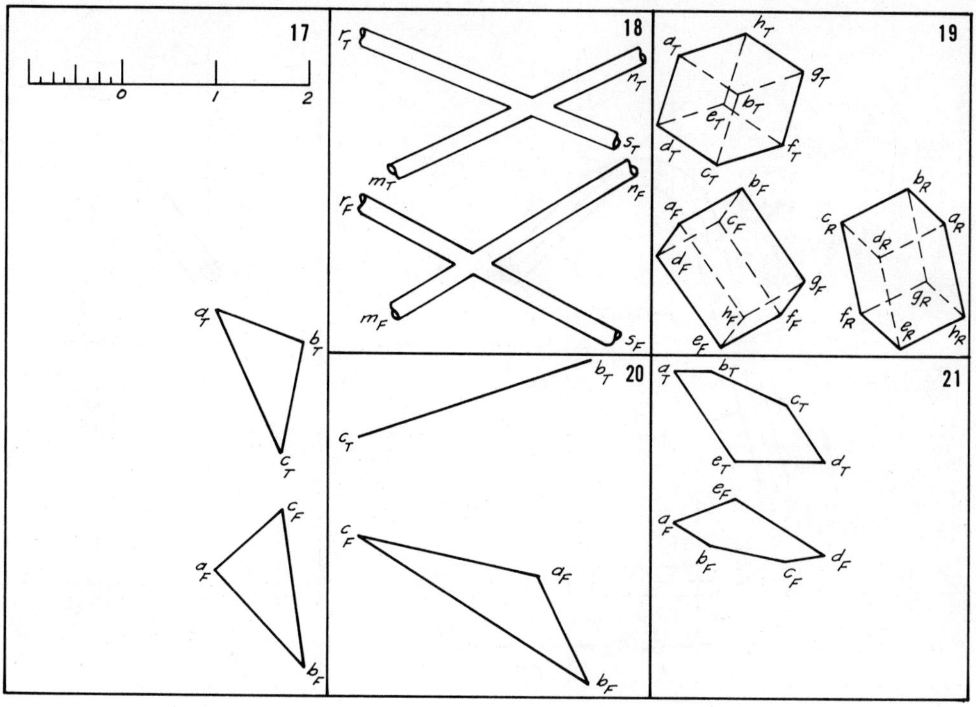

Figure 21-25
Group IV.

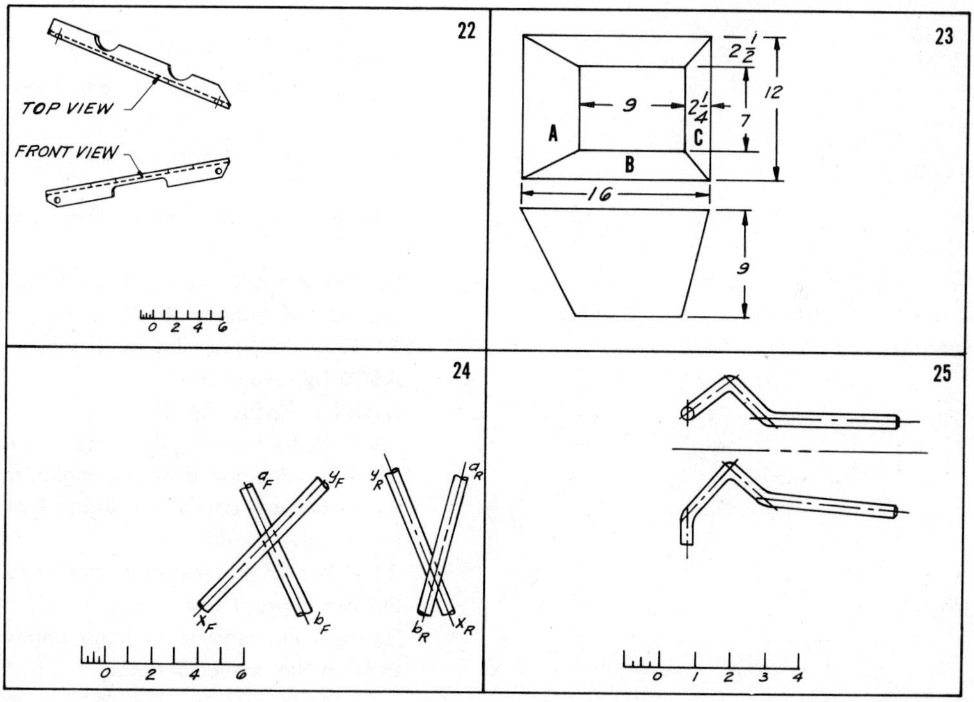

Figure 21-26
Group V.

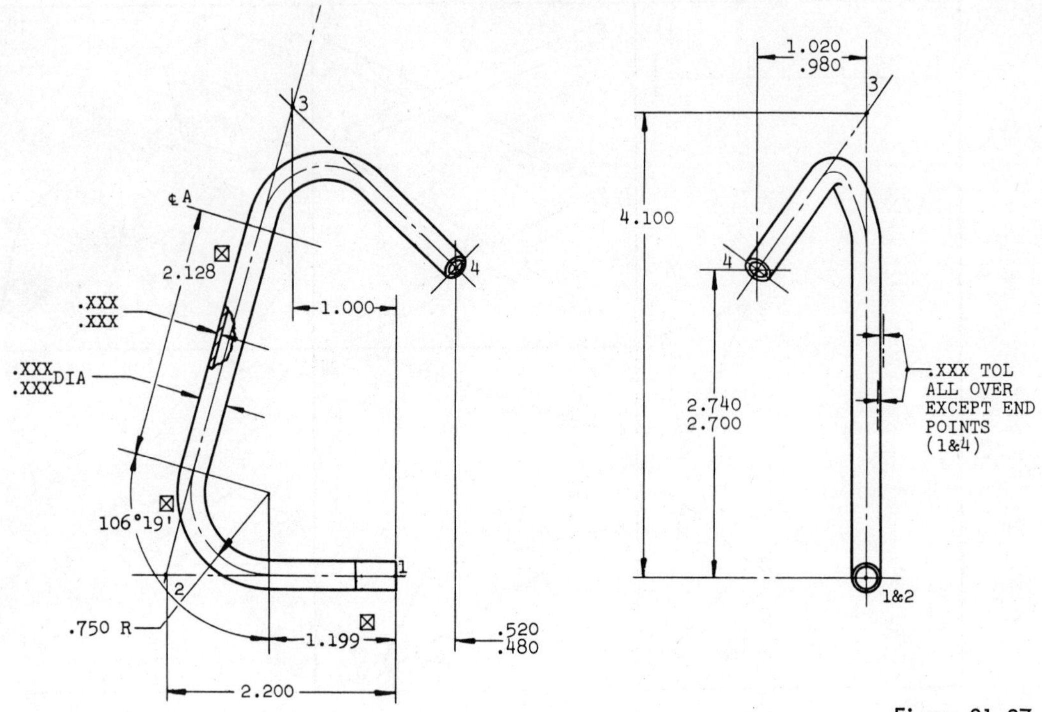

Figure 21-27
Tubular member.

Group IV, Fig. 21-25.

17 Determine the true size and shape of plane **ABC**.

18 Complete the views of the two rods, showing visibility.

19 Determine visibility of the edges of the block.

20 Line **AB** is 2-1/8 inches long. Complete the top view of triangle **ABC**. Solve by revolution.

21 Find the true size and shape of plane **ABCD** by revolution.

GROUP V, Fig. 21-26.

22 Find the true length of the retainer.

23 Determine the dihedral angles formed between plates **A** and **B**, and **B** and **C** of the chute illustrated.

24 What is the minimum clearance between the two support rods?

25 Find the amount of bend angle for each bend in the connector rod.

26 Find the bend angle at point 3 of the tubular member shown in Fig. 21-27.

Developments and intersections 22

The material in this section deals with a study of two phases of engineering drafting which are commonly referred to as developments and intersections. Developments involve the construction of full-size layouts of different shaped surfaces. Intersections are concerned with the location of lines of intersection between various geometrically shaped objects such as cylinders, cones, and prisms. Application of developments and intersections may be found in fabricating sheetmetal and plate structures, pattern making, paper and plastic work and in numerous other types of industrial processes.

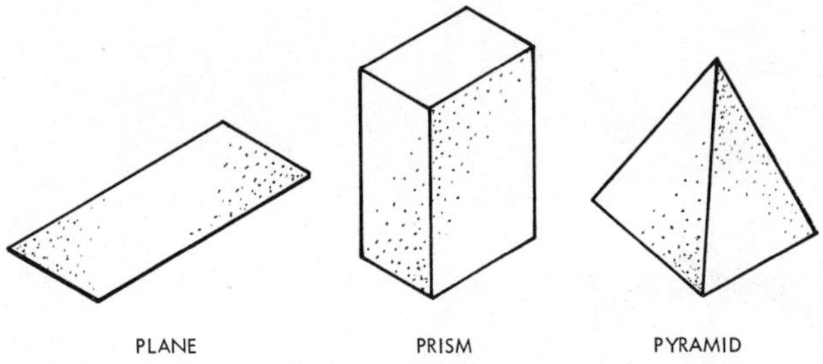

Figure 22-1
Examples of plane-surfaced figures.

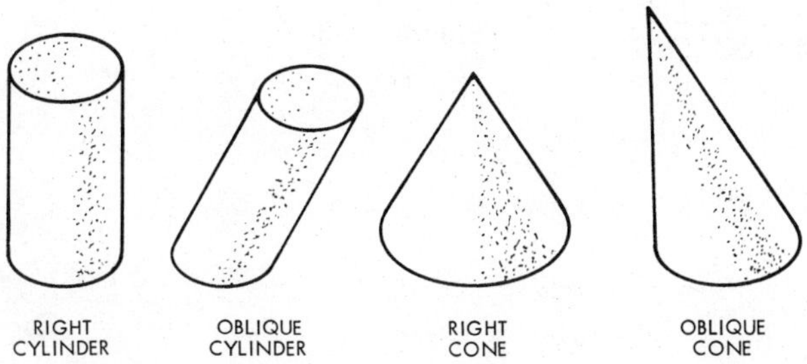

Figure 22-2
Examples of single-curved surfaces.

22.1 Classification of surfaces

A surface is a geometric form generated by a straight or curved line. The two main groups of surfaces are known as ruled and double-curved surfaces.

Ruled surfaces. A ruled surface is one which has straight line elements. Such a surface may be classified as a plane, single-curved surface, and a warped surface. A plane is a surface generated by a straight line moving in such a manner that one point on the line touches another straight line as the generating line moves parallel to its original position. See Fig. 22-1. A single curved surface is one which is generated by moving a straight line in contact with a curved line so that any two consecutive positions of the generating line either intersect or are parallel. See Fig. 22-2. A warped surface is one in which no two consecutive elements are in the same plane. See Fig. 22-3.

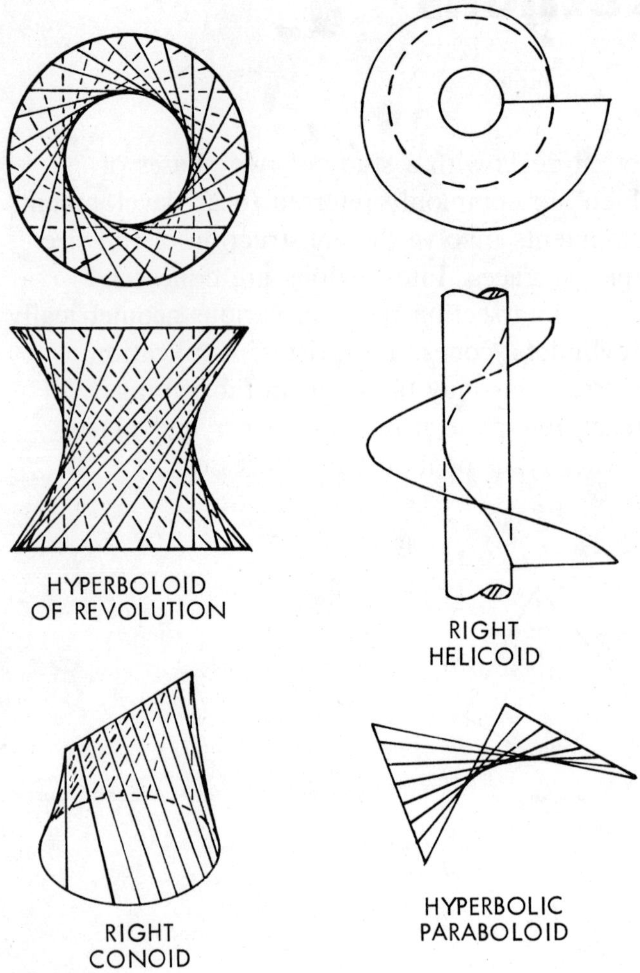

Figure 22-3
Examples of warped surfaces.

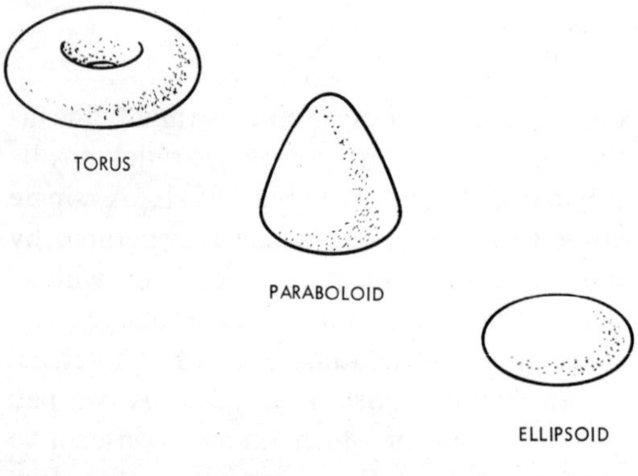

Figure 22-4
Examples of double-curved surfaces.

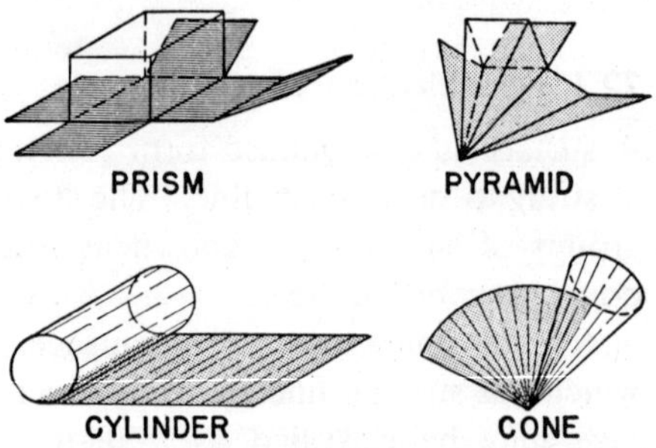

Figure 22-5
Development refers to the unfolding of the surfaces of an object.

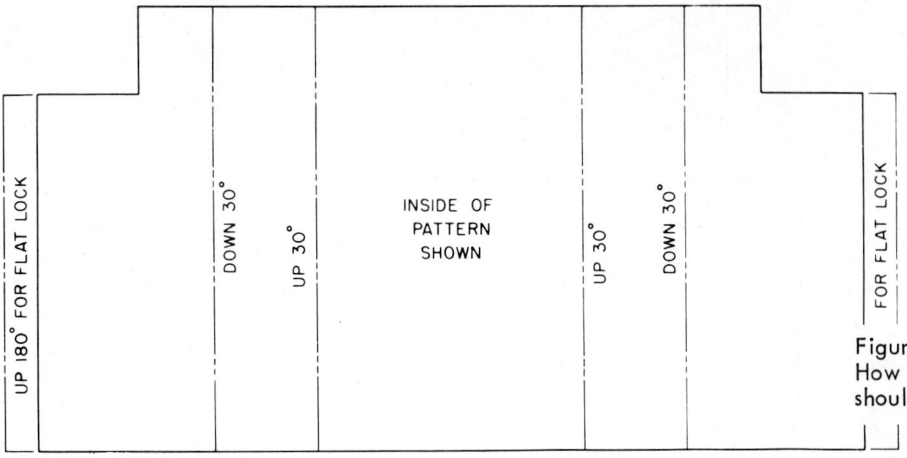

Figure 22-6
How a development should be specified.

Double-curved surfaces. A double curved surface is a surface which is formed only by a moving curved line. Examples of such surfaces are: sphere, torus, ellipsoid, etc. See Fig. 22-4.

22.2 Developments

A surface which can be rolled out or unfolded without distortion is said to be developable. Any object composed of single-curved surfaces is developable. See Fig. 22-5. Warped and double-curved surfaces are non-developable because consecutive elements cannot be brought into a flat plane without distortion. These surfaces can be developed only by approximation, which is obtained by means of triangulation.

22.3 Patterns

A pattern is a flat outline or stretchout of a developed surface. The pattern is usually prepared with drawing instruments on paper and the stretchout then transferred to the required material.

When a pattern is used repeatedly, it is generally made of metal. This type of metal pattern is often referred to as a template or master pattern.

Developed views for use as a pattern or template must be drawn with accuracy consistent with the function of the part. The development should be plainly marked "Development of____," "Pattern for____," or "Template for____." See Fig. 22-6. If elements of the surface are shown, they should be drawn as phantom lines. Bends should be clearly indicated and the angle of bend specified as the angle turned up or down from the flat. Metal for seams should be shown with a phantom line and the seam positions clearly marked.[1]

22.4 Methods of surface development

The three methods used to develop surfaces are known as parallel line, radial line and triangulation. The parallel line method is used to develop patterns for prisms and cylinders. The radial line method is used to develop surfaces of regular tapering forms, such as cones and pyramids. The triangulation method is used to develop warped and double-curved surfaces which are considered non-developable.

22.5 Development of a truncated rectangular pipe

1 Draw elevation and plan views of the required pipe as shown in Fig. 22-7.
2 Draw the stretchout line *KL* at the same level as *XY* of the elevation view. On this line lay off the perimeter distances *EF, FH, HG* and *GE,* taken from the plan view, and construct perpendicular elements representing the edges to be folded at points 1, 2, 3, and 4.
3 Project a dotted line from *C* on the elevation view to intersect elements 1, 4 and 1. Project a dotted line from *D* intersecting elements 2 and 3.

1. Extracted from *Projections ASA Y14.3-1957* (New York: The American Society of Mechanical Engineers, 1957).

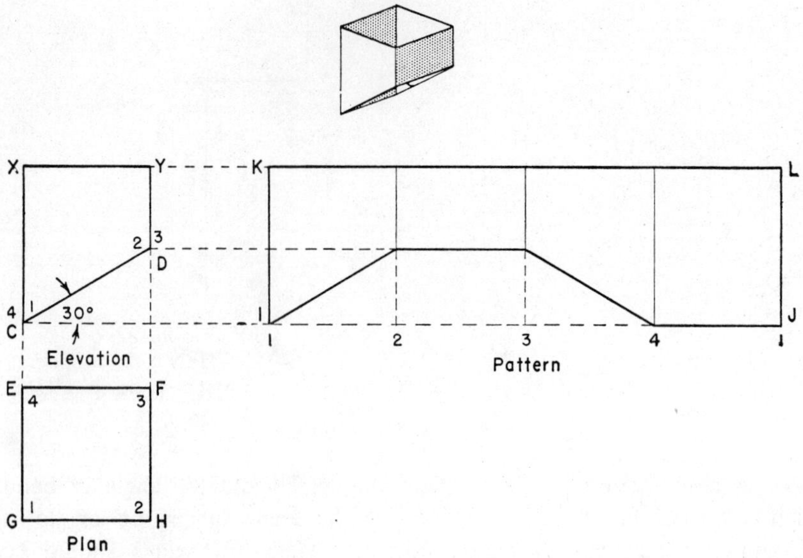

Figure 22-7
How to develop a pattern for a truncated rectangular pipe.

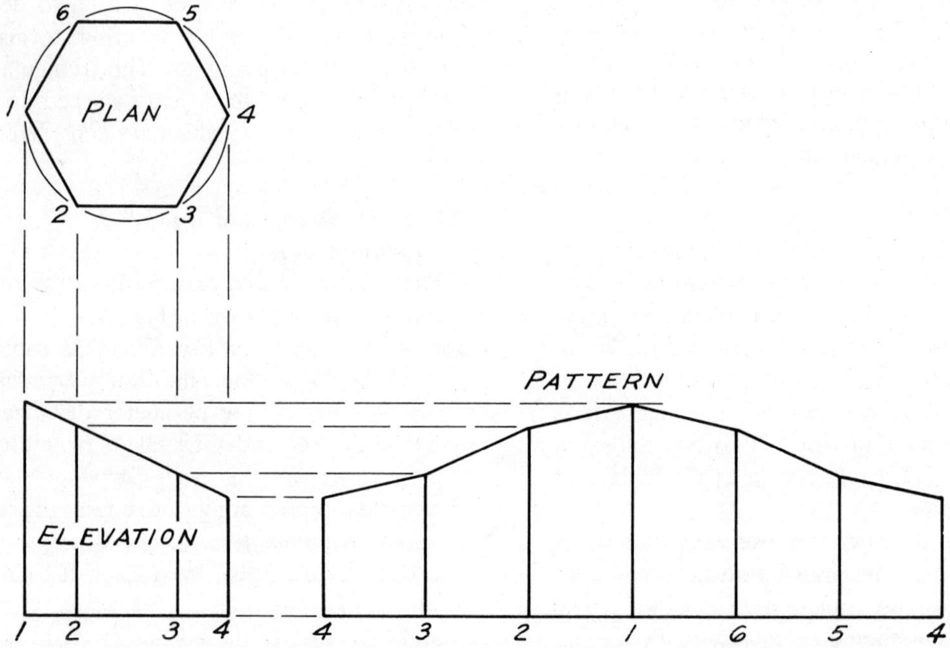

Figure 22-8
How to develop a pattern for a truncated hexagonal pipe.

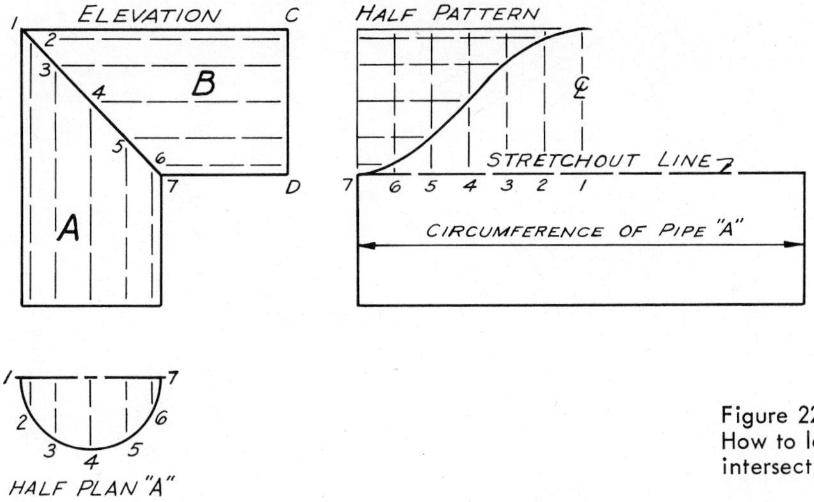

Figure 22-9
How to lay out a pattern for two intersecting pipes at an angle.

4 Connect these points with straight lines, completing the pattern.

22.6 Development of a truncated hexagonal pipe

Draw an elevation and plan view of the hexagonal pipe as shown in Fig. 22-8. On the stretchout line, lay out the six lateral edges, 1-2, 2-3, 3-4, etc., taken from the plan view. From these points draw perpendicular elements equal to the corresponding edges of the view. Connect the ends of these elements, thus completing the development.

22.7 Intersection and development of two circular pipes at an angle

Draw an elevation of pipes *A* and *B* with a 45° miter line. See Fig. 22-9. Draw a half plan view of pipe *A* and divide it into any number of equal parts. Number these spaces as shown. Project the points from the plan view to the miter line on the elevation and across pipe *B* to line *CD*.

Draw the stretchout line equal to the circumference of pipe *A*, and on it, working to the left of the centerline, lay out the points to correspond with the numbered points on the half plan *A*. Project the points from the mitered line in the elevation view to the corresponding vertical elements on the stretchout. The intersections of these lines form the points for the contour of the pattern.

Since pipe *B* is similar to pipe *A*, the pattern for both pipes will be identical.

22.8 Development of a circular pipe intersecting a flat surface.

Draw an elevation view of pipe *E* with line *BC* representing the diameter of the pipe and the mitered line *DF* having the desired angle for the plane of intersection. See Fig. 22-10. Using *BC* as a diameter, draw a semicircle and divide it into any number of equal parts. Project these points to the mitered line *DF*.

Draw the stretchout line for the pipe equal to one-half the circumference, and on it lay out the spaces from the plan view *E*. Project the points from the mitered line *DF* to the corresponding elements on the stretchout. The intersection of these lines will provide the contour of the half pattern for the pipe.

To find the opening in the flat plane *A*, lay out the desired length and width of the plane. Draw a semicircle above the flat plane to represent the plan view of the intersecting pipe and divide it into the same number of equal spaces as in the plan view of pipe *E*. The intersections of lines drawn from these points with the projections from corresponding points on the mitered line *DF* will provide the contour of the opening.

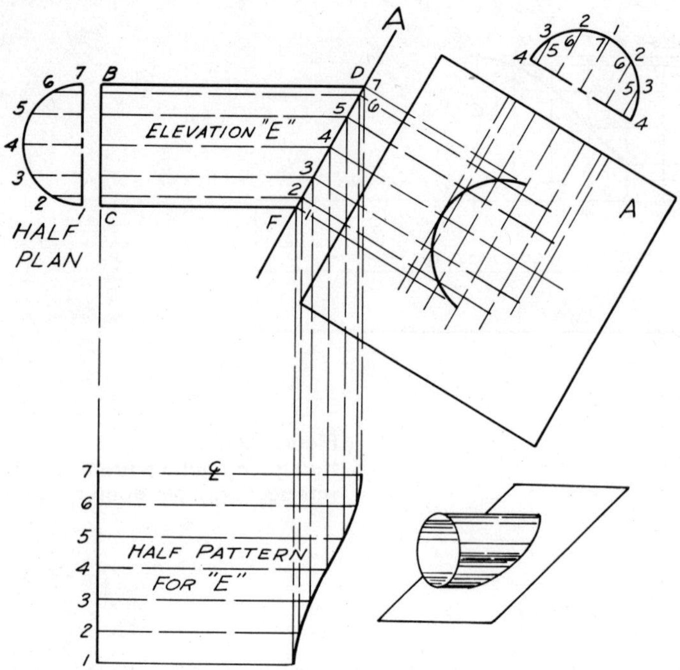

Figure 22-10
How to develop patterns for a circular pipe intersecting a plane surface.

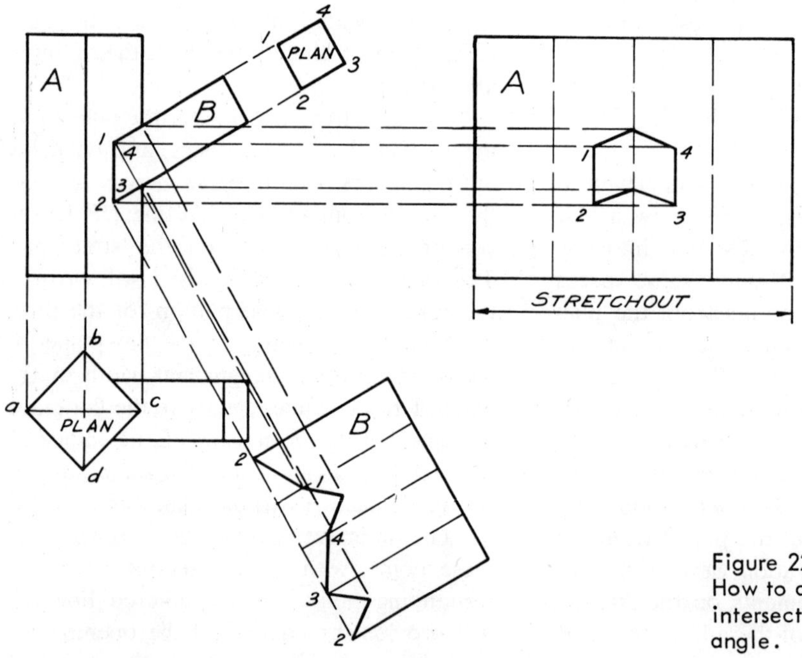

Figure 22-11
How to develop a pattern of two intersecting square pipes at an angle.

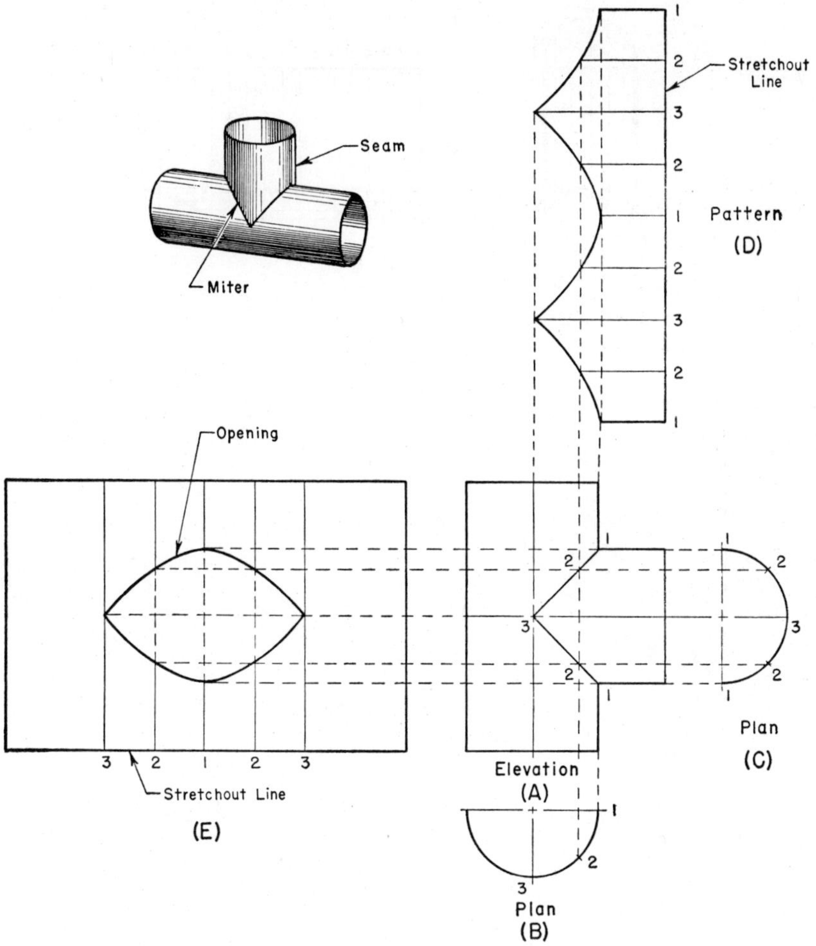

Figure 22-12
How to develop patterns for a 90° T-joint with like diameters.

22.9 Intersection and development of two square pipes at an angle

Draw an elevation and plan view of the two intersecting square pipes as shown in Fig. 22-11. Lay out the pattern for the vertical pipe *A* and locate the opening 1-2-3-4 by projecting the intersecting points of the two pipes in the elevation.

Draw the stretchout for the slanted pipe *B* and project the intersecting points of the two pipes from the elevation view.

22.10 Development of patterns for a 90° T-joint with like diameters

Draw an elevation view of two pipes as shown in Fig. 22-12, one at right angles to the other.

At one end of each pipe draw semicircles *B* and *C,* and divide each into any number of equal parts, numbering the division points as shown. Project lines through the numbered division points to both cylinders and mark their points of intersection to form the mitered lines.

Draw the stretchout line for pattern *D,* and on it lay off the divisions spaced on the semicircle of cylinder *C*. Draw lines through these points. From the points where the corresponding elements of each pipe intersect, project lines to intersect the elements on the

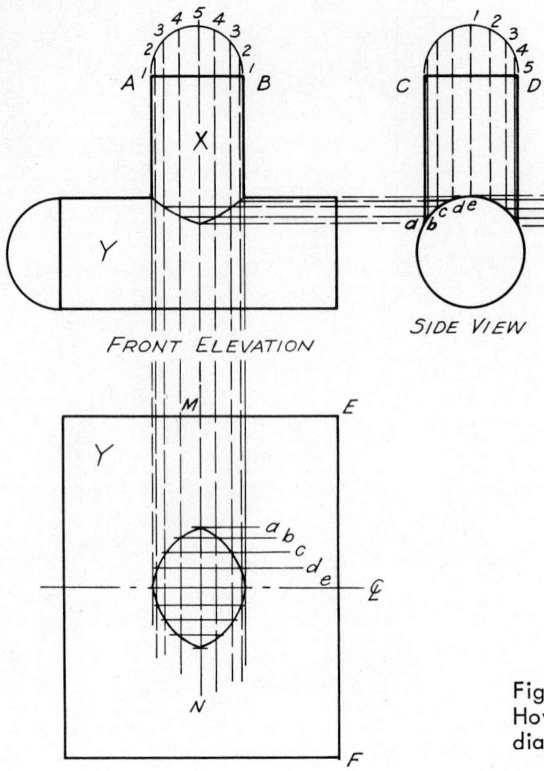

Figure 22-13
How to develop patterns for a 90° T-joint of unlike diameters.

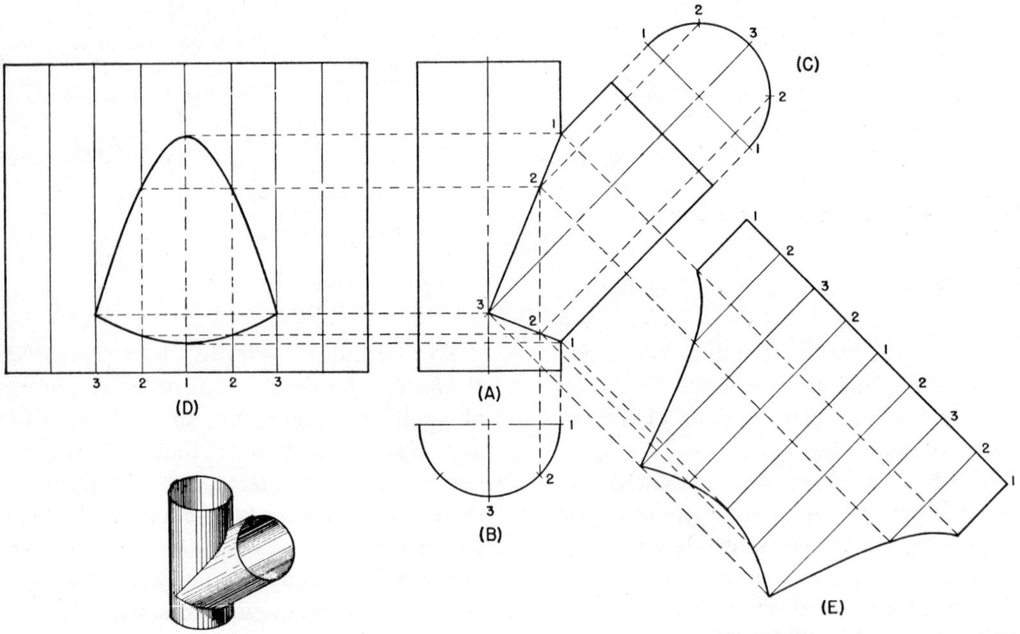

Figure 22-14
How to develop patterns for an angle intersection of cylinders of like diameters.

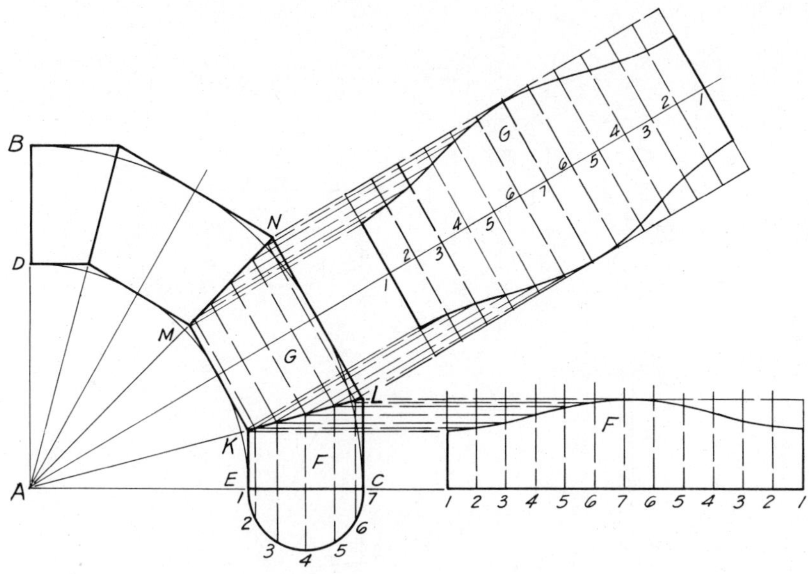

Figure 22-15
How to develop patterns for a four-piece elbow.

stretchout. Connect the intersections on the stretchout thus located with an irregular curve to complete pattern *D*.

Draw the stretchout line *E* for pipe *B* by laying out the true length of the circumference of that cylinder and locate the element spacings from plan *B*. Then draw lines through these division points. Project lines from the semicircle of plan view *C* until they intersect the corresponding elements of the stretchout. Connect the intersection points with an irregular curve.

22.11 Development of patterns for a 90° T-joint with unlike diameters

Draw an elevation view of pipes *X* and *Y* of the desired diameters. On line *AB* scribe a semicircle and divide it into any number of equal parts. See Fig. 22-13. Since the cylinders have unlike diameters, draw also a side view of the intersecting cylinders. Turn this view of the cylinders around to bring the point numbered 1 on the semicircle to show in the center position.

Draw line *A′B′* for the stretchout and lay out the divisions, numbering them as shown in Fig. 22-13. The true outline of the intersection is then found by projecting lines from the side view of cylinder *X* to the corresponding elements on the stretchout.

To find the opening of cylinder *Y*, lay out *EF* to represent the true circumference of cylinder *Y*. Project the elements of cylinder *X* to this plane. Starting at the centerline on the stretchout plane, lay off distances *ed, dc, cb, ba,* taken along the arc of the side view, on the corresponding projected elements from pipe X. The intersection of these points will produce the correct opening for the intersecting pipe.

22.12 Development of pipes of like diameters intersecting at an angle.

The method for laying out an angle intersection of two cylinders is similar to that for laying out an intersection of cylinders of like diameters. Any desired angle may be used. Details for making the stretchouts for the two cylinders are shown in Fig. 22-14. The only point that needs to be observed is to see that the centerline of cylinder *A* intersects the centerline of cylinder *C*.

22.13 Development of a four-piece elbow

Draw arcs *BC* and *DE*. See Fig. 22-15. Divide arc *BC* into three equal parts and

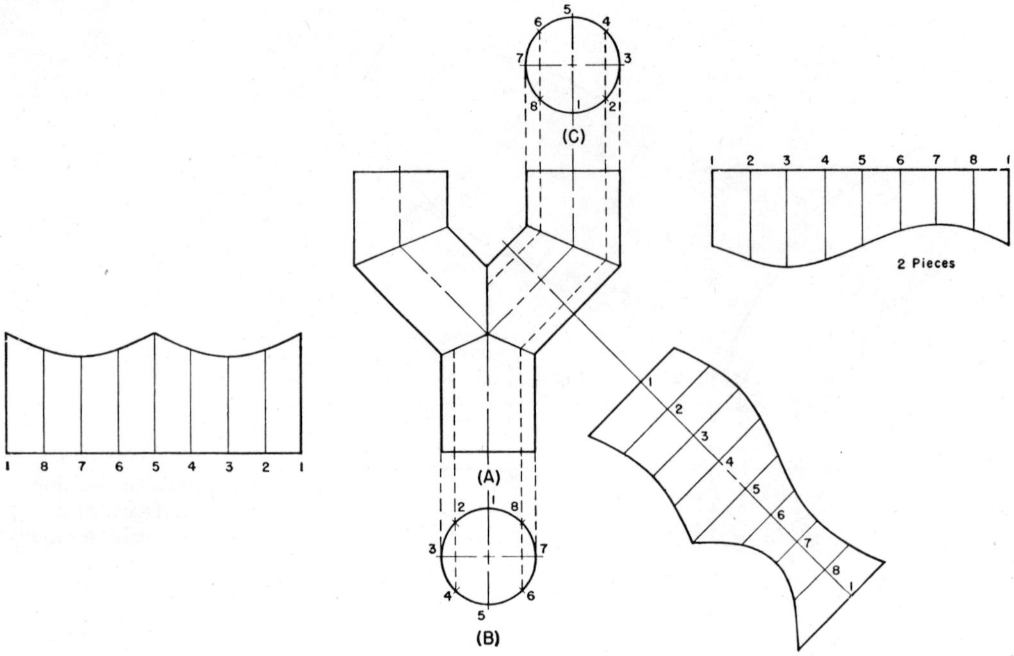

Figure 22-16
How to develop patterns for twin elbows.

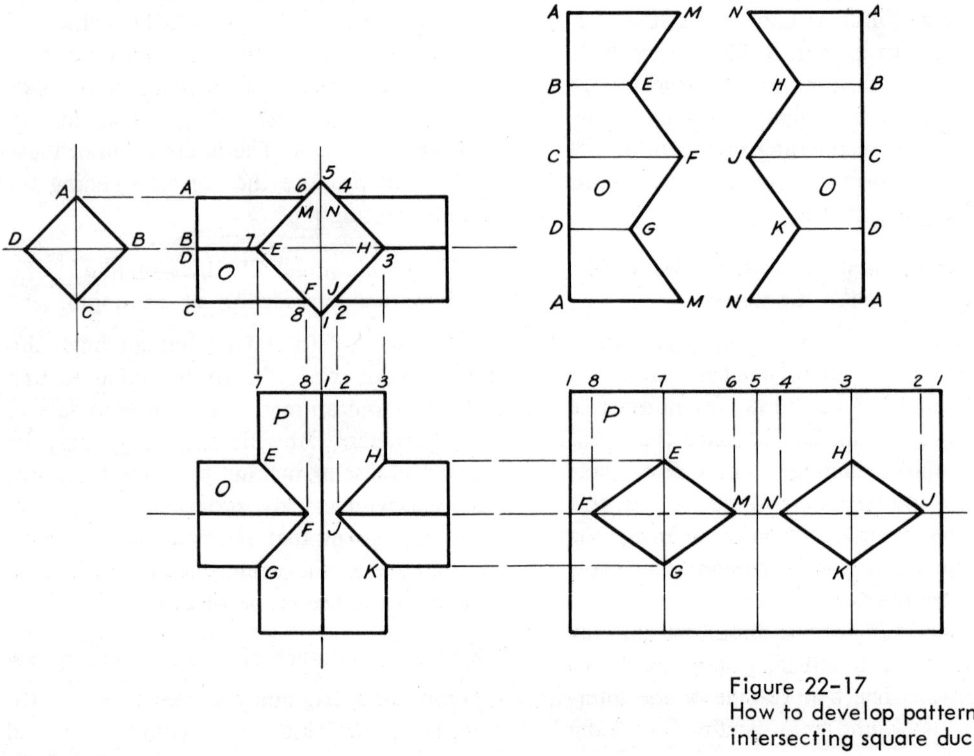

Figure 22-17
How to develop patterns for two intersecting square ducts.

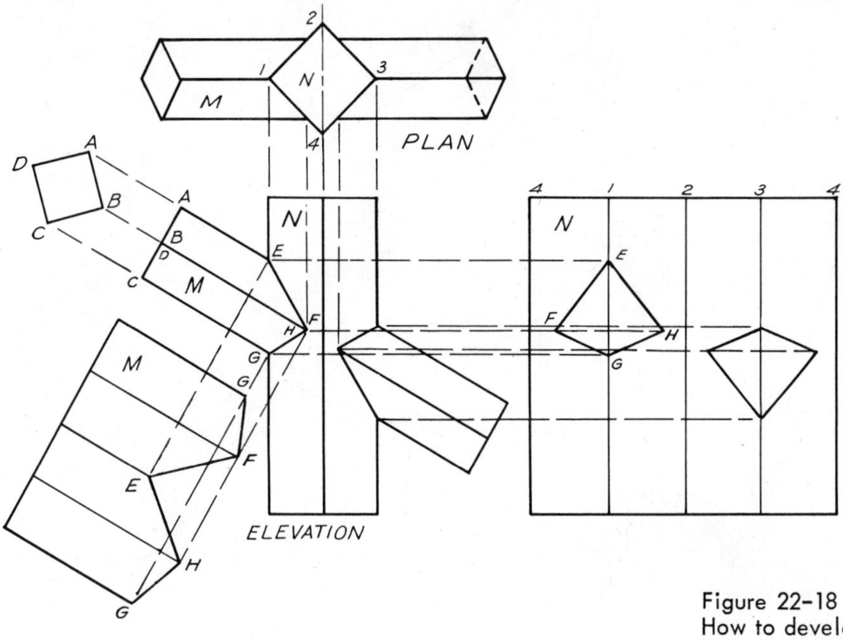

Figure 22-18
How to develop patterns for intersecting oblique ducts.

bisect each of these divisions. From these bisectors draw lines to center *A*, which provide the miter lines of the elbow. Draw the semicircle *EC* and divide it into any number of equal parts. From these points project lines to intersect miter lines *KL* and *MN*.

Draw the stretchout line for section *F* and on it lay off the correct number of divisions to represent the true circumference of the elbow. Draw vertical lines through these points. Project lines from elbow *F* to the corresponding elements on the stretchout and connect these intersections with a curved line.

Follow a similar procedure to lay out the pattern for section *G*. Actually pattern *G* may be laid out by duplicating the miter line contour of pattern *F*.

Since the remaining two patterns will be identical to those just found, only *F* and *G* should be developed.

22.14 Developing patterns for twin elbows

Construct an elevation and plan view of the pipes. See Fig. 22-16. Divide the plan view into any number of equal parts and project the points as shown. The stretchouts are developed in the same manner as described in Sub-section 22.13.

22.15 Development of two square ducts at right angles

Construct an elevation and plan view of ducts *O* and *P* and label the points as shown in Fig. 22-17. Draw the stretchout line for duct *P* and on it lay out the lateral sides taken from the plan view. Find the required openings by projecting the points from duct *O* in the elevation view.

Draw the stretchout lines for duct *O* and lay out the lateral sides *A,B,C,D* taken from the plan view of duct *O*. Find the true lengths of duct *O* in the plan view, such as *AM, BE, CF,* etc., and lay them out on the stretchout lines.

22.16 Development of square ducts intersecting at an angle

The intersection and development of the two oblique ducts in Fig. 22-18 is very similar to Fig. 22-17. An elevation and plan view of the ducts are drawn and the sides correctly labeled. The contour for ducts *M* and *N* are obtained by laying out the lateral sides and projecting the corresponding points from the elevation.

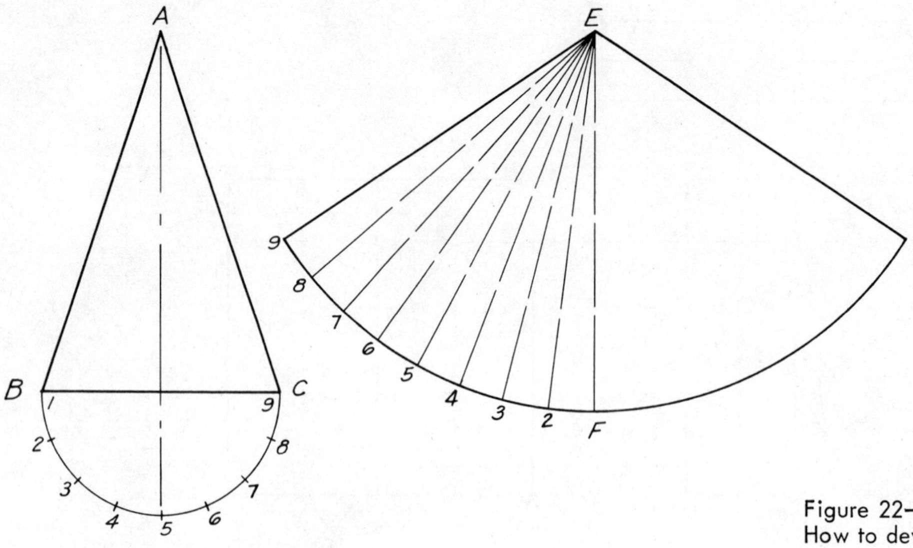

Figure 22-19
How to develop a cone.

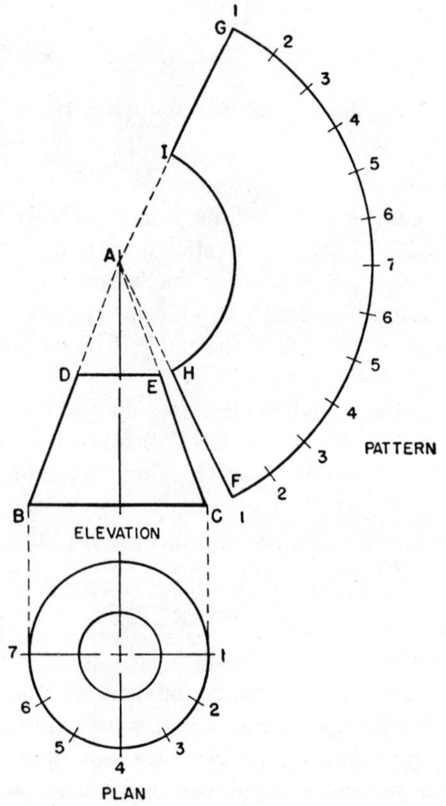

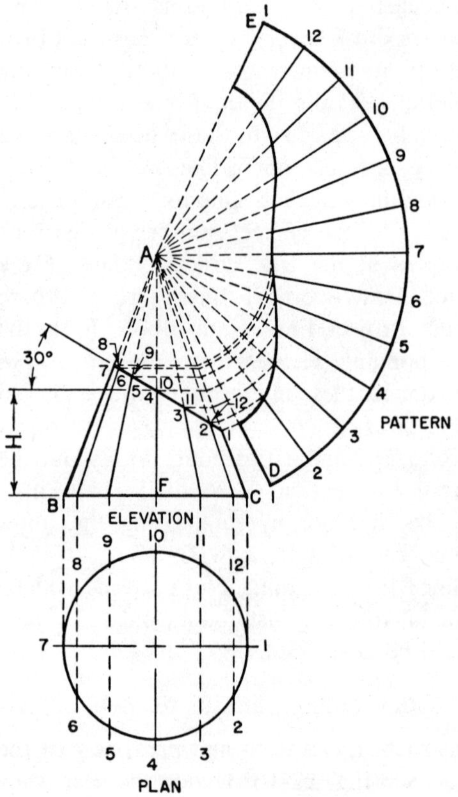

Figure 22-20
How to develop a frustum of a right cone cut parallel to its base.

Figure 22-21
How to develop a pattern for a truncated right cone cut at an angle.

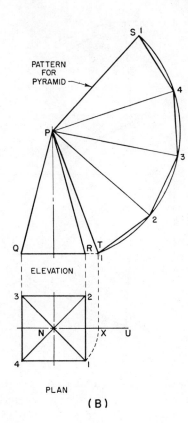

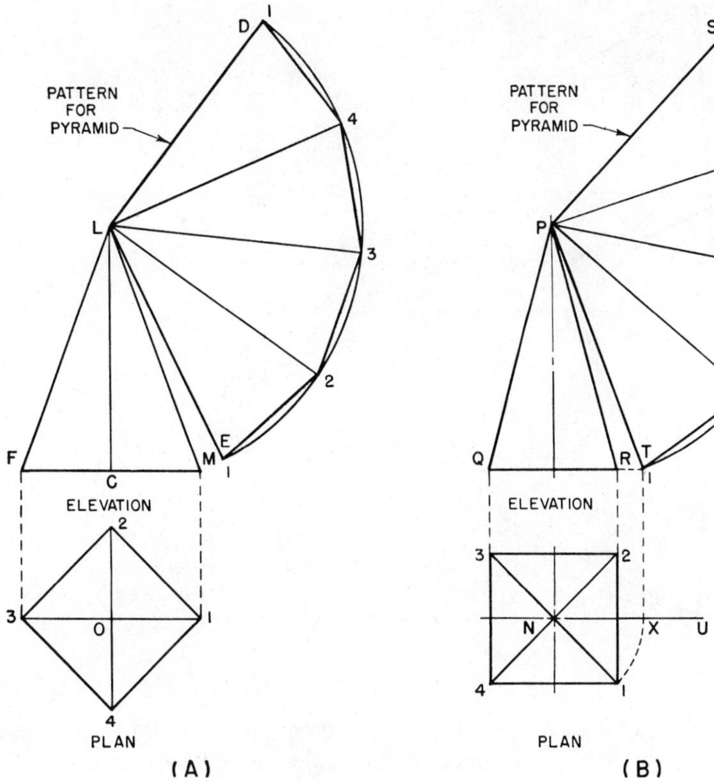

Figure 22-22
Two methods of developing a pattern for a pyramid having a square base.

22.17 Development of a cone

To lay out a pattern for a cone, draw a full-size front view of the cone as triangle *ABC* in Fig. 22-19. Using the base *BC* of the triangle as a diameter draw a semicircle. Divide this semicircle into any number of equal parts, numbering them 1,2,3,4, etc.

With side *AB* or *AC* of the triangle *ABC* as a radius, draw an arc of unlimited length with *E* as a center to represent one boundary of the stretchout. Then draw line *EF* to intersect this arc at *F*. Beginning at *F*, lay off the distances that were spaced on the semicircle. Since this semicircle represents only half of the circumference of the base of the cone, it will be necessary to lay out an equal length for the opposite half of the same arc. From the end points on the arc, draw straight lines to the center *E*.

22.18 Development of a frustum of a right cone

The procedure for laying out a frustum of a cone is very similar to that of a regular cone except that two arcs are drawn from the apex *A* having radii of *AB* and *AD*. See Fig. 22-20.

22.19 Development of a truncated right cone cut at an angle

Draw the front view of the cone *ABC* with its truncating line. See Fig. 22-21. Bisect line *BC* and, using *BF* as a radius, draw the plan view of the base. Divide the circle into any number of equal parts and number them 1,2,3,4, etc. Project lines from these points to the base line *BC* and extend them to the apex of the cone at *A*. Number the lines at the truncating line as shown.

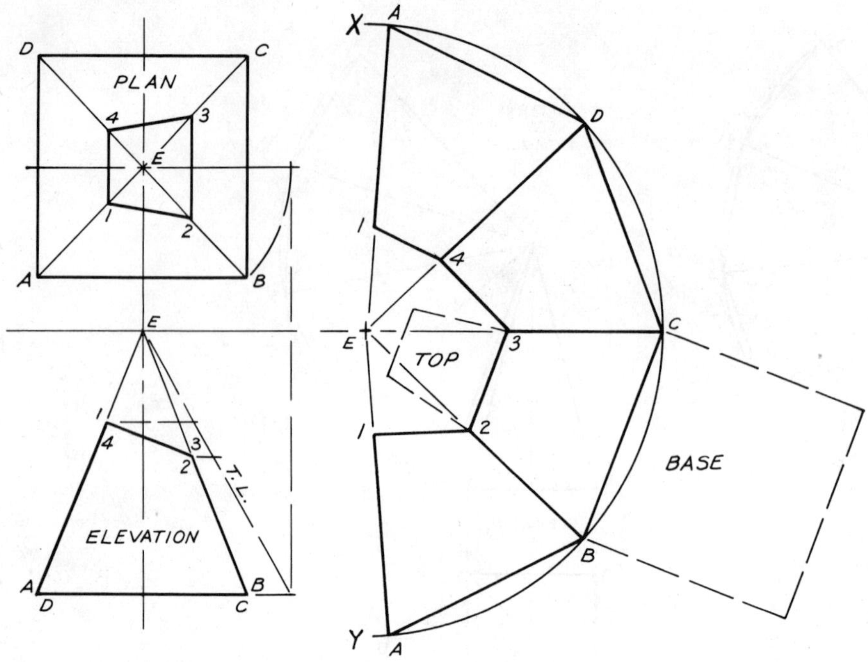

Figure 22-23
How to develop a truncated pyramid.

With *AB* as a radius, draw the stretchout arc *DE*. On this stretchout line lay out the same divisions as those that were spaced on the base circle and number them in the same order. Connect each point with the apex *A* by means of light construction lines.

To obtain the true lengths of the elements for the pattern, project lines horizontally from the points on the truncating line to *AC*. Set the compass from *A* to each of these points and scribe arcs to intersect the corresponding element on the pattern.

Connect these intersecting points with a curved line.

22.20 Development of a pyramid having a square base

The important consideration in the development of a pyramid is to find the true slant length of the elevation. This is found by constructing the base of the elevation so that it is parallel to the center line at the widest part of the plan view.

Fig. 22-22 illustrates two methods of developing patterns for a pyramid. In method *A*, the plan view is arranged with its widest part parallel to the base of the elevation. Hence the slant line *LM* appears in its true length. If the plan view is drawn as in method *B*, the slant line *PR* is not the true length because the widest part of the plan is not parallel to the base of the elevation. Therefore, to ascertain the actual length of the slant line, first extend the centerline *NU* of the plan. With *N* as a center and *N*-1 as a radius, scribe an arc to intersect *NU* at *X*. From *X* project a line vertically to the extension of base line *OR* in the elevation. Finally, draw line *PT* which now becomes the true length of slant line *PR*.

22.21 Development of a truncated pyramid

Draw an elevation and plan view of the pyramid with a truncating line 1-2. See Fig. 22-23.

Find the true length of the slant line as described in Sub-section 22.20, and draw the stretchout arc *XY*.

On the stretchout arc lay off the true sides of the base as *CD, DA, CB* and *BA*. Project lines through these points to center *E*.

Now find the true lengths of the lateral edges from the elevation view and transfer them to the stretchout as *A*1, *B*2, *C*3, etc.

If a bottom base and top are required, draw them in as shown.

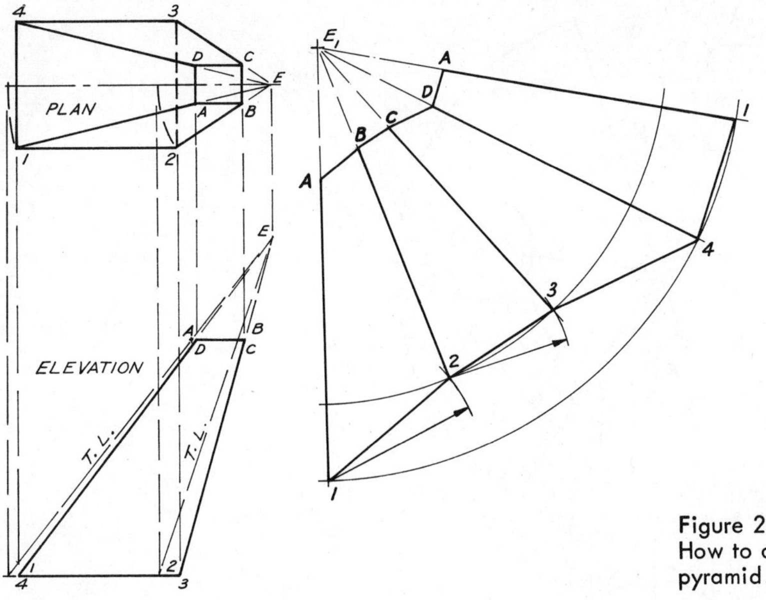

Figure 22-24
How to develop a truncated oblique pyramid.

22.22 Development of a truncated oblique pyramid

Draw an elevation and plan view of the truncated oblique pyramid and label the edges as shown in Fig. 22-24.

Determine the true lengths of elements *E*1 and *E*2 as previously described. With the true lengths of *E*1 and *E*2 as radii, scribe two stretchout arcs from E_1.

Beginning at 1 on the outer arc, lay off the base lengths taken from the plan view 1-2, 2-3, etc., so as to intersect the corresponding stretchout arcs. From these points draw radial lines to E_1. Lay off the true lengths of the lateral edges, and connect the points with straight lines.

22.23 Development of a cylinder intersecting a cone at right angles

Draw an elevation and plan view of cone *X* and horizontal cylinder *Y* as illustrated in Fig. 22-25. Divide the plan view of cylinder *Y* into equal spaces and number them as shown. Project these points horizontally to intersect the cone element *BC*.

From the points of intersection on line *BC,* drop vertical lines to intersect the center line *ab* in the plan view. With *O* as the center and radii equal to *O*-4, *O*-3-5, *O*-2-6, *O*-1-7, etc., scribe arcs as shown.

Draw a plan end view of cylinder *Y* on the plan view of cone *X* and number the points as indicated. From these points, draw horizontal lines to intersect the corresponding numbered arcs at 1′, 2′, 3′, etc. Draw vertical lines to intersect similarly numbered horizontal elements in the elevation view. The intersections found will provide the miter line for the cylinder and cone.

To draw the pattern for the cone, develop the stretchout in the usual manner for a regular cone. To find the opening for the intersecting cylinder, draw arcs on the stretchout of the cone using *B* as a center, and *B*-4, *B*-3-5, etc., as radii. Lay out the distances taken along the arcs from the center line *ab* to the points of intersection 1′, 2′, etc., in the plan view, on the corresponding arcs in the stretchout of the cone. A line drawn through these points will produce the true opening.

To develop the pattern for cylinder *Y,* lay out a stretchout line equal to the circumference of the cylinder. Project the points from the mitered line in the elevation to intersect the corresponding elements on the stretchout.

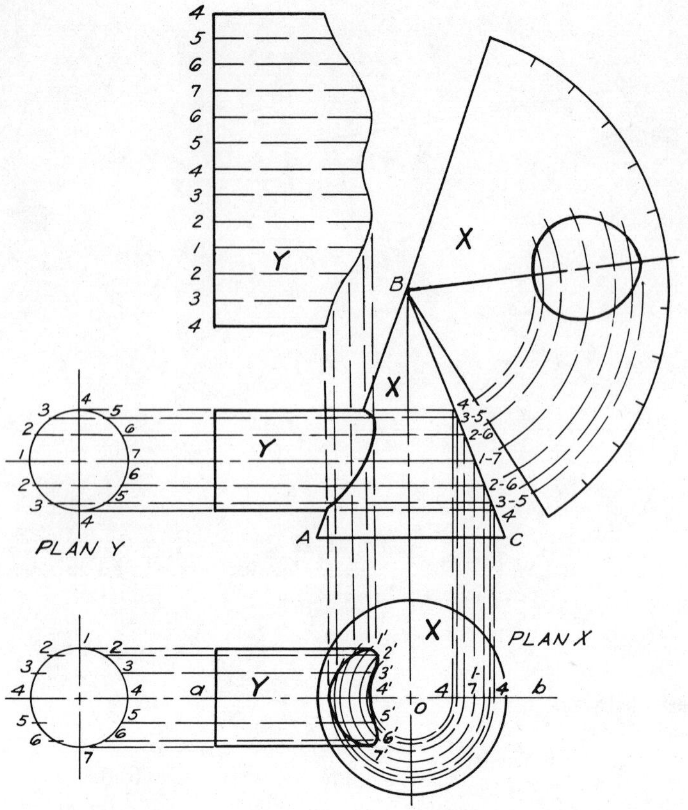

Figure 22-25
How to develop a cylinder intersecting a cone at right angles.

22.24 Development of a cone intersecting a cylinder obliquely

Draw an elevation and plan view of the cone and cylinder as shown in Fig. 22-26. Extend the sides of the cone *B* in the elevation to the base line 1-7. On this base line scribe a semicircle and divide it into any number of equal parts. Project these points to the base line and draw radial lines to center *R*.

On center line *DE,* draw the plan view for cone *B* and divide into equal parts. Extend the points on the plan view *B* to the plan view *A* so they will intersect vertical lines drawn from the base line 1-7 in the elevation. Where these lines intersect, draw radial lines to R′. From the points where the radial lines cut the circle for plan *A,* draw vertical lines to the corresponding cone elements in the elevation. The intersection of these lines will provide the miter line for cone *B*.

Using *R* as a center, draw an arc to represent the stretchout line for cone *B* as well as additional arcs from the points on miter line 1-7. The intersection of these arcs with the radial lines in the stretchout will provide the contour of cone *B*.

Draw the patterns for cylinder *A* and extend horizontal lines from the miter line 1-7 in the elevation. Find the opening in pattern *A* by transferring the circular distances 1-2, 1-3, 1-4, etc., from the center line *DE* on plan view *A* to the stretchout. The intersection of these points with the corresponding horizontal lines will produce the correct curvature for the opening.

22.25 Development of transition piece—square to square

Draw an elevation and plan view of the piece and label the plan as shown in Fig. 22-27. Draw line *FG* equal in length to the

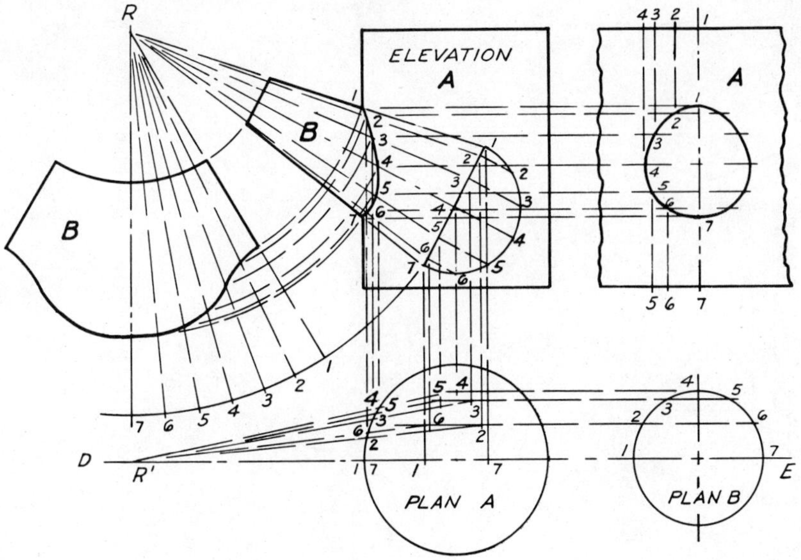

Figure 22-26
How to develop a pattern of a cone intersecting a cylinder obliquely.

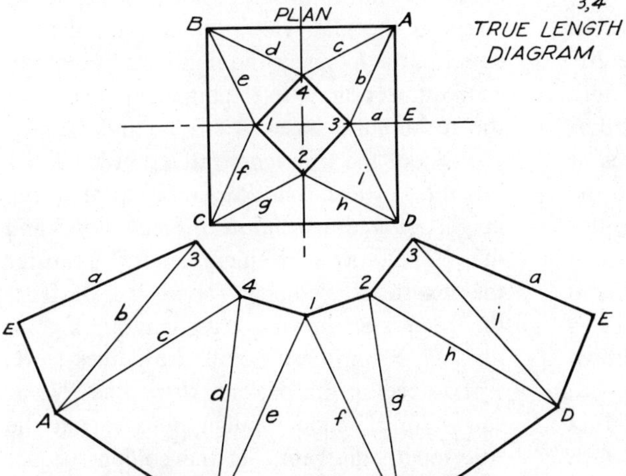

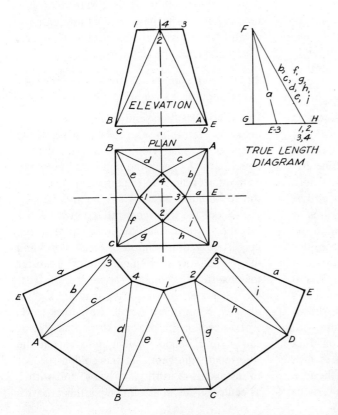

Figure 22-27
How to develop a pattern of a square-to-square transition piece.

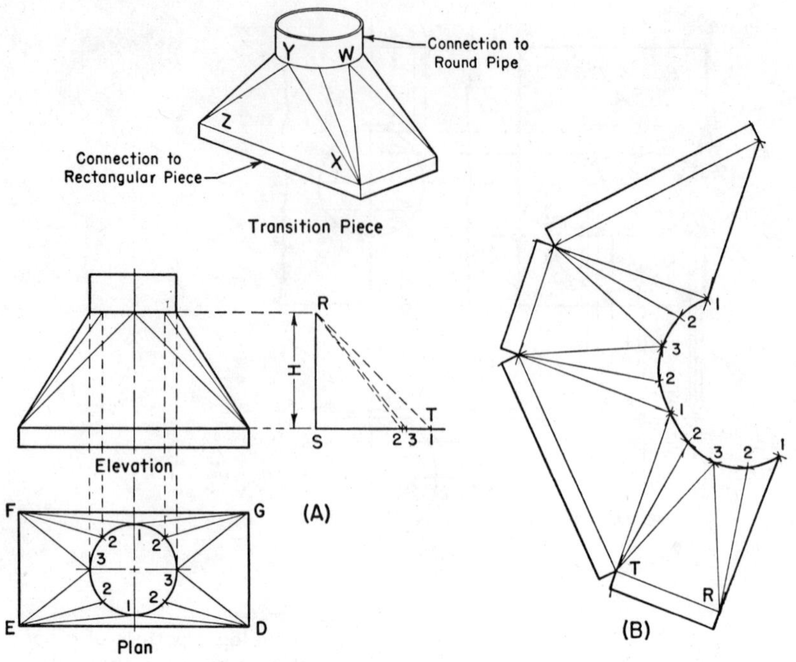

Figure 22-28
How to develop a pattern of a rectangular-to-round transition piece.

true height of the part in elevation and line *GH* of indefinite length.

With *G* as the center, lay out on line *GH* distances equal to *D*-2, *D*-3, *A*-3, *A*-4, etc., from the plan view. Draw a line from points 1, 2, 3, 4, to *F*. This line represents the true lengths of elements *b, c, d, e, f, g, h,* and *i* in the plan view. Next lay out the true length of *E*-3 on line *GH* which is shown as line *a* in the true length diagram.

To develop the pattern, draw line *BC* in the bottom view equal in length to line *BC* in the plan view. With *F*-1 as the true length taken from the true length diagram and *B* and *C* as centers, scribe intersecting arcs at 1. Then draw elements from *B* and *C* to the intersecting arcs at 1. With 1 as the center and the distances 1-2 and 1-4 from the plan view, scribe arcs at 2 and 4. With *B* and *C* as centers, *F*-2 as the true length, and *F*-4 as a radius, intersect the previously drawn arcs at 2 and 4. Connect these points with elements *C*-2 and *B*-4. Similarly construct triangles *D*-2-C, *A*-4-B, *D*-2-3 and *A*-4-3. Now using *A* and *D* as centers and the true distance of *AE* and *ED* in the plan view as a radius, scribe arcs at *E* and *E*. With 3 and 3 as centers and the true distance of *E*-3 taken as *F*-E-3 in the true length diagram as a radius, draw arcs to intersect at *E* and *E*. This completes the pattern.

22.26 Development of transition piece—rectangular to round

Draw an elevation and plan view of the piece as shown in Fig. 22-28. Divide the circle in the plan view into any number of equal parts. Connect the numbered points of each quarter circle to the adjacent corners of the rectangular bases *D, E, F,* and *G*.

Lay out the true length diagram by drawing the vertical line *RS* equal to the true height of the transition in elevation, and line *ST* of any convenient length. Transfer the length of elements *D*1, *D*2, *D*3, from the plan view to the true length diagram line *ST*. From these points draw lines to *R*.

To develop the pattern, draw line *R*1, as shown in *B,* equal in length to *R*1 in the true length diagram. Set the compass equal to distance 1-2 in the plan view, and with 1 as center strike an arc. Intersect this arc with

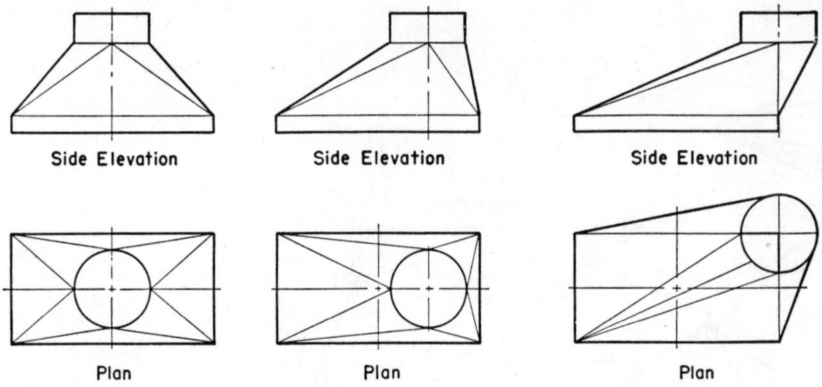

Centers in Line in Both Directions
(A)

Centers in Line in One Direction
(B)

Centers Out of Line in Both Directions

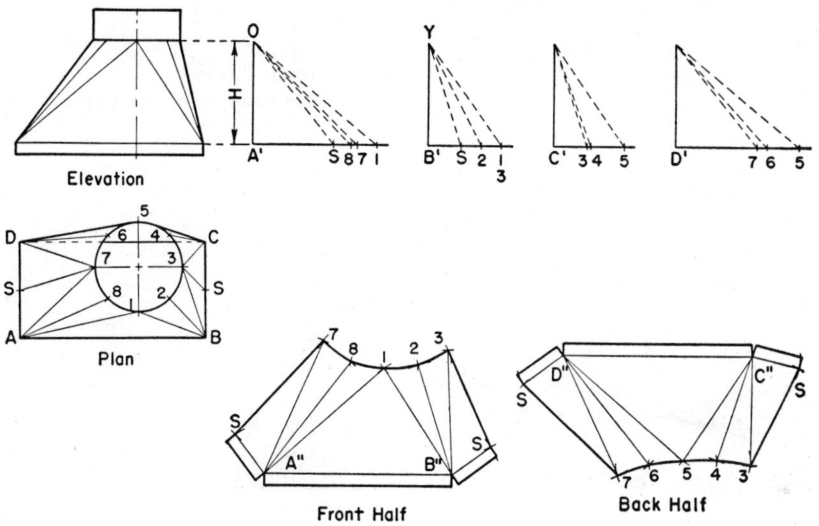

Figure 22-29
How to develop a pattern of rectangular-to-round offset piece.

an arc using *R* as a center and a radius equal to the true length of *R*2. Connect *R* and 2 with a line. Strike an arc using 2 as center and a radius 2-3 of the plan view. Intersect this arc using *R* as center and a radius of the true length *R*3. Connect points 1, 2, and 3 with a curve. Set the compass equal to *EF* of the plan view and with *R* as center, strike an arc. Intersect this arc with an arc using 3 as a center and a radius equal to the true length *R*3. Draw the triangle *R*3*T*.

Complete the pattern by adding the remaining parts in a similar order.

22.27 Development of transition piece—rectangular to round-offset

Draw an elevation and plan view of the piece. See Fig. 22-29. Divide the round end into any number of equal parts and draw element lines to the corners *A,B,C,* and *D*. Label each element as shown.

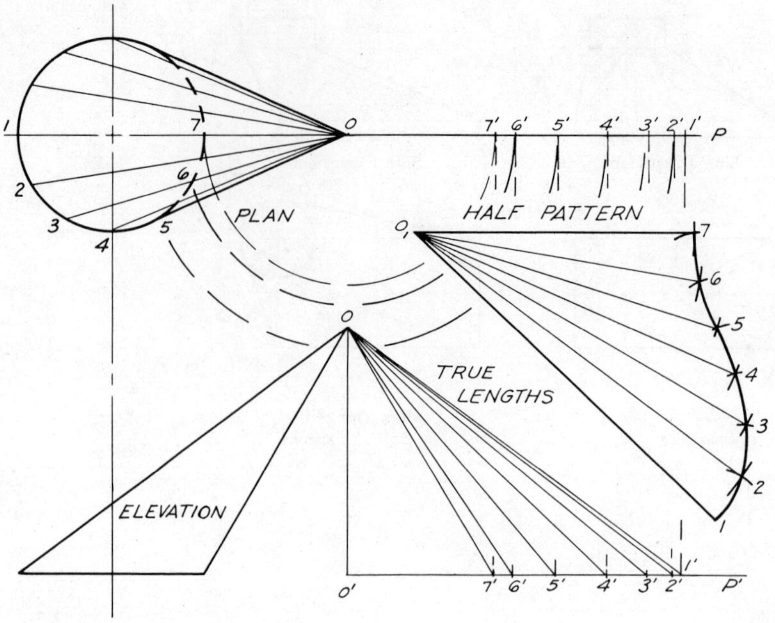

Figure 22-30
How to develop a pattern for an oblique cone.

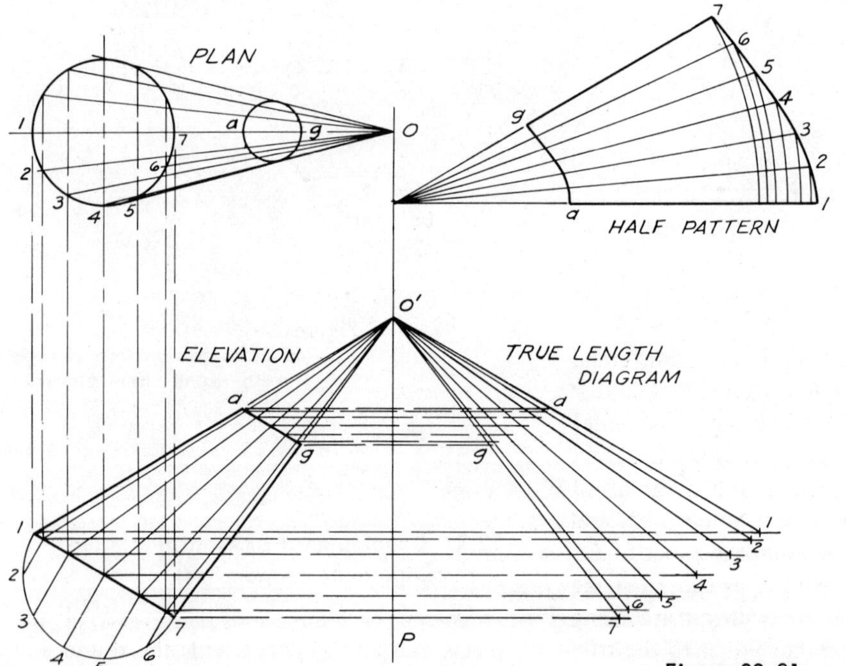

Figure 22-31
How to develop a pattern for a transition piece between two circular openings of different diameters.

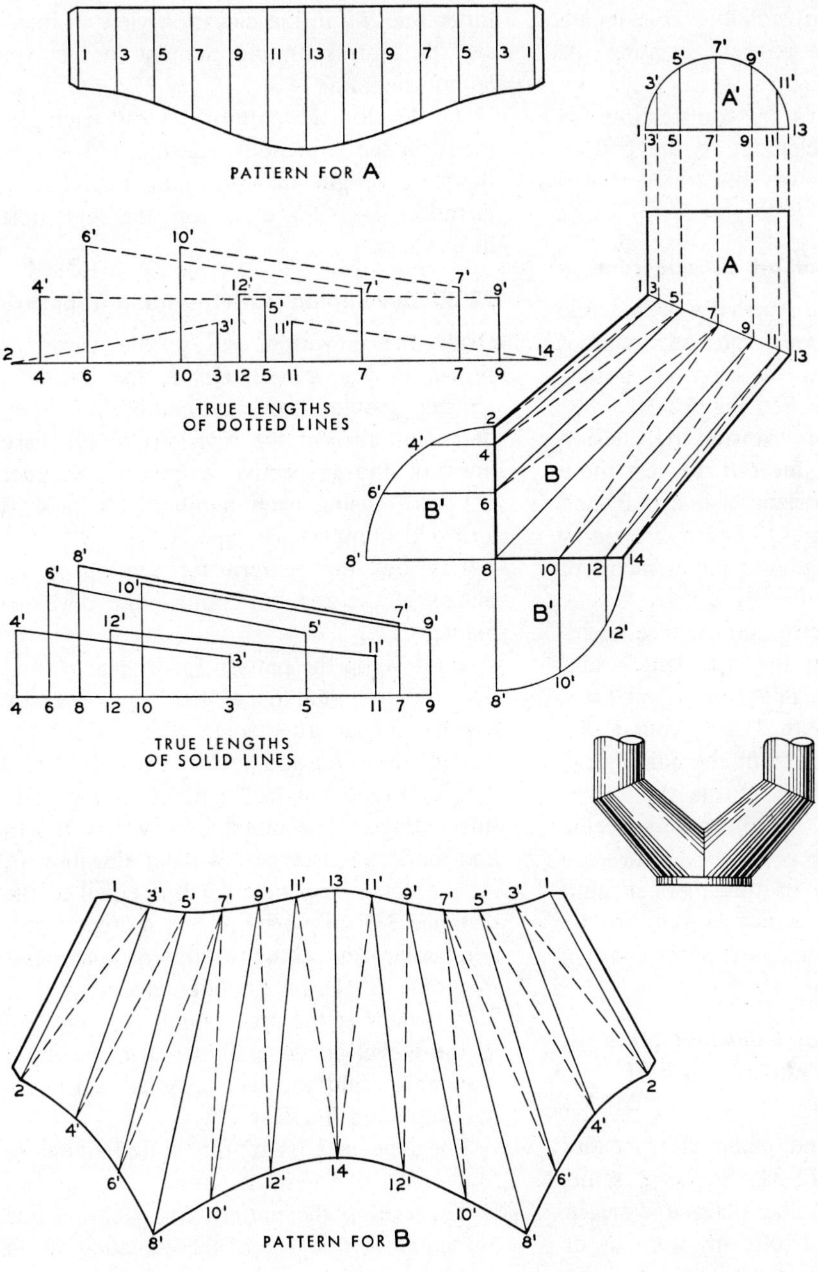

Figure 22-32
How to develop patterns for a Y branch.

Since this piece contains numerous lines, it is advisable to construct four true length diagrams to facilitate ease in locating the various lines.

Develop the pattern by transferring the true length of each element to the pattern as described in previously illustrated transition pieces.

22.28 Development of an oblique cone

Draw an elevation and plan view of the cone and divide the plan view into any number of equal parts. From the division points, draw radial lines to *O*. See Fig. 22-30.

With *O* as a center, transfer the division points in the plan to line *OP*. Project these points down to the horizontal line *O′*P′ and draw lines to meet at *O*. These lines now represent the true lengths of the elements of the oblique cone.

To lay out the pattern, find the true length of element *O*-1′ from the true length diagram and with O_1 in any convenient location scribe an arc. With 1 as a center and a radius 1-2 obtained from the plan view, draw an arc at 2. With O_1 as the center and the true length 2′ as the radius, scribe an arc intersecting the previously drawn arc at point 2. Continue in this manner until all the true elements are laid out on the stretchout. Connect the base points with a smooth curve.

22.29 Development of transition piece connecting two cylindrical pipes of different diameters

Draw an elevation and plane view of the transition. See Fig. 22-31. Scribe a semicircle on the base of the oblique cone in elevation and divide it into any number of equal parts. Project these points to the base line 1-7 and to the plan view. From these points draw radial lines to *O* and *O′*.

From the points on base line 1-7 in the elevation view, draw horizontal lines of indefinite length to the true length diagram. Find the true length of each element by transferring the distances *O*-1, *O*-2, *O*-3, etc., in the plan to these corresponding horizontal lines, measuring from vertical line *O′P*. From each of these points, draw radial lines to *O′*. Draw horizontal lines from the miter line *a-g* in the elevation view to intersect the corresponding element in the true length diagram.

To develop the pattern, lay out each element on the stretchout, starting with *a*-1 in the true length diagram and the chordal distances 1-2, 2-3, etc., from the semicircle in elevation.

22.30 Developing patterns for a Y branch

Draw the elevation and profile views as shown in Fig. 22-32. Divide the half and quarter profiles into any number of equal parts and project the divisions to the base lines of the respective cylinders. Number all points using even numbers for pipe *B* and odd numbers for pipe *A*.

Lay out the pattern for section *A* by means of the regular parallel line development.

To develop the pattern for branch *B*, first find the true lengths of the slant lines by constructing a true length diagram for the dotted lines and another for the solid lines. To determine the true lengths of the solid lines, draw a horizontal line of any length and mark off distance 3-4 from elevation *B*. At 3 erect a perpendicular line equal to the distance 3-3′ in profile *A′*. At 4 erect a perpendicular line equal to the distance 4-4′ in profile *B′*. Draw a line connecting points 3′-4′ which is the true length for line 3-4 in the elevation view. Proceed in a similar manner to find the true lengths of the remaining solid lines.

The true lengths of the dotted lines are found in a like manner.

To develop the pattern for *B*, draw line 1-2 equal to line 1-2 of the elevation. With point 2 as center and a radius equal to the true length dotted line 2-3′, strike an arc at 3′. Set the compass to space 1-3′ of profile *A′* and with 1 as the center intersect the arc at point 3′. With the true length solid line 3′-4′ as a radius and point 3′ as a center, strike an arc at 4′. Set the compass to space 2-4′ of *B′* and with point 2 as the center, cut arc at point 4′. Continue in a similar manner until all the true length lines are drawn in their respective positions.

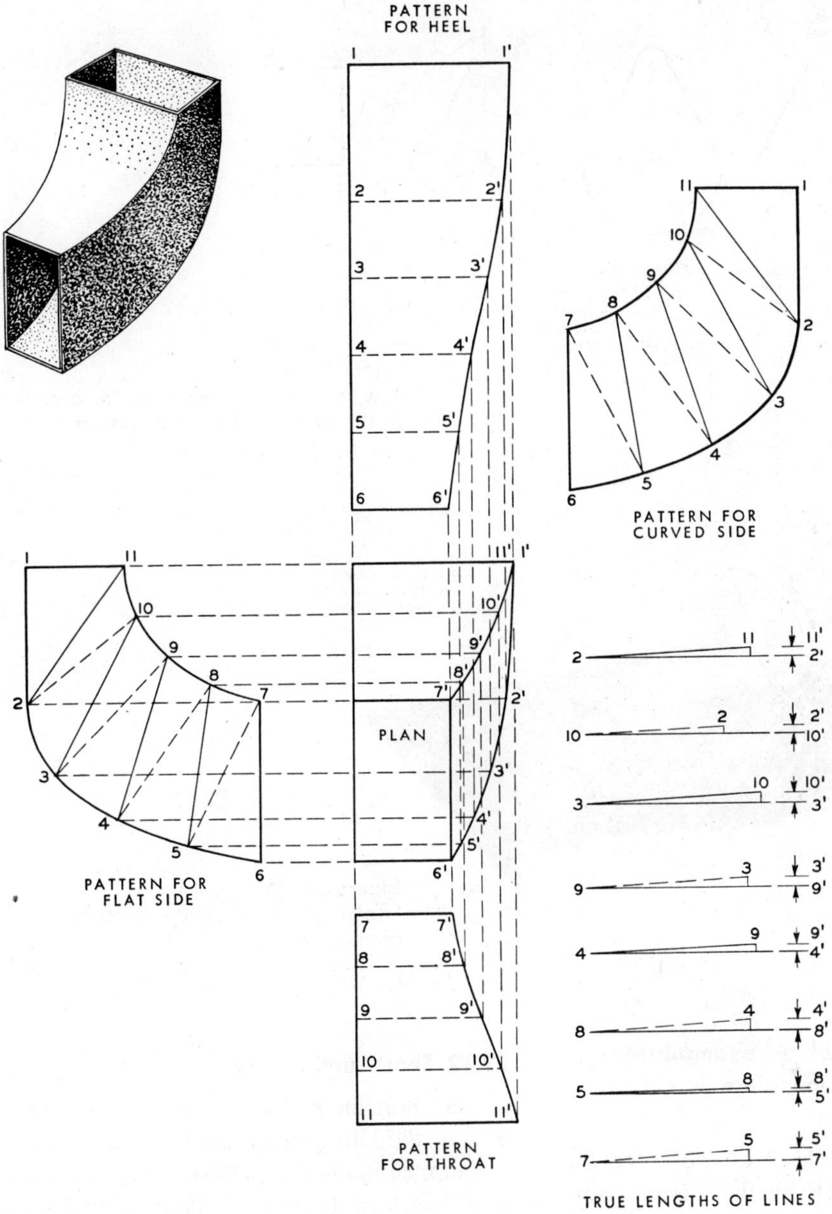

Figure 22-33
How to develop a rectangular-to-rectangular transition piece with one flat side.

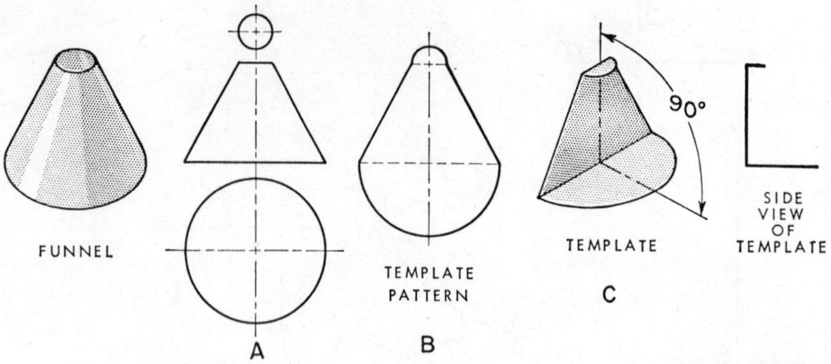

Figure 22-34
How to prepare a template for a cone by the short method development.

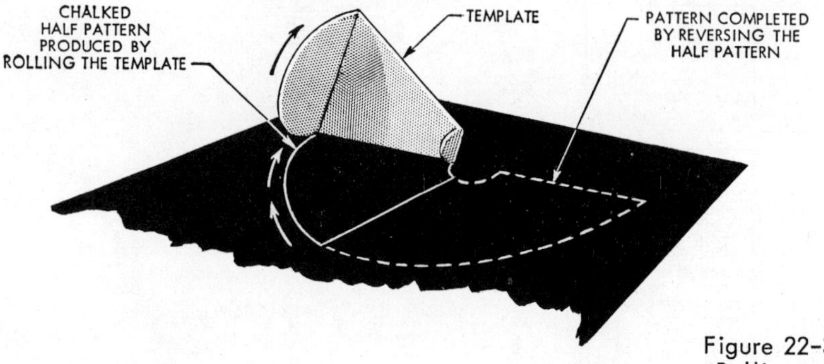

Figure 22-35
"Rolling" the template to obtain the cone pattern.

22.31 Development of a rectangular-to-rectangular transition piece having one flat side

Draw the necessary views of the piece as shown in Fig. 22-33. Divide the curved edges of the side view into any number of equal parts and connect the points with solid and dotted lines. From these points project lines to the plan view.

Lay out the throat and heel patterns by parallel line development,

To develop the pattern for the curved side, lay out true length diagrams for the slant lines in the flat side. The base of each triangle is found by measuring between the appropriate vertical lines on the plan view. Lay out the pattern using these true length lines as described in Sub-section 22.30.

22.32 Short method development[2]

The short method of pattern development is a method frequently used by sheetmetal layout men in making patterns. This method, also known as the *rollout method,* eliminates much time and effort in preparing developments. Basically it consists of making a sheetmetal template and then rolling the template on paper. To better illustrate this process, assume that a funnel or truncated cone is to be developed. First draw a front, bottom and top view of the cone as shown in *A* of Fig. 22-34. Next lay out the cone with one half of its top and bottom attached as in *B*. Now bend the half circles represent-

2. Ralph W. Poe, *Short Method of Pattern Development* (Middletown, Ohio: Armco Steel Corp., 1950).

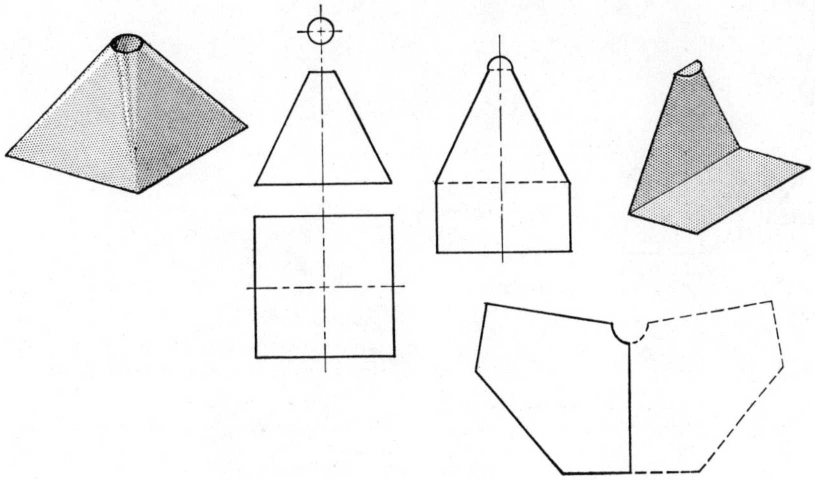

Figure 22-36
Short method pattern development for a square-to-round fitting.

ing one half of the top and bottom openings of the cone at right angles to the cross section. The pattern is produced by chalking the edges of the template and rolling it over a sheet of soft, black building paper. An alternate method is to brush the edges of the template with oil and roll it over layout paper. In each case distinct lines result which provide the stretchout of the pattern as shown in Fig. 22-35.

22.33 Representative applications of the short method development technique

Figures 22-36, 22-37, 22-38, and 22-39 show the short method of developing some representative types of patterns commonly encountered in sheetmetal work. These patterns are more complex than the layout for a simple cone, but the same principles of construction apply.

22.34 Bend allowance

In laying out sheetmetal templates, allowances must be made wherever the metal is to be bent to avoid cracking. Two methods are used to calculate bend allowance. One method involves the calculation of the material required to bend around a given radius by means of the following empirical formula:

$$B.A. = N(0.01745 \times R + 0.0078 \times T),$$

where $B.A.$ = bend allowance,
N = number of degrees in bend,
R = radius of bend,
and T = thickness.

The resulting allowance is then added to the tangent point dimensions. See Fig 22-40.

To eliminate the time consuming task of making the necessary calculations for each required bend, special bend allowance charts are available which provide the correct allowance for materials of different thicknesses and bends of different radii. See Fig. 22-41. The following example uses the bend allowance empirical formula.

Find the total length of a 1/8″ fitting to be bent 90° over a 1/4″ radius, having tangent dimensions of 4-1/4″ and 3-1/8″. See Fig. 22-40.

$B.A.$ for 1° = .00534
$B.A.$ for 90° = .00534 × 90 = .480
Tang. Dim. = 4-1/4 + 3-1/8 = 7-3/8″
Total Length = 7-3/8 + .480 = 7.855″

The second method of determining bend allowance is by means of *setback*. Set-

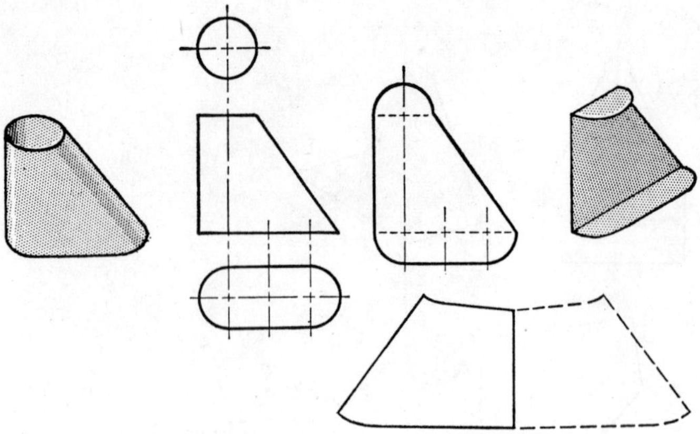

Figure 22-37
Short method pattern development for an off-center oval-to-round fitting.

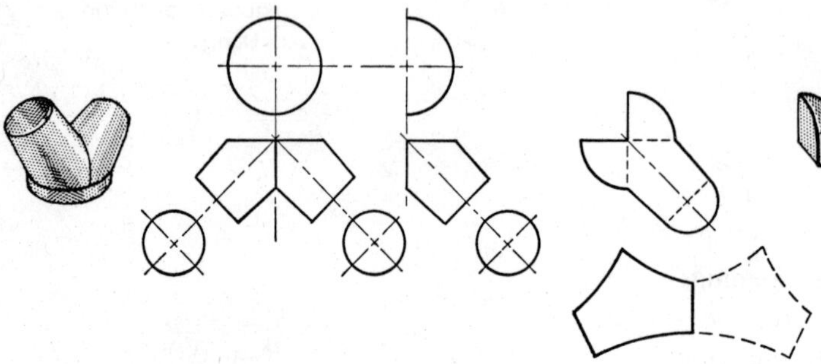

Figure 22-38
Short method pattern development for a Y fitting.

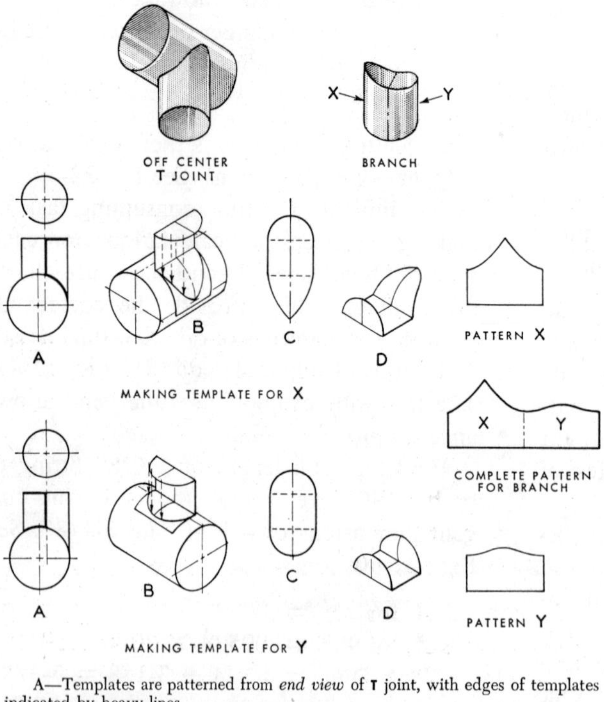

A—Templates are patterned from *end view* of T joint, with edges of templates indicated by heavy lines.

B—Partially finished template is bent around pipe. Outline of lower part is obtained by sighting over upper half circle, or guiding a square around upper half circle and tracing its course on the bent part of the template.

C—Template flattened out.

D—Finished template bent to conform to pipe.

Figure 22-39
Short method pattern development for an off-center T joint.

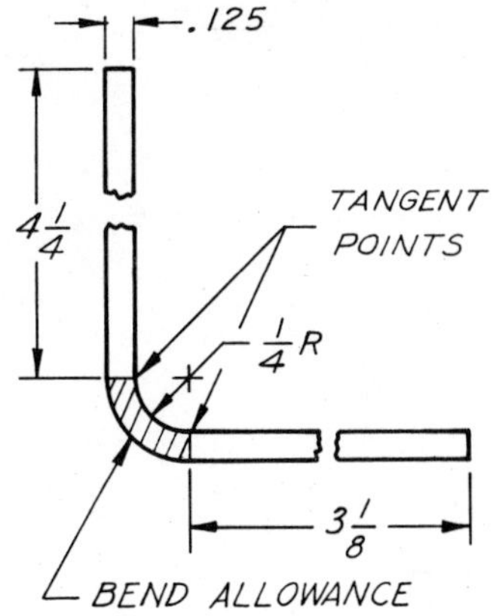

Figure 22-40
Bend allowance is always added to the tangent point dimensions.

Top No. in Each Space = Bend Allowance for 90° Bends										Bottom No. in Each Space = Bend Allowance Constant for 1°										
Bend Radii / Thickness	.031	.063	.094	.125	.156	.188	.219	.250	.281	.313	.344	.375	.438	.500	.531	.625	.656	.750	.781	1.000
.013	.058 .00064	.108 .00120	.157 .00174	.205 .00228	.254 .00282	.304 .00338	.353 .00392	.402 .00446	.450 .00500	.501 .00556	.549 .00610	.598 .00664	.697 .00774	.794 .00883	.843 .00937	.991 .01101	1.039 .01155	1.187 .01319	1.236 .01373	1.580 .01755
.016	.060 .00067	.110 .00122	.159 .00176	.208 .00231	.256 .00285	.307 .00342	.355 .00395	.404 .00449	.453 .00503	.503 .00559	.552 .00613	.600 .00667	.699 .00777	.796 .00885	.845 .00939	.993 .01103	1.041 .01157	1.189 .01321	1.238 .01375	1.582 .01758
.019 and .020	.062 .00069	.113 .00125	.161 .00179	.210 .00233	.259 .00287	.309 .00343	.358 .00397	.406 .00452	.455 .00506	.505 .00561	.554 .00616	.603 .00670	.702 .00780	.799 .00888	.848 .00942	.995 .01106	1.044 .01160	1.192 .01324	1.240 .01378	1.584 .01760
.022	.064 .00071	.114 .00127	.163 .00181	.212 .00235	.260 .00289	.311 .00345	.359 .00399	.408 .00453	.457 .00508	.507 .00563	.556 .00617	.604 .00672	.703 .00782	.801 .00890	.849 .00944	.997 .01108	1.046 .01162	1.193 .01326	1.242 .01380	1.586 .01762
.025	.066 .00074	.116 .00129	.165 .00184	.214 .00238	.263 .00292	.313 .00348	.362 .00402	.410 .00456	.459 .00510	.509 .00566	.558 .00620	.607 .00674	.705 .00784	.803 .00892	.851 .00946	.999 .01110	1.048 .01164	1.195 .01328	1.244 .01382	1.588 .01764
.028	.068 .00076	.119 .00132	.167 .00186	.216 .00240	.265 .00294	.315 .00350	.364 .00404	.412 .00458	.461 .00512	.511 .00568	.560 .00622	.609 .00676	.708 .00786	.805 .00894	.854 .00948	1.001 .01112	1.050 .01167	1.198 .01331	1.246 .01385	1.590 .01767
.031 and .032	.071 .00079	.121 .00134	.170 .00189	.218 .00243	.267 .00297	.317 .00353	.366 .00407	.415 .00461	.463 .00515	.514 .00571	.562 .00625	.611 .00679	.710 .00789	.807 .00897	.856 .00951	1.004 .01115	1.052 .01169	1.200 .01333	1.249 .01387	1.593 .01770
.038	.075 .00084	.126 .00140	.174 .00194	.223 .00248	.272 .00302	.322 .00358	.371 .00412	.419 .00466	.468 .00520	.518 .00576	.567 .00630	.616 .00684	.715 .00794	.812 .00902	.861 .00956	1.008 .01120	1.057 .01174	1.205 .01338	1.253 .01392	1.597 .01775
.040	.077 .00085	.127 .00141	.176 .00195	.224 .00249	.273 .00303	.323 .00359	.372 .00413	.421 .00468	.469 .00522	.520 .00577	.568 .00632	.617 .00686	.716 .00796	.813 .00904	.862 .00958	1.010 .01122	1.058 .01176	1.206 .01340	1.255 .01394	1.599 .01776
.050 and .051		.134 .00149	.183 .00203	.232 .00258	.280 .00312	.331 .00368	.379 .00422	.428 .00476	.477 .00530	.527 .00586	.576 .00640	.624 .00694	.723 .00804	.821 .00912	.869 .00966	1.017 .01130	1.066 .01184	1.213 .01348	1.262 .01402	1.606 .01784
.063 and .064		.144 .00160	.192 .00214	.241 .00268	.290 .00322	.340 .00378	.389 .00432	.437 .00486	.486 .00540	.536 .00596	.585 .00650	.634 .00704	.732 .00814	.830 .00922	.878 .00976	1.026 .01140	1.075 .01194	1.222 .01358	1.271 .01412	1.615 .01794
.072			.198 .00220	.247 .00274	.296 .00328	.346 .00384	.394 .00438	.443 .00492	.492 .00546	.542 .00602	.591 .00656	.639 .00710	.738 .00820	.836 .00929	.885 .00983	1.032 .01147	1.081 .01201	1.228 .01365	1.277 .01419	1.621 .01801
.078			.202 .00225	.251 .00279	.300 .00333	.350 .00389	.399 .00443	.447 .00497	.496 .00551	.546 .00607	.595 .00661	.644 .00715	.743 .00825	.840 .00933	.889 .00987	1.036 .01152	1.085 .01206	1.233 .01370	1.281 .01424	1.625 .01806
.081			.204 .00227	.253 .00281	.302 .00335	.352 .00391	.401 .00445	.449 .00499	.498 .00554	.548 .00609	.598 .00664	.646 .00718	.745 .00828	.842 .00936	.891 .00990	1.038 .01154	1.087 .01208	1.235 .01372	1.283 .01426	1.627 .01808
.091			.212 .00235	.260 .00289	.309 .00343	.359 .00399	.408 .00453	.456 .00507	.505 .00561	.555 .00617	.604 .00671	.653 .00725	.752 .00835	.849 .00944	.898 .00998	1.045 .01162	1.094 .01216	1.242 .01380	1.290 .01434	1.634 .01816
.094			.214 .00237	.262 .00291	.311 .00346	.361 .00401	.410 .00456	.459 .00510	.507 .00564	.558 .00620	.606 .00674	.655 .00728	.754 .00838	.851 .00946	.900 .00999	1.048 .01164	1.096 .01218	1.244 .01382	1.293 .01436	1.636 .01818
.102				.268 .00298	.317 .00352	.367 .00408	.416 .00462	.464 .00516	.513 .00570	.563 .00626	.612 .00680	.661 .00734	.760 .00844	.857 .00952	.906 .01006	1.053 .01170	1.102 .01224	1.249 .01388	1.298 .01442	1.642 .01825
.109				.273 .00303	.321 .00357	.372 .00413	.420 .00467	.469 .00521	.518 .00575	.568 .00631	.617 .00685	.665 .00739	.764 .00849	.862 .00958	.910 .01012	1.058 .01176	1.107 .01230	1.254 .01394	1.303 .01448	1.647 .01830
.125				.284 .00316	.333 .00370	.383 .00426	.432 .00480	.480 .00534	.529 .00588	.579 .00644	.628 .00698	.677 .00752	.776 .00862	.873 .00970	.922 .01024	1.069 .01188	1.118 .01242	1.266 .01406	1.314 .01460	1.658 .01842
.156					.355 .00394	.405 .00450	.453 .00504	.502 .00558	.551 .00612	.601 .00668	.650 .00722	.698 .00776	.797 .00886	.895 .00994	.943 .01048	1.091 .01212	1.140 .01266	1.287 .01430	1.336 .01484	1.680 .01867
.188						.427 .00475	.476 .00529	.525 .00583	.573 .00637	.624 .00693	.672 .00747	.721 .00801	.820 .00911	.917 .01019	.966 .01073	1.114 .01237	1.162 .01291	1.310 .01455	1.359 .01510	1.702 .01892
.203								.535 .00595	.584 .00649	.634 .00704	.683 .00759	.731 .00813	.830 .00923	.928 .01031	.976 .01085	1.124 .01249	1.173 .01303	1.320 .01467	1.369 .01521	1.713 .01903
.218								.546 .00606	.594 .00660	.645 .00716	.693 .00770	.742 .00824	.841 .00934	.938 .01042	.987 .01097	1.135 .01261	1.183 .01315	1.331 .01479	1.380 .01533	1.724 .01915
.234								.557 .00619	.606 .00673	.656 .00729	.705 .00783	.753 .00837	.852 .00947	.950 .01055	.998 .01109	1.146 .01273	1.194 .01327	1.342 .01491	1.391 .01545	1.735 .01928
.250								.568 .00631	.617 .00685	.667 .00741	.716 .00795	.764 .00849	.863 .00959	.961 .01068	1.009 .01122	1.157 .01286	1.206 .01340	1.353 .01504	1.402 .01558	1.746 .01940

Figure 22-41
Bend allowance chart.
Eastman Kodak Co.

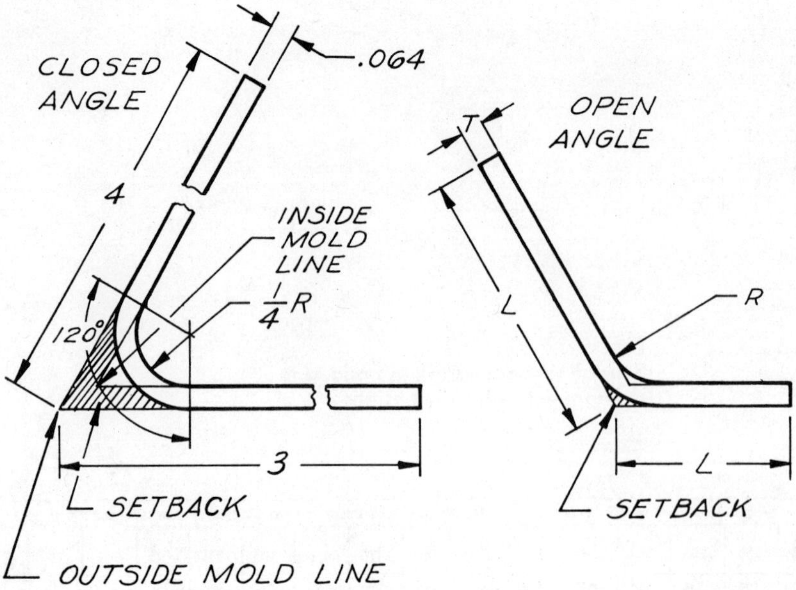

Figure 22-42
Setback is subtracted from the sum of the outside dimensions.

back is simply the difference between the sum of the outside dimensions of the angle and the actual distance needed to form the angle. See Fig. 22-42. The amount of setback is found by using a setback chart as shown in Fig. 22-43. Once the amount of setback is determined for a given bend radius and metal thickness, it is deducted from the outside dimensions of the angle. Example:

Find the setback required to calculate the exact length of a .064″ metal fitting having a 1/4″ bend radius of 120° and outside dimensions of 4″ and 3″. See Fig. 22-42.

$$\begin{aligned} \text{Degrees in bend} &= 120^\circ \\ \text{Thickness} &= .064 \\ \text{Radius} &= .25 \\ K \text{ from Table} &= 1.732 \\ \text{Setback} &= 1.732\ (.064 + .25) \\ &= 1.732 \times .314 \\ &= .544 \end{aligned}$$

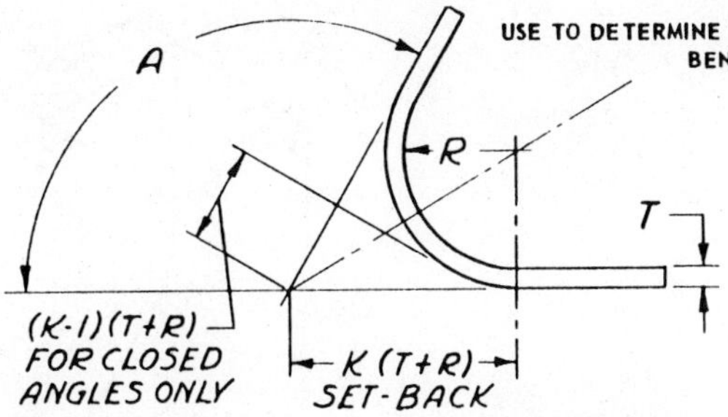

USE TO DETERMINE THE DISTANCE BETWEEN THE MOLD LINE AND THE BEND LINE OF SHEET METAL FLANGES

EXAMPLE ·

DEGREES IN BEND (A) = 120°
GAGE (T) = .032
RADIUS = .125
K (FROM TABLE) = 1.732
SET-BACK = 1.732 (.032+.125)
1.732 X .157
= .272

A	K	A	K	A	K	A	K
1°	.00873	51°	.47697	101°	1.2131	151°	3.8667
2°	.01745	52°	.48773	102°	1.2349	152°	4.0108
3°	.02618	53°	.49858	103°	1.2572	153°	4.1653
4°	.03492	54°	.50952	104°	1.2799	154°	4.3315
5°	.04366	55°	.52057	105°	1.3032	155°	4.5107
6°	.05241	56°	.53171	106°	1.3270	156°	4.7046
7°	.06116	57°	.54295	107°	1.3514	157°	4.9151
8°	.06993	58°	.55431	108°	1.3764	158°	5.1445
9°	.07870	59°	.56577	109°	1.4019	159°	5.3995
10°	.08749	60°	.57735	110°	1.4281	160°	5.6713
11°	.09629	61°	.58904	111°	1.4550	161°	5.9758
12°	.10510	62°	.60086	112°	1.4826	162°	6.3137
13°	.11393	63°	.61280	113°	1.5108	163°	6.6911
14°	.12278	64°	.62487	114°	1.5399	164°	7.1154
15°	.13165	65°	.63707	115°	1.5697	165°	7.5957
16°	.14054	66°	.64941	116°	1.6003	166°	8.1443
17°	.14945	67°	.66188	117°	1.6318	167°	8.7769
18°	.15838	68°	.67451	118°	1.6643	168°	9.5144
19°	.16734	69°	.68728	119°	1.6977	169°	10.385
20°	.17633	70°	.70021	120°	1.7320	170°	11.430
21°	.18534	71°	.71329	121°	1.7675	171°	12.706
22°	.19438	72°	.72654	122°	1.8040	172°	14.301
23°	.20345	73°	.73998	123°	1.8418	173°	16.350
24°	.21256	74°	.75355	124°	1.8807	174°	19.081
25°	.22169	75°	.76733	125°	1.9210	175°	22.904
26°	.23087	76°	.78128	126°	1.9626	176°	28.636
27°	.24008	77°	.79543	127°	2.0057	177°	38.188
28°	.24933	78°	.80978	128°	2.0503	178°	57.290
29°	.25862	79°	.82434	129°	2.0965	179°	114.590
30°	.26795	80°	.83910	130°	2.1445	180°	infinite
31°	.27732	81°	.85408	131°	2.1943		
32°	.28674	82°	.86929	132°	2.2460		
33°	.29621	83°	.88472	133°	2.2998		
34°	.30573	84°	.90040	134°	2.3558		
35°	.31530	85°	.91633	135°	2.4142		
36°	.32492	86°	.93251	136°	2.4751		
37°	.33459	87°	.94896	137°	2.5386		
38°	.34433	88°	.96569	138°	2.6051		
39°	.35412	89°	.98270	139°	2.6746		
40°	.36397	90°	1.00000	140°	2.7475		
41°	.37388	91°	1.0176	141°	2.8239		
42°	.38386	92°	1.0355	142°	2.9042		
43°	.39391	93°	1.0538	143°	2.9887		
44°	.40403	94°	1.0724	144°	3.0777		
45°	.41421	95°	1.0913	145°	3.1716		
46°	.42447	96°	1.1106	146°	3.2708		
47°	.43481	97°	1.1303	147°	3.3759		
48°	.44523	98°	1.1504	148°	3.4874		
49°	.45573	99°	1.1708	149°	3.6059		
50°	.46631	100°	1.1917	150°	3.7320		

Figure 22-43
Setback chart. Convair Div., General Dynamics Corp.

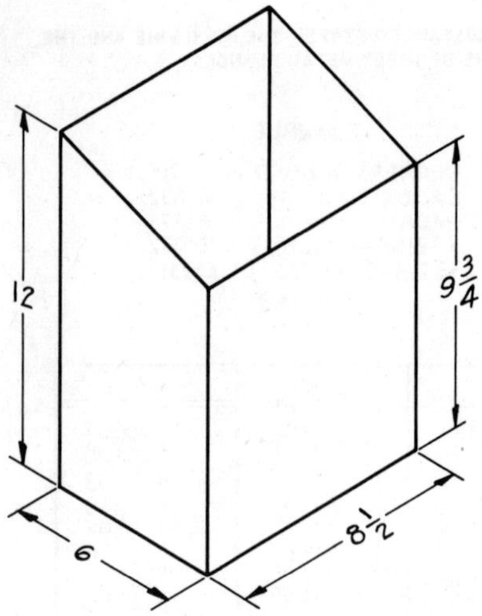

Figure 22-44
Problem 1.

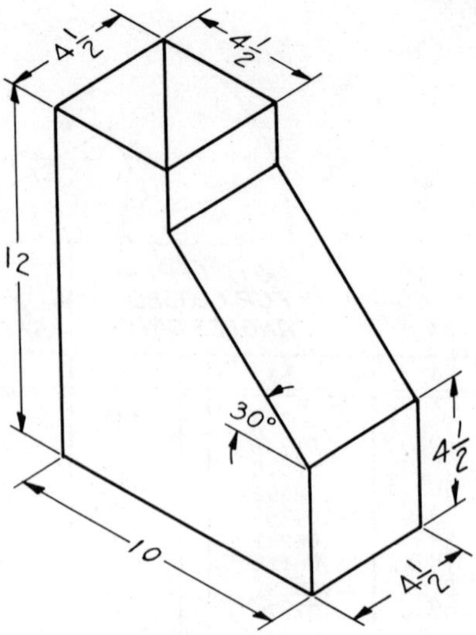

Figure 22-46
Problem 3.

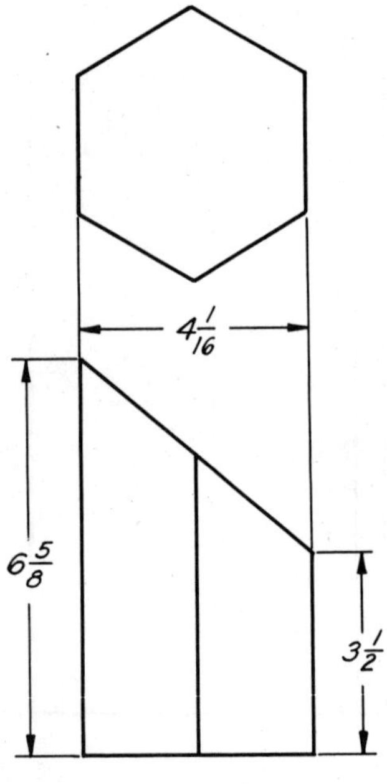

Figure 22-45
Problem 2.

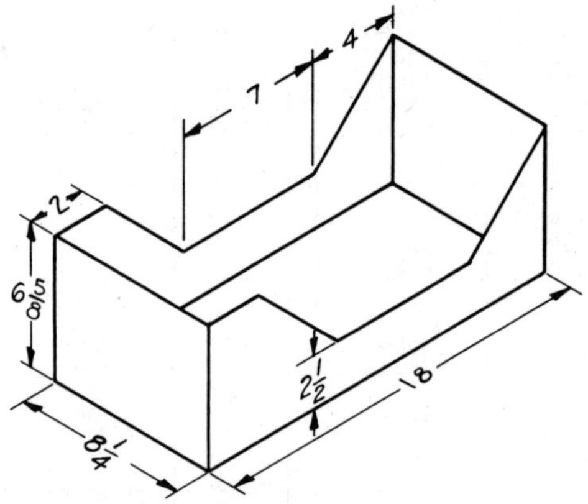

Figure 22-47
Problem 4.

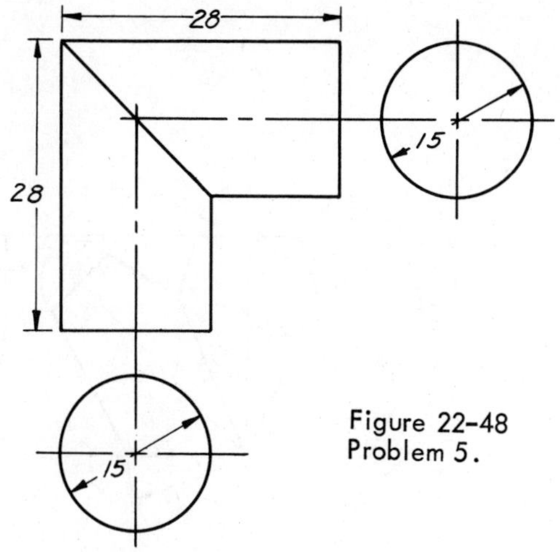

Figure 22–48
Problem 5.

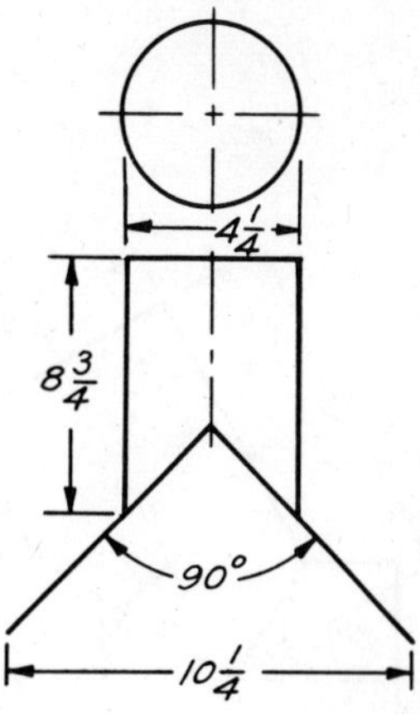

Figure 22–50
Problem 7.

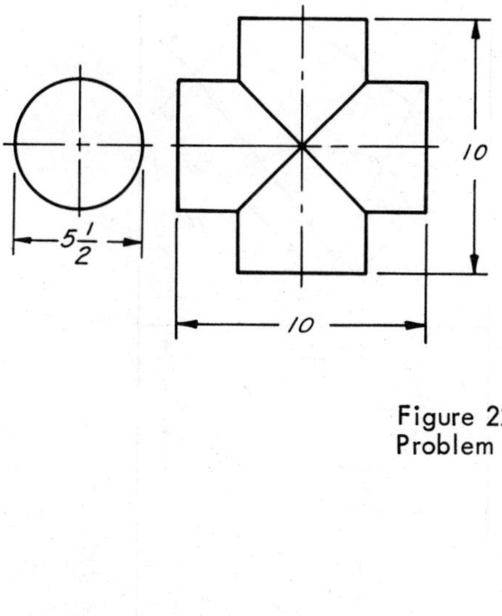

Figure 22–49
Problem 6.

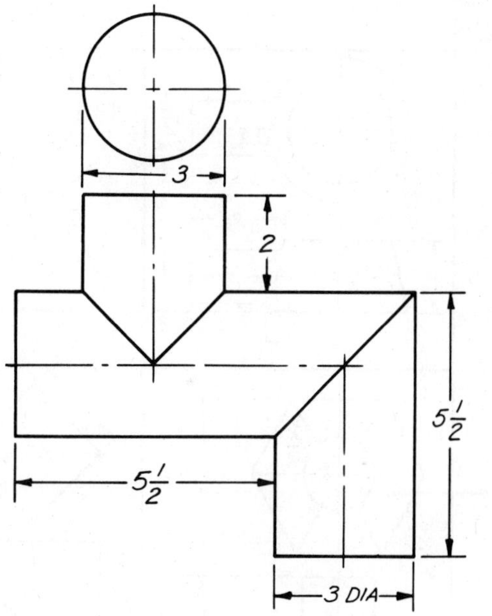

Figure 22–51
Problem 8.

Problems, section 22

Group I. Make stretchout patterns of the lateral surfaces of each of the problems shown in Figs. 22-44 to 22-53. In problem 4, include bottom.

Group II. Determine the intersections and lay out the patterns for the lateral surfaces of the problems shown in Fig. 22-54. Make full size or to scale as assigned.

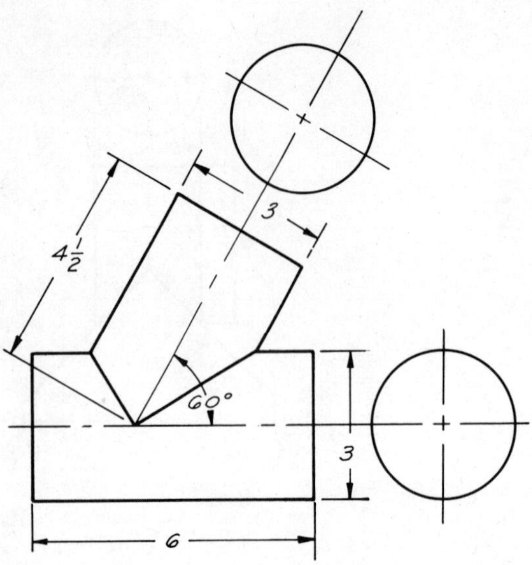

Figure 22-52
Problem 9.

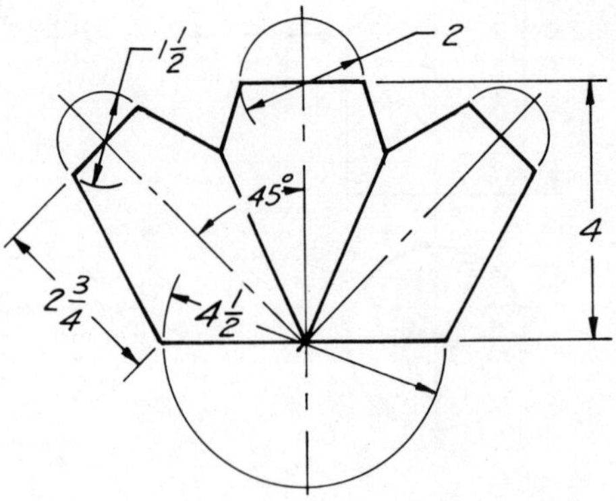

Figure 22-53
Problem 10.

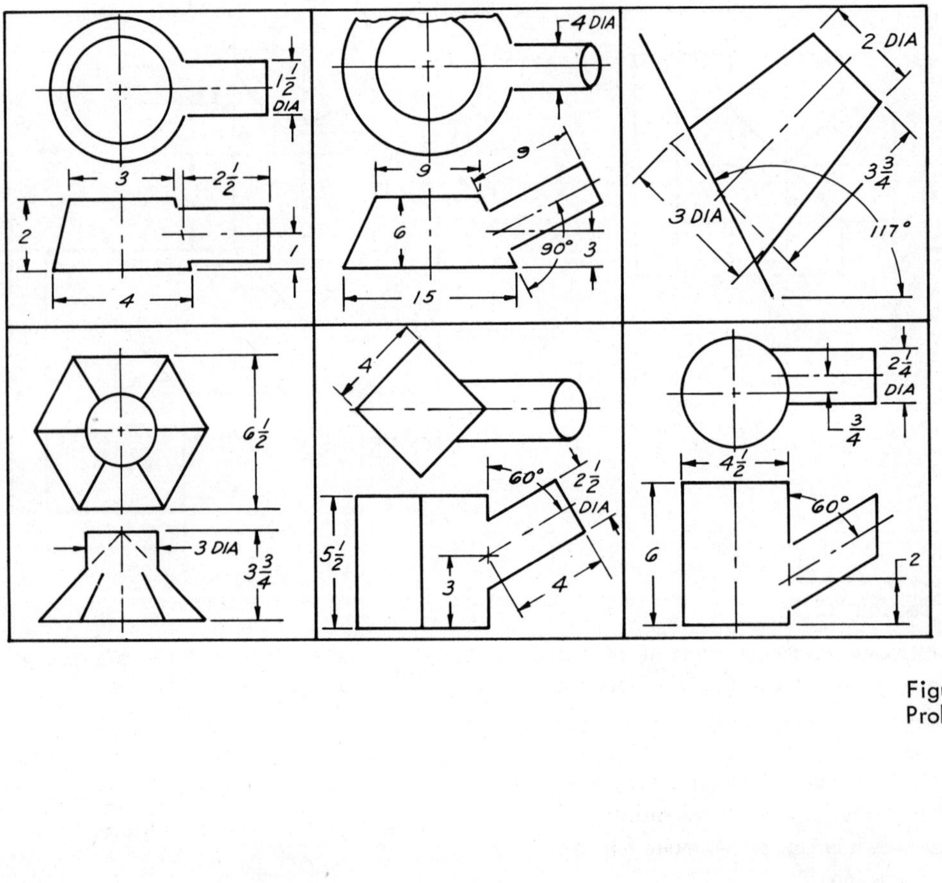

Figure 22-54
Problems 11-16.

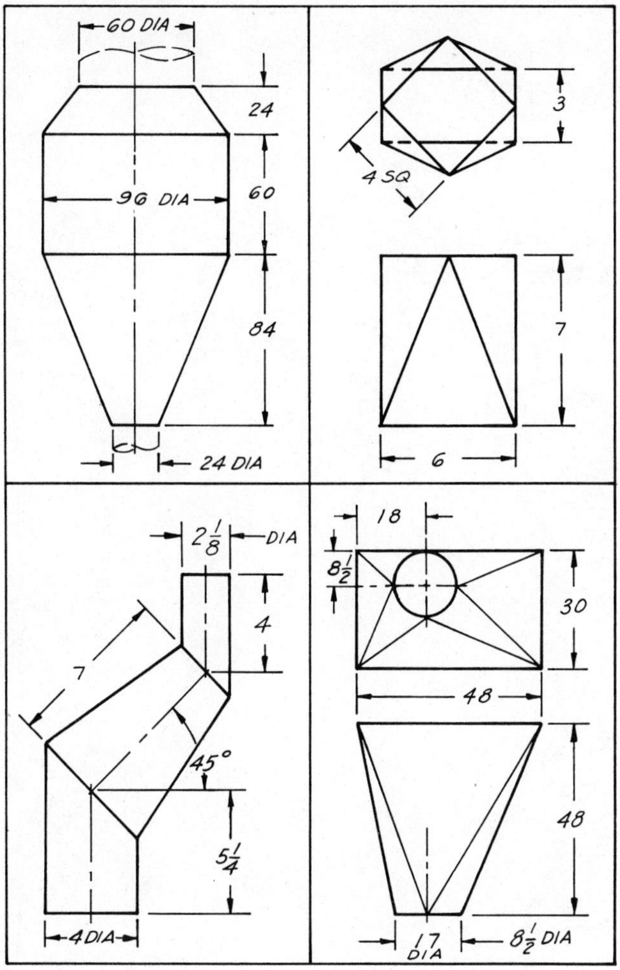

Figure 22-55
Problems 17-20.

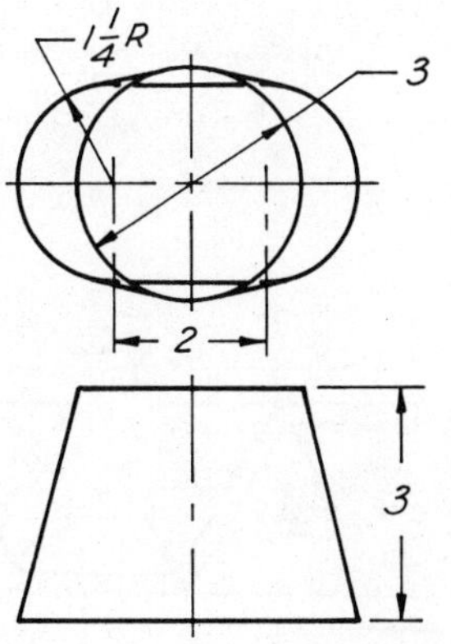

Figure 22-56
Problem 21.

Group III. Prepare full size or scale patterns of the lateral surfaces of the problems included in Fig. 22-55 as assigned.

Group IV. Using the "rollout method" for pattern development, prepare stretchouts of the transitions shown in Figs. 22-56 and 22-57. Cut out the patterns and assemble.

Group V. Determine the length of the cross-sections shown in Figs. 22-58 and 22-59, using bend allowance and setback tables.

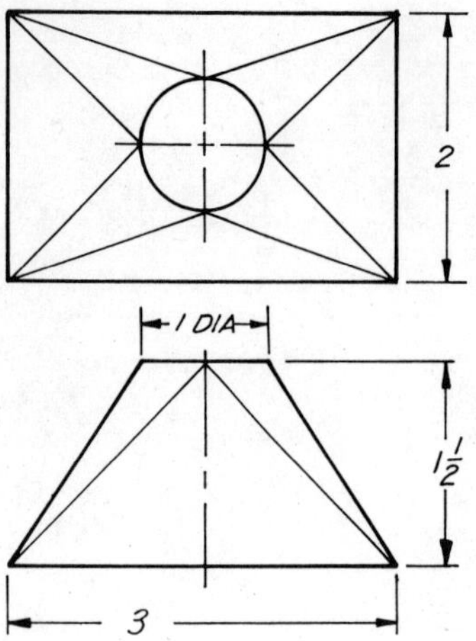

Figure 22-57
Problem 22.

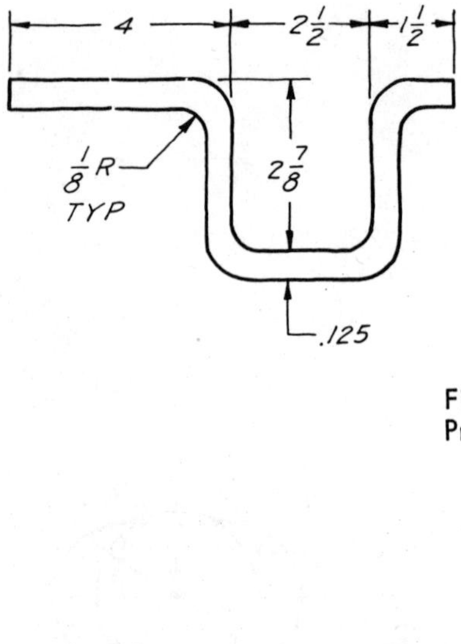

Figure 22-58
Problem 23.

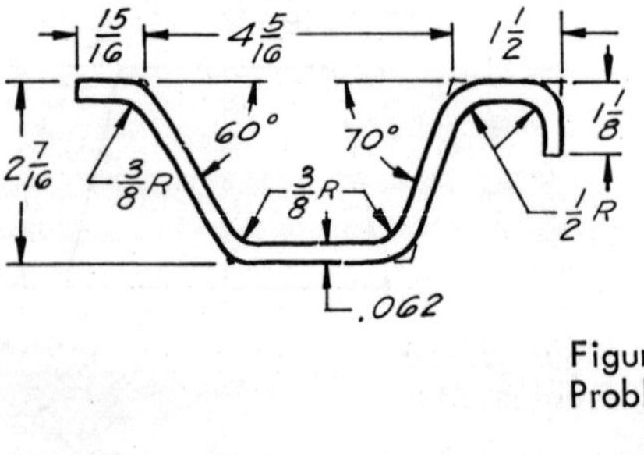

Figure 22-59
Problem 24.

Graphs and charts* 23

The function of a graphical system is to diagram the relationships between a quantity of numerical values to: (1) eliminate the time consuming mental effort of sorting them into a pattern, and (2) determine the approximate numerical values of many combinations of several factors without tedious calculation. A system of graphs and charts is used therefore to create a visual impression of the correlation of tabulated data, which not only reduces the amount of mental effort, but also makes the pattern of the data more easily remembered.

The application of graphs and charts in the fields of science, engineering, statistics, accounting and advertising to present easily understood facts is universal. The wide range of uses for graphical data tabulation has brought about the development of a variety of types of graphs and charts, each of which serves a particular need for a particular purpose.

It is virtually impossible to include in one section a description of all the types of graphs and charts utilized by various technical and scientific groups. Accordingly, the more common graphs and charts will be discussed quite thoroughly and the lesser used types will be described only briefly.

23.1 Types of graphs and charts

The intended function of a graph or chart determines the format that should be employed to present the subject matter. These questions should be answered prior to selecting the format: (1) Will the graph or chart be used to determine numerical values? This is called a *quantitative* graph. Or will the graph or chart merely represent a comparison of the numerical values? This is called a *qualitative graph.* (2) Is the graph or chart intended exclusively for scientific or technical purposes, or is it intended for advertising, selling, or informing the general public?

It is apparent that graphs or charts may serve many purposes, but the most important function should be established. With answers to the questions in the preceding paragraph, it then becomes possible to select the most effective format. The following is a list of the more common types of graphs and charts; each will be described in this section:

1 Rectangular coordinate graph.
2 Semi-logarithmic graph.
3 Logarithmic graph.
4 Bar chart.
5 Percentage bar chart.
6 Pie chart.
7 Pictorial chart.
8 Flow chart.
9 Operation process chart.
10 Organization chart.
11 Polar coordinate graph.
12 Trilinear chart.
13 Nomograph or alignment chart.

23.2 Rectangular coordinate graph

This graph is probably the most widely used to present data quantitatively or qualitatively. The rectangular coordinate graph is designed to emphasize the amount of numerical change.

*This section was written by Robert Angerman, Project Engineer, Ingersoll Kalamazoo Division, Borg-Warner Corp.

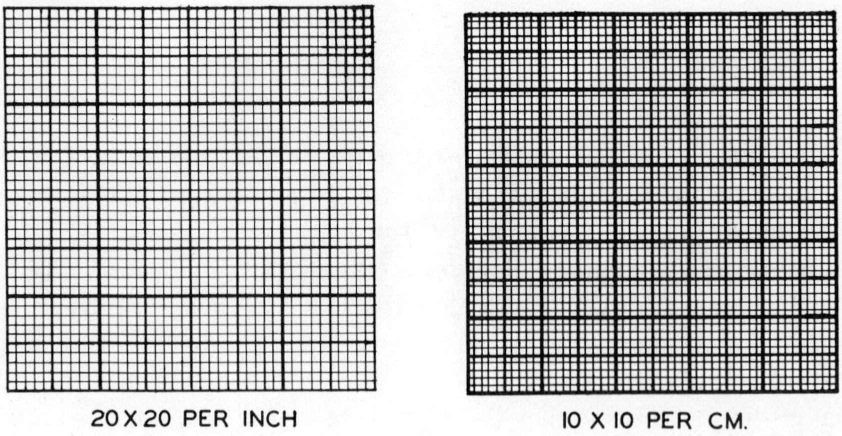

Figure 23-1
Two common types of graph paper for rectangular coordinate graphs.

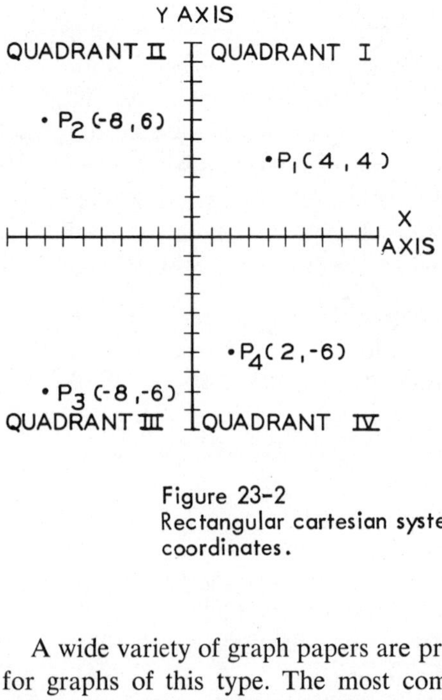

Figure 23-2
Rectangular cartesian system of coordinates.

A wide variety of graph papers are printed for graphs of this type. The most common is 8-1/2″ x 11″ and is divided into squares one-twentieth of an inch on a side with every fifth line darkened. Another form, frequently employed for laboratory reports, has one millimeter squares with every fifth line darkened. See Fig. 23-1. Other papers have 16 x 16, 12 x 12, 10 x 10, 8 x 8, 6 x 6, and 4 x 4 divisions to the inch. Still others have the conventional spacing vertically, but the horizontal spacings are divided into days, months, and years.

The method of presenting the data is based upon the rectangular cartesian system of coordinates and consists of two perpendicular lines intersecting at the origin. The horizontal line is known as the *X axis* and the vertical line as the *Y axis*. The *X* and *Y* axes are referred to as the *coordinate axes*. The coordinate axes separate the four quadrants which are numbered I, II, III, and IV. See Fig. 23-2. Each point (*P*) to be plotted contains the distance from the origin on the *X* axis (abscissa) and the distance from the origin on the *Y* axis (ordinate), listed in that order. Since the majority of engineering and scientific data is concerned with positive values of the abscissa and ordinate, most graphs incorporate Quadrant I only.

The rectangular coordinate graph is prepared in the following manner:

1 *Select the graph paper.* Knowing the range of values to be plotted, choose the graph paper having the greatest distance between divisions that will permit plotting all values. This will ensure having a readable graph. Qualitative graphs should have the range of values of both variables start with zero; in other words, the intersection of the coordinate axes is zero. An accurate comparison of the numerical values of the plotted points on a qualitative graph cannot be made unless the entire distance from the *x* and *y* axes is shown. Quantitative graphs do not require a zero origin. When the dependent variable varies as a power of the independent

variable ($Y = X^2$), consideration should be given to using logarithmic graph paper, since the plotted values will be in a straight line rather than a curve.

2 *Draw the coordinate axes, determine the variable for each axes and select and mark the scale.* Draw the *X* axis at the bottom of the sheet and the *Y* axis at the left, leaving an inch inside the edge, which is adequate room for lettering. The independent variables are normally plotted as abscissas and the dependent variables as ordinates. Select a scale that permits the divisions on the rectangular coordinate graph paper to assume values of 1, 2, 3, 4, etc., or a power of ten multiplied by 1, 2, 3, 4, etc. The scale selected determines the visual change in the dependent variable. An incorrect choice of scales may give the impression of rapid change even though this is not true. Fig. 23-3 shows the same data plotted using different scales. If more than one dependent variable is to be plotted on the graph a separate axis must be provided. See Fig. 23-4. Number the unit values of the heavy divisions along each axis so they are readable from the bottom. If decimals are used, the decimal point should have a zero prefix; for example, 0.25. Utilize the power of ten to reduce the amount of lettering; 10,000 becomes 1×10^4 or 0.00001 becomes 1×10^{-5}. The abscissa values usually increase from left to right and the ordinate from bottom to top. See Fig. 23-5. This graph may be used in a report covering a typical physics laboratory experiment.

3 *Plot the data.* Plot the positions determined by the values of the abscissa and ordinate. Encircle the dots to make the location of each point clearly evident. If more than one curve is to be plotted on a graph, make use of these symbols to differentiate the curves: triangle, square, cross, double circle, etc. (See Fig. 23-4) Make certain that the symbols will not obliterate the plotted points. Since the accuracy of the graph is dependent upon the proper placement of the plotted points, the location of each point should be verified. It is customary to eliminate the symbols on points that are plotted at

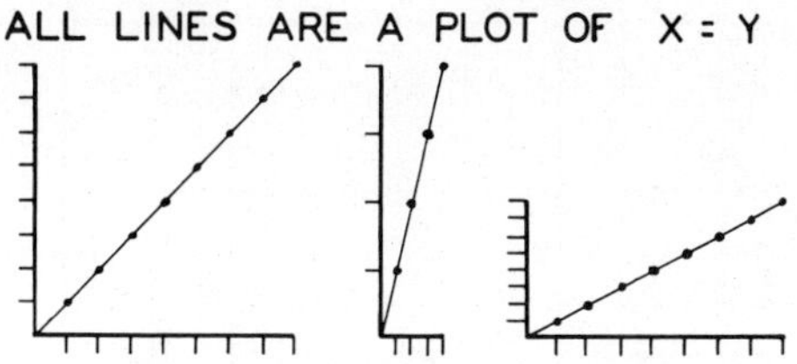

Figure 23-3
Change in visual impression is possible by altering the scale of the graph.

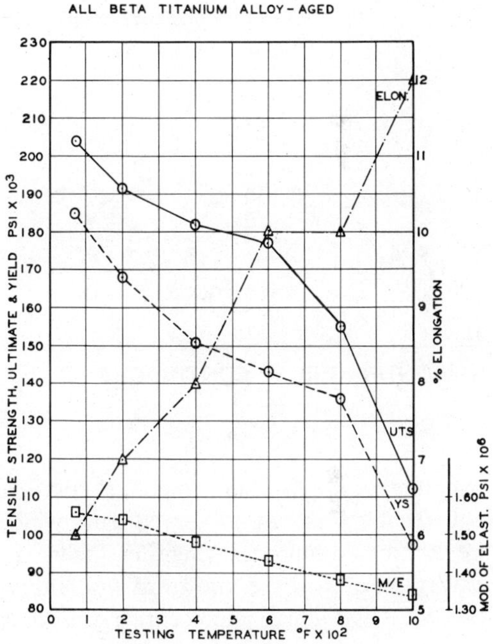

Figure 23-4
Several dependent variables may be used on a graph.

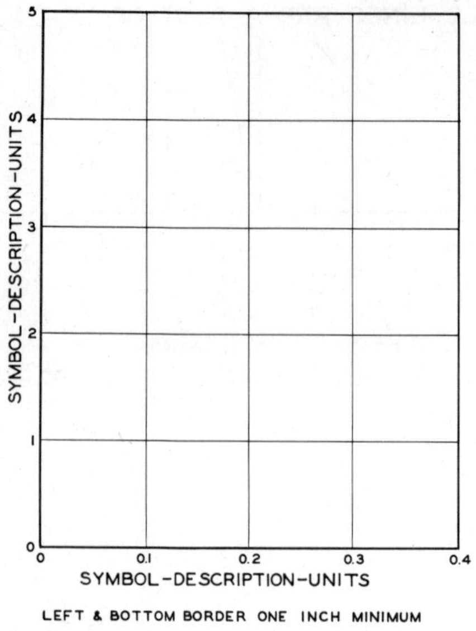

Figure 23-5
Graph construction method.

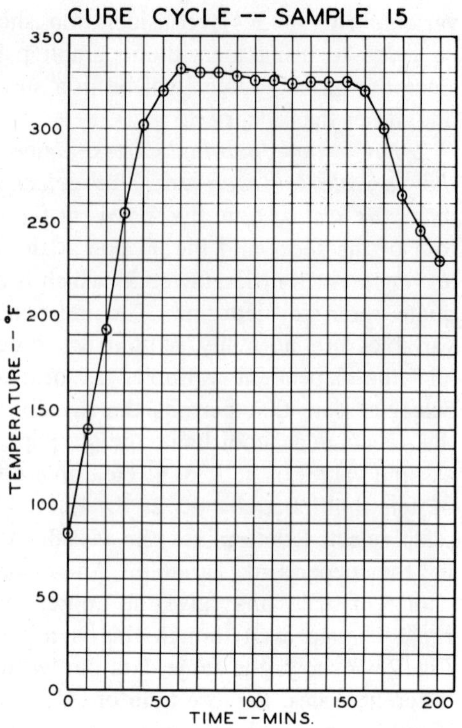

Figure 23-7
A complete rectangular graph.

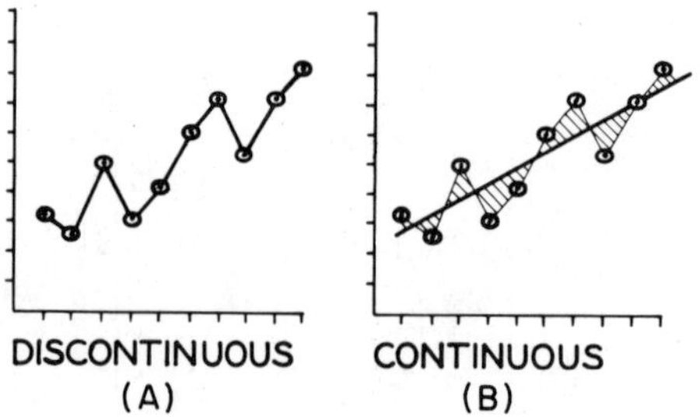

Figure 23-6
Method of representing discontinuous and continuous data.

computed positions of mathematical curves.

4 *Draw the curves.* Observed data, which are not based upon a scientific theory or mathematical law, are known as *discontinuous data.* The curve representing this data is drawn by connecting the plotted points with straight lines as shown in *A* of Fig. 23-6. For continuous data, a smooth curve should be drawn which distributes the points on either side and has as nearly as possible distances alternately on one side and on the other.[1] A method, which may assist in drawing a smooth curve, consists of drawing straight lines between the plotted points and then drawing the curve to intersect the lines so that the sum of the areas of the triangles formed by the broken line are approximately equal on each side of the curve. See *B* of Fig. 23-6.

Curves should be drawn with solid lines, if possible. When more than one curve is required on a graph, the type of line may be varied—dashed, dotted, etc.—to differentiate the curves; however, the most important curve should be solid. Curves on a quantitative graph should be drawn very sharp and fine to facilitate accurate reading. The curves on qualitative graphs should be drawn heav-

1. The best line requires that the sum of the squares of the deviations on one side of the curve equals the sum of the squares of the deviations on the other side. This theory of least squares is a theory of probability.

ier. Curves should not be drawn through the symbols.

5 *Letter the graph.* Each axis should be lettered with a brief description and the unit of measurement, using standard abbreviations when space is limited. Letter a brief description near each curve. When the curves are located close to each other, a leader should be used to differentiate them.

The title for the graph should be brief, complete, descriptive, and lettered symmetrically over the graph. It should give the name of the curve, the name of the engineer and/or draftsman, the name of the institution or source, and the date. Any relevant information concerning the nature of the experiment or the causes of irregularity in the plotted data may be included. This information is placed at the right side either at the top or bottom to give a balanced graph. It is common to remove the grid lines with alcohol in the area to be used for the title to permit lettering in an open space for emphasis. A rectangular coordinate graph is shown in Fig. 23-7.

23.3 Semi-logarithmic graph

This graph is used for presenting data qualitatively and quantitatively to indicate a rate of change, rather than an amount of change as in a rectangular coordinate graph. Semi-logarithmic graph paper has equally spaced divisions on one axis and logarithmic scaled divisions on the other and is sometimes known as *ratio ruled* paper. Measurement of the slope of the curve determines the rate of increase or decrease; a straight line indicates a constant rate of change. This type of graph should be used whenever one variable increases in a geometric progression or other non-linear manner and the other variable increases arithmetically, or if it is necessary to show a percentage of change. See Fig. 23-8. A semi-logarithmic graph is drawn in the same manner as the rectangular coordinate graph. Care must be exercised to interpolate the location of points logarithmically on the logarithmic scaled axis.

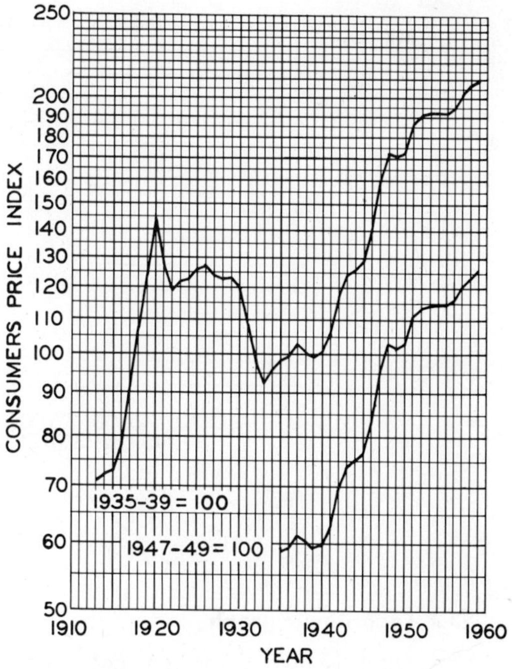

Figure 23-8
A semi-logarithmic graph showing Bureau of Labor statistics-price index.

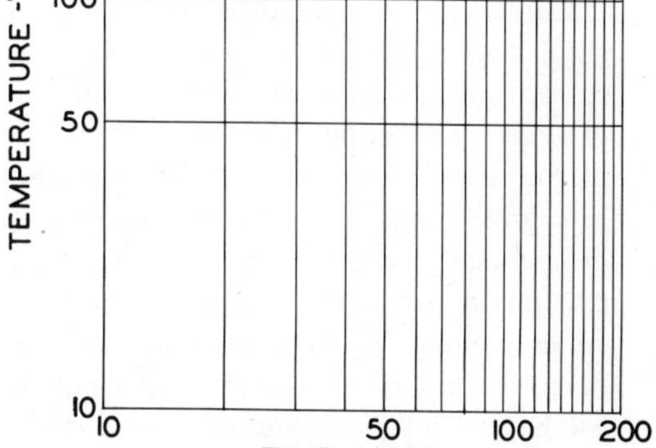

Figure 23-9
A typical logarithmic graph.

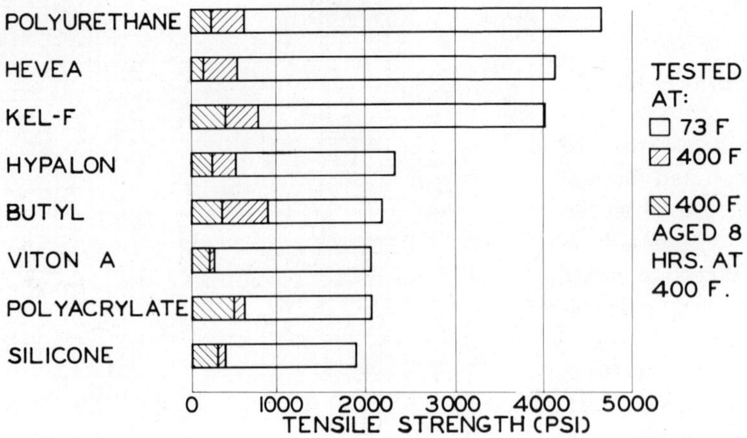

Figure 23-10
A bar chart showing the effect of temperature upon elastomer strength.

23.4 Logarithmic graph

This graph is used to present data qualitatively or quantitatively. Some of its advantages include (1) the representation of large numerical values with short graphical distances, (2) straight line graphs when the dependent variables are proportional to a constant power of the independent variables and (3) the errors which may occur in plotting or reading the graph are a constant percentage.

Logarithmic graph paper has both axes scaled in divisions proportional to the logarithms of numbers and is sometimes known as *log paper*. These printed forms are available in one or more cycles. Part cycle and split cycle forms are also available.

Curves are easily plotted on logarithmic graph paper because two points determine a straight line, as does one point and the slope of a line. The slope of a line is the tangent of the angle it makes with the horizontal axis and is equal to the exponent of the independent variable. Fig. 23-9 shows the two point- and one point-slope method of curve plotting. If the logarithms are taken of both sides of an equation, the equation will have a slope intercept form $y = mx + b$ and can be plotted on rectangular coordinate paper by substituting the logarithms of the variables. It is easier to use logarithmic coordinates and plot the points directly than use the logarithms of the variables and plot them on rectangular coordinates. All other aspects of graph making explained for rectangular coordinate graphs apply to this type. Care must be taken to interpolate logarithmically and not arithmetically as was done on rectangular coordinate graphs.

23.5 Bar chart

Bar charts are used extensively in literature for the general public. They present a graphic picture and give a pictorial summary of data that can be easily understood by a non-technical person who has little knowledge of graphs. A bar chart is sometimes known as a barograph, pipe-organ chart or a staircase chart. There are no standard printed forms available for bar charts. The practice is to use rectangular coordinate paper to prepare the rough draft and then to trace the draft for final publication.

The bar chart is so called because of the heavy bars which appear on the chart to proportionately represent the amount of a numerical value. These bars should be made to start from zero and may be placed vertically or horizontally. The scale should be the same for each bar and should be lettered along the bottom or left side of the chart to permit reading the approximate numerical values. If it is necessary to indicate the exact values, they should be lettered next to and parallel to the bars. To place the values at the end of the bars would give a false impression of greater length. The name of the items represented should be lettered on the appropriate axis and a title should be included. Fig. 23-10 shows a typical bar chart.

23.6 Percentage bar chart

This type of chart is a form of area diagram used extensively in non-technical literature to present graphically a comparison between related quantities that must be expressed in percentages. See Fig. 23-11. The total length of the bar represents 100 per cent. The bar is subdivided proportionately and each division is cross hatched differently. The description of each division should be lettered on one side of the bar. The percentage of the division should be lettered on the opposite side or on the bar itself. If the percentages are placed on the bar, the cross hatching should be drawn in later. Positioning the bars vertically simplifies lettering the chart, whereas the readability is improved if the bars are placed horizontally because horizontal distances are judged more easily.

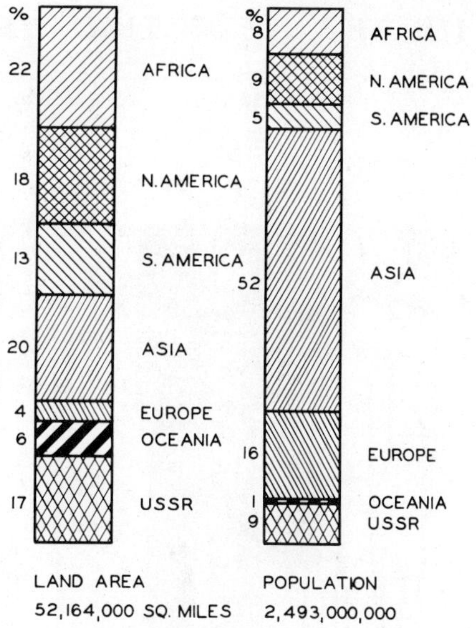

Figure 23-11
A percentage bar chart is used to present data that must be expressed in percentages.

23.7 Pie chart

The pie chart is used more frequently than the percentage bar chart because it is so easy to construct. Its principal function is to present a graphic comparison of related quantities expressed in a percentage. This chart is in the form of a circle in which its area represents 100 per cent. The subdivisions are readily calculated because they are a proportionate amount of the entire circle.

To determine the number of degrees in each of the segments, multiply the percentage that the segment will represent by 3.6. Draw the circle and then draw the divisions using a protractor to measure the calculated degrees. Describe the nature of each quantity and its percentage. Cross hatch each segment differently or use various colors. Complete the chart by lettering the title. A sample pie chart is presented in Fig. 23-12.

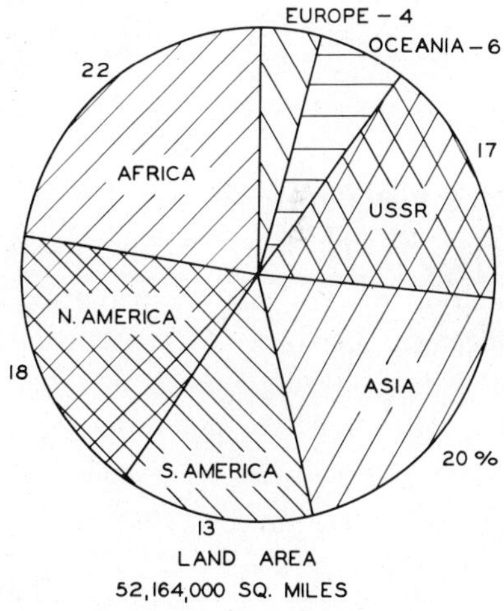

Figure 23-12
A pie chart is frequently used to graphically compare related quantities when they must be expressed in percentage.

Figure 23-13
A pictorial chart uses realistic figures to present factual data.

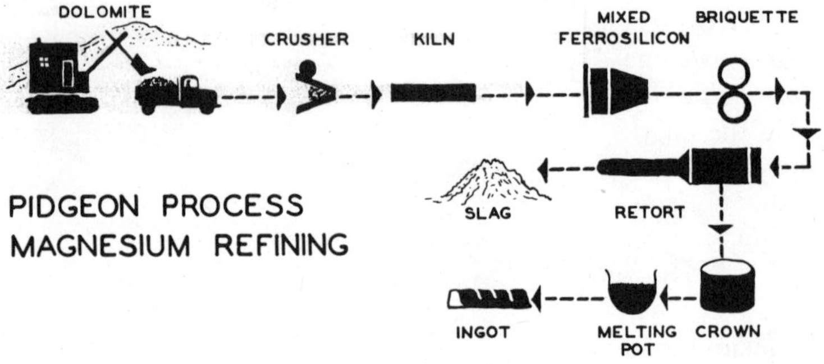

Figure 23-14
A flow chart conveys a pictorial description of the movement, travel, or flow of some particular process.

23.8 Pictorial chart

The pictorial chart is also used to present data in reports that are to be read by non-technical persons. It is particularly adaptable for showing information pertaining to population, costs, expenditures, etc. Some of the common symbols selected to represent the data are human figures, animals, hard money, etc. The symbols are made in proportionate sizes or amounts to illustrate the unit to be described. To be really effective, a pictorial chart must display symbols that tell the story and stimulate the imagination—symbols that are not the time-worn, hackneyed variety which are too frequently seen. A pictorial chart, sometimes called a pictogram, is essentially a variation of the bar chart and is drawn in the same manner. The bars are replaced with symbols as shown in Fig. 23-13.

23.9 Flow chart

The flow chart is a form of pictorial chart used to correlate and present data in a simple and understandable manner. Industrial engineers and chemical engineers use the flow chart to show a concise, pictorial description of a process to non-technical persons. A touch of artistry is again helpful in selecting meaningful and unique symbols. Fig. 23-14 illustrates this type.

23.10 Operation process chart

This chart is used by industrial engineers to present data in a concise, readable and understandable manner concerning the operations, materials and inspections necessary to fabricate a product. The chart is very similar in purpose to the flow chart and differs only in construction and intended usage. The information is normally drawn in rough form to determine the finished size and then made into a finished chart. Data such as departmental number, machine number, job classification of operator, time allowances, etc., can be included but care must be taken not to make the chart so complex that the relationship between the various operations is obscured. The four symbols used to describe the essential processes are shown in the key in Fig. 23-15. Horizontal lines depict the flow of material and the vertical lines show the work performed. It is customary to chart first the item of the assembly requiring the greatest amount of work. Operational symbols are placed at intervals of approximately 1/2″ in the order in which they occur. The description of the operation is lettered to the right of the symbol and those operations which change the condition of the raw material are numbered for reference. The items are shown joining the subassemblies and the major assembly at the appropriate points. A complete operation process chart is shown in Fig. 23-15.

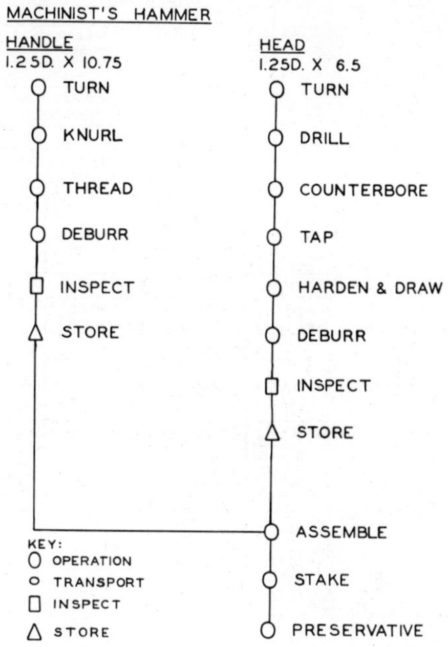

Figure 23-15
An operation process chart is used to present data concerning the operations, materials and inspection required to fabricate a product.

23.11 Organization chart

The organization chart describes the formal organization of a group of persons, offices, or organization functions. Draftsmen are frequently called upon to draw such a chart for publication and should be aware of the conventions used. The form may differ slightly from one organization to another, but these variances occur in the majority of charts. The most important office is always centered at the top of the chart. The name of the office and frequently the name of the person performing the duties of the office are lettered inside a rectangular box. Solid lines are drawn from this box to the next echelon of offices. Only those positions reporting directly to the chief officer are included in this line. The names of these offices and officers are boxed and lettered. The process is repeated for the next levels. Care must be taken to position the boxes in a pattern pleasing to the eye and in the proper relative level in the organization. See Fig. 23-16. Dotted lines are sometimes used to denote cooperation and advice between members of the same level.

23.12 Polar coordinate graph

The use of polar coordinates often simplifies the calculation of values. The data is plotted on polar coordinate paper, commonly called by that name. The most popular uses of polar coordinate graphs are in recording instruments having circular plotting paper and to represent intensity of light

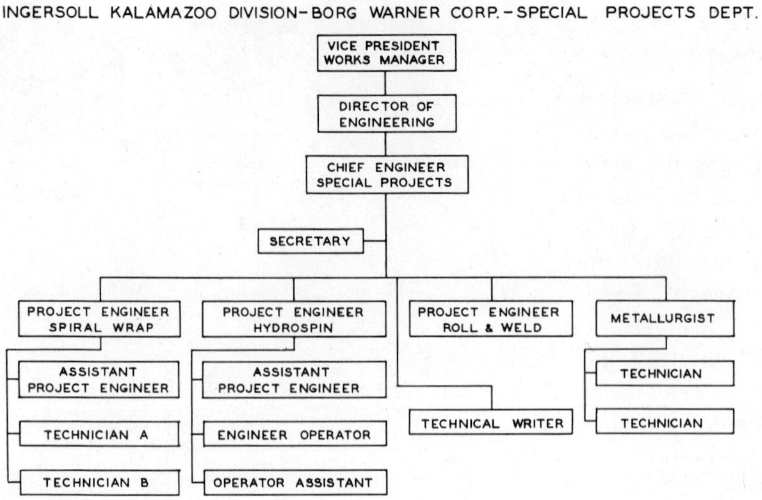

Figure 23-16
An organization chart describes the relationship of a group of people or offices in an organization.

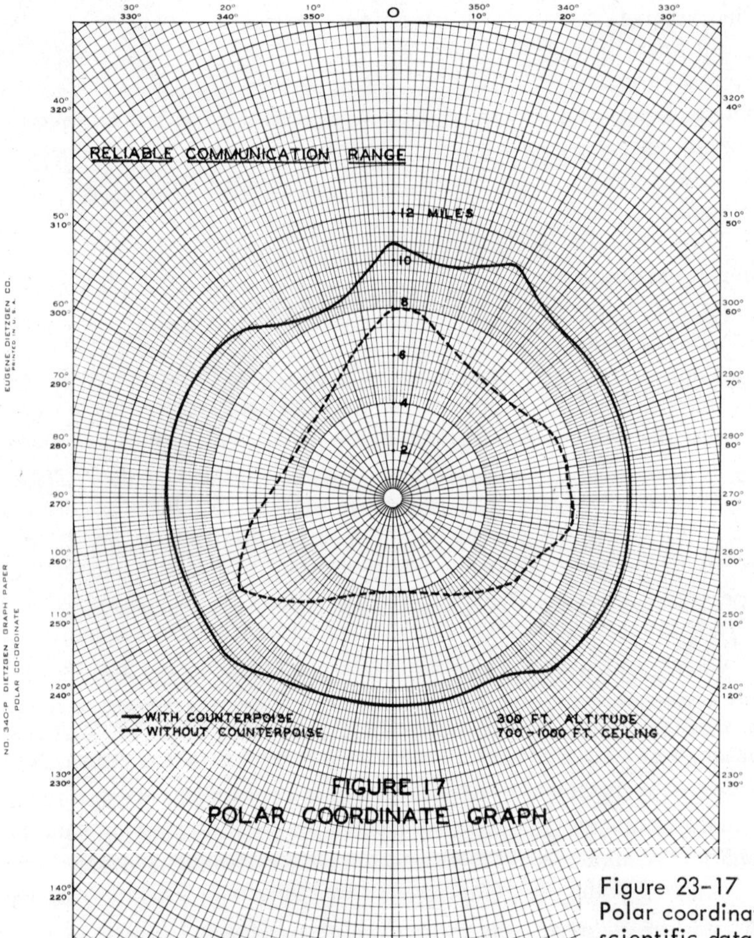

Figure 23-17
Polar coordinate graphs are used to represent scientific data such as intensity of heat and light.

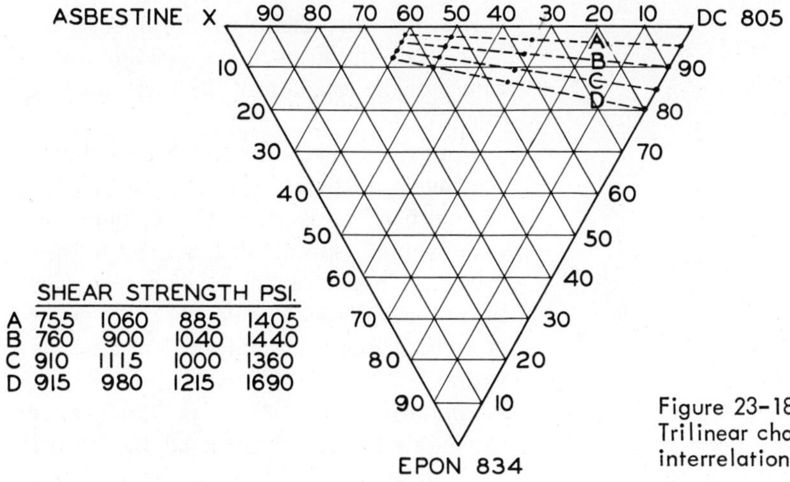

Figure 23-18
Trilinear charts are used to show the interrelations between three variables.

or heat at various distances from the source. Fig. 23-17 shows a typical polar coordinate graph. It is possible, by using trigonometry, to convert the polar coordinates to rectangular coordinates or vice versa if a more readable graph will result.

23.13 Trilinear chart

This chart is used to present the interrelations between three variable items such as chemical compounds, mixtures, solutions or alloys. Essentially it is an area chart, with the altitude of the triangle equalling 100 per cent. It is based upon the premise that the sum of the three perpendiculars from a point equals the altitude. Since the altitude equals 100 per cent, the perpendiculars are the proportionate amount of the percentage of the three variables. The chart is constructed by dividing two sides of the triangle into equal percentage divisions and then drawing lines through these points parallel to the sides of the triangle. Fig. 23-18 illustrates a trilinear chart.

23.14 Alignment chart

Alignment charts or *nomographs* are used extensively as quantitative graphs to easily and quickly determine the numerical values of formulae having three or more variables. Since the majority of nomographs are complicated and difficult to construct, it is unusual to develop one unless its frequency of use is great enough to warrant the effort. Once completed, however, they will justify the time spent because of the ease and rapidity with which the values of the variables are determined without resorting to tedious and laborious computations. Each chart must be constructed to fit the particular relationships that are to be depicted. Essentially, a nomograph consists of a graphical representation of the relationship that exists between the several variables of an equation by means of scaled lengths of the variables along straight or curved axes positioned in such a way that a straight line will intersect the axes at the points satisfying the equation. It is a graphical equation with three or more variables and only one unknown value. Usually the engineer or scientist will develop the nomograph and the draftsman will reproduce the format so that it can be used repeatedly without becoming worn or illegible.

Nomograph terms. Prior to discussing the design and construction of alignment charts, it is essential that the definitions of various terms and expressions be understood as they apply to this type of graph.

Constant. A symbol which represents a fixed numerical value, incapable of change

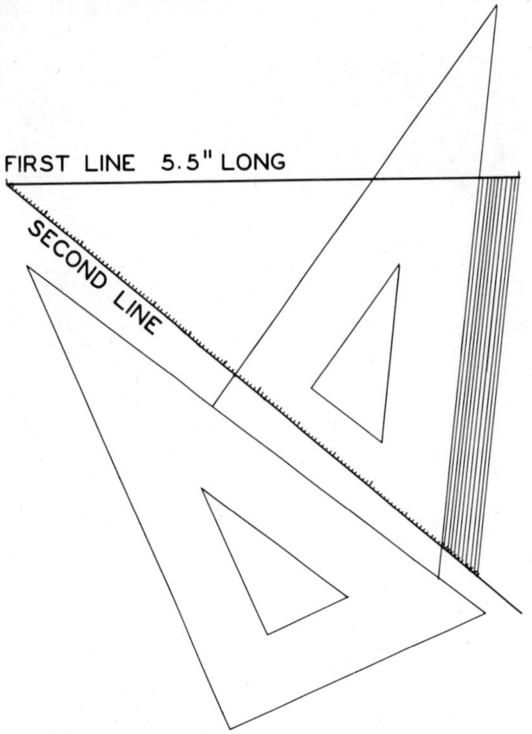

Figure 23-19
Dividing a line into equal segments to develop a uniform nomograph scale.

during a particular discussion.

Variable. A symbol which may assume various values during a discussion.

Function. A dependent variable is said to be a function of an independent variable when both are so related in a formula that to each arbitrary value assigned to the first (independent) there corresponds one or more definite values of the other variable (dependent). This condition is usually written in abbreviated form as $f(x)$ which is read "Function of x" not as "f multiplied by x."

Example: In the expression $x^2 + 3x + 5$, x is the independent variable and the expression is the dependent variable or function of x. If the expression were written as the formula, $y = f(x) = x^2+3+5$, then y is a function of x.

The equations that will be used in the following charts will have functions of different independent variables, such as $f(x) + f(y) = f(z)$; *or* $f(u)$ multiplied by $f(v) = f(w)$.

Scale. A graduated straight or curved line. These graduations may have equal distances between them (uniform scale) or may have distances corresponding to the values of the function of the variable (functional scale).

Both types of scales have been used in the previously discussed types of graphs, but it has not been necessary to fit a certain length scale within a specific distance. Since this is necessary in the drawing of alignment charts, the following procedure describes the method of constructing both uniform and functional scales.

Uniform nomograph scale. When a uniform scale is to be constructed, the first step is to solve the function for the upper and lower limits of the independent variable and then determine the length of the scale. For example, when the function of $f(x) = x^2 + 3x + 5$ is solved for $f(x)$ with x varying from zero to 10 the scale must contain 130 units reading from 5 to 135. If this scale must be constructed in 6.5 inches, it is possible to divide the distance (6.5″) by 130 units giving a value of 0.05″ per unit. Since this is an easily measured value it is possible to rule off one-hundred thirty 0.05″ increments to make the uniform scale.

If the same function having the same limits had to be drawn as a 5.5″ long uniform scale, it would not be feasible or possible to measure increments of 0.0423077″ length. In cases of this sort it is easier to divide the scale geometrically in the following manner. Draw a straight line 5.5″ long. Draw another straight line at an angle to the first line passing through the end of the line. On the second line lay out one-hundred thirty equally spaced units (the length of a unit is not important). Draw a straight line between the opposite end of the first line and the one-hundred thirtieth division of the second line. Continue to draw lines from the division marks on the second line to the first line parallel to the one-hundred thirtieth division line. The intersection of these parallel lines with the first line will mark the uniform scale desired. To complete the scale, number the intersection points from 5 to 135. This method is shown in Fig. 23-19.

X	0	1	2	3	4	5	6	7	8	9	10
$\frac{X}{2}$	0	0.5	1.0	1.5	2.0	2.5	3.0	3.5	4.0	4.5	5.0
$\left(\frac{X}{2}\right)^2$	0	0.25	1.00	2.25	4.00	6.25	9.00	12.25	16.00	20.25	25.00
$.2\left(\frac{X}{2}\right)^2$	0	0.05	0.20	0.45	0.80	1.35	1.80	2.45	3.20	4.05	5.00

PROPORTIONALITY CONSTANT $= \frac{5}{25-0} = 0.2$

Figure 23-20
Tabulated calculations of a five inch long functional scale of $f(x) = (x/2)^2$.

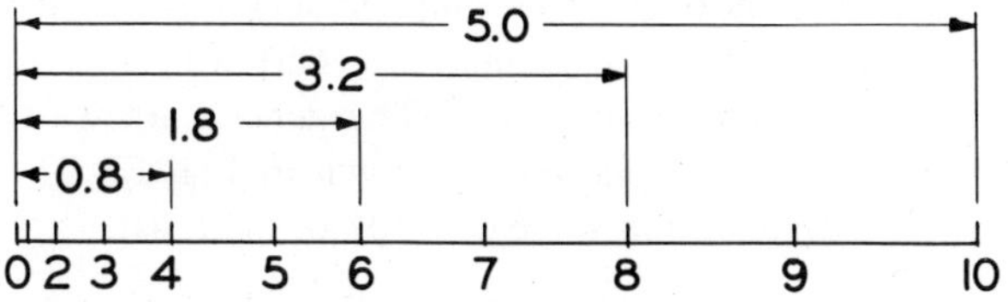

Figure 23-21
Functional scale of $f(x) = (x/2)^2$ with x ranging from zero to ten.

Functional nomograph scale. The construction of a functional scale is best accomplished in steps and the data recorded in tabular form. As in the uniform scale, the upper and lower limits of the independent variable and the length of the scale will be known or must be selected. If it is desired to construct a functional scale of the function $f(x) = (x/2)^2$ with values of x ranging from 0 to 10 within a five-inch space, use the following steps (see Fig. 23-20):

1 Record the values of the independent variable in the table.
2 Compute the numerical value of the function for each value of the independent variable.
3 Calculate the proportionality factor by dividing the length of the scale by the difference between the upper and lower values of the function.
4 Multiply the numerical values of the function by the proportionality factor to determine the scaled length of each value.
5 Lay out the computed distances on a straight line and record the value of the independent variable for each distance.

A functional scale based upon logarithmic values can be graduated in the same manner, but a simpler method may be used to reduce the calculation and construction time. Following the geometrical method described in the uniform scale construction, draw the first line to the desired length and then graduate this line using a printed log scale.

Nomograph equations. The general equation for a large number of nomographs is: $f_1(x) + f_2(x) \cdot f_3(y) = f_4(z)$, where f_1 and f_2 are different functions of the same independent variable x; f_3 is a function of y which is multiplied by $f_2(x)$, and $f_4(z)$ is a function of z. Since the variables y and z appear in only one term each they will show on the nomograph as two parallel straight lines. The independent variable x appears in two terms and is normally a curved line. If $f_1(x)$ equals *0* the chart will take the form

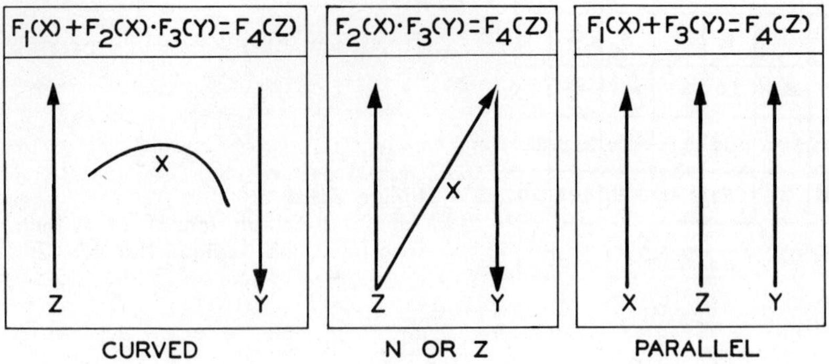

Figure 23-22
Basic forms of nomographs.

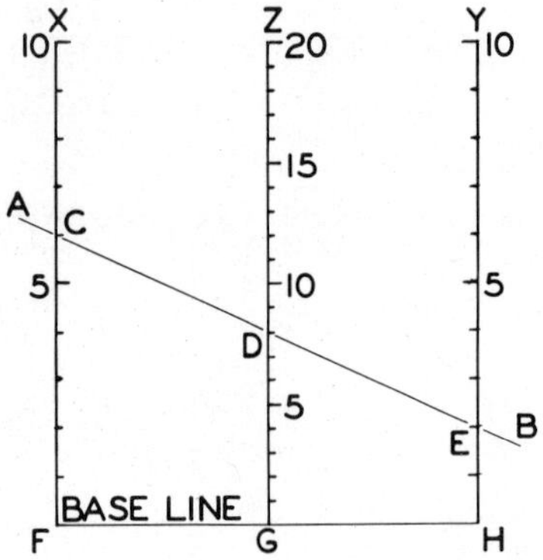

Figure 23-23
Constructing a parallel scale nomograph where X + Y = Z.

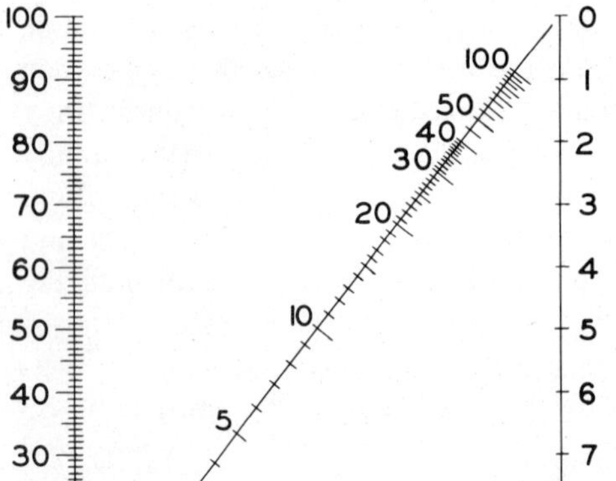

Figure 23-24
Construction of an N or Z scale nomograph in which X·Y = Z.

of an N or Z when uniform scales are used. If $f_2(x)$ is a constant, the chart will consist of three parallel lines. The general form of the three equations is shown in Fig. 23-22. The equation for each type of chart is:

Curved: $f_1(x) + f_2(x) \cdot f_3(y) = f_4(z)$

N or Z: $f_2(x) \cdot f_3(y) = f_4(z)$

Parallel: $f_1(x) + f_3(y) = f_4(z)$

Parallel scale nomograph. The parallel scale nomograph, to depict the values of equation $f_1(x) + f_3(y) = f_4(z)$, is constructed as follows: Draw three parallel lines, X, Y and Z at equal distances apart. Draw a line intersecting all three and call this the base line. The base line does not necessarily have to be drawn perpendicular to the three vertical lines. Lay off a series of equally spaced divisions starting at the base line for the outer lines X and Y. Lay off divisions on line Z using a spacing equal to half that used in the outer lines. See Fig. 23-23. Number all divisions as shown.

Draw any straight line, such as AB, intersecting lines X, Y and Z at C, D, and E, respectively. Lines AB, X, Y and the base line form a trapezoid $FCEH$. Since line Z is equidistant from CF and EH, the length of DG is equal to half the sum of the length of CF and EH. This is the reason for making the divisions on line Z half as long as the divisions on lines X and Y. It now becomes evident that every straight line intersecting the three lines will solve the equation $f_1(x) + f_3(y) = f_4(z)$ because the value of the function of x plus the value of the function

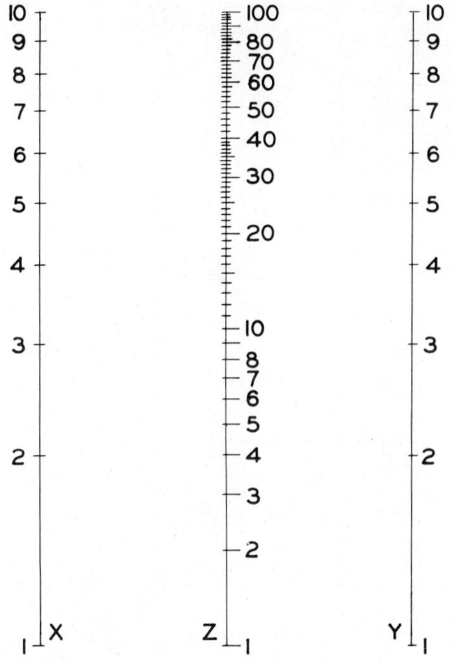

Figure 23-25
Parallel scale nomograph using logarithmic values.

of y can be read as a value of the function of z on line Z. To use the nomogram for subtraction, convert the equation to the form $f_1(x) = f_4(z) - f_3(y)$. The difference between the values of z and y can be read on line X. It is obvious that this is too simple a relationship to spend time constructing a nomograph, but the basic concept will be used later.

N or Z scale nomograph. The N or Z scale nomograph, which solves the equation $f_2(x) \cdot f_3(y) = f_4(z)$, is made in the following manner: Draw the outer vertical lines Y and Z and lay off the divisions using uniform spacing. It is necessary to have the origins opposite each other rather than on the same base line as done previously. See Fig. 23-24. Draw the diagonal line connecting the origins of the lines Y and Z. The diagonal becomes line X. To graduate line X, use any value of Y and align with various values of Z with a straight edge. The intersection of the straight edge with line X is the location of the value of Z, divided by Y. In reality, a functional scale is constructed along the diagonal in this manner. It is now possible to determine the value of Z by aligning the X and Y values and reading the graduation at the intersection point with line Z. This method of constructing the nomograph to solve equations involving multiplication has the advantage of using uniform scales on the vertical lines and permitting easy construction of the functional scale.

Another method for constructing a nomograph to solve multiplication equations involves the use of the previously described parallel scale. It is well known that adding the logarithms of numbers will yield the product of the numbers. The equation $f_2(x) \cdot f_3(y) = f_4(z)$ is identical to the equation $\log f_2(x) + \log f_3(y) = \log f_4(z)$. It is therefore possible to use the parallel scale form to multiply by using a logarithmic scale instead of the uniform spacing. Lines X and Y have identical scale division spacings starting with one instead of zero at the base line. Line Z has a double log scale as shown in Fig. 23-25.

23.15 Application of a nomograph

The difficulty in making nomographs is not caused by the basics just presented. The problem is essentially that of applying the basic approach to various equations when designing a nomograph. To eliminate the cut-and-try method generally used, it has been found helpful to reduce the equations to some form of expressions. When this is done, it is possible to choose the scale that should be used for each of the vertical lines and the relative distances between the lines. The expressions, choice of scales, and distances between lines are given in Fig. 23-26. The scales, drawn to their proper logarithmic value, are presented in Fig. 23-27.

The method of preparing the nomograph can best be presented by an example. Assume that a nomograph is desired to express the relationship between the volume (V) of a right circular cylinder with the cylinder's radius (r) and height (h). The formula, $V = \pi r^2 h$, is reduced to the expression $Z = XY^2$. By referring to Fig. 23-26, it is found that there are five combinations of scales to depict this

EXPRESSION	SCALE			RATIO
	X	Y	Z	$L_X : L_Y$
$Z = XY$	1	1	3	1:1
	1	3	4	2:1
	1	4	5	3:1
	3	1	4	1:2
	3	3	5	1:1
	3	5	6	2:1
	4	1	5	1:3
	4	4	6	1:1
	5	3	6	1:2
$Z = XY^2$	1	1	4	2:1
	2	2	5	2:1
	3	1	5	1:1
	3	3	6	2:1
	5	1	6	1:2
$Z = XY^3$	1	1	5	3:1
	3	2	6	2:1
	4	1	6	1:1
$Z = XY^4$	3	1	6	2:1
$Z = X^2Y^2$	1	1	5	1:1
	1	3	6	2:1
	3	1	6	1:2
$Z = X^2Y^4$	1	1	6	2:1
$Z = X^3Y^3$	1	1	6	1:1
$Z^4 = XY$	1	4	1	3:1
	3	3	1	1:1
	4	1	1	1:3
	5	5	3	1:1
$Z^4 = X^3Y^3$	2	2	3	1:1

EXPRESSION	SCALE			RATIO
	X	Y	Z	$L_X : L_Y$
$Z^2 = XY$	1	1	1	1:1
	1	4	3	3:1
	2	2	2	1:1
	3	3	3	1:1
	3	5	4	2:1
	4	4	4	1:1
	4	1	3	1:3
	5	3	4	1:2
	5	5	5	1:1
$Z^2 = XY^2$	3	1	3	1:1
	3	3	4	2:1
	5	1	4	1:2
	5	3	5	1:1
$Z^2 = XY^3$	1	1	3	3:1
	3	2	4	2:1
	4	1	4	1:1
	5	2	5	1:1
$Z^2 = XY^4$	3	1	4	2:1
	5	1	5	1:1
$Z^2 = X^2Y^2$	1	2	4	2:1
	3	2	5	1:1
$Z^2 = X^3Y^3$	1	1	4	1:1
	2	2	5	1:1
	3	3	6	1:1
$Z^2 = X^3Y^4$	2	1	5	1:1
$Z^4 = XY^3$	1	1	1	3:1
	2	2	2	3:1
	3	3	3	3:1

EXPRESSION	SCALE			RATIO
	X	Y	Z	$L_X : L_Y$
$Z^3 = XY$	1	3	1	2:1
	1	4	2	3:1
	3	1	1	1:2
	3	3	2	1:1
	3	5	3	2:1
	4	1	2	1:3
	4	4	3	1:1
	5	3	3	1:2
$Z^3 = XY^2$	1	1	1	2:1
	2	2	2	2:1
	3	1	2	1:1
	3	3	3	2:1
	5	1	3	1:2
$Z^3 = XY^3$	1	1	2	3:1
	3	2	3	2:1
	4	1	3	1:1
$Z^3 = XY^4$	3	1	3	2:1
	5	3	5	2:1
$Z^3 = X^2Y^2$	1	1	2	1:1
	1	3	3	2:1
	5	1	3	1:2
$Z^3 = X^2Y^3$	1	2	3	2:1
$Z^3 = X^2Y^4$	1	1	3	2:1
	3	3	5	2:1
$Z^3 = X^3Y^4$	2	3	5	2:1
$Z^4 = XY^2$	3	1	1	1:1
	5	3	3	1:1
$Z^4 = XY^4$	5	1	3	1:1

Figure 23-26
This chart includes expressions, scales and ratios for designing a variety of nomographs.

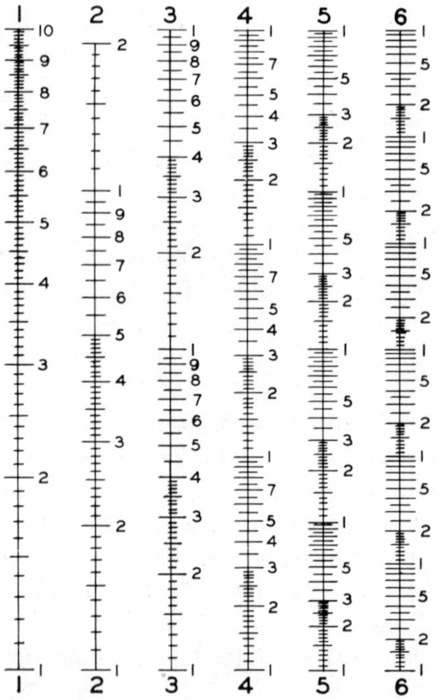

Figure 23-27
Scales which may be used for Fig. 23-26.

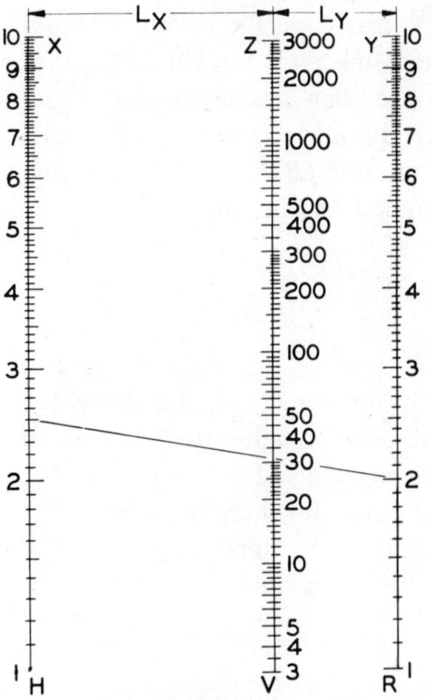

Figure 23-28
Right circular cylinder volume V = $\pi r^2 h$.

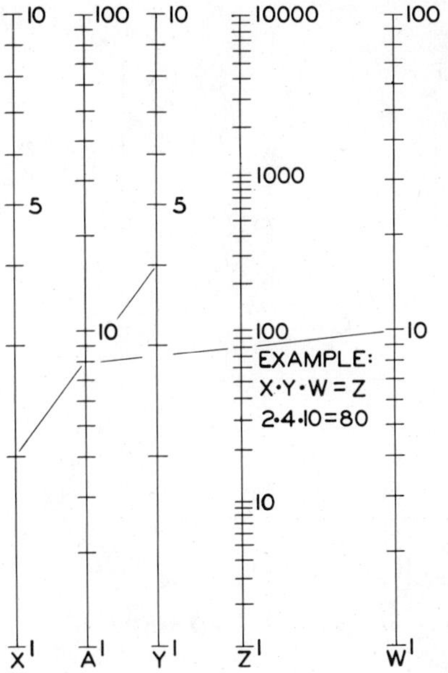

Figure 23-29
Nomograph showing the multiplication of three variables.

relationship. For ease in reading, it is best to use the scale that has the greatest distance between divisions. If the first set is selected, line X and Y will be drawn as scale 1 and Z as scale 4. The L_x:L_y ratio column given in Fig. 23-26 establishes the distance of the X and Y lines from the Z line. In the example, locate line Y any desired distance from line Z and then draw line X twice that distance from Z to satisfy the L_x:L_y ratio of 2:1. See Fig. 23-28.

The scales for lines X and Y do not have to be indexed with respect to each other. When these two scales are drawn, a construction line should be drawn at the proper location of line Z. The formula should be solved for V with any value of r and h. Using $r = 2''$ and $h = 2.5''$, V becomes 31.416 cubic inches. A straight edge should be used to align the 2 on the R scale and 2.5 on the H scale. A mark should be made on the V line at the point of intersection with the straight edge. A copy of scale 4 should be positioned along the vertical construction line with its 31.416 value on the intersection point that was previously drawn. Locating the height of line Z in this manner removes the necessity for calculating the value of each of the scales at a base line through the three lines to establish their relative height.

The expressions listed in Fig. 23-26 can be extended to cover an even wider variety of equations by observing the following:

1 Constants do not alter the form of the nomograph, they only shift the location of the Z scale up or down. Z was such a constant in the example just described.

2 If the variables appear as a quotient, $Z = X/Y^2$, the expression $Z = XY^2$ should be used with scale Y being drawn upside down.

3 When an equation has more than three variables, $Z = (X)(Y)(W)$, it should be drawn in two stages as: $A = (X)(Y)$ and $Z = (A)(W)$. An example is shown in Fig. 23-29.

4 If the equation has a trigonometric function of the form $z = \sin x/y^2$, the expression $z = x^1/y^2$ should be used, with $x^1 = \sin x$. The scale should be graduated by the method used to develop a functional scale.

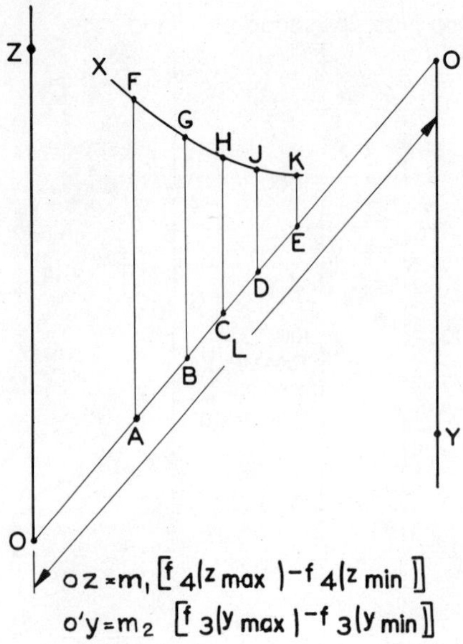

Figure 23-30
Construction of a curved scale nomograph.

23.16 Curved scale nomographs

The curved scale nomograph which satisfies the equation $f_1(x) + f_2(x) \cdot f_3(y) = f_4(z)$ is constructed in the following manner:

Draw two lines Z and Y parallel to each other. See Fig. 23-30. Select the location of the origin on each line and letter them O and O' respectively. Connect these two points with a straight line. It is not necessary for the line OO' to be perpendicular to lines Z and Y. Lay off the scale

$$m_1 \left[f_4(z_{\max}) - f_4(z_{\min})\right]$$

on line Z. The total length of the Z scale is equal to OZ. Lay off the scale

$$m_2 \left[f_3(y_{\max}) - f_3(y_{\min})\right]$$

on line Y, with the total length equal to $O'Y$. The length of line OO' is designated L. Fig. 23-30 also includes an imaginary configuration of the curved line X and the method of plotting the curve. The quotient

$$\frac{m_1 f_2(x) l}{m_1 f_2(x) + m_2}$$

is used to calculate the distances of points A, B, C, D, and E from the origin O measured along the line OO' for various values of X. Lines are then drawn through these plotted points parallel to line Z. The distances from the line OO' to the curved line X are determined by the quotient

$$\frac{m_1 m_2 f_1(x)}{m_1 f_2(x) + m_2}.$$

Points F, G, H, J, and K represent the plotted distance from line OO' calculated by the equation. The positive values will be plotted above the line and the negative values below. These plotted points form the basis for drawing line X. Any line intersecting the three scales will solve the equation

$$f_1(x) + f_2(x) \cdot f_3(y) = f_4(z).$$

This general background on curved scale nomographs can be best illustrated with an example to show the steps necessary to complete this type of alignment chart. If it is desired to develop a nomograph to determine the chordal height and length of a chord for a circle it is necessary to put the equation $d^2 = 8rh - 4h^2$ in standard form:

$$f_1(x) + f_2(x) \cdot f_3(y) = f_4(z)$$
$$-4h^2 + 8h \cdot r = d^2.$$

The length of increments for various values of h along the OO' line will be calculated by the quotient: $\dfrac{(m_d)(8h)(l)}{(m_d)(8h) + (m_r)}$,

where $m_d = m_1$, $m_r = m_2$, and $8h = f_2(x)$.

The vertical distances are determined by the quotient: $\dfrac{(m_d)(m_r)(-4h^2)}{(m_d)(8h) + (m_r)}$, where $-4h^2 = f_1(x)$.

It is planned to fit the nomograph into a space four by five inches. The OZ and $O'Y$ lines may both be five inches long with a four-inch perpendicular distance between them. The following ranges of values will provide the desired information: d varies from 0 to 20, r varies from 0 to 10, h varies from 1 to 10.

EQUATION	1	2	3	4	5	6	7	8	9	10
1	1.067	1.829	2.401	2.846	3.202	3.493	3.735	3.940	4.116	4.269
2	-0.042	-0.143	-0.281	-0.444	-0.625	-0.818	-1.021	-1.231	-1.446	-1.667

Figure 23-31
Tabulated data for the construction of the curved scale nomograph in Fig. 23-32.

The value of m_d and m_r should be calculated next using the preceding information:

$$m_d = \frac{5''}{(d^2_{max} - d^2_{min})} = 0.0125$$

$$m_r = \frac{5''}{(r_{max} - r_{min})} = 0.5.$$

The value of l should be calculated by the equation $l = \sqrt{(5)^2 + (4)^2}$ because it happens to be the hypotenuse of the triangle OYO'. This calculation yields a value of 6.403 for l. The quotients

$$\frac{(m_d)(8h)(l)}{(m_d)(8h) + (m_r)} \text{ and } \frac{(m_d)(m_r)(-4h^2)}{(m_d)(8h) + (m_r)}$$

then become

$$\frac{(0.0125)(8)(h)(6.403)}{(0.0125)(8)(h) + (0.5)}$$

and

$$\frac{(0.0125)(0.5)(-4)(h^2)}{(0.0125)(8)(h) + (0.5)}$$

which reduces to

$$\frac{0.6403h}{0.1h + 0.5} \text{ and } \frac{-0.025\,h^2}{0.1h + 0.5}.$$

By applying the desired range of values for h to the above quotients the distances from the origin on line D can be calculated. In addition, the vertical length of the lines to determine the locus of points on line H can be determined. These values are included in the table of Fig. 23-31. Now that all the necessary values for the various lines have been calculated the chart can be drawn. See Fig. 23-32. Scale D is drawn on the left side using a functional scale because D is squared. Scale R is drawn as a uniform scale. Both of these scales are 5 inches long and are 4 inches apart to fulfill the space restriction. The lengths presented in the table are scaled on a light construction line connecting the origins of scales D and R. The vertical distances are then measured from the construction line and the points for the H curve are plotted. These points are the location of the value of h given in the table. The curve is then drawn using these points. A straight line through the three scales will solve the equation $d^2 = 8rh - 4h^2$.

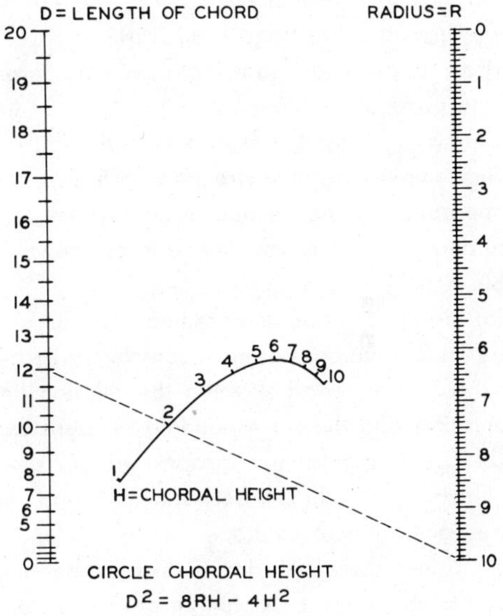

Figure 23-32
Curved scale nomograph.

TABLE I. PROBLEMS 1, 2.

Elements	Percent
Oxygen	46.43
Silicon	27.77
Aluminum	8.14
Iron	5.12
Calcium	3.62
Sodium	2.85
Potassium	2.60
Magnesium	2.09
Titanium	.63
Phosphorus	.13
Hydrogen	.13
All Others	.49

Problems, section 23

1 Using the values shown in Table I of the occurrence of chemical elements in the earth's crust, draw a percentage bar chart.

2 Draw a pie chart showing the same information given in Problem 1.

3 During a study to determine the optimum curing temperature of a structural adhesive, the temperature of the heated platen press was recorded at various time intervals as shown in Table II.

(a) Using rectangular coordinate graph paper 20 x 20 divisions per inch, construct a graph for a technical report showing the relation between time and the corresponding temperature.

(b) Using logarithmic graph paper show graphically the relation between time and the corresponding temperature.

(c) Using the graph drawn in (b), determine the rate of increase in temperature per unit time between 68°F. and 200°F. (0 to 15 minutes) and the decrease in temperature per unit time between 300°F. and 152°F. (85 to 100 minutes).

4 Calculate the values of the following equations and plot the curve for quantitative purposes:

(a) $\mathbf{Y} = \mathbf{x}^3 - 12\,\mathbf{x} + 16$ **x** varies from 0 to 5

(b) $\mathbf{Y}^2 = 4\mathbf{x}$ **x** varies from 0 to 4

(c) $\mathbf{Y}^2 = \dfrac{144 - 9x^2}{16}$ **x** varies from −4 to +4

(d) $\mathbf{Y} = \sin \mathbf{x}$ **x** varies from 0° to 360°

(e) $\mathbf{Y} = \cos \mathbf{x}$ **x** varies from 0° to 360°

(f) $\mathbf{Y} = \log \mathbf{x}^2$ **x** varies from 1 to 10

(g) $\mathbf{Y} = \dfrac{1}{\mathbf{x}^2}$ **x** varies from 1 to 10

TABLE II. PROBLEM 3.

Time (min.)	Temperature	Time (Min.)	Temperature
0	68°F	40	300°F
3	95	45	300
5	115	50	300
10	165	60	300
12	190	65	300
13	199	70	300
14	201	75	301
15	200	76	302
16	200	77	299
17	201	78	300
18	200	79	300
19	210	80	300
20	218	85	300
25	259	86	285
30	292	87	273
31	301	88	260
32	300	90	238
33	300	95	190
35	300	100	152

5 Construct a nomograph of the formula $\mathbf{x} + \mathbf{y} = \mathbf{z}$. Symbol **x** varies from 0 to 20 and **y** from 0 to 10. The scales should have enough division marks to ensure accurate readings on the **z** scale.

6 Construct a nomograph for the multiplication of numbers from 1 to 100 using an **N** or **Z** scale. Repeat using a parallel scale.

7 Construct a nomograph for determining the minutes required to machine one inch of material using the formula: Speed (RPM) × feed (ins./rev.) = (ins./min.). The speed can vary from 3 to 400 RPM and the feed from 0.006 to 0.100 (ins./rev.).

8 Construct a nomograph for determination of height in feet of the Francis formula $\mathbf{Q} = 3.33\ \mathbf{BH}^{3/2}$ where **Q** = cubic feet per second which varies from 0 to 80 and **B** varies from 0 to 10 feet.

9 Make a bar chart showing the number of men and women students in your school in the first, second, third and fourth years. Obtain data from the registrar.

10 Make a semi-logarithmic chart showing the comparative rate of growth of the five largest American cities during the past 50 years. The data can be obtained from U.S. Census Bureau reports.

11 Determine the organizational structure of the department of your school or city government of your instructor's choice and construct an organization chart.

12 Collect information showing the various steps to manufacture an item of goods. Draw a flow chart.

Tool drawing 24

Mass production of finished goods involves the use of countless tools and machines to perform a vast number of operations, many of them complex. To achieve quality products on a low-cost, competitive basis, production tools must be designed that will permit rapid and economical fabrication. See Fig. 24-1. The responsibility of producing such equipment rests with the tool designer or tool engineer.

Tool design is a highly specialized field involving the creation of jigs, fixtures, dies and gages. The individual concerned with this phase of engineering must have a good knowledge of materials, a general understanding of shop practices, mechanical ingenuity and skill in drafting. The main function of this section is to familiarize the student with some of the basic elements of tool design and the type of drafting involved.

Figure 24-1
Machining operations require that parts to be worked on must be located and held securely to maintain uniform degree of accuracy.

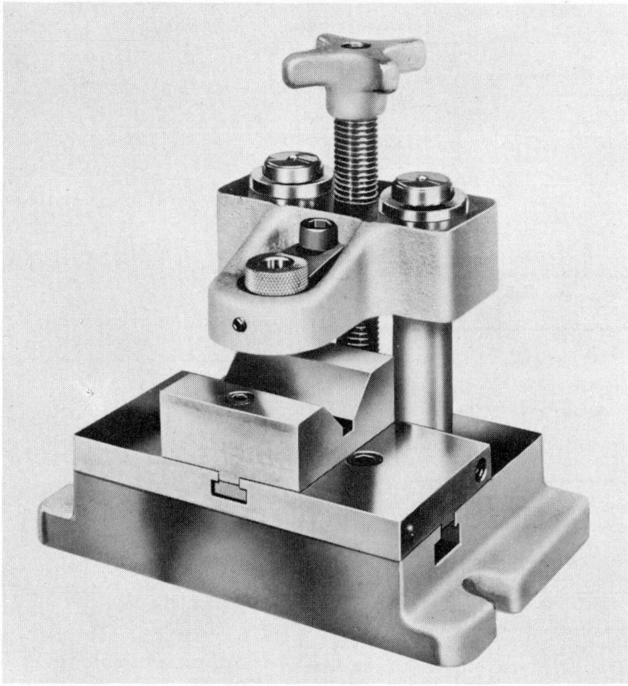

Figure 24–2
A jig is used in drilling, reaming, counterboring, and tapping operations. Rockford Engineered Products Co.

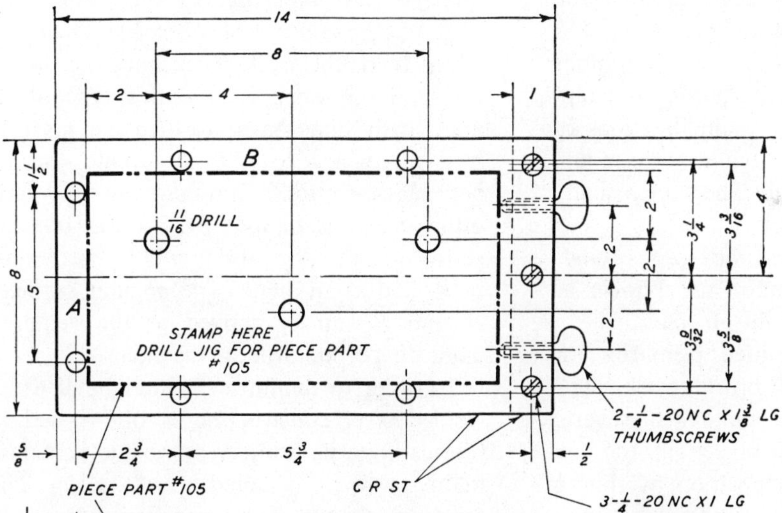

Figure 24–3
In simple flatwork, drilling is often done by using a plate-type drill jig.

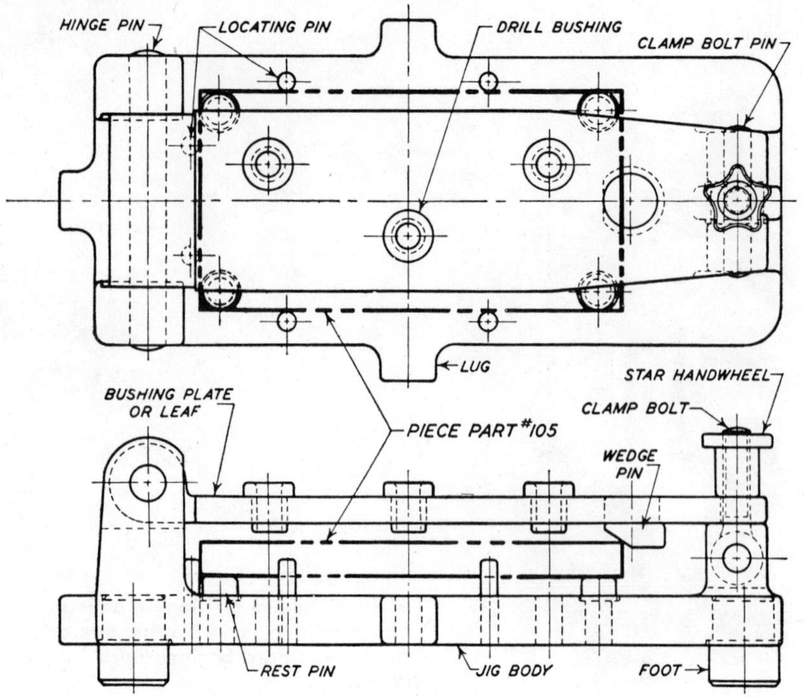

Figure 24-4
A jig in which the plate containing the drill bushings is hinged to facilitate loading and unloading is known as a leaf jig.

24.1 Jigs

Jigs are devices which are used in performing identical operations easily and rapidly with uniformity of precision. Jigs are specifically adapted for such operations as drilling, reaming, counterboring and tapping. See Fig. 24-2. The main functions of jigs are to hold the workpiece in position and to guide the cutting tool. They are usually movable on the worktable.

There are many types and sizes of jigs. Some of the more common are known as plate jig, box jig, and built-up jig.

The *plate jig* is intended primarily for operations to be done on flatwork. The design consists of a steel plate with several pins that locate the workpiece in the jig. The work is clamped in position by thumb screws. Hardened drill bushings are often omitted from jigs of this type when an extremely high degree of accuracy is not required. See Fig. 24-3.

An adaptation of the plate jig is sometimes constructed by pivoting the plate as a hinge to allow loading and unloading the workpiece. This form of plate jig is often referred to as a *leaf jig*. See Fig. 24-4.

A *box jig* consists of a box-like enclosure which holds the workpiece. Since the operations on the workpiece in this type of jig are usually done on more than one surface, it is necessary to turn or rotate the jig between operations. Consequently, this jig is often called a *tumble jig*. In the box jig shown in Fig. 24-5, the two holes at *C* must be drilled at an angle. The angular surfaces *A* and *B* can be moved at the required angle to permit drilling the holes.

In order to minimize the weight of a jig, welded steel construction is often used in fabricating a jig body. When made in such a manner, the jig is called a *built-up jig*. The resulting rigidity and comparative lightness in weight are advantages of this type. See Fig. 24-6.

Other commonly used jigs are the index jig, shaft drill jig and universal jig. The universal jig is particularly valuable since it can be adapted for machining many sizes of similar parts. See Fig. 24-7.

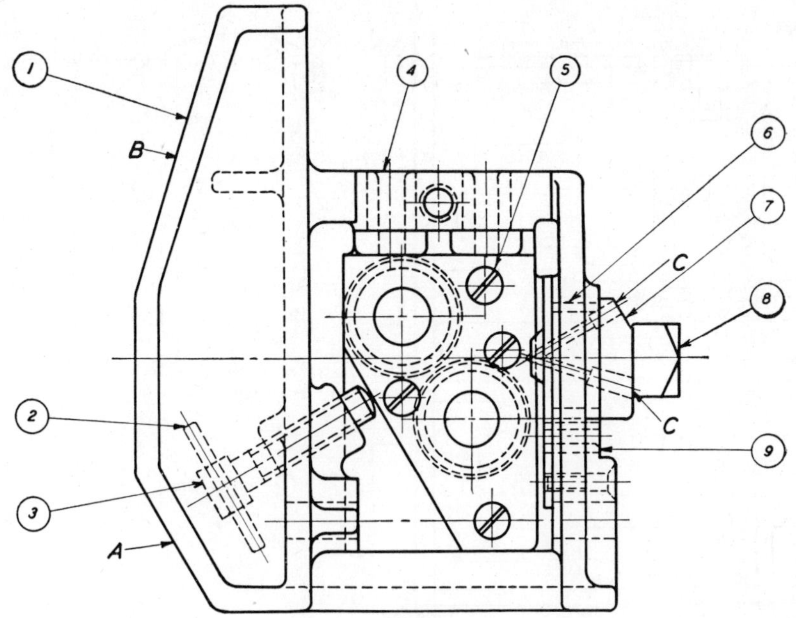

PLAN
PLAN VIEW SHOWS LEAF PLATE REMOVED

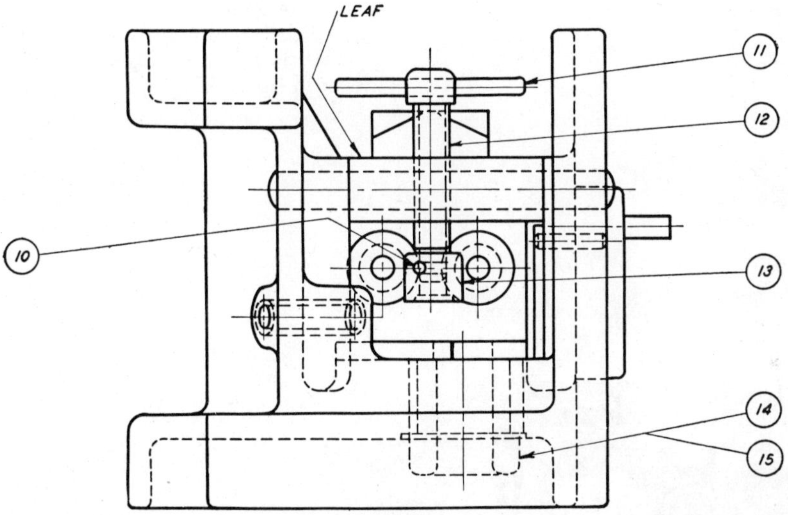

FRONT ELEVATION

DET. NO.	DESCRIPTION
1	JIG BODY
2	CLAMPING SCREW PIN
3	CLAMPING SCREW
4	DRILL BUSHING
5	FLAT HEAD MACH. SCREW
6	LINER BUSHING
7	DRILL PLATE
8	QUARTER TURN THUMBSCREW
9	HEADLESS DRILL BUSHING
10	FLOATING CLAMP PIN
11	TOP CLAMPING SCREW PIN
12	TOP CLAMPING SCREW
13	TOP CLAMPING SCREW FLOAT
14	SLIP DRILL BUSHING
15	SLIP REAM BUSHING

Figure 24-5
When work is to be done in more than one plane on the workpiece, a tumble jig is used.

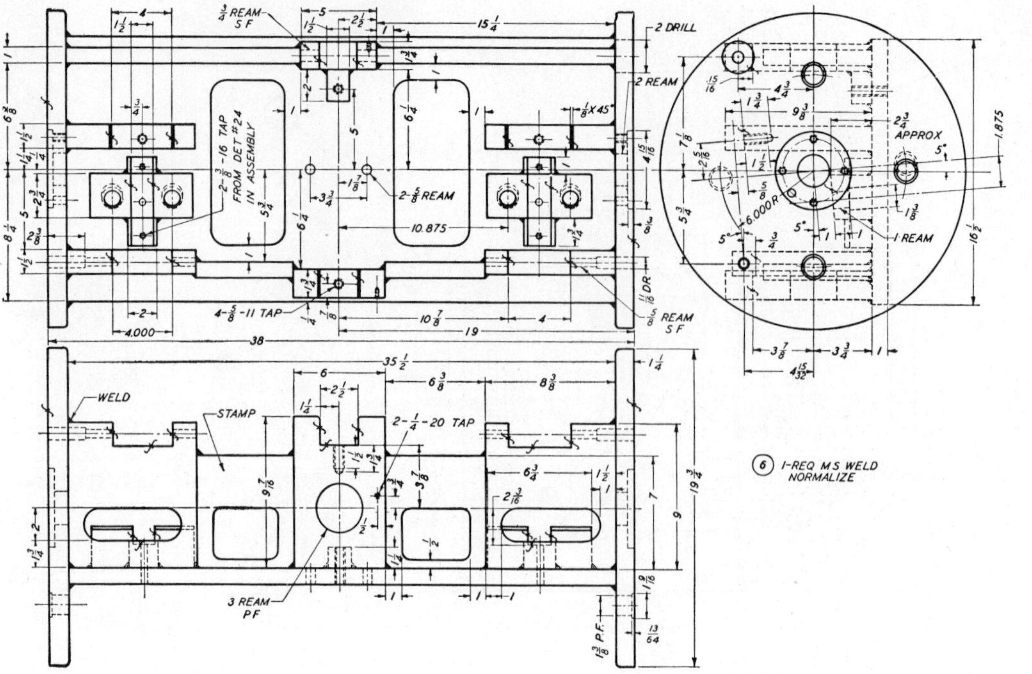

Figure 24-6
Welded steel construction is often used to fabricate light-weight, rigid jig bodies.

Figure 24-7
A universal type jig is often used when similar parts are to be machined. Cleveland Universal Jig Co.

Figure 24-8
A fixture is designed to be clamped in a fixed position on a movable table which carries the workpiece to the cutting or shap-tool. Cincinnati Milling Machine Co.

24.2 Fixtures

Fixtures are also locating and holding devices but unlike jigs they are clamped in a fixed position and are not free to move or guide the cutting tool. They are used to perform operations requiring facing, boring, milling, grinding, welding, etc.

The many different types of fixtures are all designed for some specific operation. As such they are often identified according to the operation that is to be done on the workpiece, as: milling fixture, grinding fixture, welding fixture. These fixtures are normally clamped to a moving table which carries the work to the machining tool. For example, a milling fixture is fastened to the milling machine table and the table movement then carries the firmly supported workpiece past the revolving cutter or cutters. See Fig. 24-8.

24.3 Essential features of jigs and fixtures

Jigs and fixtures contain three principal units: body, nest, and clamps. A vast assortment of components for these units are available commercially. The problem of the tool designer is often that of resolving which of these commercial parts are best adaptable for the required jig or fixture and then incorporating them into his design.

Body. Frequently the critical task is that of designing the most suitable body or frame to fit the workpiece. In general, the body must be constructed to (1) permit ease of loading and unloading the workpiece, (2) provide clear visibility of all locating points so each successive workpiece can be placed in the same position, (3) incorporate suitable clamping devices to prevent movement of the piece while the operation is being performed, and (4) be strong enough to withstand any forces which may be encountered.

Ordinarily, the accepted practice is to equip a jig body with four feet to ensure stability. The use of a flat base is inadvisable because of the difficulty in maintaining a true level surface, especially since there is always a tendency for chips to lodge under the plate. Furthermore, in a drilling operation, a jig without feet often results in the drill cutting through the plate and going into the drill press table. Standard jig feet are commercially available which can be pressed into drilled and reamed holes in the bottom of the jig body or can be fastened with screws. Fig. 24-9 illustrates two types of standard jig feet.

BUTTON JIG FEET

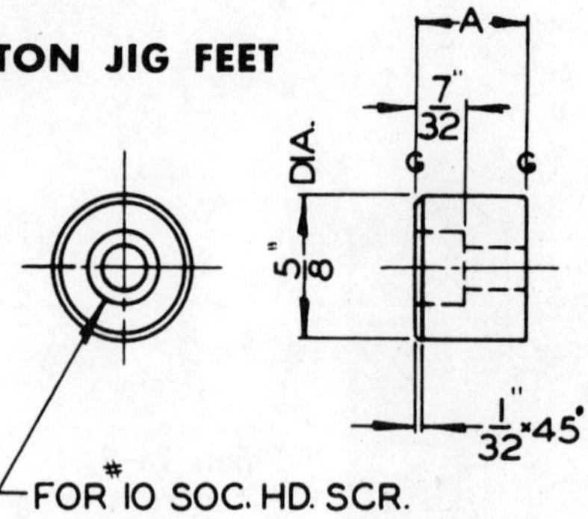

Rust-proof black finish

Machine Steel—HARDENED AND GROUND

PART NO.	A
BJF 250	1/4
BJF 375	3/8
BJF 500	1/2
BJF 625	5/8
BJF 750	3/4
BJF 875	7/8
BJF 1000	1

10-32 FLAT HEAD MACH. SCREW (THIS SIZE ONLY) — BJF 250

10-32 SOCKET HEAD SCREW — BJF 375 through BJF 1000

SCREWS ARE FURNISHED

REST BUTTONS (ALSO USED AS JIG FEET)

Rust-proof black finish

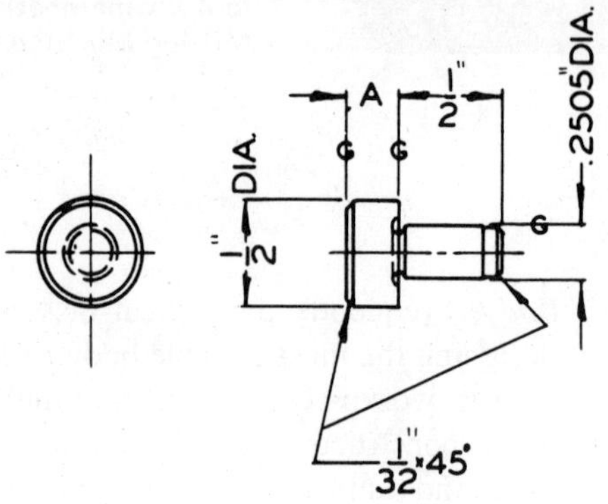

PART NO.	A
RB 141	1/4
RB 142	3/8
RB 143	1/2

STEM DIA AND HEAD THICKNESS ARE HELD +.0005 −.0000

Machine Steel —HARDENED AND GROUND

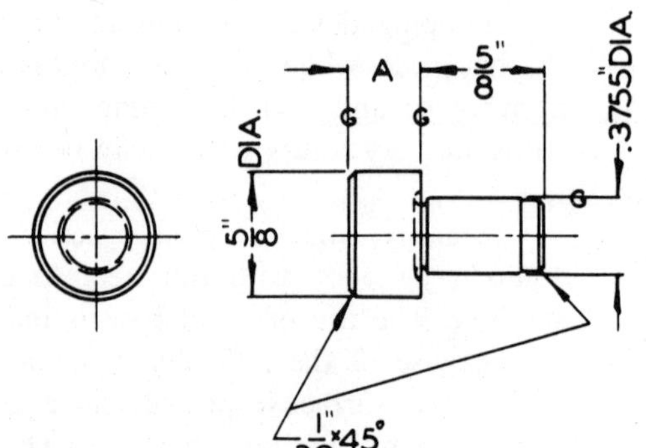

PART NO.	A
RB 381	1/4
RB 382	3/8
RB 383	1/2
RB 384	5/8
RB 385	3/4

Rust-proof black finish

LEAD IS GROUND ON STEM TO ASSIST IN ASSEMBLY

Figure 24-9
Jigs are often equipped with standard type feet to provide a firm base as well as prevent chips from becoming lodged under the jig. Morton Machine Works

Figure 24-10
A fixture must provide some simple means for fastening it securely to the table.

Inasmuch as a fixture is clamped in a fixed position, its base normally consists of a flat plate. Various means are then provided for holding the fixture in position. The type of holding device depends upon where the fixture is to be clamped. Thus in a milling fixture, the base is generally designed with slots to accommodate the T-bolts which fit into the milling machine table. See Fig. 24-10. In the case of a lathe fixture, a cylindrical plug may be welded to the base plate so it can be inserted in the lathe chuck.

Nest. A jig or fixture must contain surfaces, commonly referred to as the nest, that will support and locate parts accurately and consistently. As a rule, adequate location is achieved by using three or four locators. The most common type of locators are pins, vee blocks, pads or buttons. See Fig. 24-11. For most jigs and fixtures these units can be procured commercially. Pins have the advantage of cheapness and simplicity. The important factor is the arrangement of the pins to avoid any possibility of chips or dirt from becoming lodged in corners, or burrs on the workpiece hindering true contact with the pins. Vee blocks are particularly suitable for locating round pieces. Pads or buttons are frequently employed for supporting flat surfaces.

Clamping devices. One of the most important features of any jig or fixture is its provisions for clamping the workpiece. A variety of clamps are commercially manufactured and the responsibility of the tool designer is to select the most effective device for the particular jig or fixture which he is designing. Several common types of clamps are shown in Fig. 24-12.

The following are some of the basic considerations governing the selection of proper clamping devices:

1 The clamp must have correct bearing points or contact surfaces so sufficient pressure can be applied to hold the work securely during machining.
2 The clamp must be able to withstand hard usage.
3 The clamp must have positive clamping action to prevent the workpiece from getting loose during the machining operation.
4 The clamp must be quick-acting, simple to handle, and easy to control and guide.

Tool guides. A jig utilizes a guide to limit and control the path of the cutting tool. The

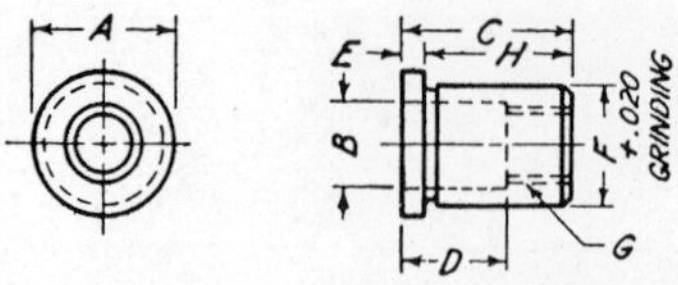

STYLE	A	B	C	D	E	F	G	H
1	9/16	.3125	3/4	1/2	3/32	7/16	1/4-24	21/32
2	7/8	.4375	1	5/8	1/8	11/16	3/8-24	7/8
3	1	.5625	1 5/16	3/4	5/32	13/16	1/2-20	1 5/32
4	1 9/16	.8750	1 3/4	1 1/8	1/4	1 1/4	3/4-16	1 1/2

LOCATOR RETAINER

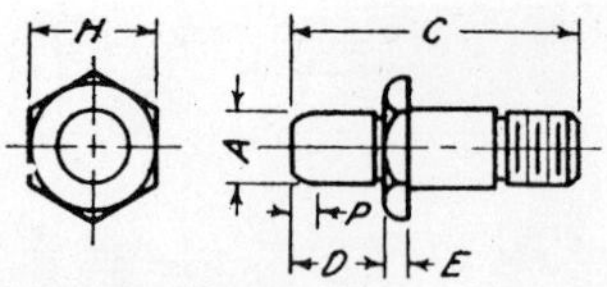

STYLE	A	C	D	E	H	P
C1	3/32-5/16	1 1/4	7/16	3/32	1/2	3/32
C2	5/16-7/16	1 5/8	1/2	1/8	11/16	1/8
C3	7/16-5/8	2 1/8	11/16	5/32	7/8	3/16
C4	5/8-1	3	1	1/4	1 1/4	9/32

LOCATING REST PAD

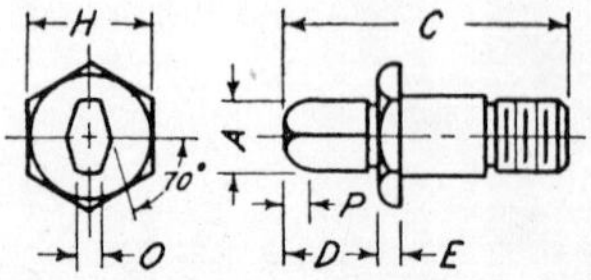

STYLE	A	C	D	E	H	P	O
R1	3/32-5/16	1 1/4	7/16	3/32	1/2	3/32	1/3
R2	5/16-7/16	1 5/8	1/2	1/8	11/16	1/8	OF
R3	7/16-5/8	2 1/8	11/16	5/32	7/8	3/16	A
R4	5/8-1	3	1	1/4	1 1/4	9/32	DIM.

A-WILL BE GROUND TO SIZE GIVEN MINUS .0003
UNLESS OTHERWISE SPECIFIED. TOTAL LIMIT .0002

RELIEVED LOCATING PIN REST PAD

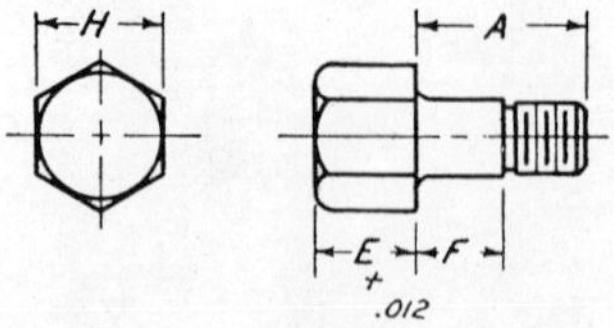

STYLE	A	E	F	H
B1	3/4	3/32-3/4	3/8	1/2
B2	1	1/8-3/4	1/2	11/16
B3	1 5/16	3/16-3/4	5/8	7/8
B4	1 3/4	1/4-3/4	1	1 1/4

REST BUTTONS HAVE STOCK ON E
DIM. FOR FINISHING

REST BUTTON

Figure 24-11
Jigs and fixtures must be equipped with locators to provide a secure rest for the workpiece. Cincinnati Milling Machine Co.

guide is in the form of a bushing. Either the press-fit or slip-fit type of bushings are used. Both are standard items and available commercially in the head or headless style and in many different sizes. The press-fit bushing is mostly limited for low production runs where replacement due to wear is not essential. For high production runs the slip-fit type is preferable because it is easy to remove when a change must be made. See Fig. 24-13.

24.4 Principles of jigs and fixture design

The following rules are given as the main points to be considered in the designing of jigs and fixtures.[1]

1 Before laying out the jig or fixture, decide upon the locating points and outline a clamping arrangement.
2 Make all clamping and binding devices as quick-acting as possible. Such devices may be purchased outside from various manufacturers and should be used whenever possible.
3 In selecting locating points, see that two component parts of a machine can be located from corresponding points and surfaces.
4 Make the jig "fool-proof". Arrange it so that the work cannot be inserted except in the correct way.
5 For rough castings, make some of the locating points adjustable.
6 Locate clamps so that they will be in the best position to resist the pressure of the cutting tool during the operation.
7 If possible, make all clamps integral parts of the jig or fixture.
8 Avoid complicated clamping arrangements, which are liable to wear or get out of order.

1. *Engineering and Drafting Reference Book* (Providence: Brown and Sharpe Manufacturing Co.).

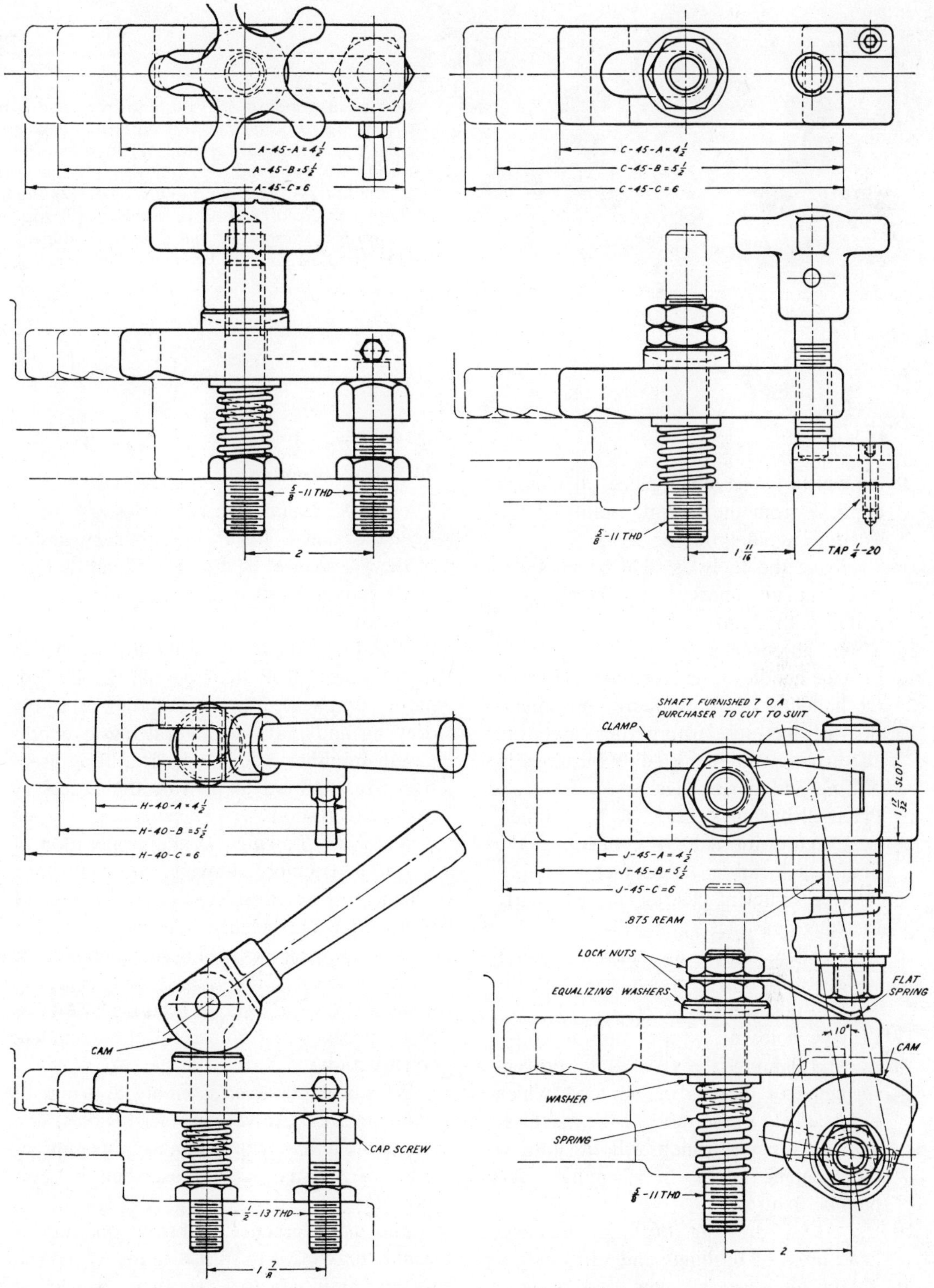

Figure 24-12
Clamps for jigs and fixtures should be durable, effective and quick acting.
Siewek Tool Company

Figure 24-13
Hardened standard drill bushings are used with a drill jig to guide the cutting tool. Important parts are: (1) locating pin, (2) locating retainer, (3) relieved locating pin, (4) flat clamp, (5) lockscrew, (6) round end clamp, (7) shoulder liner, (8) plain renewable bushing, (9) slip renewable bushing, (10) head press-fit bushing (11) headless liner. Universal Engineering Co.

9 As nearly as possible, place all clamps opposite from the bearing points of the work, to avoid springing.
10 To make the tools as light as possible, core out all unnecessary metal, consistent with rigidity.
11 Round all corners.
12 Provide handles wherever they will make the handling of the jig more convenient.
13 Provide feet, preferably four, opposite all surfaces containing guide bushings in drilling and boring jigs.
14 Place all bushings inside of the geometrical figure formed by connecting the points of location of the feet.
15 Provide sufficient clearance, particularly for rough castings.
16 If possible, make all locating points visible to the operator when placing the work in position.
17 Provide holes or escapes for the chips.
18 Locate clamping lugs so as to prevent springing of fixtures on all tools which must be held to the table of the machine. Provide tongues which will fit slots in the machine tables, in all milling and planing fixtures.
19 Use ASA drill jig bushings; namely, head press fit bushings and slip renewable bushings on all new tool designs.
20 Use liners where slip renewable bushings are used.
21 Use headless liners for all general applications.

24.5 Tool drawing

The tool designer usually resorts to a freehand sketch for the preliminary design of the jig, fixture, or die. The sketch is then made into a finished drawing.

Drawings of simple tools are often confined to a single assembly drawing which incorporates all of the essential details. For more complicated tools, both an assembly drawing and parts detail drawings are prepared. In either case standard drafting practices are followed to provide the necessary shape description.

Assembly drawings. In the preparation of any tool assembly drawing, the first thing which must be considered is the number of views that are needed. As in any other form of drawing the guiding rule is to include sufficient views so that the assembly is clearly understood. The use of sectional views is often necessary to illustrate the complete construction.

Whenever possible, assembly drawings of tools should be made full scale unless the size of the unit is such as to make this impractical. A reduced scale must then be employed.

The usual practice in laying out an assembly drawing is to start with the workpiece — the required tool is then developed around it. The workpiece is drawn with a red pencil or red ink in all views, using either solid or phantom lines. When prints are made later the red lines of the work-

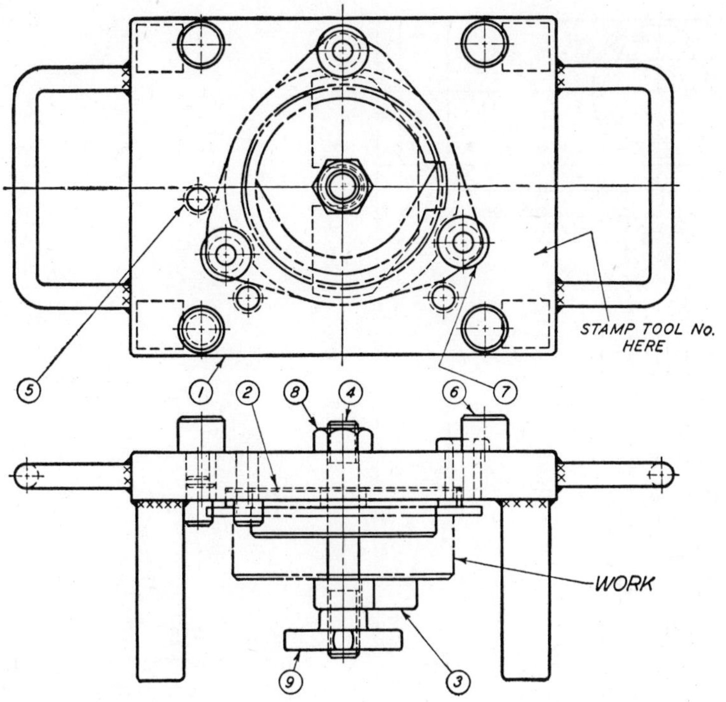

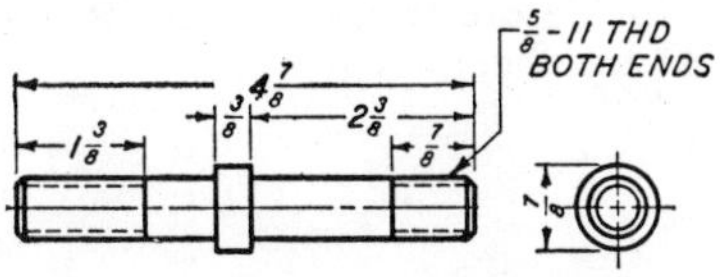

(4) 1-REQD CRS CYAN

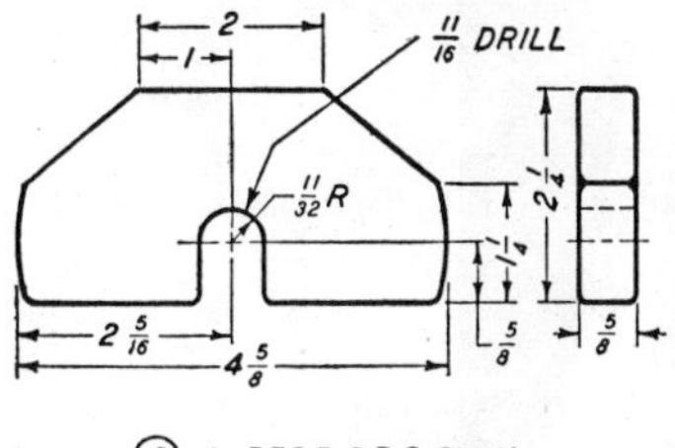

(3) 1-REQD CRS CYAN

DET	REQD	MATL	STOCK SIZE	REMARKS
9	1	STD	$2\frac{1}{2}$ HAND KNOB	
8	1	STD	$\frac{5}{8}$-11-HEX NUT	
7	3		XLO #O-23 BUSHINGS	
6	4	CRS	1 DIA x $1\frac{5}{8}$	
5	3	TS	$\frac{5}{8}$ DIA x $1\frac{1}{8}$	HDN AND GRD
4	1	CRS	$\frac{7}{8}$ DIA x 5	CYAN
3	1	CRS	$\frac{5}{8}$ x $2\frac{1}{4}$ x $4\frac{3}{4}$	CYAN
2	1	MS	$5\frac{1}{8}$ DIA x $1\frac{1}{8}$	CARB HDN AND GRD
1	1	MS	WELDED CONST	HDN & GRD

Figure 24-14
The assembly drawing of a tool should show the workpiece in position as well as the essential parts of the tool.

piece will appear as faint lines and thereby become readily distinguishable from outlines of the tool.

All of the essential parts included in the assembly must be properly identified. The most common practice is to designate them by means of small numbered balloons pointing to the parts. See Fig. 24-14. These parts are then described in the material list.

Many manufacturers of jig, fixture, and die components provide template drawings for the convenience of tool draftsmen. These

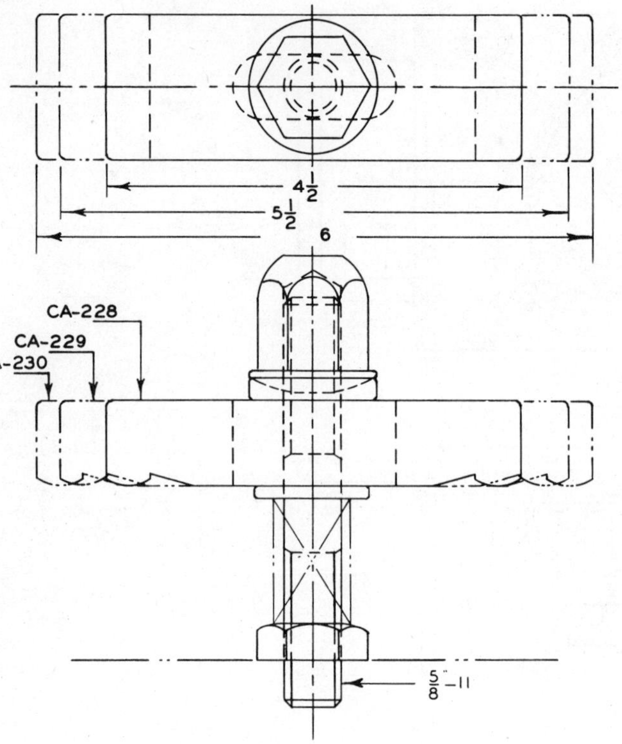

Figure 24-15
This tracing template, printed full size in a suppliers catalog, is a valuable aid to the tool draftsman. Morton Machine Works

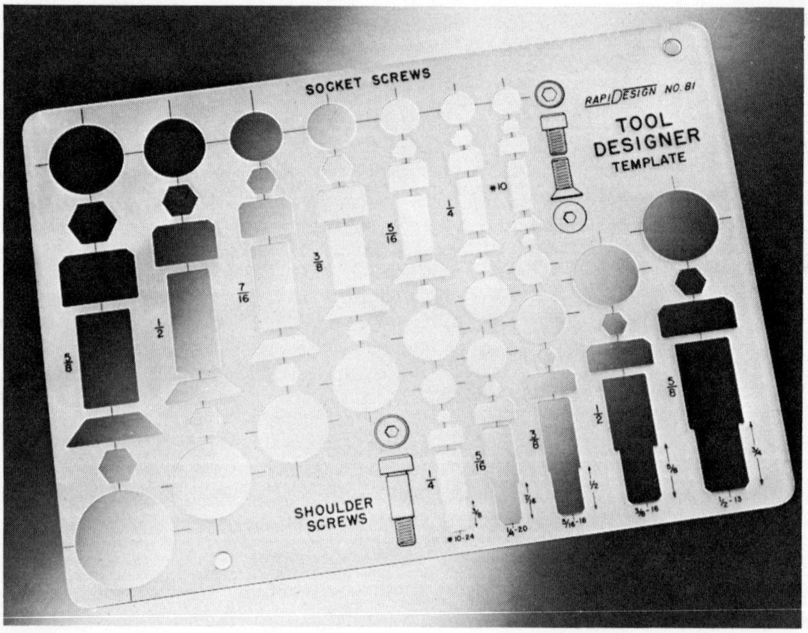

Figure 24-16
This template provides the outlines for many of the fasteners used in tool drafting. RapiDesign

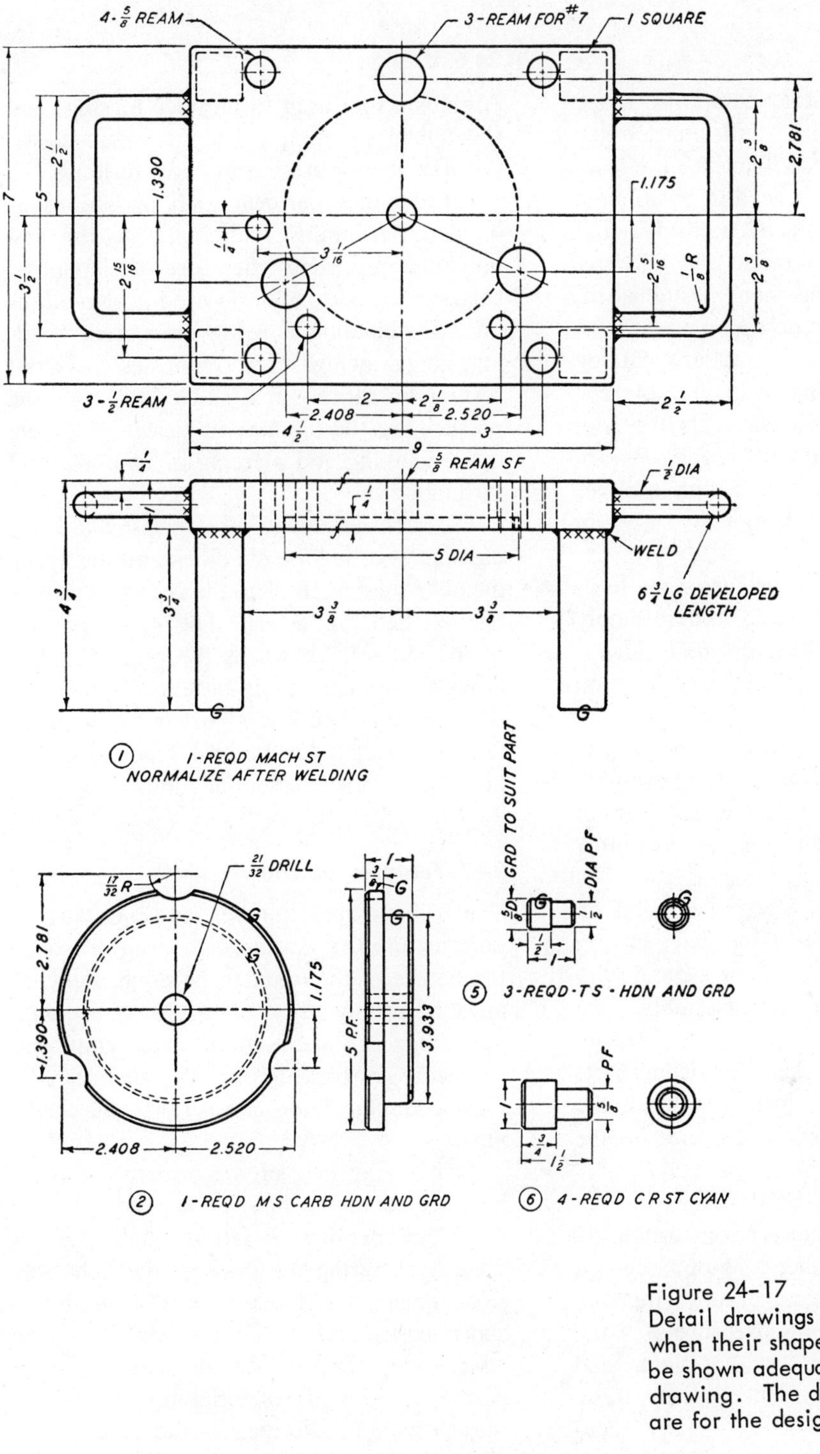

Figure 24-17
Detail drawings of tools are made when their shape description cannot be shown adequately in an assembly drawing. The details included here are for the design shown in Fig. 24-14.

drawings of the suppliers' components are made full size, half-size, and quarter-size so that they may be placed beneath the tracing medium and simply traced in position as a part of the tool design. This ensures that adequate working clearances are allowed, proper clamping arrangements established, and valuable drafting time saved.

A typical sheet from a supplier's catalog suitable for tracing is shown in Fig. 24-15.

Another valuable time saver is the tool designer template, shown in Fig. 24-16, which provides the draftsman with outlines for the fasteners most frequently used in tool drawing.

If no separate detail drawings of the individual parts are to be made, the assembly drawing will show all of the essential dimensions. Otherwise, only critical location dimensions are given.

For some relatively simple tools, one sheet will frequently contain the assembly plus such details of parts which cannot adequately be described on the assembly itself.

A bill of material is always included on the assembly sheet with each part clearly described and numbered to correspond with the parts called out on the assembly. The specifications include stock sizes before machining. A separate sheet for listing parts is used only in special instances when the design of the tool cannot accommodate the material list on the same sheet.

Detail drawings. Detail drawings of tool parts follow all of the conventions ordinarily used in detailing any other type of assembly. See Fig. 24-17. Individual parts of the tool are detailed on the same size sheets as the assembly drawing, and usually more than one detail appears on a sheet. Only those views are included which will ensure accurate shape description. Sectional and auxiliary views are drawn if greater clarity is achieved. Standard parts that can be purchased commercially should never be detailed, but are merely called out in the list of materials on the assembly drawing.

24.6 Dies

A die is a tool used to produce forgings and sheetmetal stampings. The two main classification of dies are cutting and forming.

Cutting dies perform such operations as blanking, trimming, piercing, shearing and notching. Forming dies are designed to shape metal parts and are used in operations involving bending, flanging, embossing, beading, and drawing. Very often dies carry out several operations in a single stroke of the press. Thus the die may be designed to perform blanking and piercing or blanking and forming.

Dies consist of two main parts; the lower member is called the die block and the upper member the punch. The die is mounted in a die set. See Fig. 24-18. The upper portion of the die set, known as the punch holder, holds the punch and is fastened to the ram of the press. The lower part, referred to as the die shoe, holds the die block, locating pins, and other essential units. See Fig. 24-19.

24.7 Features of cutting dies

The size, shape, number and position of punches used in cutting dies is governed by the nature of the work to be done. Punches must be rigidly fastened to ensure accurate performance. Various methods are employed to secure cutting dies in the die set, the most common being cap screws and dowel pins.

In blanking or piercing operations, relief is provided in the hole of the die to allow the blank or slug to fall through. This is done by tapering the sides of the hole at a small angle. The taper extends to within a short distance of the face of the die, from which point the sides of the hole are made parallel to provide material for sharpening the die without altering the size of the hole. This relief angle is usually not less than 1/4 degree and not more than 1-1/2 degrees. The straight sided part of the hole usually is not greater than 3/16 inch.

As a rule, the clearance between the punch and the die is approximately five

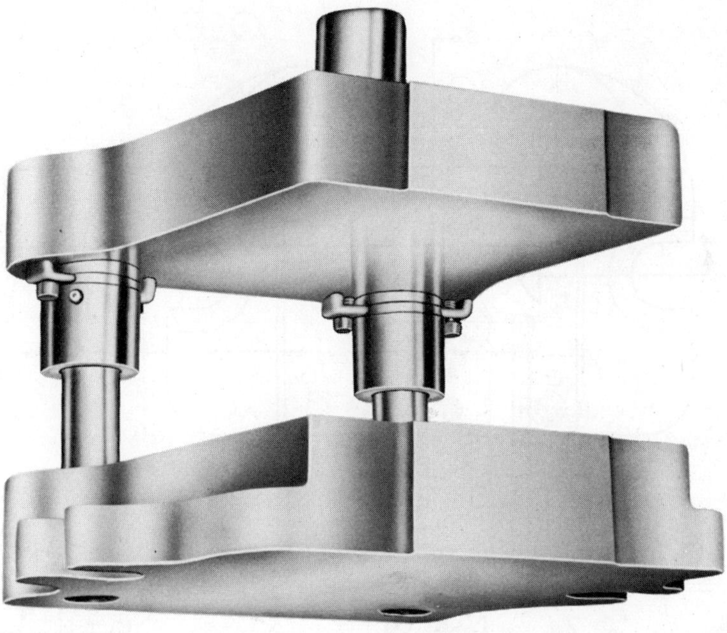

Figure 24-18
Punches and die blocks are mounted in die sets such as these. Danly Machine Specialties, Inc.

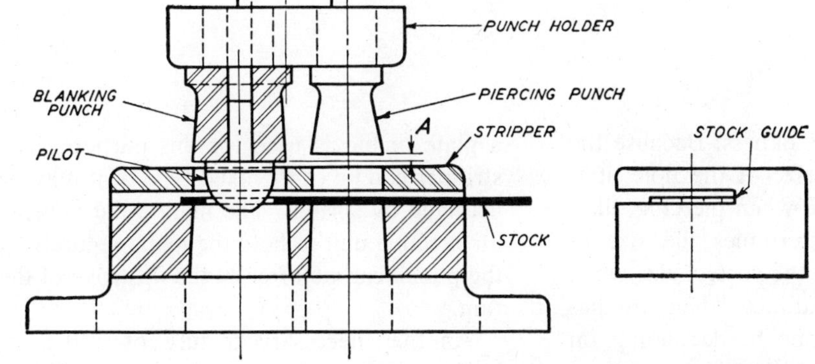

Figure 24-19
A die is used for producing stampings or to form metal parts. The simple progressive die shown here pierces and blanks the workpiece.

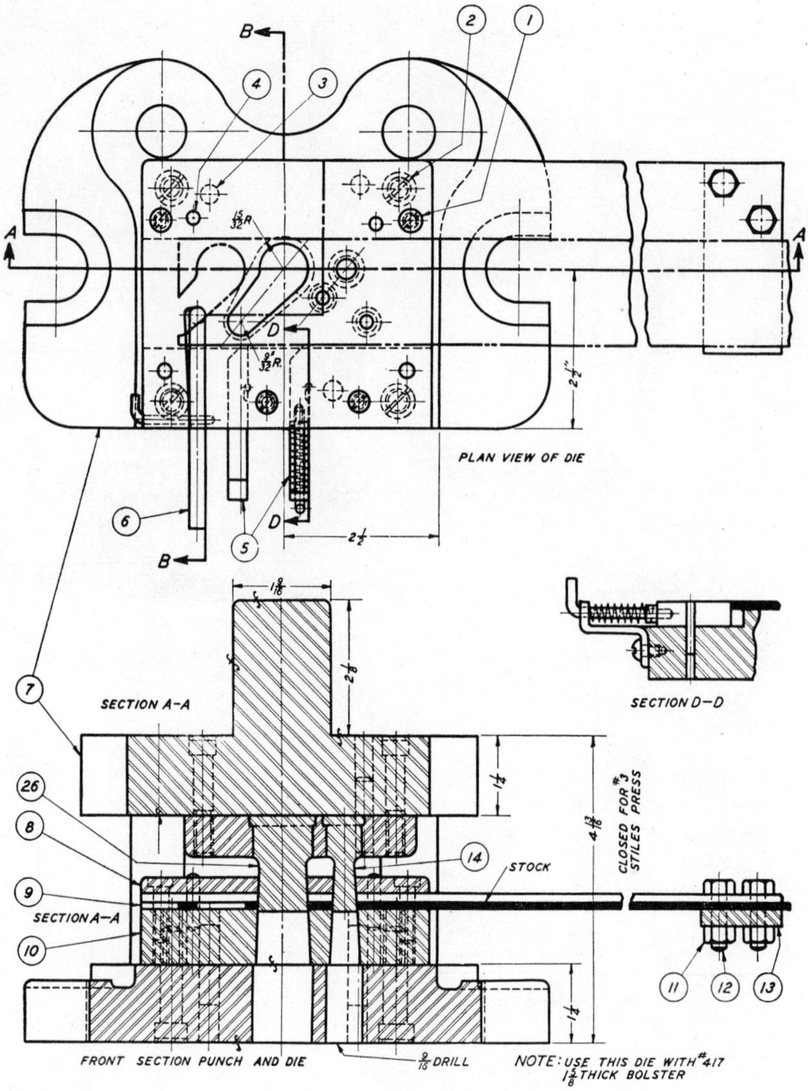

Figure 24-20A

per cent of the stock thickness. Because the punch determines the size of the hole, it is made to the proper size when piercing; likewise, since the die determines the size of the blank, it is made to the correct size when producing blanks. Clearances then are figured on the die, or punch, depending on whether piercing or blanking is to be done.

Generally, dies include some form of a stripper. A stripper is simply a device that frees the metal from around the punch after the cutting operation is completed. Either a plate or bar is used for this purpose. The stripper can be of the fixed type or it may be actuated by springs. The main point is using an effective unit to hold the metal securely so the punch can pull free of the upstroke of the ram.

Another necessary feature of a die set is the locating pins. These pins, as in the case of jigs and fixtures, must ensure the correct placement of the metal in the die set. Fig. 24-20 (A,B,C) is a cutting die set showing the stripper plate and locating stop.

Figures 24-20A and B show a progressive piercing and blanking die equipped with a stripper to free the metal and a locating stop for correct positioning of the metal. Figure 24-20C (next page) is a Bill of Material for the die.

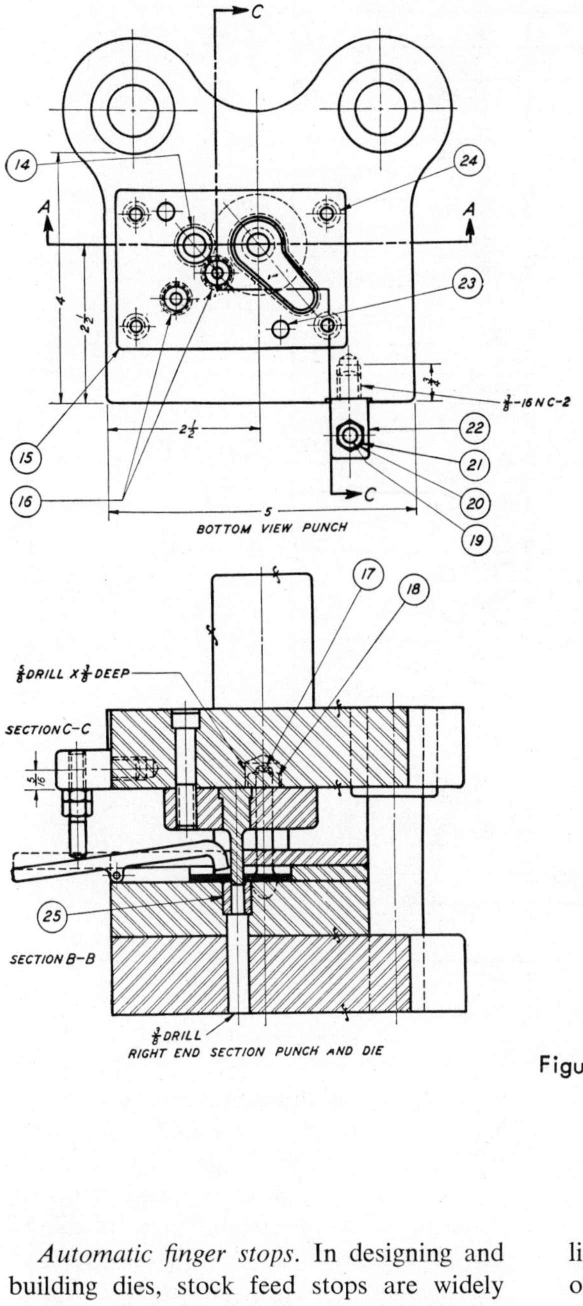

Figure 24-20B

Automatic finger stops. In designing and building dies, stock feed stops are widely used to automatically stop the stock in the correct position just prior to piercing, shearing or blanking operations. They are designed so that they can be applied easily to almost any type of blanking die.

In the illustration, Fig. 24-21, it will be noted that the operator feeds the stock against the gage pin. The set screw in the punch holder strikes the lever, lifting the gage pin so that it clears the stock. This pin lies on the stock during the down stroke of the press. As the punch rises on the upstroke the stock is again free to be fed forward, the gage pin drops back into the hole that has just been blanked, and the stock comes to a stop as it was in the original position.

24.8 Features of forming dies

As previously defined, the function of a forming die is to form metal parts such as utensils, metal furniture, oil pans, automo-

BILL OF MATERIALS				
DET	DESCRIPTION	MATERIAL	FIN. STOCK SIZE	REQ.
1	FLAT FILLISTER HEAD MACH. SCREW	STANDARD	1/4-20NC X 7/8 LG	4
2	FLAT FILLISTER HEAD MACH. SCREW	STANDARD	3/8-16NC X 1 1/2 LG	4
3	DOWEL PIN	STANDARD	5/16 DIA X 1 1/4 LG	3
4	DOWEL PIN	STANDARD	1/4 DIA X 7/8 LG	4
5	FINGER STOP	STANDARD	5/16 X 3/8 X 2 3/8 LG	2
6	AUTOMATIC STOP	STANDARD	1/4 X 3 3/8 LG	1
7	DIE SET—BAUMBACH A575	STANDARD	4 X 5 LG	1
8	STRIPPER PLATE	C R ST	1/4 X 4 1/4 X 4 3/4 LG	1
9	GUIDE	C R ST	1/4 X 1 1/4 X 15 LG	1
10	DIE BLOCK	COLONIAL SIX STEEL	7/8 X 4 1/4 X 4 3/4 LG	1
11	HEXAGON NUT	STANDARD	1/4-20NC	2
12	HEXAGON BOLTS	STANDARD	1/4-20NC X 7/8 LG	2
13	REST	C R ST	1/4 X 1 1/4 X 3 LG	1
14	.438 DIA PIERCING PUNCH	COLONIAL SIX STEEL	11/16 DIA X 1 1/2 LG	1
15	PUNCH PLATE	#1040 S A E ST	5/8 X 2 1/2 X 3 3/4 LG	1
16	.136 DIA PIERCING PUNCH	COLONIAL SIX STEEL	9/16 DIA X 1 1/2 LG	2
17	PILOT	TOOL ST	.437 DIA X 2 1/8	1
18	HEXAGON NUT	STANDARD	1/4-20NC	1
19	PIN	C R ST	1/4 DIA X 1 3/4 LG	1
20	LOCK NUT	STANDARD	1/4-20NC	1
21	HEXAGON NUT	STANDARD	1/4-20NC	1
22	PIN HOLDER	C R ST	5/8 X 5/8 X 1 9/16 LG	1
23	DOWEL PIN	STANDARD	1/4 DIA X 1 LG	2
24	FLAT FILLISTER HEAD MACH SCREW	STANDARD	5/16-18NC X 1 5/8 LG	4
25	BUTTON DIE	COLONIAL SIX STEEL	1/2 DIA X 1/2 LG	2
26	BLANKING PUNCH	COLONIAL SIX STEEL	1 3/32 X 1 19/32 X 1 31/32 LG	1

Figure 24-20C

tive and airplane parts and countless other products. Forming is accomplished by subjecting a piece of metal to pressure over special shaped dies. These dies may be very simple in design or extremely complex.

Since the forming process causes metal to bend, curl or stretch, the dies must permit the metal to flow into the required form smoothly and precisely. Accordingly, dies must be designed with special features so they can perform the required functions. For example, in the case of bending, sufficient compensation must be made for springback; that is, a certain allowance is required in the die design to overform the angle of bend. Otherwise, when pressure is released, the metal has a tendency to spring back slightly. With no provision for springback, the resulting bend would be less than the required bend angle. The amount allowed for springback depends on the elasticity of the metal and quite often the degree of bend.

Proper elongation or stretching of metal is made possible by incorporating the correct bend radius in the die. The size of radius is governed by such factors as angle of bend, kind and thickness of metal. If the proper radius is not included, the metal will have a tendency to bulge or wrinkle when it is compressed. Moreover, during a forming operation, the lack of correct radius will usually cause the metal to crack. A typical forming die is shown in Fig. 24-22.

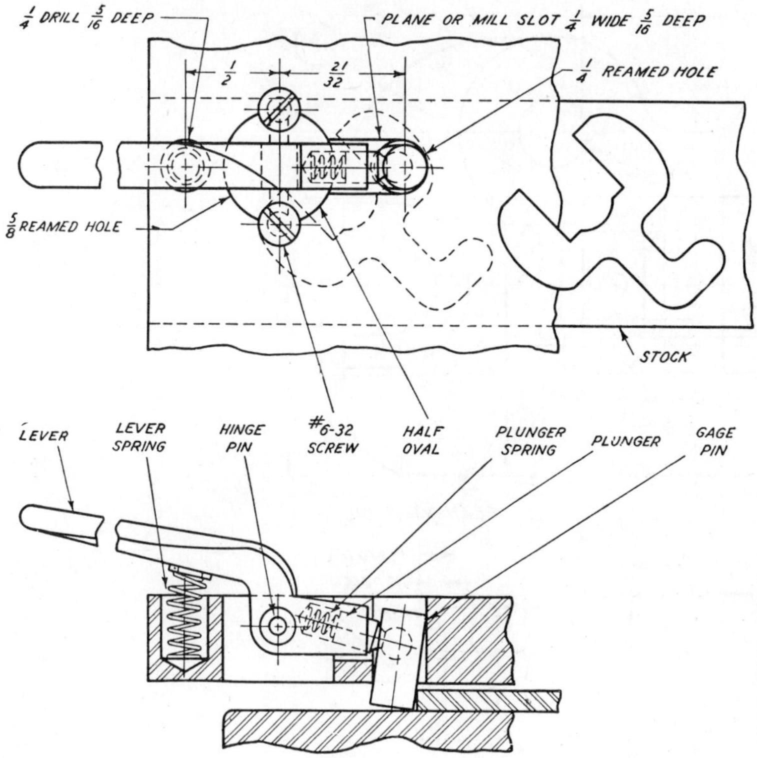

Figure 24–21
Commercially available automatic stock stops are often incorporated into the design for blanking dies. Danly Machine Specialties, Inc.

A unique forming operation used especially in the aviation industry is known as the Guerin Process. This process is particularly adaptable for forming parts from aluminum, light gage stainless steel, and sheet metal. The process utilizes a rubber pad that forces the metal against the form block.

24.9 Basic steps in laying out a die

The following illustrates the basic steps in laying out a simple die:

1 Draw a front, top and side view of the material strip. Use a red line to represent the material.
2 Draw the three views of the die block around the material strip.
3 Draw in the required punch. Show a bottom view of the punch in the upper right hand corner. Include all screws and dowels to secure the punch to the punch holder.
4 Insert the locating pins that will locate the material strip.
5 Draw in the stripper that is to remove the material strip from around the blanking punch.
6 Determine the size of the die set and complete the outline of the die set.
7 Place all required dimensions and notes.
8 Prepare a material list.
9 Prepare detail drawings of complicated parts that cannot be readily determined from the assembly drawing.

24.10 Fixed gages

Fixed gages are indispensable tools in the production of duplicate parts. They are used for checking purposes to ensure a uniform degree of accuracy. The many different types of gages are classified as work gages, inspection gages, and master gages. Work gages are those employed by the operator for checking a particular operation.

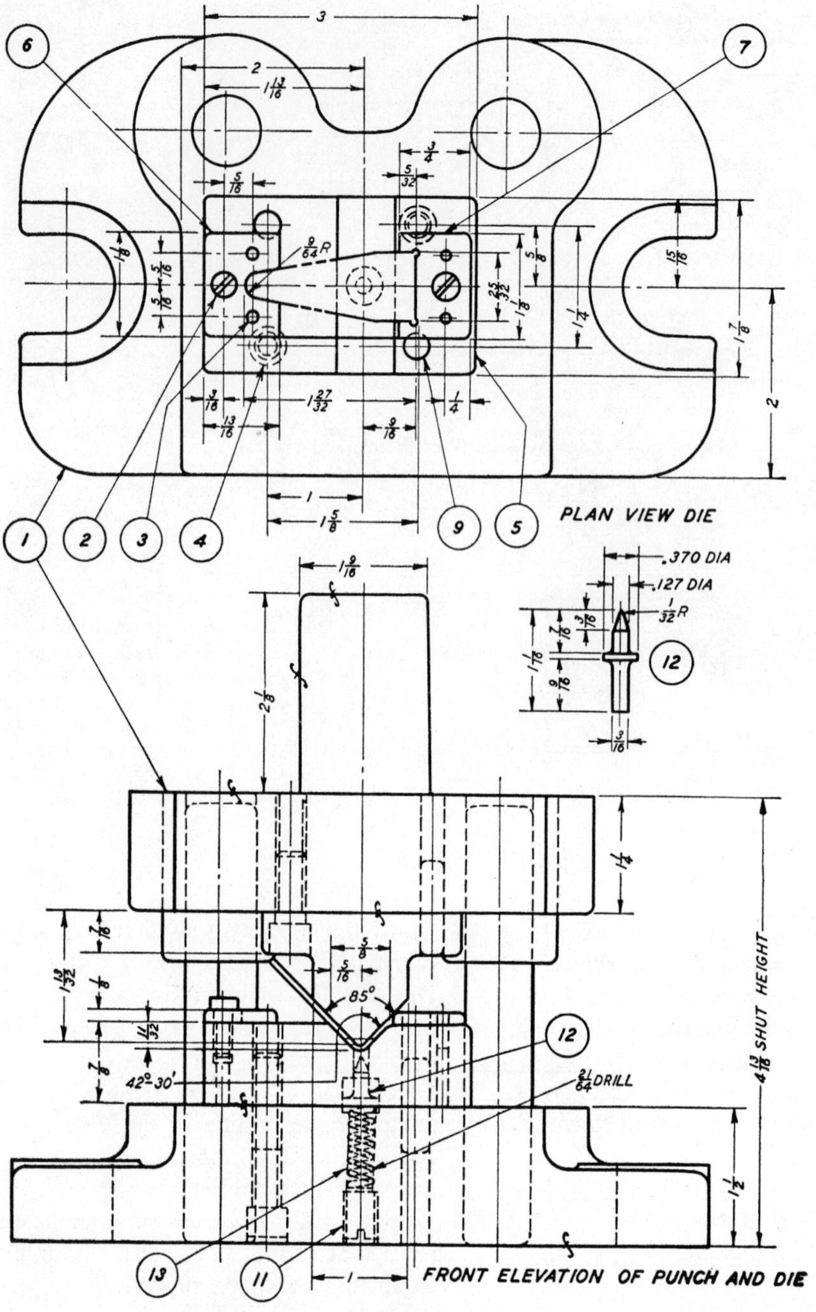

Figure 24-22
Forming dies may be simple or complex in design. The die shown here will bend the workpiece to a 90° angle. Notice that it is designed to over-bend the piece by 5° to allow for spring-back.

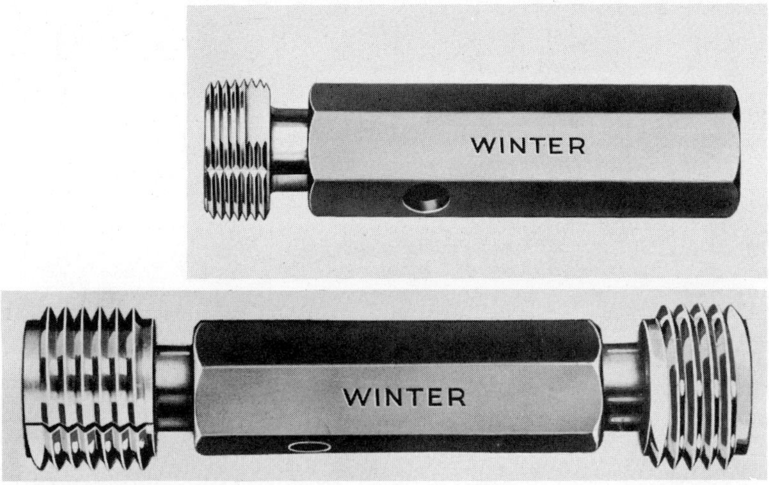

THREAD GAGES

PLUG GAGE

Figure 24-23
Plug gages are used for checking the accuracy of straight, tapered, bored or threaded holes.

Inspection gages are used by the inspector for checking the finished product. Master gages are reference tools intended primarily to check inspection gages periodically.

Many gages have been more or less standardized and can be obtained commercially. Others fall in a special category and must be designed for specific work. The following are a few of the more common gages:

Plug gages. These gages are used to check the inside of holes. They may be of the plain variety for checking straight, tapered, reamed, or bored holes, or threaded for ascertaining the accuracy of threaded holes. One end of the plug gages is marked "Go" and the opposite end "No-Go". Thus if the "Go" end fits the hole and the "No-Go" does not, then the hole is considered to be correctly machined. See Fig. 24-23.

Snap gages. These gages are designed to check dimensions between faces or shoulders on shafts or finished surfaces. They, too, are marked "Go" and "No-Go". See Fig. 24-24.

Ring gages. Gages of this type are employed to check the diameter of round pieces and function on the same "Go" and "No-Go" principle. See Fig. 24-25.

24.11 Gaging fixtures

To facilitate the checking of some parts, a special fixture is often required. Such fixtures are designed to hold the finished part while one or more gaging operations are performed. These fixtures must be designed specifically for the component being fabricated.

The important factors in the designing of gaging fixtures are (1) ease by which parts to be checked can be inserted and removed, and (2) adequate locating pins to ensure uniform positioning of the part. Fig. 24-26 illustrates a simple gaging fixture.

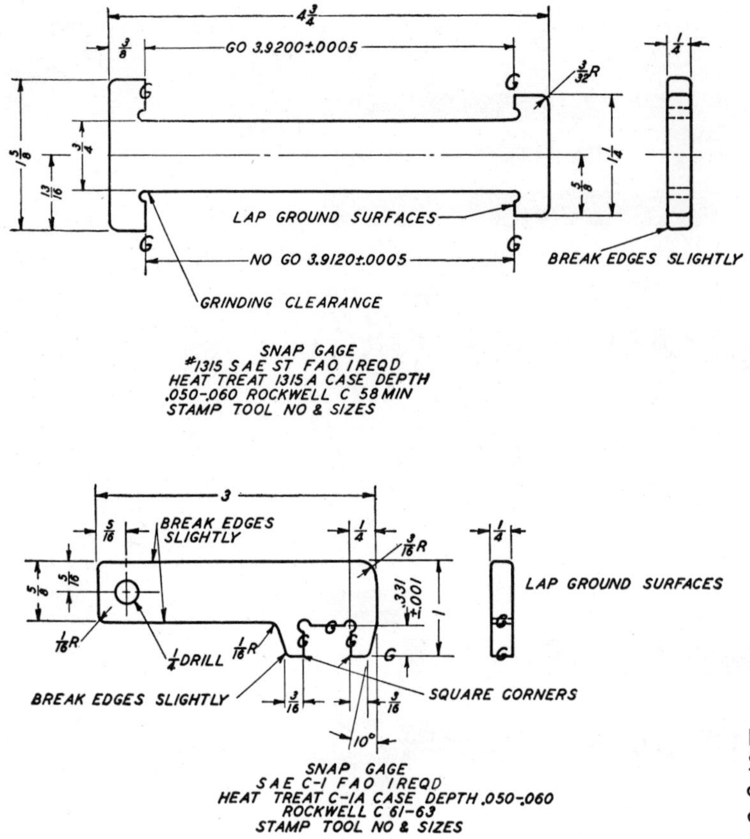

Figure 24-24
Snap gages are used to check finished surfaces or shoulders on shafts.

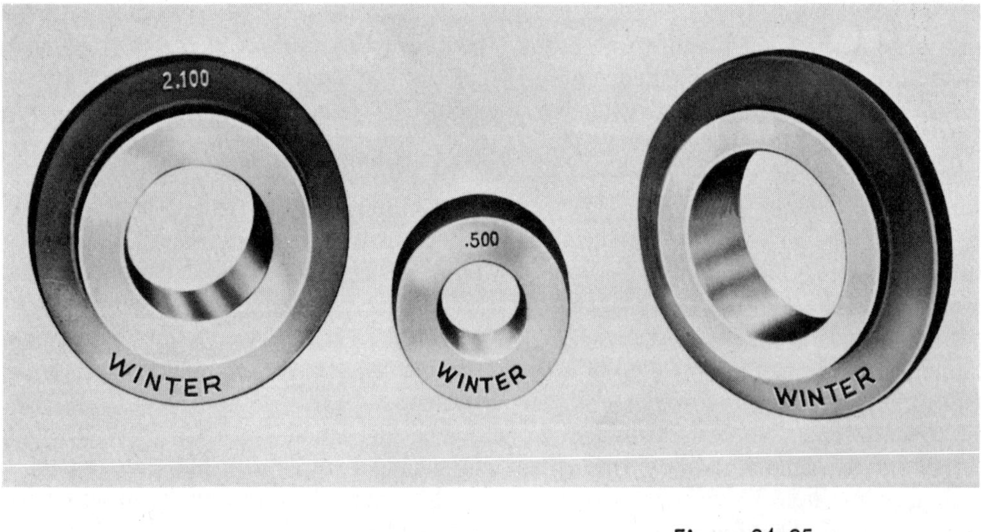

Figure 24-25
Ring gages are used to check plain and threaded shafts.

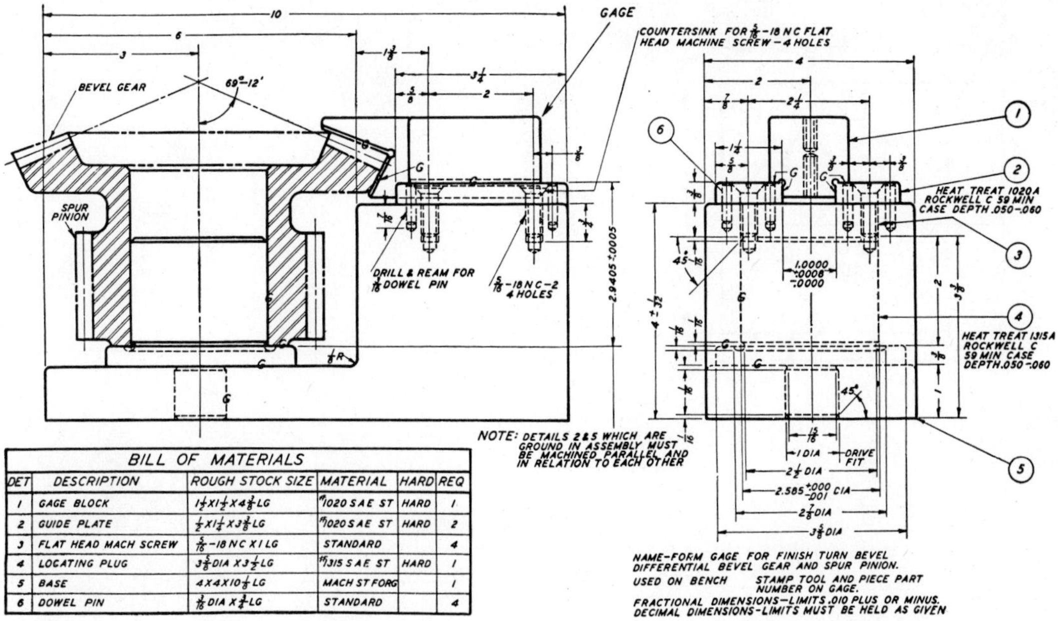

BILL OF MATERIALS

DET	DESCRIPTION	ROUGH STOCK SIZE	MATERIAL	HARD	REQ
1	GAGE BLOCK	1 1/2 X 1 1/2 X 4 3/8 LG	#1020 SAE ST	HARD	1
2	GUIDE PLATE	1/2 X 1 1/4 X 3 3/8 LG	#1020 SAE ST	HARD	2
3	FLAT HEAD MACH SCREW	5/16-18 NC X 1 LG	STANDARD		4
4	LOCATING PLUG	3 5/8 DIA X 3 1/2 LG	#1315 SAE ST	HARD	1
5	BASE	4 X 4 X 10 1/8 LG	MACH ST FORG		1
6	DOWEL PIN	3/16 DIA X 3/4 LG	STANDARD		4

Figure 24-26
Gaging fixtures are often needed to simplify the process of checking.

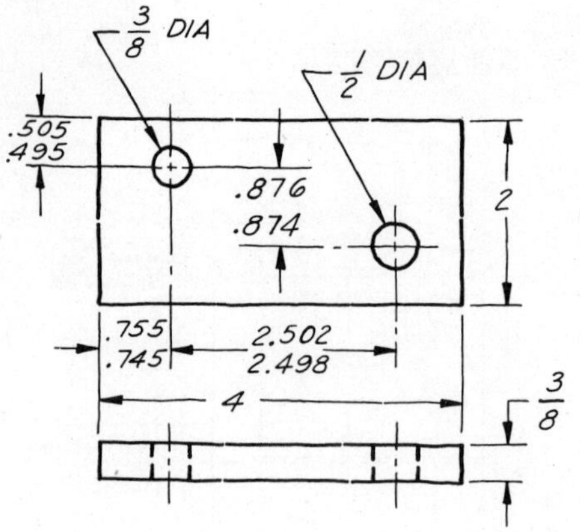

Figure 24-27
Problem 1.

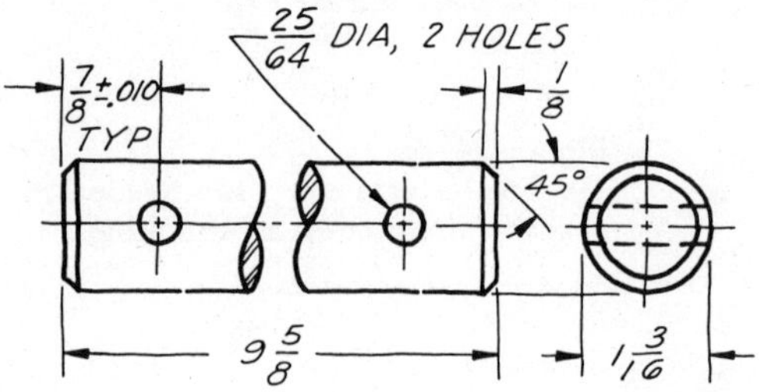

Figure 24-28
Problem 2.

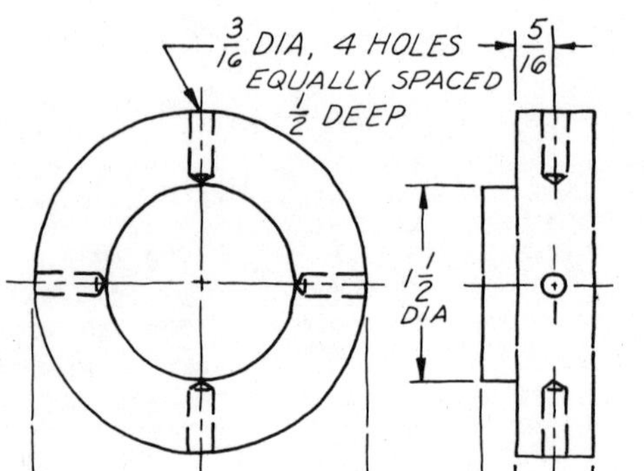

Figure 24-29
Problem 3.

Problems, section 24

1 Design a plate jig for drilling two holes in the part shown in the sketch of Fig. 24-27. Use head-type, press fit bushings.

2 Design a jig for drilling the holes in the shaft shown in the sketch of Fig. 24-28.

3 Design a jig for drilling the holes in the disk shown in the sketch of Fig. 24-29.

4 Draw a box jig for drilling the holes in the support sketched in Fig. 24-30.

5 Design a milling fixture to hold the connecting rod sketched in Fig. 24-31 during a straddle milling operation to face off the ends.

6 Produce the drawings for a complete die to blank and pierce the piece shown in the sketch of Fig. 24-32. Material: .064 half-hard cold rolled steel.

7 Prepare complete drawings for the design of a blanking die to stamp the part shown in the sketch of Fig. 24-33.

8 Make a set of drawings for a die to bend down the two semi-circular ends 90° for the part shown in the sketch of Fig. 24-33.

9 Design a gage to check the lengths of the shoulders for the pin shown in the sketch of Fig. 24-34.

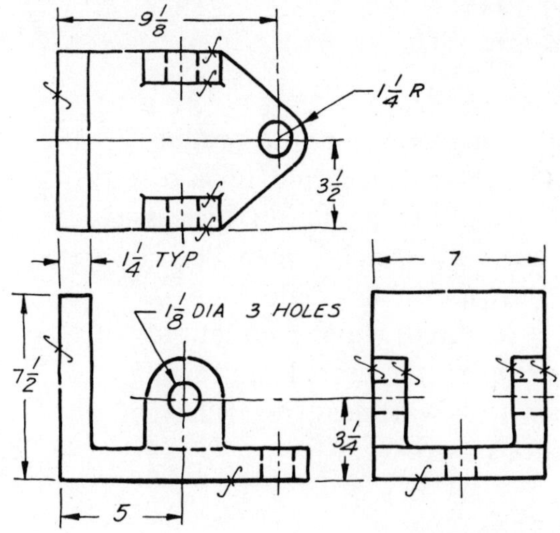

Figure 24-30
Problem 4.

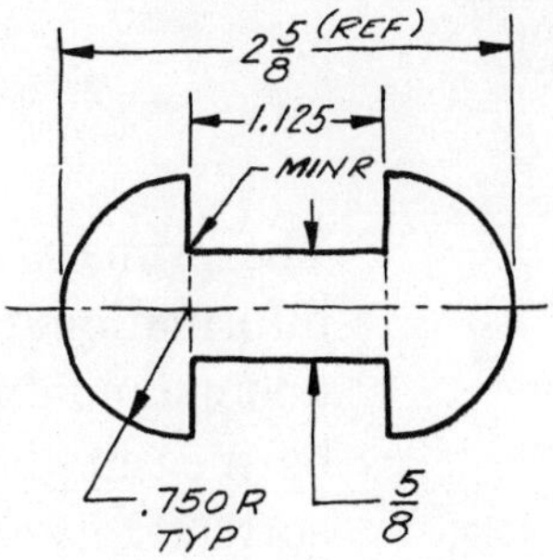

Figure 24-33
Problem 7.
Problem 8.

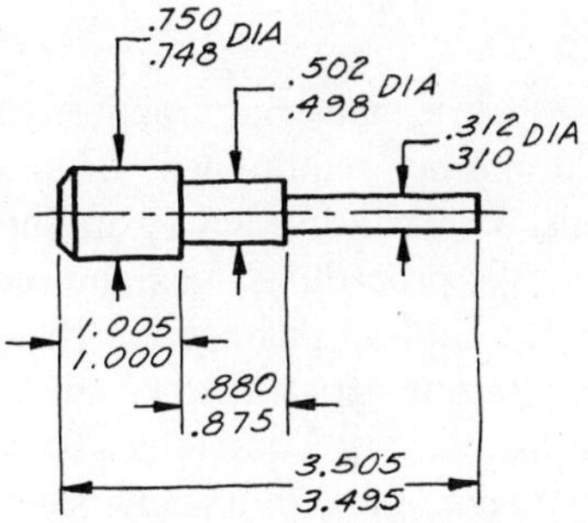

Figure 24-34
Problem 9.

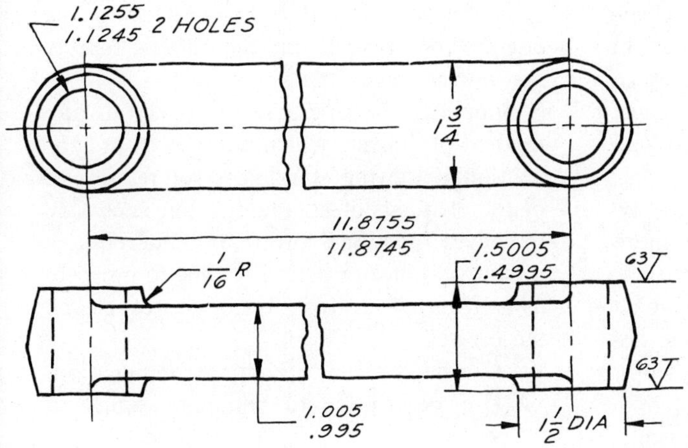

Figure 24-31
Problem 5.

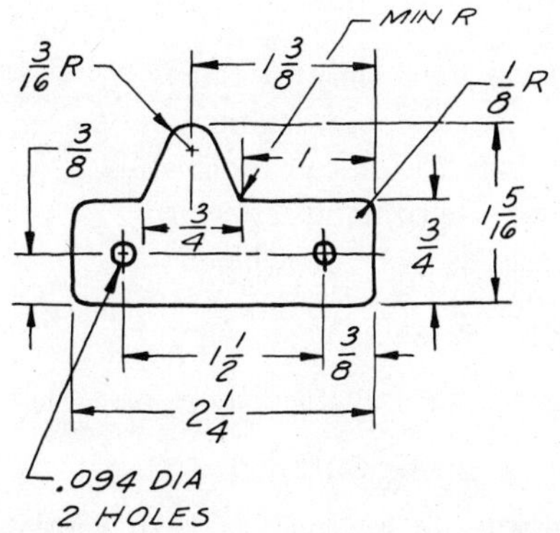

Figure 24-32
Problem 6.

Simplified drafting* 25

The primary function of an engineering drawing is to produce information that is complete, concise and accurate in a readily understandable form. The quality of a drawing must of necessity be measured according to the ease with which it can be interpreted correctly by the individual who must use it. It should state exactly and unequivocally what is required, leaving no latitude of misreading or unwarranted discretion by the user. If a drawing fails to achieve this objective then it is worthless, regardless of the conventional drafting representations used.

Modern industrial practices have imposed still another requirement on drawings: they must be produced rapidly and on time. Competitive procedures demand economies in all levels of an engineering structure. Hence the drafting department of any industry must be just as cost conscious as those involved in design, production and sales.

Reduction in drafting costs can be effected in several ways, some of the more important being:

1 Use of standardized components which can be represented by typewritten descriptions rather than by detail drawings.
2 Use of drafting aids.
3 Elimination of lost motion in transmitting drafting assignments.
4 Employment of competent draftsmen.
5 Simplification of drafting procedures.

The material in this section deals principally with the last mentioned factor—simplification of drafting procedures.

25.1 What is simplified drafting?

The emphasis in industrial drafting rooms today is on speed. Time saved in the drafting department reflects on the overall productivity of the entire organization. That is why simplification of drafting practices is being encouraged by industry. In the final analysis, the end result of design and drafting is the proper fabrication and operation of those components which appear on drawings. The end result is not graphic or art presentation. To the manufacturing or engineering organization, the esthetic aspects of drawing have little value.

Simplified drafting may be defined as any method of drafting which deviates from conventional drawing standards, yet retains all of the elements of communication necessary to convey functional information but requires a relatively shorter period of time to prepare. This form of drafting encompasses eleven basic rules:

1 Use description to eliminate delineation.
2 Use description to eliminate projected views.
3 Omit elaborate, repetitive, pictorial details.
4 Use keyed legends to indicate standard items.
5 Use dotted lines only to clarify.
6 Use hatching for clarification only.
7 Use symbols to indicate hole sizes.
8 Avoid the use of hand lettering.
9 Avoid the use of arrowheads.
10 Use ordinate dimensioning when appropriate.
11 Make freehand drawings where possible.

*Prepared with the assistance of J. H. Bergen, formerly Director, Engineering Services Laboratory, American Machine and Foundry Co.

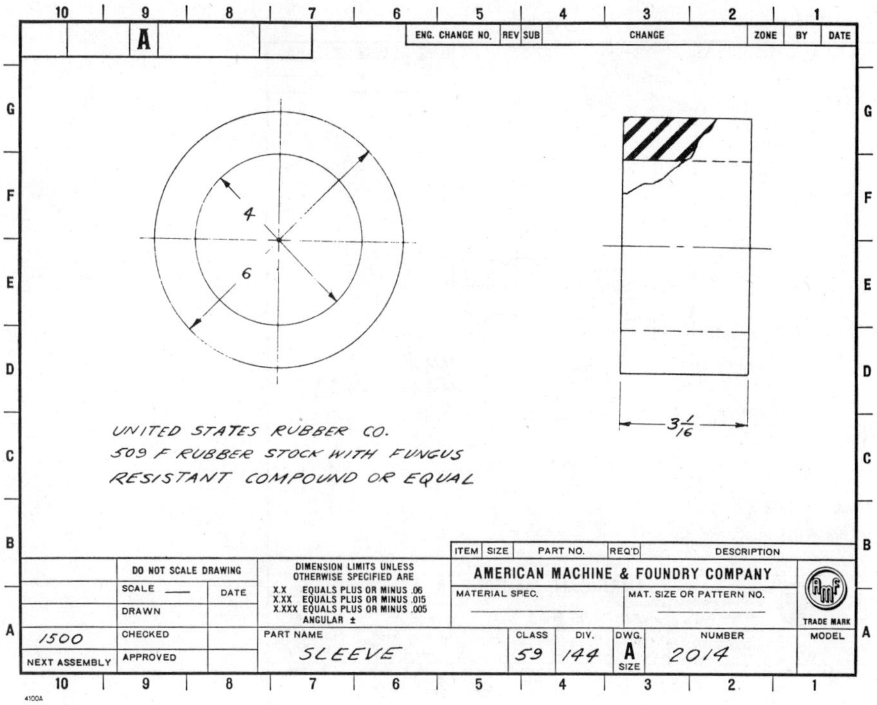

Figure 25-1
Conventional method.

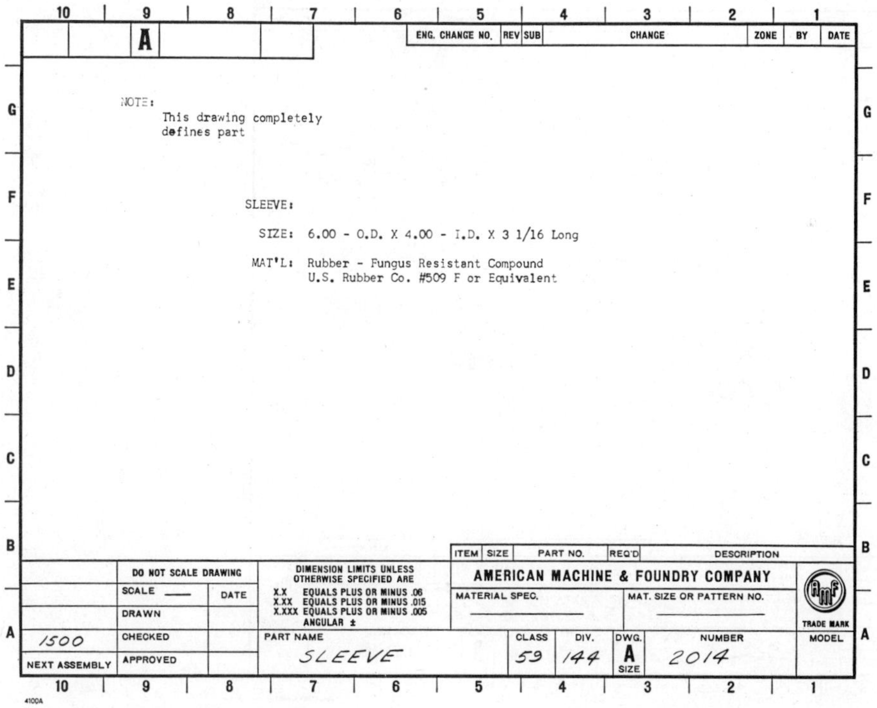

Figure 25-2
Simplified method.

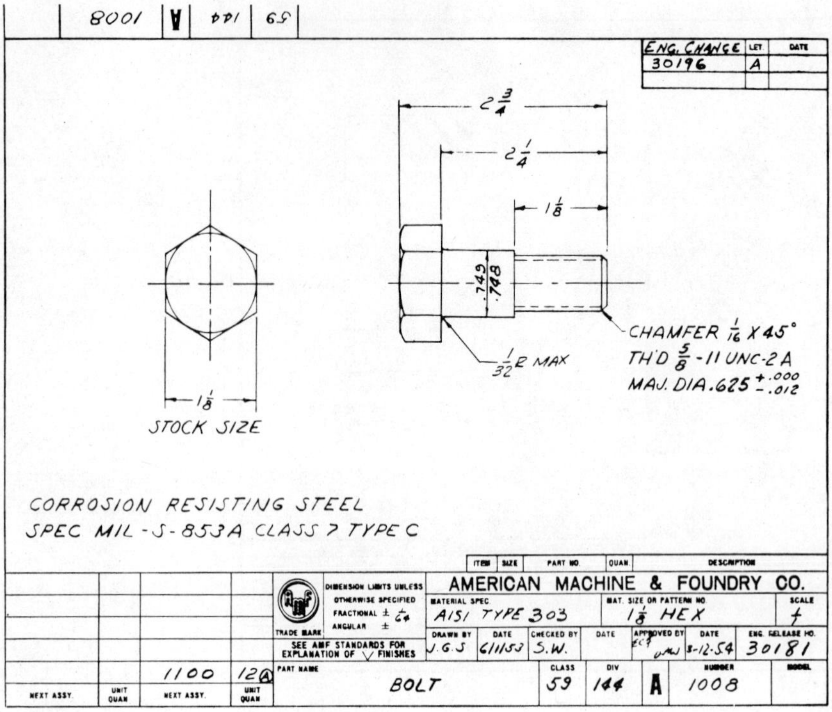

Figure 25-3
Conventional method.

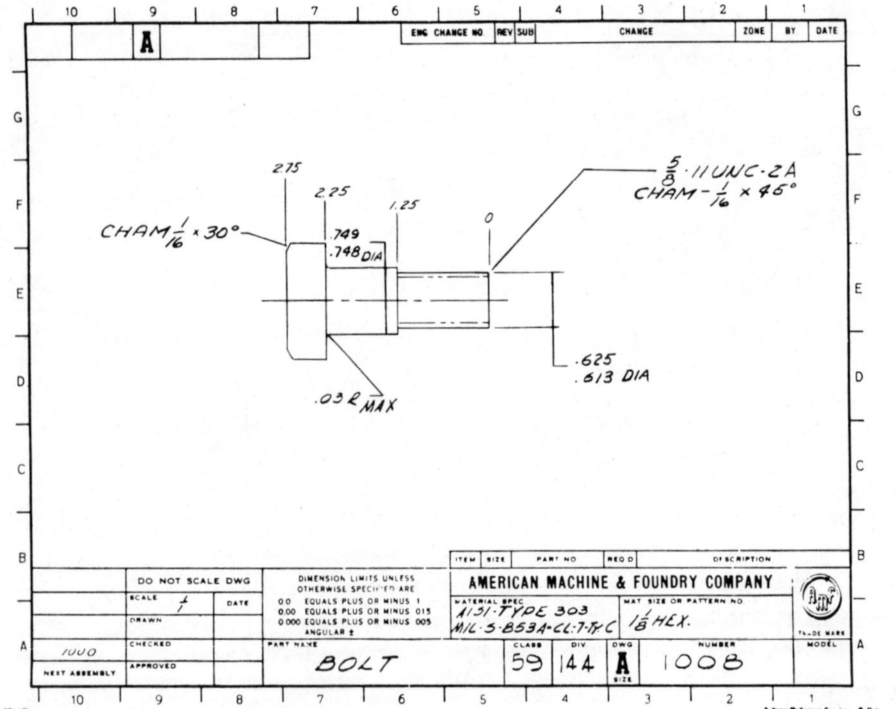

Figure 25-4
Simplified method.

25.2 Use description to eliminate delineation

The drawing of many simple parts such as bolts, nuts, washers, fittings, gears, tubing, gaskets, seals, etc., can be eliminated entirely. Instead describe these units either in the list of materials or as a non-picture drawing by word description alone.

Fig. 25-1 illustrates the conventional way of drawing a sleeve. If the simplified process is used, the same sleeve would be shown by a description as in Fig. 25-2.

25.3 Use description to eliminate projected views

Avoid projected views unless the shape of the item requires the preparation of additional views for clarity; instead use word description. For example, the thickness of a part can often be shown on a plan view instead of a projected view.

Place all dimension figures and notes horizontally to facilitate lettering and reading. Wherever possible eliminate dimension lines. Abbreviate words whenever clarity is not impaired and refrain from using periods.

Very often a few words will be sufficiently descriptive to make an extra view unnecessary. Thus, such words as *diameter, square, on centerline* or *hexagon* can be used to supplement the given view without having to show additional details.

A typical example of this rule is illustrated in Figs. 25-3 and 25-4.

25.4 Omit elaborate, pictorial, or repetitive detail

A good example of how details can be omitted from a drawing without sacrificing clarity is shown in Fig. 25-6 as contrasted with its conventional counterpart in Fig. 25-5.

Work simplification can be achieved by using broken lines to represent the *O.D., P.D.,* and *R.D.,* of a gear rather than drawing the gear teeth. On threaded parts, instead of showing the actual threads, use dotted lines or a description.

25.5 Use keyed legends to indicate nuts, bolts and other hardware

The main function of an assembly drawing is to show the arrangement and location of parts. In the conventional assembly drawing as illustrated in Fig. 25-7, the practice is to draw as well as to number the standard parts. By eliminating the outline of these parts, except where they are necessary to indicate position or to check for clearance, and using keyed legends only, considerable time can be saved. See example in Fig. 25-8.

25.6 Avoid use of dotted lines that do not add clarification

Dotted lines often tend to clutter a view and result in confusion. Therefore, in the simplified method, omit dotted lines unless they are absolutely essential. Notice the amount of drafting time that can be saved by comparing the conventional drawing in Fig. 25-9 and the simplified version in Fig. 25-10.

25.7 Only use cross-hatching to add clarification

In drawing sectional views, do not use cross-hatching unless it is necessary for clarity. When required, resort to partial cross-hatching done freehand.

Refrain from cross-hatching as a means of identifying materials. Identification of materials can be more adequately and easily done in the list of materials or covering specifications. See examples in Figs. 25-11 and 25-12.

25.8 Use symbols to indicate various hole sizes

Considerable drafting time can be saved by eliminating circles to represent holes. Instead use symbols to designate required holes. Notice in Fig. 25-14 how much detail can be avoided by using the simplified method as contrasted with the conventional method in Fig. 25-13. *(Text continued on page 717)*

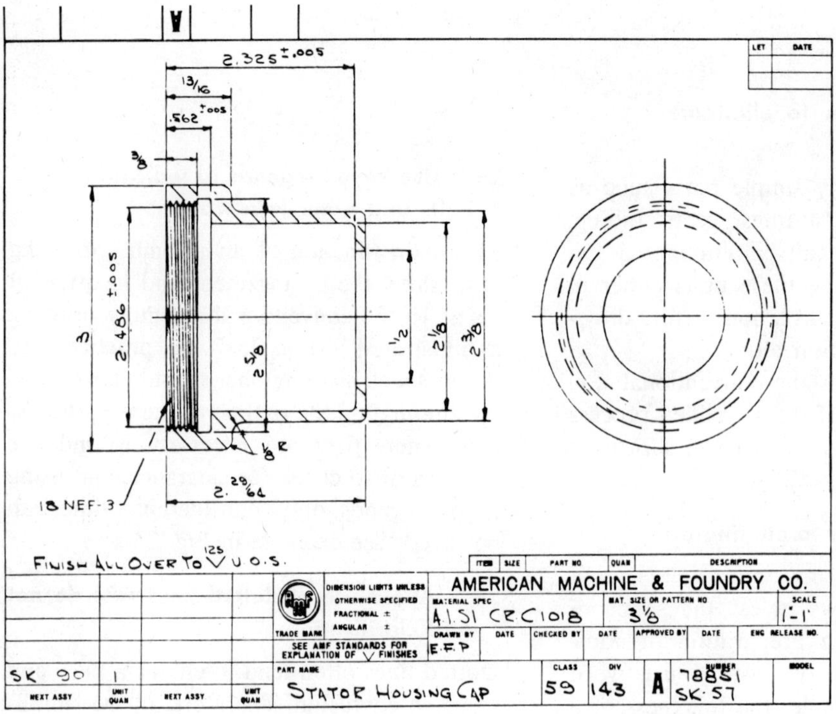

Figure 25-5
Conventional method.

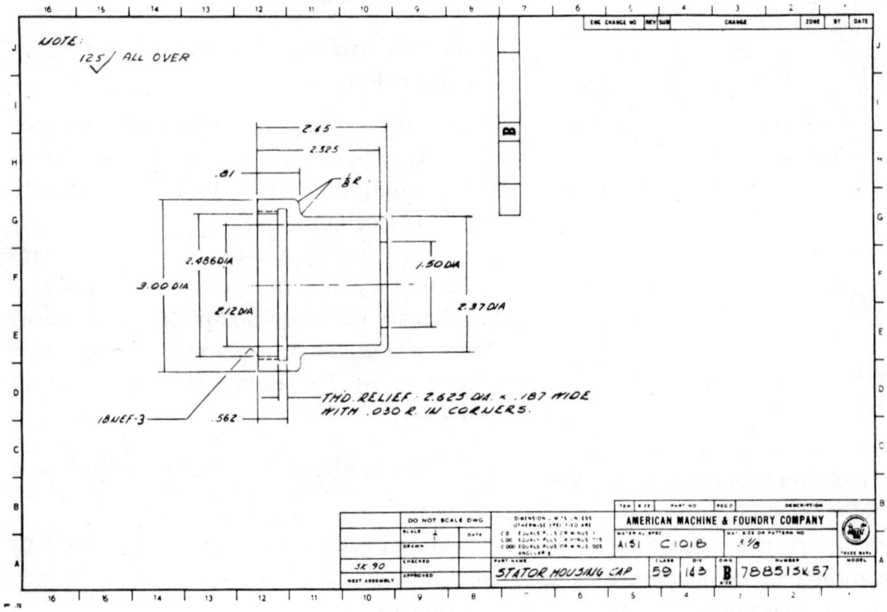

Figure 25-6
Simplified method.

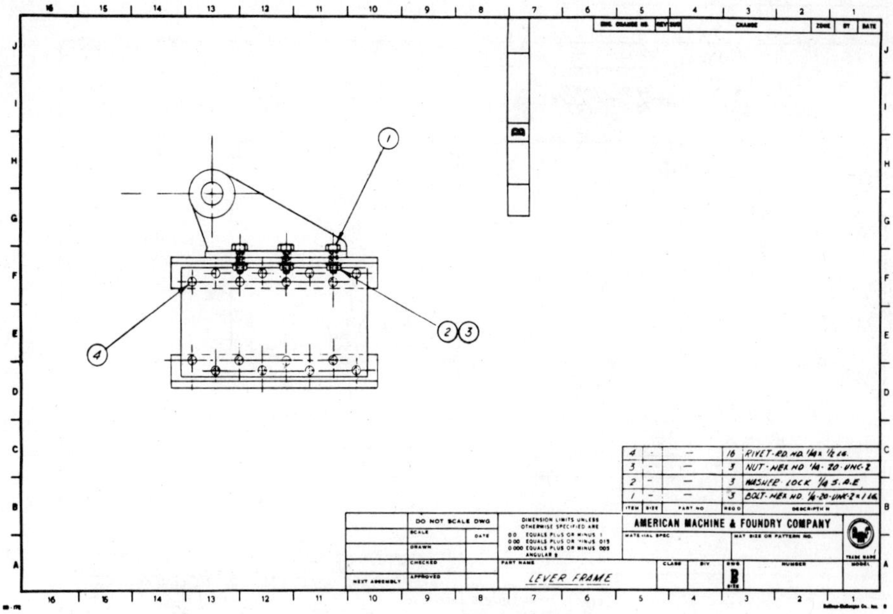

Figure 25-7
Conventional method.

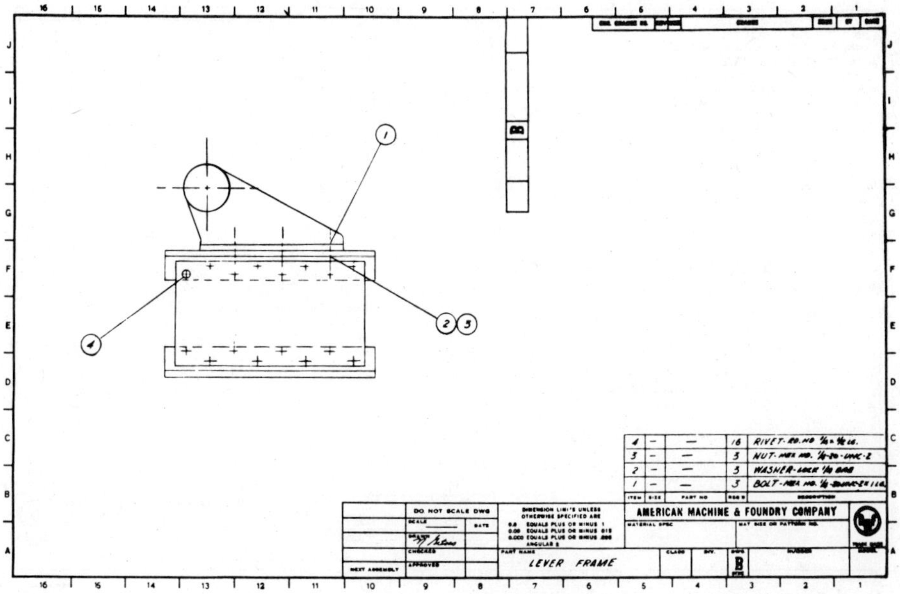

Figure 25-8
Simplified method.

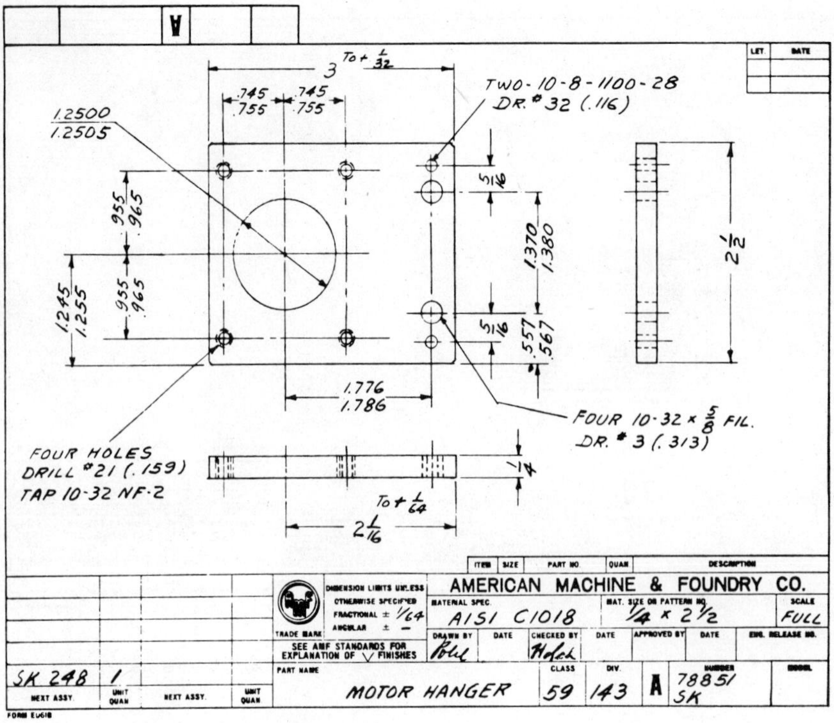

Figure 25-9
Conventional method.

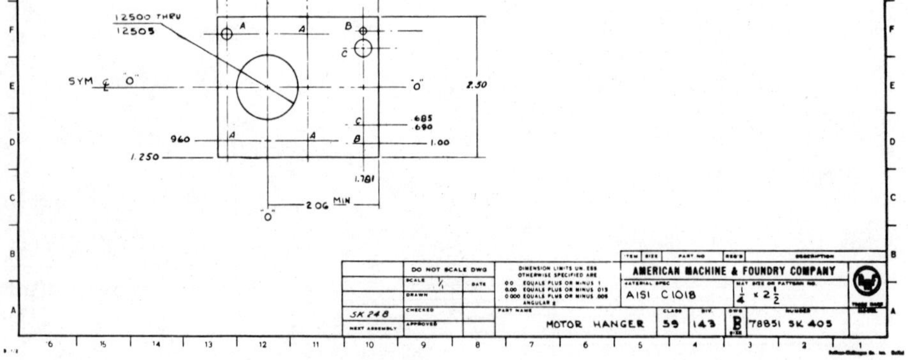

Figure 25-10
Simplified method.

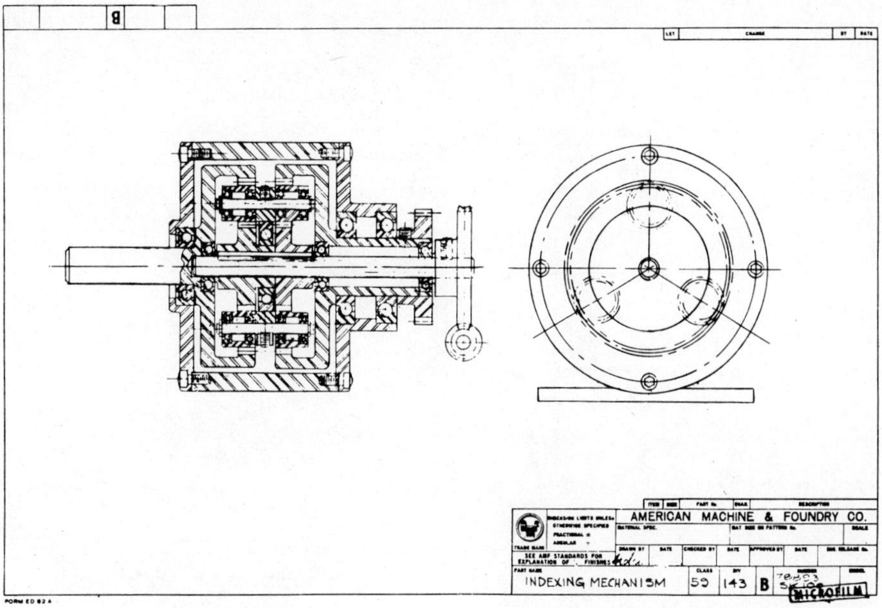

Figure 25-11
Conventional method.

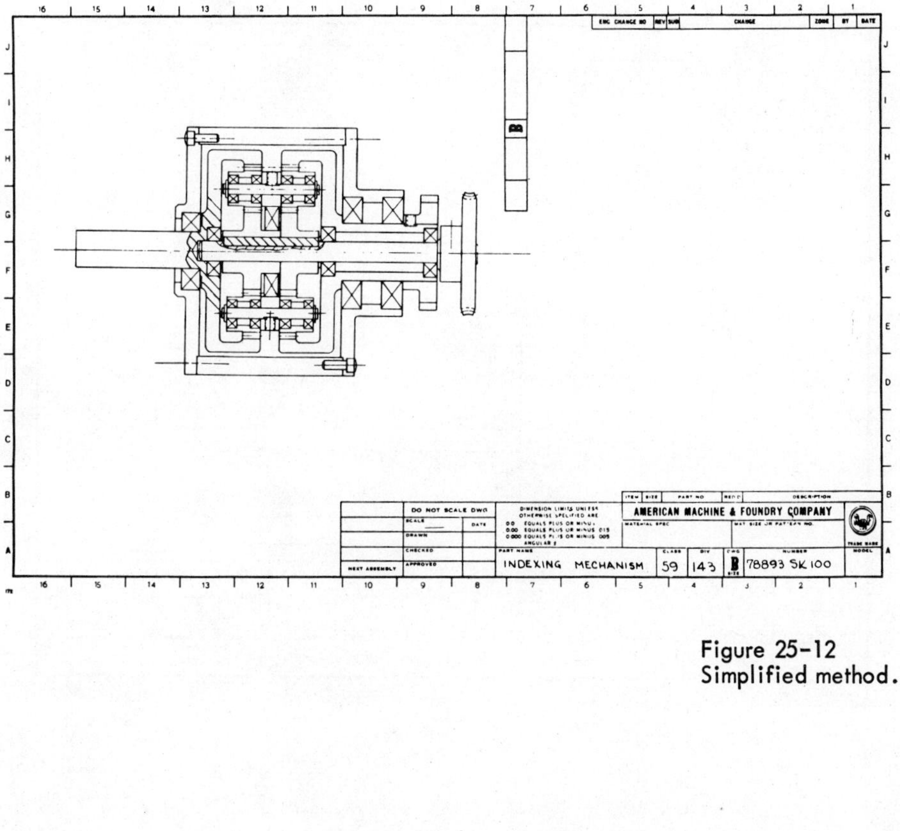

Figure 25-12
Simplified method.

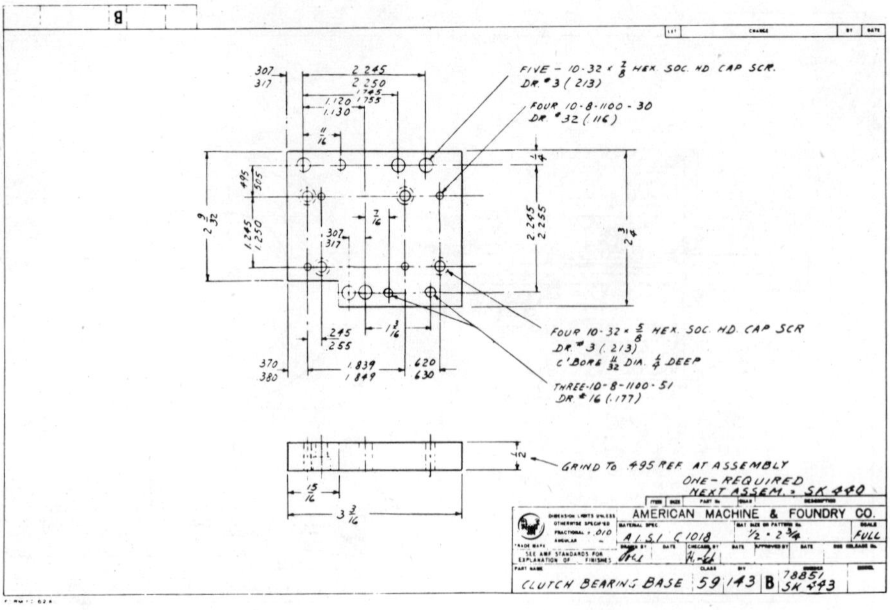

Figure 25-13
Conventional method.

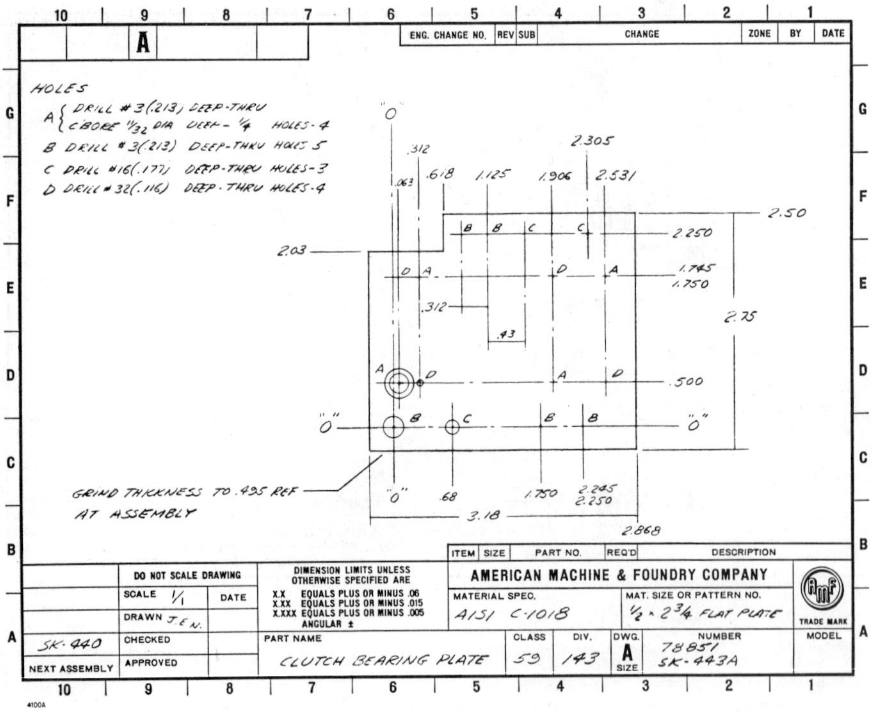

Figure 25-14
Simplified method.

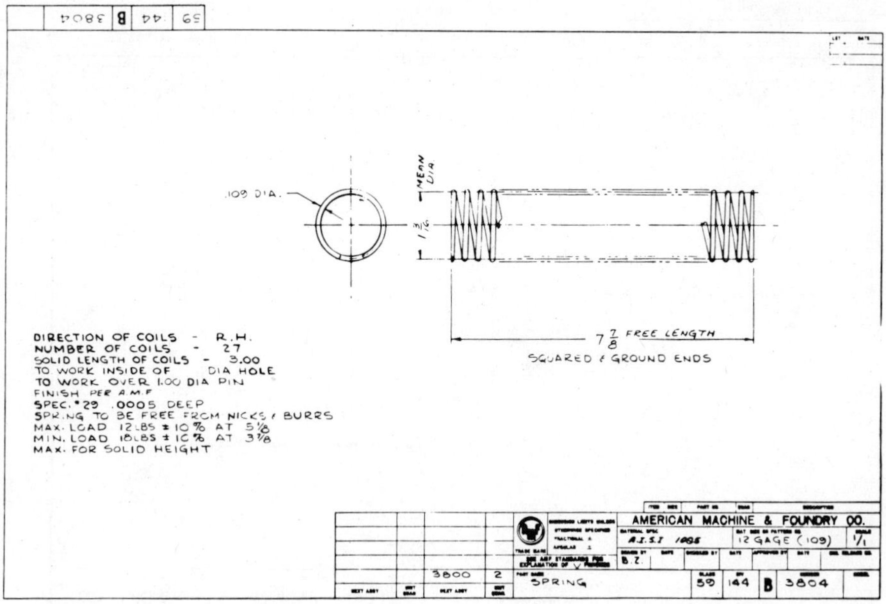

Figure 25-15
Conventional method.

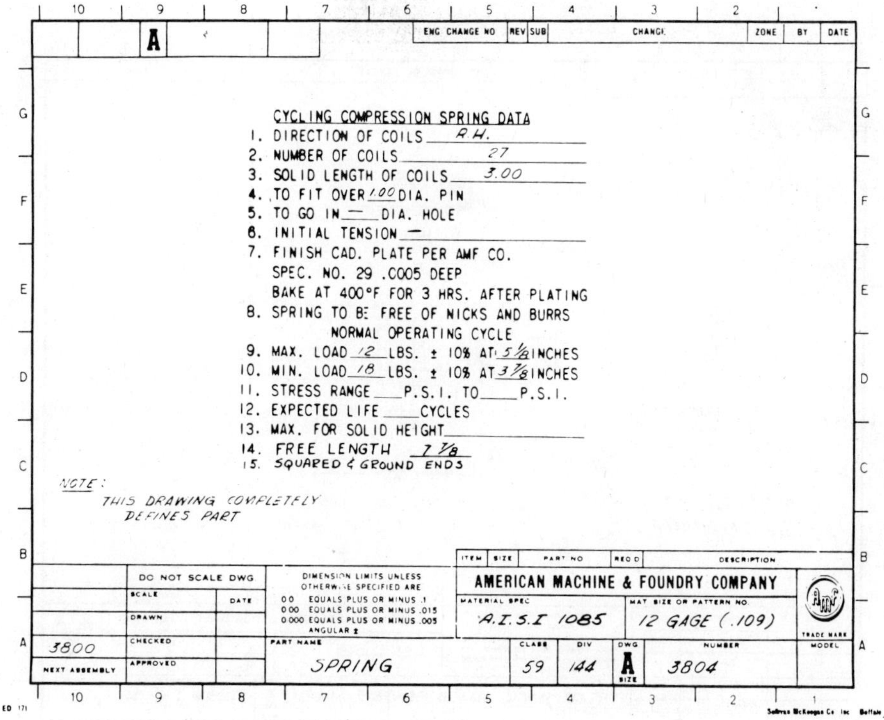

Figure 25-16
Simplified method.

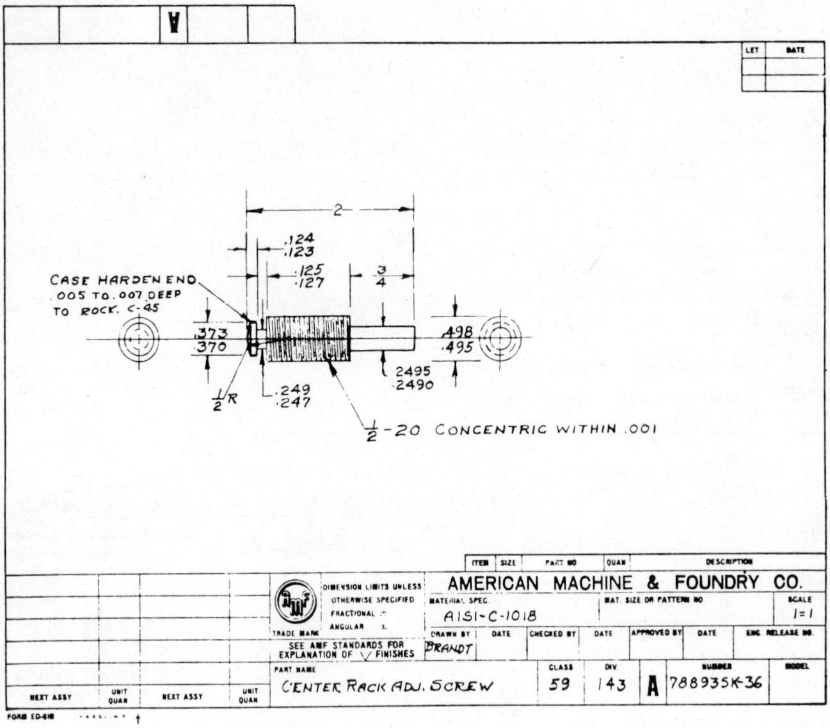

Figure 25-17
Conventional method.

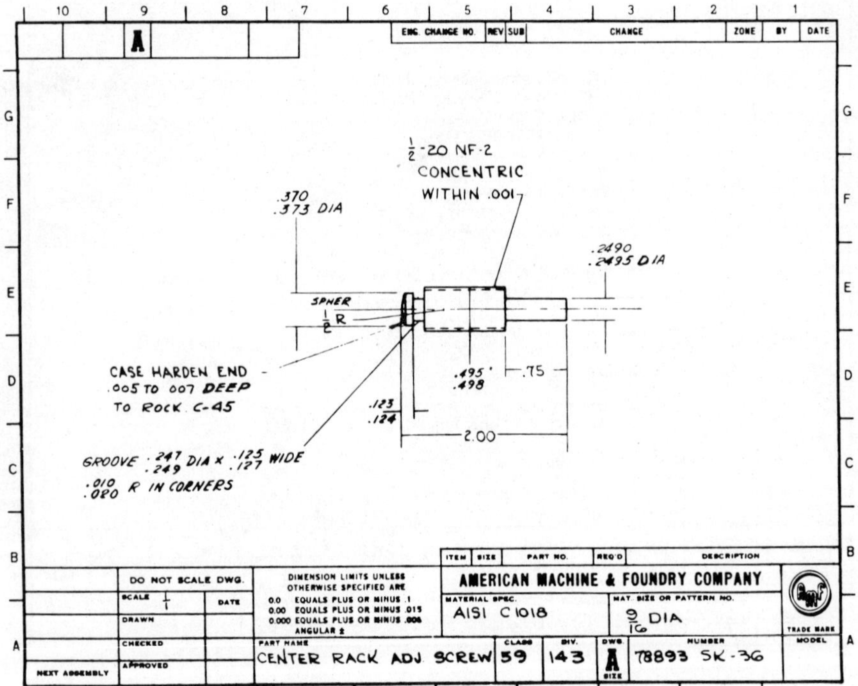

Figure 25-18
Simplified method.

25.9 Avoid the use of hand lettering

Drawings often require a considerable amount of lettering either for notes, material lists, title blocks, etc. Providing this information by hand lettering is a time consuming task. Therefore, whenever possible use a typewriter. See Figs. 25-15 and 25-16.

25.10 Avoid the use of arrowheads

Arrowheads on dimension lines and leaders do serve a useful purpose, nevertheless considerable time is required to make them. This does not mean that all arrowheads should arbitrarily be omitted from a drawing. If clarity is not sacrificed, such arrowheads should be eliminated. On the other hand, if by their omission the readability of the drawing is impaired, then it would be foolish to omit them.

Observe that by dispensing with arrowheads the readability of the drawing in Fig. 25-18 as contrasted with the one in Fig. 25-17 is not jeopardized.

25.11 Using ordinate dimensioning

Drawing simplification is generally achieved by using the ordinate system of dimensioning. With this method, dimensions are measured from several base surfaces or centerlines, thereby reducing considerably the number of conventional dimension and extension lines which often tend to clutter up a drawing. The ordinate system in addition to shortening the drafting time, minimizes the need for the shopman to add dimensions, which he must do when dimensions are given by increments in the conventional drawing.

Notice how much easier it is to prepare the drawing in Fig. 25-20 than the one in Fig. 25-19.

25.12 Make freehand drawings where possible

Making freehand sketches instead of instrument drawings is a great time saver. Freehand sketches do not presume sloppy, careless or substandard work. Their use simply recognizes the fact that drawings are designed to convey engineering information; they are not ornamental pictures.

Freehand drawings, if made with reasonable care, will retain all of the essential accuracy and information of conventional drawings. They are particularly valuable in detailing from assembly drawings or layouts, and in producing simple working drawings, assemblies, schematics and electrical diagrams. Complicated parts can usually be drawn on translucent paper placed over a grid board cover or on drawing paper having non-reproducible blue grid lines. Figs. 25-21 and 25-22 illustrate an item drawn by the conventional and simplified method.

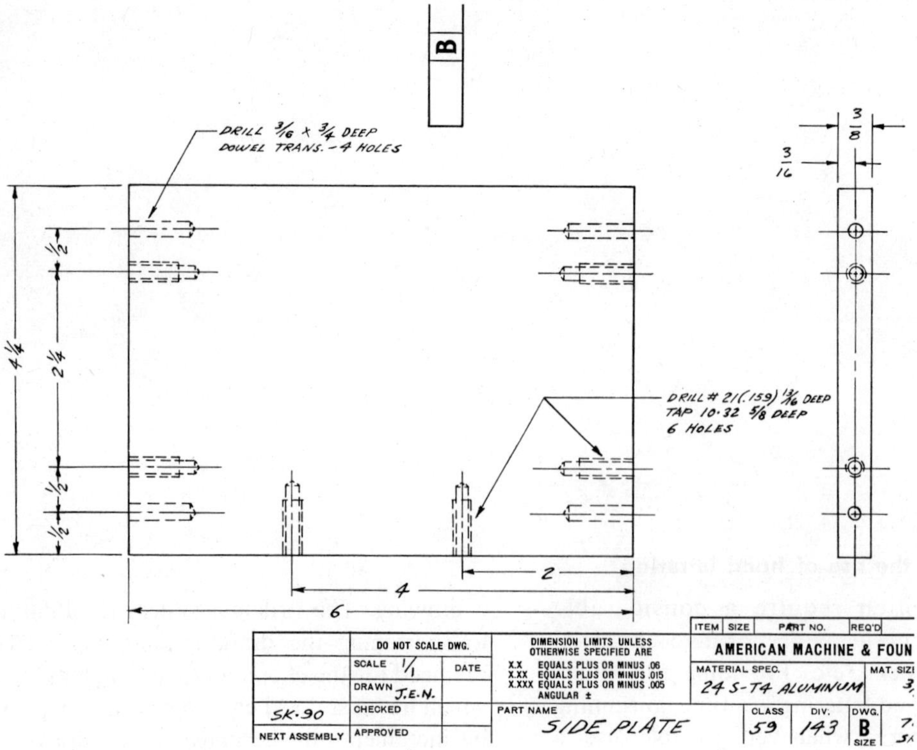

Figure 25-19
Conventional method.

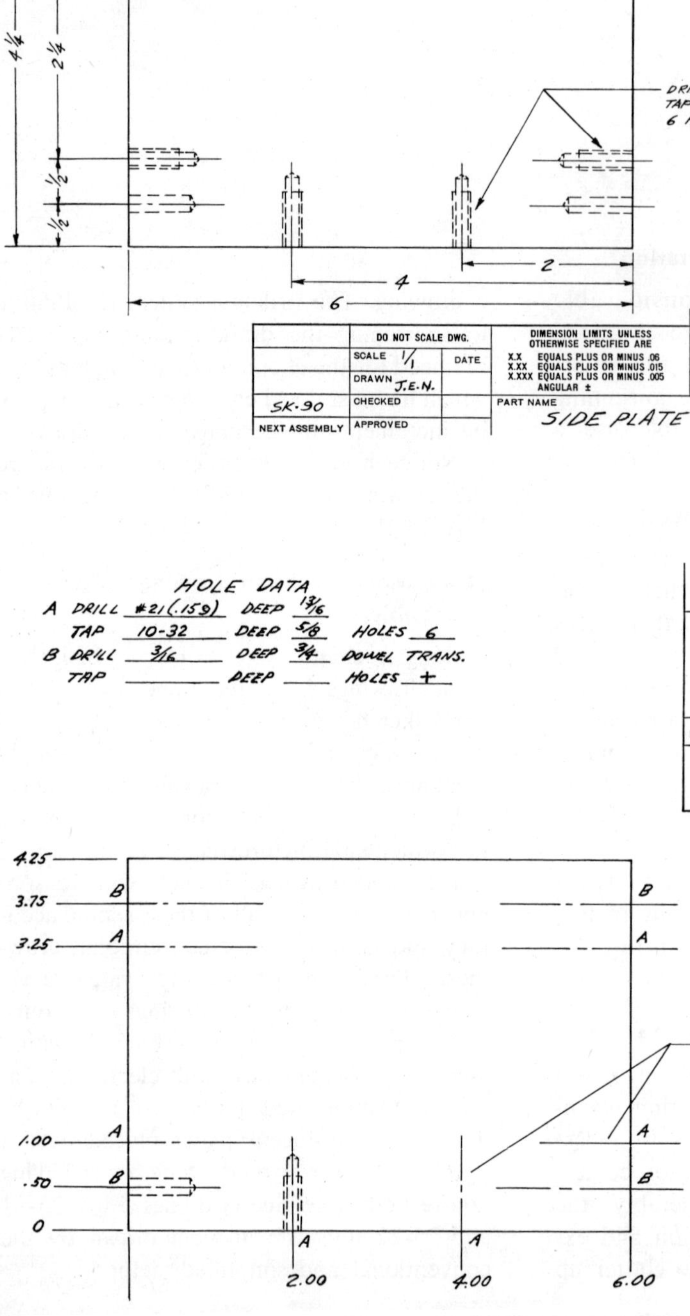

Figure 25-20
Simplified method.

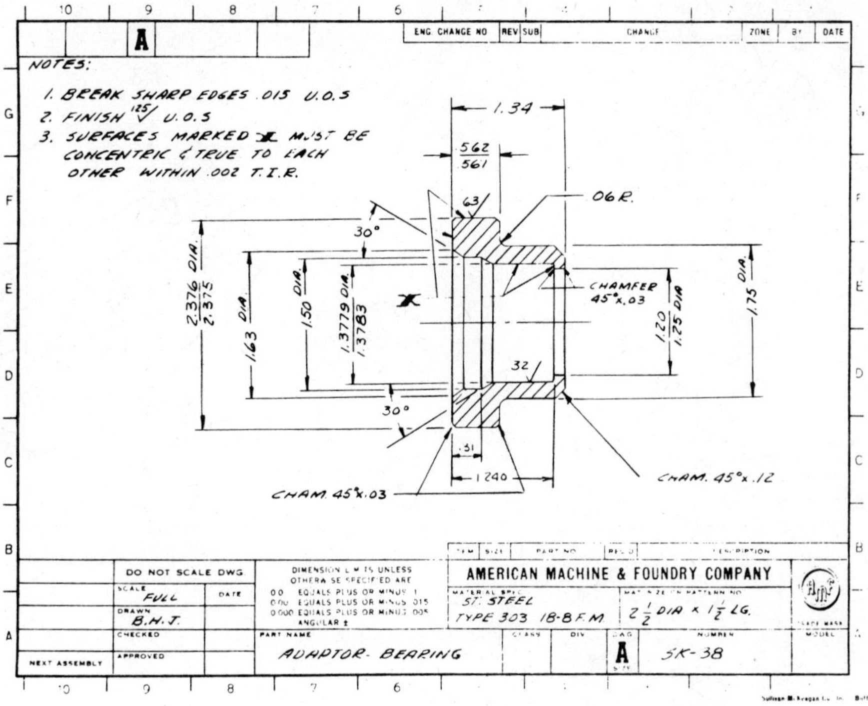

Figure 25–21
Conventional method.

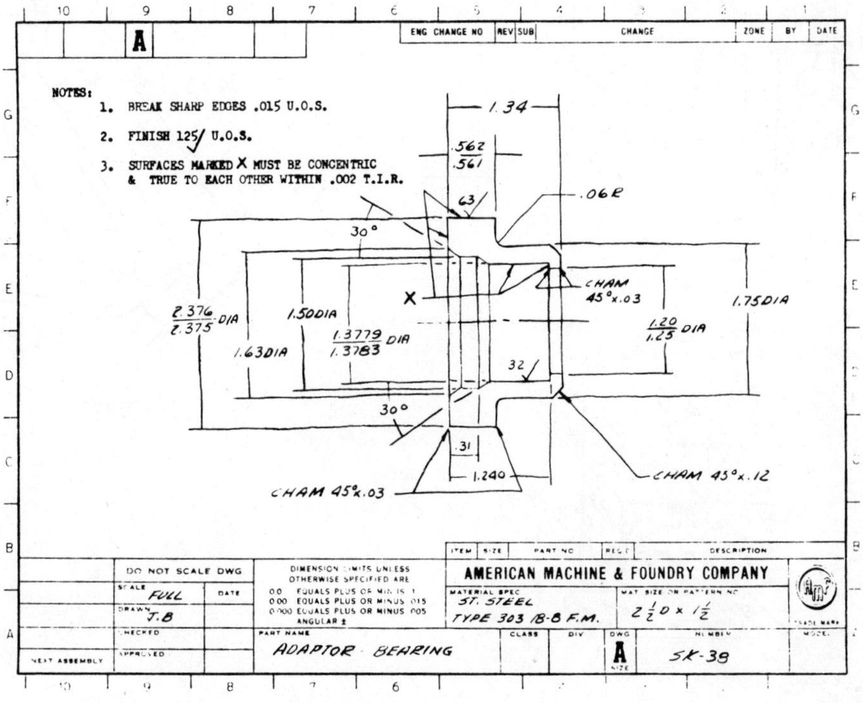

Figure 25–22
Simplified method.

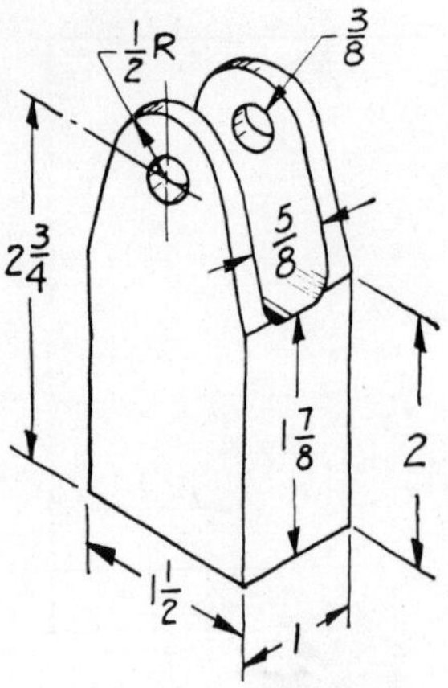

Figure 25-23
Pivot Mount.

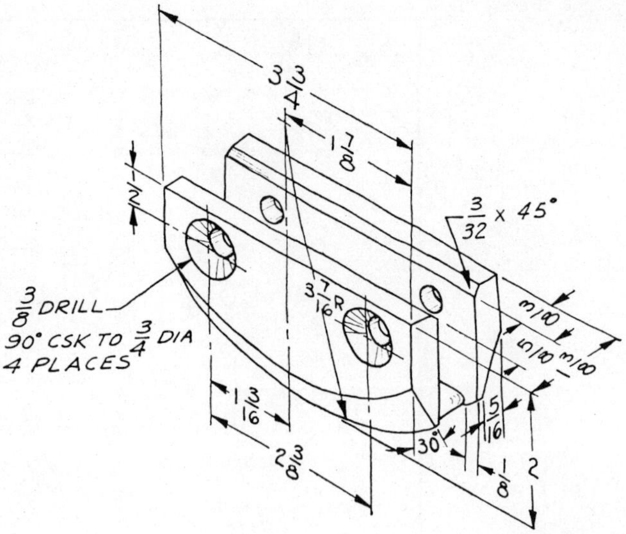

Figure 25-26
Counterweight.

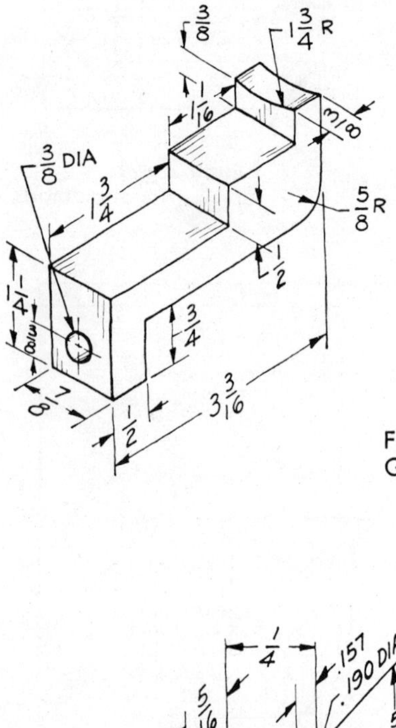

Figure 25-24
Gage Stop.

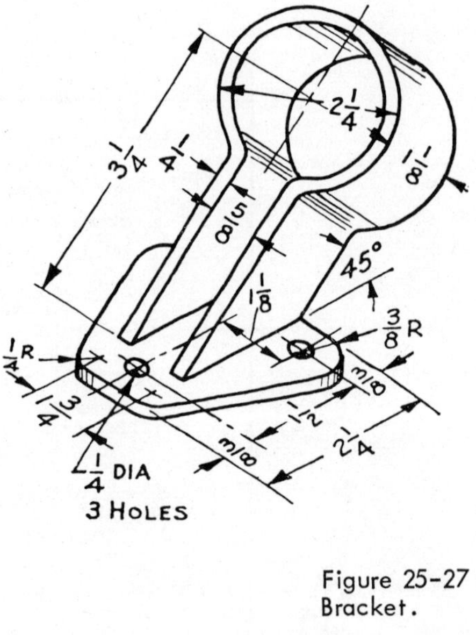

Figure 25-27
Bracket.

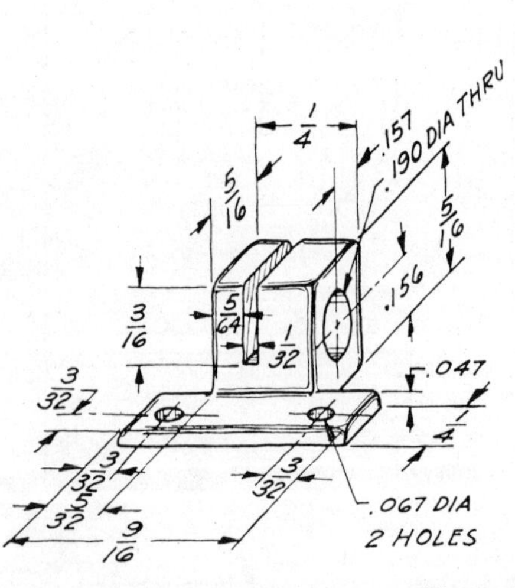

Figure 25-25
Gyro Bracket.

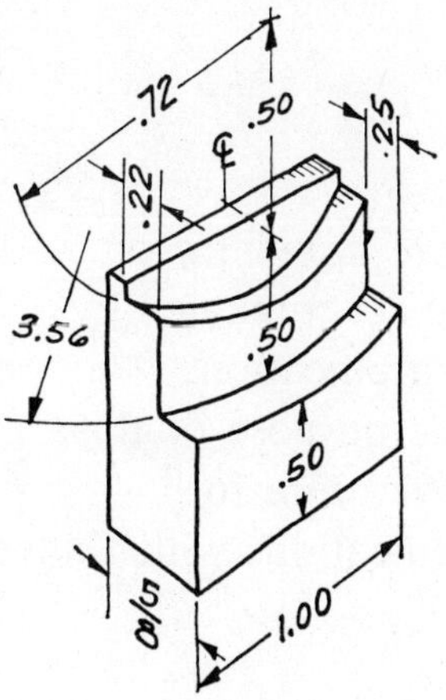

Figure 25–28
Door Catch.

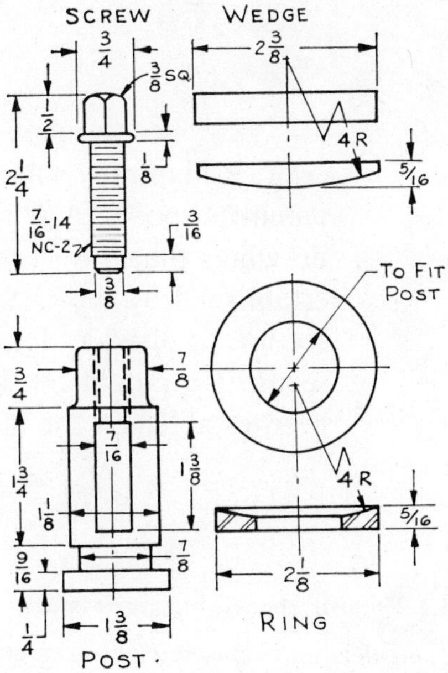

Figure 25–30
Tool Post.

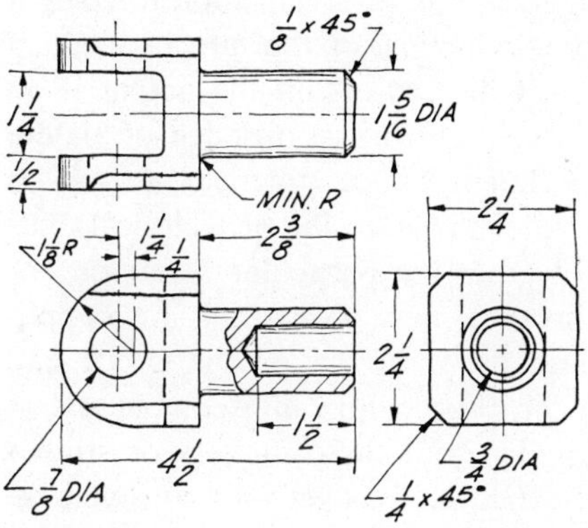

Figure 25–29
Terminal.

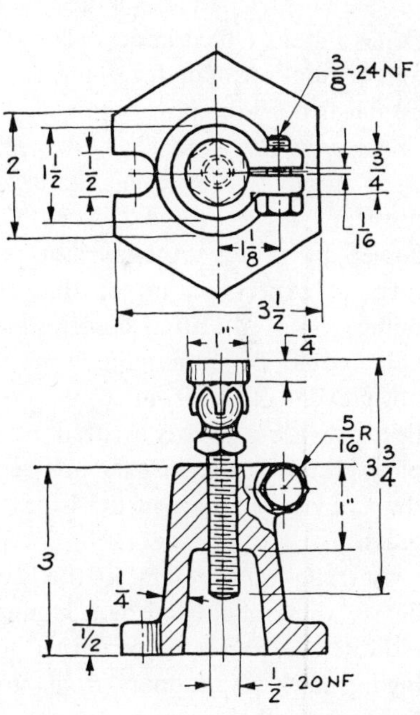

Figure 25–31
Leveling Jack.

Problems, section 25

1-9 Make detail drawings of the parts shown in Figs. 25-23 to 25-31 using simplified drafting practices.

Patent drawings 26

A draftsman may sometimes be required to prepare drawings for patent purposes. Any request for a patent must be accompanied by drawings that have been prepared according to specifications established by the U.S. Patent Office. It is not the purpose of this section to provide detailed information on the procedure for securing a patent but merely to describe the specifications which have been established for making patent drawings.

26.1 Patent, copyright, trade-mark

A *patent* is an exclusive right granted to an individual to exclude others from making, using, or selling a useful invention for the term of 17 years throughout the United States. Any person may obtain a patent who invents or discovers any new and useful process, machine, manufacture, or composition of matter, or any new and useful improvements. A patent is issued by the United States Patent Office in accordance with rules and regulations (in legal terms, a *statute*) established by the government.

A *copyright* is an exclusive right granted to an author to prevent his literary, dramatic, musical and/or artistic work from being copied by others. A copyright protects the form of expression rather than the subject matter. Thus a written description of a machine could be copyrighted but this would not prevent others from copying the description providing it was written in their form of expression. Copyrights are registered in the Copyright Office in the Library of Congress.

A *trade-mark* refers to the word, letter, device, or symbol used by a manufacturer to indicate the source or owner of goods bearing his mark. Trade-mark rights are intended to prevent others from using the same name on similar goods but do not restrict others from making the same goods. Trade-marks which are used in interstate or foreign commerce may be registered in the Patent Office.

26.2 Patent attorneys and patent agents[1]

The preparation of an application for patent and the conducting of the proceedings in the Patent Office to obtain the patent is an undertaking requiring knowledge of patent law and Patent Office practice as well as knowledge of the scientific or technical matters involved in the particular invention.

The inventor may prepare his own application and file it in the Patent Office and conduct the proceedings himself, but unless he is familiar with these matters or studies them in detail, he may get into considerable difficulties. While a patent may be obtained in many cases by persons not skilled in this work, there would be no assurance that the patent obtained would adequately protect the particular invention.

Most inventors employ the services of patent attorneys or patent agents to do the work for them. The statute gives the Patent Office the power to make rules and regulations governing the recognition of patent attorneys and agents to practice before the Patent Office, and persons who are not recognized by the Patent Office for this practice are not permitted by law to represent inventors. The Patent Office maintains a register of attorneys and agents. To be admitted to this register, a person must comply with the regu-

1. *General Information Concerning Patents* (Washington, D.C.: U.S. Department of Commerce, March, 1954).

lations prescribed by the Office, which now require a showing of the necessary qualifications and the passing of an examination.

The Patent Office registers both attorneys at law and persons who are not attorneys at law. The former persons are now referred to as "patent attorneys" and the latter persons are referred to as "patent agents." Insofar as the work of preparing an application for patent and conducting the prosecution in the Patent Office is concerned, patent agents are usually just as well qualified as patent attorneys, although patent agents cannot conduct patent litigation in the courts or perform various services which the local jurisdiction considers as practicing law. For example, a patent agent could not draw up a contract relating to a patent, such as an assignment or a license, if the state in which he resides considers drawing contracts as practicing law.

26.3 Drawing required[2]

A drawing is required by the statute for practically all inventions except compositions of matter or processes.

The drawing must show every feature of the invention specified in the claims and is required by the Office rules to be in a particular form. See Fig. 26-1. The Office specifies the size of the sheet on which the drawing is made, the type of paper, the margins, and other details relating to the making of the drawing. The reason for specifying the standards in detail is that the drawings are printed and published in a uniform style when the patents are issued, and the drawing must also be such that it can be readily understood by persons using the patent descriptions.

26.4 Standards for drawings[3]

The complete drawing is printed and published when the patent is issued, and a copy is attached to the patent. This work is done by the photolithographic process, the sheets of drawing being reduced about one-third in size. In addition, a reduction of a selected portion of the drawings of each application is published in the Official Gazette. Therefore it is necessary for these and other reasons that the character of each drawing be brought as nearly as possible to a uniform standard of execution and excellence, suited to the requirements of the reproduction process and of the use of the drawings, to give the best results in the interests of inventors, of the Office, and of the public.

2. *Ibid.*
3. *Ibid.*

26.5 Paper and ink[4]

Drawings must be made upon pure white paper of a thickness corresponding to two-ply or three-ply Bristol board. The surface of the paper must be calendared and smooth and of a quality which will permit erasure and correction. To secure perfectly black solid lines, India ink alone must be used for pen drawings. The use of white pigment to cover lines is not acceptable.

26.6 Size of sheet and margins[5]

The size of a sheet on which a drawing is made must be exactly 10 by 15 inches. One inch from its edges a single marginal line is to be drawn, leaving the "sight" precisely 8 by 13 inches. Within this margin all work must be included. One of the shorter sides of the sheet is regarded as its top, and, measuring down from the marginal line, a space of not less than 1-1/4 inches is to be left blank for the heading of title, name, number, and date, which will be applied subsequently by the Office in a uniform style. See Fig. 26-2.

26.7 Character of lines[6]

All drawings must be made with drafting instruments or by a photolithographic process which will give satisfactory reproduction characteristics. Every line and letter (signatures included) must be absolutely black. This direction applies to all lines however fine, to shading, and to lines representing cut surfaces in sectional views. All lines must be clean, sharp, and solid; fine or crowded lines

4. *Ibid.*
5. *Ibid.*
6. *Ibid.*

Aug. 5, 1952 H. M. SCHLEGEL Des. 167,427

PHOTOGRAPHIC SLIDE PROJECTOR

Filed Sept. 11, 1951

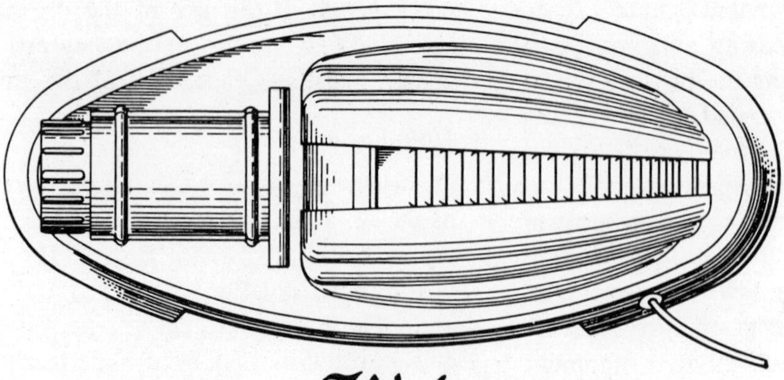

Fig. 1

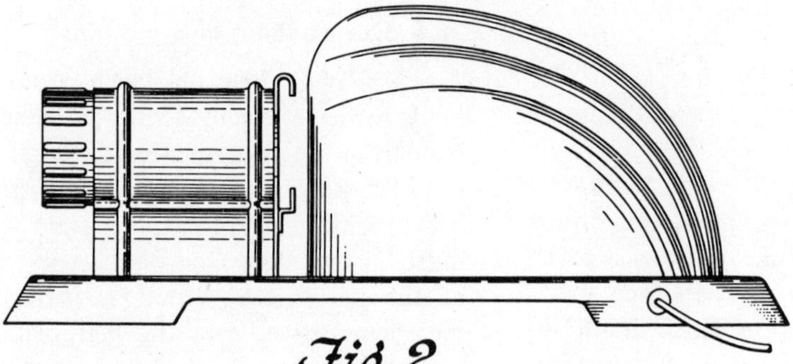

Fig. 2

Fig. 3

Fig. 4

INVENTOR.
HEROLD M. SCHLEGEL
BY

Oct. 20, 1959 S. M. BOOTH 2,909,082

AUTOMATIC FEED AND DEPTH CONTROL FOR A DRILL PRESS

Filed Sept. 6, 1956 3 Sheets-Sheet 1

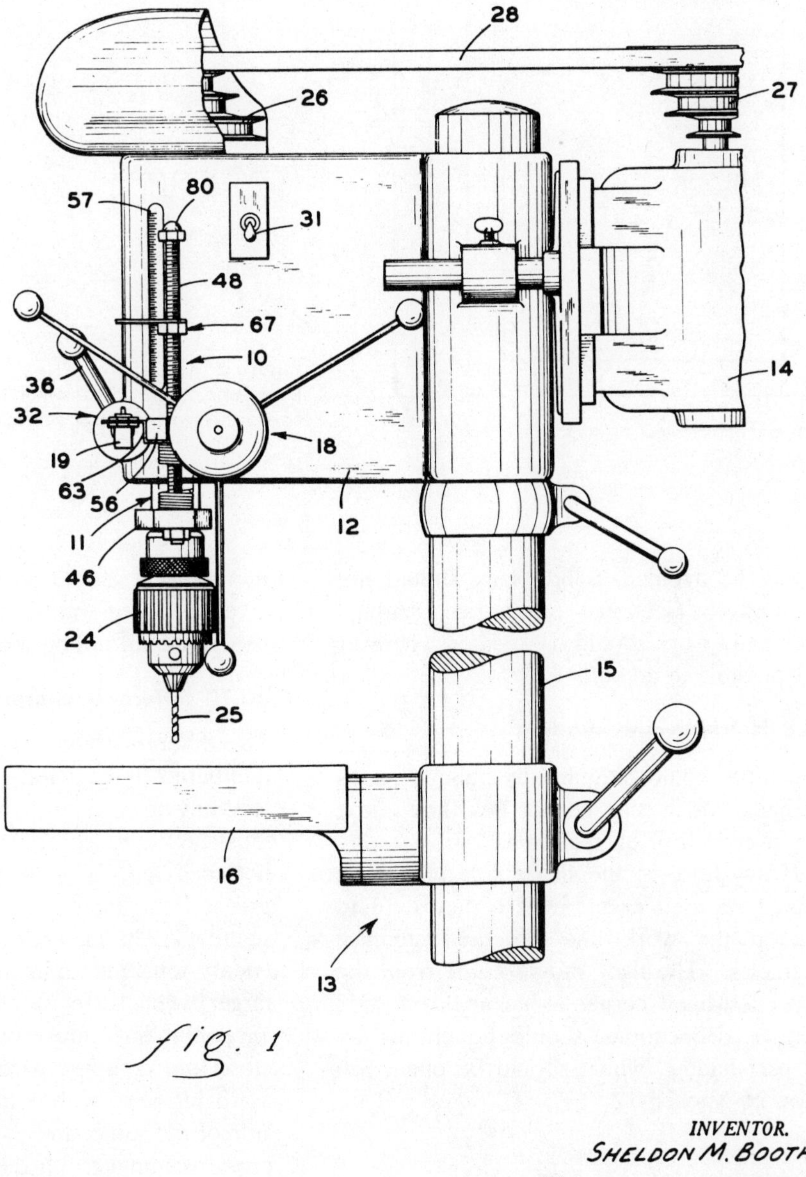

INVENTOR.
SHELDON M. BOOTH
BY
Woodhams Blanchard & Flynn
ATTORNEYS

Figure 26-1
A drawing must show every feature of the invention specified.

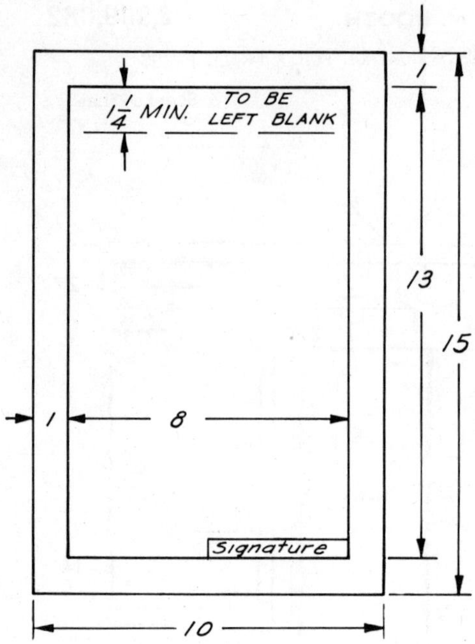

Figure 26-2
Drawings of inventions must have a sheet format conforming to these specifications.

should be avoided. Solid black should not be used for sectional or surface shading. Free-hand work should be avoided wherever it is possible to do so.

26.8 Hatching and shading[7]

Hatching should be made by oblique parallel lines, which may be not less than about one-twentieth of an inch apart.

Heavy lines on the shade side of objects should be used except where they tend to thicken the work and obscure reference characters. The light should come from the upper left-hand corner at an angle of 45°. Surface delineations should be shown by proper shading, which should be open. See Figs. 26-3 to 26-12.

26.9 Scale[8]

The scale of a drawing ought to be large enough to show the mechanism without crowding when the drawing is reduced in reproduction. Views of portions of the mechanism on a larger scale should be used when necessary to show details clearly. Two or more sheets should be used if one does not give sufficient room, but the number of sheets should not be more than is necessary.

26.10 Reference characters[9]

The different views should be consecutively numbered figures. Reference numerals (letters may be used but numerals are preferred) must be plain, legible, carefully formed, and not encircled. They should if possible, measure at least one-eighth of an inch in height so that they may bear reduction to one twenty-fourth of an inch; they may be slightly larger when there is sufficient room. Reference numerals must not be placed in the close and complex parts of the drawing so as to interfere with a thorough comprehension of the same, and therefore should rarely cross or mingle with the lines. When necessarily grouped around a certain part, they should be placed at a little distance, at the closest point where there is available space, and connected by lines with the parts to which they refer. They should not be placed upon hatched or shaded surfaces but when necessary, a blank space may be left in the

7. *Ibid.*
8. *Ibid.*
9. *Ibid.*

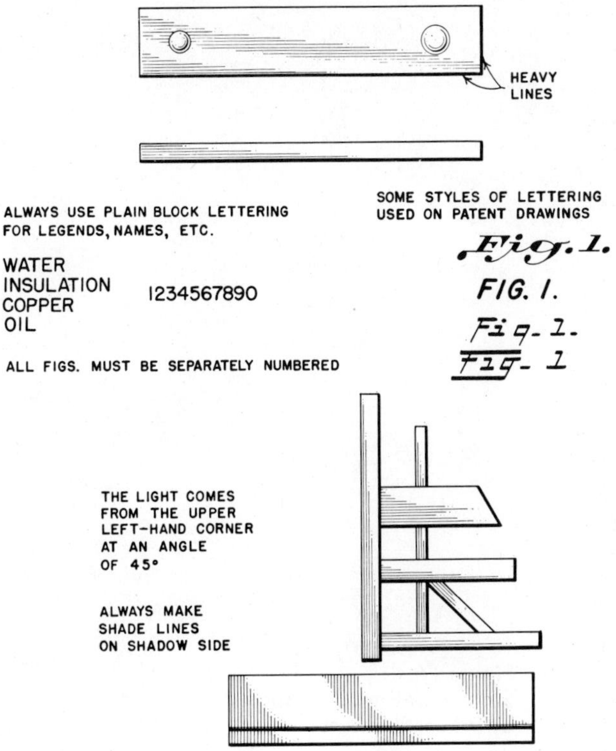

Figure 26-3
Letters and figures of reference must be carefully formed. Several types of lettering and figure marks are shown; however, the draftsman may use any style of lettering that he chooses.

hatching or shading where the character occurs, so that it shall appear perfectly distinct and separate from the work.

The same part of an invention appearing in more than one view of the drawing must always be designated by the same character, and the same character must never be used to designate different parts.

26.11 Symbols, legends[10]

Graphical drawing symbols for conventional elements may be used when appropriate, subject to approval by the Office. The elements for which such symbols are used must be adequately identified in the specification. While descriptive matter on drawings is not permitted, suitable legends may be used, or may be required in proper cases, as in diagrammatic views and flow sheets. The lettering should be as large as, or larger than, the reference characters.

10. *Ibid.*

26.12 Location of signature and names[11]

The signature of the applicant, or the name of the applicant and signature of the attorney or agent, may be placed in the lower right-hand corner of each sheet within the marginal line, or may be placed below the lower marginal line.

26.13 Views[12]

The drawing must contain as many figures as may be necessary to show the invention; the figures should be consecutively numbered if possible, in the order in which they appear. The figures may be plan, elevation, section, or perspective views, and detail views of portions or elements, on a larger scale if necessary may also be used. Exploded views, to show the relationship or order of assembly of various parts, are permissible; the sepa-

(Text continued on page 732)

11. *Ibid.*

12. *Ibid.*

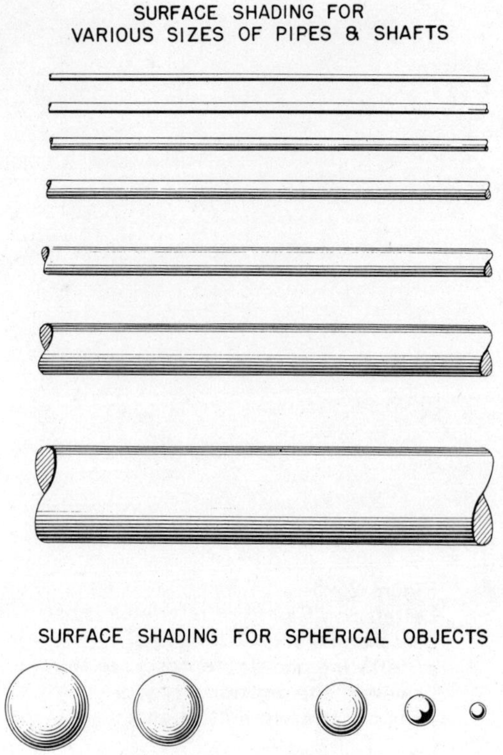

Figure 26-4
Surface delineations should be shown by proper shading.

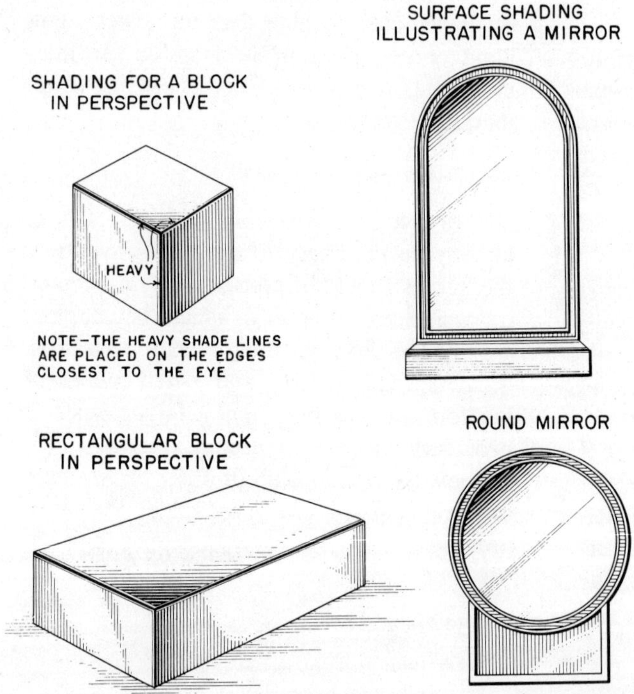

Figure 26-5
Heavy shade lines on perspective views are placed on the edges closes to the eye. The rule of the light coming from the upper left-hand corner at a 45° angle does not apply to perspective views.

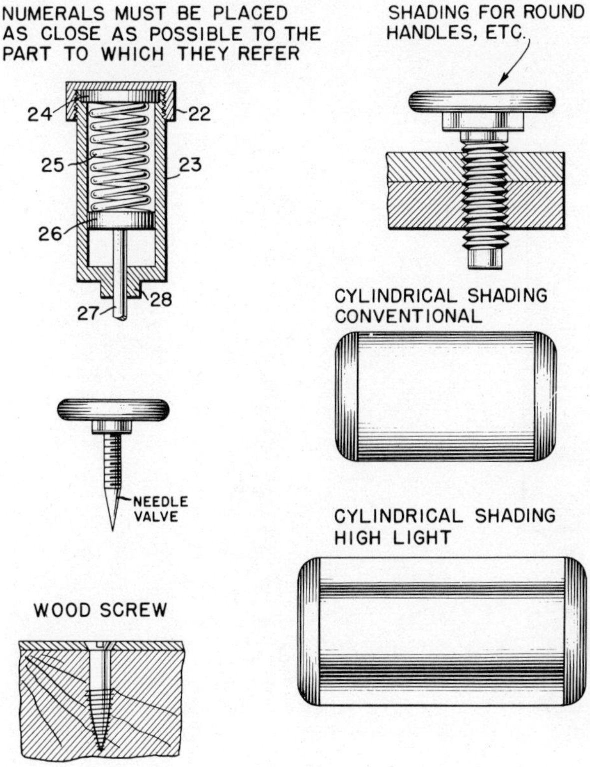

Figure 26-6
Placing of reference characters, shading and sectioning methods.

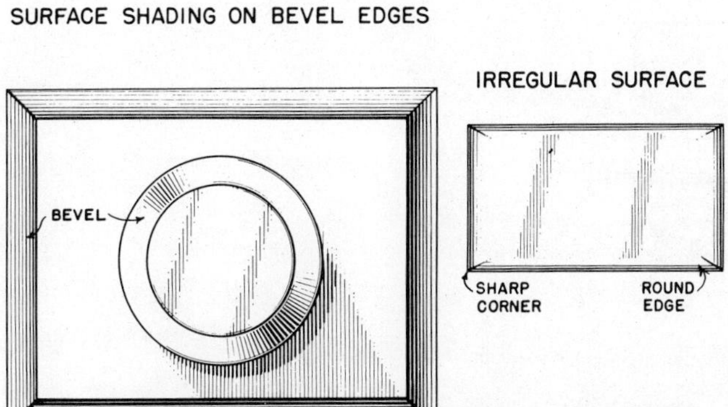

Figure 26-7
Methods of shading various kinds of surfaces.

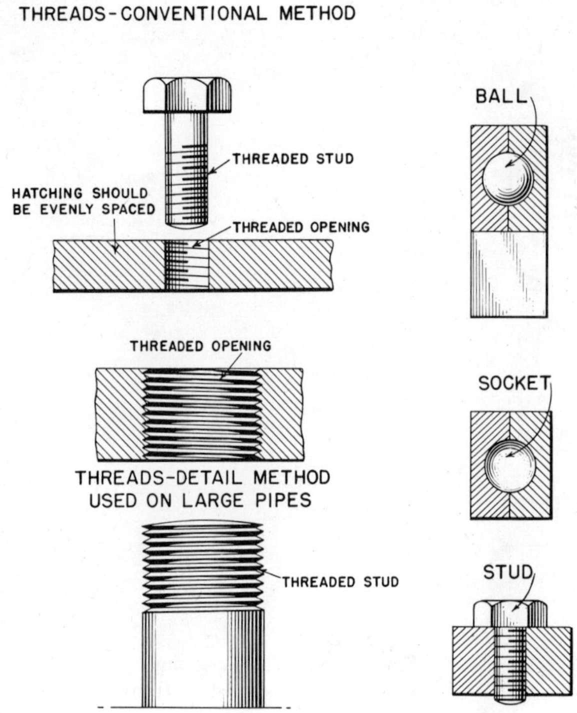

Figure 26-8
Methods of showing threads and spherical surfaces.

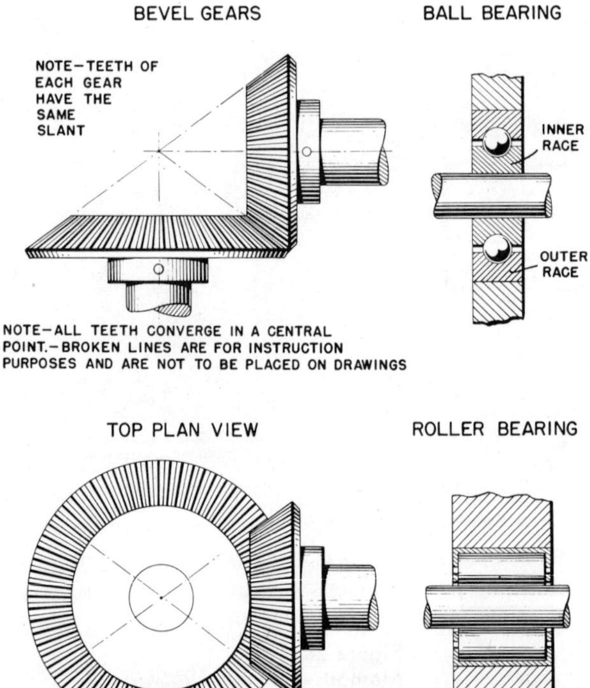

Figure 26-9
Methods of showing bevel gears and bearings.

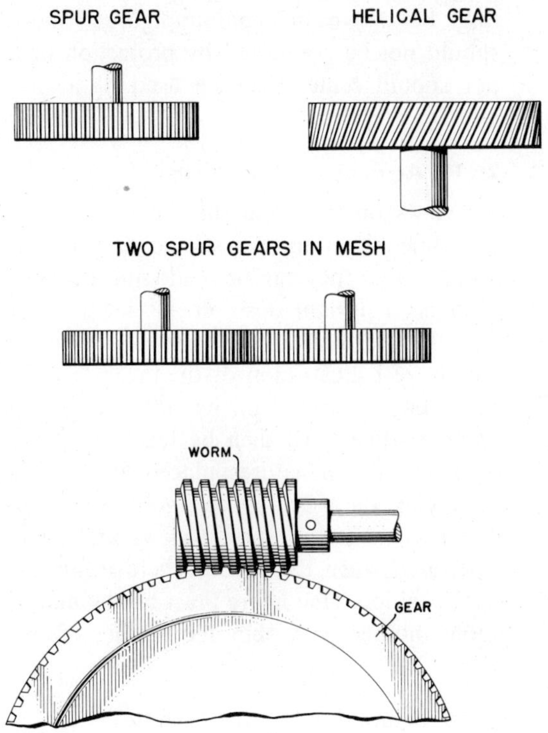

Figure 26-10
Methods of showing various gears.

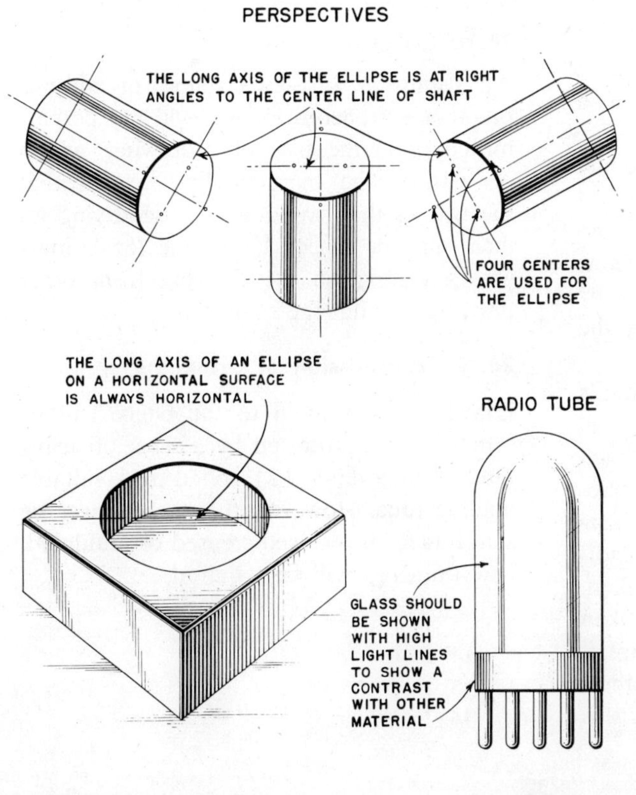

Figure 26-11
Figures are in perspective, showing shading and position of long axis.

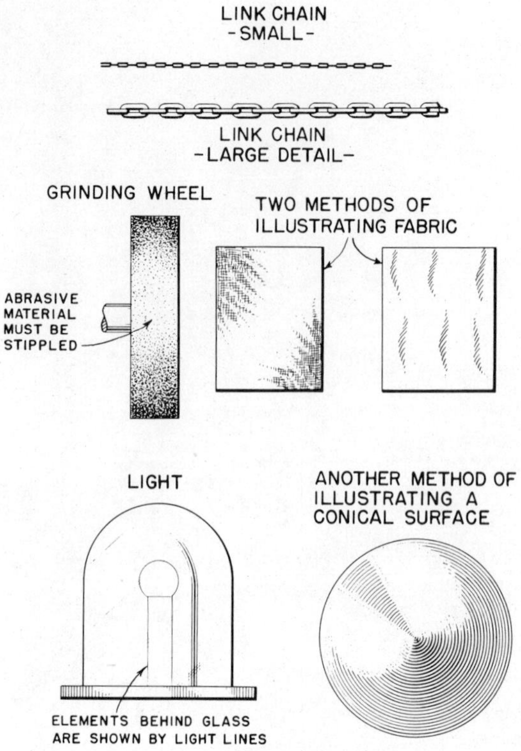

Figure 26-12
Methods of showing link chains, abrasive material, fabrics, glass, and conical surfaces.

rated parts of the same figure are embraced by a bracket.

When necessary, a view of a large machine or device in its entirety may be broken and extended over several sheets if there is no loss in facility of understanding the view. The different parts should be identified by the same figure number but followed by the letters *a, b, c,* etc., for each part.

The plane upon which a sectional view is taken should be indicated on the general view by a broken line, the ends of which should be designated by numerals corresponding to the figure number of the sectional view and have arrows applied to indicate the direction in which the view is taken. A moved position may be shown by a broken line superimposed upon a suitable figure if this can be done without crowding; otherwise, a separate figure must be used for this purpose. Modified forms of construction can only be shown in separate figures. Views should not be connected by projection lines nor should center lines be used.

26.14 Arrangement of views[13]

All views on the same sheet must stand in the same direction and should, if possible, stand so that they can be read with the sheet held in an upright position. If views longer than the width of the sheet are necessary for the clearest illustration of the invention, the sheet may be turned on its side. The space for a heading must then be reserved at the right and the signatures placed at the left, occupying the same space and position on the sheet as in the upright views and being horizontal when the sheet is held in an upright position. One figure must not be placed upon another or within the outline of another.

26.15 Figure for Official Gazette[14]

The drawing should, as far as possible, be so planned that one of the views will be suitable for publication in the Official Gazette as the illustration of the invention.

26.16 Extraneous matter[15]

An agent's or attorney's stamp, or address, or other extraneous matter, will not be permitted upon the face of a drawing, within or without the marginal line, except that the title of the invention and identifying indicia may be placed below the lower margin to distinguish the drawing from other drawings filed at the same time.

26.17 Transmission of drawings[16]

Drawings transmitted to the Office can be sent (1) flat, protected by a sheet of heavy binder's board, or (2) rolled in a suitable mailing tube. However, they must never be sent folded. If received creased or mutilated, new drawings will be required.

13. *Ibid.*
14. *Ibid.*
15. *Ibid.*
16. *Ibid.*

BROADHEAD
HUNTING ARROW

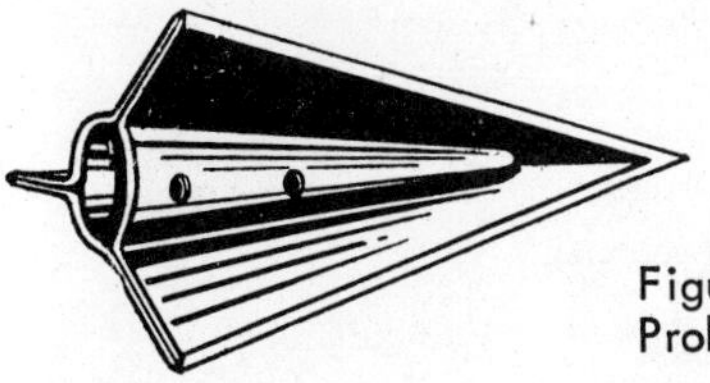

Figure 26-13
Problem 1.

POKER CHIP
RACK

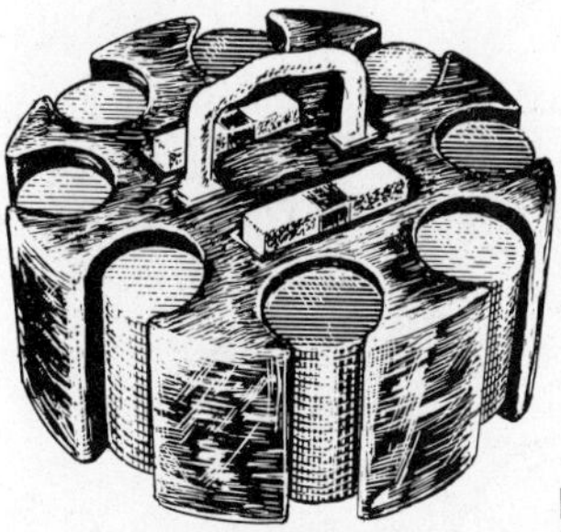

Figure 26-14
Problem 2.

RIFLE
FOREARM TIP

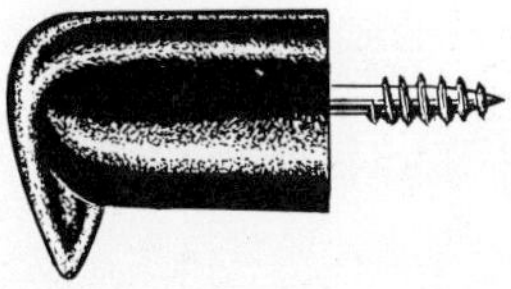

Figure 26-15
Problem 3.

ALUMINUM
STORM DOOR

Figure 26-16
Problem 4.

CLOCK
DUST COVER

Figure 26-17
Problem 5.

WHISTLE

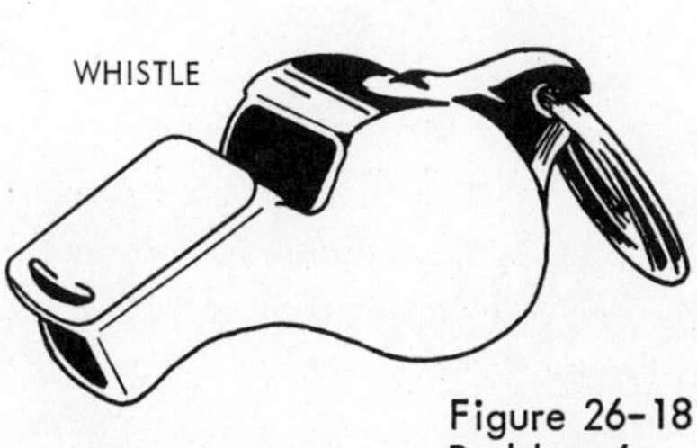

Figure 26-18
Problem 6.

Problems, section 26

1-13 Assume that the products illustrated in Figs. 26-13 to 26-25 are patentable. Prepare patent drawings of any selected or assigned detail of the products chosen, incorporating all drawing regulations as prescribed by the Patent Office. Shade the product according to the practices shown in Figs. 26-3 to 26-12. Assume all shape sizes.

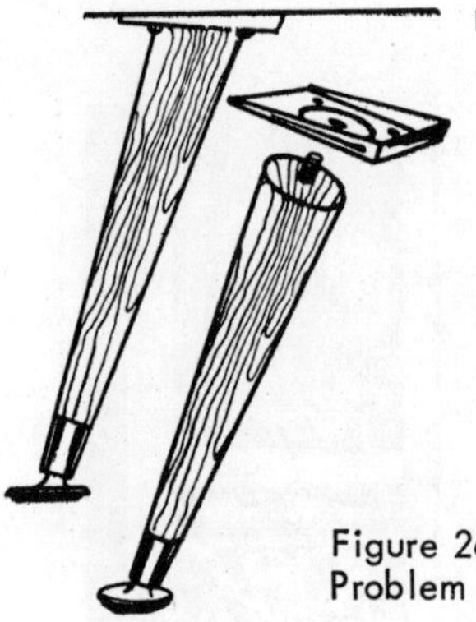

Figure 26-19
Problem 7.

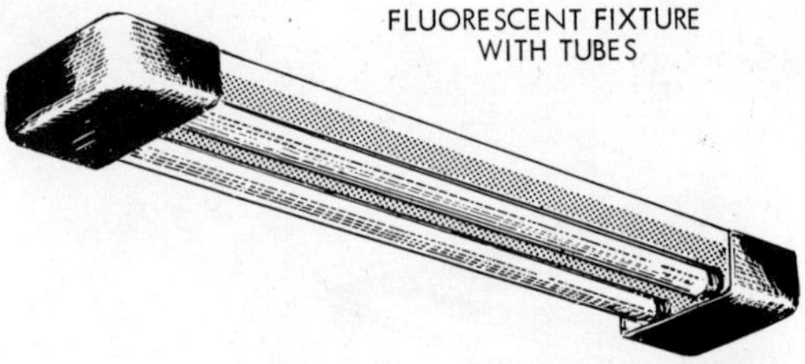

Figure 26-22
Problem 10.

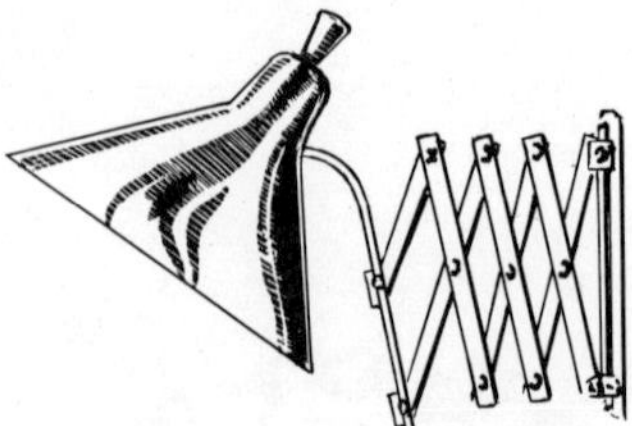

Figure 26-23
Problem 11.

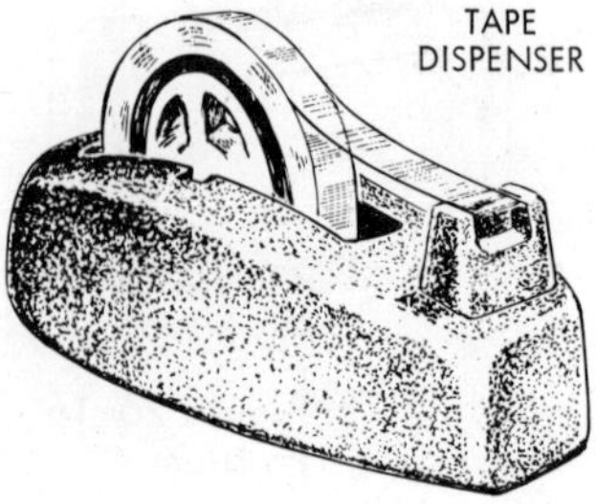

Figure 26-20
Problem 8.

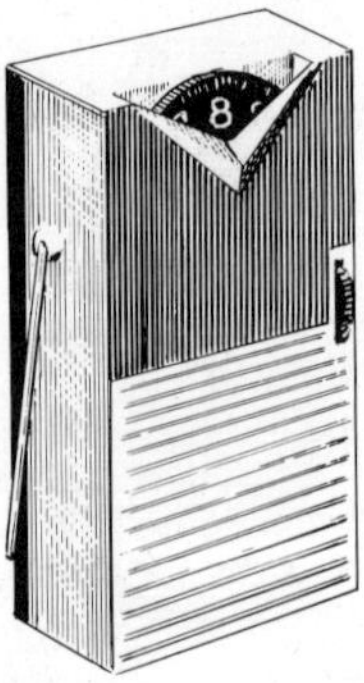

Figure 26-21
Problem 9.

Figure 26-24
Problem 12.

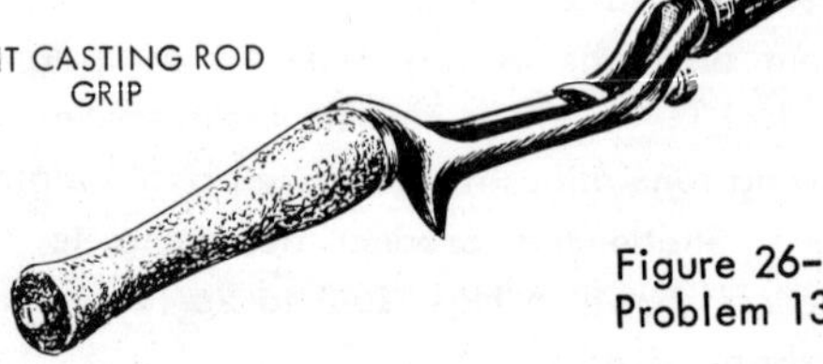

Figure 26-25
Problem 13.

Reproductions of drawings 27

prepared by
Frederick Post Company

A reproduction is a copy of printed, written, or drawn material, in either a negative or positive form, to any scale—larger, smaller, or identical to the original, and done by any of several different processes.

The avenue of visual communication to be considered here is that of reproducing a line drawing. The achievement of the industrial draftsman—the original drawing—seldom reaches the production areas; it is the reproduced print that is used by the fabricators.

Each technical drawing normally represents a sizeable expenditure of engineering and drafting time. Frequently a single such document is worth thousands of dollars. Original drawings are obviously too valuable for actual shop or field use. However, apart from the cost, the use of the original only would be impractical in this age of speed and mass production, which requires multiple copies in the planning and production operations. Modern graphic reproduction machines and materials fulfill this need with legible and inexpensive prints.

Visual communication by means of graphic reproduction has not only accelerated industrial development, but has also permitted standardization of parts, simplification of effort, and greater diversification of industry over the entire earth. No longer is it necessary, or even desirable, for each industrial unit to be completely self-sufficient.

27.1 Graphic reproduction processes

In general, the graphic reproduction processes available today can be divided into five major classifications:

1 The iron process.
2 The diazo process.
3 The silver process.
4 The electrostatic process.
5 The heat process.

Each process has its advantages and disadvantages. Each is "best" for a particular application or type of work. Some processes are more permanent, less subject to soiling; others are especially suited to small, intermittent work. Some processes are better for continuous, long-run production; still others adapt themselves to shifts in production schedules and therefore are more flexible.

27.2 The iron process

Blueprints. The blueprint or ferro-prussiate process used for graphic reproductions is well over 100 years old, having been discovered in England in 1840. It is a negative process, producing prints with a white image on a blue background from a subject having dark lines on a light background. The process consists of exposing sensitized material to ultra-violet light which has passed through a translucent drawing or master. Exposure to ultraviolet (actinic) light creates a chemical reaction in the exposed area. The process is completed by developing in a water wash, fixing by an oxidizing agent (usually potassium bichromate), rewashing in water and drying.

Most blueprint machines in use today do all of these operations in one continuous pass through the machine, taking the sensitized material in roll form. See Fig. 27-1. It is difficult to apply this process to cut sheets because of the complete immersions required in the development. As a consequence, high wet-strength paper, made with

Figure 27–1
With this continuous blueprint machine a large number of prints can be produced in a short time.

a rag pulp content of 50% or more, is normally used.

The widespread use of the word blueprint has led many people to believe it to be a general term applicable to all types of reproductions. Actually, blueprinting is a separate and distinct process. Reproductions by any other process are not blueprints, nor do they possess the advantages of blueprints.

Blueprints are the lowest in cost of any of the commonly used reproduction processes. The material can be used under normal roomlight conditions giving a print that is permanent, resistant to soiling, resistant to aging, and with no objectionable odor.

Disadvantages of blueprinting include the high initial cost and maintenance costs of equipment, a high scrap loss, and a high labor cost for the final trimming of the prints.

Brownprints. The brownprint process is akin to the blueprint process in that it is primarily an iron process. However, silver nitrate is included in the light sensitive ferro compound which is coated on the paper so that the resultant color after exposure to actinic light is a deep brown-black. The brownprint paper stock is usually translucent so the resultant copy becomes a permanent negative master which can be used in the manufacture of wet blue line blueprints, for example.

The development of the brownprint substitutes a hypo bath in place of the potassium bichromate wash in the blueprint process.

Wash-off prints. This process is a modification of the brownprint iron process of reproduction, and is used primarily with a brownprint or some other similar intermediate in the development of a positive reading reproduction. Cloth is generally used for this type of reproduction.

The advantage of this process is that all sensitized coating, save the actual exposed line, is washed away in the development, leaving a drawing surface equal to that of uncoated cloth. It is considered a permanent type of reproduction.

27.3 The diazo process

This process, unlike the iron process, produces a positive reading print directly, giving dark lines on a white background.

Dry whiteprints. The whiteprint or dry diazo process makes use of the principle that light-sensitive diazonium salts will form an azo dye when coupled with certain coal tar derivatives in an alkaline environment, providing the salts are not exposed to the light. Varying the azo dye component makes it possible to develop practically any color in the spectrum.

The process involves exposing the sensitized material to ultraviolet (actinic) light through a translucent material or drawing whose image prevents exposure in specified areas. See Fig. 27-2. The light decomposes the diazo in the exposed areas making it incapable of compounding into an azo dye. Alkalizing the coupler by means of an ammonia atmosphere then develops the color in the unexposed areas. This is also known as the ammonia process. Fig. 27-3 shows a machine for producing dry whiteprints.

Dry sepiaprints. This process is identical to the dry whiteprint except that the dye color formed is a deep yellow-brown. The process is used primarily to make master copies of an original on translucent paper or other material.

Wet whiteprints. This type of diazo print is basically identical to the dry. The only difference is that the coupler is applied to the diazo as a wet solution after the diazo has been exposed to ultraviolet light. The resultant prints or reproductions are damp and have to be dried before use.

Wet sepia prints. These are identical to the whiteprints, except that a different coupler is used so that the resultant positive print has deep yellow-brown lines. The base stock used in this case is usually a translucent material.

27.4 General information concerning the iron and diazo processes

In all of the preceding paragraphs, nothing was mentioned about specific base materials, speeds of printing, or development, because these light sensitive solutions can, and probably have been, coated on the thinnest of papers to the thickest of foils. The speed of printing is dependent on the concentration of the coating of the light sensitive solution, the type of machine used, the translucency of the subject drawing base, and the opacity of the drawn line. The development rate has as many variables.

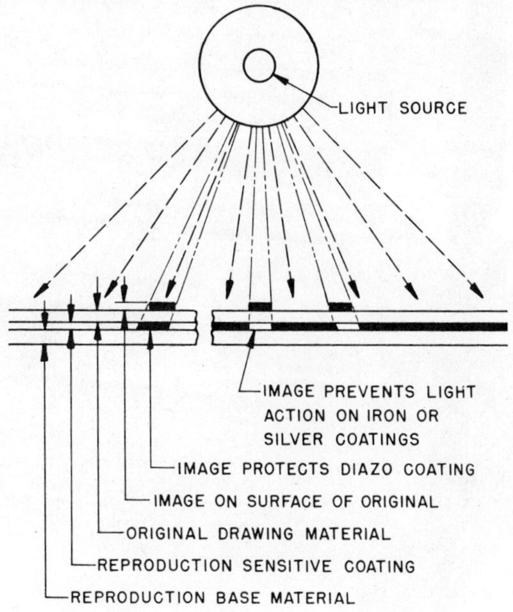

Figure 27-2
The Diazo process produces a positive print having dark lines on a white background.

The general practice is to expose the iron process at such a rate that the lines are clear and white, and the diazo process at the rate that results in a slightly discolored background.

The iron process gives a permanent reproduction, whereas the diazo process produces what is considered to be a less permanent reproduction.

27.5 The silver process

The oldest process of reproduction is that which uses the light sensitive properties of the silver haloids and silver nitrate compounds. This is primarily the field of photog-

Figure 27-3
This is an example of a Diazo process reproduction machine which speedily performs all of the essential reproduction operations. Copymation Corp.

raphy—a process that has so expanded and become so diversified, that the modifications when used for graphic reproductions many times overshadow the basic process. The sensitized solution can be coated on practically any base material. The process lends itself easily to reduction and enlargements of graphic illustrations, and is used basically for the development of permanent reproductions, the rejuvenation of old graphic illustrations, and the development of translucent master copies from opaque originals.

Some of the sensitized coatings have to be handled under dark-room conditions, whereas others can be handled in subdued room light. Some of the sensitized materials are exposed when in direct contact with the graphic subject; others have this subject projected on them from a distance. Certain sensitized materials create a positive print from a positive original; others result in a negative print from a positive original. A number of sensitized materials are exposed by having the light pass through the original to the sensitized coating, while others are exposed by having the light pass through the sensitized coating first and bouncing back from the original to the sensitized coating. Several sensitized coatings require the light to pass through a yellow filter; others do not.

However, in every case, the development after exposure is by standard photographic materials, water, hypo, and fixer. The reproductions must be dried before use.

The trade names under which the silver process is known are: Microfilming, Autopositives, Autofax, Refax, Lithoprint, Reflex, Photocopy, Photostat, Photocontact, Rectigraph, Dupro, Cronaflex, and many others.

27.6 The electrostatic process

In this process the base material, either metal or paper, is coated with zinc oxide in an insulating resin binder. The zinc oxide is then given an electrostatic charge that is dissipated when exposed to ultraviolet light. When a graphic illustration shadows this light, either by projection or by being in direct contact with the coating, the electrostatic charge of all of the zinc oxide particles is eliminated except in the shadowed areas, and an invisible latent electrostatic image of the graphic illustration remains on the base material.

The base material is then dusted with an opposite electrostatically charged black powder that adheres to the base material only in those areas still containing charged zinc oxide, just as the north pole of a magnet adheres to the south pole of another magnet. This image is then transferred to a translucent material or offset plate and made permanent by heat fusion. If the original base material is translucent, no transfer is necessary prior to the fusion by heat.

Xerography is a trade name of this type of process. The main disadvantages are that the prints are contrasty and often lack definition.

27.7 The heat process

Just as some chemicals show a marked change when subjected to light radiation, there are others that are affected by heat radiation. In this process the base material is coated with a heat sensitive chemical. When a graphic illustration is held in close contact with this coating, between a low grade heat source and the coating, those areas (lines) that are dark permit the sensitized coating to absorb more heat than the blank areas. The excess heat absorbed changes the color of the chemical coating to a blue-black, and the resultant reproduction is a positive copy of the original.

The disadvantages of this process at present are limitation in size and critical heat range, and the fact that some non-metallic colors cannot be reproduced.

27.8 Summary

From the preceding discussion it can be summarized that, depending on the type and size of the reproduction desired and its usage, the reproducing of a drawing is a matter involving one of five basic processes, with many modifications of each, using various types of equipment and a wide selection of base materials. See chart in Fig. 27-4.

By custom, two words have emerged to distinguish these processes from each other. A *print* is an expendable production such as those made by the blueprinting method or the diazo method. A *reproduction* is considered to be a permanent copy of the original such as those made by the silver process.

BASE MATERIAL \ PROCESS	IRON	DIAZO	SILVER	ELECTRO-STATIC	HEAT
Paper	X	X	X	X	X
Cloth	X	X	X		
Acetate Film		X	X		
Polyester Film		X	X		
Aluminum Foil		X	X	X	
Metal			X		
Glass			X		

Figure 27-4
This chart illustrates the various types of base materials required for different reproduction processes.

27.9 Trade tricks: diazo process intermediates

The cost of an original drawing and the hazards of wear and tear which occur even in normal usage have combined to make necessary and desirable the use of intermediate reproductions. By the use of the intermediate in place of the original for the manufacture of prints, the original can be retained in the files in perfect condition and the intermediate replaced only when necessary.

The following techniques show how sepia intermediates can be used to cut drafting hours. With imagination and observation, the draftsman can develop additional ways to save time. In some cases, depending upon the original and the work involved, various combinations of these suggested techniques can be applied to obtain the best results.

Corrector fluids—for small or scattered areas. One of the most common drafting room time-savers involves the use of corrector fluids, rather than re-drawing or tracing an original on which corrected data is desired.

Liquid eradicators are available for making line deletions on standard prints, as well as on intermediates. This method is well adapted to alteration of drawings when a portion of the details is obsolete or when certain design and dimensions must be changed.

Drawings that require alteration are reproduced directly from the unchanged original on an intermediate. Unwanted lines on the intermediate are removed by application of corrector fluid. New data is then drawn in the corrected area. The desired number of prints is later processed from the corrected intermediate.

The intermediate is now a new master, capable of producing copies of the revised drawing or record at any future time. The original master drawing can be kept on file in its unchanged form.

Scissors editing—for large area changes. When an original is to be modified, an intermediate print is made. The intermediate is then adapted by scissors-editing. This procedure is a quick and easy way to save time and labor.

Undesired portions of the intermediate are cut out with scissors or blade. The edited intermediate can then be reproduced without any trace of corrections on the finished prints.

This intermediate application is most useful when large sections are to be removed. If additions are desired in the cutout section, another intermediate is made directly from the scissors-edited intermediate, and new data is drawn on this second intermediate.

In making a diazo intermediate, a little background (under-exposure) is advisable since this will improve the intensity of the lines on the resulting prints. Print quality naturally is slightly reduced with each successive intermediate that is made.

Block-out method—to delete small areas. Sections of an intermediate print that are too small to be cut away easily can be blocked out. Ink, pencil, or any other opaquing material over the area to be deleted is used.

The corrected portion will appear as a dark image on the finished diazo positive print. This is a particularly suitable application of the intermediate technique, as it is usually not desirable to insert a blocked-out section on the original drawing.

When new dimensions or other data are required over the block-out area, they can often be inserted by means of colored pencil or ink. However, the block-out method is used primarily to remove obsolete matter.

When time is particularly important, the block-out technique is suggested for quick, on-the-spot alterations.

Masking—for selecting or deleting large areas. The masking technique is based on the reproduction principle that the sensitized surface on diazo papers can be burned out by the printing machine's ultra-violet light.

If portions of the sensitized sheet are covered by an opaque mask and then fed through the printer light source only, the sensitized paper in the areas that are not covered will be burned out. Then, when the mask is removed and the print is made (exposed *and* developed) in the normal manner, those portions of the original which are over the burned-out areas of the sensitized paper will not be reproduced. Regardless of the shape of the sections to be deleted, a mask can be designed to ensure reproduction of the selected parts only.

This masking procedure can be followed in making prints from a selected area on an original, or in making an intermediate to be used as a print-making master, whether additions are desired in the selected area or not.

The sequence of the operation is as follows. Step 1: Cut out a mask with opaque paper. Step 2: Place mask over sensitized paper and feed through the light source section only. Step 3: Follow normal printing and developing procedure with the original, but without the mask.

Transparent matte tape—to add variable data. With its matte surface on one side and adhesive on the other, transparent mending tape can be used for many time-saving applications other than mending.

This tape is functionally an intermediate which can take dimensions drawn on the matte surface. It can be applied to paper, cloth or film and becomes an integral part of any original or intermediate.

Many engineering departments have standard unit drawings with identical design, except for variable dimensions. One master drawing without dimensions can be used to produce a complete file of standard units by means of intermediates, with the dimensions added, as needed, via the transparent matte tape method.

As a job order is received, dimensions, symbols and other engineering variables can be applied by tape additions for the particular data desired without the necessity of complete re-drawing, thus saving valuable drawing hours.

Non-reproducible blue—for drafting rooms and business systems. Certain shades of blue and violet do not block ultra-violet light. As a consequence, such lines will not reproduce on prints.

Detailed entries on drawings or records when made with non-reproducible materials will not appear on the prints. For example, this is used in business systems to prevent confidential data from appearing on finished copies intended for general distribution. It can also be used in cases where subject matter is necessary on both sides of a form, yet facsimile copies are required of one side only.

Experimental layout work can be done on an original or on an intermediate, yet prints can be quickly made showing only the data that had been originally drawn.

The best non-reproducible line is sharp but light, in preference to broad heavy lines which normally will reproduce faintly. However, with the recent increased use of the "phantom-line" technique, there are several specially adapted materials available that provide high visual density yet will not show in reproduction.

A variety of "phantom-line" products on the market today are suitable for non-reproducible applications: printers ink, fountain pen ink, pencil and typewriter ribbons in addition to special pencils.

Successive additions—using a matte surface film intermediate. This idea can be applied to engineering drawings, bills of material and parts lists. It can also save time in payroll, accounting and inventory procedures.

The constant data is printed on a film intermediate from a translucent original. Variable additions are then added to the film intermediate with pen and ink, typewriter or pencil. After prints have been made from the matte film, these additions are easily removed with a damp cloth, carbon tetrachloride, or eraser.

A succession of variable data can be recorded over and over, using the same diazo film intermediate because of its durability and the ease of making additions and deletions. This economical application more than justifies the original cost of matte film. A few jobs made easier by this application:

1 Procedures requiring an unchanging printed form to which variable entries are made and where copies of the completed forms are desired.
2 Questionnaires to be completed by the recipient, copies of which are desired on return to the distributing office.
3 Reproduction of endorsements.
4 Maintenance of lists subject to continuous addition.

Pick-off transfer—with use of matte tape. Use of transparent matte tape to transfer columns of figures can eliminate tedious transcription time and avoid the possibility of human error. This is a completely different method from the previous example.

The third column made on a diazo film intermediate in Fig. 27-5 was originally blank. Note that the pencil entries in the first column have been transferred to the last column. This is done by (1) placing the adhesive side of the tape over the pencil figures in the first column, (2) removing the tape in order to pick off the numeral impressions from the film, and (3) permanently placing the tape that bears the image of these numbers onto the last column. The resulting prints carry all data desired without lengthy entry work on original or intermediate, and the film intermediate can be changed

Cat. No.	Description	Annual Sales	Maximum	Revised Order
2965W	Chemistry	1364	9 75	1364
2967	Isometric	879	7 01	879
2968	Holometer	2771	18 50	2771
2969	Planner	506	6 28	506

Figure 27-5
Transparent matte tape is used to transfer columns of figures.

later for other variable data.

When experimenting, allow a little extra tape to hold onto. Otherwise it will be difficult to lift up from the matte film. Then merely apply direct finger pressure over the applied tape to pick-off the desired data. It is also possible to pick-off certain data in pen or typewriter ink.

The pick-off transfer technique can also be applied to a high quality tracing medium that has the characteristics of translucent film.

Composite grouping—from several originals. The intermediate technique is especially useful and appropriate when several different drawings (or more often sections of the drawings) are desired on one reproduction master.

An intermediate is made from each original (or portion of original) involved, and the resulting intermediates are cut and formed to the locations wanted in the new overall pattern by the use of transparent mending tape.

Subsequent standard prints can then be processed without noticeable traces of the patching. If the details on the original drawings are sufficiently strong, another intermediate can be printed from the composite intermediates that have been taped, thus providing a reproduction master for subsequent print-making.

Composite overlays—from several originals. Where two or three highly transparent original drawings are available from which data is to be combined into a single composite for future prints, a single master intermediate may be obtained without making separate intermediates.

The overlay method involves super-imposing the two originals into the desired location (identical register is best if the design subjects permit). The overlayed originals are exposed on a sensitized intermediate, then developed to get the composite reproduction.

Composite reproductions, as illustrated in the previous method as well as in the overlay technique just now described, frequently can eliminate costly re-drawing or re-tracing hours. These suggestions often make it possible to inexpensively combine valuable originals into a single master.

Pre-printing of constant data. There are occasions where certain constant data is frequently used over and over—not only in forms, bills of material and parts lists, but also in drawings.

Under such conditions, consideration can be given to printing such data directly onto the sensitized surface of the diazo paper (or on the reverse side) by means of standard offset or letterpress printing. Sensitized materials can be printed in this manner, just as regular commercial papers, with no harm to the chemical emulsions on the sensitized surface.

In subsequent print-making, the pre-printed image will obviously appear very satisfactorily on the resulting print, as will the added detail drawn onto the master.

A printing house can handle the letterpress or offset work necessary to add the constant data desired through this preprinting technique, thus saving hours of repetitious drawing or typing.

27.10 Trade tricks: silver process

The silver process is often used instead of the diazo process intermediates to save un-

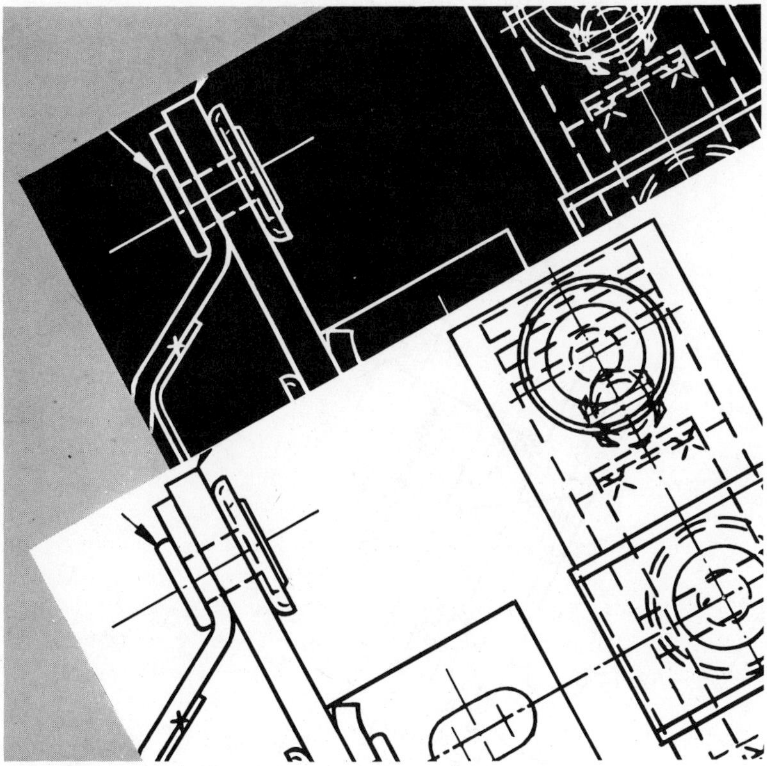

Figure 27-6
Negative to positive—directly.

told hours of drafting time. The fundamental reason for the use of one over the other is the permanency of the reproduction desired. The silver process results in a permanent reproduction; the diazo process does not. The procedures of scissor editing, blockout, masking, successive additions, composite grouping, and composite overlays, as described for diazo intermediates, are also applicable with the silver process. Furthermore, it adapts itself to many other time saving aids as well. For example, using the silver process, it is possible to:

1 Make an opaque or a transparent positive directly from an opaque negative, or transparent negative.
2 Make an opaque or transparent positive directly from an opaque or transparent positive.
3 Reverse (1) or (2).
4 Make an enlargement or reduction of an opaque or transparent subject.

Figs. 27-6, 27-7, and 27-8 illustrate three silver process reproductions.

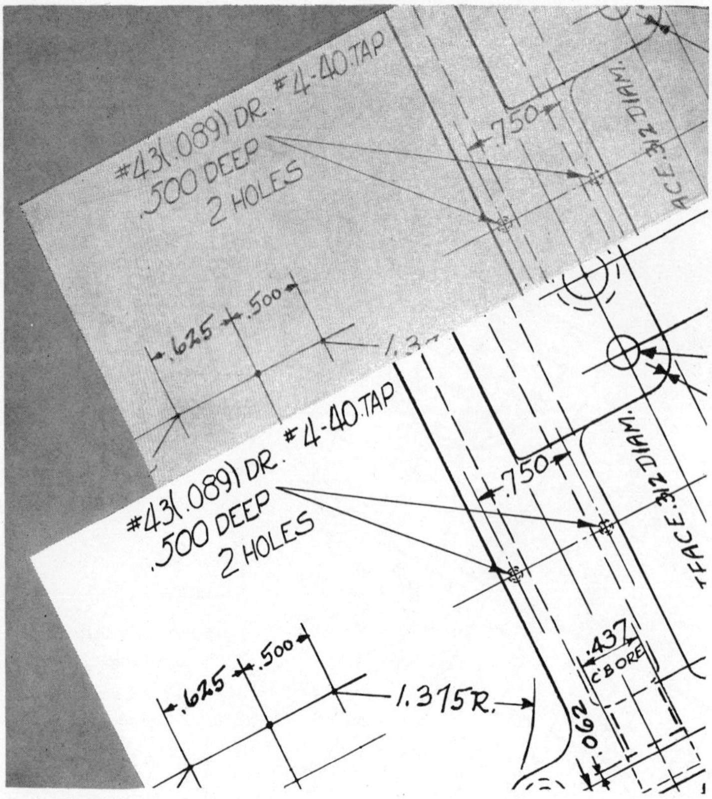

Figure 27-7
Positive to positive—directly.

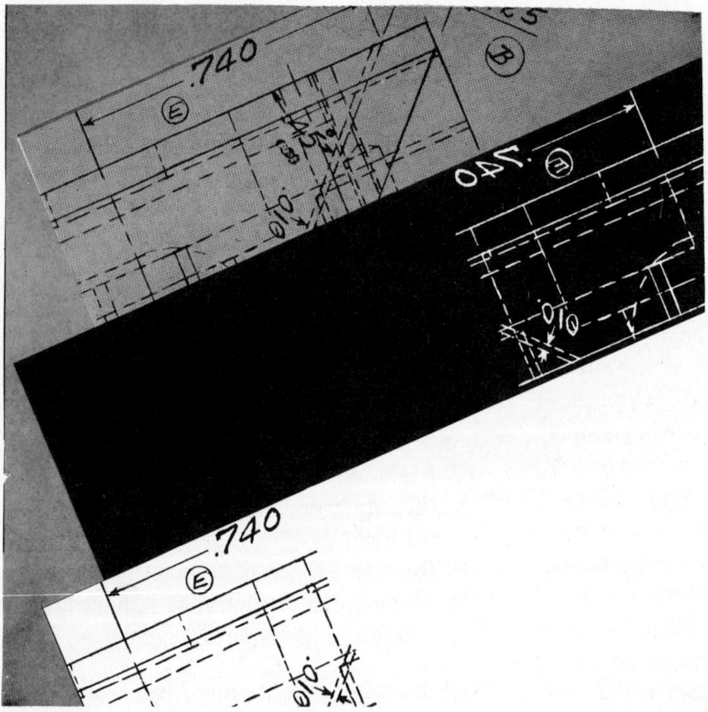

Figure 27-8
Positive to negative to positive with blockout operation at the negative stage.

APPENDIX CONTENTS

ABBREVIATIONS USED ON DRAWINGS

A

Absolute	ABS
Accelerate	ACCEL
Access Panel	AP
Accessory	ACCESS.
Account	ACCT
Actual	ACT.
Adapter	ADPT
Addendum	ADD.
Adjust	ADJ
Advance	ADV
Aeronautic	AERO
Aeronautical Material Specifications	AMS
Aeronautical Standards	AS
After	AFT.
Aggregate	AGGR
Air Condition	AIR COND
Aircraft	ACFT
Allowance	ALLOW
Alloy	ALY
Alternate	ALT
Alternating Current	AC
Altitude	ALT
Aluminum	AL
Ambient	AMB
American Standard	AMER STD
American Standard Elevator Codes	ASEC
American Wire Gage	AWG
Ammeter	AM
Amount	AMT
Ampere	AMP
Amphibian—Amphibious	AMPH
Amplifier	AMPL
Anneal	ANL
Antenna	ANT.
Anti-Aircraft	AA
Anti-Friction Bearing	AFB
Apartment	APT.
Apparatus	APP
Approved	APPD
Approximate	APPROX
Arc Weld	ARC/W
Area	A
Armament	ARMT
Armature	ARM.
Armor Plate	ARM-PL
Army Air Forces	AAF
Army Navy	AN
Army Navy Aeronautical	ANA
Army Service Forces	ASF
Arrange	ARR
Asbestos	ASB
Asphalt	ASPH
Assemble	ASSEM
Assembly	ASSY
Assistant	ASST
Associate	ASSOC
Association	ASSN
Atomic	AT
Atomic Hydrogen Weld	AT/W
Audible	AUD
Audio Frequency	AF
Authorized	AUTH
Automatic	AUTO.
Auxiliary	AUX
Avenue	AVE
Average	AVG
Aviation	AVI
Avoirdupois	AVDP

B

Babbitt	BAB
Back Feed	BF
Back Pressure	BP
Back to Back	B to B
Backface	BF
Balance	BAL
Ball Bearing	BB
Barrel	BBL
Base Line	BL
Base Plate	BP
Battery	BAT.
Baume′	BE
Bearing	BRG
Bell and Flange	B&F
Bell and Spigot	B&S
Bench Mark	BM
Bending Moment	M
Between	BET.
Between Centers	BC
Bevel	BEV
Bill of Material	B/M
Birmingham Wire Gage	BWG
Blank	BLK
Board	BD
Boiler	BLR
Bolster	BOLS
Bolt Circle	BC
Both Faces	BF
Both Sides	BS
Both Ways	BW
Bottom	BOT
Bottom Chord	BC
Bottom Face	BF
Bracket	BRKT
Brake	BK
Brake Horsepower	BHP
Brass	BRS
Brazing	BRZG
Break	BRK
Brinnell Hardness	BH
British Standard	BR STD
British Thermal Units	BTU
Broach	BRO
Bronze	BRZ
Brown & Sharp	B&S
Building	BLDG
Building Line	BL
Bulkhead	BHD
Bureau. of Standards	BU STD
Bushing	BUSH.
Button	BUT.
By-Pass	BYP

C

Cabinet	CAB.
Cab Over Engine	COE
Cadmium Plate	CD PL
Calculate	CALC
Caliber	CAL
Candlepower	CP
Capacity	CAP.
Cap Screw	CAP SCR
Carbon	C
Carburetor	CARB
Carburize	CARB
Carriage	CRG
Carton	CTN
Case Harden	CH
Cast (Used with Other Materials	C
Cast Iron	CI
Cast Iron Pipe	CIP
Cast Steel	CS
Casting	CSTG
Castle Nut	CAS NUT
Catalogue	CAT.
Cavity	CAV
Ceiling	CLG
Cement	CEM
Center	CTR
Center Line	CL
Center of Gravity	CG
Center Punch	CP
Center to Center	C to C
Centigrade	C
Centrifugal	CENT.
Ceramic	CER
Chamfer	CHAM
Change	CHG
Change Notice	CN
Change Order	CO
Channel	CHAN
Check	CHK
Chemical	CHEM
Chord	CHD
Chrome Molybdenum	CR MOLY
Chromium Plate	Cr PL
Chrome Vanadium	CR VAN.
Circle	CIR
Circuit	CKT
Circular Pitch	CP
Circumference	CIRC
Clamp	CLP
Cleanout	CO
Clearance	CL
Clockwise	CW
Closet	CLO
Coated	CTD
Coaxial	COAX
Cold Drawn	CD
Cold Drawn Steel	CDS
Cold Finish	CF
Cold Punched	CP
Cold Rolled Steel	CRS
Column	COL
Combination	COMB.
Command	COM
Commercial	COML
Commercial Quality	CQ
Commutator	COMM
Companion	COMP
Complete	COMPL
Compound	COMP
Compressor	COMPR
Concentric	CONC
Concrete	CONC
Condition	COND
Constant	CONST
Construction	CONST
Container	CNTR
Continue	CONT
Contract	CONT
Contractor	CONTR

Contractor Furnished
Equipment ....CFE
Control ....CONT
Conveyor ....CNVR
Copper Plate ....COP. PL
Correct ....CORR
Corrosion Resistant ....CRE
Corrosion Resistant
Steel ....CRES
Corrugate ....CORR
Cotter ....COT.
Cotton Webbing ....COT. WEB.
Counter Clockwise ....CCW
Counter
Electromotive Force ..CEMF
Counterbore ....CBORE
Counterdrill ....CDRILL
Counterpunch ....CPUNCH
Countersink ....CSK
Countersink
Other Side ....CSK-O
Coupling ....CPLG
Cowling ....COWL.
Crankcase ....CRKC
Cross Arm ....XARM
Cross Section ....XSECT
Cubic ....CU
Cubic Feet per Minute ....CFM
Cubic Feet per Second ....CFS
Cubic Foot ....CU FT
Cubic Inch ....CU IN.
Cubic Yard ....CU YD
Current ....CUR.
Cyanide ....CYN
Cycle ....CY
Cylinder ....CYL

D

Decalcomania ....DECAL
Decimal ....DEC
Deck ....DK
Dedendum ....DED
Deep Drawn ....DD
Degree ....(°) DEG
Density ....D
Department ....DEPT
Design ....DSGN
Designed Water Line .....DWL
Detail ....DET
Develop ....DEV
Diagonal ....DIAG
Diagram ....DIAG
Diameter ....DIA
Diametal Pitch ....DP
Diaphragm ....DIAPH
Direct Current ....DC
Discharge ....DISCH
Ditto ....DO.
Division ....DIV
Dovetail ....DVTL
Dowel ....DWL
Downspout ....DS
Drafting ....DFTG
Draftsman ....DFTSMN
Drawing ....DWG
Drawing List ....DL
Drill ....DR
Drill Rod ....DR
Drive ....DR
Drive Fit ....DF
Drop Forge ....DF
Duplex ....DX
Duplicate ....DUP

E

Each ....EA
Eccentric ....ECC
Effective ....EFF
Effective Horsepower .....EHP
Efficiency ....EFF
Elastic Limit ....EL
Elbow ....ELL
Electric ....ELEC
Electromotive Force ......EMF
Elementary ....ELEM
Elevate ....ELEV
Elevation ....EL
Elongation ....ELONG
Enamel ....ENAM
Enclose ....ENCL
End to End ....E to E
Engine ....ENG
Engineer ....ENGR
Engineering ....ENGRG
Engineering
Change Order ....ECO
Entrance ....ENT
Envelope ....ENV
Equal ....EQ
Equipment ....EQUIP.
Equipment
& Spare Parts ....E&SP
Equivalent ....EQUIV
Estimate ....EST
Excavate ....EXC
Exchange ....EXCH
Executive ....EXEC
Exhaust ....EXH
Existing ....EXIST.
Expansion (Joint) ....EXP
Explosion Proof ....EP
Extension ....EXT
Exterior ....EXT
Extra Heavy ....X HVY
Extra Strong ....X STR
Extrude ....EXTR

F

Fabricate ....FAB
Face to Face ....F to F
Fahrenheit ....F
Far Side ....FS
Federal ....FED.
Federal Specifications ....FS
Federal Stock Number ....FSN
Feeder ....FDR
Feet ....(′) FT
Feet Board Measure ......FBM
Feet per Minute ....FPM
Feet per Second ....FPS
Female ....FEM
Fiber ....FBR
Figure ....FIG.
Fillet ....FIL
Fillister ....FIL
Finish ....FIN.
Finish All Over ....FAO
Fire Door ....F DR
Fire Hose ....FH
Fire Hydrant ....FHY
Fireproof ....FPRF
Fitting ....FTG
Fixture ....FIX.
Flange ....FLG
Flashing ....FL
Flat ....F
Flat Head ....FH
Flexible ....FLEX.
Floor ....FL
Floor Drain ....FD
Floor Line ....FL
Fluid ....FL
Fluorescent ....FLUOR
Foot ....(′) FT
Foot Candle ....FC
Forged Steel ....FST
Forging ....FORG
Forward ....FWD
Foundation ....FDN
Foundry ....FDRY
Fractional ....FRAC
Fractional Horsepower ...FHP
Frame ....FR
Framework ....FRWK
Frequency ....FREQ
Front ....FR
Furnish ....FURN
Fuselage ....FUS

G

Gage or Gauge ....GA
Gallon ....GAL
Galvanize ....GALV
Galvanized Iron ....GI
Galvanized Steel ....GS
Galvanized
Steel Wire Rope ......GSWR
Gasket ....GSKT
General ....GEN
Generator ....GEN
Girder ....G
Glass ....GL
Government ....GOVT
Grade ....GR
Grade Line ....GL
Graphic ....GRAPH.
Graphite ....GPH
Grid ....G
Grind ....GRD
Grommet ....GROM
Groove ....GRV

H

Half-Hard ....½H
Half-Round ....½RD
Handle ....HDL
Hanger ....HGR
Hard ....H
Hard-Drawn ....HD
Harden ....HDN
Hardware ....HDW
Head ....HD
Headless ....HDLS
Heat ....HT
Heat Treat ....HT TR
Heavy ....HVY
Height ....HGT
Hexagon ....HEX
High Frequency ....HF
High-Pressure ....HP
High-Speed ....HS
High-Speed Steel ....HSS
High-Tensile Cast Iron ...HTCI
High-Tensile Steel ....HTS
Highway ....HWY
Horizontal ....HOR
Horsepower ....HP
Hot Rolled ....HR
Hot Rolled Steel ....HRS

Hour ....HR
Hundredweight ....CWT
Hydraulic ....HYD
Hydrostatic ....HYDRO

I

Ignition ....IGN
Impregnate ....IMPG
Inboard ....INBD
Incandescent ....INCAND
Inch ....(″) IN.
Incorporated ....INC
Indicate ....IND
Industrial ....IND
Inside Diameter ....ID
Inspect ....INSP
Install ....INSTL
Insulate ....INS
Interchangeable ......INTCHG
Intercommunication INTERCOM
Interior ....INT
Internal ....INT
International Annealed Copper Standard ....IACS
International Pipe Standard ....IPS
Interphone Control Station ..ICS
Intersect ....INT
Iron I
Iron-Pipe Size ....IPS
Irregular ....IRREG
Issue ....ISS

J

Job Order ....JO
Joint ....JT
Joint Army-Navy ....JAN
Journal ....JNL
Junction ....JCT
Junior ....JR

K

Key ....K
Keyseat ....KST
Keyway ....KWY
Kiln-Dried ....KD
Kilocycle ....KC
Kilowatt Hour ....KWH
Kip (1000 lb) ....K
Knocked Down ....KD
Knockout ....KO

L

Laboratory ....LAB
Lacquer ....LAQ
Laminate ....LAM
Lateral ....LAT
Lavatory ....LAV
Lead Covered LC
Leading Edge ....LE
Left L
Left Hand ....LH
Length ....LG
Length Over All ....LOA
Letter ....LTR
Light ....LT
Limit ....LIM
Line L
Linear ....LIN
Liquid ....LIQ
Lithograph ....LITHO
Locate ....LOC
Long ....LG
Low Frequency ....LF
Low Pressure ....LP
Low-Speed ....LS
Lubricate ....LUB
Lumber ....LBR

M

Machine ....MACH
Machine Steel ....MS
Magnaflux ....M
Maintenance ....MAINT
Male & Female ....M&F
Malleable ....MALL.
Malleable Iron ....MI
Manual ....MAN.
Manufacture ....MFR
Manufactured ....MFD
Manufacturing ....MFG
Marine ....MAR.
Mark ....MK
Material ....MATL
Material List ....ML
Maximum ....MAX
Mechanical ....MECH
Median ....MED
Memorandum ....MEMO
Metal ....MET.
Meter (Instrument or Measure of Length ....M
Mezzanine ....MEZZ
Micro ....μ or U
Micrometer ....MIC
Miles ....MI
Miles per Gallon ....MPG
Miles per Hour ....MPH
Military ....MIL.
Millimeter ....MM
Minimum ....MIN
Minute ....(′) MIN
Miscellaneous ....MISC
Mixture ....MIX.
Model ....MOD
Mold Line ....ML
Molded ....MLD
Molding ....MLDG
Month ....MO
Monument ....MON
Morse Taper ....MOR T
Motor ....MOT
Mounted ....MTD
Mounting ....MTG
Multiple ....MULT
Music Wire Gage ....MWG

N

Name Plate ....NP
National ....NATL
National Aircraft Standards .....NAS
National Electrical Code ..NEC
Natural ....NAT
Naval Architect ....NA
Near Face ....NF
Near Side ....NS
Negative ....NEG
New British Standard (Imperial Wire Gage) ..NBS
Nipple ....NIP.
Nominal ....NOM
Noon ....M
Normal ....NOR
North ....N
Not to Scale ....NTS
Number ....NO.

O

Obsolete ....OBS
Octagon ....OCT
Office ....OFF.
On Center ....OC
One Pole ....1 P
Opening ....OPNG
Opposite ....OPP
Optical ....OPT
Ordnance ....ORD
Original ....ORIG
Ounce ....OZ
Outboard ....OUTBD
Outlet ....OUT.
Outside Diameter ....OD
Overall ....OA
Overflow ....OVFL
Overhead ....OVHD
Oxidized ....OXD

P

Pack ....PK
Packing ....PKG
Page ....P
Pair ....PR
Panel ....PNL
Paragraph ....PAR.
Parallel ....PAR.
Parkway ....PKWY
Part ....PT
Passage ....PASS.
Patent ....PAT.
Pattern ....PATT
Peck ....PK
Penny (Nails, etc) ....d
Permanent ....PERM
Perpendicular ....PERP
Phenolic ....PHEN
Phosphor Bronze ......PH BRZ
Pick Up ....PU
Piece ....PC
Piece Mark ....PC MK
Pint ....PT
Pipe Tap ....PT
Pitch ....P
Pitch Circle ....PC
Pitch Diameter ....PD
Plaster ....PLAS
Plastic ....PLSTC
Plate ....PL
Plumbing ....PLMB
Pneumatic ....PNEU
Point ....PT
Pole ....P
Polish ....POL
Porcelain ....PORC
Port ....P
Portable ....PORT.
Position ....POS
Potential ....POT.
Pound ....LB
Pounds per Square Inch ....PSI
Power ....PWR
Precast ....PRCST
Prefabricated ....PREFAB
Preferred ....PFD
Prepare ....PREP
Press ....PRS
Pressure ....PRESS.
Pressure Angle ....PA.
Primary ....PRI
Process ....PROC

Production .... PROD.
Production Order .... PO
Profile .... PF
Project .... PROJ
Proposed .... PROP.
Publication .... PUB
Pull Box .... PB
Pull Button Switch . PULL B SW
Punch .... PCH
Purchase .... PUR
Push Button .... PB

Q

Quadrant .... QUAD.
Quality .... QUAL
Quantity .... QTY
Quart .... QT
Quarter-Hard .... ¼ H
Quarter-Round .... ¼ RD
Quartermaster Corps ..... QMC

R

Radial .... RAD
Radius .... R
Railroad .... RR
Railway .... RY
Ream .... RM
Reassemble .... REASM
Received .... RECD
Receptacle .... RECP
Record .... REC
Rectangle .... RECT
Rectifier .... RECT
Reduce .... RED.
Reducer .... RED.
Reference .... REF
Reference Line .... REF L
Register .... REG
Regulator .... REG
Reinforce .... REINF
Relative Humidity .... RH
Relay .... REL
Relief .... REL
Remove .... REM
Renewable .... REN
Reproduce .... REPRO
Require .... REQ
Required .... REQD
Requisition .... REQ
Retard .... RET.
Return .... RET.
Reverse .... REV
Revise .... REV
Revolution .... REV
Revolutions per Minute ... RPM
Right .... R
Right Hand .... RH
Rivet .... RIV
Rockwell Hardness .... RH
Roller Bearing .... RB
Root Diameter .... RD
Round .... RD

S

Schedule .... SCH
Schematic .... SCHEM
Screw .... SCR
Sea Level .... SL
Seamless .... SMLS
Secondary .... SEC
Section .... SECT.
Semi-Finished .... SF
Semi-Fixed .... SFXD
Semi-Steel .... SS
Serial .... SER
Serrate .... SERR
Set Screw .... SS
Sewer .... SEW.
Shaft .... SFT
Sheathing .... SHTHG
Sheet .... SH
Shop Order .... SO
Short Wave .... SW
Shoulder .... SHLD
Shut Off Valve .... SOV
Side .... S
Similar .... SIM
Sink .... SK
Sketch .... SK
Sleeve .... SLV
Sleeve Bearing .... SB
Slotted .... SLOT.
Small .... SM
Socket .... SOC
Soft .... S
Soil Pipe .... SP
Space .... SP
Spare .... SP
Special .... SPL
Special Treatment Steel .... STS
Specific Gravity .... SP GR
Specification .... SPEC
Speed .... SP
Spherical .... SPHER
Split Phase .... SP PH
Spot Faced .... SF
Spring .... SPG
Square .... SQ
Squirrel Cage .... SQ CG
Stainless .... STN
Stainless Steel .... SST
Stairway .... STWY
Standard .... STD
Starboard .... STBD
Station .... STA
Steel .... STL
Stock .... STK
Storage .... STG
Straight .... STR
Street .... ST
Stress Anneal .... SA
Strip .... STR
Structural .... STR
Substitute .... SUB
Substructure .... SUBSTR
Summary .... SUM.
Supercharge .... S-CHG
Superintendent .... SUPT
Supersede .... SUPSD
Superstructure ..... SUPERSTR
Supervise .... SUPV
Supplement .... SUPP
Supply .... SUP
Surface .... SUR
Survey .... SURV
Switch .... SW
Switch and Relay Types
  Single Pole Switch .... SP SW
  Single Pole Single
    Throw Switch .... SPST SW
  Single Pole Double
    Throw Switch ... SPDT SW
  Double Pole Switch ... DP SW
  Double Pole Single
    Throw Switch ... DPST SW
  Double Pole Double
    Throw Switch ... DPDT SW
  Triple Pole Switch .... 3P SW
  Triple Pole Single
    Throw Switch .... 3PST SW
  Triple Pole Double
    Throw Switch ... 3PDT SW
  4 Pole Switch .... 4P SW
  4 Pole Single
    Throw Switch .... 4PST SW
  4 Pole Double
    Throw Switch ... 4PDT SW
  etc
Switchboard .... SWBD
Switchgear .... SWGR
Symbol .... SYM
Symmetrical .... SYM
Synchronous .... SYN
Synthetic .... SYN
System .... SYS

T

Tabulate .... TAB.
Tangent .... TAN.
Taper .... TPR
Technical .... TECH
Technical Manual .... TM
Technical Report .... TR
Tee .... T
Teeth per Inch .... TPI
Temperature .... TEMP
Template .... TEMP
Tensile Strength .... TS
Tension .... TENS.
Terminal .... TERM.
That is .... IE
Thermal .... THRM
Thick .... THK
Thousand .... M
Thousand Foot Pounds .. KIP-FT
Thousand Pound .... KIP
Thread .... THD
Threads per Inch .... TPI
Through .... THRU
Timber .... TMBR
Time .... T
Time Delay .... TD
Tobin-Bronze .... TOB BRZ
Toggle .... TGL
Tolerance .... TOL
Tongue & Groove .... T&G
Tool Steel .... TS
Tooth .... T
Total .... TOT.
Total Indicator Reading .... TIR
Trailing Edge .... TE
Training .... TNG
Transfer .... TRANS
Transformer .... TRANS
Transmission .... XMSN
Transportation .... TRANS
Truss .... T
Tubing .... TUB.
Typical .... TYP

U

Ultimate .... ULT
Ultra-High Frequency .... UHF
United States Gage ...... USG
United States Standard .... USS
Universal .... UNIV

V

Vacuum .... VAC
Valve V
Vandyke .... VD
Vapor Proof .... VAP PRF

Varnish .... VARN
Velocity V
Vent Pipe .... VP
Ventilate .... VENT.
Vertical .... VERT
Very-High Frequency ..... VHF
Vibrate .... VIB
Vitreous .... VIT
Volt V
Voltmeter .... VM
Volume .... VOL

W

Wall .... W
Washer .... WASH.
Water Line .... WL
Watt .... W
Week .... WK
Weight .... WT
West .... W
Wheel Base .... WB
Width .... W
Wire .... W
With .... W/
Without .... W/O
Woodruff .... WDF
Wrought .... WRT
Wrought Iron .... WI

X Y Z

Yard .... YD
Year .... YR

ABBREVIATIONS RELATING TO SCREW THREADS

Screw-Thread Standards
- American National Coarse Thread .... NC
- American National Fine Thread .... NF
- American National Extra Fine Thread .... NEF
- American National Special Pitch, etc, Thread ..... NS
- American National Pitch Thread .. 8N, 12N, or 16N
- American National Acme Thread .... NA
- American National Taper Pipe Thread .... NPT
- American National Straight Pipe Thread in Pipe Couplings .... NPSC

American National Straight Pipe Threads for Dry Seal Pressure Tight Joint . NPSF
American National Taper Pipe Threads for Dry Seal Pressure Tight Joints NPTF
American National Straight Pipe Threads for Mechanical Joints .. NPSM
American National Straight Pipe Threads for Locknuts and Locknut Pipe Threads .... NPSL
American National Straight Pipe Threads for Hose Couplings and Nipples .. NPSH
American National Taper Pipe Threads for Railing Fixtures .... NPTR
American Truncated Whitworth Coarse Thread .... TWC
American Truncated Whitworth Fine Thread .... TWF
American Truncated Whitworth Special Thread .... TWS
Unified National Coarse Thread .... UNC
Unified National Fine Thread .... UNF
Unified National Special Thread .... UNS

ENGINEERING SOCIETIES AND INDUSTRIAL ASSOCIATIONS

American Association of Engineers .... AAE
American Boiler Manufacturers' Association & Affiliated Industries ... ABMA
American Bureau of Shipping .... ABS
Air Conditioning & Refrigerating Machinery Association .... ACRMA
American Chemical Society .... ACS
American Concrete Institute .... ACI
American Electrochemical Society .... AES
American Electroplaters Society .... AES
American Engineering Council .... AEC
American Foundrymen's Association .... AFA
American Gas Association .... AGA
American Gear Manufacturers' Association ... AGMA
American Institute of Architects .... AIA
American Institute of Chemical Engineers ... AICE
American Institute of Electrical Engineers ... AIEE
American Institute of Mining & Metallurgical Engineers .... AIMME
American Institute of Steel Construction ..... AISC
American Iron & Steel Institute .... AISI
American Petroleum Institute .... API
American Railway Engineering Association .. AREA
American Railway Bridge & Building Association .. ARBBA
American Society of Aeronautical Engineers ..... ASAE
American Society of Civil Engineers .... ASCE
American Society of Engineers and Architects .... ASEA
American Society of Heating & Ventilating Engineers .... ASHVE
American Society of Lubricating Engineers .. ASLE
American Society of Mechanical Engineers .... ASME
American Society for Metals .... ASM
American Society of Refrigerating Engineers . ASSE
American Society of Safety Engineers .... ASSE
American Society of Sanitary Engineering .... ASSE
American Society for Steel Treating .... ASST
American Society for Testing Materials ...... ASTM
American Society of Tool Engineers .... ASTE
American Standards Association .... ASA
American Steel Foundrymen's Association ..... ASFA
American Telephone & Telegraph Co. ..... AT&TCO
American Transit Association .... ATA
American Water Works Association .... AWWA
American Welding Society . AWS
American Wood Preservers Association ... AWPA
Anti-Friction Bearing Manufacturers' Association .... AFBMA
Association of American Railroads .... AAR
Association of American Steel Manufacturers ... AASM
Association of Iron & Steel Engineers .... AISE
Automobile Manufacturers' Association .... AMA
Canadian Standards Association .... CSA
Canadian Lumbermen's Association .... CLA
Compressed Air Institute .. CAI
Edison Electric Institute .... EEI
Electrochemical Society ..... ES

Gas Appliances Manufacturers' Association . . GAMA
Hydraulic Institute . . . . HI
Illuminating Engineering Society . . . . IES
Institute of Radio Engineers . . . . IRE
Institute of Traffic Engineers . . . . ITE
Insulated Power Cable Engineers' Association . . IPCEA
Joint Electron Tube Engineering Council . . JETEC
Manufacturers Standardization Society of the Valve and Fittings Industry . . . . MSS
National Advisory Committee for Aeronautics . . . . . . NACA
National Aircraft Standards . . . . NAS
National Bureau of Standards . . . . NBS
National Association of Manufacturers . . . . NAM
National Conservation Bureau . . . . NCB
National Electrical Manufacturers Association . . NEMA
National Hardwood Lumber Association . . . NHLA
National Housing Agency . . NHA
National Lumber Manufacturers Association . . . . NLMA
National Machine Tool Builders' Association . NMTBA
National Petroleum Association . . . . NPA
National Safety Council . . . NSC
Oil Heat Institute of America . . . . OHIA
Radio Manufacturers Association . . . . RMA
Refrigeration Equipment Manufacturers' Association . . . . REMA
Society for the Advancement of Management . . . . SAM
Society of Automotive Engineers . . . . SAE
Society of Fire Engineers . . . SFE
Society of Industrial Engineers . . . . SIE
Society of Military Engineers . . . . SME
Society of Tractor Engineers . . . . STE
Standards Engineers Society . . . . SES
Underwriters' Laboratories, Inc. UL

HARDNESS CONVERSION NUMBERS

FOR STEEL

Based on Rockwell Hardness

ROCKWELL				BRINELL				
C Scale 150 Kg., 120° Cone	B Scale 100 Kg., 1/16" Ball	15-N Scale 15 Kg., Superficial Brale Penetrator	30-N Scale 30 Kg., Superficial Brale Penetrator	Hardness No.	Diam. 3000 Kg., 10 mm. Ball	Vickers	Shore Scleroscope	Tensile Strength 1000 Lb./Sq. Inch
68	...	93.2	84.4	...	...	940	97	...
67	...	92.9	83.6	...	...	900	95	...
66	...	92.5	82.8	...	...	865	92	...
65	...	92.2	81.9	739	...	832	91	...
64	...	91.8	81.1	722	2.28	800	88	...
63	...	91.4	80.1	705	2.31	772	87	...
62	...	91.1	79.3	688	2.33	746	85	...
61	...	90.7	78.4	670	2.36	720	83	...
60	...	90.2	77.5	654	2.40	697	81	...
59	...	89.8	76.6	634	2.43	674	80	326
58	...	89.3	75.7	615	2.47	653	78	315
57	...	88.9	74.8	595	2.51	633	76	305
56	...	88.3	73.9	577	2.55	613	75	295
55	...	87.9	73.0	560	2.58	595	74	287
54	...	87.4	72.0	543	2.63	577	72	278
53	...	86.9	71.2	525	2.67	560	71	269
52	...	86.4	70.2	512	2.71	544	69	262
51	...	85.9	69.4	496	2.75	528	68	253
50	...	85.5	68.5	481	2.79	513	67	245
49	...	85.0	67.6	469	2.83	498	66	239
48	...	84.5	66.7	455	2.87	484	64	232
47	...	83.9	65.8	443	2.91	471	63	225
46	...	83.5	64.8	432	2.94	458	62	219
45	...	83.0	64.0	421	2.98	446	60	212
44	...	82.5	63.1	409	3.02	434	58	206
43	...	82.0	62.2	400	3.05	423	57	201
42	...	81.5	61.3	390	3.09	412	56	196
41	...	80.9	60.4	381	3.12	402	55	191
40	...	80.4	59.5	371	3.16	392	54	186
39	...	79.9	58.6	362	3.19	382	52	181
38	...	79.4	57.7	353	3.24	372	51	176
37	...	78.8	56.8	344	3.28	363	50	172
36	(109)	78.3	55.9	336	3.32	354	49	168
35	...	77.7	55.0	327	3.37	345	48	163
34	(108)	77.2	54.2	319	3.41	336	47	159
33	...	76.6	53.3	311	3.45	327	46	154
32	(107)	76.1	52.1	301	3.51	318	44	150
31	(106)	75.6	51.3	294	3.54	310	43	146
30	...	75.0	50.4	286	3.59	302	42	142
29	...	74.5	49.5	279	3.63	294	41	138
28	(104)	73.9	48.6	271	3.69	286	41	134
27	(103)	73.3	47.7	264	3.74	279	40	131
26	...	72.8	46.8	258	3.78	272	38	127
25	...	72.2	45.9	253	3.81	266	38	124
24	(101)	71.6	45.0	247	3.84	260	37	121
23	100	71.0	44.0	243	3.88	254	36	118
22	99	70.5	43.2	237	3.93	248	35	115
21	...	69.9	42.3	231	3.98	243	35	113
20	98	69.4	41.5	226	4.02	238	34	110

WEIGHTS OF MATERIALS

Material	Avg. Wt. per Cu. Ft.	Material	Avg. Wt. per Cu. Ft.
Aluminum	167.1	Mahogany, Honduras, dry	35
Brass, cast	519	Manganese	465
Brass, rolled	527	Masonry, granite or limestone	165
Brick, common and hard	125	Nickel, rolled	541
Bronze, copper 8, tin 1	546	Oak, live, perfectly dry, .88 to 1.02	59.3
Cement, Portland, 376 lbs. net per bbl	110–115	Pine, white, perfectly dry	25
Concrete, conglomerate, with Portland cement	150	Pine, yellow, southern dry	45
Copper, cast	542	Plastics, molded	74–137
Copper, rolled	555	Rubber, manufactured	95
Fibre, hard	87	Slate, granulated	95
Fir, Douglas	31	Snow, freshly fallen	5–15
Glass, window or plate	162	Spruce, dry	29
Gravel, round	100–125	Steel	489.6
Iron, cast	450	Tin, cast	459
Iron, wrought	480	Walnut, black, perfectly dry	38
Lead, commercial	710	Water, distilled or pure rain	62.4
		Zinc or spelter, cast	443

CIRCUMFERENCES AND AREAS OF CIRCLES

Dia	Circum	Area	Dia	Circum	Area	Dia	Circum	Area	Dia	Circum	Area
1/64	0.0491	0.0002	1	3.1416	0.7854	3	9.4248	7.0686	5	15.7080	19.635
1/32	0.0982	0.0008	1/16	3.3379	0.8866	1/16	9.6211	7.3662	1/16	15.9043	20.129
1/16	0.1964	0.0031	1/8	3.5343	0.9940	1/8	9.8175	7.6699	1/8	16.1007	20.629
3/32	0.2945	0.0059	3/16	3.7306	1.1075	3/16	10.0138	7.9798	3/16	16.2970	21.135
1/8	0.3927	0.0123	1/4	3.9270	1.2272	1/4	10.2102	8.2958	1/4	16.4934	21.648
5/32	0.4909	0.0192	5/16	4.1233	1.3530	5/16	10.4065	8.6179	5/16	16.6897	22.166
3/16	0.5890	0.0276	3/8	4.3197	1.4849	3/8	10.6029	8.9462	3/8	16.8861	22.691
7/32	0.6872	0.0376	7/16	4.5160	1.6230	7/16	10.7992	9.2806	7/16	17.0824	23.221
1/4	0.7854	0.0491	1/2	4.7124	1.7671	1/2	10.9956	9.6211	1/2	17.2788	23.758
9/32	0.8836	0.0621	9/16	4.9087	1.9175	9/16	11.1919	9.9678	9/16	17.4751	24.301
5/16	0.9817	0.0767	5/8	5.1051	2.0739	5/8	11.3883	10.321	5/8	17.6715	24.850
11/32	1.0799	0.0928	11/16	5.3014	2.2365	11/16	11.5846	10.680	11/16	17.8678	25.406
3/8	1.1781	0.1105	3/4	5.4978	2.4053	3/4	11.7810	11.045	3/4	18.0642	25.967
13/32	1.2763	0.1296	13/16	5.6941	2.5802	13/16	11.9773	11.416	13/16	18.2605	26.535
7/16	1.3745	0.1503	7/8	5.8905	2.7612	7/8	12.1737	11.793	7/8	18.4569	27.100
15/32	1.4726	0.1726	15/16	6.0868	2.9483	15/16	12.3700	12.177	15/16	18.6532	27.688
1/2	1.5708	0.1964	2	6.2832	3.1416	4	12.5664	12.566	6	18.8496	28.274
17/32	1.6690	0.2217	1/16	6.4795	3.3410	1/16	12.7627	12.962	1/8	19.2423	29.465
9/16	1.7672	0.2485	1/8	6.6759	3.5466	1/8	12.9591	13.364	1/4	19.6350	30.680
19/32	1.8653	0.2769	3/16	6.8722	3.7583	3/16	13.1554	13.772	3/8	20.0277	31.919
5/8	1.9635	0.3068	1/4	7.0686	3.9761	1/4	13.3518	14.185	1/2	20.4204	33.183
21/32	2.0617	0.3382	5/16	7.2649	4.2000	5/16	13.5481	14.607	5/8	20.8131	34.472
11/16	2.1598	0.3712	3/8	7.4613	4.4301	3/8	13.7445	15.033	3/4	21.2058	35.785
23/32	2.2580	0.4057	7/16	7.6576	4.6664	7/16	13.9408	15.466	7/8	21.5984	37.122
3/4	2.3562	0.4418	1/2	7.8540	4.9087	1/2	14.1372	15.904	7	21.9911	38.485
25/32	2.4544	0.4794	9/16	8.0503	5.1572	9/16	14.3335	16.349	1/8	22.3838	39.871
13/16	2.5525	0.5185	5/8	8.2467	5.4119	5/8	14.5299	16.800	1/4	22.7765	41.282
27/32	2.6507	0.5591	11/16	8.4430	5.6727	11/16	14.7262	17.257	3/8	23.1692	42.718
7/8	2.7489	0.6013	3/4	8.6394	5.9396	3/4	14.9226	17.721	1/2	23.5619	44.179
29/32	2.8471	0.6450	13/16	8.8357	6.2126	13/16	15.1189	18.190	5/8	23.9546	45.664
15/16	2.9452	0.6903	7/8	9.0321	6.4918	7/8	15.3153	18.665	3/4	24.3473	47.173
31/32	3.0434	0.7371	15/16	9.2284	6.7771	15/16	15.5116	19.147	7/8	24.7400	48.707

DISTANCE ACROSS CORNERS OF HEXAGONS AND SQUARES

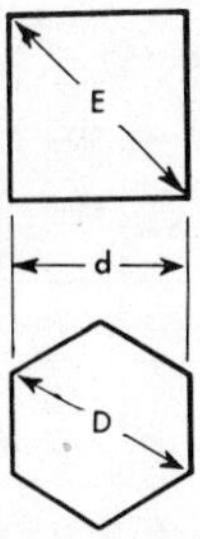

$D = 1.1547\,d$
$E = 1.4142\,d$

d	D	E	d	D	E	d	D	E
1/4	0.2886	0.3535	1 1/4	1.4434	1.7677	2 5/16	2.6702	3.2703
9/32	0.3247	0.3977	1 9/32	1.4794	1.8119	2 3/8	2.7424	3.3587
5/16	0.3608	0.4419	1 5/16	1.5155	1.8561	2 7/16	2.8145	3.4471
11/32	0.3968	0.4861	1 11/32	1.5516	1.9003	2 1/2	2.8867	3.5355
3/8	0.4329	0.5303	1 3/8	1.5877	1.9445	2 9/16	2.9583	3 6239
13/32	0.4690	0.5745	1 13/32	1.6238	1.9887	2 5/8	3.0311	3.7123
7/16	0.5051	0.6187	1 7/16	1.6598	2.0329	2 11/16	3.1032	3.8007
15/32	0.5412	0.6629	1 15/32	1.6959	2.0771	2 3/4	3.1754	3.8891
1/2	0.5773	0.7071	1 1/2	1.7320	2.1213	2 13/16	3.2476	3.9794
17/32	0.6133	0.7513	1 17/32	1.7681	2.1655	2 7/8	3.3197	4.0658
9/16	0.6494	0.7955	1 9/16	1.8042	2.2097	2 15/16	3.3919	4.1542
19/32	0.6855	0.8397	1 19/32	1.8403	2.2539	3	3.4641	4.2426
5/8	0.7216	0.8839	1 5/8	1.8764	2.2981	3 1/16	3.5362	4.3310
21/32	0.7576	0.9281	1 21/32	1.9124	2.3423	3 1/8	3.6084	4.4194
11/16	0.7937	0.9723	1 11/16	1.9485	2.3865	3 3/16	3.6806	4.5078
23/32	0.8298	1.0164	1 23/32	1.9846	2.4306	3 1/4	3.7527	4.5962
3/4	0.8659	1.0606	1 3/4	2.0207	2.4708	3 5/16	3.8249	4.6846
25/32	0.9020	1.1048	1 25/32	2.0568	2.5190	3 3/8	3.8971	4.7729
13/16	0.9380	1.1490	1 13/16	2.0929	2.5632	3 7/16	3.9692	4.8613
27/32	0.9741	1.1932	1 27/32	2.1289	2.6074	3 1/2	4.0414	4.9497
7/8	1.0102	1.2374	1 7/8	2.1650	2.6516	3 9/16	4.1136	5.0381
29/32	1.0463	1.2816	1 29/32	2.2011	2.6958	3 5/8	4.1857	5.1265
15/16	1.0824	1.3258	1 15/16	2.2372	2.7400	3 11/16	4.2579	5.2149
31/32	1.1184	1.3700	1 31/32	2.2733	2.7842	3 3/4	4.3301	5.3033
1	1.1547	1.4142	2	2.3094	2.8284	3 13/16	4.4023	5.3917
1 1/32	1.1907	1.4584	2 1/32	2.3453	2.8726	3 7/8	4.4744	5.4801
1 1/16	1.2268	1.5026	2 1/16	2.3815	2.9168	3 15/16	4.5466	5.5684
1 3/32	1.2629	1.5468	2 3/32	2.4176	2.9610	4	4.6188	5.6568
1 1/8	1.2990	1.5910	2 1/8	2.4537	3.0052	4 1/8	4.7631	5.8336
1 5/32	1.3351	1.6352	2 5/32	2.4898	3.0494	4 1/4	4.9074	6.0104
1 3/16	1.3712	1.6793	2 3/16	2.5259	3.0936	4 3/8	5.0518	6.1872
1 7/32	1.4073	1.7235	2 1/4	2.5981	3.1820	4 1/2	5.1961	6.3639

FRACTIONAL, NUMBER, AND LETTER SIZES FOR TWIST DRILLS

Drill No.	Frac.	Deci.	Drill No.	Frac.	Deci.	Drill No.	Frac.	Deci.	Drill No.	Frac.	Deci.
80	—	.0135	42	—	.0935	7	—	.201	X	—	.397
79	—	.0145	—	3/32	.0938	—	13/64	.203	Y	—	.404
—	1/64	.0156				6	—	.204			
78	—	.0160	41	—	.0960	5	—	.206	—	13/32	.406
77	—	.0180	40	—	.0980	4	—	.209	Z	—	.413
			39	—	.0995				—	27/64	.422
76	—	.0200	38	—	.1015	3	—	.213	—	7/16	.438
75	—	.0210	37	—	.1040	—	7/32	.219	—	29/64	.453
74	—	.0225				2	—	.221			
73	—	.0240	36	—	.1065	1	—	.228	—	15/32	.469
72	—	.0250	—	7/64	.1094	A	—	.234	—	31/64	.484
			35	—	.1100				—	1/2	.500
71	—	.0260	34	—	.1110	—	15/64	.234	—	33/64	.516
70	—	.0280	33	—	.1130	B	—	.238	—	17/32	.531
69	—	.0292				C	—	.242			
68	—	.0310	32	—	.116	D	—	.246	—	35/64	.547
—	1/32	.0313	31	—	.120	—	1/4	.250	—	9/16	.562
			—	1/8	.125				—	37/64	.578
67	—	.0320	30	—	.129	E	—	.250	—	19/32	.594
66	—	.0330	29	—	.136	F	—	.257	—	39/64	.609
65	—	.0350				G	—	.261			
64	—	.0360	—	9/64	.140	—	17/64	.266	—	5/8	.625
63	—	.0370	28	—	.141	H	—	.266	—	41/64	.641
			27	—	.144				—	21/32	.656
62	—	.0380	26	—	.147	I	—	.272	—	43/64	.672
61	—	.0390	25	—	.150	J	—	.277	—	11/16	.688
60	—	.0400				—	9/32	.281			
59	—	.0410	24	—	.152	K	—	.281	—	45/64	.703
58	—	.0420	23	—	.154	L	—	.290	—	23/32	.719
			—	5/32	.156				—	47/64	.734
57	—	.0430	22	—	.157	M	—	.295	—	3/4	.750
56	—	.0465	21	—	.159	—	19/64	.297	—	49/64	.766
—	3/64	.0469				N	—	.302			
55	—	.0520	20	—	.161	—	5/16	.313	—	25/32	.781
54	—	.0550	19	—	.166	O	—	.316	—	51/64	.797
			18	—	.170				—	13/16	.813
53	—	.0595	—	11/64	.172	P	—	.323	—	53/64	.828
—	1/16	.0625	17	—	.173	—	21/64	.328	—	27/32	.844
52	—	.0635				Q	—	.332			
51	—	.0670				R	—	.339			
50	—	.0700	16	—	.177	—	11/32	.344	—	55/64	.859
			15	—	.180				—	7/8	.875
49	—	.0730	14	—	.182	S	—	.348	—	57/64	.891
48	—	.0760	13	—	.185	T	—	.358	—	29/32	.906
—	5/64	.0781	—	3/16	.188	—	23/64	.359	—	59/64	.922
47	—	.0785				U	—	.368			
46	—	.0810	12	—	.189	—	3/8	.375	—	15/16	.938
			11	—	.191				—	61/64	.953
45	—	.0820	10	—	.194	V	—	.377	—	31/32	.969
44	—	.0860	9	—	.196	W	—	.386	—	63/64	.984
43	—	.0890	8	—	.199	—	25/64	.391	—	1	1.000

TAP DRILL SIZES FOR UNIFIED AND AMERICAN THREADS

SCREW THREAD		TAP DRILL	SCREW THREAD		TAP DRILL
No. or Diameter	Threads per Inch	Size or Number	No. or Diameter	Threads per Inch	Size or Number
0	80	3/64	5/16	18	F
				24	1
1	64	53	3/8	16	5/16
	72			24	Q
2	56	50	7/16	14	U
	64			20	25/64
3	48	47	1/2	13	27/64
	56	45		20	29/64
4	40	43	9/16	12	31/64
	48	42		18	33/64
5	40	38	5/8	11	17/32
	44	37		18	37/64
6	32	36	3/4	10	21/32
	40	33		16	11/16
8	32	29	7/8	9	49/64
	36			14	13/16
10	24	25	1	8	7/8
	32	21		12	59/64
12	24	16	1 1/8	7	63/64
	28	14		12	1 3/64
1/4	20	7	1 1/4	7	17/64
	28	3		12	1 11/64

AMERICAN STANDARD BOLTS, NUTS AND HEXAGON HEAD CAP SCREWS
(For full information see ASA B18.2-1960 and B18.6.2-1956)

Normal Size or Basic Major Dia. of Thread	Body Dia. (Max.)	REGULAR BOLTS							HEX CAP SCREWS			REGULAR NUTS						
		Width Across Flats (Max.)		Width Across Corners (Max.)		Height (Max.)			Width Across		Height	Width Across Flats (Max.)		Width Across Corners (Max.)		Thickness		(Max.)
		Sq.	Hex.	Sq.	Hex.	Sq.	Hex.	Semi-Fin Hex.	Flats (Max.)	Corners (Max.)	(Max.)	Sq.& Hex.	Semi-Fin.Hex.	Sq.	Hex.;Semi-Fin.Hex.	Sq.& Hex.	Semi-Fin.Hex.	Semi-Fin. Hex-Jam
1/4	.260	3/8	7/16	.530	.505	.188	.188	.163	7/16	.505	.163	7/16	7/16	.619	.505	.235	.219	.157
5/16	.324	1/2	1/2	.707	.577	.220	.235	.211	1/2	.577	.211	9/16	9/16	.795	.650	.283	.267	.189
3/8	.388	9/16	9/16	.795	.650	.268	.268	.243	9/16	.650	.243	5/8	5/8	.884	.722	.346	.330	.221
7/16	.452	5/8	5/8	.884	.722	.316	.316	.291	5/8	.722	.291	3/4	3/4	1.061	.866	.394	.378	.253
1/2	.515	3/4	3/4	1.061	.866	.348	.364	.323	3/4	.866	.323	13/16	13/16	1.149	.938	.458	.442	.317
9/16	-	-	-	-	-	-	-	-	13/16	.938	.371	7/8*	7/8	-	1.010	.521*	.505	.349
5/8	.642	15/16	15/16	1.326	1.083	.444	.444	.403	15/16	1.083	.403	1	1	1.414	1.155	.569	.553	.381
3/4	.768	1-1/8	1-1/8	1.591	1.299	.524	.524	.483	1-1/8	1.299	.483	1-1/8	1-1/8	1.591	1.299	.680	.665	.446
7/8	.895	1-5/16	1-5/16	1.856	1.516	.620	.604	.563	1-5/16	1.516	.563	1-5/16	1-5/16	1.856	1.516	.792	.776	.510
1	1.022	1-1/2	1-1/2	2.121	1.732	.684	.700	.627	1-1/2	1.732	.627	1-1/2	1-1/2	2.121	1.732	.903	.887	.575
1-1/8	1.149	1-11/16	1-11/16	2.386	1.949	.780	.780	.718	1-11/16	1.949	.718	1-11/16	1-11/16	2.386	1.949	1.030	.999	.639
1-1/4	1.277	1-7/8	1-7/8	2.652	2.165	.876	.876	.813	1-7/8	2.165	.813	1-7/8	1-7/8	2.652	2.165	1.126	1.094	.751
1-3/8	1.404	2-1/16	2-1/16	2.917	2.382	.940	.940	.878	2-1/16	2.382	.878	2-1/16	2-1/16	2.917	2.382	1.237	1.206	.815
1-1/2	1.531	2-1/4	2-1/4	3.182	2.598	1.036	1.036	.974	2-1/4	2.598	.974	2-1/4	2-1/4	3.182	2.598	1.348	1.317	.880
1-5/8	1.658	2-7/16	-	3.447	-	1.132	-	-	-	-	-	-	2-7/16	-	2.815+	-	1.429	.944
1-3/4	1.785	-	2-5/8	-	3.031	-	1.196	1.134	-	-	-	-	2-5/8	-	3.031+	-	1.540	1.009
1-7/8	-	-	-	-	-	-	-	-	-	-	-	-	2-13/16	-	3.248+	-	1.651	1.073
2	2.039	-	3	-	3.464	-	1.388	1.263	-	-	-	-	3	-	3.464+	-	1.763	1.138
2-1/4	2.305	-	3-3/8	-	3.897	-	1.548	1.423	-	-	-	-	3-3/8	-	3.897+	-	1.970	1.251
2-1/2	2.559	-	3-3/4	-	4.330	-	1.708	1.583	-	-	-	-	3-3/4	-	4.330+	-	2.193	1.505
2-3/4	2.827	-	4-1/8	-	4.763	-	1.869	1.744	-	-	-	-	4-1/8	-	4.763+	-	2.415	1.634
3	3.081	-	4-1/2	-	5.196	-	2.060	1.935	-	-	-	-	4-1/2	-	5.196+	-	2.638	1.763

*Hex Only   + Semi-Fin Hex Only   NOTE: All dimensions in inches.

SLOTTED HEAD SCREWS
(For full information see ASA B18.6-1947)

Dimensions of Round Head Machine Screws

Nominal Size	D: Max Diameter of Screw	A: Head Diameter Max	A: Head Diameter Min	H: Height of Head Max	H: Height of Head Min	J: Width of Slot Max	J: Width of Slot Min	T: Depth of Slot Max	T: Depth of Slot Min
0	0.060	0.113	0.099	0.053	0.043	0.023	0.016	0.039	0.029
1	0.073	0.138	0.122	0.061	0.051	0.026	0.019	0.044	0.033
2	0.086	0.162	0.146	0.069	0.059	0.031	0.023	0.048	0.037
3	0.099	0.187	0.169	0.078	0.067	0.035	0.027	0.053	0.040
4	0.112	0.211	0.193	0.086	0.075	0.039	0.031	0.058	0.044
5	0.125	0.236	0.217	0.095	0.083	0.043	0.035	0.063	0.047
6	0.138	0.260	0.240	0.103	0.091	0.048	0.039	0.068	0.051
8	0.164	0.309	0.287	0.120	0.107	0.054	0.045	0.077	0.058
10	0.190	0.359	0.334	0.137	0.123	0.060	0.050	0.087	0.065
12	0.216	0.408	0.382	0.153	0.139	0.067	0.056	0.096	0.072
1/4	0.250	0.472	0.443	0.175	0.160	0.075	0.064	0.109	0.082
5/16	0.3125	0.590	0.557	0.216	0.198	0.084	0.072	0.132	0.099
3/8	0.375	0.708	0.670	0.256	0.237	0.094	0.081	0.155	0.117
7/16	0.4375	0.750	0.707	0.328	0.307	0.094	0.081	0.196	0.148
1/2	0.500	0.813	0.766	0.355	0.332	0.106	0.091	0.211	0.159
9/16	0.5625	0.938	0.887	0.410	0.385	0.118	0.102	0.242	0.183
5/8	0.625	1.000	0.944	0.438	0.411	0.133	0.116	0.258	0.195
3/4	0.750	1.250	1.185	0.547	0.516	0.149	0.131	0.320	0.242

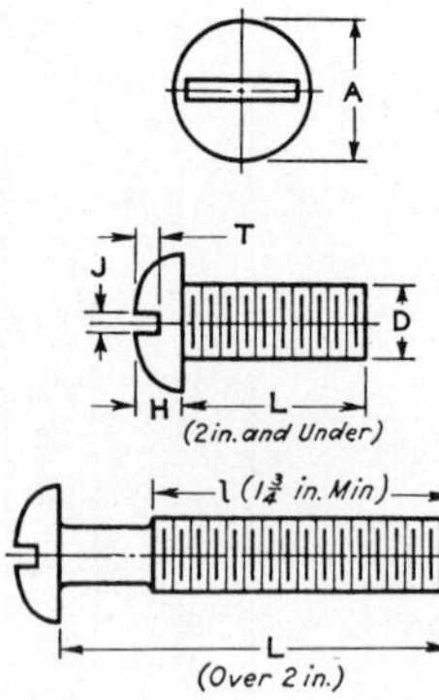

All dimensions are given in inches.

Dimensions of Flat Head Machine Screws

Nominal Size	D: Max Diameter of Screw	A: Head Diameter Max Sharp	A: Head Diameter Min Sharp	A: Absolute Min with Max S	H: Height of Head Max	H: Height of Head Min	J: Width of Slot Max	J: Width of Slot Min	T: Depth of Slot Max	T: Depth of Slot Min
0	0.060	0.119	0.105	0.101	0.035	0.026	0.023	0.016	0.015	0.010
1	0.073	0.146	0.130	0.126	0.043	0.033	0.026	0.019	0.019	0.012
2	0.086	0.172	0.156	0.150	0.051	0.040	0.031	0.023	0.023	0.015
3	0.099	0.199	0.181	0.175	0.059	0.048	0.035	0.027	0.027	0.017
4	0.112	0.225	0.207	0.200	0.067	0.055	0.039	0.031	0.030	0.020
5	0.125	0.252	0.232	0.225	0.075	0.062	0.043	0.035	0.034	0.022
6	0.138	0.279	0.257	0.249	0.083	0.069	0.048	0.039	0.033	0.024
8	0.164	0.332	0.308	0.300	0.100	0.084	0.054	0.045	0.045	0.029
10	0.190	0.385	0.359	0.348	0.116	0.098	0.060	0.050	0.053	0.034
12	0.216	0.438	0.410	0.397	0.132	0.112	0.067	0.056	0.060	0.039
1/4	0.250	0.507	0.477	0.462	0.153	0.131	0.075	0.064	0.070	0.046
5/16	0.3125	0.635	0.600	0.581	0.191	0.165	0.084	0.072	0.088	0.058
3/8	0.375	0.762	0.722	0.700	0.230	0.200	0.094	0.081	0.106	0.070
7/16	0.4375	0.812	0.771	0.743	0.223	0.190	0.094	0.081	0.103	0.066
1/2	0.500	0.875	0.831	0.802	0.223	0.186	0.106	0.091	0.103	0.065
9/16	0.5625	1.000	0.950	0.919	0.260	0.220	0.118	0.102	0.120	0.077
5/8	0.625	1.125	1.069	1.035	0.298	0.253	0.133	0.116	0.137	0.088
3/4	0.750	1.375	1.306	1.267	0.372	0.319	0.149	0.131	0.171	0.111

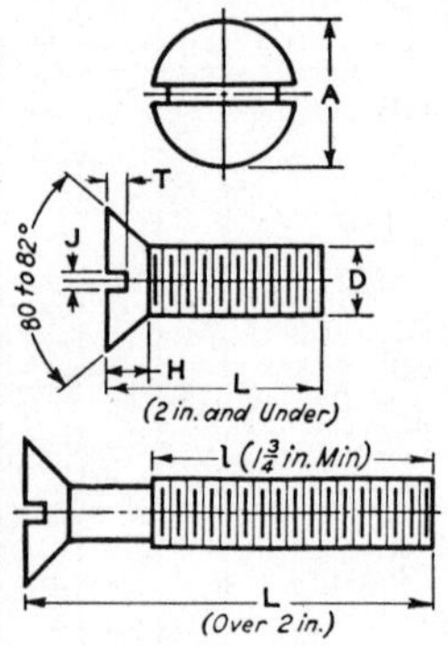

Dimensions of Fillister Head Machine Screws

Nominal Size	D: Max Diameter of Screw	A: Head Diameter Max	A: Head Diameter Min	H: Height of Head Max	H: Height of Head Min	O: Total Height of Head Max	O: Total Height of Head Min	J: Width of Slot Max	J: Width of Slot Min	T: Depth of Slot Max	T: Depth of Slot Min
0	0.060	0.096	0.083	0.045	0.037	0.059	0.043	0.023	0.016	0.025	0.015
1	0.073	0.118	0.104	0.053	0.045	0.071	0.055	0.026	0.019	0.031	0.020
2	0.086	0.140	0.124	0.062	0.053	0.083	0.066	0.031	0.023	0.037	0.025
3	0.099	0.161	0.145	0.070	0.061	0.095	0.077	0.035	0.027	0.043	0.030
4	0.112	0.183	0.166	0.079	0.069	0.107	0.088	0.039	0.031	0.048	0.035
5	0.125	0.205	0.187	0.088	0.078	0.120	0.100	0.043	0.035	0.054	0.040
6	0.138	0.226	0.208	0.096	0.086	0.132	0.111	0.048	0.039	0.060	0.045
8	0.164	0.270	0.250	0.113	0.102	0.156	0.133	0.054	0.045	0.071	0.054
10	0.190	0.313	0.292	0.130	0.118	0.180	0.156	0.060	0.050	0.083	0.064
12	0.216	0.357	0.334	0.148	0.134	0.205	0.178	0.067	0.056	0.094	0.074
1/4	0.250	0.414	0.389	0.170	0.155	0.237	0.207	0.075	0.064	0.109	0.087
5/16	0.3125	0.518	0.490	0.211	0.194	0.295	0.262	0.084	0.072	0.137	0.110
3/8	0.375	0.622	0.590	0.253	0.233	0.355	0.315	0.094	0.081	0.164	0.133
7/16	0.4375	0.625	0.589	0.265	0.242	0.368	0.321	0.094	0.081	0.170	0.135
1/2	0.500	0.750	0.710	0.297	0.273	0.412	0.362	0.106	0.091	0.190	0.151
9/16	0.5625	0.812	0.768	0.336	0.308	0.466	0.410	0.118	0.102	0.214	0.172
5/8	0.625	0.875	0.827	0.375	0.345	0.521	0.461	0.133	0.116	0.240	0.193
3/4	0.750	1.000	0.945	0.441	0.406	0.612	0.542	0.149	0.131	0.281	0.226

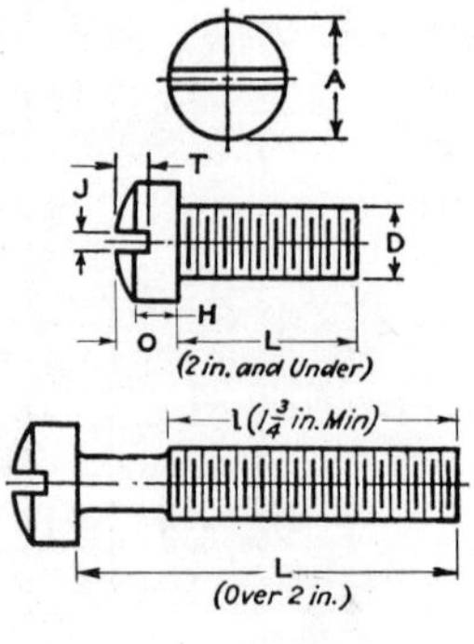

SLOTTED HEAD SCREWS
(For full information see ASA B18.6-1947)

Dimensions of Oval Head Machine Screws

Nominal Size	D	A			H		O		J		T	
	Max Diameter of Screw	Head Diameter			Height of Head		Total Height of Head		Width of Slot		Depth of Slot	
		Max Sharp	Min Sharp	Absolute Min with Max S	Max	Min	Max	Min	Max	Min	Max	Min
0	0.060	0.119	0.105	0.101	0.035	0.026	0.056	0.041	0.023	0.016	0.030	0.025
1	0.073	0.146	0.130	0.126	0.043	0.033	0.068	0.052	0.026	0.019	0.038	0.031
2	0.086	0.172	0.156	0.150	0.051	0.040	0.080	0.063	0.031	0.023	0.045	0.037
3	0.099	0.199	0.181	0.175	0.059	0.048	0.092	0.073	0.035	0.027	0.052	0.043
4	0.112	0.225	0.207	0.200	0.067	0.055	0.104	0.084	0.039	0.031	0.059	0.049
5	0.125	0.252	0.232	0.225	0.075	0.062	0.116	0.095	0.043	0.035	0.067	0.055
6	0.138	0.279	0.257	0.249	0.083	0.069	0.128	0.105	0.048	0.039	0.074	0.060
8	0.164	0.332	0.308	0.300	0.100	0.084	0.152	0.126	0.054	0.045	0.088	0.072
10	0.190	0.385	0.359	0.348	0.116	0.098	0.176	0.148	0.060	0.050	0.103	0.084
12	0.216	0.438	0.410	0.397	0.132	0.112	0.200	0.169	0.067	0.056	0.117	0.096
1/4	0.250	0.507	0.477	0.462	0.153	0.131	0.232	0.197	0.075	0.064	0.136	0.112
5/16	0.3125	0.635	0.600	0.581	0.191	0.165	0.290	0.249	0.084	0.072	0.171	0.141
3/8	0.375	0.762	0.722	0.700	0.230	0.200	0.347	0.300	0.094	0.081	0.206	0.170
7/16	0.4375	0.812	0.771	0.743	0.223	0.190	0.345	0.295	0.094	0.081	0.210	0.174
1/2	0.500	0.875	0.831	0.802	0.223	0.186	0.354	0.299	0.106	0.091	0.216	0.176
9/16	0.5625	1.000	0.950	0.919	0.260	0.220	0.410	0.350	0.118	0.102	0.250	0.207
5/8	0.625	1.125	1.069	1.035	0.298	0.253	0.467	0.399	0.133	0.116	0.285	0.235
3/4	0.750	1.375	1.306	1.267	0.372	0.319	0.578	0.497	0.149	0.131	0.353	0.293

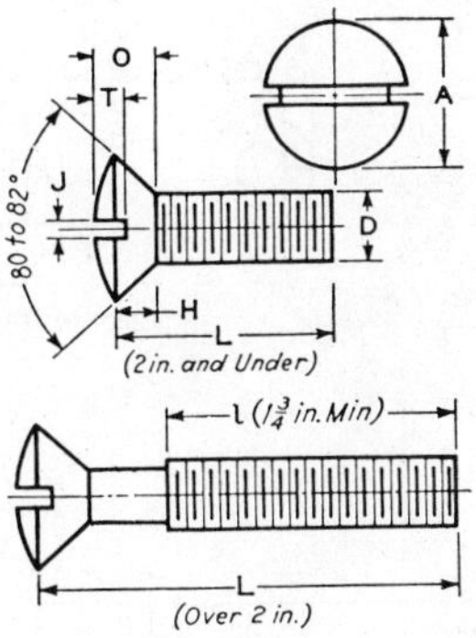

Dimensions of Truss Head Machine Screws

Nominal Size	D	A		H		J		T		R
	Max Diameter of Screw	Head Diameter		Height of Head		Width of Slot		Depth of Slot		Radius
		Max	Min	Max	Min	Max	Min	Max	Min	Max
2	0.086	0.194	0.180	0.053	0.044	0.031	0.023	0.031	0.022	0.129
3	0.099	0.226	0.211	0.061	0.051	0.035	0.027	0.036	0.026	0.151
4	0.112	0.257	0.241	0.069	0.059	0.039	0.031	0.040	0.030	0.169
5	0.125	0.289	0.272	0.078	0.066	0.043	0.035	0.045	0.034	0.191
6	0.138	0.321	0.303	0.086	0.074	0.048	0.039	0.050	0.037	0.211
7	0.151	0.352	0.333	0.094	0.081	0.048	0.039	0.054	0.041	0.231
8	0.164	0.384	0.364	0.102	0.088	0.054	0.045	0.058	0.045	0.254
10	0.190	0.448	0.425	0.118	0.103	0.060	0.050	0.068	0.053	0.283
12	0.216	0.511	0.487	0.134	0.118	0.067	0.056	0.077	0.061	0.336
1/4	0.250	0.573	0.546	0.150	0.133	0.075	0.064	0.087	0.070	0.375
5/16	0.3125	0.698	0.666	0.183	0.162	0.084	0.072	0.106	0.085	0.457
3/8	0.375	0.823	0.787	0.215	0.191	0.094	0.081	0.124	0.100	0.538
7/16	0.4375	0.948	0.907	0.248	0.221	0.094	0.081	0.142	0.116	0.619
1/2	0.500	1.073	1.028	0.280	0.250	0.106	0.091	0.161	0.131	0.701
9/16	0.5625	1.198	1.149	0.312	0.279	0.118	0.102	0.179	0.146	0.783
5/8	0.625	1.323	1.269	0.345	0.309	0.133	0.116	0.196	0.162	0.863
3/4	0.750	1.573	1.511	0.410	0.368	0.149	0.131	0.234	0.182	1.024

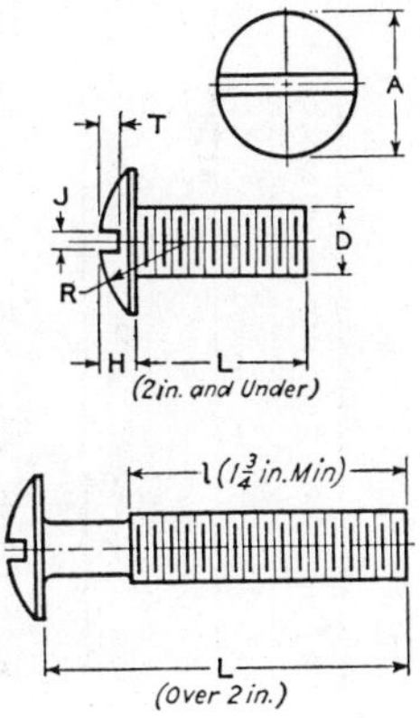

Dimensions of Binding Head Machine Screws

Nominal Size	D	A		O		J		T		F		U		X	
	Max Diameter of Screw	Head Diameter		Total Height of Head		Width of Slot		Depth of Slot		Height of Oval		Diameter of Undercut		Depth of Undercut	
		Max	Min	Max	Min	Max	Min	Max	Min	Max	Min	Max	Min	Max	Min
2	0.086	0.181	0.171	0.046	0.041	0.031	0.023	0.030	0.024	0.018	0.013	0.141	0.124	0.010	0.005
3	0.099	0.208	0.197	0.054	0.048	0.035	0.027	0.036	0.029	0.022	0.016	0.162	0.143	0.011	0.006
4	0.112	0.235	0.223	0.063	0.056	0.039	0.031	0.042	0.034	0.025	0.018	0.184	0.161	0.012	0.007
5	0.125	0.263	0.249	0.071	0.064	0.043	0.035	0.048	0.039	0.029	0.021	0.205	0.180	0.014	0.009
6	0.138	0.290	0.275	0.080	0.071	0.048	0.039	0.053	0.044	0.032	0.024	0.226	0.199	0.015	0.010
8	0.164	0.344	0.326	0.097	0.087	0.054	0.045	0.065	0.054	0.039	0.029	0.269	0.236	0.017	0.012
10	0.190	0.399	0.378	0.114	0.102	0.060	0.050	0.077	0.064	0.045	0.034	0.312	0.274	0.020	0.015
12	0.216	0.454	0.430	0.130	0.117	0.067	0.056	0.089	0.074	0.052	0.039	0.354	0.311	0.023	0.018
1/4	0.250	0.513	0.488	0.153	0.138	0.075	0.064	0.105	0.088	0.061	0.046	0.410	0.360	0.026	0.021
5/16	0.3125	0.641	0.609	0.193	0.174	0.084	0.072	0.134	0.112	0.077	0.059	0.513	0.450	0.032	0.027
3/8	0.375	0.769	0.731	0.234	0.211	0.094	0.081	0.163	0.136	0.094	0.071	0.615	0.540	0.039	0.034

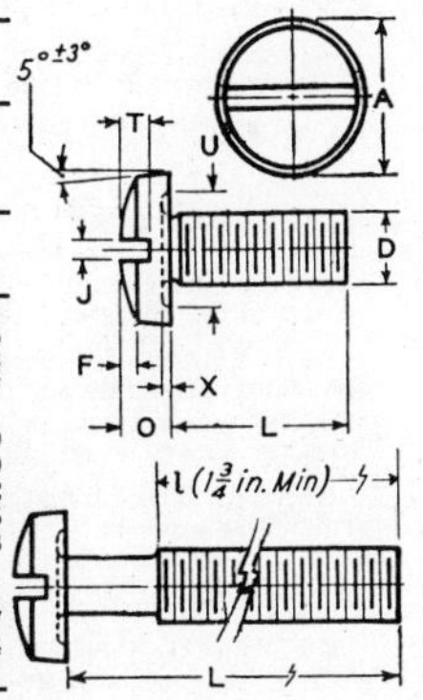

SOCKET SET SCREWS
(For full information see ASA B18.3-1954)

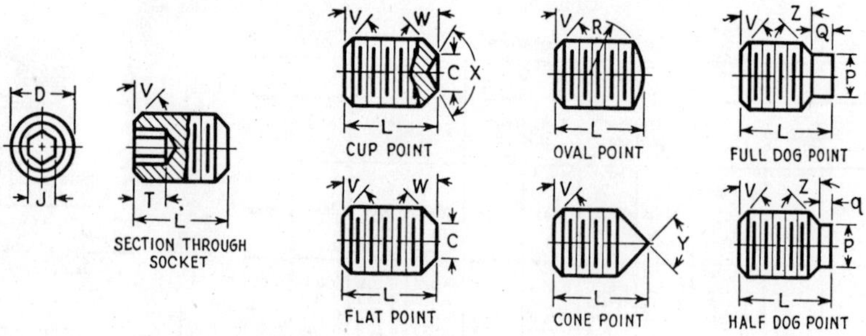

Dimensions of Hexagonal Socket Set Screws

D	C		R	Y		P		Q	q	J		T
Nominal Diameter	Cup and Flat[3] Point Diameter		Oval Point Radius	Cone Point Angle[3]		Full Dog Point and Half Dog Point [1], [2], [3]				Socket Width Across Flats		Key Engagement[4]
				118° ±2° for these Lengths and Under	90° ±2° for these Lengths and Over	Diameter		Full	Half			
	Max	Min				Max	Min			Max	Min	Min
0	0.033	0.027	3/64	1/16	5/64	0.040	0.037	0.030	0.015	0.0285	0.028	0.022
1	0.040	0.033	0.055	5/64	3/32	0.049	0.045	0.037	0.019	0.0355	0.035	0.028
2	0.047	0.039	1/16	3/32	7/64	0.057	0.053	0.043	0.022	0.0355	0.035	0.028
3	0.054	0.045	5/64	7/64	1/8	0.066	0.062	0.050	0.025	0.051	0.050	0.040
4	0.061	0.051	0.084	1/8	5/32	0.075	0.070	0.056	0.028	0.051	0.050	0.040
5	0.067	0.057	3/32	1/8	3/16	0.083	0.078	0.06	0.03	0.0635	1/16	0.050
6	0.074	0.064	7/64	1/8	3/16	0.092	0.087	0.07	0.035	0.0635	1/16	0.050
8	0.087	0.076	1/8	3/16	1/4	0.109	0.103	0.08	0.04	0.0791	5/64	0.062
10	0.102	0.088	9/64	3/16	1/4	0.127	0.120	0.09	0.045	0.0947	3/32	0.075
12	0.115	0.101	5/32	3/16	1/4	0.144	0.137	0.11	0.055	0.0947	3/32	0.075
1/4	0.132	0.118	3/16	1/4	5/16	5/32	0.149	1/8	1/16	0.1270	1/8	0.100
5/16	0.172	0.156	15/64	5/16	3/8	13/64	0.195	5/32	5/64	0.1582	5/32	0.125
3/8	0.212	0.194	9/32	3/8	7/16	1/4	0.241	3/16	3/32	0.1895	3/16	0.150
7/16	0.252	0.232	21/64	7/16	1/2	19/64	0.287	7/32	7/64	0.2207	7/32	0.175
1/2	0.291	0.270	3/8	1/2	9/16	11/32	0.334	1/4	1/8	0.2520	1/4	0.200
9/16	0.332	0.309	27/64	9/16	5/8	25/64	0.379	9/32	9/64	0.2520	1/4	0.200
5/8	0.371	0.347	15/32	5/8	3/4	15/32	0.456	5/16	5/32	0.3155	5/16	0.250
3/4	0.450	0.425	9/16	3/4	7/8	9/16	0.549	3/8	3/16	0.3780	3/8	0.300
7/8	0.530	0.502	21/32	7/8	1	21/32	0.642	7/16	7/32	0.5030	1/2	0.400
1	0.609	0.579	3/4	1	1 1/8	3/4	0.734	1/2	1/4	0.5655	9/16	0.450
1 1/8	0.689	0.655	27/32	1 1/8	1 1/4	27/32	0.826	9/16	9/32	0.5655	9/16	0.450
1 1/4	0.767	0.733	15/16	1 1/4	1 1/2	15/16	0.920	5/8	5/16	0.6290	5/8	0.500
1 3/8	0.848	0.808	1 1/32	1 3/8	1 5/8	1 1/32	1.011	11/16	11/32	0.6290	5/8	0.500
1 1/2	0.926	0.886	1 1/8	1 1/2	1 3/4	1 1/8	1.105	3/4	3/8	0.7540	3/4	0.600
1 3/4	1.086	1.039	1 5/16	1 3/4	2	1 5/16	1.289	7/8	7/16	1.0040	1	0.800
2	1.244	1.193	1 1/2	2	2 1/4	1 1/2	1.474	1	1/2	1.0040	1	0.800

[1]Where usable length of thread is less than nominal diameter, half dog point shall be used.

[2]Allowable eccentricity of dog point axis with respect to the screwaxis shall not exceed 3 per cent of the nominal diameter of the screw and shall in no case exceed 0.005 in.

[3]CHAMFERS AND POINT ANGLES. $W = 45^\circ + 5^\circ, -0^\circ$; $X = 118^\circ \pm 5^\circ$; Y = (see Table 4); $Z = 35^\circ + 5^\circ, -0^\circ$.

[4]These dimensions apply to cup and flat point screws one diameter in length or longer. For screws shorter than one diameter in length, and for other types of points, socket to be as deep as practicable.

SOCKET END CHAMFER (V). Socket end of screw shall be flat and chamfered. The flat shall be normal to the axis of the screw and the chamfer (V) shall be at an angle of $35^\circ + 5^\circ, -0^\circ$ with the surface of the flat. The chamfer shall extend to the bottom of the thread and the edge between flat and chamfer shall be slightly rounded.

LENGTH (L). The length of the screw shall be measured overall on a line parallel to the axis. The difference between consecutive lengths shall be as follows:
(a) for screw lengths 1/8 to 5/8 in. difference = 1/16 in.
(b) for screw lengths 5/8 to 1 in. difference = 1/8 in.
(c) for screw lengths 1 to 4 in. difference = 1/4 in.
(d) for screw lengths 4 to 6 in. difference = 1/2 in.

LENGTH TOLERANCE. Allowable tolerance on length (L) shall be 3 per cent on lengths 2 in. and under with a minimum of 0.020 in., one-half to be applied plus and one-half minus; on lengths over 2 in. to 6 in. plus or minus 1/32 in.; on lengths over 6 in. plus or minus 1/16 in.

THREADS shall be Class 3 A.

MATERIAL. Steel, high-grade alloy, hardened by quenching in oil from the hardening temperature, and tempered to a Rockwell "C" hardness of 45-53.

SOCKET HEAD CAP SCREWS
(For full information see ASA B18.3-1954)

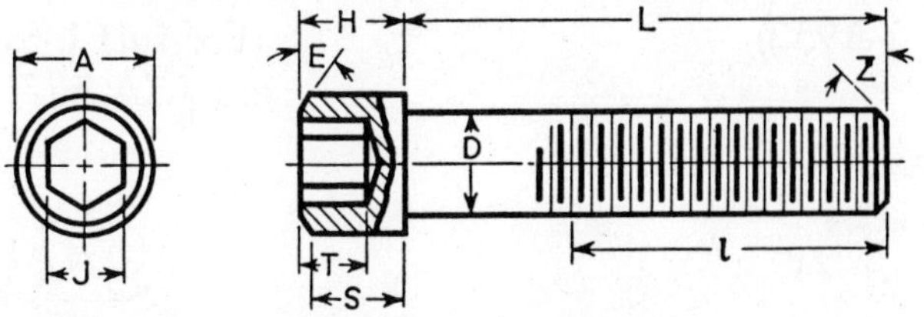

Dimensions of Hexagonal Socket Head Cap Screws

D			A		H		S			J		T
Body Diameter[1]			Head Diameter[2]		Head Height[3]		Head Side-Height[3]			Socket Width Across Flats		Key Engagement
Nom	Max	Min	Max	Min	Max	Min	Nom	Max	Min	Max	Min	Min
0	0.060	0.0583	0.0960	0.0926	0.0600	0.0574	0.055	0.056	0.054	0.051	0.050	0.025
1	0.0730	0.0711	0.1180	0.1142	0.0730	0.0702	0.067	0.068	0.066	0.051	0.050	0.031
2	0.0860	0.0840	0.140	0.136	0.086	0.083	0.079	0.081	0.078	0.0635	1/16	0.038
3	0.0990	0.0968	0.161	0.157	0.099	0.096	0.091	0.093	0.089	0.0791	5/64	0.044
4	0.1120	0.1096	0.183	0.178	0.112	0.109	0.103	0.105	0.101	0.0791	5/64	0.051
5	0.1250	0.1226	0.205	0.200	0.125	0.122	0.115	0.117	0.113	0.0947	3/32	0.057
6	0.1380	0.1353	0.226	0.221	0.138	0.134	0.127	0.129	0.125	0.0947	3/32	0.064
8	0.1640	0.1613	0.270	0.265	0.164	0.160	0.150	0.152	0.148	0.1270	1/8	0.077
10	0.1900	0.1867	5/16	0.306	0.190	0.185	0.174	0.176	0.172	0.1582	5/32	0.090
12	0.2160	0.2127	11/32	0.337	0.216	0.211	0.198	0.200	0.196	0.1582	5/32	0.103
1/4	0.2500	0.2464	3/8	0.367	1/4	0.244	0.229	0.232	0.226	0.1895	3/16	0.120
5/16	0.3125	0.3084	7/16	0.429	5/16	0.306	0.286	0.289	0.283	0.2207	7/32	0.151
3/8	0.3750	0.3705	9/16	0.553	3/8	0.368	0.344	0.347	0.341	0.3155	5/16	0.182
7/16	0.4375	0.4326	5/8	0.615	7/16	0.430	0.401	0.405	0.397	0.3155	5/16	0.213
1/2	0.5000	0.4948	3/4	0.739	1/2	0.492	0.458	0.462	0.454	0.3780	3/8	0.245
9/16	0.5625	0.5569	13/16	0.801	9/16	0.554	0.516	0.520	0.512	0.3780	3/8	0.276
5/8	0.6250	0.6191	7/8	0.863	5/8	0.616	0.573	0.577	0.569	0.5030	1/2	0.307
3/4	0.7500	0.7436	1	0.987	3/4	0.741	0.688	0.693	0.684	0.5655	9/16	0.370
7/8	0.8750	0.8680	1 1/8	1.111	7/8	0.865	0.802	0.807	0.797	0.5655	9/16	0.432
1	1.0000	0.9924	1 5/16	1.297	1	0.989	0.917	0.922	0.912	0.6290	5/8	0.495
1 1/8	1.1250	1.1165	1 1/2	1.483	1 1/8	1.113	1.031	1.037	1.025	0.7540	3/4	0.557
1 1/4	1.2500	1.2415	1 3/4	1.733	1 1/4	1.238	1.146	1.152	1.140	0.7540	3/4	0.620
1 3/8	1.3750	1.3649	1 7/8	1.855	1 3/8	1.361	1.260	1.267	1.253	0.7540	3/4	0.682
1 1/2	1.5000	1.4899	2	1.979	1 1/2	1.485	1.375	1.382	1.368	1.0040	1	0.745

[1]BODY DIAMETER (D) refers to the unthreaded portion of the screw and the maximum diameter conforms to the basic diameter or size of the screw.

[2]CONCENTRICITY of head, body and thread shall be such as to permit acceptance when checked with a compound go gage which will gage the maximum diameters of these parts simultaneously. This gage shall have the head and body diameters at their maximum values (see Columns D and A, Table 1) but expressed to four decimal places and the pitch diameter at the maximum value allowed for Class 3A American Standard Screw Threads. (B1.1)

[3]HEAD CHAMFER (E). The head shall be flat and chamfered. The flat shall be normal to the axis of the screw and the chamfer (E) shall be at an angle of $30^\circ \pm 2^\circ$ with the surface of the flat. The edge between flat and chamfer shall be slightly rounded.

LENGTH UNDER HEAD (L). The length of the screw shall be measured, on a line parallel to the axis, from the plane of the bearing surface under the head to the plane of the point. The difference between consecutive lengths shall be as follows:

(a) for screw lengths 1/8 to 1 in. shall be 1/8 in.
(b) for screw lengths 1 to 3 1/2 in. shall be 1/4 in.
(c) for screw lengths 3 1/2 to 6 in. shall be 1/2 in.

LENGTH TOLERANCE. The allowable tolerance on the length (L) under the head on lengths 2 inches and under shall be 3 per cent of the nominal length with a minimum of 0.030 in., two-third to be applied plus and one-third minus. On lengths over 2 in. to 6 in. plus or minus 1/32 in. and on lengths over 6 in. plus or minus 1/16 in.

THREAD LENGTH (l). The length of the screw thread is measured from the extreme point to the last completethread and shall be as follows:

for National Coarse:
- $l = 2D + \frac{1}{2}$ in. (where this length of thread would be greater than half the screw length)
- $l = \frac{1}{2} L$ (where this length of thread would be greater than $2D + \frac{1}{2}$ in.)

for National Fine:
- $l = 1\frac{1}{2}D + \frac{1}{2}$ in. (where this length of thread would be greater than three-eighths the screw length)
- $l = \frac{3}{8} L$ (where this length of thread would be greater than $1\frac{1}{2}D + \frac{1}{2}$ in.)

Screws too short to allow application of these formulas shall be threaded as close to the head as practicable.

SCREW POINT CHAMFER (Z). The point shall be flat and chamfered. The flat shall be normal to the axis of the screw and the chamfer (Z) shall be at an angle of $35^\circ + 5^\circ - 0^\circ$ with the plane of the flat. The chamfer shall extend to the bottom of the thread and the edge between flat and chamfer shall be slightly rounded.

MATERIAL. Steel, high-grade alloy, hardened by quenching in oil from the hardening temperature, and tempered to a Rockwell "C" hardness of 36-43.

THREADS. Threads shall be Class 3 A.

PLAIN WASHERS
(For full information see ASA B27.2-1953)

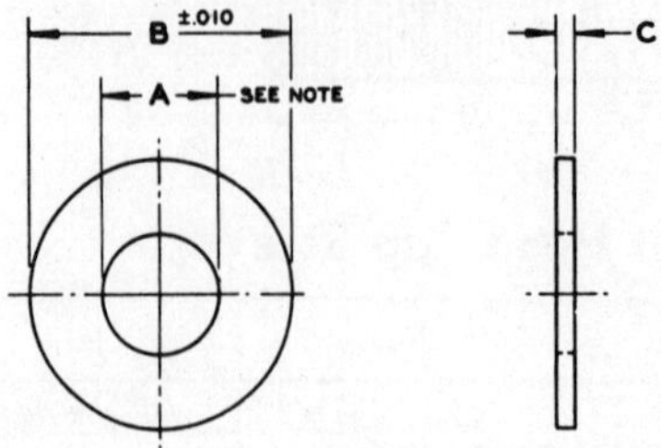

Inside Diameter	Outside Diameter	Thickness, C
A	B	Nom
5/64	3/16	0.020
3/32	7/32	0.020
3/32	1/4	0.020
1/8	1/4	0.022
1/8	5/16	0.032
5/32	5/16	0.035
5/32	3/8	0.049
11/64	13/32	0.049
3/16	3/8	0.049
3/16	7/16	0.049
13/64	15/32	0.049
7/32	7/16	0.049
7/32	1/2	0.049
15/64	17/32	0.049
1/4	1/2	0.049
1/4*	9/16	0.049
1/4*	9/16	0.065
17/64	5/8	0.049
9/32	5/8	0.065
5/16	3/4	0.065
5/16	7/8	0.065
11/32	11/16	0.065
3/8	3/4	0.065
3/8	7/8	0.083
3/8	1 1/8	0.065
13/32	13/16	0.065
7/16	7/8	0.083
7/16	1	0.083
7/16	1 3/8	0.083
15/32	59/64	0.065
1/2	1 1/8	0.083
1/2	1 1/4	0.083
1/2	1 5/8	0.083
17/32	1 1/16	0.095
9/16	1 1/4	0.109
9/16	1 3/8	0.109
9/16	1 7/8	0.109
19/32	1 3/16	0.095
5/8	1 3/8	0.109

Inside Diameter	Outside Diameter	Thickness, C
A	B	Nom
5/8	1 1/2	0.109
5/8	2 1/8	0.134
21/32	1 5/16	0.095
11/16	1 1/2	0.134
11/16	1 3/4	0.134
11/16	2 3/8	0.165
13/16	1 1/2	0.134
13/16	1 3/4	0.148
13/16	2	0.148
13/16	2 7/8	0.165
15/16	1 3/4	0.134
15/16	2	0.165
15/16	2 1/4	0.165
15/16	3 3/8	0.180
1 1/16	2	0.134
1 1/16	2 1/4	0.165
1 1/16	2 1/2	0.165
1 1/16	3 7/8	0.238
1 3/16	2 1/2	0.165
1 1/4	2 3/4	0.165
1 5/16	2 3/4	0.165
1 3/8	3	0.165
1 7/16	3	0.180
1 1/2	3 1/4	0.180
1 9/16	3 1/4	0.180
1 5/8	3 1/2	0.180
1 11/16	3 1/2	0.180
1 3/4	3 3/4	0.180
1 13/16	3 3/4	0.180
1 7/8	4	0.180
1 15/16	4	0.180
2	4 1/4	0.180

NOTE: Tolerance ±0.005 on inside diameter to and including 7/32 inside diameter; ±0.010 on inside diameter greater than 7/32 with exception of two 1/4 × 9/16 sizes marked with an asterisk on which two sizes the tolerance is ±0.005.

MEDIUM SPRING LOCK WASHERS
(For full information see ASA B27.1-1950)

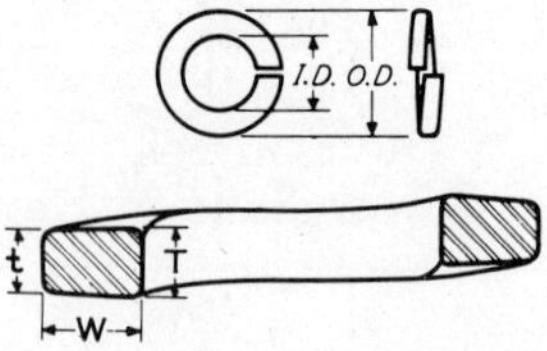

Nominal Size	Inside Diameter Min	Washer Sections (Min) Width w	Thickness (T+t)/2	Outside Diam Max*
0.086 (No. 2)	0.088	0.035	0.020	0.175
0.099 (No. 3)	0.102	0.040	0.025	0.198
0.112 (No. 4)	0.115	0.040	0.025	0.212
0.125 (No. 5)	0.128	0.047	0.031	0.239
0.138 (No. 6)	0.141	0.047	0.031	0.253
0.164 (No. 8)	0.168	0.055	0.040	0.296
0.190 (No. 10)	0.194	0.062	0.047	0.337
0.216 (No. 12)	0.221	0.070	0.056	0.380
1/4	0.255	0.109	0.062	0.493
5/16	0.319	0.125	0.078	0.591
3/8	0.382	0.141	0.094	0.688
7/16	0.446	0.156	0.109	0.784
1/2	0.509	0.171	0.125	0.879
9/16	0.573	0.188	0.141	0.979
5/8	0.636	0.203	0.156	1.086
11/16	0.700	0.219	0.172	1.184
3/4	0.763	0.234	0.188	1.279
13/16	0.827	0.250	0.203	1.377
7/8	0.890	0.266	0.219	1.474
15/16	0.954	0.281	0.234	1.570
1	1.017	0.297	0.250	1.672
1 1/16	1.081	0.312	0.266	1.768
1 1/8	1.144	0.328	0.281	1.865
1 3/16	1.208	0.344	0.297	1.963
1 1/4	1.271	0.359	0.312	2.058
1 5/16	1.335	0.375	0.328	2.156
1 3/8	1.398	0.391	0.344	2.253
1 7/16	1.462	0.406	0.359	2.349
1 1/2	1.525	0.422	0.375	2.446

All dimensions are given in inches.

*The maximum outside diameters specified allow for the commercial tolerances on cold drawn wire and hot rolled rod.

SQUARE AND FLAT STOCK KEY SIZES

Shaft Diameter	Sq. Key Sizes	Flat Key Sizes
1/2 - 9/16	1/8	1/8 x 3/32
5/8 - 7/8	3/16	3/16 x 1/8
15/16 - 1 1/4	1/4	1/4 x 3/16
1 5/16 - 1 3/8	5/16	5/16 x 1/4
1 7/16 - 1 3/4	3/8	3/8 x 1/4
1 13/16 - 2 1/4	1/2	1/2 x 3/8
2 5/16 - 2 3/4	5/8	5/8 x 7/16
2 7/8 - 3 1/4	3/4	3/4 x 1/2

WOODRUFF KEY SIZES

Shaft Diameter	Key Numbers	Shaft Diameter	Key Numbers
5/16 - 3/8	204	1 1/16 - 1 1/8	606, 607, 608, 609
7/16 - 1/2	304, 305	1 3/16	607, 608, 609
9/16 - 5/8	404, 405	1 1/4 - 1 5/16	607, 608, 609, 810
11/16 - 3/4	404, 405, 406	1 3/8 - 1 7/16	608, 609, 810
13/16	505, 506	1 1/2 - 1 5/8	808, 809, 810, 812
7/8 - 15/16	505, 506, 507	1 11/16 - 1 3/4	809, 810, 812
1	606, 607, 608	1 13/16 - 2	1011, 1012

TAPER PIN DIMENSIONS
(Taper 1/4 inch per foot)

No. of Taper Pin	Diameter Large End D+	Approximate Size D D	Range in Lengths L	Shaft Diameter *	Drill Size Before Reamer
6/0	0.078	5/64	3/8-3/4	7/32	No. 53
5/0	0.094	3/32	1/2-1	1/4	No. 47
4/0	0.109	7/64	1/2-1	5/16	No. 42
3/0	0.125	1/8	1/2-1	3/8	No. 37
2/0	0.141	9/64	1/2-1 1/4	7/16	No. 31
0	0.156	5/32	1/2-1 1/4	1/2	No. 28
1	0.172	11/64	5/8-1 1/4	9/16	No. 25
2	0.193	3/16	3/4-1 1/2	5/8	No. 19
3	0.219	7/32	3/4-1 3/4	3/4	No. 12
4	0.250	1/4	3/4-2	13/16	No. 3
5	0.289	19/64	1-2 1/4	7/8	1/4
6	0.341	11/32	1 1/4-3	1	9/32
7	0.409	13/32	2-3 3/4	1 1/4	11/32
8	0.492	1/2	2-4 1/2	1 1/2	13/32

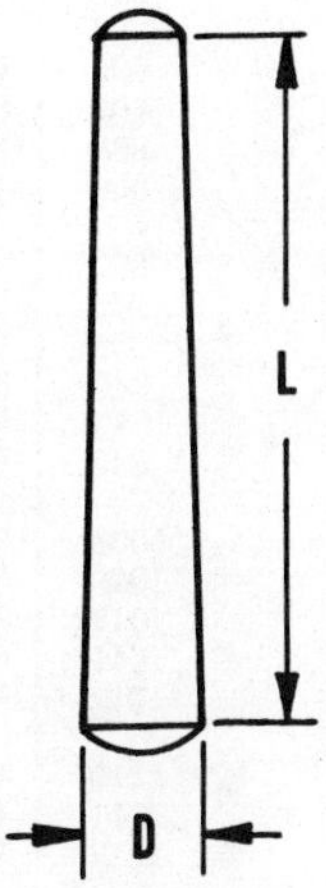

*Suggested sizes—Not Standard

+ To find diameter at small end of pin, multiply length L by 0.0208 and subtract product from large end diameter D.

WOODRUFF KEYS, KEYSLOTS
(For full information see ASA B17f-1955)

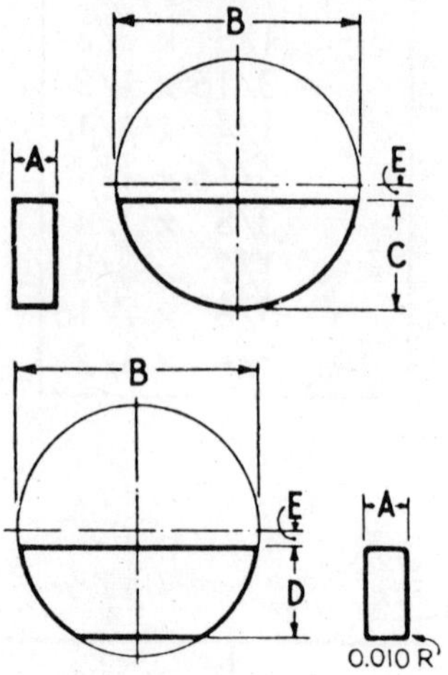

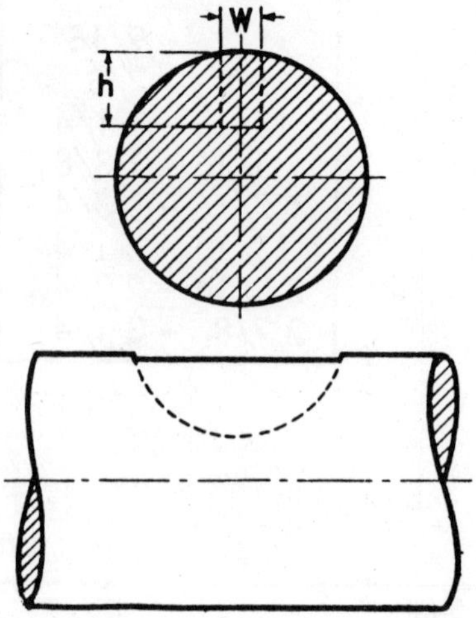

Key[1] Number	Nominal Key Size A × B	Height of Key C Max.	Height of Key D Max.	Distance Below Center E
204	1/16 × 1/2	0.203	0.194	3/64
304	3/32 × 1/2	.203	.194	3/64
305	3/32 × 5/8	.250	.240	1/16
404	1/8 × 1/2	.203	.194	3/64
405	1/8 × 5/8	.250	.240	1/16
406	1/8 × 3/4	.313	.303	1/16
505	5/32 × 5/8	.250	.240	1/16
506	5/32 × 3/4	.313	.303	1/16
507	5/32 × 7/8	.375	.365	1/16
606	3/16 × 3/4	.313	.303	1/16
607	3/16 × 7/8	.375	.365	1/16
608	3/16 × 1	.438	.428	1/16
609	3/16 × 1 1/8	.484	.475	5/64
807	1/4 × 7/8	.375	.365	1/16
808	1/4 × 1	.438	.428	1/16
809	1/4 × 1 1/8	.484	.475	5/64
810	1/4 × 1 1/4	.547	.537	5/64
811	1/4 × 1 3/8	.594	.584	3/32
812	1/4 × 1 1/2	.641	.631	7/64
1008	5/16 × 1	.438	.428	1/16
1009	5/16 × 1 1/8	.484	.475	5/64
1010	5/16 × 1 1/4	.547	.537	5/64
1011	5/16 × 1 3/8	.594	.584	3/32
1012	5/16 × 1 1/2	.641	.631	7/64
1210	3/8 × 1 1/4	.547	.537	5/64
1211	3/8 × 1 3/8	.594	.584	3/32
1212	3/8 × 1 1/2	.641	.631	7/64

All dimensions given in inches.

Key[1] Number	Nominal Key Size A × B	Keyslot Width W	Keyslot Depth h Max.
204	1/16 × 1/2	0.0630	0.1718
304	3/32 × 1/2	0.0943	0.1561
305	3/32 × 5/8	0.0943	0.2031
404	1/8 × 1/2	0.1255	0.1405
405	1/8 × 5/8	0.1255	0.1875
406	1/8 × 3/4	0.1255	0.2505
505	5/32 × 5/8	0.1568	0.1719
506	5/32 × 3/4	0.1568	0.2349
507	5/32 × 7/8	0.1568	0.2969
606	3/16 × 3/4	0.1880	0.2193
607	3/16 × 7/8	0.1880	0.2813
608	3/16 × 1	0.1880	0.3443
609	3/16 × 1 1/8	0.1880	0.3903
807	1/4 × 7/8	0.2505	0.2500
808	1/4 × 1	0.2505	0.3130
809	1/4 × 1 1/8	0.2505	0.3590
810	1/4 × 1 1/4	0.2505	0.4220
811	1/4 × 1 3/8	0.2505	0.4690
812	1/4 × 1 1/2	0.2505	0.5160
1008	5/16 × 1	0.3130	0.2818
1009	5/16 × 1 1/8	0.3130	0.3278
1010	5/16 × 1 1/4	0.3130	0.3908
1011	5/16 × 1 3/8	0.3130	0.4378
1012	5/16 × 1 1/2	0.3130	0.4848
1210	3/8 × 1 1/4	0.3755	0.3595
1211	3/8 × 1 3/8	0.3755	0.4065
1212	3/8 × 1 1/2	0.3755	0.4535

All dimensions given in inches.

LARGE RIVETS (MANUFACTURED SHAPES)
(For full information see ASA B18.4-1960)

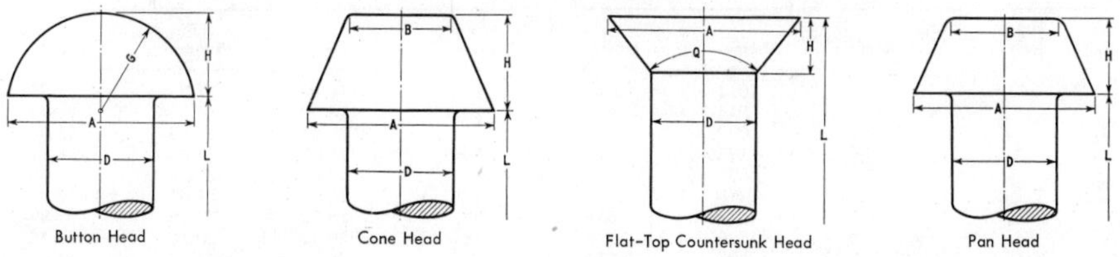

Button Head

Diameter of Body D		Diameter of Head A	Height of Head H	Radius of Head G
Nominal	Max	Max	Max	
1/2	0.520	0.938	0.406	0.443
5/8	0.655	1.157	0.500	0.553
3/4	0.780	1.390	0.593	0.664
7/8	0.905	1.609	0.687	0.775
1	1.030	1.828	0.781	0.885

Cone Head

Diameter of Body D		Major Diameter of Head A	Minor Diameter of Head B	Height of Head H
Nominal	Max	Max	Max	Max
1/2	0.520	0.938	0.532	0.469
5/8	0.655	1.157	0.649	0.578
3/4	0.780	1.390	0.781	0.687
7/8	0.905	1.609	0.898	0.797
1	1.030	1.828	1.016	0.906

Flat-Top Countersunk Head

Diameter of Body D		Diameter of Head A	Depth of Head H	Included Angle of Head Q Deg
Nominal	Max	Max	Max	
1/2	0.520	0.936	0.281	78
5/8	0.655	1.194	0.343	78
3/4	0.780	1.421	0.406	78
7/8	0.905	1.647	0.469	78
1	1.030	1.873	0.531	78

Pan Head

Diameter of Body D		Major Diameter of Head A	Minor Diameter of Head B	Height of Head H
Nominal	Max	Max	Max	Max
1/2	0.520	0.863	0.563	0.381
5/8	0.655	1.063	0.688	0.469
3/4	0.780	1.278	0.828	0.556
7/8	0.905	1.478	0.953	0.643
1	1.030	1.678	1.078	0.731

All dimensions given in inches.

CAST STEEL WEIGHT COMPUTATIONS

Weight in Pounds of a Lineal Foot of Round, Square, and Octagon Steel

Size in Inches	Round	Octagon	Square	Size in Inches	Round	Octagon	Square
1/16	.010	.011	.013	2 1/2	16.69	17.65	21.25
1/8	.042	.044	.053	2 5/8	18.40	19.45	23.43
3/16	.094	.099	.120	2 3/4	20.20	21.28	25.00
1/4	.167	.177	.212	2 7/8	22.07	23.28	28.10
5/16	.261	.277	.333	3	24.03	25.36	30.60
3/8	.376	.398	.478	3 1/8	26.08	27.50	33.20
7/16	.511	.542	.651	3 1/4	28.20	29.28	35.92
1/2	.668	.708	.850	3 3/8	30.42	32.10	38.73
9/16	.845	.896	1.076	3 1/2	32.71	34.56	41.65
5/8	1.043	1.107	1.328	3 5/8	35.09	37.05	44.68
11/16	1.270	1.331	1.608	3 3/4	37.56	39.69	47.82
3/4	1.502	1.584	1.913	3 7/8	40.10	42.35	51.05
13/16	1.763	1.860	2.245	4	42.73	45.07	54.40
7/8	2.044	2.156	2.603	4 1/4	48.24	50.78	61.41
15/16	2.347	2.482	2.989	4 1/2	54.07	57.04	68.85
1	2.670	2.817	3.400	4 3/4	60.25	63.55	76.71
1 1/8	3.379	3.568	4.303	5	66.76	70.42	85.00
1 1/4	4.173	4.407	5.312	5 1/4	73.60	77.63	93.72
1 3/8	5.040	5.331	6.428	5 1/2	80.77	85.21	102.80
1 1/2	6.008	6.344	7.650	5 3/4	88.29	93.13	112.40
1 5/8	7.051	7.446	8.978	6	96.14	101.40	122.40
1 3/4	8.178	8.635	10.410	7	130.90	138.10	166.60
1 7/8	9.388	9.918	11.950	8	171.00	180.30	217.60
2	10.680	11.280	13.660	9	216.30	228.01	275.40
2 1/8	12.060	12.710	15.350	10	267.00	281.60	340.00
2 1/4	13.520	14.240	17.220	11	323.10	340.80	411.40
2 3/8	15.070	15.880	19.180	12	386.79	405.60	492.48

STANDARD SHEET GAUGES and WEIGHTS

Ga. No.	Carbon Sheets (To USS or Mfrs. ga.) Thickness in Inches	Carbon Sheets Weight per sq. Ft. in Lbs.	Galv. Sheets (To galv. sht. ga.) Weight per Sq. Ft. in Lbs.	Stainless Sheets (To Stainless Sheet Gauge) Thickness in Inches	Wt. per Sq. Ft. in Lbs. Straight Chrome	Wt. per Sq. Ft. in Lbs. Chrome Nickel
	1/4", & over are plates					
7	.1793	7.500	....	....	....	....
8	.1644	6.875	....	....	....	....
9	.1494	6.250	....	....	....	....
10	.1345	5.625	5.7812	.140625	5.7937	5.9062
11	.1196	5.000	5.1562	.125000	5.1500	5.2500
12	.1046	4.375	4.5312	.109375	4.5063	4.5937
13	.0897	3.750	3.9062	.093750	3.8625	3.9375
14	.0747	3.125	3.2812	.078125	3.2187	3.2812
15	.0673	2.812	2.9687	.070312	2.8968	2.9531
16	.0598	2.500	2.6562	.062500	2.5750	2.6250
17	.0538	2.250	2.4062	.056250	2.3175	2.3625
18	.0478	2.000	2.1562	.050000	2.0600	2.1000
19	.0418	1.750	1.9062	.043750	1.8025	1.8375
20	.0359	1.500	1.6562	.037500	1.5450	1.5750
21	.0329	1.375	1.5312	.034375	1.4160	1.4437
22	.0299	1.250	1.4062	.031250	1.2875	1.3125
23	.0269	1.125	1.2812	.028125	1.1587	1.1813
24	.0239	1.000	1.1562	.025000	1.0300	1.0500
25	.0209	.875	1.0312	.021875	.9013	.9187
26	.0179	.750	.9062	.018750	.7725	.7875
27	.0164	.6875	.8437	.017187	.7081	.7218
28	.0149	.625	.7812	.015625	.6438	.6562
29	.0135	.5625	.7187	.014062	.5794	.5906
30	.0120	.500	.6562	.012500	.5150	.5250

STRUCTURAL RIVETS

Length of Rivets Required for Various Grips Including Amount Necessary to Form One Head

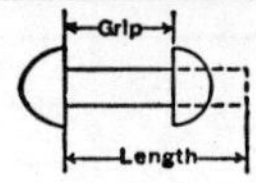

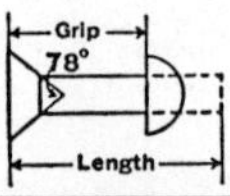

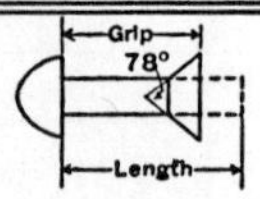

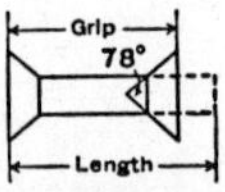

Grip in Inches	1/2"	5/8"	3/4"	7/8"	1"	1 1/8"	1 1/4"	1/2"	5/8"	3/4"	7/8"	1"	1 1/8"	1 1/4"
	Diameter of Rivet — Length of Rivet							Diameter of Rivet — Length of Rivet						
1/2	1 5/8	1 7/8	1 7/8	2	2 1/8	...	..	1	1	1 1/8	1 1/4	1 1/4		
5/8	1 3/4	2	2	2 1/8	2 1/4	...	...	1 1/8	1 1/4	1 1/4	1 3/8	1 3/8	.	..
3/4	1 7/8	2 1/8	2 1/8	2 1/4	2 3/8	...	...	1 3/8	1 3/8	1 3/8	1 1/2	1 1/2	.	
7/8	2	2 1/4	2 1/4	2 3/8	2 1/2	...	...	1 1/2	1 1/2	1 1/2	1 5/8	1 5/8	...	...
1	2 1/4	2 3/8	2 3/8	2 1/2	2 5/8	2 3/4	2 7/8	1 5/8	1 5/8	1 5/8	1 3/4	1 3/4	1 7/8	1 7/8
1 1/8	2 3/8	2 1/2	2 1/2	2 5/8	2 3/4	2 7/8	3	1 3/4	1 3/4	1 7/8	1 7/8	1 7/8	2	2
1 1/4	2 1/2	2 5/8	2 5/8	2 3/4	2 7/8	3	3 1/8	2	2	2	2	2	2 1/8	2 1/8
1 3/8	2 5/8	2 3/4	2 3/4	2 7/8	3	3 1/8	3 1/4	2 1/8	2 1/8	2 1/8	2 1/4	2 1/4	2 3/8	2 3/8
1 1/2	2 7/8	3	3	3 1/8	3 1/4	3 3/8	3 1/2	2 1/4	2 1/4	2 1/4	2 3/8	2 3/8	2 1/2	2 1/2
1 5/8	3	3 1/8	3 1/8	3 1/4	3 3/8	3 1/2	3 5/8	2 3/8	2 3/8	2 3/8	2 1/2	2 1/2	2 5/8	2 5/8
1 3/4	3 1/8	3 1/4	3 1/4	3 1/2	3 1/2	3 3/4	3 7/8	2 5/8	2 5/8	2 5/8	2 5/8	2 5/8	2 3/4	2 3/4
1 7/8	3 1/4	3 3/8	3 3/8	3 5/8	3 5/8	3 7/8	4	2 3/4	2 3/4	2 3/4	2 3/4	2 3/4	2 7/8	2 7/8
2	3 1/2	3 1/2	3 5/8	3 3/4	3 3/4	4	4 1/8	2 7/8	2 7/8	2 7/8	2 7/8	2 7/8	3	3
2 1/8	3 5/8	3 5/8	3 3/4	3 7/8	3 7/8	4 1/8	4 1/4	3 1/8	3	3	3	3	3 1/8	3 1/8
2 1/4	3 3/4	3 7/8	3 7/8	4	4 1/8	4 1/4	4 3/8	3 1/4	3 1/8	3 1/8	3 1/8	3 1/4	3 1/4	3 1/4
2 3/8	4	4	4	4 1/8	4 1/4	4 3/8	4 1/2	3 3/8	3 3/8	3 3/8	3 3/8	3 3/8	3 3/8	3 3/8
2 1/2	4 1/8	4 1/8	4 1/8	4 1/4	4 3/8	4 1/2	4 5/8	3 1/2	3 1/2	3 1/2	3 1/2	3 1/2	3 5/8	3 5/8
2 5/8	4 1/4	4 1/4	4 1/4	4 3/8	4 1/2	4 5/8	4 3/4	3 3/4	3 5/8	3 5/8	3 5/8	3 5/8	3 3/4	3 3/4
2 3/4	4 3/8	4 3/8	4 3/8	4 1/2	4 5/8	4 3/4	4 7/8	3 7/8	3 3/4	3 3/4	3 3/4	3 3/4	3 7/8	3 7/8
2 7/8	4 5/8	4 5/8	4 5/8	4 5/8	4 3/4	4 7/8	5	4	3 7/8	3 7/8	3 7/8	3 7/8	4	4

STEEL WIRE GAUGES and DECIMAL EQUIVALENTS

Ga. No.	Birmingham Wire Gauge or Stubs Ga. Thickness, In.	Birmingham Wire Gauge or Stubs Ga. Wt. per Sq. Ft.	Brown & Sharpe or American Wire	Steel Wire Gauge (Washburn & Moen)	Ga. No.	Birmingham Wire Gauge or Stubs Ga. Thickness, In.	Birmingham Wire Gauge or Stubs Ga. Wt. per Sq. Ft.	Brown & Sharpe or American Wire	Steel Wire Gauge (Washburn & Moen)
3	.259	10.567	.2294	.2437	17	.058	2.366	.0453	.0540
4	.238	9.710	.2043	.2253	18	.049	1.999	.0403	.0475
5	.220	8.976	.1819	.2070	19	.042	1.714	.0359	.0410
6	.203	8.282	.1620	.1920	20	.035	1.428	.0320	.0348
7	.180	7.344	.1443	.1770	21	.032	1.306	.0285	.0317
8	.165	6.732	.1285	.1620	22	.028	1.142	.0253	.0286
9	.148	6.038	.1144	.1483	23	.025	1.020	.0226	.0258
10	.134	5.467	.1019	.1350	24	.022	.898	.0201	.0230
11	.120	4.896	.0907	.1205	25	.020	.816	.0179	.0204
12	.109	4.447	.0808	.1055	26	.018	.734	.0159	.0181
13	.095	3.876	.0720	.0915	27	.016	.653	.0142	.0173
14	.083	3.386	.0641	.0800	28	.014	.571	.0126	.0162
15	.072	2.938	.0571	.0720	29	.013	.530	.0113	.0150
16	.065	2.652	.0508	.0625	30	.012	.490	.0100	.0140

DRILL JIG BUSHINGS
(For full information see ASA B5.6–1949)

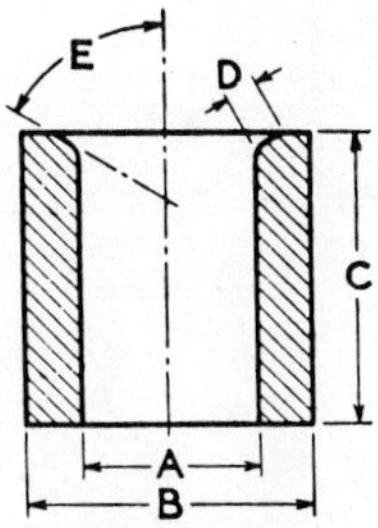

PRESS FIT, HEADLESS WEARING BUSHING

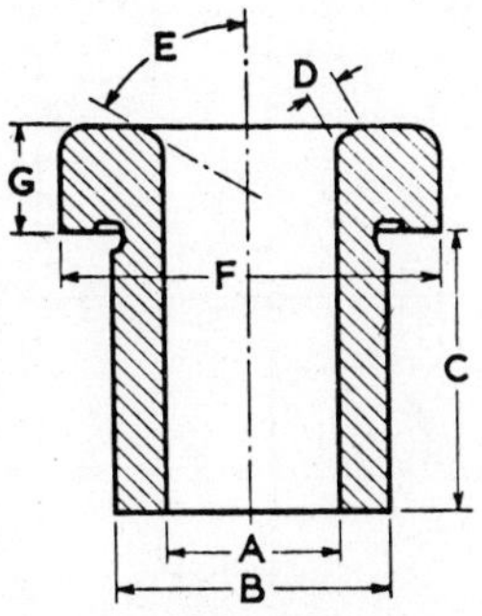

PRESS FIT, HEAD TYPE WEARING BUSHING

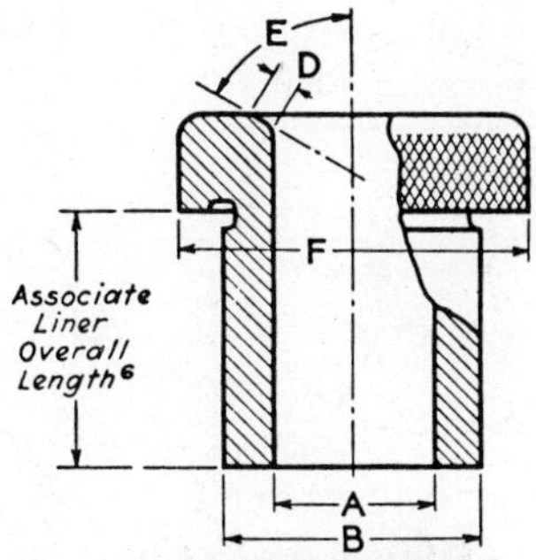

SLIP TYPE, RENEWABLE WEARING BUSHING

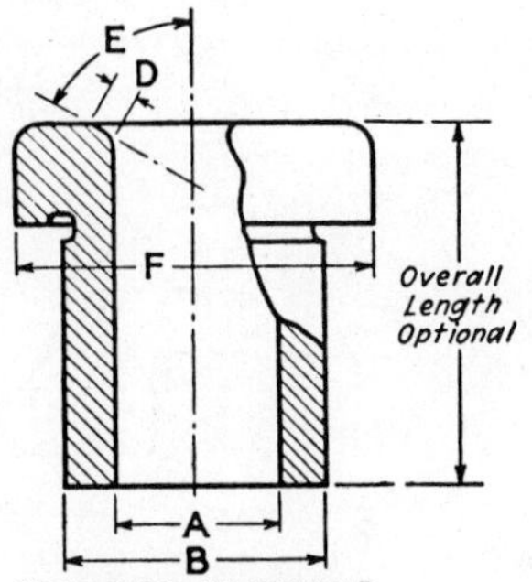

FIXED TYPE, RENEWABLE WEARING BUSHING

Press Fit Wearing Bushings—Headless and Head Types

Range of Hole Size A		Body Diameter B					Body Length C			Width of Chamfer D	Head Diameter F	Head Height G
		Unfinished			Finished							
From	Up to and Including	Nominal	Max	Min	Max	Min	Short	Medium	Long		Max	Max
0.0156	0.0625	5/32	0.166	0.161	0.1578	0.1575	5/16	.....	1/2	1/32	1/4	3/32
0.0630	0.0995	13/64	0.213	0.208	0.2046	0.2043	5/16	.....	1/2	1/32	5/16	3/32
0.1024	0.1378	1/4	0.260	0.255	0.2516	0.2513	5/16	.....	1/2	1/32	3/8	3/32
0.1406	0.1875	5/16	0.327	0.322	0.3141	0.3138	5/16	1/2	3/4	1/32	7/16	1/8
0.1910	0.2500	13/32	0.421	0.416	0.4078	0.4075	5/16	1/2	3/4	1/16	17/32	5/32
0.2520	0.3125	1/2	0.520	0.515	0.5017	0.5014	5/16	1/2	3/4	5/64	5/8	7/32
0.3160	0.4219	5/8	0.645	0.640	0.6267	0.6264	1/2	3/4	1	3/32	13/16	7/32
0.4375	0.5000	3/4	0.770	0.765	0.7518	0.7515	1/2	3/4	1	7/64	15/16	7/32
0.5156	0.6250	7/8	0.895	0.890	0.8768	0.8765	3/4	1	1 3/8	7/64	1 1/8	1/4
0.6406	0.7500	1	1.020	1.015	1.0018	1.0015	3/4	1	1 3/8	7/64	1 1/4	5/16
0.7656	1.0000	1 3/8	1.395	1.390	1.3772	1.3768	3/4	1	1 3/8	9/64	1 5/8	3/8
1.0156	1.3750	1 3/4	1.770	1.765	1.7523	1.7519	1	1 3/8	1 3/4	9/64	2	3/8
1.3906	1.7500	2 1/4	2.270	2.265	2.2525	2.2521	1	1 3/8	1 3/4	7/32	2 1/2	3/8

Renewable Wearing Bushings—Slip and Fixed Head Types

Range of Hole Size A		Body Diameter B			Width of Chamfer D	Head Diameter F
From	Up to and Including	Nominal	Max	Min		Max
0.0000	0.1562	5/16	0.3125	0.3123	1/32	5/8
0.1610	0.3125	1/2	0.5000	0.4998	5/64	15/16
0.3160	0.5000	3/4	0.7500	0.7498	7/64	1 1/4
0.5156	0.7500	1	1.0000	0.9998	7/64	1 5/8
0.7656	1.0000	1 3/8	1.3750	1.3747	9/64	2
1.0156	1.3750	1 3/4	1.7500	1.7497	9/64	2 1/2
1.3906	1.7500	2 1/4	2.2500	2.2496	7/32	3

PUNCH AND DIE SETS
(For full information see ASA B5.25-1950)

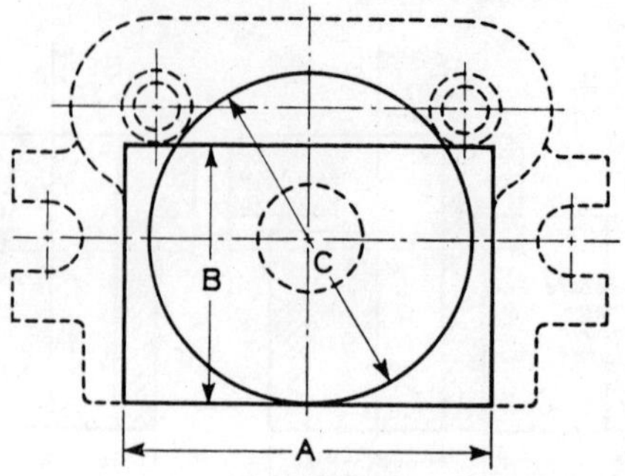

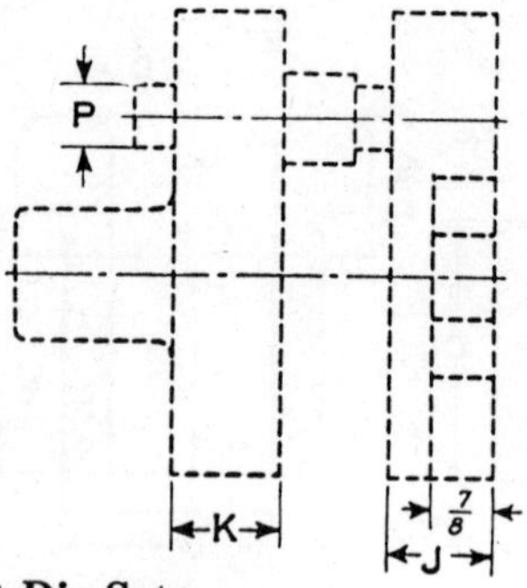

Dimensions of Back-Post Die Sets

Die Area			Thickness				Min Guide-post Diam
Right to Left	Front to Back	Diameter	Die Holder J		Punch Holder K		
A	B	C	From	To	From	To	P
3	3	3	1	1 1/4	1	..	3/4
4	4	4	1 3/8	1 3/4	1 1/4	..	1
4	6	...	1 1/2	2 3/4	1 1/4	2 1/4	1
5	4	...	1 3/8	1 3/4	1 1/4	..	1
5	5	5	1 1/2	2	1 1/4	1 3/4	1
5	8	...	1 1/2	3	1 1/4	2 1/4	1
6	3	...	1 1/2	2	1 1/4	1 3/4	1
6	4	5	1 1/2	2 3/4	1 1/4	2 1/4	1
6	6	6 1/2	1 1/2	2 1/2	1 1/4	2 1/4	1
6	9	...	1 1/2	3 1/4	1 1/4	2 1/4	1 1/4
7	5	5 3/4	1 1/2	3	1 1/4	2 1/4	1
7	7	7 1/2	1 1/2	2 1/2	1 1/4	2 1/4	1
7	10	...	1 5/8	3 1/4	1 3/8	2 1/4	1 1/4
8	4	...	1 1/2	2 1/2	1 1/4	2 1/4	1
8	6	7	1 1/2	3	1 1/4	2 1/4	1
8	8	8 1/2	1 1/2	2 1/2	1 1/4	2 1/4	1
9	12	...	1 3/4	3 1/2	1 1/2	2 1/4	1 1/2
10	5	...	1 1/2	2 1/2	1 1/4	1 3/4	1 1/4
10	7	...	1 3/8	2 3/4	1 3/8	2 1/4	1 1/4
10	10	10	1 5/8	2 3/4	1 3/8	2 1/4	1 1/4
10	14	...	1 7/8	3 3/4	1 5/8	2 3/4	1 1/2
11	9	10	1 3/4	3 1/2	1 1/2	2 1/4	1 1/4
12	4	...	1 3/4	2 1/4	1 1/2	2	1 1/4
12	6	...	1 1/2	2 1/2	1 1/2	2	1 1/4
12	12	12 1/2	1 3/4	3 1/2	1 3/4	2 1/4	1 1/2
12	16	...	2	3 3/4	1 3/4	2 3/4	1 1/2
14	8	...	1 3/4	3 1/4	1 5/8	2 3/4	1 1/2
14	10	11 1/4	1 3/4	3 1/4	1 5/8	2 3/4	1 1/2
14	14	14	1 3/4	3 1/4	1 5/8	2 1/4	1 1/2
15	5	...	1 1/2	2 1/2	1 1/2	2	1 1/2
15	9	...	1 1/2	2 1/2	1 1/2	2	1 1/2

Shank Diameters and Lengths
(Back-Post Die Sets)

Diameter	1 1/2	1 9/16*	2	2 1/2	3
Length	2 1/8	2 1/8	2 7/8	2 7/8	2 7/8

CAST-IRON SCREWED FITTINGS
(For full information see ASA B16.4-1953)

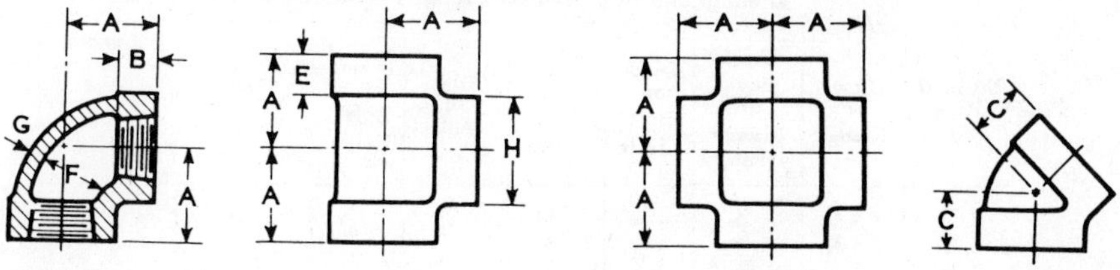

90° ELBOW TEE CROSS 45° ELBOW

125-Lb Screwed Fittings

Nominal Pipe Size	Center to End, Elbows, Tees, and Crosses A	Center to End, 45-Deg Elbows C	Length of Thread, Min B	Width of Band, Min E	Inside Diameter of Fitting F Max	Inside Diameter of Fitting F Min	Metal Thick-ness G	Outside Diameter of Band, Min H
1/4	0.81	0.73	0.32	0.38	0.584	0.540	0.110	0.93
3/8	0.95	0.80	0.36	0.44	0.719	0.675	0.120	1.12
1/2	1.12	0.88	0.43	0.50	0.897	0.840	0.130	1.34
3/4	1.31	0.98	0.50	0.56	1.107	1.050	0.155	1.63
1	1.50	1.12	0.58	0.62	1.385	1.315	0.170	1.95
1 1/4	1.75	1.29	0.67	0.69	1.730	1.660	0.185	2.39
1 1/2	1.94	1.43	0.70	0.75	1.970	1.900	0.200	2.68
2	2.25	1.68	0.75	0.84	2.445	2.375	0.220	3.28
2 1/2	2.70	1.95	0.92	0.94	2.975	2.875	0.240	3.86
3	3.08	2.17	0.98	1.00	3.600	3.500	0.260	4.62
3 1/2	3.42	2.39	1.03	1.06	4.100	4.000	0.280	5.20
4	3.79	2.61	1.08	1.12	4.600	4.500	0.310	5.79
5	4.50	3.05	1.18	1.18	5.663	5.563	0.380	7.05
6	5.13	3.46	1.28	1.28	6.725	6.625	0.430	8.28
8	6.56	4.28	1.47	1.47	8.725	8.625	0.550	10.63
10	8.08	5.16	1.68	1.68	10.850	10.750	0.690	13.12
12	9.50	5.97	1.88	1.88	12.850	12.750	0.800	15.47

250-Lb Screwed Fittings

Nominal Pipe Size	Center to End, Elbows, Tees, and Crosses A	Center to End, 45-Deg Elbows C	Length of Thread, Min B	Width of Band, Min E	Inside Diameter of Fitting F Max	Inside Diameter of Fitting F Min	Metal Thick-ness G	Outside Diameter of Band, Min H
1/4	0.94	0.81	0.43	0.49	0.584	0.540	0.18	1.17
3/8	1.06	0.88	0.47	0.55	0.719	0.675	0.18	1.36
1/2	1.25	1.00	0.57	0.60	0.897	0.840	0.20	1.59
3/4	1.44	1.13	0.64	0.68	1.107	1.050	0.23	1.88
1	1.63	1.31	0.75	0.76	1.385	1.315	0.28	2.24
1 1/4	1.94	1.50	0.84	0.88	1.730	1.660	0.33	2.73
1 1/2	2.13	1.69	0.87	0.97	1.970	1.900	0.35	3.07
2	2.50	2.00	1.00	1.12	2.445	2.375	0.39	3.74
2 1/2	2.94	2.25	1.17	1.30	2.975	2.875	0.43	4.60
3	3.38	2.50	1.23	1.40	3.600	3.500	0.48	5.36
3 1/2	3.75	2.63	1.28	1.49	4.100	4.000	0.52	5.98
4	4.13	2.81	1.33	1.57	4.600	4.500	0.56	6.61
5	4.88	3.19	1.43	1.74	5.663	5.563	0.66	7.92
6	5.63	3.50	1.53	1.91	6.725	6.625	0.74	9.24
8	7.00	4.31	1.72	2.24	8.725	8.625	0.90	11.73
10	8.63	5.19	1.93	2.58	10.850	10.750	1.08	14.37
12	10.00	6.00	2.13	2.91	12.850	12.750	1.24	16.84

All dimensions given in inches.

CAST-IRON PIPE FLANGES AND FLANGED FITTINGS
(For full information see ASA B16.1-1960)

Dimensions of Cast-Iron Flanges and Bolts

Nominal Pipe Size	Diam of Flange	Thickness of Flange (Min)	Diam of Bolt Circle	Number of Bolts	Diam of Bolts	Diam of Bolt Holes	Length of Bolts	Length of Bolt-Stud With Two Nuts
1	4 1/4	7/16	3 1/8	4	1/2	5/8	1 3/4	....
1 1/4	4 5/8	1/2	3 1/2	4	1/2	5/8	2	....
1 1/2	5	9/16	3 7/8	4	1/2	5/8	2	....
2	6	5/8	4 3/4	4	5/8	3/4	2 1/4	....
2 1/2	7	11/16	5 1/2	4	5/8	3/4	2 1/2	....
3	7 1/2	3/4	6	4	5/8	3/4	2 1/2	....
3 1/2	8 1/2	13/16	7	8	5/8	3/4	2 3/4	....
4	9	15/16	7 1/2	8	5/8	3/4	3	....
5	10	15/16	8 1/2	8	3/4	7/8	3	....
6	11	1	9 1/2	8	3/4	7/8	3 1/4	....

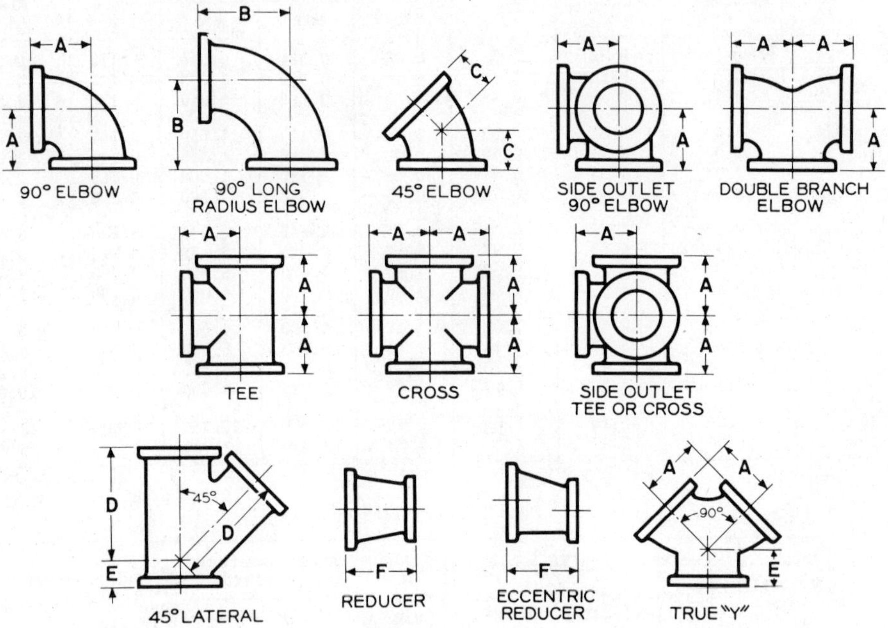

Dimensions of Elbows, Double Branch Elbows, Tees, Crosses, Laterals, True Y's (Straight Sizes), and Reducers

Nominal Pipe Size	Inside Diam of Fittings	Center to Face 90 Deg Elbow Tees, Crosses True "Y" and Double Branch Elbow A	Center to Face 90 Deg Long Radius Elbow B	Center to Face 45 Deg Elbow C	Center to Face Lateral D	Short Center to Face True "Y" and Lateral E	Face to Face Reducer F	Diam of Flange	Thickness of Flange (Min)	Wall Thickness
1	1	3 1/2	5	1 3/4	5 3/4	1 3/4	....	4 1/4	7/16	5/16
1 1/4	1 1/4	3 3/4	5 1/2	2	6 1/4	1 3/4	....	4 5/8	1/2	5/16
1 1/2	1 1/2	4	6	2 1/4	7	2	....	5	9/16	5/16
2	2	4 1/2	6 1/2	2 1/2	8	2 1/2	5	6	5/8	5/16
2 1/2	2 1/2	5	7	3	9 1/2	2 1/2	5 1/2	7	11/16	5/16
3	3	5 1/2	7 3/4	3	10	3	6	7 1/2	3/4	3/8
3 1/2	3 1/2	6	8 1/2	3 1/2	11 1/2	3	6 1/2	8 1/2	13/16	7/16
4	4	6 1/2	9	4	12	3	7	9	15/16	1/2
5	5	7 1/2	10 1/4	4 1/2	13 1/2	3 1/2	8	10	15/16	1/2
6	6	8	11 1/2	5	14 1/2	3 1/2	9	11	1	9/16

AMERICAN STANDARD WELDED AND SEAMLESS STEEL PIPE DATA

Nominal Pipe Size	Outside Diameter	WALL THICKNESS Standard Weight *	Extra Strong **	Double Extra Strong	WEIGHT PER FOOT Standard Weight +	Extra Strong	Double Extra Strong
1/8	.405	.068	.095	-	.244	.314	-
1/4	.540	.088	.119	-	.424	.535	-
3/8	.675	.091	.126	-	.567	.738	-
1/2	.840	.109	.147	.294	.850	1.087	1.714
3/4	1.050	.113	.154	.308	1.130	1.473	2.440
1	1.315	.133	.179	.358	1.678	2.171	3.659
1-1/4	1.660	.140	.191	.382	2.272	2.996	5.214
1-1/2	1.900	.145	.200	.400	2.717	3.631	6.408
2	2.375	.154	.218	.436	3.652	5.022	9.029
2-1/2	2.875	.203	.276	.552	5.79	7.66	13.70
3	3.500	.216	.300	.600	7.58	10.25	18.58
3-1/2	4.000	.226	.318	-	9.11	12.51	-
4	4.500	.237	.337	.674	10.79	14.98	27.54
5	5.563	.258	.375	.750	14.62	20.78	38.55
6	6.625	.280	.432	.864	18.97	28.57	53.16
8	8.625	.322	.500	.875	28.55	43.39	72.42
10	10.750	.365	.500	-	40.48	54.74	-
12	12.750	.375	.500	-	49.56	65.42	-

Dimensions in inches, weights in pounds.

*Same as ASA B36.10 "Schedule 40" Pipe, except 12-inch diameter.

**Same as ASA B36.10 "Schedule 80" Pipe, except 10 and 12-inch diameter.

+ Plain Ends

ACME SCREW THREADS
(For full information see ASA B1.5-1952)

Limiting Diameter	Threads per Inch	Limiting Diameter	Threads per Inch	Limiting Diameter	Threads per Inch	Limiting Diameter	Threads per Inch
1/4	16	3/4	6	1 1/2	4	3	2
5/16	14	7/8	6	1 3/4	4	3 1/2	2
3/8	12	1	5	2	4	4	2
7/16	12	1 1/8	5	2 1/4	3	4 1/2	2
1/2	10	1 1/4	5	2 1/2	3	5	2
5/8	8	1 3/8	4	2 3/4	3		

TAPER AND STRAIGHT PIPE THREADS
(For full information see ASA B2.1-1945)

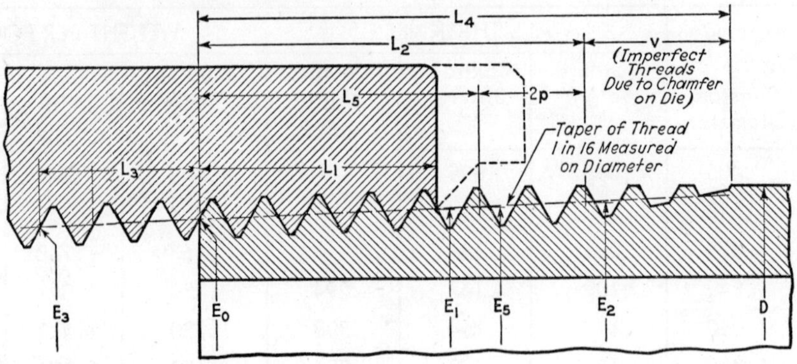

Basic Dimensions, American Standard Taper Pipe Thread

Nominal Pipe Size	Outside Diameter of Pipe	Threads per Inch	Pitch of Thread	Pitch Diameter at Beginning of External Thread	Hand-Tight Engagement			Effective Thread, External		
					Length L_1		Diam	Length L_2		Diam E_2
	D	n	p	E_0	In.	Thds	E_1	In.	Thds	In.
1/16	0.3125	27	0.03704	0.27118	0.160	4.32	0.28118	0.2611	7.05	0.28750
1/8	0.405	27	0.03704	0.36351	0.180	4.86	0.37476	0.2639	7.12	0.38000
1/4	0.540	18	0.05556	0.47739	0.200	3.60	0.48989	0.4018	7.23	0.50250
3/8	0.675	18	0.05556	0.61201	0.240	4.32	0.62701	0.4078	7.34	0.63750
1/2	0.840	14	0.07143	0.75843	0.320	4.48	0.77843	0.5337	7.47	0.79179
3/4	1.050	14	0.07143	0.96768	0.339	4.75	0.98887	0.5457	7.64	1.00179
1	1.315	11 1/2	0.08696	1.21363	0.400	4.60	1.23863	0.6828	7.85	1.25630
1 1/4	1.660	11 1/2	0.08696	1.55713	0.420	4.83	1.58338	0.7068	8.13	1.60130
1 1/2	1.900	11 1/2	0.08696	1.79609	0.420	4.83	1.82234	0.7235	8.32	1.84130
2	2.375	11 1/2	0.08696	2.26902	0.436	5.01	2.29627	0.7565	8.70	2.31630
2 1/2	2.875	8	0.12500	2.71953	0.682	5.46	2.76216	1.1375	9.10	2.79062
3	3.500	8	0.12500	3.34062	0.766	6.13	3.38850	1.2000	9.60	3.41562
3 1/2	4.000	8	0.12500	3.83750	0.821	6.57	3.88881	1.2500	10.00	3.91562
4	4.500	8	0.12500	4.33438	0.844	6.75	4.38712	1.3000	10.40	4.41562
5	5.563	8	0.12500	5.39073	0.937	7.50	5.44929	1.4063	11.25	5.47862
6	6.625	8	0.12500	6.44609	0.958	7.66	6.50597	1.5125	12.10	6.54062
8	8.625	8	0.12500	8.43359	1.063	8.50	8.50003	1.7125	13.70	8.54062
10	10.750	8	0.12500	10.54531	1.210	9.68	10.62094	1.9250	15.40	10.66562
12	12.750	8	0.12500	12.53281	1.360	10.88	12.61781	2.1250	17.00	12.66562
14 OD	14.000	8	0.12500	13.77500	1.562	12.50	13.87262	2.2500	18.90	13.91562
16 OD	16.000	8	0.12500	15.76250	1.812	14.50	15.87575	2.4500	19.60	15.91562
18 OD	18.000	8	0.12500	17.75000	2.000	16.00	17.87500	2.6500	21.20	17.91562
20 OD	20.000	8	0.12500	19.73750	2.125	17.00	19.87031	2.8500	22.80	19.91562
24 OD	24.000	8	0.12500	23.71250	2.375	19.00	23.86094	3.2500	26.00	23.91562

Dimensions, Internal Straight Pipe Threads in Pipe Couplings
(Pressure-Tight Joints *With* Lubricant or Sealer)

Nominal Pipe Size	Number of Threads per Inch	Pitch Diameter		Minor Diameter
		Max	Min	Min
1/8	27	0.3782	0.3713	0.342
1/4	18	0.4951	0.4847	0.440
3/8	18	0.6322	0.6218	0.577
1/2	14	0.7851	0.7717	0.715
3/4	14	0.9956	0.9822	0.925
1	11 1/2	1.2468	1.2305	1.161
1 1/4	11 1/2	1.5915	1.5752	1.506
1 1/2	11 1/2	1.8305	1.8142	1.745
2	11 1/2	2.3044	2.2881	2.219
2 1/2	8	2.7739	2.7504	2.650
3	8	3.4002	3.3768	3.277
3 1/2	8	3.9005	3.8771	3.777
4	8	4.3988	4.3754	4.275

All dimensions given in inches.

Dimensions, External and Internal Straight Pipe Threads for Mechanical Joints
(Free Fitting)

Nominal Pipe Size	Threads per Inch	External Thread				Internal Thread			
		Major Diameter		Pitch Diameter		Minor Diameter		Pitch Diameter	
		Max	Min	Max	Min	Max	Min	Max	Min
1/8	27	0.399	0.393	0.3748	0.3713	0.357	0.350	0.3783	0.3748
1/4	18	0.527	0.516	0.4899	0.4847	0.463	0.453	0.4951	0.4899
3/8	18	0.664	0.654	0.6270	0.6218	0.600	0.590	0.6322	0.6270
1/2	14	0.826	0.813	0.7784	0.7717	0.744	0.731	0.7851	0.7784
3/4	14	1.036	1.023	0.9889	0.9822	0.955	0.941	0.9956	0.9889
1	11 1/2	1.296	1.280	1.2386	1.2305	1.197	1.181	1.2468	1.2386
1 1/4	11 1/2	1.641	1.625	1.5834	1.5753	1.542	1.526	1.5916	1.5834
1 1/2	11 1/2	1.880	1.864	1.8223	1.8142	1.781	1.764	1.8305	1.8223
2	11 1/2	2.354	2.338	2.2963	2.2882	2.254	2.238	2.3044	2.2963
2 1/2	8	2.846	2.822	2.7622	2.7505	2.702	2.679	2.7739	2.7622
3	8	3.472	3.448	3.3885	3.3768	3.329	3.305	3.4002	3.3885
3 1/2	8	3.972	3.949	3.8888	3.8771	3.829	3.806	3.9005	3.8888
4	8	4.470	4.447	4.3871	4.3754	4.327	4.304	4.3988	4.3871
5	8	5.533	5.509	5.4493	5.4376	5.389	5.366	5.4610	5.4493
6	8	6.589	6.566	6.5060	6.4943	6.446	6.423	6.5177	6.5060

INDEX